ENCYCLOPEDIA OF PHYSICS

EDITED BY

S. FLÜGGE

VOLUME XXV/1

CRYSTAL OPTICS · DIFFRACTION

WITH 242 FIGURES

SPRINGER-VERLAG
BERLIN · GÖTTINGEN · HEIDELBERG
1961

HANDBUCH DER PHYSIK

HERAUSGEGEBEN VON

S. FLÜGGE

BAND XXV/1

KRISTALLOPTIK · BEUGUNG

MIT 242 FIGUREN

SPRINGER-VERLAG
BERLIN · GÖTTINGEN · HEIDELBERG
1961

Printed in Germany

Druck der Universitätsdruckerei H. Stürtz AG., Würzburg

Inhaltsverzeichnis.

Crystal Optics.

By

G. N. Ramachandran and S. Ramaseshan.

With 99 Figures.

A. Polarisation of light.

1. States of polarisation of light: Poincaré sphere. α) Light is a transverse electromagnetic wave and the nature of the vibration of the electric displacement vector in the plane normal to the direction of wave propagation defines the state of polarisation of a light beam. In a completely polarised beam[1], the vibration may be either linear in any azimuth at right angles to the propagation direction, or elliptical, with the major axis at any azimuth. The ratio of the axes of the ellipse can have any value and the sense of the ellipse may again be right or left handed. The two limiting cases of elliptic vibrations are linear and circular vibrations. Correspondingly, the light beam would be said to be elliptically, linearly or circularly polarised.

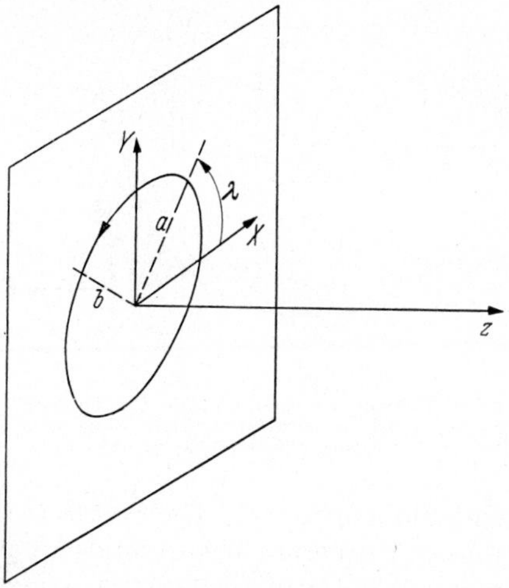

Fig. 1. Elliptically polarised light.

A general state of polarisation can thus be described by two quantities: (a) the orientation of the major axis of the ellipse, which may be specified by the angle λ which it makes with a given direction in the wave front and (b) the ratio of the axes of the ellipse (b/a, $b<a$). The sense of the ellipse could be specified by making the axial ratio positive for left-rotating ellipses and negative for right-rotating ellipses. The terms right and left-rotation are with respect to an observer looking towards the source of light. If the electric displacement vector rotates clockwise with progress of time, then it is right-rotating. At any instant of time the terminus of the electric displacement vector therefore forms a right-handed screw in space for a right elliptically polarised light beam.

Throughout this article, we shall imagine the light to be propagated along OZ (when not specified otherwise), which is taken to be horizontal (Fig. 1). The other two axes are taken horizontal (OX) and vertical (OY), the three together forming a right-handed system of co-ordinates.

The orientation of the major axis of the ellipse is given by the angle (λ) which it makes with the horizontal (OX) measured in the counter-clockwise direction,

[1] The descriptions of unpolarised and partially polarised beams of light are given in Sects. 8 and 11.

as seen by an observer looking towards the source. The ellipticity is defined by another angle ω, given by $\tan\omega = b/a$. The two angles λ and ω, which we shall denote by azimuth and ellipticity[1], uniquely specify the state of polarisation of a beam of light and all possible states of polarisation are covered by the range 0 to π of λ and the range $-\pi/4$ to $\pi/4$ of ω (taken together).

β) Poincaré sphere. The states of polarisation of a light beam can be uniquely represented by a point on the surface of a sphere of unit radius, whose latitude and longitude have the values 2ω, 2λ. This representation may be called the Poincaré representation and the sphere, the Poincaré sphere, after H. POINCARÉ who first suggested this idea[2]. The range of values of 2λ and 2ω required for describing all possible states of polarisation are therefore $2\lambda = 0$ to 2π, and $2\omega = -\pi/2$ to $\pi/2$, which covers the surface of the sphere completely. Thus all possible states of polarisation are represented by points on a sphere, there being a one-to-one correspondence between the points on the sphere and the various states of polarisation. A reversal of the direction of the major axis changes λ by π and therefore 2λ by 2π. It is the same state as before and is represented by the same point on the Poincaré sphere.

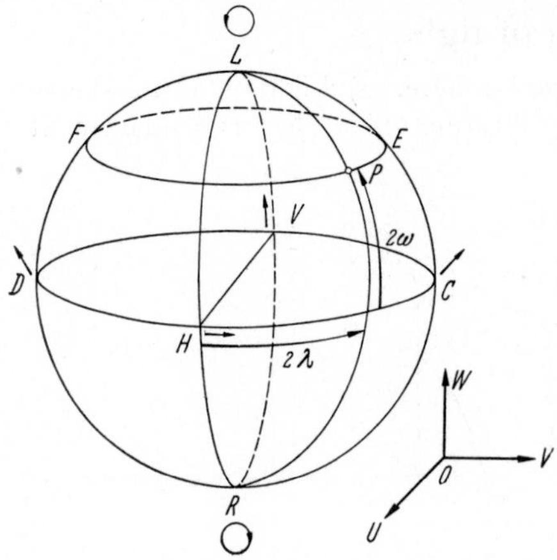

Fig. 2. The POINCARÉ sphere. A point P of longitude 2λ and latitude 2ω represents an elliptic vibration of azimuth λ and ellipticity ω.

Fig. 2 gives a picture of the Poincaré sphere. The points H and V represent horizontal and vertical linearly polarised light. Both are on the equator ($2\omega = 0$) and are at an angle π apart. L and R are the poles of the sphere and represent left and right circular vibrations. All linear states of polarisation are represented by points on the equator $HCVD$, the longitude being equal to twice the angle made with the horizontal. The points C and D, which are $\pi/2$ away from H and V thus correspond to linear vibrations at $\pm\pi/4$. All elliptical states having the same orientation (λ) of their major axes are represented by points on the meridian (LPR) of longitude 2λ. All ellipses having the same axial ratio ($b/a = \tan\omega$) are represented by points on the latitude circle (EPF) of latitude 2ω.

We shall, in general, call a beam of polarised light, whose state is represented by a point P on the Poincaré sphere, as light of polarisation state P. Similarly, a device which produces light of polarisation state P will be called "polariser P". A device which transmits light of polarisation state P completely is then called "analyser P". As will be seen later, it will be necessary to consider the orthogonal co-ordinate axes $OUVW$ in the space of the Poincaré sphere. These axes are respectively parallel to HV, DC and LR.

In crystal optics, we shall be interested in the changes produced in the state of polarisation of a beam of light traversing an anisotropic medium. The Poincaré representation is admirably suited for this purpose, and we shall therefore deal with some of the fundamental properties of the Poincaré sphere in this chapter.

---

[1] In spite of its ambiguity it has been decided to use the term "ellipticity" for the sake of convenience in preference to such terms as angle of ellipticity etc. When the "ellipticity" is small the ellipse is highly elongated, and it becomes a line in the limit when the "ellipticity" is zero.

[2] H. POINCARÉ: Théorie Mathématique de la Lumière, Vol. II, Chap. XII. Paris 1892.

A knowledge of spherical trigonometry is required for this purpose, which may be readily obtained from the books listed in footnote[1]. Wherever possible, a perspective diagram of the sphere will be given, but for some purposes, the stereographic projection is more convenient. Details regarding the stereographic projection and its properties will be found in any textbook on crystallography, and the books listed in footnote[2] may be referred to in particular. The pole L is taken to be above the plane in all the projections; points on the sphere below the plane of the paper are indicated by a circle around the symbol representing the point, e.g. Ⓐ.

In spite of its elegance and simplicity, the Poincaré sphere representation of polarisation states is not discussed in most textbooks and works of reference on optics. An account of the Poincaré sphere and its use in the study of the transmission of light in optically active birefringent crystals is contained in POCKELS' Lehrbuch ([2], pp. 11—13 and 309—313). Since then, a fair number of original investigations appear to have made use of this representation[3]. The advantages of the Poincaré representation in studies on crystal optics and analysis of polarised light were pointed out in a recent paper of RAMACHANDRAN and RAMASESHAN[4]. A review of some of the application of the Poincaré sphere has been given by JERRARD, more recently[5].

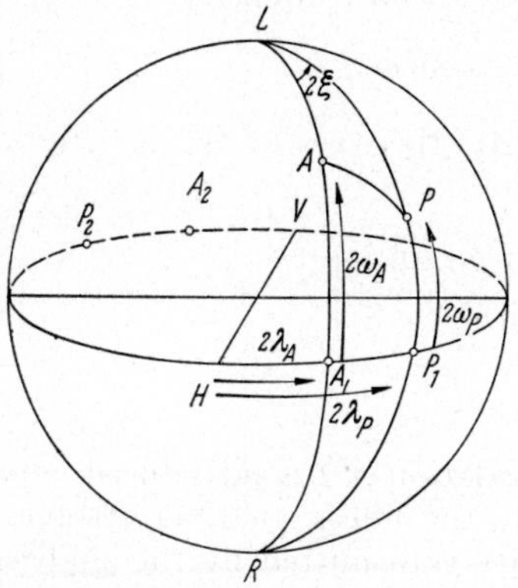

a

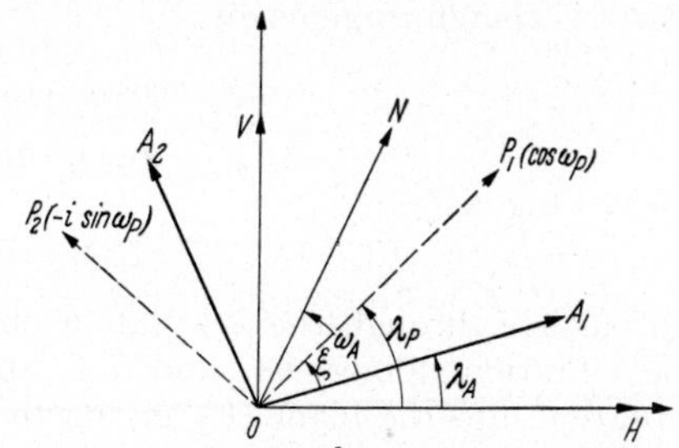

b

Fig. 3 a and b. Light of state P is incident on an analyser A. Fraction of intensity transmitted is $\cos^2 \frac{1}{2} \widehat{PA}$.

2. Intensity transmitted by an analyser when light of arbitrary polarisation is incident on it[6]. In Fig. 3, let the analyser be represented by the state A, $(2\lambda_A, 2\omega_A)$. We wish to determine the fraction of a light beam of polarisation P, $(2\lambda_P, 2\omega_P)$

[1] W. J. MCLELLAND and T. PRESTON: A treatise on spherical trigonometry with applications to spherical geometry. London 1897. — I. TODHUNTER and J. G. LEATHEM: Spherical trigonometry. London 1911.

[2] S.L. PENFIELD: Amer. J. Sci. **11**, 1, 115 (1901); **14**, 249 (1902). — E. BOEKE: Die Anwendung der stereographischen Projection bei kristallographischen Untersuchungen. Berlin: Bornträger 1911. See also C.S. BARRETT: Structure of Metals. New York: McGraw-Hill 1943.

[3] J. BEQUEREL: Commun. Phys. Lab. Univ. Leiden No. 91 C (1928); 221 A (1930). — L. CHAUMONT: C. R. Acad. Sci., Paris **150**, 1604 (1913). — Ann. Chim. Phys. Paris (9) **4**, 101 (1915). — C.A. SKINNER: J. Opt. Soc. Amer. **10**, 490 (1925). — R.E. WRIGHT: J. Opt. Soc. Amer. **20**, 529 (1930). — G. BRUHAT and P. GRIVET: J. Phys. Radium **6**, 12 (1935). — Y. BJORNSTAHL: Phys. Z. **42**, 437 (1939). — Z. Instrumentenkde. **59**, 425 (1939). — O. SNELLMAN and Y. BJORNSTAHL: Kolloid-Beih. **52**, 403 (1941). — M.F. BOKOTEIN: J. Techn. Phys. USSR. **18**, 673 (1948). — G.N. RAMACHANDRAN and V. CHANDRASEKHARAN: Proc. Ind. Acad. Sci. A **33**, 199 (1951). — S. RAMASESHAN and V. CHANDRASEKHARAN: Current Sci. **20**, 150 (1951). — S. RAMASESHAN: Proc. Ind. Acad. Sci. A **34**, 32 (1951). — J. Ind. Inst. Sci. **37**, 195 (1955). — S. PANCHARATNAM: Proc. Ind. Acad. Sci., A **41**, 130, 137 (1955); A **42** 86, 235 (1955); A **44**, 247, 398 (1956); A **45**, 402; A **46**, 1, 280 (1957). — G. DESTRIAU and J. PROUTEAU: J. Phys. Radium **110**, 53 (1949).

[4] G.N. RAMACHANDRAN and S. RAMASESHAN: J. Opt. Soc. Amer. **42**, 49 (1952).

[5] H.G. JERRARD: J. Opt. Soc. Amer. **44**, 630 (1954).

[6] U. FANO: J. Opt. Soc. Amer. **39**, 859 (1949). — G.N. RAMACHANDRAN and S. RAMASESHAN: J. Opt. Soc. Amer. **42**, 49 (1952).

which is transmitted by this analyser. It is well known that a $\lambda/4$ plate with its slow axis OA_1 (Fig. 3b) at azimuth λ_A, followed by a linear analyser N at an angle ω_A to the slow axis, constitutes an elliptic analyser A. The action of the $\lambda/4$ plate is to reduce the ellipse A into a linear vibration parallel to the linear analyser and the ellipse A_a (antipodal to A) to a linear vibration perpendicular to it. When light of polarisation P is incident on this analyser it is easily seen that the light transmitted by it does not depend on the construction of the analyser, for an elliptic vibration P can be resolved into two orthogonal vibrations A and A_a in one and only one way, the intensity of the former component being transmitted by the analyser A. Hence without any loss of generality we may use the specific analyser described above for deducing the magnitude of the fraction transmitted.

This is done by resolving the incident light into two linear components P_1 and P_2 parallel to the axes of the ellipse, the latter lagging in phase by $\pi/2$. Thus the displacements along these two directions are for unit intensity

$$u_{P_1} = \cos\omega_P, \qquad u_{P_2} = -i\sin\omega_P. \tag{2.1}$$

The incident light resolved along OA_1 and OA_2 (the axes of the quarter wave plate) is therefore given by

$$\left.\begin{aligned} u_{A_1} &= \cos\omega_P\cos\xi + i\sin\omega_P\sin\xi, \\ u_{A_2} &= \cos\omega_P\sin\xi - i\sin\omega_P\cos\xi \end{aligned}\right\} \tag{2.2}$$

where (Fig. 3b)

$$\xi = (\lambda_P - \lambda_A).$$

On passage through the $\lambda/4$ plate a phase retardation $\pi/2$ is introduced between the vibrations along OA_1 and OA_2 and finally the linear analyser resolves the vibration into the plane ON giving the intensity transmitted by the analyser as

$$u_A = u_{A_1}\cos\omega_A + i\,u_{A_2}\sin\omega_A. \tag{2.3}$$

Thus the intensity transmitted by the analyser is

$$|u_A|^2 = \cos^2\xi\cos^2(\omega_A - \omega_P) + \sin^2\xi\sin^2(\omega_A + \omega_P).$$

This can be transformed, after some manipulation, into the form

$$|u_A|^2 = \tfrac{1}{2} + [\tfrac{1}{2}\sin 2\omega_P\sin 2\omega_A + \tfrac{1}{2}\cos 2\omega_P\cos 2\omega_A\cos 2(\lambda_P - \lambda_A)].$$

From the spherical triangle LPA of Fig. 3a we have the quantity within the square brackets to be equal to $\cos\widehat{PA}$, so that

$$|u_A|^2 = \tfrac{1}{2} + \tfrac{1}{2}\cos\widehat{PA} \tag{2.4}$$

or

$$|u_A|^2 = \cos^2\tfrac{1}{2}\widehat{PA}. \tag{2.5}$$

Thus, the fraction of the intensity of light of the polarisation state P which is transmitted by the analyser A is $\cos^2\frac{1}{2}\widehat{PA}$ where $\widehat{PA}$ is the length of the arc joining P and A on the Poincaré sphere. This elegant result has a number of important applications, as will be seen below.

In particular, it is seen that if $\widehat{PA} = \pi$, i.e., the states of polarisation P and A are represented by opposite points on the Poincaré sphere, then no light is transmitted. Thus, these two states are orthogonal to one another. An analyser A transmits completely light of state A, while it completely cuts out light of state

A_a, A_a being the point antipodal to A. When arc $\widehat{PA}$ varies from 0 to π the transmitted fraction decreases from unity (P coincident with A) to zero (for P opposite to A). In particular, if A is a linear vibration, then the state A_a corresponds to the perpendicular linear vibration. If A is a left circular vibration corresponding to L, the orthogonal state is a right circular vibration, then A_a corresponds to R. If A corresponds to a general ellipse, then the orthogonal state A_a is the corresponding "crossed" ellipse which has its major and minor axes interchanged with respect to the former and has also the opposite sense of description.

In many applications, one is interested in the variations in the intensity of light transmitted by an analyser set close to extinction. In such a case, it is more convenient to consider the smaller arc $\widehat{PA_a}$ rather than the larger arc $\widehat{PA}$ which will be nearly π in value. The fraction of the intensity transmitted is then given by

$$t_a = \sin^2 \tfrac{1}{2}\, \widehat{PA_a}. \tag{2.6}$$

3. Effect of linear birefringence represented on the Poincaré sphere. In crystal optics a common problem that occurs is the following: When a beam of particular state of elliptic polarisation (P_1) is incident on a crystal plate, what will be the intensity and the state of polarisation P_2 of the emergent light. The crystal resolves the incident light into two specific polarised beams in different states of polarisation which are propagated with different velocities and, if the crystal is absorbing, with different absorption coefficients. In the case of a transparent crystal, the component beams will be in opposite states of polarisation A, A_a. When the specific states of opposite polarisation are linear, circular or elliptic, we shall refer to the medium as linearly, circularly or elliptically birefringent. One of the important results of the Poincaré representation, which makes it so useful in crystal optics, is that the state P_2 of the emergent light can be obtained from the state P_1 of the incident light by the simple geometrical operation of rotating the sphere about the axis AA_a through an angle Δ, where Δ is the phase advance of A over A_a introduced by the crystal. We shall first consider the case of a linearly birefringent medium.

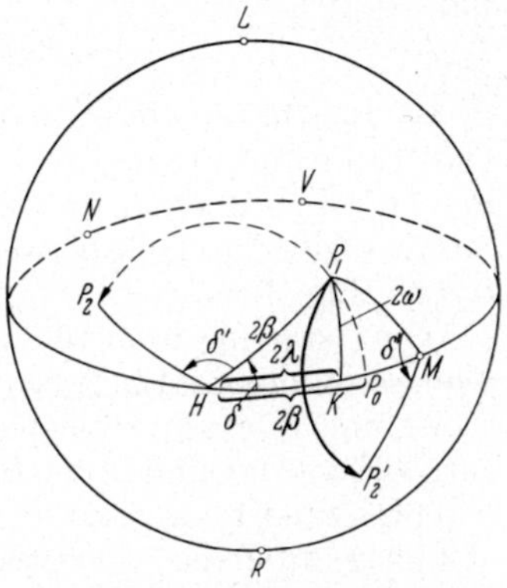

Fig. 4. Effect of linear birefringence. A phase difference δ' introduced between two linear orthogonal states M and N is equivalent to an anti-clockwise rotation through an angle δ' about the faster state M.

Let the two linear states of polarisation which are propagated unchanged through the medium be H and V (Fig. 4) and let the phase difference introduced between them due to the passage through the medium be δ, H leading V by δ. Suppose unit intensity of linearly polarised light at azimuth β represented on the equator by P_0 ($HP_0 = 2\beta$ in Fig. 4) be incident on the crystal. This may be resolved along H and V giving the components $\cos\beta$ and $\sin\beta$. Let this be converted into an elliptical beam represented by the point P_1 as a result of the phase difference δ introduced. Let this ellipse have an azimuth λ and ellipticity ω. Resolving the vibration along H and V, we have, for unit intensity, the two amplitudes to be

$$u_1 = \cos\omega\cos\lambda + i\sin\omega\sin\lambda, \tag{3.1}$$

$$u_2 = \cos\omega\sin\lambda - i\sin\omega\cos\lambda, \tag{3.2}$$

while their phases ε_1 and ε_2 are given by

$$\tan \varepsilon_1 = \tan \omega \tan \lambda, \tag{3.3}$$

$$\tan \varepsilon_2 = - \tan \omega \cot \lambda. \tag{3.4}$$

The amplitudes of the two components must be equal to $\cos \beta$ and $\sin \beta$, so that we have

$$\left.\begin{aligned} \cos^2 \beta &= \cos^2 \omega \cos^2 \lambda + \sin^2 \omega \sin^2 \lambda, \\ \sin^2 \beta &= \cos^2 \omega \sin^2 \lambda + \sin^2 \omega \cos^2 \lambda. \end{aligned}\right\} \tag{3.5}$$

The two equations are equivalent and can be put in the form

$$\cos 2\beta = \cos 2\omega \cos 2\lambda. \tag{3.6}$$

The phase difference between the two is given by

$$\delta = \varepsilon_1 - \varepsilon_2,$$

so that

$$\tan (\varepsilon_1 - \varepsilon_2) = \frac{2 \tan \omega}{1 - \tan^2 \omega} \frac{1}{2} (\tan \lambda + \cot \lambda) \tag{3.7}$$

and

$$\tan \delta = \tan 2\omega / \sin 2\lambda. \tag{3.8}$$

We thus have two relations (3.6) and (3.8) between the quantities ω, λ and β, δ. They can be interpreted very simply by saying that the point P_1 is obtained from P_0 by rotating it about the axis HV through an angle δ. Both Eqs. (3.6) and (3.8) can be verified to hold between the elements of the right angled spherical triangle HP_1K (Fig. 4).

Thus, starting from the linear polarisation state P_0, the effect of introducing a phase difference δ between the components H and V (H leading V by δ) is to rotate the representative point about the axis HV by an angle δ, measured anticlockwise looking from H to V. It follows from this that, if the initial state is represented by a point P_1, now considered as a general point, then the effect of a phase difference δ' between H and V is to bring P_1 to P_2 by a rotation through an angle δ' about HV.

So also, if the phase difference δ' is not between the linear states H and V but between the two states of linear polarisation of azimuth α and $\alpha + \pi/2$ represented on the Poincaré sphere by points M and N, of longitude 2α, $\pi + 2\alpha$ on the equator, the representative point is rotated by an angle δ' about the axis MN (from P_1 to P_2').

Similarly, if a phase difference δ is introduced between left- and right-circular vibrations, the effect can readily be shown to be equivalent to rotating the sphere through an angle δ about LR. Suppose the incident beam is linearly polarised parallel to OX, represented by the point H on the equator. Following FRESNEL, we may resolve the linear vibration into two circular vibrations (which are in phase along OX). If the left rotating circle (L) is advanced in phase by $\delta/2$ while the other (R) is retarded by $\delta/2$ (phase difference $= \delta$), it may be shown that the two together will produce a linear vibration at azimuth $\delta/2$. The corresponding representative point remains on the equator, but is at longitude δ. It is obtained from the original state by a rotation through an angle δ about LR. The proof is directly generalised to any linear vibration. Considering any ellipse as made up of two linear vibrations at right angles but with a phase difference of $\pi/2$, it will be seen that both components will be rotated by $\delta/2$ by introducing a phase difference of δ between L and R. Thus the axial ratio of the ellipse is unaffected, but its azimuth is rotated[1] by $\delta/2$; the latitude of the representative point on the Poincaré sphere is unchanged but its longitude increases by δ. This is equivalent to rotating the point through an angle δ about LR.

Thus, the effect of linear or circular birefringence, and the consequent introduction of a phase difference δ between two orthogonal linear or circular states of polarisation, can be determined by finding the effect of a rotation of the Poincaré sphere through an angle δ about the appropriate axis of rotation. These results are in fact consequences of even more general properties regarding the addition of *any* two orthogonally polarised beams (see Sect. 4).

4. Coherent addition of polarised beams[2]. α) *Direct interference of two polarised beams.* Suppose we have a pair of orthogonal analysers A and A_a. Then it follows from the results (3.4) and (3.5) that the intensities transmitted by the two analysers would be constant for all states of polarisation (P) for which the arc $\widehat{PA}$ (and therefore also the arc $\widehat{PA_a}$) is the same. Thus, the locus of points on the Poincaré sphere representing the states of polarisation for which a definite fraction f is transmitted by the analyser A is a small circle of centre A and radius $\widehat{PA}$ where

$$\cos^2 \tfrac{1}{2}\,\widehat{PA} = f. \tag{4.1}$$

For all these states, the analyser A_a will transmit a fraction

$$\cos^2 \tfrac{1}{2}\,\widehat{PA_a} = \sin^2 \tfrac{1}{2}\,\widehat{PA} = 1 - f.$$

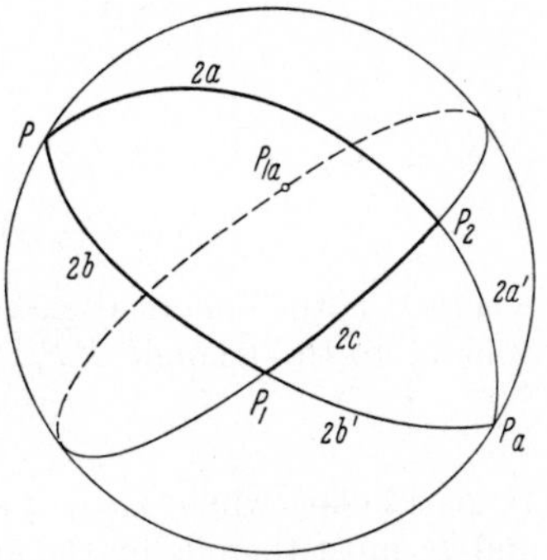

Fig. 5. Coherent addition of polarised beams. When a beam of intensity I and any state P is decomposed into two beams in the states P_1 and P_2, their intensities I_1 and I_2 are given by Eqs. (4.5) and (4.6); the phase difference is the supplement of half the area of the triangle $P_1 P_a P_2$.

The above result may be used to work out the resultant of the coherent addition of two beams of polarised light, say 1 and 2, whose states are represented by points P_1 and P_2 on the Poincaré sphere (Fig. 5) and whose intensities are I_1 and I_2 respectively. The resultant is the state P. Denote the arcs PP_2, PP_1, and P_1P_2 by $2a$, $2b$, $2c$ respectively, and similarly the arcs P_aP_2 and P_aP_1 by $2a'$, $2b'$ respectively. Let P_{1a} be the state opposite to P_1 and resolve the beam 2 into the state P_1 and P_{1a}, the intensities of which will be $I_2 \cos^2 c$ and $I_2 \sin^2 c$ respectively. The intensity of the resolved component of the combined beam along P may be obtained by the usual formula for combining two vibrations in the same state. The resultant intensity is

$$I_{P_1} = I_1 + I_2 \cos^2 c + 2\sqrt{I_1 I_2} \cos c \cos \delta. \tag{4.2}$$

The intensity of the resolved component of the combined beam in the state P_{1a} is

$$I_{P_{1a}} = I_2 \sin^2 c. \tag{4.3}$$

Since the beams of intensity I_{P_1} and $I_{P_{1a}}$ are orthogonal, the resultant intensity is just the sum of the two, independent of the phase difference between them. Thus,

$$I = I_1 + I_2 + 2\sqrt{I_1 I_2} \cos c \cos \delta \tag{4.4}$$

[1] This uses the fact that the phase difference *between* the components is unaltered by the operation of rotation. We shall not prove this, as a general proof for elliptic birefringence is given in Sect. 4.

[2] S. Pancharatnam: Proc. Ind. Acad. Sci. A **44**, 247 (1956).

and we may conveniently refer to δ as the phase difference between the two beams themselves though they are in different states of polarisation.

Now, the intensities of the resolved component of the resultant I in the state P_{1a} and of I_2 also in the state P_{1a} must be equal, since P_1 is orthogonal to P_{1a}. Hence

$$I \sin^2 b = I_2 \sin^2 c$$

or

$$I_2 = I \sin^2 b / \sin^2 c\,. \tag{4.5}$$

Similarly,

$$I_1 = I \sin^2 a / \sin^2 c\,. \tag{4.6}$$

Hence

$$\cos\delta = \frac{I - I_1 - I_2}{2\sqrt{I_1 I_2}\cos c} = \frac{\sin^2 c - \sin^2 b - \sin^2 a}{2 \sin a \sin b \cos c} \tag{4.7}$$

$$= \frac{1 - \cos^2 c - \cos^2 b' - \cos^2 a'}{2 \cos a' \cos b' \cos c} \tag{4.8}$$

or

$$\cos\delta = \cos \tfrac{1}{2}\,\varepsilon' \tag{4.9}$$

where ε' is the spherical excess or area of the spherical triangle $P_1 P_2 P_a$ which is colunar to the triangle $P P_1 P_2$. Thus

$$\delta = \pi \pm \tfrac{1}{2}\,\varepsilon'\,. \tag{4.10}$$

In particular, when $\delta = 0$, $\frac{1}{2}\varepsilon' = \pi$ or the spherical excess is 2π. The points P and P_a must then lie on the great circle passing through P_1 and P_2, P lying on the shorter arc $P_1 P_2$.

Thus, given I_1, I_2 and δ, one can first calculate I from Eq. (4.4) and then the spherical arcs a and b from Eqs. (4.5) and (4.6) which immediately fix the representative point P of the resultant, except for an ambiguity in the sign of δ, which is present also in Eq. (4.10). The ambiguity can be removed by a consideration of the combination of orthogonal states and a comparison with the conventions adopted in Sect. 3.

Suppose P_2 tends to the point P_{1a} i.e., $2c \to \pi$. Then, the triangle $P_1 P P_2$ becomes a lune in the limit (Fig. 6a). Denote the angle between the great circles $P_1 P_2 P_{1a}$ and $P_1 P P_{1a}$ at P as Δ. Then the spherical excess of the colunar triangle is $\varepsilon' = 2(\pi - \Delta)$. Thus, we have

$$\Delta = \pm\,\delta\,. \tag{4.11}$$

Further since the beams are orthogonal

$$I = I_1 + I_2 \tag{4.12}$$

and

$$\left.\begin{aligned} I_1/I &= \sin^2 b = \cos^2 a\,,\\ I_2/I &= \sin^2 a = \cos^2 b\,. \end{aligned}\right\} \tag{4.13}$$

If the phase relationship is kept constant and I_2/I_1 is altered, the resultant state moves along the locus for which Δ is constant i.e. along a great circle (e.g. $P_1 P P_{1a}$ of Fig. 6a). On the other hand, if the ratio I_2/I_1 is given and the phase difference δ is varied, then the resultant occurs in a small circle whose axis is $P_1 P_2$ (i.e. $P_1 P_{1a}$). It is however necessary to define the condition when the two have the same phase, which may be done by taking some great circle through $P_1 P_2$ as the standard of reference (say the one marked $\delta = 0$ in Fig. 6a). Then, for any given δ, the resultant P lies on a great circle rotated from the standard through an angle δ. Thus two position are possible corresponding to $\Delta = \pm\,\delta$.

We have already shown (Sect. 3) that for the case of linear birefringence the upper positive sign is to be taken if P_1 leads P_2 in phase. From considerations of analytical continuity the same must be true for adjacent axes of rotation and hence for any axis of rotation of the Poincaré sphere. We have thus proved the proposition stated in Sect. 3 namely that *the effect of any elliptic birefringence is represented by an anticlockwise rotation about the point representing the faster state.*

This result for orthogonal vibrations may be used to resolve the ambiguity in (4.10) for the case of non-orthogonal vibrations by the method of analytical continuity, giving

$$\delta = \pi - \tfrac{1}{2}\,\varepsilon' \tag{4.14}$$

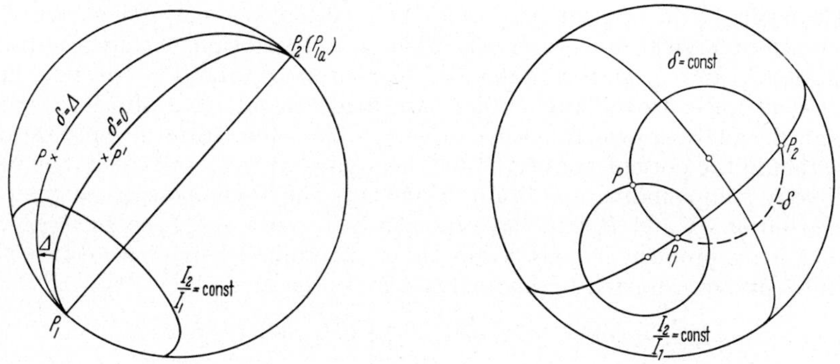

a b

Fig. 6 a and b. Locus of the resultant state of polarisation P when the ratio of the intensities of two beams P_1 and P_2 or their phase difference is varied the cther remaining constant. (a) States P_1, P_2 of the combining beams are orthogonal. (b) States P_1, P_2 non-orthogonal.

where ε' is to be counted positive if the sequence of points $P_1 P_a P_2$ (and therefore the sequence $P_1 P_2 P$) is described in a counter-clockwise sense on the surface of the sphere.

The necessity for defining the condition of zero phase difference occurs only in the case of orthogonal vibrations because one cannot be "resolved" into the other. When P_1 and P_2 are not orthogonal, then the resolved component of one along the other can be compared for specifying their phase difference. The resultant intensity is then a maximum, when the phase difference is zero as seen from Eq. (4.4), and the resultant state of polarisation lies on the arc $P_1 P_2$ directly joining P_1 and P_2. When the two beams are opposite in phase, the intensity is a minimum and the resultant state lies on the greater segment $(P_1 P_a P_2)$ of the great circle through P_1 and P_2.

It follows from Eqs. (4.5) and (4.6) that, when the phase difference between the two beams is altered without altering the ratio of their intensities, then $\sin^2 a/\sin^2 b$ is a constant. The locus of P is then a small circle, with its centre on the great circle through P_1 and P_2 (Fig. 6b). On the other hand, if the ratio of the intensities is altered, keeping the phase difference constant, then ε' is a constant, and the locus of P is again a small circle, but passing through P_1 and P_2, with its centre of the great circle which is the perpendicular bisector of the arc $P_1 P_2$ (Fig. 6b). When P_1 and P_2 are orthogonal, the former family of small circles are all perpendicular to the diameter $P_1 P_2$ and the latter all become great circles passing through P_1 and P_2 (Fig. 6a).

β) Interference of two beams after resolution by an analyser. Given a vibration in state P_1 (Fig. 5) its resolved components in the orthogonal states P and P_a

can be said to be in phase by choosing the arc $P P_2 P_a$ as the standard arc defining the zero of phase difference for two orthogonal states. Considering a second vibration in state P_2, let us also resolve it into its components in the states P and P_a. Let δ' be the phase advance of the P-component of the vibration in state P_2 over the P-component of the vibration in state P_1; and similarly let δ'' be the difference in the phases of the P_a-components of the vibrations in states P_2 and P_1 respectively. Then from a consideration of the results of the preceding sub-section,

$$\delta' - \delta'' = \hat{P} \tag{4.15}$$

where $\hat{P}$ is the angle $P_1 \hat{P} P_2$, counted positive if (on looking from P to P_a) an anticlockwise rotation brings arc $P P_1$ to arc $P P_2$.

The result of the last paragraph may be used to discuss a problem of common occurrence in crystal optics (see e.g. Chap. C). Two beams 1 and 2 initially of intensities I_1 and I_2 and in states of polarisation P_1 and P_2—the first having a phase advance δ over the second—are made to interfere after transmission through an analyser which resolves them to the same state of polarisation P. (Note that in the present context P does *not* represent the resultant state obtained by directly compounding the beams 1 and 2.) The P-components of the beams of polarisation P_1 and P_2 will have intensities $I_1 \cos^2 b$ and $I_2 \cos^2 a$ respectively and our main problem in this section is to determine their phase difference δ'. The intensity transmitted by an analyser P is then given by

$$I_P = I_1 \cos^2 b + I_2 \cos^2 a + 2\sqrt{I_1 I_2} \cos a \cos b \cos \delta'. \tag{4.16}$$

Similarly the P_a-component of the resultant beam will have an intensity

$$I_{P_a} = I_1 \sin^2 b + I_2 \sin^2 a + 2\sqrt{I_1 I_2} \sin a \sin b \cos \delta''. \tag{4.17}$$

The intensity I of the resultant beam, obtained by directly compounding 1 and 2, is obtained by adding (4.16) and (4.17) using (4.15):

$$I = I_1 + I_2 + 2\sqrt{I_1 I_2}\{\cos a \cos b \cos \delta' + \sin a \sin b \cos (\delta' - \hat{P})\}.$$

By applying the standard expressions for the spherical excess of a triangle this reduces to

$$I = I_1 + I_2 + 2\sqrt{I_1 I_2} \cos c \cos (\delta' + \tfrac{1}{2}\varepsilon) \tag{4.18}$$

where ε represents the area or spherical excess of the triangle $P P_1 P_2$ itself (counted positive if the sequence of points P, P_1, P_2 describe the periphery of the triangle in a counter-clockwise sense).

Comparing (4.18) with (4.4) we obtain the interesting result that if two beams initially have a phase difference δ then after passage through an analyser their phase difference becomes

$$\delta' = \delta - \tfrac{1}{2}\varepsilon, \tag{4.19}$$

i.e., an additional phase difference $-\frac{1}{2}\varepsilon$ is introduced in the process of analysation. The intensity transmitted by the analyser (i.e., the intensity obtained by the interference of the resolved components) is obtained by substituting (4.19) in (4.16):

$$I_P = I_1 \cos^2 b + I_2 \cos^2 a + 2\sqrt{I_1 I_2} \cos a \cos b \cos (\delta - \tfrac{1}{2}\varepsilon). \tag{4.20}$$

The limiting case when the states of polarisation P_1 and P_2 become oppositely polarised is of particular importance (Fig. 6a). In this case, if the beams have been originally derived by the decomposition of a beam in state P', we must take the great circle $P_1 P' P_2$ as defining the condition of zero phase difference. It follows from (4.19) (since ε becomes now the area of a lune) that on passing through an analyser P the resolved component of the first beam lags behind that of the second by an angle Δ which denotes the angle $P P_1 P'$ (measured positive in a counter-clockwise sense). Thus, for example, when two circularly polarised beams in opposite states are incident on a linear (or elliptic) analyser, the phase difference between the transmitted beams is altered by 2ϑ when the azimuth of the analyser is rotated (as a whole) through an angle ϑ—a result which finds application in certain types of phase-contrast microscopes which use crystal-optic elements[1].

5. Propagation of light through an optical system (no absorption). *α) Non-absorbing optical elements of infinitesimal thickness.* We wish to investigate the change in the state of polarisation of a beam of light of polarisation state P as a result of its passing through a number of optical elements. Each element is considered to be either (a) a parallel plate of birefringent material, with principal planes oriented at an arbitrary azimuth, or (b) an optically active material, which only rotates the azimuth of the elliptically polarised beam. Systems of this type were considered by JONES[2] making use of a matrix calculus and his papers may be referred to for examples and for further details. The matrix method of JONES is also discussed in Sect. 12. The overall effect can however be readily worked out by the use of the Poincaré sphere.

Before proceeding to the general case we shall first consider a special case of such combination, which is of particular interest, viz., when the effect of each optical element is infinitesimal in magnitude. An example is that of a birefringent optically active crystal. Although strictly the medium must be considered to have the properties of both birefringence and optical activity and should be treated as such in a rigorous theory (see Chap. B), one may also picture the crystal to be made up of alternate infinitesimal layers of equal thickness exhibiting alternately, only linear birefringence and only optical activity. A thickness dz of the optically active birefringent medium can on the above picture be regarded as a linearly birefringent element producing a retardation $d\delta = \delta' \, dz$, and an optically active element producing a rotation $d\varrho = \varrho' \, dz$ where δ' and ϱ' define respectively the retardation per unit thickness in the absence of optical activity and the optical rotatory power in the absence of linear birefringence. Suppose the principal axes of the birefringent element are at azimuth α and $\alpha + \pi/2$, represented by M and N (Fig. 7) of which M is the faster axis. Then the effect of passage through these two optical elements is to rotate the Poincaré sphere through angles $d\delta$ and $2d\varrho$ in an anti-clockwise direction about MN and LR respectively (Fig. 7). The addition of two infinitesimal rotations follow the law of vectorial addition and the resultant is independent of the sequence and is a rotation through an angle $d\Delta = \sqrt{(d\delta)^2 + (2d\varrho)^2}$ about the axis EF which is in the plane of MN and LR and makes an angle 2χ with NM where

$$2\chi = \arctan \frac{2d\varrho}{d\delta} = \arctan \frac{2\varrho'}{\delta'} . \tag{5.1}$$

For unit thickness of a birefringent, optically active crystal, the resultant effect is an anti-clockwise rotation of the Poincaré sphere through an angle

$$\Delta' = \sqrt{\delta'^2 + (2\varrho')^2} \tag{5.2}$$

[1] See e.g. BENNETT, OSTERBERG, JUPNIK and RICHARDS: Phase Microscopy, Chap. 3. New York 1951.

[2] R.C. JONES: J. Opt. Soc. Amer. **31**, 488, 493, 500 (1941).

about the axis EF, where the elliptic state E is propagated with the faster velocity.

Thus, the most general type of non-absorbing crystal (or optical element) is one which leads to a rotation of the Poincaré sphere about an axis EF, which is neither the polar axis LR nor does it lie in the equatorial plane. Analogous to the purely birefringent crystal, in which linear vibrations parallel to its principal directions are propagated unchanged, and the purely optically active crystal without birefringence, in which L and R are propagated unchanged, light of polarisation states E and F will be propagated unchanged in this crystal. This is so because a rotation of the sphere about EF leaves E and F unchanged. These states are two crossed ellipses which are orthogonal to each other.

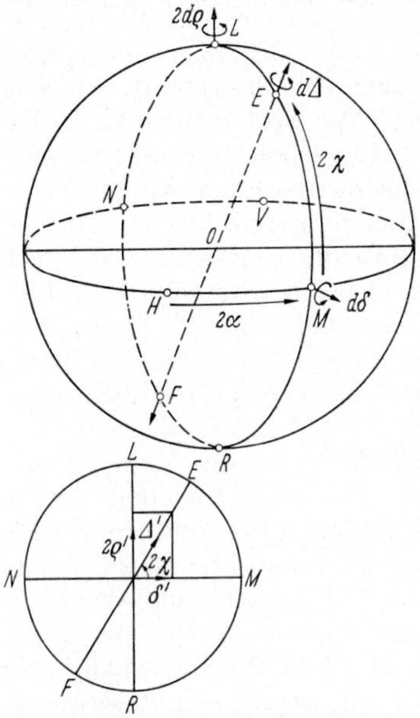

Fig. 7. Effect of a non-absorbing crystal exhibiting birefringence and optical activity. If δ' is the phase difference due to birefringence alone and ϱ' the optical rotation in the absence of birefringence, the resultant effect is a rotation of the Poincaré sphere through an angle Δ' about the axis EF.

In such a crystal, incident light of arbitrary state of polarisation P_0 is split up into the two orthogonal elliptical states E and F, which are propagated unchanged in state, but with a relative phase retardation Δ' per unit thickness. On emergence, they recombine, and the resultant state P is obtained from P_0 by a rotation of the Poincaré sphere about the axis EF, as shown in Sect. 4. The optical phenomena in such crystals are treated in Chap. B.

Since the emerging waves are orthogonally polarised they do not interfere and the emergent intensity will be the same as the incident intensity. The crystal will therefore be transparent as is to be expected. Vice versa, the operation for a thin layer of any non-absorbing optical element must necessarily be a rotation through an infinitesimal angle $d\Delta = \Delta' dz$ about some axis EF. This can be resolved into three infinitesimal rotations $d\Delta_1$, $d\Delta_2$, $d\Delta_3$ about the axes HV, CD, and LR respectively. These axes correspond to the co-ordinate axes OU, OV, OW in Poincaré space (Fig. 2). Thus, the effect of a general infinitesimal (non-absorbing) optical element on the state of polarisation of light passing through it is describable by means of three infinitesimal rotations about OU, OV and OW.

β) Combined effect of a series of transparent plates. We now return to the problem stated at the beginning of the section, viz., the passage of polarised light through a series of transparent parallel plates of finite thickness. For a linearly birefringent plate producing a relative phase retardation δ, the effect is to rotate the Poincaré sphere about an axis in the equatorial plane through the angle δ. The orientation of the axis is known from the orientation of the principal plane. So also, if ϱ is the rotation produced by the optically active plate (ϱ is positive for left-rotation), then the effect is to rotate the sphere through an angle 2ϱ about LR. (If the system also contains plates possessing both linear birefringence and optical activity, the effect of any such plate is to rotate the sphere about a given axis EF through a given angle Δ.)

The resultant of two successive rotations about two axes is again a rotation about some other axis of the sphere which may be determined either analytically or graphically by the construction illustrated in Fig. 8. The combined effects of the successive rotations of the Poincaré sphere may in this manner be replaced finally by a single rotation about some general axis in Poincaré space, i.e., the combination will be equivalent to a single elliptically birefringent plate (of the type discussed in the preceding sub-section), which shows differential retardation for two orthogonally polarised elliptic states. Alternatively, the resultant single rotation of the sphere can be resolved into two rotations about perpendicular axes—the first may be about LR and the other will then be about some axis in the equatorial plane which may be determined by the construction of Fig. 8. Thus the combination is equivalent to a system containing two elements, one a rotator and the other a retardation plate.

Since rotations about non-parallel axes are non-commutative operations, it is necessary to specify the exact sequence of the various elements. Interchanging any two of them would in general lead to a change in the final state of polarisation. The complete solution in the important case when all the plates exhibit only linear birefringence is given in Sect. 74.

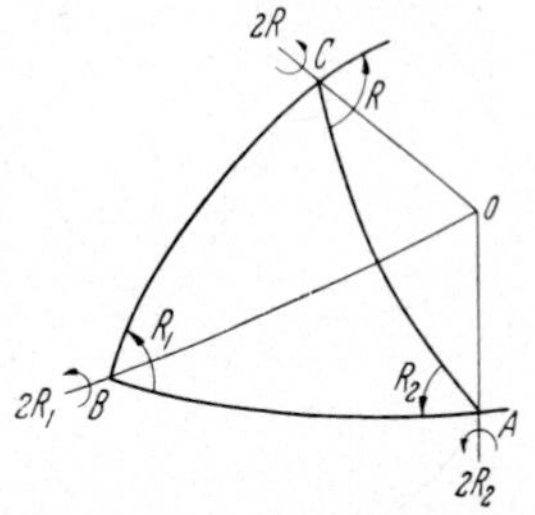

Fig. 8. Construction for the composition of two rotations. A rotation about AO through twice the internal angle at A followed by a rotation about BO through twice the internal angle at B is equivalent to a rotation about CO through twice the external angle at C.

6. Effect of absorption and dichroism—no birefringence[1]. The effect of an isotropic absorption would only lead to a reduction in intensity, without any change in the polarisation state. On the other hand, if the medium exhibits linear dichroism, with the principal planes along M_k and N_k (Fig. 9), then the absorption coefficients for the linear vibrations M_k and N_k will be different. Let these be k_1 and k_2 say for amplitude. In consequence, if a general elliptic vibration is resolved along M_k and N_k, then the components would be attenuated differently during the passage through the crystal plate, and on emergence the polarisation state would be changed.

If F_{k_0} and G_{k_0} are the *amplitudes* of the resolved components of the incident beam of the unit intensity along M_k and N_k, then it follows from Eq. (2.5) that

$$F_{k_0} = \cos\eta_0, \quad G_{k_0} = \sin\eta_0 \tag{6.1}$$

where $2\eta_0$ is the angular distance between P_0 and M_k on the Poincaré sphere. Thus

$$G_{k_0}/F_{k_0} = \tan\eta_0. \tag{6.2}$$

As a result of absorption, the amplitudes of the two components are reduced by factors $e^{-k_1 z}$ and $e^{-k_2 z}$ and in consequence the resolved components on emergence are

$$F_k = F_{k_0}\, e^{-k_1 z}, \tag{6.3}$$

$$G_k = G_{k_0}\, e^{-k_2 z}, \tag{6.4}$$

and if P is the state of polarisation of the emergent light and 2η is the arc $\widehat{PM_k}$, then

$$\tan\eta = \tan\eta_0\, e^{(k_1-k_2)z}. \tag{6.5}$$

If we consider a medium exhibiting pure linear dichroism i.e., with no birefringence, the relative phase difference between the M_k and N_k components of P_0 is

[1] S. PANCHARATNAM: Proc. Ind. Acad. Sci. A **42**, 86 (1955).

unaltered. This restricts the locus of P to the great circular arc $M_k P_0 N_k$ (as shown in the discussion in Sect. 4). Hence the position of P is as indicated in Fig. 9. It moves towards the less absorbed component, i.e., towards or away from M_k along the arc $M_k P_0 N_k$, according as k_1 is $>$ or $< k_2$.

The infinitesimal operation of linear dichroism corresponds to the passage through an infinitesimal distance dz. If we put $k = (k_1 - k_2)$ and denote the length of the arc $M_k P_0$ by s_k then it follows from (6.5) that

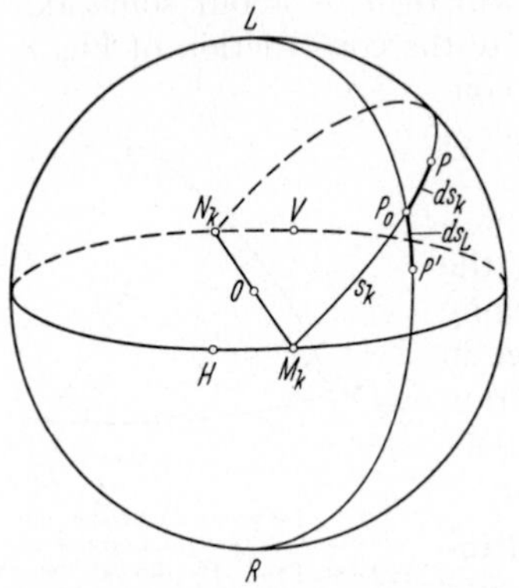

Fig. 9. Effect of dichroism on the state of polarisation. If M_k and N_k are the principal axes of linear dichroism, the initial state P_0 moves to P towards the less absorbed component along a great circle. In the case of circular dichroism, it moves to P' along the meridian of longitude.

$$\tan(\eta + d\eta) = \tan\eta \, e^{k\,dz}$$
$$= \tan\eta\,(1 + k\,dz)$$

or

$$k\,dz \tan\eta = d(\tan\eta) = \sec^2\eta\, d\eta .$$

Hence

$$d s_k = 2 d\eta = k \sin s_k \, dz. \qquad (6.6)$$

Thus, the arc $\widehat{PM_k}$ becomes larger if k is positive, and *vice-versa*.

Similarly, if the medium exhibits circular dichroism i.e., the two circular vibrations L and R are differently absorbed, then the effect on the polarisation state of a beam of light is described in a manner similar to that given above (on the Poincaré sphere). Let k be equal to $(k_L - k_R)$. Then, if s_L is the length of the arc LP_0, then on passing through an infinitesimal thickness dz, the point P_0 moves along the great circular arc LP_0R by a distance

$$d s_L = k \sin s_L \, dz , \qquad (6.7)$$

an equation exactly analogous to Eq. (6.6).

The most general case possible is one in which the medium exhibits differential absorption for two crossed ellipses, say E and F. In this case, the state P_0 goes to the state P as a result of passage through the medium, and if k_E and k_F are the absorption coefficients for light of polarisation states E and F and $k = (k_E - k_F)$ and $s_E = \text{arc}\ \widehat{EP}$ then

$$d s_E = k \sin s_E \, dz \qquad (6.8)$$

and P lies on the great circle EPF. In all these cases it is assumed that the medium exhibits no birefringence.

Analogous to Eq. (6.5), one could also obtain an equation for the position of the final state of polarisation P for a finite thickness also in the cases represented by (6.7) and (6.8).

7. Propagation of light through an optical system with absorption. It was mentioned in Sect. 5 that the infinitesimal operation in the most general case of birefringence is a rotation through an angle $d\Delta$ about a general axis, which could be resolved into three components $d\Delta_1, d\Delta_2, d\Delta_3$ about OU, OV, OW respectively. From the vectorial law of addition of infinitesimal rotations it can be shown that, if P, Q, R, are the direction cosines of the direction EF referred to OU, OV, OW, then

$$d\Delta_1 = P\,d\Delta, \quad d\Delta_2 = Q\,d\Delta, \quad d\Delta_3 = R\,d\Delta \qquad (7.1)$$

so that

$$(d\Delta)^2 = (d\Delta_1)^2 + (d\Delta_2)^2 + (d\Delta_3)^2 . \qquad (7.2)$$

A closely analogous result can be derived from the infinitesimal operation of dichroism[1]. The operation, as seen from Eq. (6.8), is a movement of the representative point P away from E by an amount ds proportional to $\sin \widehat{EP} = dk$ (say), where dk stands for $k\,ds$. This may be shown to be equivalent to the resultant of three such elementary operations of dichroism associated with OU, OV, OW and of strength $P\,dk$, $Q\,dk$, $R\,dk$ respectively. Thus, the point P is displaced away from OU in the great circle UPU' by an amount

Similarly,

$$\left.\begin{aligned} ds_1 &= P\,dk \sin \widehat{UP} = dk_1 \sin \widehat{UP}. \\ ds_2 &= Q\,dk \sin \widehat{VP} = dk_2 \sin \widehat{VP}, \\ ds_3 &= R\,dk \sin \widehat{WP} = dk_3 \sin \widehat{WP}, \end{aligned}\right\} \tag{7.3}$$

and the resultant of these three displacements (which is independent of the sequence, with infinitesimal operations) is equivalent to

$$ds = dk \sin \widehat{EP}. \tag{7.4}$$

It also follows that

$$(dk)^2 = (dk_1)^2 + (dk_2)^2 + (dk_3)^2. \tag{7.5}$$

The most general type of optical medium will be both birefringent and dichroic. In such a case, for an infinitesimal thickness, the effect of birefringence is given by the three quantities $d\Delta_1, d\Delta_2, d\Delta_3$ and that of dichroism by dk_1, dk_2, dk_3. Thus, six quantities have to be specified to describe the variation in the state of polarisation of the transmitted light. In addition, two more quantities are required to describe fully the light beam, namely its amplitude and its absolute phase. The changes occurring in amplitude and phase while passing through an infinitesimal thickness of the crystal may be defined by a mean absorption coefficient K and a mean refractive index n. These two quantities cannot be represented on the Poincaré sphere, which only represents the state of polarisation, without specifying the amplitude or the absolute phase.

It can be shown that an infinitesimal layer of such a medium exhibits differential absorption and differential retardation with respect to two non-orthogonal elliptic states (see Chap. B in Sect. 52). Hence the propagation through a finite thickness of a homogeneous medium of this type can be handled by the application of the results of Sect. 4. However, the propagation through an optical system of elements, which are of finite thickness and some of which are absorbing cannot be conveniently worked out by means of the Poincaré sphere—at least no geometrical analysis of this method appears to have been worked out. The problem can however be analysed by matrix methods (Sects. 12 and 13) particularly by the method introduced by JONES.

8. Incoherent addition of light beams. Partially polarised light[2]. The discussion so far had been confined to completely polarised beams of light and the decomposition and coherent addition of such beams which occurs during passage through an anisotropic medium. We shall now consider the state of polarisation of a mixture of two perfectly polarised incoherent beams, whose states of polarisation are different.

[1] We are here considering the case of orthogonal dichroism, i.e. that in which the different absorbed states are oppositely polarised. It can be shown that non-orthogonal dichroism can be resolved into orthogonal birefringence together with orthogonal dichroism for infinitesimal operations.

[2] U. FANO: J. Opt. Soc. Amer. **39**, 859 (1949). — G.N. RAMACHANDRAN: J. Madras Univ. B **22**, 277 (1952). — See also Sect. 17.

This is best discussed by using the intensity formula (2.4). Suppose P_1 and P_2 are the states of the two completely polarised beams whose intensities are in the ratio of $f_1:f_2$ and that these two beams are mixed incoherently. Thus, there is no phase correlation between the two, and if we allow the beam to pass through the analyser A, then the total intensity is just the sum of the intensities of the two beams transmitted by A. Remembering that the intensity of the resultant is the sum of the components, it follows from Eq. (2.4) that the fraction of the resultant beam which is transmitted by A is

$$\left.\begin{aligned} t_A &= \tfrac{1}{2} f_1 (1+\cos \widehat{P_1 A}) + \tfrac{1}{2} f_2 (1+\cos \widehat{P_2 A}) \\ &= \tfrac{1}{2} + \tfrac{1}{2} (f_1 \cos \widehat{P_1 A} + f_2 \cos \widehat{P_2 A}). \end{aligned}\right\} \tag{8.1}$$

If we indicate unit vectors along OP_1 and OP_2 by $\boldsymbol{P}_1$ and $\boldsymbol{P}_2$ and that along OA by $\boldsymbol{A}$, then we have

$$\left.\begin{aligned} t_A &= \tfrac{1}{2} + \tfrac{1}{2} (f_1 \boldsymbol{P}_1 + f_2 \boldsymbol{P}_2) \cdot \boldsymbol{A} \\ &= \tfrac{1}{2} + \tfrac{1}{2} \boldsymbol{p} \cdot \boldsymbol{A} \end{aligned}\right\} \tag{8.2}$$

where

$$\boldsymbol{p} = f_1 \boldsymbol{P}_1 + f_2 \boldsymbol{P}_2. \tag{8.3}$$

Obviously, Eqs. (8.2) and (8.3) hold for any analyser A, and (8.2) is the generalised form of Eq. (2.4) which in our present notation may be written in the form:

$$t_A = \tfrac{1}{2} + \tfrac{1}{2} \boldsymbol{P} \cdot \boldsymbol{A} \tag{8.4}$$

where $\boldsymbol{P}$ is now a unit vector parallel to OP. The intensities transmitted by an analyser of two beams having the same $\boldsymbol{P}$ will be identical and following STOKES, we may assume that these beams are identical in all other respects. The generalised equation for an incoherent mixture of two completely polarised beams is (8.3), and the magnitude of the vector $\boldsymbol{p}$ is given by

$$|\boldsymbol{p}| = |\boldsymbol{p}_1 + \boldsymbol{p}_2| \leqq p_1 + p_2 = 1$$

where

$$\boldsymbol{p}_1 = f_1 \boldsymbol{P}_1 \quad \text{and} \quad \boldsymbol{p}_2 = f_2 \boldsymbol{P}_2. \tag{8.5}$$

Thus, the state of polarisation of the mixed beam may be defined by the vector $\boldsymbol{p}$, whose magnitude $p<1$. In Poincaré space, the state may be represented by a point *within or on the surface* of the sphere of unit radius. If it is on the surface, then it represents completely polarised light.

We shall now examine the nature of the light beam represented by a point P, not lying on the surface of the Poincaré sphere (Fig. 10). Let the length of the vector OP be p, whose magnitude is less than unity. If we examine this light beam by an analyser A, then from Eq. (8.2), the fraction of the intensity transmitted by it is

$$t_A = \tfrac{1}{2} + \tfrac{1}{2} p \cos \alpha \tag{8.6}$$

where α is the angle between OP and OA. Obviously, this is maximum and minimum corresponding to $\cos\alpha = \pm 1$, i.e. $\alpha = 0$ or π. The corresponding positions of A are shown in Fig. 10 as A_1 and A_2, and in both cases, OA_1 or OA_2 is parallel to OP; only they are directed in opposite senses. The maximum and minimum values are:

$$t_{A_1} = \tfrac{1}{2} + \tfrac{1}{2} p \quad \text{and} \quad t_{A_2} = \tfrac{1}{2} - \tfrac{1}{2} p. \tag{8.7}$$

Thus, unlike with completely polarised light, there is no complete extinction of the light beam at any setting of the elliptic analyser, nor is there complete transmission. Such a beam of light would be called partially polarised. Since the maximum and minimum of transmitted intensity occurs at the orthogonal settings A_1 and A_2 of the analyser, one may say that the polarised part of the light beam has the state represented by A_1 and that there is in addition an unpolarised component. The relative proportion of the two is readily worked out from Eq. (8.6), which may be put in the form:

$$\left.\begin{aligned} t_A &= \tfrac{1}{2}(1-p) + \left(\tfrac{1}{2} + \tfrac{1}{2}\cos\alpha\right) \\ &= \tfrac{1}{2}u + p\left(\tfrac{1}{2} + \tfrac{1}{2}\cos\alpha\right). \end{aligned}\right\} \tag{8.8}$$

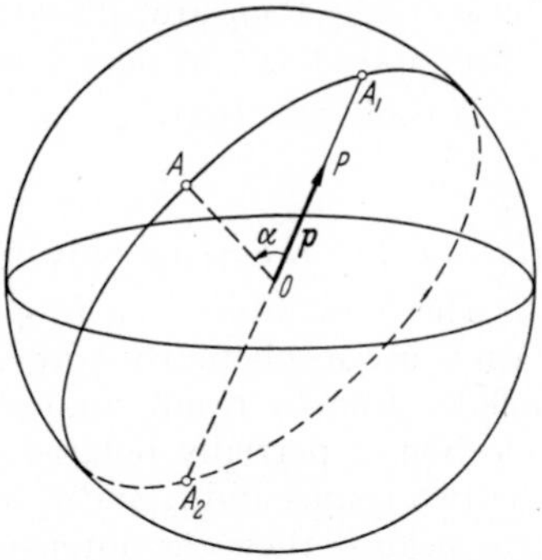

Fig. 10. Poincaré representation of partially polarised light. The state of a partially polarised beam is represented by the Poincaré vector $\boldsymbol{p}$ whose length p is the degree of polarisation and whose orientation A_1 represents the state of polarisation of the completely polarised part. The vector $I\boldsymbol{p}$ is called the Stokes vector.

Here, $\frac{1}{2} + \frac{1}{2}\cos\alpha$ is the fraction of the intensity of a completely polarised beam of state represented by A_1, which would be transmitted by an analyser A. Thus, the beam consists of a fraction p of completely polarised light of the state A_1 and a fraction $u = (1-p)$ of unpolarised light, half of which is transmitted by any analyser.

This then is the description of partially polarised light, of degree of polarisation p. If $p=0$, we get completely unpolarised light; the corresponding representative point coincides with the centre of the Poincaré sphere and any analyser would transmit half of its intensity. The state of partially polarised beam can be represented by a point P within the Poincaré sphere of unit radius, the two limiting cases being a *completely* polarised beam, represented by a point on the *surface* and an unpolarised beam, represented by the centre.

9. Stokes parameters. The geometrical representation in Poincaré space of partially polarised light discussed above can be given an analytical form by taking the components of the Poincaré vector along the three co-ordinate axes OU, OV, OW. If these components are denoted by u, v, w then obviously,

$$u^2 + v^2 + w^2 = 1. \tag{9.1}$$

The intensity I of the light beam and the three components of the vector $I\boldsymbol{p}$ namely Iu, Iv, Iw are called the four "Stokes Parameters" of the beam of light. They are respectively denoted by the symbols

$$I, \quad M(=Iu), \quad C(=Iv), \quad S(=Iw). \tag{9.2}$$

The vector $I\boldsymbol{p}$ may be called the Stokes vector $\boldsymbol{\Sigma}$ of the light beam.

The above parameters were first introduced by Stokes[1] in connection with his studies on polarised light more than a century ago. Many of the theorems discussed below were proved by him even then. In fact the concept of unpolarised and partially polarised light which he put forward so long ago is remarkably modern and is consistent with quantum mechanical concepts. The Stokes parameters have however found very few applications until recently. Soleillet[2] used them for a study of fluorescence, while Perrin[3] developed a general theory of the polarised components in light scattering in terms of Stokes parameters.

[1] C. G. Stokes: Trans. Cambridge Phil. Soc. **9**, 399 (1852).
[2] P. Soleillet: Ann. Phys., Paris **12**, 23 (1929).
[3] F. Perrin: J. Chem. Phys. **10**, 415 (1942).

It was CHANDRASEKHAR[1] who drew pointed attention to the advantages ot these parameters in optical studies. MUELLER[2] has made a systematic use of these parameters in a course on optics but unfortunately this treatment has never been published *in extenso*. Since then, Stokes parameters have figured in several papers[3], some of which are mentioned in the later sections. The relationship between the Poincaré sphere and Stokes parameters is discussed by FANO[4] and RAMACHANDRAN[5] while a few reviews have also appeared recently[6].

It is obvious that

$$I \geqq \sqrt{M^2 + C^2 + S^2}, \tag{9.3}$$

the equality occurring only for completely polarised light.

The most interesting property of the Stokes parameters is that, if two light beams are incoherently added, then their Stokes parameters are additive. This follows from a result analogous to Eq. (8.3), which holds for the incoherent addition of partially polarised beams. If $\boldsymbol{p}_1$ and $\boldsymbol{p}_2$ are the Poincaré vectors of the two beams and f_1 and f_2 are the fractions of the intensity contributed by the two beams, then the intensity of the resultant beam of intensity I which is transmitted by an analyser A is

$$\left.\begin{aligned} I_A &= I f_1 (\tfrac{1}{2} + \tfrac{1}{2}\boldsymbol{p}_1 \cdot \boldsymbol{A}) + I f_2 (\tfrac{1}{2} + \tfrac{1}{2}\boldsymbol{p}_2 \cdot \boldsymbol{A}) \\ &= \tfrac{1}{2} I [1 + (f_1 \boldsymbol{p}_1 + f_2 \boldsymbol{p}_2) \cdot \boldsymbol{A}] \\ &= \tfrac{1}{2} I [1 + \boldsymbol{p} \cdot \boldsymbol{A}] \end{aligned}\right\} \tag{9.4}$$

where

$$\boldsymbol{p} = f_1 \boldsymbol{p}_1 + f_2 \boldsymbol{p}_2. \tag{9.5}$$

If now I_1 and I_2 are the intensities of the two beams, and the resultant is I, we have

$$I = I_1 + I_2 \tag{9.6}$$

and

$$I \boldsymbol{p} = I f_1 \boldsymbol{p}_1 + I f_2 \boldsymbol{p}_2 = I_1 \boldsymbol{p}_1 + I_2 \boldsymbol{p}_2 \tag{9.7}$$

giving

$$M = M_1 + M_2, \qquad C = C_1 + C_2, \qquad S = S_1 + S_2. \tag{9.8}$$

The result can obviously be generalised to the incoherent addition of any number of light beams, and each Stokes parameter of the resultant beam would be the sum of the corresponding parameters of the component beams.

The intensity formula (9.4) can now be put in terms of the Stokes parameters. Suppose the elliptic analyser A corresponds to an azimuth λ of the major axis and an ellipticity ω. Then the latitude and longitude of A are 2ω and 2λ, and its three components along OU, OV, OW are

$$\cos 2\omega \cos 2\lambda, \qquad \cos 2\omega \sin 2\lambda, \qquad \sin 2\omega.$$

Thus,

$$I_A = \tfrac{1}{2} [I + M \cos 2\omega \cos 2\lambda + C \cos 2\omega \sin 2\lambda + S \sin 2\omega]. \tag{9.9}$$

---

[1] S. CHANDRASEKHAR: Astrophys. J. **105**, 424 (1947). — Radiative Transfer, pp. 24—37. London 1950.

[2] H. MUELLER: M.I.T. Course (8.26), Spring 1945. — J. Opt. Soc. Amer. **38**, 661 (1948).

[3] B.H. BILLINGS and E.H. LAND: J. Opt. Soc. Amer. **38**, 819 (1948). — B.H. BILLINGS: J. Opt. Soc. Amer. **41**, 966 (1951); **42**, 72 (1952).

[4] U. FANO: J. Opt. Soc. Amer. **39**, 859 (1949).

[5] G.N. RAMACHANDRAN: J. Madras Univ. B **22**, 277 (1952).

[6] M.J. WALKER: Amer. J. Phys. **22**, 170 (1954). — W.H. MCMASTER: Amer. J. Phys. **22**, 351 (1954). — G.V. ROZENBERG: Uspekhi Fiz. Nauk **56**, 77 (1955).

This formula gives the intensity transmitted by a general elliptic analyser of light having the Stokes parameters I, M, C, S and its variation with the azimuth and ellipticity of the analyser.

Various methods could be worked out for determining the Stokes parameters of a beam of light by making use of the variation with ω, λ of the transmitted intensity. A straightforward method, however, follows from Eq. (9.4)[1]. Suppose one determines by a photometer the intensity transmitted by the following analysers: a linear analyser set at angles (a) 0°, (b) 90°, (c) 45°, (d) −45° and (e) a left circular analyser and (f) a right circular analyser. Let the measured intensities be respectively denoted by $I_0, I_{90}, I_{45}, I_{-45}, I_L$ and I_R. Then we have from (9.2) and (9.4),

$$\left.\begin{aligned} I_0 &= \tfrac{1}{2}(I+M), & I_{90} &= \tfrac{1}{2}(I-M),\\ I_{45} &= \tfrac{1}{2}(I+C), & I_{-45} &= \tfrac{1}{2}(I-C),\\ I_L &= \tfrac{1}{2}(I+S), & I_R &= \tfrac{1}{2}(I-S) \end{aligned}\right\} \tag{9.10}$$

so that

$$M = (I_0 - I_{90}), \quad C = (I_{45} - I_{-45}), \quad S = (I_L - I_R), \tag{9.11}$$

$$I = (I_0 + I_{90}) = (I_{45} + I_{-45}) = (I_L + I_R). \tag{9.12}$$

Actually, only four of the six measurements are independent, but the others serve as a check.

10. Incoherent addition and decomposition of polarised beams. When two partially polarised beams are incoherently added, the resultant Poincaré vector is given by Eq. (9.5) and the Stokes parameters are additive. More generally, if $\boldsymbol{p}$ is the Poincaré vector representing the state of polarisation of a beam obtained by incoherently adding fractions f_j of a number of beams of state $\boldsymbol{p}_j$ ($j=1$ to n), then

$$\boldsymbol{p} = \sum_{j=1}^{n} f_j \boldsymbol{p}_j \tag{10.1}$$

since the magnitudes of all the vectors $\boldsymbol{p}_j \leqq 1$ and $\Sigma f_j = 1$, it follows that $\boldsymbol{p} \leqq 1$ as it should be. What is more interesting is the fact that

$$p \leqq \sum f_j p_j \tag{10.2}$$

which follows from Eq. (10.1). Thus, the degree of polarisation of the resulting beam is less than the mean degree of polarisation of the component beams. In other words, the degree of polarisation always decreases on mixing light beams incoherently. In the special case, when the polarised components of all the added beams are of the same state, there is no change.

A particularly vivid example of this is obtained when two completely polarised beams are mixed. If the two are not of the same state, the resulting beam is only partially polarised. If the two are orthogonally polarised, then $\boldsymbol{P}_1 = -\boldsymbol{P}_2$, so that on mixing equal proportions of the two, $\boldsymbol{p} = \frac{1}{2}\boldsymbol{P}_1 + \frac{1}{2}\boldsymbol{P}_2 = 0$ i.e., the beam has zero degree of polarisation, or it is unpolarised. Thus, unpolarised light can be obtained by incoherently superposing any two orthogonally polarised beams in equal proportions. If the two are not mixed in equal proportions, then a partially polarised beam is produced, the state of the polarised part being that of the stronger component.

Conversely, suppose we wish to resolve a beam of partially polarised light represented by the Poincaré vector $\boldsymbol{p}$ into a sum of two incoherent oppositely

[1] U. Fano: Phys. Rev. **93**, 121 (1954).

polarised beams. This can be done in one and only one way[1]. If $\boldsymbol{P}_1$ and $\boldsymbol{P}_2$ are the Poincaré vectors (modulus unity) into which the vector $\boldsymbol{p}$ is to be resolved then obviously $\boldsymbol{P}_1$, $\boldsymbol{P}_2$ and $\boldsymbol{p}$ must be coplanar. Consequently, if $\boldsymbol{P}_1$ and $\boldsymbol{P}_2$ are oppositely directed, then all the three vectors must be parallel, which makes the resolution unique (except when $\boldsymbol{p}=0$). Also, if f_1 and f_2 are the fractions of the total intensity of the two resolved beams, then

$$f_1\boldsymbol{P}_1+f_2\boldsymbol{P}_2=\boldsymbol{p}$$

giving

$$p=f_1-f_2. \tag{10.3}$$

This together with $f_1+f_2=1$ gives

$$f_1=\tfrac{1}{2}(1+p), \quad f_2=\tfrac{1}{2}(1-p). \tag{10.4}$$

If $p=0$ then $f_1=f_2=\frac{1}{2}$ and therefore completely unpolarised light can be resolved into two equal beams of any pair of orthogonally polarised beams.

If the restriction that the two components should be orthogonally polarised is removed, then the resolution of an arbitrary state of polarisation ($\boldsymbol{p}$) into an incoherent sum of two completely polarised beams of states $\boldsymbol{P}_1$ and $\boldsymbol{P}_2$ is not unique. In fact, the only condition is that $\boldsymbol{P}_1, \boldsymbol{P}_2, \boldsymbol{p}$ should be coplanar[2] and $\boldsymbol{p}$ should be contained in the angle between $\boldsymbol{P}_1$ and $\boldsymbol{P}_2$. Thus, one has the interesting result that, while two polarised beams combine to produce a partially polarised beam whose state can be uniquely specified, the resolution of the latter beam into two completely polarised beams is not at all unique (unless the state of one of the component beams is given).

11. Partially coherent light beams. *α) Interference of two partially coherent beams*[3]. The most general case of the interference of two completely polarised beams of intensities I_1 and I_2 occurs when they are *partially* coherent, i.e., when there exists only a partial correlation between the fluctuations in the absolute phases and intensities of the beams. The correlation may be expressed in terms of a degree of coherence γ and the effective phase advance δ of the first beam P_1 over the second, or alternatively, in terms of two correlation parameters C' and S'. The former parameters are defined by

$$\langle|\sqrt{i_1 i_2}|\,e^{i\delta_t}\rangle=\gamma\,|\sqrt{I_1 I_2}|\,e^{i\delta} \tag{11.1}$$

while the latter are defined as

$$\left.\begin{aligned} C' &= 2\langle\sqrt{i_1 i_2}\cos\delta_t\rangle = 2\gamma\sqrt{I_1 I_2}\cos\delta,\\ S' &= 2\langle\sqrt{i_1 i_2}\sin\delta_t\rangle = 2\gamma\sqrt{I_1 I_2}\sin\delta \end{aligned}\right\} \tag{11.2}$$

where $\langle a\rangle$ stands for the average value of a.

Here i_1 and i_2 are the instantaneous intensities of the beams in the states of polarisation $\boldsymbol{P}_1$ and $\boldsymbol{P}_2$ and δ_t is the instantaneous phase advance of the first vibration over the second. The state of polarisation of the vibration obtained by their composition will obviously be fluctuating rapidly, giving us a new picture of a partially polarised beam—into which we must briefly digress.

[1] G.N. RAMACHANDRAN: J. Madras Univ. B **22**, 277 (1952). This result was first proved by an analytical method by C.G. STOKES [Mathematical and Physical Papers, Cambridge **3**, 233 (1901)].

[2] For more details, see U. FANO: J. Opt. Soc. Amer. **39**, 859 (1949). An example of such a resolution occurs in Sect. 70γ.

[3] S. PANCHARATNAM: Proc. Ind. Acad. Sci. A **44**, 247, 398 (1956); A **45**, 1 (1957).

Let σ be a vector (drawn from the centre of the Poincaré sphere) whose length is equal to the instantaneous intensity of the resultant (partially polarised) beam, and whose point of intersection with the Poincaré sphere defines the instantaneous state of polarisation. Then the parameters which are observable in usual experiments are

$$I = \langle i \rangle, \qquad \boldsymbol{\Sigma} = \langle \boldsymbol{\sigma} \rangle. \tag{11.3}$$

The relation that the present representation $(I, \boldsymbol{\Sigma})$ of the state of a partially polarised beam bears to the representation introduced previously, is made obvious by writing down the expression for the intensity I_P transmitted by an analyser P which will be the average of the instantaneously transmitted intensity:

$$I_P = \langle \tfrac{1}{2}(i + \boldsymbol{\sigma} \cdot \boldsymbol{P}) \rangle = \tfrac{1}{2}(I + \boldsymbol{\Sigma} \cdot \boldsymbol{P}). \tag{11.4}$$

If we write $\boldsymbol{\Sigma} = I\boldsymbol{p}$, then $\boldsymbol{p}$ is the Poincaré vector representing the state of polarisation of the beam, which had been introduced by a simpler procedure in Sect. 8 [see e.g. Eq. (8.2)]. Thus $\boldsymbol{\Sigma}$ is the three-component part of the Stokes vector, which we shall for brevity refer to as the Stokes vector of the light beam. The component of the Stokes vector parallel to any direction is given by a formula of the type (9.11) since we have from (11.4)

$$I_P - I_{-P} = \boldsymbol{\Sigma} \cdot \boldsymbol{P}. \tag{11.5}$$

Returning to the problem of the addition of two completely polarised but partially coherent beams, the resultant intensity may be obtained by averaging a formula of the type (4.4) for the momentary intensity, using (11.2):

$$I = I_1 + I_2 + 2\gamma \sqrt{I_1 I_2} \cos c \cos \delta \tag{11.6}$$

where $2c$ is the angle between $\boldsymbol{P}_1$ and $\boldsymbol{P}_2$.

The intensity transmitted by an analyser P if introduced in the path of the interfering beams is similarly obtained by averaging a formula of the type (4.20) for the momentary intensity transmitted using (11.1); and hence I_p will be given again by the expression (4.20) except that the third term will be multiplied by the degree of coherence γ. The Stokes vector of the resultant beam obtained by directly compounding two partially coherent beams in states $\boldsymbol{P}_1$ and $\boldsymbol{P}_2$ may now be determined by using (11.5) to find the x, y and z components of $\boldsymbol{S}$—by taking x, y and z to lie successively along these coordinate axes. Referring to Fig. 11, we take the x-axis along the direction of $(\boldsymbol{P}_1 - \boldsymbol{P}_2)$—which bisects externally the angle between $\boldsymbol{P}_1$ and $\boldsymbol{P}_2$; the y-axis is taken along the direction of the internal bisector $(\boldsymbol{P}_1 + \boldsymbol{P}_2)$ and the z-axis along the perpendicular direction $(\boldsymbol{P}_1 \times \boldsymbol{P}_2)$. It can then be shown that

$$\boldsymbol{\Sigma} = \boldsymbol{\Sigma}_1 + \boldsymbol{\Sigma}_2 + \boldsymbol{\Sigma}_{12} \tag{11.7}$$

where $\boldsymbol{\Sigma}_1 = I_1 \boldsymbol{P}_1$ and $\boldsymbol{\Sigma}_2 = I_2 \boldsymbol{P}_2$ are the Stokes vectors of the two interfering beams and $\boldsymbol{\Sigma}_{12}$ is a vector arising because of the interference of the beams [cf. e.g. Eq. (9.7)]; the vector $\boldsymbol{\Sigma}_{12}$ is given by

$$\left.\begin{aligned} (\Sigma_{12})_x &= 0, & \text{(a)}\\ (\Sigma_{12})_y &= 2\gamma \sqrt{I_1 I_2} \cos \delta = C', & \text{(b)}\\ (\Sigma_{12})_z &= 2\gamma \sqrt{I_1 I_2} \sin \delta \sin c = S' \sin c. & \text{(c)} \end{aligned}\right\} \tag{11.8}$$

On the basis of the above discussion it may be shown that just as a partially polarised beam may be regarded as a mixture of completely polarised and unpolarised light, so also two partially coherent (but completely polarised) beams may be pictured in the following way: an independent fraction γ^2 of the intensity of one beam may be regarded as completely coherent with the whole of the second beam having a phase advance δ with respect to it.

The result in the limiting case when the two interfering beams become orthogonally polarised may be deduced either as a special case of the problem discussed above, or independently. Here $\boldsymbol{P}_1$ and $\boldsymbol{P}_2$ lie respectively along the positive and negative directions of the x-axis, the arc $P_1 Y P_2$ being taken as defining the arc of zero phase difference for the orthogonal states $\boldsymbol{P}_1$ and $\boldsymbol{P}_2$. The resultant partially polarised beam $(I, \boldsymbol{\Sigma})$ is now given by

$$\left.\begin{aligned} I &= I_1 + I_2; & \Sigma_x &= I_1 - I_2; \\ \Sigma_y &= 2\gamma\sqrt{I_1 I_2}\cos\delta = C'; & \Sigma_z &= 2\gamma\sqrt{I_1 I_2}\sin\delta = S'. \end{aligned}\right\} \tag{11.9}$$

A beam $(I, \boldsymbol{\Sigma})$ in any state of polarisation can always be decomposed into two completely polarised beams in any given state though the component beams will in general be partially coherent; for example even unpolarised light can be decomposed into two non-orthogonal polarised beams which will then be partially coherent with one another (see Sect. 70). We shall not however quote the results for the general problem which is the converse of that discussed above.

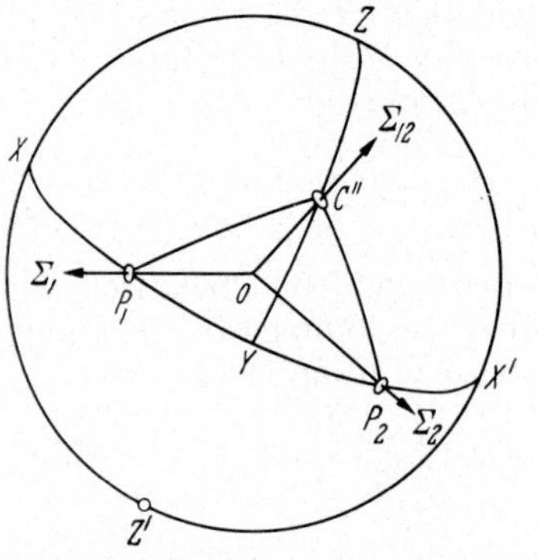

Fig. 11. Composition of two non-orthogonally polarised beams $\boldsymbol{\Sigma}_1$ and $\boldsymbol{\Sigma}_2$. The Stokes vector of the resultant partially polarised beam is the sum

$$\boldsymbol{\Sigma}_1 + \boldsymbol{\Sigma}_2 + \boldsymbol{\Sigma}_{12}.$$

β) Partial coherence and partial polarisation. It is seen from (11.6) that the visibility of fringes obtained by the interference of two completely polarised beams is affected in a similar manner by two factors namely the degree of coherence γ and the factor $\cos c$, which specifies the difference in the states of polarisation. Nevertheless these two factors must be carefully distinguished; for example two orthogonally polarised beams can never give rise to interference in intensity and yet may be completely coherent (combining to yield an elliptic vibration). Similarly two beams may be in the same state of polarisation and yet at the same time be completely incoherent. In general the beams can be tested for partial coherence after transmission through an analyser which resolves them into the same state. It is convenient to adjust the setting of the analyser so that the intensity of the transmitted beams are equal. The degree of coherence is then given by the visibility of the fringes, V. The latter is defined by

$$V = \frac{I_{\max} - I_{\min}}{I_{\max} + I_{\min}}, \tag{11.10}$$

and the relation $\gamma = V$ is readily obtained from Eq. (11.6) remembering that the interfering beams are in the same state of polarisation ($\cos c = 1$). Here $I_{\max}$ and $I_{\min}$ correspond to the cases when the phase differences of the final beams are respectively 0 and π. Similarly by direct interference experiments, without resolving the beam through an analyser, the factor $\gamma\cos c$ may be determined, being equal to the visibility of this system of fringes. Since γ is known from the previous experiment, the non-orthogonality factor may be separated out. The physical interpretation of the degree of coherence γ is that an independent fraction γ^2 of the intensity of one beam is completely coherent with the other beam (having a phase advance of δ over the other).

As an example of two partially coherent pencils we may mention the two completely separate pencils emerging from a calcite rhomb when a partially polarised pencil is incident on the first face. This example leads us to the relation between partial polarisation and partial coherence. When a partially polarised beam is resolved into two orthogonally polarised beams, the component beams can only be incompletely coherent. In particular the state of partial polarisation of a beam could itself be specified by regarding it as the sum of two partially coherent beams which are linearly polarised in two orthogonal states H and V. This forms the basis of the conventional presentation of the Stokes parameters. In fact the Stokes parameters of a beam with reference to axes on the wavefront corresponding to H and V are then defined as the values taken by the quantities on the right-hand side of Eq. (11.9). However in such a representation the invariant character (namely the state of partial polarisation) of the given beam is not immediately evident since the degree of coherence of the component beams itself varies with the orientation of the two orthogonal axes. For example, at one extreme the given partially polarised beam can always be resolved into two orthogonal states which are completely incoherent and at the other extreme, if the orthogonal beams are chosen such that the component beams have equal intensity, their degree of coherence will be a maximum, being equal to the degree of polarisation of the beam. By picturing a partially polarised beam as one in which the instantaneous state of polarisation fluctuates (as in Sect. 11 α) the Stokes vector may then be directly obtained using the Poincaré sphere without recourse to the concepts of partial coherence. Alternatively the Stokes vector may be introduced as in Sect. 9 where only the extreme concepts of coherence and incoherence and of completely polarised and unpolarised light are used.

12. Propagation of light through an optical system. Changes in the state of polarisation. *α) Use of Stokes representation.* Although Stokes parameters have been introduced essentially to represent unpolarised or partially polarised light, they may be used equally well for completely polarised light. In this case,

$$I^2 = M^2 + C^2 + S^2 \tag{12.1}$$

so that the Stokes vector $\boldsymbol{\Sigma}$, or its three components M, C, S can be used to represent both intensity and the state of polarisation. Consequently in this case, all statements regarding the transformation of the Stokes vector will be equally valid for the Poincaré vector, provided the medium is transparent.

The effect of passage through a finite thickness of a transparent birefringent plate has been shown to be a rotation through an angle Δ about some axis OR in the Poincaré space. The corresponding operator may be represented by a matrix

$$R = T\,U\,T^{-1} \tag{12.2}$$

where T is the operator for the transformation of axes which brings OU to OR and U is the operator for a rotation through an angle about OU.

Explicitly, U takes the form

$$\begin{pmatrix} 1 & 0 & 0 \\ 0 & \cos\Delta & -\sin\Delta \\ 0 & \sin\Delta & \cos\Delta \end{pmatrix} \tag{12.3a}$$

which for an infinitesimal rotation $d\Delta$ takes the form

$$\begin{pmatrix} 1 & 0 & 0 \\ 0 & 1 & -d\Delta \\ 0 & d\Delta & 1 \end{pmatrix}. \tag{12.3b}$$

The matrix of the operator in the case of dichroism is not so simple and is not independent of the polarisation state of the incident beam. In fact the total absorption also depends on the state of polarisation of the incident beam [see Eq. (12.5) below].

When the medium exhibits both birefringence and dichroism, then the effect of an infinitesimal thickness on the polarisation state may be expressed by a product of two matrices, one representing the operation of linear birefringence and the other the operation of linear dichroism, the product being independent of the order when both are infinitesimal. It appears that, in the Poincaré representation, problems are best worked out by means of geometrical methods, rather than by the use of matrices given here.

β) Mueller matrices. The matrices discussed above relate only to completely polarised beams, and for coherent additions of such beams. When incoherent mixtures of light beams are considered, then the resultant beam is partially polarised, and in such cases, the Stokes parameters I, M, C, S should be used to denote its intensity and state of polarisation. The effect of the passage of light through a depolarising system (i.e., a system in which the components of the emergent light are not perfectly coherent) may then be described by a 4×4 matrix $\mathfrak{M}$ having 16 elements. If $\mathfrak{S}$ is the column vector with components $I, M, C, S,$ then,

$$\mathfrak{S}' = \mathfrak{M}\mathfrak{S}. \tag{12.4}$$

We shall call the matrix $\mathfrak{M}$ the Mueller matrix, after Professor MUELLER[1] who advocated the systematic use of these matrices, although the relation (12.4) had been used earlier by other workers[2,3].

The matrices could also be used even in the case when the system introduces depolarisation. For example for the infinitesimal operation of dichroism the Mueller matrix is given by

$$\mathfrak{M} = \begin{pmatrix} 1-2K\,dz & -P\,dK & -Q\,dK & -R\,dK \\ -P\,dK & 1-2K\,dz & 0 & 0 \\ -Q\,dK & 0 & 1-2K\,dz & 0 \\ -R\,dK & 0 & 0 & 1-2K\,dz \end{pmatrix} \tag{12.5}$$

where the notation of Sect. 7 is used, K representing the mean of the absorption coefficients for the two crossed elliptic states.

The Mueller matrices have 16 coefficients; actually one more is necessary to define the absolute phase. If there is no depolarisation, then $I^2 = M^2 + C^2 + S^2$ and it can be shown that 9 identities occur between the Mueller coefficients, so that 7 independent coefficients are required to describe the change in the state of polarisation.

The Mueller matrices in the general form are useful in the study of the polarisation and intensity of light scattering[4].

13. Jones matrix method[5]. JONES has developed a different matrix method for studying the propagation of light through an optical system, of the type

---

[1] H. MUELLER: J. Opt. Soc. Amer. **38**, 661 (1948).

[2] F. PERRIN: J. Chem. Phys. **10**, 415 (1942). — S. CHANDRASEKHAR: Radiative Transfer, London 1950.

[3] R.C. JONES: J. Opt. Soc. Amer. **37**, 107 (1947).

[4] F. PERRIN: J. Chem. Phys. **10**, 415 (1942).

[5] R.C. JONES: J. Opt. Soc. Amer. **31**, 488, 500 (1941).

discussed in the previous section. The method is based on the idea that any elliptic vibration can be represented as the resultant of a coherent addition of two linear vibrations at right angles (e.g. OX and OY) with appropriate amplitudes and phases. The elliptic vibrations can be then represented completely (amplitude, phase and polarisation state) by the column vector[1]

$$\vec{D} = \begin{pmatrix} A_1 \\ A_2 \end{pmatrix} \tag{13.1}$$

where A_1 and A_2 are the resolved components of the electric displacement vector $\boldsymbol{D}$ along OX and OY, and are in general complex numbers. The intensity is $I = |A_1|^2 + |A_2|^2$ while the complex ratio A_2/A_1 describes its polarisation state. The azimuth λ and the ellipticity ω of the ellipse are related to A_1 and A_2 as follows: If $\tan\alpha = \frac{|A_1|}{|A_2|}$ and $\delta = \varepsilon_1 - \varepsilon_2$ where ε_1 and ε_2 are the phases of A_1 and A_2 then

$$\left.\begin{aligned} \tan 2\lambda &= \cos\delta \tan 2\alpha, \\ \sin 2\omega &= \sin\delta \sin 2\alpha. \end{aligned}\right\} \tag{13.2}$$

The effect of an optical component, e.g., a birefringent, absorbing or dichroic plate, or a combination of such plates, would be to change both A_1 and A_2, so that the effect may be represented by a 2×2 matrix with complex elements

$$\vec{D'} = \mathsf{M}\vec{D}. \tag{13.3}$$

For a non-absorbing plate, there is no change in the intensity and the matrix M is therefore unitary i.e., $\det M = 1$, which makes $|D'| = |D|$. Suppose that the plate exhibits only linear birefringence (retardation plate) and the principal axes are parallel to OX and OY. If φ_1, φ_2 are the phase retardation for vibrations parallel to OX and OY respectively and we set $\varphi = \frac{1}{2}(\varphi_1 + \varphi_2)$ and $\gamma = \frac{1}{2}(\varphi_1 - \varphi_2)$, then obviously M takes the form $e^{i\varphi}\,\mathsf{G}$, where

$$\mathsf{G} = \begin{pmatrix} e^{i\gamma} & 0 \\ 0 & e^{-i\gamma} \end{pmatrix}. \tag{13.4}$$

If we are only interested in the state of polarisation of the emergent beam, then $\exp i\varphi$ may be omitted.

If the principal axes are inclined at angles β and $\beta + \frac{\pi}{2}$ to OX, then the matrix is

$$\mathsf{M}(\beta) = \mathsf{S}(\beta)\,\mathsf{G}\,\mathsf{S}(-\beta) \tag{13.5}$$

where $\mathsf{S}(\beta)$ is the rotation matrix

$$\begin{pmatrix} \cos\beta & -\sin\beta \\ \sin\beta & \cos\beta \end{pmatrix}. \tag{13.6}$$

If the plate exhibits only circular birefringence (rotator), then the effect is to rotate the plane of polarisation. If the rotation is ϱ, and the mean absolute phase retardation is φ, then the matrix is simply $e^{i\varphi}\,\mathsf{S}(\varrho)$ and the effect of the plate on the state of polarisation of the light beam is completely represented by $\mathsf{S}(\varrho)$.

---

[1] Jones has used the components of the electric vector $\boldsymbol{E}$ for this purpose. In anisotropic media, it is the displacement vector $\boldsymbol{D}$ that should represent the light vibrations.

It can be readily shown[1] that for light of a given wavelength, an optical system containing any number of retardation plates and rotators is equivalent to a system containing only two elements—one a retardation plate and the other a rotator. This has already been shown from the Poincaré representation in Sect. 5.

In fact, it follows from the group theory of three dimensional rotations that any unitary 2×2 matrix with unit determinant may be associated with the rotation of a sphere in a unique manner[2]. Thus the Jones matrix method is identically equivalent to the Poincaré sphere representation, as far as the polarisation state of a light beam is concerned.

Suppose the optical element is linearly dichroic, with its principal axes parallel to OX and OY (partial polariser). Then, its matrix is $e^{i\varphi}\,\mathbf{P}$ where

$$\mathbf{P} = \begin{pmatrix} p_1 & 0 \\ 0 & p_2 \end{pmatrix}, \quad 0 \leqq p_1 \leqq 1, \quad 0 \leqq p_2 \leqq 1. \tag{13.7}$$

For a perfect polariser one of the p's will be zero. The more general dichroic element will be discussed in Sect. 14.

The matrix representing the combined effect of a succession of optical elements would be the product of the matrices representing the effects of the individual elements (taken in the proper sequence). Using these results several elegant equivalence theorems of the type given above have been derived by JONES (see Sect. 74).

14. Experimental determination of the Jones matrix[3]. Explicitly written, the Eq. (13.3) takes the form

$$\begin{pmatrix} A_1' \\ A_2' \end{pmatrix} = \begin{pmatrix} m_1 & m_4 \\ m_3 & m_2 \end{pmatrix} \begin{pmatrix} A_1 \\ A_2 \end{pmatrix} \tag{14.1}$$

where m_1, m_2, m_3, m_4 are complex numbers. The following is a procedure which may be used to determine the real and imaginary parts of these four numbers. It is assumed that the state of the light beam is completely reversed, if it traverses the system in the reverse direction.

(i) Use incident light linearly polarised parallel to OX (i.e., $A_2=0$) and determine the state of polarisation of the emergent light by an elliptic analyser. This gives the ratio $A_2'/A_1' = c_1$ (say). Then

$$c_1 = \frac{m_3}{m_1}. \tag{14.2}$$

(ii) Use incident light linearly polarised parallel to OY and determine the ratio $A_2'/A_1' = c_2$ (say). Then

$$c_2 = \frac{m_2}{m_4}. \tag{14.3}$$

(iii) Reverse the system and repeat the procedure (i) with this. Let the ratio be c_3. Then

$$c_3 = \frac{m_4}{m_1}. \tag{14.4}$$

[1] See H. HURWITZ jr. and R.C. JONES: J. Opt. Soc. Amer. **31**, 493 (1941) for a proof by the matrix method.

[2] C. ECKART: Rev. Mod. Phys. **2**, 305 (1930).

[3] R.C. JONES: J. Opt. Soc. Amer. **37**, 110 (1947).

As a check, the procedure (ii) may be repeated in the reverse position giving

$$c_4 = \frac{m_2}{m_3}. \tag{14.5}$$

This is not an independent determination, for

$$c_1 c_4 = c_2 c_3. \tag{14.6}$$

However, it provides two checks, namely for the real and imaginary parts of Eq. (14.6).

The matrix $\mathbf{M}$ may then be written in the form

$$\mathbf{M} = c \begin{pmatrix} 1 & c_3 \\ c_1 & c_2 c_3 \end{pmatrix} \tag{14.7}$$

where c is a complex number.

(iv) Determine the transmitted intensity for unpolarised light (T_{unpol}). This is given by

$$T_{\text{unpol}} = \tfrac{1}{2} \sum |m_1|^2 \tag{14.8}$$

so that

$$|c|^2 = \frac{2\, T_{\text{unpol}}}{1 + |c_1|^2 + |c_3|^2 + |c_2 c_3|^2}. \tag{14.9}$$

(v) Determine the absolute phase of the transmitted light. This serves to determine the real and imaginary parts of c, and completes the determination.

It may be mentioned that each of the measurements, under (i), (ii) and (iii) consists of two determinations, namely the orientation and ratio of the axes of the ellipses or the real and imaginary parts of the ratio c, so that in fact the five determinations give $(3 \times 2 + 2)$ i.e., 8 parameters.

Even if the principle of reciprocity does not hold for the system, all the matrix elements can be determined by replacing procedure (iii) by the following:

(vi) Use incident light linearly polarised at 45° to OX, i.e., $A_1 = A_2$, and determine $c_6 = A_2'/A_1'$. Then

$$c_6 = \frac{m_3 + m_2}{m_1 + m_4} \tag{14.10}$$

so that

$$c_3 = \frac{c_6 - c_1}{c_2 - c_6}. \tag{14.11}$$

As a check, a determination may be made with incident light linearly polarised at $-45°$ to OX, which gives

$$c_7 = \frac{c_3 - c_2}{c_1 - c_4}. \tag{14.12}$$

Then

$$\frac{c_6 - c_1}{c_2 - c_6} = \frac{c_7 - c_1}{c_1 - c_2} \tag{14.13}$$

each being equal to c_3.

15. Differential matrix operators[1]. In the previous section, we considered the effect of optical elements of finite thickness. We may now define a differential operator $\mathbf{N}$, such that $\mathbf{M}$ is an integral of $\mathbf{N}$:

$$\mathbf{N}_z = \lim_{z' \to z} \frac{\mathbf{M}_{z,z'} - 1}{z' - z}. \tag{15.1}$$

[1] R.C. Jones: J. Opt. Soc. Amer. **38**, 671 (1948).

Since $M_{z,z'} = M'_z/M_z$ we have

$$N_z = \lim_{z' \to z} \frac{M_{z'} - M_z}{z' - z} M^z_{-1} \tag{15.2}$$

or

$$N = \frac{dM}{dz} M^{-1}. \tag{15.3}$$

Integrating this equation, one obtains the formal result

$$M_z = \exp(N_z). \tag{15.4}$$

It may be readily verified that the N matrices transform exactly like the M matrices when the optical element is rotated. Thus, if N becomes N' by a rotation through an angle β then

$$N' = S(\beta)\, N\, S(-\beta). \tag{15.5}$$

The differential operators are very useful for discussing the case when the medium exhibits both general birefringence (linear as well as circular), as well as general dichroism. Now, a general 2×2 matrix requires eight quantities to specify it completely, namely the real and imaginary parts of its four elements. Let us suppose therefore that a thin slice of the plate of thickness $\tau (\ll 1)$ is made up of 8 laminae, each of thickness $\frac{1}{8}\tau$, and each having a different property as listed below. The differential matrices of the eight laminae are denoted by N_k and let $\Theta_k = \frac{1}{8} N_k$. Then, we have

$$M_k = \exp\left(\frac{N_k \tau}{8}\right) = \exp(\Theta_k \tau). \tag{15.6}$$

Thus, the matrix of the operator corresponding to the passage through all the eight laminae is

$$M = M_8 M_7 \ldots M_1 = 1 + \sum_{k=1}^{8} \Theta_k \tau + \Theta[\tau^2] \tag{15.7}$$

in the limit when $\tau \to 0$,

$$M = 1 + \sum_{1}^{8} \Theta_k \tau = 1 + N\tau \quad \text{(say)} \tag{15.8}$$

where N is the differential matrix operator of the sandwich of eight plates. Thus,

$$N = \sum_{k=1}^{8} \Theta_k. \tag{15.9}$$

The eight matrices, corresponding to the eight elementary operations may be defined as shown in Table 1.

It is obvious that any 2×2 matrix N whatsoever can be written in the form (15.9) by choosing suitable values for the eight parameters η, k, g_0, g_{45}, ϱ, p_0, p_{45} and μ. Of these, the first two represent the changes in phase and amplitude of the beam, while the other six denote the changes in the state of polarisation.

Although the six elementary operators of birefringence and dichroism, viz., Θ_3 to Θ_8 take a simple form in the 2×2 matrix representation, their physical content is best understood in terms of the Poincaré representation. Thus, it appears as if an unusual type of resolution is involved in representing the linear birefringence of a crystal plate with its principal axes kept at an arbitrary azimuth α. If g is the birefringence, the N matrix is

$$N = \begin{pmatrix} i g \cos 2\alpha & i g \sin 2\alpha \\ i g \sin 2\alpha & -i g \cos 2\alpha \end{pmatrix} \tag{15.10}$$

Table 1. *The eight elementary* $\boldsymbol{\Theta}$ *matrices.*

$\boldsymbol{\Theta}_1 = -\eta \begin{pmatrix} i & 0 \\ 0 & i \end{pmatrix}$	The parameter η is the propagation constant, or the phase retardation per unit thickness, and is thus related to the index refraction n by $\eta = 2\pi\, n/\lambda$.
$\boldsymbol{\Theta}_2 = -k \begin{pmatrix} 1 & 0 \\ 0 & 1 \end{pmatrix}$	The parameter k is the amplitude absorption coefficient to the base e per unit thickness, and is thus related to the extinction coefficient $\varkappa$ by $k = 2\pi\,\varkappa/\lambda$.
$\boldsymbol{\Theta}_3 = g_0 \begin{pmatrix} i & 0 \\ 0 & -i \end{pmatrix}$	The parameter g_0 is a measure of that part of the linear birefringence which is parallel with the co-ordinate axes. It is equal to one-half of the difference between the two principal propagation constants, i.e., $g_0 = \frac{1}{2}(\eta_y - \eta_x)$ and is thus positive when the fast (smaller index) axis is parallel with the x axis.
$\boldsymbol{\Theta}_4 = g_{45} \begin{pmatrix} 0 & i \\ i & 0 \end{pmatrix}$	The parameter g_{45} is a measure of that part of the linear birefringence which is parallel with the bisectors of the co-ordinate axes. It is equal to one-half of the difference between the two principal propagation constants, i.e., $g_{45} = \frac{1}{2}(\eta_{-45} - \eta_{45})$ and is thus positive when the fast axis bisects the positive x and y axes.
$\boldsymbol{\Theta}_5 = \varrho \begin{pmatrix} 0 & -1 \\ 1 & 0 \end{pmatrix}$	The parameter ϱ is a measure of the circular birefringence, and is equal to the rotation (in the positive direction) of the plane of linearly polarised light, in radians per unit thickness. It is equal to half of the difference of propagation constants for right and left circularly polarised lights, i.e. $\varrho = \frac{1}{2}(\eta_R - \eta_L)$ and is positive for crystals which are laevo-rotatory.
$\boldsymbol{\Theta}_6 = p_0 \begin{pmatrix} 1 & 0 \\ 0 & -1 \end{pmatrix}$	The parameter p_0 is a measure of that part of the linear dichroism which is parallel with the co-ordinate axes. It is equal to one-half of the difference of the two principal absorption coefficients, i.e. $p_0 = \frac{1}{2}(k_y - k_x)$ and is thus positive when the more highly transmitting axis is parallel with the x axis.
$\boldsymbol{\Theta}_7 = p_{45} \begin{pmatrix} 0 & 1 \\ 1 & 0 \end{pmatrix}$	The parameter p_{45} is a measure of that part of the linear dichroism which is parallel with the bisectors of co-ordinate axes. It is equal to one-half of the difference between the two principal absorption coefficients, i.e. $p_{45} = \frac{1}{2}(k_{-45} - k_{45})$ and is thus positive when the more highly transmitting axis bisects the positive x and y axes.
$\boldsymbol{\Theta}_8 = \mu \begin{pmatrix} 0 & -i \\ i & 0 \end{pmatrix}$	The parameter μ is a measure of the circular dichroism, and is equal to half of the difference of the absorption coefficients for left and right circularly polarised lights, i.e., $\mu = \frac{1}{2}(k_R - k_L)$. The parameter is positive for crystals which are more transparent for right polarised light.

which is to be compared with

$$\boldsymbol{\Theta}_3 + \boldsymbol{\Theta}_4 = \begin{pmatrix} i\, g_0 & i\, g_{45} \\ i\, g_{45} & -i\, g_0 \end{pmatrix}. \tag{15.11}$$

Thus,

$$g_0 = g\cos 2\alpha, \quad g_{45} = g\sin 2\alpha \quad \text{and} \quad g^2 = \sqrt{g_0^2 + g_{45}^2}. \tag{15.12}$$

In the Poincaré representation, the points representing azimuths 0 and 45° are actually at right angles, so that the resolution given by (15.12) is very natural.

The six elementary operators $\boldsymbol{\Theta}_3$ to $\boldsymbol{\Theta}_8$ can be divided into two groups, the first three representing birefringence and the second three representing dichroism. The following identification with the operators mentioned in Sect. 7 is then obvious:

$$\left.\begin{aligned} \boldsymbol{\Theta}_3\, \boldsymbol{\Theta}_4\, \boldsymbol{\Theta}_5 &\to \text{rotations } d\Delta_1\, d\Delta_2\, d\Delta_3, \\ \boldsymbol{\Theta}_6\, \boldsymbol{\Theta}_7\, \boldsymbol{\Theta}_8 &\to \text{displacements } d s_1\, d s_2\, d s_3. \end{aligned}\right\} \tag{15.13}$$

Thus, there is a one to one correspondence between the matrix method of JONES and the Poincaré representation and the associated matrix method involving Stokes parameters which was discussed in the first part of Sect. 12. However, in both matrix methods, the formulae are simple only for elementary operations. The problem of the passage of light through a finite thickness of medium exhibiting both birefringence and dichroism is best discussed by using the geometry of the Poincaré sphere. This is done in the succeeding chapters of this article.

The Jones matrices are applicable only for completely polarised beams. Of the eight coefficients which occur, one represents the absolute phase, leaving seven to describe the change in state of polarisation. This is also the number of independent coefficients in the Mueller matrices in the corresponding case.

16. Quantum mechanical description of polarisation[1]. The "state" of electromagnetic radiation can be described in quantum mechanics by a wave function, whose variables are the amplitudes of each of the basic states of a complete set. For a particular frequency and direction of propagation, the complete set consists of just two states of opposite polarisation. They are orthogonal, since light in one of the states (say P) is completely admitted by the analyser P while if the beam is in the other state P_a, then it is completely rejected by it. Any two opposite states of polarisation can be taken as a basic set. We shall however choose them to be states of linear polarisation parallel to OX and OY, and designate the normalized wave function by φ_1, φ_2. Then, a beam of completely polarised radiation may be represented by the wave function:

$$\psi = A_1 \varphi_1 + A_2 \varphi_2 \tag{16.1}$$

where A_1 and A_2 are complex. If we set $|A_1|^2$ and $|A_2|^2$ equal to the intensities of the two components, then $|\psi|^2$ gives the intensity of the beam. JONES' representation is identical in content with this quantum mechanical picture. If we represent the wave function ψ by the column vector $\begin{pmatrix} A_1 \\ A_2 \end{pmatrix}$, then the matrix method of Sects. 13 and 14 can be carried over *in toto* for the quantum mechanical description.

Consider now the 2×2 matrix

$$\varrho_{ij} = A_i A_j^* . \tag{16.2}$$

This matrix also has four components, analogous to the four components of A_1 and A_2, and they are the observables of the system. However, the absolute phase is lost by the multiplication with complex conjugates, and only three of them are independent, there being one linear relation between them, namely

$$\operatorname{Det} \varrho_{ij} = 0 . \tag{16.3}$$

The four Stokes parameters are just linear combinations of the four matrix elements ϱ_{ij}[2]. In fact,

$$I = \varrho_{11} + \varrho_{22}, \quad M = \varrho_{11} - \varrho_{22}, \quad C = \varrho_{12} + \varrho_{21}, \quad S = i(\varrho_{21} - \varrho_{12}) . \tag{16.4}$$

[1] For a detailed account of quantum mechanical theory of elliptically polarised photons, see G. ARAKI: Progr. Theor. Phys. **1**, 125 (1946); **2**, 1 (1947); Phys. Rev. **74**, 472 (1948) and the references given therein.

[2] D.L. FALKOFF and J.E. McDONALD: J. Opt. Soc. Amer. **41**, 861 (1951). The application of Stokes parameters for the treatment of polarisation in quantum mechanics is discussed by U. FANO: Phys. Rev. **93**, 121 (1954).

This may be proved as follows. Suppose the state of polarisation of the beam is an ellipse of amplitude A, with azimuth λ and ellipticity ω. Then

$$\left.\begin{aligned} A_1 &= A\,(\cos\omega\cos\lambda - i\sin\omega\sin\lambda)\,,\\ A_2 &= A\,(\cos\omega\sin\lambda - i\sin\omega\cos\lambda)\,. \end{aligned}\right\} \tag{16.5}$$

This gives

$$\left.\begin{aligned} \varrho_{11}+\varrho_{22} &= |A_1|^2+|A_2|^2 = A^2 = I\,,\\ \varrho_{12}-\varrho_{22} &= |A_1|^2-|A_2|^2 = A^2\cos 2\omega\cos 2\lambda = M\,,\\ \varrho_{12}+\varrho_{21} &= A_1A_2^* + A_2A_1^* = A^2\cos 2\omega\sin 2\lambda = C\,,\\ i\,(\varrho_{21}-\varrho_{12}) &= i\,(A_2A_1^* - A_1A_2^*) = A^2\sin 2\omega = S\,. \end{aligned}\right\} \tag{16.6}$$

For a completely polarised beam, the condition Det $\varrho_{ij}=0$ gives

$$I^2 = M^2 + C^2 + S^2. \tag{16.7}$$

The additivity law of Stokes parameters for incoherent addition of light beams follows from the result that the ϱ-matrices are additive for incoherent superposition of states. Suppose we have N completely polarised beams described by the wave-functions

$$\psi^\alpha = c_1^\alpha\varphi_1 + c_2^\alpha\varphi_2 \qquad (\alpha = 1 \text{ to } N). \tag{16.8}$$

Then, for incoherent superposition, we have

$$\langle c_i^\alpha c_j^\beta\rangle = c_i^\alpha c_j^\beta\,\delta_{\alpha\beta}. \tag{16.9}$$

Hence

$$\langle\varrho_{ij}\rangle = \Big\langle\sum_{\alpha\beta} c_i^\alpha c_j^{\beta *}\Big\rangle = \sum_\alpha c_i^\alpha c_j^{\alpha *} = \sum_{\alpha=1}^{N}\varrho_{ij}^\alpha. \tag{16.10}$$

By a direct application of the Schwarz inequality, it follows that

$$\mathrm{Det}\,\langle\varrho_{ij}\rangle \geqq 0 \tag{16.11}$$

so that for the resultant beam

$$I^2 \geqq M^2 + C^2 + S^2, \tag{16.12}$$

a result which we have already seen. The equality holds in (16.11) and (16.12) only when all the beams are in the same state; when it is not so, the resultant beam is only partially polarised.

The generalisation of the additivity law (16.10) to the incoherent superposition of partially polarised beams is obvious, and thus, STOKES' theorem (Sect. 9) follows also from the quantum mechanical formulation.

The intensity formula (8.4), namely

$$t_A = \tfrac{1}{2}\,(1 + \boldsymbol{P}\cdot\boldsymbol{A})$$

may also be derived from the quantum mechanical representation[1]. This however represents only the *mean* fraction of the photons in the beam accepted by the analyser A. A discussion of the fluctuations in the number of photons passed by the analyser is more complicated[2].

17. Nature of unpolarised and partially polarised light. It was mentioned earlier that natural or completely unpolarised light may be obtained by incoherently

[1] G. ARAKI: Phys. Rev. **74**, 472 (1948). — U. FANO: J. Opt. Soc. Amer. **39**, 859 (1949). See also R.H. DALITZ: Proc. Phys. Soc. Lond. **65**, 175 (1952).

[2] U. FANO: J. Opt. Soc. Amer. **41**, 58 (1951). See also the references given therein.

superposing equal proportions of oppositely polarised radiation. Any pair of oppositely polarised beams may be used and they all lead to the same state, namely unpolarised light. It follows from this that any analyser transmits exactly half the intensity of a beam of unpolarised light.

Although the above picture of unpolarised light is perfectly consistent and in conformity with quantum mechanics, it may be worthwhile to consider some of the earlier ideas. BREWSTER supposed that natural light is made up of two plane polarised waves, with their vibration directions at right angles and being propagated independently. FRESNEL put forward the hypothesis that natural light consists of plane polarised light in which the azimuth of polarisation varied rapidly and assumed all possible values. It is obvious that the point representing its polarisation state would then rapidly move along the equator of the Poincaré sphere. The resulting state would be represented by the centre, as is to be expected. A slightly better picture would be to assume that all directions of linear vibration are taken up at random, but with equal probability. In any case, as has been discussed in Sect. 11, provided the variations occur in a time much less than the period of observation, the beam would exhibit all the properties of natural light.

An attempt was made by LANGSDORF and DU BRIDGE[1] to verify the Fresnel-hypothesis. They obtained interference fringes with unpolarised light using a biprism, and then introduced in the paths of the two beams optically active media which rotate the plane of polarisation by $+45°$ and $-45°$ respectively. The fringes then completely vanished and the field of view had only uniform illumination[2], and continued to remain so even if viewed through a linear analyser at any azimuth. The latter observation can be explained because in both beams only the components with vibrations parallel to the analyser would be transmitted by the analyser. The vibration directions of these were however, originally at right angles, so that the phase difference between them will vary at random and no interference fringes would be formed. The same result also follows from FRESNEL's picture, as was shown by LANGSDORF and DU BRIDGE.

On the other hand, if we resolve the unpolarised beam into its two opposite circularly polarised components L and R then the optically active media in the two beams would not change the state of polarisation, but would introduce a relative phase difference of $\pm\frac{\pi}{2}$ according as it is L or R. Consequently, the fringe system would be present if observed through a circular analyser L or R, but would be displaced by $\pm\frac{1}{4}$ fringe from the appearance when the two liquid cells were not there. This is actually what was observed.

These beautiful experiments clearly show that the various alternative methods of decomposing an unpolarised light beam are all valid. However, it must be mentioned that all possible orientations of elliptic vibrations of definite ellipticity (b/a) would not lead to unpolarised light, but only to partially (circularly) polarised light. Only if both senses of rotation are equally probable would the resultant behave as unpolarised light. Similarly, if all possible (elliptical) states of polarisation are occupied with equal probability, i.e., the representative points on the Poincaré sphere are uniformly distributed over its surface area, then again the resultant is unpolarised light.

---

[1] A. LANGSDORF and L.A. DU BRIDGE: J. Opt. Soc. Amer. **24**, 1 (1934).

[2] A similar observation was made as early as 1864 by STEFAN who obtained Talbot bands with a plate of quartz of thickness 5 mm cut perpendicular to the optic axis and found the bands to vanish in the orange region, for which the optical rotation was 90°. See R.W. WOOD: J. Opt. Soc. Amer. **24**, 4 (1934).

Thus, an unpolarised light beam occurs in what might be called a "mixed" state in the quantum mechanical sense. Consequently, one would obtain uniform results for experiments made on such a beam only if the period of observation is large compared with the time over which coherence exists. It is known that in any atomic system, the light emitted as a result of a transition between two precisely defined quantum states must be completely polarised. Consequently, if a system emits unpolarised, or partially polarised light, then this must be attributed to (*a*) the fact that a number of closely spaced levels are involved in the emission, and (*b*) the fact that the individual emitters may be oriented differently. If the gas is subjected to a strong magnetic field, then the different components can be separated spectroscopically and then each is found to be completely polarised. In such a case, each component corresponds to a transition between two precisely defined states of the atom.

Thus, complete polarisation of the emitted light is observed only if the states of the emitter are precisely defined both before and after emission. If either is incompletely defined, then the light emitted is also incompletely polarised[1]. In fact, if a beam of light is precisely monochromatic, then it must also be completely polarised. Even if it consists of several components derived from different sources, and not expected to be connected with one another, the phase relationships between the components beams remain the same for all time if the frequencies are identically equal. Consequently, the resultant must have a unique state of polarisation[2]. For the same reason, a beam of unpolarised monochromatic light would appear to be elliptically polarised if it is observed over a period of time small compared to the reciprocal of the frequency width $\Delta\nu$ of the line. It is immaterial if the small line breadth is due to the characteristics of the source, or if it is obtained by means of a narrow band filter. The state of polarisation would however change with time and if one makes measurements over time intervals large compared to $1/\Delta\nu$, then all possible states would be occupied, and only average values would be observed. It is interesting to note that not only the state of polarisation, but the intensity also should fluctuate with time. A detailed discussion of the statistical properties of unpolarised light is given by HURWITZ[2], based on the conventional decomposition of elliptically polarised light into two linear states at right angles, viz., OX and OY. They however follow much more simply from the Poincaré representation, and two of the interesting results are derived below.

As mentioned earlier, unpolarised light is represented by a point at the centre of the Poincaré sphere, and this would be true on the average if all points on the Poincaré sphere are occupied with equal probability. Assuming this to be the case then it is obvious that the quantity $\sin^2\omega$ is uniformly distributed between 0 and 1. Now,

$$\sin 2\omega = 2\sin\omega\cos\omega = 2ab/(a^2+b^2) \tag{17.1}$$

which last function has been shown by HURWITZ to be uniformly distributed between 0 and 1. So also, if we consider ellipses of varying ellipticity, then the median value of ω is that value which divides the area of the sphere into two equal halves, i.e., $\sin 2\omega = \frac{1}{2}$, which gives $2\omega = 30^\circ$ or $\omega = 15^\circ$. The corresponding axial ratio of the ellipse is 0.268, a rather surprising result, when not pictured in terms of the Poincaré sphere.

[1] U. FANO: J. Opt. Soc. Amer. **39**, 859 (1949).
[2] H. HURWITZ jr.: J. Opt. Soc. Amer. **35**, 525 (1945).

18. Production of polarised light[1]. *α) Production of plane polarised light.* Completely polarised light may be obtained from unpolarised light or partially polarised light by using one of three methods: (a) passing it through a strongly dichroic crystal, (b) removing by suitable means one of the two polarised components into which a beam of light is split up in a birefringent medium, and (c) by reflection from a surface at a suitable angle or by refraction at oblique incidence through a pile of plates.

(a) In a dichroic crystal, two orthogonal states of linear polarisation are absorbed differently, sometimes with very different absorption coefficients. Consequently, one component may be reduced only by a small fraction. For instance a crystal of tourmaline, cut parallel to the optic axis and of thickness one millimeter, transmits very little of the component with its vibration direction parallel to the optic axis. HERAPATH[2] found that crystals of iodoquinine sulphate was even more strongly dichroic, a thickness of 0.1 mm being sufficient to absorb almost completely one of the components, but this did not receive any practical application until recently. It was only some twenty years ago that large crystals of herapathite could be grown[3].

However, it is possible to obtain an oriented deposit of colloidal herapathite crystals in a transparent base of nitrocellulose or plastic and this works very well as a polariser. Other materials, even more dichroic than herapathite have been prepared, and in this way polarisers useful for various spectral ranges, even going up to 2.8 μ in the infrared have been prepared[4,5]. We shall refer to such polarising filters as polaroids though this is a commercial name given to one particular brand.

b) The difference in the refractive indices of the two polarised components in an anisotropic medium may be used to obtain total reflection of the component with the lower index. This is used in the well-known Nicol prism and similar polarisers like the Glan-Thomson prism. Sometimes, the two components are separated by refraction, as in the so-called double image prisms.

(c) Complete polarisation can be obtained by reflection at the Brewsterian angle from an isotropic material[6]. The corresponding transmitted beam must also be completely polarised. This method is useful in the infrared region. Using selenium, which has a high refractive index (about 2.9), a degree of polarisation of nearly 99% is possible for an angular range of incidence 59 to 77°[7].

Another method is to use a pile of plates, so that the degree of polarisation of the transmitted beam increases as it passes through successive plates. Usually four or five plates are sufficient. This method has been used in recent years for obtaining polarised infrared rays[8], using selenium, tellurium and silver

---

[1] A good review of the earlier work related to the production and measurements of polarised light is available in the articles of SZIVESSY [*1*] and details of apparatus are given in this article and in that by SCHULZ [*9*]. Only the principles are discussed here. A more recent account is by W. HELLER in the chapter on Polarimetry in "Physical Methods of Organic Chemistry". Ed. A. WEISSBERGER. New York 1949.

[2] W. B. HERAPATH: Phil. Mag. **3**, 161 (1852).

[3] F. BERNAUER: Fortschr. Min. **19**, 22 (1935).

[4] E. H. LAND: J. Opt. Soc. Amer. **41**, 957 (1951).

[5] The characteristics of the optimum polariser is discussed by C. D. WEST and R. C. JONES: J. Opt. Soc. Amer. **41**, 976, 982 (1951). — The spectral properties of high extinction polarisers are discussed by L. BAXTER, A. S. MAKAS and W. A. SCHURCLIFF: J. Opt. Soc. Amer. **46**, 229 (1956).

[6] W. KONIG: Handbuch der Physik, Vol. 20, p. 141. 1928.

[7] A. H. PFUND: Astrophys. J. **24**, 19 (1906). — J. Opt. Soc. Amer. **37**, 558 (1947).

[8] A. ELLIOTT, E. J. AMBROSE and R. TEMPLE: J. Opt. Soc. Amer. **38**, 212 (1948).

chloride[1]. With eight thin films of selenium, each 3 μ thick, a degree of polarisation of 99.8% is obtained.

In a polaroid, the transmitted beam suffers no lateral deviation, but this difficulty is present in most of the other polarising devices. A method of avoiding this with the pile of plates, by using two sets of plates producing opposite displacements, has been suggested[2].

β) Production of elliptically polarised light. It is possible to produce elliptically polarised light of any desired azimuth, axial ratio and sense from a linearly polarised beam by the use of a linearly birefringent plate. With a given azimuth of vibration of the plane polarised beam N (Fig. 12), any state of polarisation P may be obtained, provided a suitable thickness of the birefringent plate is available. The orientation $\alpha, \alpha + \frac{\pi}{2}$ of the slow and fast axes of the plate with reference to that of the linear polariser and the required phase retardation ε may both be determined from the construction shown in Fig. 12. The former are given by the longitudes 2α, $2\alpha+\pi$ of the points where the great circle bisecting the arc PN cuts the equator. If 2ω, $2\lambda'$ are the latitude and longitude of P with respect to N, then,

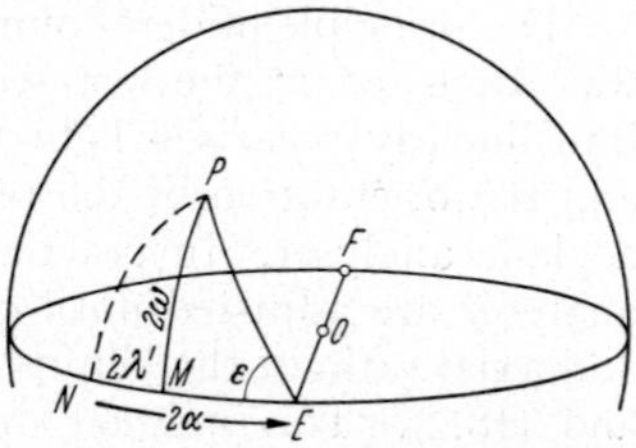

Fig. 12. Principle of the elliptic polariser. A linear vibration N is brought to the elliptic state by the action of a plate of retardation ε whose slow axis is E.

$$\tan 2\alpha = \frac{1-\cos 2\omega \cos 2\lambda'}{\cos 2\omega \sin 2\lambda'}, \tag{18.1}$$

$$\sin\varepsilon = \sin 2\omega / \sin 2\alpha . \tag{18.2}$$

With a given retardation plate, if the azimuth of both the polariser (N) and plate (E) can be arbitrarily varied, then a wide range of ellipticity can be obtained. However, there is an upper limit to the axial ratio b/a, i.e., of 2ω which can be obtained, namely $|2\omega| \leq |\varepsilon|$, which leads to $\left|\frac{b}{a}\right| \leq \tan\frac{\varepsilon}{2}$. This may be readily proved from the construction in Fig. 12 by allowing E to vary, keeping N fixed. Thus all possible states of polarisation can be obtained with a *single* birefringent plate and incident linearly polarised light only if the relative retardation is $\pi/2$, i.e., it is a quarter wave plate.

If a quarter wave plate is used, then $\varepsilon = \pi/2$, so that we have from (18.2) $\sin 2\omega = \sin 2\alpha$ and from (18.1) $2\omega = \pm 2\lambda'$. Thus the fast or slow axis of the quarter wave plate must be parallel to the major axis of the ellipse and correspondingly the polariser must be set at an angle $\lambda' = \pm\omega$ to the fast axis. This is also clear from Fig. 12.

Owing to the dispersion of refractive indices, the phase retardation varies with wavelength and the settings calculated from (18.1) and (18.2) hold good only for a definite wavelength. In particular, a quarter wave plate prepared for one wavelength is not useful for other wavelengths. An achromatic quarter wave plate, whose phase retardation is a constant over the visible region may however be obtained by combining three plates of mica[3].

[1] A review of infrared polarisers is given in Cahiers de Phys. **38**, 26. The theory of "pile" polariser, including multiple reflections is discussed by G. K. T. Conn and G. K. Eaton: J. Opt. Soc. Amer. **44**, 546, 553 (1954).

[2] A. S. Makas and W. A. Schurcliff: J. Opt. Soc. Amer. **45**, 998 (1955).

[3] The design of this, as well as of an achromatic circular polariser, was obtained employing the Poincaré representation, by S. Pancharatnam: Proc. Ind. Acad. Sci. A **41**, 130, 137 (1955). See also G. Destriau and J. Prouteau: J. Phys. Radium **10**, 53 (1949).

The retardation between two perpendicular components could be produced not only by a birefringent plate, but also by total internal reflection. In the Fresnel rhomb two successive internal reflections at the appropriate angle (calculated from the refractive index) are used to produce a total retardation of $\pi/2$ so that system acts like a $\lambda/4$ plate. The advantage of the Fresnel rhomb is that it is practically achromatic. However it displaces the incident beam, though arrangements have been suggested to get over this deficiency by employing more than two reflections.

19. Measurement of elliptically polarised light. The measurement of elliptically polarised light requires the determination of three quantities, namely the orientation of the major axis, the axial ratio and the sense. These are given respectively by the longitude (2λ), the latitude ($|2\omega|$) and the sign ($\pm$) of the latitude of the representative point on the Poincaré sphere.

The principle of determining these quantities is in essence the reverse of what was discussed in the last section. The elliptically polarised light is converted into linearly polarised light by a retardation plate set at the proper azimuth, and the orientation of the resultant plane vibration is determined by means of a plane analyser. In practice, the azimuths of both the retardation plate and analyser are adjusted until complete extinction is obtained. Then the azimuth and axial ratio of the elliptic vibration may be obtained by inverting Eqs. (18.1) and (18.2). This method, in which a retardation plate with arbitrary phase retardation is used, is originally due to MACCULLAGH[1] and STOKES[2] and it is discussed in Sect. 21. It is obvious that if ε is the phase retardation of the plate, then ellipses with axial ratio $|b/a| \geqq \tan \varepsilon/2$ cannot be measured. On the other hand, all states of polarisation can be measured by means of a single retardation plate if it is a quarter wave plate. The use of a quarter wave plate is originally due to SÉNARMONT[3] and this method is usually called after him. A defect in methods requiring the use of quarter wave plates is that such a plate will not have a relative phase retardation of $\pi/2$ for all wavelengths.

The analysis of elliptically polarised light is of interest in two types of applications: (a) determination of small relative retardations introduced by doubly refracting media (having natural birefringence), birefringence produced by stress, or flow birefringence, (b) measurement of the parameters involved in the reflection of light from surfaces. According to the particular application, simplifications in the method as well as special techniques of high accuracy have been evolved. Some of these will be discussed below, particularly with respect to the general principles involved[4].

All the methods are based essentially on the intensity formulae (2.4) to (2.6), namely that the fraction (t_A) of the intensity of light of polarisation P transmitted by an analyser A is

$$t_A = \tfrac{1}{2}(1 + \cos \widehat{PA}) = \cos^2 \tfrac{1}{2}\widehat{PA} = \sin^2 \tfrac{1}{2}\widehat{PA}_a. \tag{19.1}$$

This may be directly used to determine the azimuth λ of the ellipse. As the orientation of the analyser is varied, A travels along the equator, the arc $\widehat{PA}$ varies

[1] J. MACCULLAGH: Collected works, pp. 138, 230. Dublin and London 1880.

[2] C. G. STOKES: Mathematical and Physical Papers, Vol. 3, p. 197. Cambridge 1901.

[3] H. DE SÉNARMONT: Ann. Chim. Phys. Paris **73**, 337 (1840).

[4] Two excellent review articles have appeared recently by H. G. JERRARD: J. Opt. Soc. Amer. **38**, 35 (1948) and by M. RICHARTZ and H.Y. HSU: J. Opt. Soc. Amer. **39**, 136 (1949). They contain a survey of all the methods so far proposed, with full details of theory and practice. An earlier descriptive article is by G. SZIVESSY: Handbuch der Physik, Vol. 19, p. 926. 1928.

and is obviously largest when A lies in the same meridian as P. The point A_a is then nearest to P, and the minimum intensity transmitted is simply $\sin^2 \omega$. If we denote by β the azimuth of the analyser and by $\beta_{\min}$ the setting for minimum intensity, then clearly,

$$\lambda = \beta_{\min} - \frac{\pi}{2}. \tag{19.2}$$

20. Determination of azimuth. In practice, it is difficult to judge the setting for minimum intensity accurately, and consequently what are known as half-shade devices are used. In these, the field of view is divided into two parts, the intensities of which will vary differently and the correct setting is one in which both are equally bright. The optimum intensity of the field of view at equality varies with the observer, and it is therefore desirable that this should be capable of adjustment. So also, the difference in intensity between the two halves should rapidly increase with a slight missetting of the analyser. If J' and J'' are the intensities in the two halves for a missetting specified by the parameter $\Delta\beta$, then the sensitivity s of the device may be defined as follows:

$$\left|\frac{(J'-J'')}{(J'+J'')}\right| = \frac{1}{2} s \Delta\beta. \tag{20.1}$$

For small values of $\Delta\beta$, this gives

$$s = \frac{1}{J_0} \frac{\partial}{\partial\beta} (J' - J''). \tag{20.2}$$

Obviously, s should be large for high accuracy. The three types of half-shades commonly used are discussed below[1]. In all the three cases, if the devices are used for the direct determination of the azimuth, the sensitivity decreases with increasing angle of ellipticity. This defect can be removed by arrangements described in Sect. 21.

α) Double field analyser. Two linear analysers are used in the two halves of the field of view, the azimuth of the two being rotated with respect to each other by a small angle η. The arrangement is originally due to JELLETT[2] but several improvements have been made[3]. It consists of a Glan-Thomson prism from which a wedge-shaped piece has been removed and then cemented together. When the double field analyser is rotated, the intensities in the two halves will be equal when the major or minor axis of the ellipse is parallel to the internal bisector of the angle between the vibration directions of the two analysers. Of these, the latter is the more sensitive position, as the intensity will be less. The setting is shown on the Poincaré sphere in Fig. 13 and the condition for equality of intensity is $\widehat{A_{1a}P} = \widehat{A_{2a}P}$ which gives

$$\sin^2 \tfrac{1}{2} \widehat{A_{1a}P} = \sin^2 \tfrac{1}{2} \widehat{A_{2a}P}. \tag{20.3}$$

If β is the azimuth of the internal bisector (A in Fig. 13) then

$$\lambda = \beta - \frac{\pi}{2} \tag{20.4}$$

independent of the ellipticity.

---

[1] Experimental details and a fuller account will be found in the articles by O. SCHÖNROCK, GEIGER-SCHEEL: Handbuch der Physik, Vol. 19, p. 749, 1928; SCHULZ: Handbuch der Experimentalphysik, Vol. 18, p. 420, 1928; W. HELLER, in Physical Methods of Organic Chemistry, Ed. A. WEISSBERGER, Vol. 1, Part III, p. 1531. 1949.

[2] J.H. JELLETT: Rep. Brit. Assoc. **30**, 13 (1860).

[3] A. CORNU: Bull. Soc. Chim. **14**, 140 (1870). — O. SCHÖNROCK: Handbuch der Physik, Vol. 19, p. 750. 1928.

The half-shade angle is not variable in the Jellett prism, but is adjustable in the arrangement due to LIPPICH[1]. In this, a smaller Nicol prism is put in front of the large analysing prism, with its azimuth at an angle η to the analyser. While η can be varied in this way, the transmissions of the two halves are different, the ratio of the two being $\cos^2\eta$. If the incident light is linearly polarised, then its azimuth can be accurately determined with respect to a standard orientation. If η is small, the azimuth λ of the linear vibration is given by (20.4). If η is not small, it can be shown that

$$\lambda = \beta - \frac{\pi}{2} - \frac{\eta}{2} + \alpha \qquad (20.5)$$

where

$$\tan\alpha = \tfrac{1}{2}\tan\eta\,. \qquad (20.6)$$

There is only a constant difference $(\alpha - \frac{1}{2}\eta)$ from equation (20.4), which does not matter. However, this is not so for a general elliptic vibration, since the condition for equality of intensity is

$$\sin^2\tfrac{1}{2}\widehat{A_{1a}P} = \sin^2\tfrac{1}{2}\widehat{A_{2a}P}\cos^2\eta\,. \qquad (20.7)$$

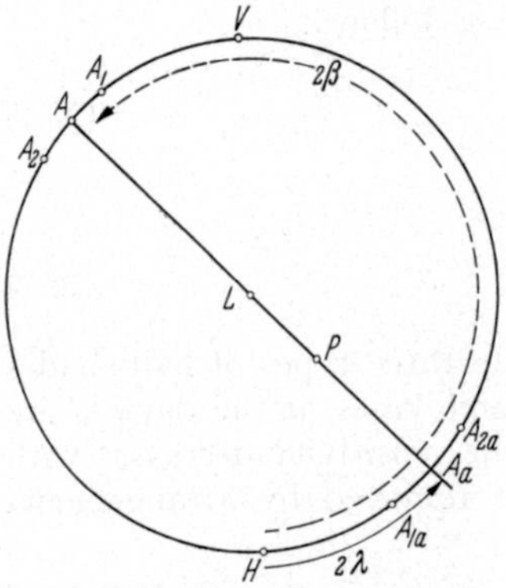

Fig. 13. Principle of the double field analyser. (Stereographic projection.)

If P is not on the equator, the difference of the solution for λ from Eq. (20.4) is not the same for all states, but depends on the ellipticity, and so a small systematic error is introduced.

In both arrangements, the sensitivity decreases with increasing angle of ellipticity.

β) Rotating biplate[2]. This consists of two thin plates of quartz (thickness about 0.05 mm) cut perpendicular to the optic axis, one dextro- and the other laevo-rotatory, and is known as a "biquartz" or Nakamura plate. Each covers half the field of view and the arrangement is put before the analyser. If $\frac{1}{2}\eta$ is the rotation of each, then one half is transparent to linear vibrations making an angle $-\frac{1}{2}\eta$ with the plane of the linear analyser while the other half is transparent for linear vibrations at azimuth $+\frac{1}{2}\eta$. The arrangement is therefore equivalent to a Jellet prism of angle η. The intensities of the two halves will be equal and darkest only if the setting of the analyser is at $\pi/2$ to the azimuth of the major axis of the incident ellipse. The Nakamura biplate is preferable to some other arrangements in which a plate of optically active material covers only one-half of the field of view. Because of the asymmetry, the loss of light due to reflection and other causes will be different in the two halves, and so precise measurements are not possible with the latter type.

A combination of two half wave plates, with their axes inclined at an angle $\frac{1}{2}\eta$ can be seen to be equivalent to an optically active plate producing a rotation η. In Fig. 14, the effect of the two half wave plates E_1F_1 and E_2F_2 is to bring the point P_0 to P_1 and then to P_2, the movement from P_0 to P_2 being equivalent to a rotation about LR through an angle η. Such a combination may therefore be used instead of the quartz plate in each half of the Nakamura biplate[3].

---

[1] F. LIPPICH: Wien. Ber. **91**, 1059 (1885).

[2] S. NAKAMURA: Zbl. Min. 267 (1905). The Nakamura half shade has been used to determine the principal directions in a doubly refracting medium of small phase difference: H. G. JERRARD: J. Opt. Soc. Amer. **42**, 259 (1956).

[3] M. RICHARTZ and H. HSU: J. Opt. Soc. Amer. **39**, 136 (1949).

γ) Doubly refracting half shade. The simplest form of this, originally due to LAURENT[1] and CHAUVIN[2] consists of a half wave plate kept in front of the analyser covering half the field of view, with one of its vibration directions at an angle $\frac{1}{2}\eta$ to that of the analyser. The portion covered by the mica has its maximum transmission for linear vibrations at an azimuth η with respect to the analyser vibration. The arrangement is therefore equivalent to a Jellet prism. The half-shade match is achieved when the vibration directions of the half-wave plate are parallel to the axes of the ellipse. By varying η, the sensitivity may be altered; but in common with the other two types, the sensitivity of this device also decreases with increasing ellipticity. Further, the device cannot be used for different wavelengths, as the retardation of the plate can be made exactly equal to a half-wave only for a definite wavelength.

A very thin sheet of mica embedded in Canada balsam and covering half the field of view is a very useful half-shade for measuring the azimuth of linearly polarised light, obtained for instance in the Stokes-MacCullagh method after passage through the retardation plate. This is known as a Brace half-shade and is widely used in the measurement of the elements of elliptically polarised light. Its principle is described in the next section. A symmetric modification of this is a biplate composed of two equally thin birefringent plates with their fast directions at a small angle to each other[3]. Another modification of the birefringent half shade consists of two equally thin birefringent plates (usually of mica) with their fast and slow directions interchanged. When such a plate is placed in front of a linear analyser the system will show an equality in the two halves only when linearly polarised light is incident on it. This system is found to be of great use in the analysis of elliptically polarised light (see Sects. 21, 23).

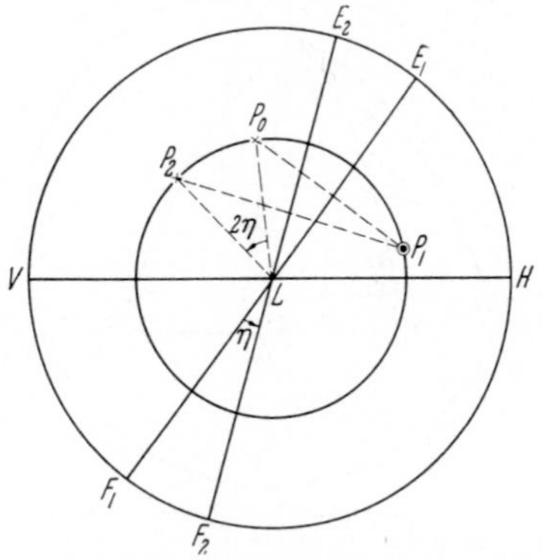

Fig. 14 Two half-wave plates with their axes inclined at $\frac{1}{2}\eta$ are together equivalent to an optically active plate producing a rotation η. (Stereographic projection.)

21. Determination of ellipticity: Direct methods. The methods which have been proposed for the determination of ellipticity generally require a knowledge of the azimuth, although in some methods both are determined by suitable techniques. The main application of the measurement of ellipticity is for determining the phase retardation introduced by a birefringent medium. In such a case, the principal directions of birefringence are known, and it is the phase difference between the two waves which must be determined. Instruments designed for this purpose are known as compensators. By having auxiliary devices to determine the azimuth of the ellipse, these can also be used to determine the ellipticity of a polarised beam. In this section also, we shall only discuss the broad principles and give only one or two examples. A complete review is available in the publications mentioned in Sect. 20.

α) Sénarmont and Stokes-MacCullagh methods. If a quarter wave plate be set with its axes parallel to the principal axes of an elliptic vibration, the emergent vibration will be linearly polarised at an azimuth α with respect to the slow axis, where α determines the ellipticity of the incident vibration, i.e., tan α is the ratio

[1] L. LAURENT: C. R. Acad. Sci., Paris **86**, 662 (1878). — J. de Phys. **3**, 183 (1874).
[2] M. CHAUVIN: Ann. de Toulouse **3**, 30 (1889).
[3] G. SZIVESSY and W. HERZOG: Z. Instrumentenkde. **58**, 229, 345 (1938).

of the two principal axes of the incident ellipse parallel to the slow and fast axes of the retardation plate (taken with a negative sign if the incident light is right-elliptic). This is the principle of the original Sénarmont method, in which the azimuth of elliptic vibration may be first determined by finding the setting of a linear analyser at which the intensity transmitted is a minimum.

As has been previously mentioned, the azimuth cannot be determined accurately in this manner when the ellipticity is not small. But if the principal axes of the $\lambda/4$ plate are not exactly coincident with those of the incident elliptic vibration, the emergent vibration not being linearly polarised cannot be completely extinguished at any setting of the linear analyser placed after the retardation plate. Hence the deficiency of the simple method can to a large extent be over-come by a method of successive approximations due to STOKES[1] and MACCULLAGH[2], which has the added advantage that it can be used even when the retardation of the plate is different from $\pi/2$. The procedure is to find by trial and error that particular setting of the retardation plate at which the emergent light can be completely extinguished at some setting of a linear analyser. The azimuths of the principal axes of the retardation plate are noted as also the orientation α with respect to these principal axes of a direction crossed with respect to the linear analyser. If the retardation of the plate is exactly $\pi/2$ the constants of the incident elliptic vibration are immediately obtained. When the retardation of the plate is $\varepsilon\,(\neq\pi/2)$ the required setting of the plate is explained in Fig. 15 using the Poincaré sphere. In the setting illustrated, the major axis M of the elliptic vibration will not coincide with the slow axis E of the retardation plate but will be inclined to it at an angle γ (arc $\widehat{EM}=2\gamma$). Since the analyser setting A is adjusted to cross out the emerging linearly polarised state, the latter coincides with A_a and therefore $\widehat{EP_0}=\widehat{EA_a}=2\alpha$. From the spherical triangle P_0ME

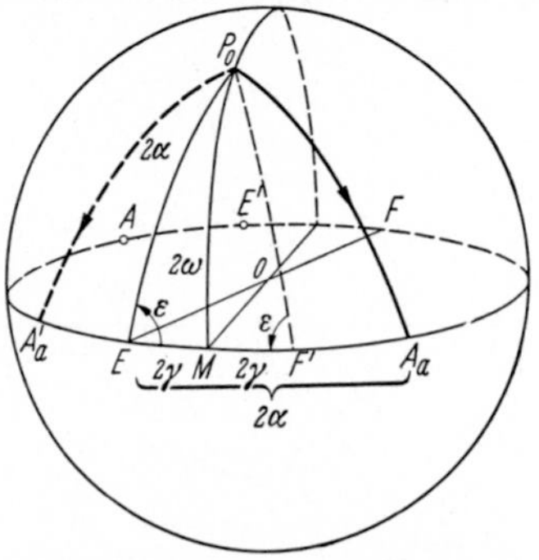

Fig. 15. The Stokes-MacCullagh method. The incident state P_0 can be reduced to a linear vibration A_a on the equator by a suitably oriented retardation plate whose slow and fast axes are E and F, and whose effect is to produce a clockwise rotation ε about the diameter EF. A symmetrical setting with the fast axis at F' is also possible, when an anti-clockwise rotation ε about F' brings P_0 to the equator at A'_a.

$$\sin 2\omega = \sin 2\alpha \sin \varepsilon, \tag{21.1}$$

$$\tan 2\gamma = \tan \alpha \cos \varepsilon. \tag{21.2}$$

Hence the azimuth γ and the ellipticity ω may be calculated if α is measured, provided, ε is known. However even a knowledge of the retardation is unnecessary if by the method of successive approximations another setting of the retardation plate and analyser at which no light emerges is obtained. This is clearly a symmetrical setting (see Fig. 15), the fast axis F' of the retardation plate being such that $\widehat{F'M}=\widehat{EM}=2\gamma$ while the anticlockwise rotation ε about F' brings P_0 to A'_a, where $\widehat{F'A'_a}=2\alpha$. The bisector of the angle between the slow axis at first setting and the fast axis at the second setting determines the azimuth of the major axis of the incident elliptic vibration. Having thus determined γ, the ellipticity

[1] C. G. STOKES: Mathematical and Physical Papers, Vol. 3, p. 197. Cambridge 1901.
[2] J. MACCULLAGH: Collected Works, pp. 138, 230. Dublin and London 1880.

is obtained from the spherical triangle P_0ME as

$$\cos 2\omega = \cos 2\alpha \sec 2\gamma. \tag{21.3}$$

[It may be noted that the unknown retardation ε of the plate may also be now determined from (21.2)—a principle used in some compensators—see e.g. Sect. 23.]

Though the oldest method, we have referred to this in some detail not only because of its great simplicity but also as most other methods are only minor modifications attempting to improve its accuracy. The following drawbacks in this method may be noted. The Sénarmont method has the apparent advantage that there are two independent operations (namely of determining the azimuth and then the ellipticity) but is inaccurate in its elementary form for reasons mentioned. The Stokes-MacCullagh method, though more accurate, requires a procedure of successive approximations. Further in neither of the methods is the half-shade principle incorporated. We shall discuss three modifications which have been suggested for incorporating the half-shade principle in the adjustments.

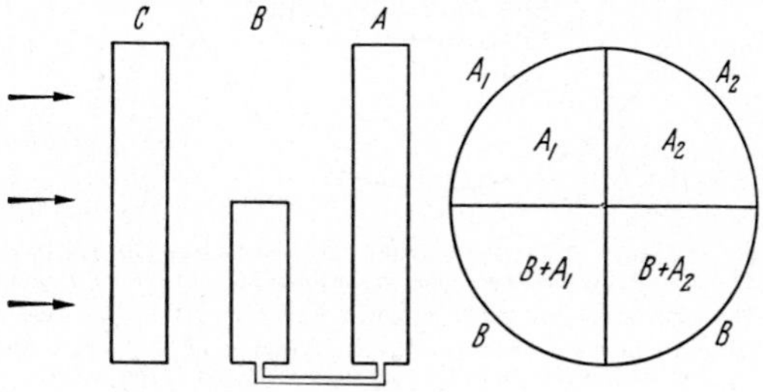

Fig. 16. Tool elliptic analyser. A = Jellett double prism, B = Brace half-shade, C = Compensator plate, A_1, A_2 = Two halves of Jellett prism.

β) The Tool half-shade method. Tool has devised an elegant half-shade method[1] making use of a Jellet prism to which is attached a Brace elliptic half-shade. The principal planes of the Brace plate are at $\pm\frac{\pi}{4}$ to the internal bisector of the angle between the vibration directions of the analyser, and the plate is kept so as to cover one-half of each half of the analyser. The arrangement is shown schematically in Fig. 16.

The setting for equality of intensity in all the four quadrants is obtained by successive approximations. The compensator and the combined analyser half-shade system are first rotated together to obtain a match for the birefringent half-shade. With the compensator fixed, the analyser system (with the attached Brace-plate) is rotated for a match of the two parts of the Jellet prism, which now affects the match already obtained for the birefringent half-shade. The two procedures are then repeated successively. Fig. 17a explains the final setting on the Poincaré sphere. In this figure E, F, E_B, F_B represent respectively the principal axes of the compensator and the Brace birefringent half-shade; P_1 and P_2 are the states incident on the upper and lower halves of the Jellet prism; A_1 and A_2 represent the azimuths of the left and right halves of the Jellet analyser and A their internal bisector. The Brace plate is attached to the Jellet prism such that arc $\widehat{AF_B}$ is a quadrant.

The actual formulae for the parameters λ and ω of the incident ellipse clearly involves, in addition to the setting of the compensator and the analyser system and the phase retardation of the compensator, also the phase retardation η of the Brace plate. These are not given here but may be obtained from the paper by Skinner[1]. Fig. 17b gives the corresponding figure when a symmetrical birefringent half-shade is used in which the two halves consist of equally thick birefringent plates but with their fast and slow axes interchanged. In this case

[1] A. Q. Tool: Phys. Rev. **31**, 1 (1910). The theory of the instrument is discussed, making use of the Poincaré representation by C. A. Skinner: J. Opt. Soc. Amer. **10**, 491 (1925).

a method of successive approximations is not required when the compensating plate is set properly (i.e., such that P_0 is brought to a point P on the equator), since whatever be the setting F_B of the birefringent half-shade, the states P_1 and P_2 emerging from its two halves will be symmetrically above and below the equator, and consequently the birefringent half-shade will appear matched. The formulae in this case are clearly identical with those for the Stokes-MacCullagh

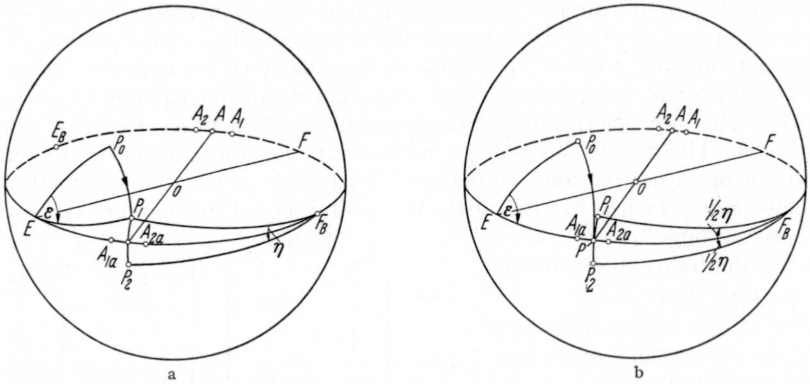

Fig. 17 a and b. Tool elliptic analyser at correct setting. (a) The incident state P_0 is brought to P_1 by the compensator; P_1 is altered to P_2 by the Brace plate in the lower half of the field, P_1 and P_2 being symmetrically above and below the equator. The birefringent half-shade is matched since $\widehat{A_{1a}P_1} = \widehat{A_{1a}P_2}$ and $\widehat{A_{2a}P_1} = \widehat{A_{2a}P_2}$; while the two halves of the Jellett prism are matched since $\widehat{A_{1a}P_1} = \widehat{A_{2a}P_1}$ and $\widehat{A_{1a}P_2} = \widehat{A_{2a}P_2}$. (b) Modified symmetric form. Here P_0 is brought to P on the equator and then converted to P_1 and P_2 respectively by the two halves of the birefringent half-shade.

method, with the added advantage of the half-shade. The retardation of the half-shade does not enter into the formulae, and a knowledge of the retardation ε can be rendered unnecessary as in that case.

γ) Double half-shade methods. RICHARTZ[1] has devised a simple, at the same time accurate, modification of the Sénarmont method for determining all the elements of an elliptically polarised beam. Half the field of view is covered by a quarter-wave plate and behind this is kept a Nakamura rotating bi-plate, with its dividing line at right angles to the edge of the quarter-wave plate (Fig. 18.) The system is backed by an analyser.

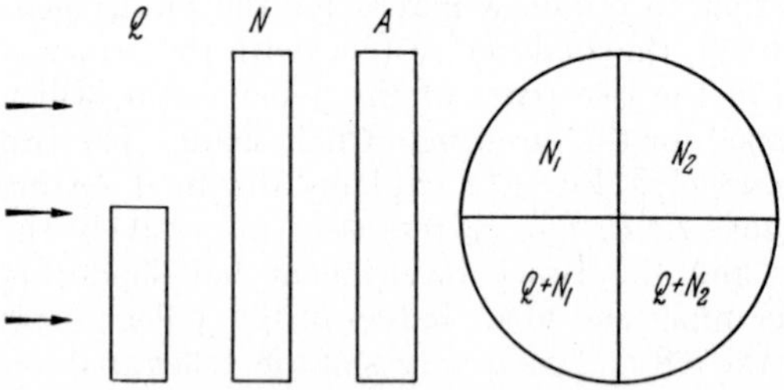

Fig. 18. Richartz double half-shade analyser. Q = quarter wave plate, N = Nakamura biplate, A = linear analyser.

Initially a principal axis of the quarter-wave plate is adjusted to be perpendicular to the vibration-direction of the analyser by keeping the combined half-shadow plate between crossed nicols and rotating it so that both pairs of the fields of view are equally bright. The elliptically polarised light is then allowed to fall on the elliptic analyser, and the whole system is rotated until the lower halves not covered by the quarter-wave plate appear equally bright. The axes of the quarter-wave plate are now parallel to those of the ellipse. The azimuth of the plane polarised light

[1] M. RICHARTZ: Z. Instrumentenkde. **60**, 358 (1940). A sensitive half-shadow device for use with a quarter-wave plate has been devised by JERRARD: J. Opt. Soc. Amer. **44**, 289 (1954). This paper may be referred to for detailed references to literature on the subject of compensators.

emerging from the $\lambda/4$ plate is determined by rotating the analyser alone until equality of intensity is obtained in the top quarters.

The polarisation states of the light emerging from the four quadrants of the half-shade system at the correct setting of the quarter wave plate are indicated in Fig. 20a by P_1, P_2, P_3', P_4', P being the state of the incident light. It will be noticed from this that the first setting for the determination of the azimuth of P will not be sensitive if the ellipticity is large (see also Sect. 19). This in turn affects the accuracy in measuring the ellipticity, although the second setting in the above arrangement is by itself very sensitive.

This points to the need for devising a half-shade system by which both the azimuth and ellipticity can be measured accurately. RAMASESHAN[1] has made a careful study of this problem and he has suggested a number of arrangements for achieving it. The essential idea is to have a system by which the point P' is accompanied by four points P_1', P_2', P_3', P_4' forming a cross with it, as shown in Fig. 20a. Then, at the correct setting, there will be equality of intensity in both the half-shade pairs only if P' is exactly on the equator and if the analyser is set at azimuth P_a', antipodal to P'. In fact, if this could be achieved, then the setting of the quarter wave plate can be made for any arbitrary setting of the analyser (although the sensitivity is maximum when it is at P_a'), by adjusting for equality of intensity in P_1' and P_2'. The analyser is then adjusted for equality in P_3' and P_4'. The measurement does not require the use of successive approximations and the first setting can be made independent of the second.

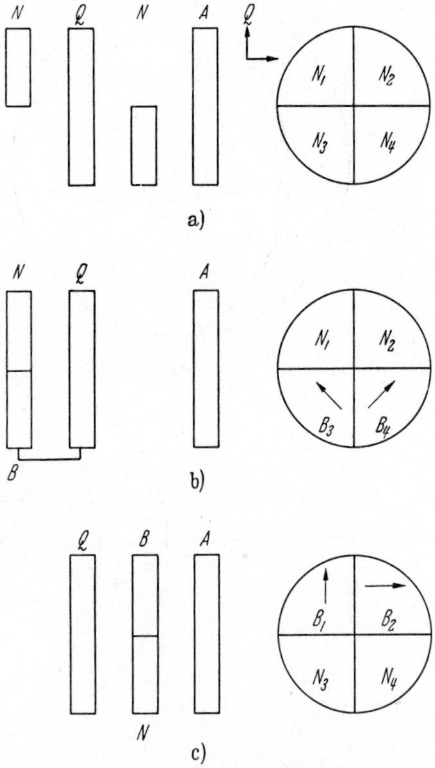

Fig. 19a—c. Different possible arrangements in RAMASESHAN's analyser. Q = quarter wave plate, N = Nakamura biplate, B = birefringent half-shade consisting of two plates of low, but equal retardation (2 to 5°), with their fast and slow axes interchanged, A = linear analyser.

Perhaps the simplest way of achieving the cross of points, when a quarter wave plate is used, is to have the quarter wave plate (Q of Fig. 19a) covering the whole field and having one Nakamura biplate in front covering the top half, and another Nakamura biplate behind it covering the bottom half. The states of polarisation of the light emerging from the upper two quarters are then represented by P_1' and P_2' (Fig. 20a) and of light emerging from the lower two quarters by P_3' and P_4'.

Two other possible types of arrangement are shown in Figs. 19b and 19c. In Fig. 19b, the upper half consists of a Nakamura biplate kept before Q, while the lower half is a double-refracting biplate, B, which is also kept before Q, but whose axes are at $\pm 45°$ to those of the quarter wave plate. The way in which P_1', P_2', P_3', P_4' are produced is shown in Fig. 20b.

[1] S. RAMASESHAN: J. Ind. Inst. Sci. **37**, 195 (1955).

In Fig. 19c, on the other hand, both the biplates are kept after the quarter wave plate. Here, the Nakamura biplate forms the lower half and leads to the points P'_3, P'_4 on the Poincaré sphere. The upper half consists of a double-refracting biplate, but its azimuth can be varied by rotating the half-shade system. The separation between P'_1 and P'_2 produced by it is maximum when its axes are at 45° to the analyser setting. Fig. 20c has been drawn corresponding to this setting.

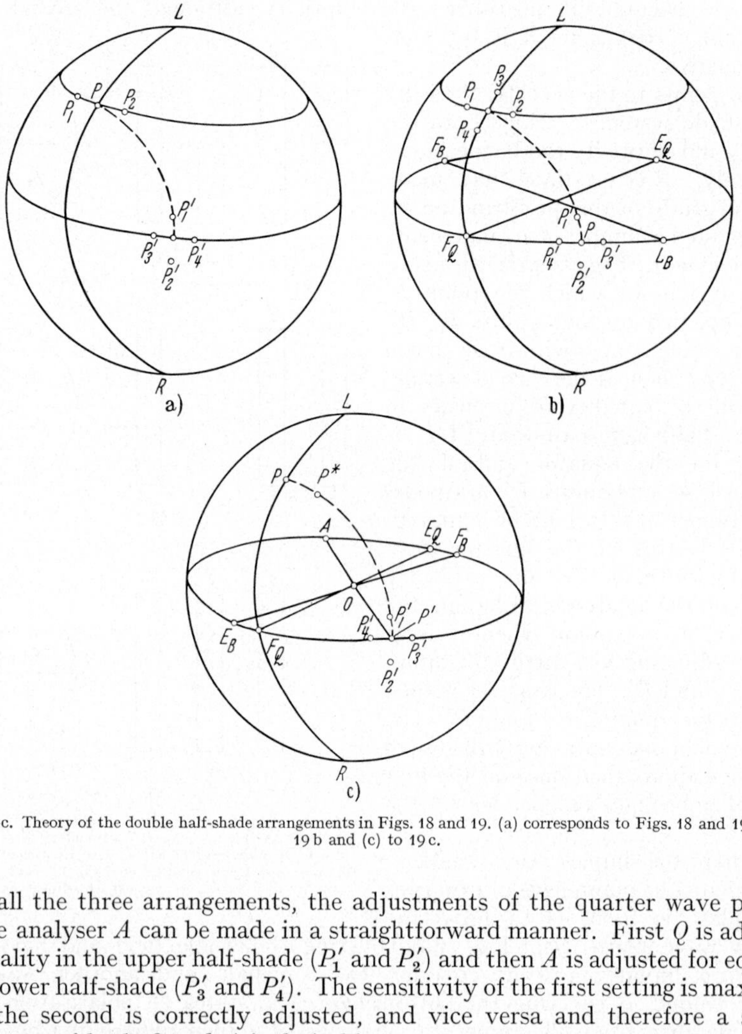

Fig. 20 a—c. Theory of the double half-shade arrangements in Figs. 18 and 19. (a) corresponds to Figs. 18 and 19 a, (b) to 19 b and (c) to 19 c.

In all the three arrangements, the adjustments of the quarter wave plate Q and the analyser A can be made in a straightforward manner. First Q is adjusted for equality in the upper half-shade (P'_1 and P'_2) and then A is adjusted for equality in the lower half-shade (P'_3 and P'_4). The sensitivity of the first setting is maximum when the second is correctly adjusted, and vice versa and therefore a second adjustment of both Q and A is desirable.

In the arrangements 19a and 19b, the effective "half-shade angle" i.e., the angular separation of the points P'_1 and P'_2 and of P'_3 and P'_4 is not a constant, independent of the ellipticity. In both, $\widehat{P'_1 P'_2}$ decreases with increasing ellipticity. So also, they are not suited for use with compensator plates whose retardation is not exactly $\pi/2$, for then the four points P'_1, P'_2, P'_3, P'_4 do not form a rectangular cross. The last arrangement (20c), on the other hand, is ideally suited for this case, since it is the final state P' which is split up into four parts with different states of polarisation. Thus, if the retardation is ε, the state P^* is brought to P' (Fig. 20c) and thence to the four states P_1', P_2', P_3', P_4', exactly as in the case of a quarter wave plate. Further, the separation $\widehat{P_1' P_2'}$ can be made the same by rotating the half-shade system alone so that the axes of the birefringent biplate are at $\pm 45°$ to the analyser. Consequently, the double half-shade arrangement in Fig. 20c can be used to locate the final setting accurately and all the measurements discussed in connection with the Stokes-MacCullagh method (Sect. 21 α) can be made with it. A brief description of the procedure is given below.

The analyser consists of a quarter wave plate or a birefringent plate producing a retardation ε whose azimuth λ_Q can be read on a graduated scale. Behind it is the double half-shade arrangement of Fig. 19c, which again can be set with the axes of the birefringent half-shade B at any azimuth λ_B. The whole is backed by a linear analyser A, whose azimuth λ_A can also be varied.

The procedure is as follows. With B and A at arbitrary positions, Q is rotated until match is obtained in the upper half-shade (1 and 2). A is then rotated to obtain match in the lower half-shade. B is then set at 45° to A and the first setting is repeated, and then the second. The whole process may be repeated if necessary; but after the second setting, small deviations of the other elements from their ideal positions will have a negligible effect on the setting of a particular element (Q or A).

δ) Crossed elliptic analysers. In many experiments in crystal optics, e.g., in determining the nature of the elliptic vibration which is transmitted without change inside a crystal (see Sects. 71 and 98) one requires a system consisting of an elliptic polariser and crossed elliptic analyser. This can be obtained as follows: The incident light falls on a linear polariser P_1 which is succeeded by a quarter wave plate Q_1. The analyser consists of another quarter wave plate Q_2 rotated through 90° with respect to Q_1, backed by a linear analyser P_2, which is also rotated 90° with respect to the initial polariser P_1. The arrangement in front constitutes an elliptic polariser, which can produce light of any desired state of polarisation, while the arrangement at the back would always cut out the light coming from the elliptic polariser and is therefore an elliptic analyser orthogonal to the former. The two together are called a pair of "crossed elliptic analysers".

In practice, the linear polariser P_1 and analyser P_2 are coupled together with their directions at right angles to form the P-system and they are capable to being rotated together. So also the two quarter wave plates Q_1, Q_2 with their fast and slow directions interchanged (which form the Q system) are capable of being rotated together. It should also be possible to couple the P-system to the Q-system at any setting and then rotate all of them together. A conventional polarisation microscope can be readily adapted for this purpose.

The principal axes of the incident elliptic vibration will be parallel to the axes of Q_1 and this can therefore be varied by rotating the quarter wave plates and the azimuth of the ellipse is thus known from the setting (λ_Q) of the Q-system. The ellipticity can be varied by rotating the P-system, and is known from the angle $(\lambda_P - \lambda_Q)$ between the polariser and the fast axis of the first quarter wave plate, being $\omega = (\lambda_P - \lambda_Q)$.

To determine the nature of the elliptic vibration propagated for example through an optically active birefringent crystal plate, the plate is placed on the stage in between the polariser and the orthogonal elliptic analyser. Both the P-system and the Q-system are adjusted until crossing is obtained. Then the azimuth and ellipticity of the state propagated unchanged is the state of the light incident from the polariser and may be obtained from the settings λ_P and λ_Q. In certain experiments it is necessary to have the incident vibration of constant ellipticity, but of variable azimuth. This can be obtained by setting $\lambda_P - \lambda_Q$ equal to ω and rotating the P- and Q-systems together. If more general sections of the Poincaré sphere have to be explored it would be necessary to use a pair of crossed birefringent plates of equal retardation $\delta \neq 90°$.

22. Compensators. In the above methods, the compensating plate which converts the elliptical vibration into a linear vibration has a fixed retardation and only its azimuth is varied. On the other hand, one could employ birefringent plates of fixed orientation, but of variable retardation. Such a plate is known as a compensator and may be obtained by using a wedge-like plate, or a combination of wedges, with their fast and slow directions interchanged. The two types most commonly used are the Babinet compensator (Fig. 21 a) and the Soleil compensator (Fig. 21 b)[1] which are usually made of quartz plates

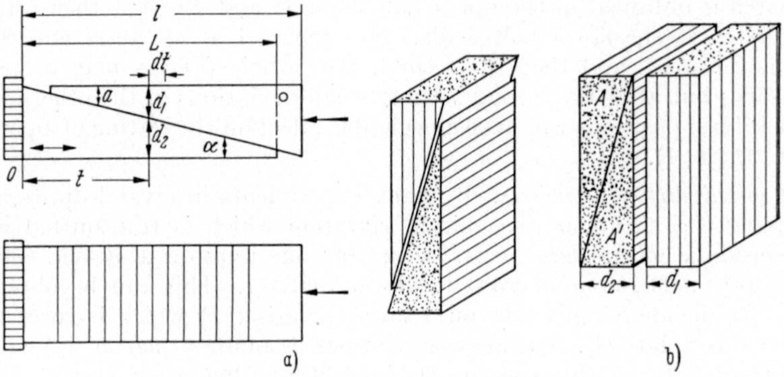

Fig. 21. (a) Babinet compensator. (b) Soleil compensator.

cut parallel to the optic axis[2]. In the Babinet compensator, the path retardation varies linearly over the breadth of the plate, while it is a constant over the whole area in the Soleil compensator. In both, the retardation may be varied by moving one of the plates, and the relative phase retardation may be varied over a few cycles in the usual designs.

In all methods involving the use of such compensators, it is necessary to know the azimuth of the elliptic vibration beforehand, as the principal directions of the compensator must be kept parallel to the axes of the ellipse. This may be done by using one of the half-shadow methods discussed earlier. However, by far a major part of the applications of compensators is for finding the retardation δ produced by a crystal plate or birefringent medium. This may be measured by keeping a linear polariser at $\pi/4$ to the principal planes, when the ellipticity of the resulting ellipse is given by $\tan \frac{1}{2}\delta$. The axes of the ellipse will be parallel to the principal directions of the crystal plate, and so the orientation of the compensator presents no problem.

In the Babinet compensator, a series of dark and bright fringes will be observed in the field of view, when linearly polarised light at azimuth $\pi/4$ is incident and an analyser is set at azimuth $\pm \frac{\pi}{4}$. The setting of the analyser does not affect

[1] For details, see G. SZIVESSY [*1*] and H. G. JERRARD: J. Opt. Soc. Amer. **38**, 35 (1948).

[2] This particular orientation is however not essential. See also G. SZIVESSY and CL. MUNSTER: Phys. Z. **36**, 101 (1935) for eliminating errors due to optical activity of quartz.

the position of the fringes, but they are clearest at $\pm\frac{\pi}{4}$ and vanish at 0 and $\frac{\pi}{4}$. If now a crystal plate is introduced with its principal directions parallel to those of the compensator, then the fringes will shift by an amount proportional to the retardation δ introduced. The shift may be directly measured, or may be compensated by moving one of the wedges. The instrument is calibrated by measuring the band-width or the movement necessary to shift the fringes through one band, which corresponds to a phase retardation of π.

The Soleil compensator is very similar to the Babinet, except that the field of view is uniform in intensity and the adjustments of the compensator are made for extinction. The calibration is done by measuring the movement of the wedges from one setting for extinction to the next. In view of the large field of view, half-shadow devices could be used in combination with it[1].

The problems connected with the accurate adjustment and the calibration of the Babinet and Soleil compensators have been discussed by JERRARD[2]. A birefringent compensator having a field of view about 25 times that of the Babinet and suitable for use in strongly convergent light, as in microscopy, has also been developed[3].

23. Compensators for measuring small ellipticity. A type of compensator, suitable for small ellipticities, may be obtained by compressing or tensioning a plate of optical glass, whereby it develops birefringence with the principal planes parallel and perpendicular to the direction of the tension. Uniform phase retardation may be obtained over the field of view with proper arrangements, and its value may be varied by adjusting the tension. This method is particularly used for measuring very small retardations of the order of $10^{-5}\cdot 2\pi$. Half-shade arrangements using such a compensator have also been described[4].

A particularly accurate arrangement, making use of two retardation plates, one as a compensator and the other as a half-shadow device has been devised by BRACE[5]. Several modifications of this have been suggested by various workers, and full details may be obtained from JERRARD'S review.

Here, we shall consider the typical arrangement. The polariser is kept at $\pi/4$ to the principal planes of the crystal plate under study, producing a phase retardation δ, and the emergent elliptical light passes through a retardation plate producing a phase difference ε of about $2\pi/50$. Behind this is kept another birefringent plate with a retardation of about $2\pi/200$, which covers half the field of view (Brace half-shade of Sect. 20). As mentioned in Sect. 21, a more satisfactory arrangement would be to have a biplate, of half the thickness, each covering half the field of view, but with their fast and slow directions interchanged. We shall develop the theory for the latter arrangement[6]. Behind the half-shade is the linear analyser.

With the polariser and analyser crossed, and keeping the principal directions of the half-shade at $\pm\frac{\pi}{4}$, the setting of the compensator for equality of intensity is indicated in Fig. 22a.

[1] H.G. JERRARD: J. Sci. Instrum. **28**, 10 (1951).

[2] H.G. JERRARD: J. Sci. Instrum. **26**, 353 (1949); **27**, 62 (1950); **27**, 164; **30**, 65 (1953).

[3] M. FRANÇON and B. SERGENT: Optica Acta **2**, 151 (1955).

[4] A. DE FOREST PALMER: Phys. Rev. **17**, 409 (1921). — H.A. BOURSE: Phys. Rev. **46**, 187 (1934).

[5] D.B. BRACE: Phil. Mag. **7**, 320 (1904). — Phys. Rev. **18**, 70 (1904); **19**, 218 (1904). — G. SZIVESSY: Z. Instrumentenkde. **57**, 49, 89 (1937).

[6] The use of the Poincaré sphere helps one to appreciate the simplicity and symmetry of the arrangement discussed here. In the theory of the Brace compensator, worked out by analytical methods by the earlier workers, the formulae are highly complicated, because of the unsymmetrical nature of the two halves of the device.

The half-shade is kept at $\pi/4$, but the compensator azimuth k can be varied, and if this is such that the elliptic vibration P_0 is converted into a linear vibration P, then there would be equality of intensity in the two halves of the field of view (Fig. 22a). The setting is independent of the position of the analyser, but the sensitivity can be greatly increased by bringing the analyser close to the setting orthogonal to P i.e., A_a coinciding with P. Let the azimuth of the analyser for this condition by $\gamma + \frac{\pi}{2}$ i.e., 2γ is the longitude of P.

Alternatively the half shade plate may be kept in front of the compensating plate and the setting of the compensator for match determined. This is independent of the polariser setting but the field will appear darkest when the polariser

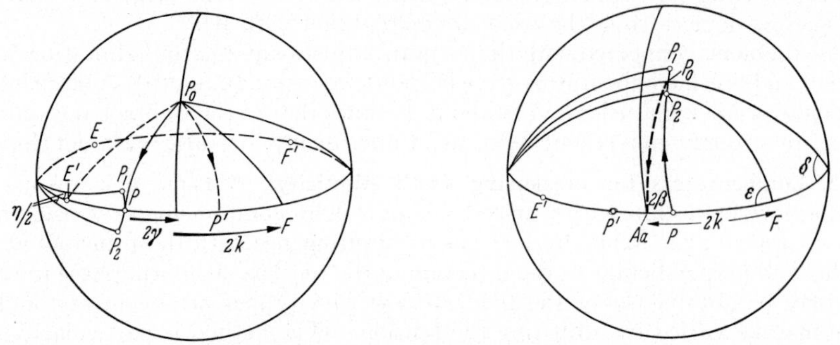

a b

Fig. 22 a and b. Diagrams (a) and (b) illustrating two possible arrangements for the Brace compensator. The rotations of the Poincaré sphere are highly exaggerated.

is turned through an angle β such that the state P_0 of the light emerging from the test plate represents a state which, if the half shade had been absent, would have been crossed out by the elliptic analyser composed of the compensator plate backed by the nicol (Fig. 22b).

The values of γ and β for the two cases, as also that of the phase retardation δ, in terms of the compensator setting k and its retardation ε are given by the following equations. They may be derived from the appropriate spherical triangles in Figs. 22a and 22b.

(a)
$$\left.\begin{aligned} \tan\delta &= \sin 2k \tan\varepsilon\,,\\ \tan 2\gamma &= \frac{1-\sec\varepsilon}{\cot 2k + \tan 2k \sec\varepsilon}\,, \end{aligned}\right\} \tag{23.1}$$

(b)
$$\left.\begin{aligned} \sin 2\beta &= \sin 4k \sin^2 \varepsilon/2\,,\\ \sin\delta &= \sin\varepsilon \sin 2k/\cos 2\beta \\ &= \frac{\sin 2k \sin\varepsilon}{\sqrt{1-\sin^2 4k \sin 4\,\varepsilon/2}}\,. \end{aligned}\right\} \tag{23.2}$$

The setting of the compensator for match of the half-shade is first determined approximately with the polariser and analyser crossed. The value of γ or β as the case may be is calculated, the polariser or analyser is kept at that position and the compensator is carefully reset for match. A second setting of the compensator is also possible, shown by $E'F'$ in Figs. 22a and 22b, for which γ and β have respectively the same values as in the previous case, except for a change of sign. Two more settings can be obtained during a full rotation of the compensator at an angle π away from the above two settings. The best method of utilising these four readings is discussed by SZIVESSY[1]. Very accurate measurements can be made in this way and an accuracy of one percent or better is claimed for measuring phase differences of the order of $1\times10^{-4}\cdot 2\pi$. As may be verified from Fig. 22 and the equations for δ, the setting of the polariser or analyser has no effect on the setting of the compensator for match of the half-shade, although it affects the sensitivity. The settings γ and β are only those for maximum sensitivity.

Several modifications may be made in the above arrangement e.g., by interchanging the position of the compensator and the half-shadow plates, or keeping either the half-shadow plate or the compensator plate, or both, in either order, before the crystal plate whose retardation is to be measured[2]. No special advantages seem to be present for any of these arrangements over the case considered above.

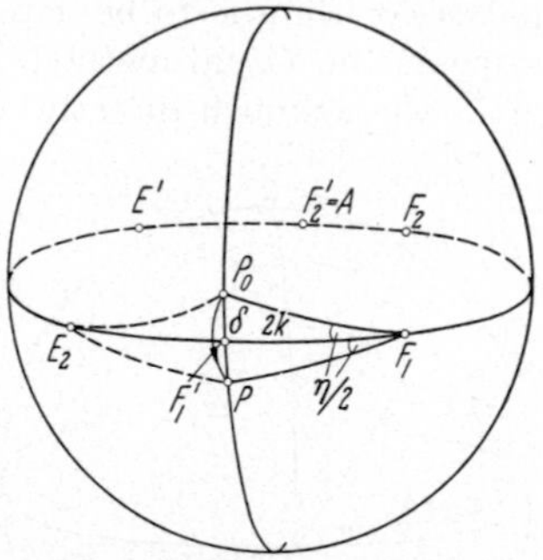

Fig. 23. Principle of SZIVESSY's compensator half-shade. The incident state P_0 is transformed to P for one half of the field of view by the compensator half-shade whose fast axis is F_1. The two halves are matched when P_0 and P are symmetrically above and below the equator, A being the analyser setting for which the field is darkest. Rotations of the Poincaré sphere are exaggerated.

A simple method, making use of a single birefringent plate both as a compensator and a half-shade has been proposed by SZIVESSY[3]. This is particularly useful for small ellipticities. The birefringent plate, whose phase retardation η is chosen to be slightly larger than twice the expected phase difference δ, is fixed to cover half the field of view. The analyser is initially kept at right angles to the major axis, and the compensator plate is rotated until equality of intensity is obtained. The setting for this is shown on the Poincaré sphere in Fig. 23 and it will be seen that there will be four possible settings of the fast axis during a rotation of π, marked by F_1, F_2, F_1', F_2' in the figure. The latter two are not of interest, because they correspond to the settings when the principal directions of the half-shadow plate are parallel and perpendicular to the analyser. If k, $\frac{\pi}{2}-k$ are the settings corresponding to F_1 and F_2, then the relation between δ and k is

$$\tan\delta = \sin 2k \tan\tfrac{1}{2}\eta. \tag{23.3}$$

Modifications of the above method, and of the Brace compensator have been suggested by SZIVESSY and HERZOG[4]. A detailed study of the Sénarmont compensator and of its modifications has been made by GABLER and SAKOB[5].

24. Photoelectric methods for the analysis of elliptically polarised light. *α) Methods using compensators.* Visual methods cannot be employed for the regions of the spectrum outside the visible, and so other methods have to be used. Photographic methods are useful, particularly in the ultraviolet[6]. The main purpose

[1] G. SZIVESSY: Z. Physik **54**, 594 (1929).
[2] For details see H. G. JERRARD: J. Opt. Soc. Amer. **38**, 35 (1948).
[3] G. SZIVESSY and A. DIERKESMAN: Ann. Phys., Lpz. **11**, 949 (1931).
[4] G. SZIVESSY and W. HERZOG: Z. Instrumentenkde. **57**, 305 (1937).
[5] F. GABLER and P. SAKOB: Z. Instrumentenkde. **58**, 301 (1938); **61**, 298 (1941). — Z. Physik **116**, 47 (1940). — Phys. Z. **42**, 319 (1941).
[6] W. VOIGT: Phys. Z. **2**, 303 (1901). — R. C. MINOR: Ann. Phys., Lpz. **10**, 581 (1903). — G. BRUHAT and M. PAUTHENIER: Rev. d'Opt. **6**, 163 (1927). — G. SZIVESSY and C. MUNSTER: Z. Physik **70**, 750 (1931). — G. SZIVESSY, A. DIERKESMANN and C. MUNSTER: Z. Physik **82**, 279 (1933). — Z. Instrumentenkde. **53**, 465 (1933). — J. BOR and B. G. CHAPMAN: Nature, Lond. **163**, 182 (1949).

of such studies have been the investigation of the optical properties of absorbing materials, from the state of polarisation of the light reflected from the surface. The relationship between the polarisation state and the optical constants, both in isotropic and anisotropic media, will be found elsewhere[1]. Here, we shall consider the main principles involved in the non-visual methods which have been proposed for measuring the characteristics of an elliptically polarised beam.

All methods use some type of detector for measuring the intensity of radiation. We shall use the term photocell for this device, although other types of detectors may be employed actually. In polarimetry, where only the azimuth of a linearly polarised beam is to be determined, the photoelectric method is in principle the same as the visual method[2]. The setting of the analyser for minimum intensity gives the azimuth directly, or the method of symmetric angles may be used, in which the settings on either side at which the intensities are equal are determined, the mean giving the setting for minimum[3]. The dark current of the photo-cell may be suppressed by modulating the incident beam, e.g. by an intermittent chopper, and using a tuned amplifier[4].

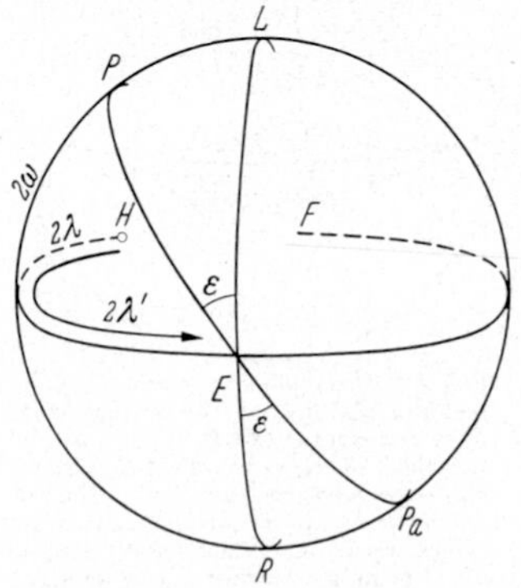

Fig. 24. Principle of the Kent and Lawson photoelectric analyser. The state of polarisation P is brought to the circular state L by a rotation ε about EF. Note that P_a is brought to R by the same operation.

BRUHAT and GRIVET[5] were the first to use the photoelectric method of analysing elliptically polarised light. However, they did not use the principle of modulation. KENT and LAWSON[6] have suggested a very ingenious method in which the ellipse is converted into a circular vibration by means of a quarter-wave plate, instead of into a linear vibration as in the usual methods. If the emergent light is fed through a rotating linear analyser to a photo-cell, then there would be no a.c. signal if the light is circularly polarised. Otherwise, it is obvious that there would be a fluctuating component in the intensity of twice the frequency of rotation of the analyser. By using a narrow band amplifier, the signal-to-noise ratio may be greatly increased.

The principle is indicated in Fig. 24. The point representing the state of polarisation of the incident light may be brought to L (or R as the case may be) by rotating it through an angle ε about EF, where the longitude of F is $\frac{\pi}{2}+2\lambda$. Thus, the principal planes of the compensator must be at $\pm\frac{\pi}{4}$ to the axes of the ellipse, and the phase retardation ε of the compensator must be variable. If the azimuth λ' and the retardation ε are adjusted so as to obtain circularly

[1] See the article by J. FRIEDEL and J. BOR: Vol. XXV, Part 2 of this Encyclopedia.

[2] G. BRUHAT and P. CHAPELAIN: C. R. Acad. Sci., Paris **195**, 370 (1932). — G. BRUHAT and A. GUINIER: C. R. Acad. Sci., Paris **196**, 762 (1933). — D.H. RANK, J.H. LIGHT and P.R. YODER: J. Sci. Instrum. **27**, 270 (1950). — G.B. LEVY, P. SCHWED and D. FERGUS: Rev. Sci. Instrum. **21**, 693 (1950).

[3] An account of this and other special techniques in photoelectric polarimetry is given by W. HELLER, Ref. 1, p. 34.

[4] Such a method has been used recently for the measurement of Faraday rotation, the modulation being obtained by running a mercury discharge lamp from 50 cycles a.c. V. SIVARAMAKRISHNAN: Proc. Ind. Acad. Sci. A **44**, 206 (1956). See also L.R. INGERSOLL and D. LIEBENBERG: J. Opt. Soc. Amer. **44**, 566 (1954).

[5] G. BRUHAT and P. GRIVET: C. R. Acad. Sci., Paris **199**, 852 (1934).

[6] C.V. KENT and J. LAWSON: J. Opt. Soc. Amer. **27**, 117 (1937).

polarised light, then

$$\lambda = \lambda' - \frac{\pi}{4}, \qquad |2\omega| = \frac{\pi}{2} - \varepsilon \tag{24.1}$$

so that

$$\left|\frac{b}{a}\right| = |\tan\omega| = \cot\frac{\varepsilon}{2}. \tag{24.2}$$

It is clear that the sense of the ellipse cannot be determined, since there is no way of distinguishing whether the state of the circularly polarised beam is L

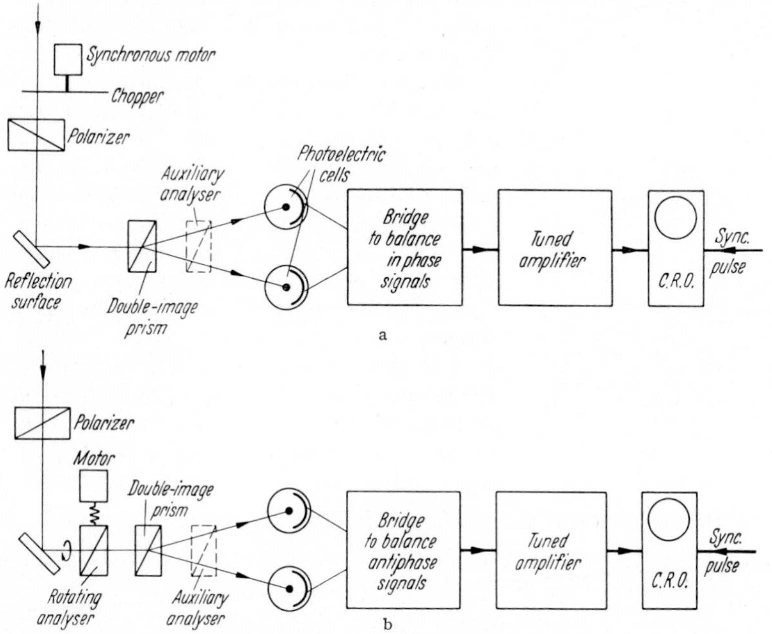

Fig. 25 a and b. Photoelectric method for analysing elliptically polarised light. (a) Using modulated light source. (b) Using rotating analyser.

or R. Thus there is an ambiguity between two orthogonal states in this method. A practical difficulty of the rotating analyser method[1] is that the photoelectric effect is dependent on the azimuth of the plane polarised light, so that the photocell is not equally sensitive for all azimuths. This difficulty may be avoided by fixing a quarter-wave plate behind the analyser at the appropriate azimuth, the two being rotated together, so that circularly polarised light is always incident on the photocell.

β) Methods without compensating plates. Two interesting methods have been suggested for the analysis of elliptically polarised light using a stationary double image prism and two photocells[2]. In both, tuned amplifiers are used and a matching circuit, which can compare the two outputs, either in phase or antiphase, is utilized for making the adjustment.

The first is a simple application of the visual[3] and photographic[4] methods, using a double image prism. The principle is shown in Fig. 25a. The double

[1] The sources of error in this method are discussed by J.F. Archard, P.L. Clegg and A.M. Taylor: Proc. Phys. Soc. Lond. B **65**, 758 (1952).

[2] J.F. Archard, P.L. Clegg and A.M. Taylor: Research, Lond. **3**, 339 (1950). — Proc. Phys. Soc. Lond. B **65**, 758 (1952).

[3] L.R. Ingersoll and J.T. Littleton: Phys. Rev. **31**, 489 (1910).

[4] G. Pfestorf: Ann. Phys., Lpz. **81**, 906 (1926).

image prism separates two perpendicular linear vibrations, and may be considered to be a double field analyser (Sect. 20) with a half-shadow angle of $\pi/2$. The two fields will be equally bright when the two bisectors of this angle are parallel to the axes of the ellipse. It may be shown that the sensitivity of the device is a maximum when the half-shadow angle is $\pi/2$, but this condition is not utilised for visual methods, since the intensity in the field of view will be too high. In a photocell, this presents no difficulty because the constant intensity may be removed by having a chopper rotating at a frequency f and observing only the components of frequency $2f$.

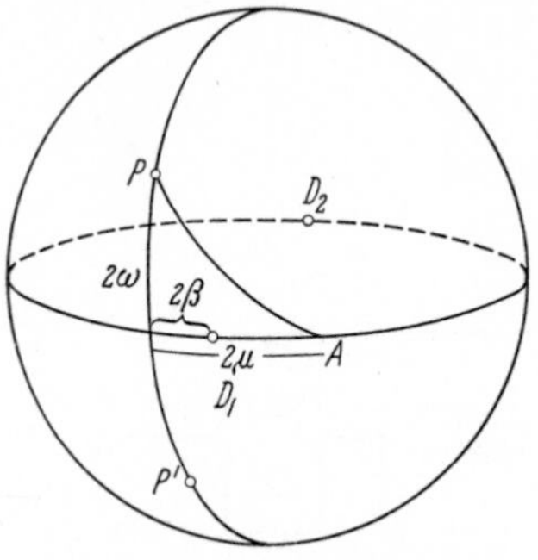

Fig. 26. Theory of the photoelectric elliptic analyser of Fig. 25b. Light of polarisation state P is passed through a rotating linear analyser and then through a double image prism which resolves it into states D_1 and D_2. The intensities in D_1 and D_2 will be in anti-phase only when P lies on the meridian through D_1 and D_2.

Having obtained the azimuth of the ellipse, the double image prism is then rotated through $\pi/4$, so that the axes of the prism are parallel to the axes of the ellipse. The ratio of the intensities in the two fields then gives b^2/a^2. Using a Wollaston double image prism, it is possible to match the two fields by means of an auxiliary analyser behind the prism. Its azimuth at equality gives directly the ellipticity $\omega (= \arctan b/a)$ of the ellipse.

The other method is rather ingenious. Here, no chopper is used, but a rotating analyser is placed in front of the double image prism (Fig. 25b). Imagine all azimuths to be measured from the major axis of the ellipse to be determined. Let β, $\beta + \frac{\pi}{2}$ be the azimuths of the two axes of the double image prism and μ that of the rotating analyser. Then the fraction of the intensity received by the photocell *1* is, referring to Fig. 26

$$\left.\begin{aligned} t_1 &= \tfrac{1}{2}(1+\cos \widehat{AP})\,[\tfrac{1}{2}(1+\cos \widehat{AD_1})] \\ &= \tfrac{1}{4}(1+\cos 2\mu\cos 2\omega)\,[1+\cos 2(\mu-\beta)]. \end{aligned}\right\} \tag{24.3}$$

Similarly

$$t_2 = \tfrac{1}{4}(1+\cos\mu\cos 2\omega)\,[1-\cos 2(\mu-\beta)]. \tag{24.4}$$

Thus

$$\left.\begin{aligned} t_{1,2} = \tfrac{1}{4}[1 &+ \{\cos 2\omega\cos 2\mu \pm \cos 2(\mu-\beta)\} + \\ &+ \cos 2\mu\cos 2\omega\cos 2(\mu-\beta)]. \end{aligned}\right\} \tag{24.5}$$

If f is the frequency of rotation of the analyser, then the second term is of frequency $2f$ while the third is of frequency $4f$. By means of a tuned circuit, the latter is eliminated. Considering only the second term, the two intensities are

$$t'_{1,2} = (\cos 2\omega \pm \cos 2\beta)\cos 2\mu \pm \sin 2\beta \sin 2\mu. \tag{24.6}$$

It is seen that only if $\beta = 0$ are the two exactly in anti-phase and the ratio of the two is then

$$\frac{t'_2}{t'_1} = -\frac{1-\cos 2\omega}{1+\cos 2\omega} = -\tan^2\omega. \tag{24.7}$$

Thus, the setting of the double image prism for this condition gives the orientation of the axes of the ellipse and the ratio of the two signals give b^2/a^2. As in the first method, an auxiliary analyser may also be used to give directly ω.

Both the methods do not give the sense of the ellipse. Unlike in KENT and LAWSON's method, the ambiguity in these methods is that the sign of ω is indeterminate, while λ is definitely fixed. The alternative choice of P is shown by P' in Fig. 26. Such an ambiguity is unavoidable if no compensators are used, and only measurements of intensities are made with analysers represented by points on the equator of the Poincaré sphere. On the other hand, these methods do not require any calibration of the compensator plates.

The photocell method has been utilised for the analysis of elliptically polarised radiation in the infrared, particularly in connection with the determination of optical constants by reflection[1].

25. Depolarisers. A depolariser is an arrangement which converts a beam of light of any state of polarisation into an unpolarised beam. Such a device finds an application for instance if the relative intensities of two differently polarised components have to be compared after passing through an instrument such as a spectrograph, where refraction through optical surfaces occur.

In the Poincaré representation, unpolarised light is represented by a point at the centre of the Poincaré sphere. Thus, if the vector $\boldsymbol{p}$ represents the state of the beam emerging from the depolariser, then it must change in such a way that its mean value is zero, i.e.,

$$\int \boldsymbol{p}\, ds = 0 \tag{25.1}$$

where s is some parameter[2]. This must happen independent of the state of polarisation of the incident beam. Since any light beam can be considered to be made up of a mixture of an unpolarised part and a completely polarised part, it is only the latter that has to be rendered unpolarised by the depolariser. Our discussion may therefore be confined to completely polarised incident light.

The effect of an optical element is to rotate the point on the Poincaré sphere about some axis. Suppose the crystal plate exhibits varying path retardation over its surface extending over a number of wavelengths. Then P would be rotated over a number of complete revolutions about the axis concerned. If the incident beam is plane polarised and the plate is optically active, the point P is rotated around the equator, and the mean value of $\boldsymbol{p}$ for an integral number of rotations is zero. However, if the incident light is elliptically polarised, such a plate will not render it unpolarised. In general, rotation about any one axis alone will not be sufficient to depolarise an incident beam, irrespective of its state of polarisation. However, if the instrument produces, in effect, rotations distributed evenly over a range of 2π about two perpendicular axes in Poincaré space, the rotations being uncorrelated, then it would act as a depolariser. This is so because any point on the sphere would be evenly distributed over its surface area by this process.

It is also possible to achieve this by means of correlated rotations about two perpendicular axes[3]. If the ratio of the two rotations is r, then the resultant Poincaré vector can be shown to be zero if r is an integer equal to, or greater than 2. The simplest case with $r=2$ was adopted by Lyot[4], who obtained the effect by using two plates of quartz, one twice the thickness of the other, both cut parallel to the optic axis, but kept one behind the other, with their axes at 45° to each other. The resultant rotations are about HV and CD which are at right angles. Lyot used this with white radiation and the thickness was quite large, so that small variations of wavelength introduced the varying phase retardations. If a similar arrangement is to be used for monochromatic light, e.g.,

---

[1] G. K. T. Conn and G. K. Eaton: J. Opt. Soc. Amer. **44**, 477, 484, 546 (1954).
[2] G. N. Ramachandran: J. Madras Univ. B **22**, 277 (1952).
[3] B. H. Billings: J. Opt. Soc. Amer. **41**, 966 (1951).
[4] B. Lyot: Ann. Obs. Astron. Phys., Paris **8**, 102 (1928).

in the study of scattering of light or the Raman effect, then two wedges, one with twice the angle as the other, but with their principal directions at 45° may be used. Here, the transmitted light would be unpolarised when averaged over the area of the depolariser. BILLINGS has suggested the use of the electro-optical effect to construct a depolariser. The electric field which is applied to the crystal (like KH_2PO_4) through which the light is transmitted is varied in a saw tooth fashion at a high frequency. The transmitted light would be unpolarised if observed for a period much larger than the period of one cycle.

B. The theory of propagation of light in anisotropic media.

I. General considerations.

26. Electromagnetic equations[1]. The four field vectors $\boldsymbol{E}$, $\boldsymbol{D}$, $\boldsymbol{H}$ and $\boldsymbol{B}$ where

$\boldsymbol{E}$ is the electric field
$\boldsymbol{D}$ is the displacement or the electric induction
$\boldsymbol{H}$ is the magnetic field
and $\boldsymbol{B}$ is the magnetic induction

define the electromagnetic field in any medium and they must satisfy MAXWELL's equations[2]. If in a medium the charge density is ϱ and the current density is $\boldsymbol{j}$ then MAXWELL's equations are given by

$$\left.\begin{aligned} \operatorname{curl} \boldsymbol{H} &= \frac{1}{c}\dot{\boldsymbol{D}} + \frac{\boldsymbol{j}}{c}, \\ \operatorname{curl} \boldsymbol{E} &= -\frac{1}{c}\dot{\boldsymbol{B}} \end{aligned}\right\} \tag{26.1}$$

and one also has the scalar relations

$$\left.\begin{aligned} \operatorname{div} \boldsymbol{D} &= \varrho, \\ \operatorname{div} \boldsymbol{B} &= 0. \end{aligned}\right\} \tag{26.1 a}$$

When a non-conducting medium is placed in an electric field, the distribution of electric charges that constitute the atoms and molecules is altered and this alteration produces a dipole moment per unit volume described by a polarisation vector $\boldsymbol{P}$. There would also be quadrupole moments (Q) and other higher order effects induced[3]. The induction $\boldsymbol{D}$ is given by

$$\boldsymbol{D} = \boldsymbol{E} + \boldsymbol{P} - \operatorname{div} Q \ldots. \tag{26.2}$$

We shall not deal with these atomistic causes but shall present the propagation of light in material media purely from the phenomenological point of view. The only *a priori* condition that one can impose is thet $\boldsymbol{D}$ must be a linear vector function of $\boldsymbol{E}$. This implies that $\boldsymbol{D}$ and $\boldsymbol{E}$ need not necessarily be in the same direction.

We shall restrict ourselves in the present Chapter to the case of electrically non-conducting media which are also at the same time "non-magnetic"—i.e.

[1] Several excellent treatises on crystal optics are available, which present the details of the various phenomena observed in crystals e.g. [*1*] to [*8*], List of References at the end of this article.

[2] Throughout this article, we shall be using Heaviside units for electromagnetic quantities so that factors like 4π will not occur in the equations.

[3] See L. ROSENFELD: Theory of Electrons. Amsterdam: North Holland Publ. Co. 1951.

ones in which the magnetisation cannot follow the rapid optical oscillations. For such media

$$\boldsymbol{j}=0, \quad \varrho=0 \quad \text{and} \quad \boldsymbol{B}=\boldsymbol{H}$$[1]

and MAXWELL's equations (26.1) and (26.1a) reduce to

$$\left.\begin{aligned} &\text{(a)} \quad \operatorname{div}\boldsymbol{D}=0, &\quad &\text{(c)} \quad \operatorname{curl}\boldsymbol{H}=\frac{1}{c}\frac{\partial\boldsymbol{D}}{\partial t},\\ &\text{(b)} \quad \operatorname{div}\boldsymbol{H}=0, &\quad &\text{(d)} \quad \operatorname{curl}\boldsymbol{E}=-\frac{1}{c}\frac{\partial\boldsymbol{H}}{\partial t}. \end{aligned}\right\} \tag{26.3}$$

In what follows, we shall be dealing essentially with the propagation of *plane* electromagnetic waves in a material medium. We are therefore interested in the solutions of MAXWELL's equations (26.3) of the form

$$\boldsymbol{E}, \boldsymbol{D}, \boldsymbol{H} = (\boldsymbol{E}_0, \boldsymbol{D}_0, \boldsymbol{H}_0)\exp\left[i\,\omega\left(t-\frac{n}{c}\,\boldsymbol{r}\cdot\mathbf{s}\right)\right], \tag{26.4}$$

where $\omega\,(=2\pi\nu)$ is the circular frequency, c is the velocity of light in vacuum, n is the refractive index, $\mathbf{s}$ is the unit vector along the wave normal and $\boldsymbol{r}$ is the vector distance of any point from the origin. The refractive index n measures the ratio of the velocity of light in vacuo to the phase velocity of the wave in the medium. It is convenient to take the velocity of light in vacuo to be unity, so that the phase velocity v is related to the refractive index by the equation $n=1/v$.

In most problems, we would be interested in the diverging bundle of rays emerging from a point source or a source of finite size. In such cases, we assume that the light disturbance can be represented by a system of mutually independent plane waves. This assumption can be fully justified from the theory of Fourier transformation, for any arbitrary disturbance can be represented as a sum of its Fourier components, each of which may be identified with a plane wave.

Thus, if $u(x, y, z, t)$ is the light amplitude at a point x, y, z at time t and $v(K_x, K_y, K_z)$ is the amplitude of its plane wave components with wave vector $\boldsymbol{K}(K_x, K_y, K_z; |K| = 1/\lambda)$, then u may be put in the form

$$u(x, y, z, t) = \iiint\limits_{-\infty}^{+\infty} v(K_x, K_y, K_z)\, e^{2\pi i(\nu t-\boldsymbol{K}\cdot\boldsymbol{r})}\, dK_x\, dK_y\, dK_z. \tag{26.5}$$

If now $u_0(x_0, y_0, z_0)$ is the light disturbance at time $t=0$, then v's can be connected with u_0 by inverting (26.5). Thus,

$$v(K_x, K_y, K_z) = \iiint\limits_{-\infty}^{+\infty} u_0(x_0, y_0, z_0)\, e^{2\pi i\boldsymbol{K}\cdot\boldsymbol{r}_0}\, dx_0\, dy_0\, dz_0. \tag{26.5a}$$

Hence, given the light field at $t=0$, that at any later time may be obtained by combining the above two equations. Thus,

$$u(x, y, z, t) = \iiint\limits_{-\infty}^{+\infty}\iiint\limits_{-\infty}^{+\infty} u_0(x_0, y_0, z_0)\, e^{2\pi i[\nu t-\boldsymbol{K}\cdot(\boldsymbol{r}-\boldsymbol{r}_0)]}\, dx_0\, dy_0\, dz_0\, dK_x\, dK_y\, dK_z. \tag{26.5b}$$

It may readily be verified that u, as defined by (26.5b), satisfies the wave equation

$$\nabla^2 u - \frac{1}{c^2}\frac{\partial^2 u}{\partial t^2} = 0$$

[1] See however Sect. 36 on Optical Activity.

with $c = v/K$ and obviously also satisfies the initial conditions at $t=0$. Thus, a superposition of plane waves satisfies the wave equation because of (26.5) and can be made to fit any required initial conditions by means of (26.5a)[1].

It must however be mentioned that Eq. (26.4) represents a disturbance which is propagated in a homogeneous isotropic medium. We shall however assume that the plane wave representation holds equally well in a homogeneous anisotropic medium. It is also supposed that there is no change in the state of polarisation. This is true in general, but not so along certain singular directions in absorbing crystals (see Sect. 56). Plane wave solutions of a more general type have been dealt with by R.C. JONES[2].

It will be seen that the operator $\frac{\partial}{\partial t}$ is equivalent to multiplication by $i\omega$ and the operator $\frac{\partial}{\partial x}$ to multiplication by $-i\omega n \frac{s_x}{c}$. Substituting these, one has

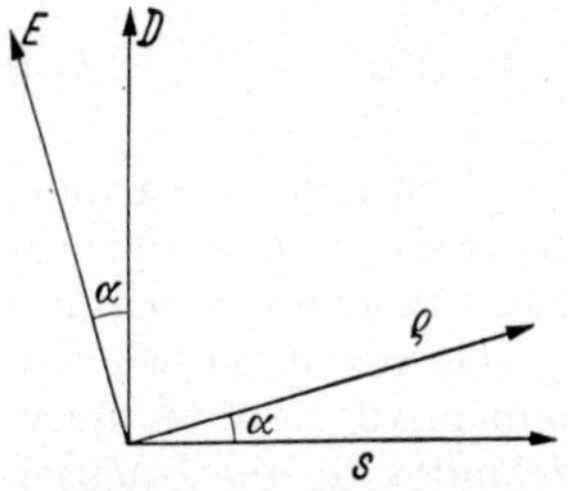

Fig. 27. Relation between vectors connected with electromagnetic wave propagation. The wave normal $\boldsymbol{s}$ is perpendicular to $\boldsymbol{D}$, the ray direction $\boldsymbol{\rho}$ is perpendicular to $\boldsymbol{E}$, while $\boldsymbol{E}, \boldsymbol{D}, \boldsymbol{\rho}$ and $\boldsymbol{s}$ are coplanar. $\boldsymbol{H}$ is normal to the plane of the paper.

$$\frac{\partial \boldsymbol{D}}{\partial t} = i\,\omega\,\boldsymbol{D}$$

and

$$\operatorname{curl} \boldsymbol{E} = i\,\omega\,\frac{n}{c}\,\boldsymbol{E}\times\boldsymbol{s}$$

and Eqs. (26.3) become

$$\left.\begin{aligned} n\,\boldsymbol{H}\times\boldsymbol{s} &= \boldsymbol{D}, \\ n\,\boldsymbol{E}\times\boldsymbol{s} &= \boldsymbol{H}. \end{aligned}\right\} \qquad (26.6)$$

Eliminating $\boldsymbol{H}$ from the two equations in (26.6) we get

$$\boldsymbol{D} = -\,n^2\,(\boldsymbol{E}\times\boldsymbol{s})\times\boldsymbol{s} = n^2\,\{\boldsymbol{E} - (\boldsymbol{E}\cdot\boldsymbol{s})\,\boldsymbol{s}\}. \qquad (26.7)$$

If the z axis is along the direction of propagation, Eq. (26.7) takes the elegant form

$$D_x = n^2 E_x, \quad D_y = n^2 E_y \quad \text{and} \quad D_z = 0. \qquad (26.8)$$

From Eqs. (26.6) one can deduce[3] that (a) $\boldsymbol{H}$ is perpendicular to $\boldsymbol{D}$, $\boldsymbol{E}$ and $\boldsymbol{s}$ and hence $\boldsymbol{D}$, $\boldsymbol{E}$ and $\boldsymbol{s}$ are coplanar; (b) the wave normal $\boldsymbol{s}$ is perpendicular to $\boldsymbol{D}$ and not necessarily to $\boldsymbol{E}$ ($\boldsymbol{s}$ being perpendicular to $\boldsymbol{E}$ in vacuum) and from Eq. (26.7) we find that (c) $\boldsymbol{D}$ is equal to the product of n^2 and the component of $\boldsymbol{E}$ along the wavefront.

The direction of ray propagation is the direction of travel of a marked element on the wavefront. In Sect. 27 we shall be considering from a wave-optical standpoint the relation between the *ray* and *wave* propagation. Here we may identify the direction of ray propagation with the direction of energy propagation, the latter being defined by the Poynting vector $\boldsymbol{E}\times\boldsymbol{H}$. The ray therefore travels along $\boldsymbol{\varrho}$ which is the unit vector perpendicular to $\boldsymbol{E}$ and coplanar with $\boldsymbol{E}, \boldsymbol{D}$ and $\boldsymbol{s}$. These results are illustrated in Fig. 27. It is clear from the diagram, as $\boldsymbol{E}, \boldsymbol{D}, \boldsymbol{\varrho}$ and $\boldsymbol{s}$ are coplanar, that if $\boldsymbol{s}$ and $\boldsymbol{\varrho}$ are at an angle α, $\boldsymbol{D}$ and $\boldsymbol{E}$ also make the same angle with each other.

It is worthwhile at this stage to give the relation between the wave and ray velocities[4]. If at time $t=0$, the points of constant phase lie on a plane AB

[1] Attempts to justify the plane wave representation were made by LAMÉ, for elastic waves in his "Leçons sur la théorie mathématique de l'élasticité", Paris 1852, and these were extended by V. VOLTERRA, Acta math. **16**, 153 (1892).

[2] R.C. JONES: J. Opt. Soc. Amer. **46**, 126 (1956).

[3] We are here describing the simple case when the solutions are *plane* polarised waves.

[4] See also Sect. 27.

(Fig. 28) and later, on a plane $A'B'$ at time t, then the normal distance between the two planes will be proportional to vt, where v is the wave velocity. The marked element of wavefront on the other hand will be propagated along $\boldsymbol{\varrho}$ making an angle α with the wave normal If the ray velocity is v_r,[1] then from Fig. 28,

$$v_r \cos\alpha = v \tag{26.9}$$

and the ray index is

$$\frac{1}{v_r} = n_r = n\cos\alpha. \tag{26.10}$$

Now Eq. (26.7) can be written in the form

$$|D| = n^2 |E| \cos\alpha = \frac{1}{v^2} |E| \cos\alpha. \tag{26.11}$$

Hence, we have the inverse relation

$$|E| = \frac{1}{n^2\cos^2\alpha} |D| \cos\alpha = \frac{1}{n_r^2} |D| \cos\alpha \tag{26.12}$$

or

$$|E| = v_r^2 |D| \cos\alpha. \tag{26.13}$$

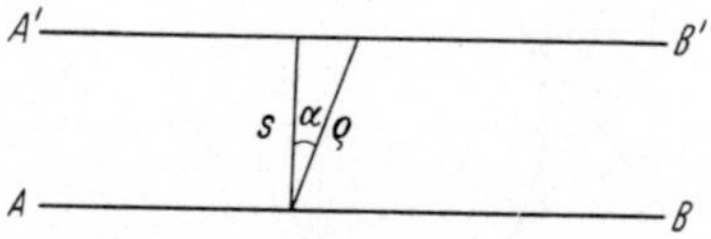

Fig. 28. Relation between ray velocity and wave velocity. AB and $A'B'$ are planes of constant phase. $\boldsymbol{s}$ is the wave normal. $\boldsymbol{\rho}$ is the ray direction along which a marked element is propagated.

Since a vector of length $|D| \cos\alpha$ along $\boldsymbol{E}$ is from Fig. 27 equal to $\boldsymbol{D} - (\boldsymbol{D}\cdot\boldsymbol{\varrho})\,\boldsymbol{\varrho}$, this gives for the vector $\boldsymbol{E}$ the equation

$$\boldsymbol{E} = \frac{1}{n_r^2} \{\boldsymbol{D} - (\boldsymbol{D}\cdot\boldsymbol{\varrho})\,\boldsymbol{\varrho}\} \tag{26.14}$$

which is exactly analogous to Eq. (26.7).

Eqs. (26.7) and (26.14) may be taken as the *fundamental equations* for developing a consistent theory of the optics of homogeneous media.

27. The wave surface, the wave velocity surface and the ray velocity surface for an anisotropic medium. In the last section the distinction between the directions of the wave normal and the ray normal was introduced specifically as a consequence of the electromagnetic theory. This was done by assuming that the direction of the ray normal—i.e. the direction of travel of a limited portion of a wavefront—may be identified with that of the Poynting vector which gives the direction of energy flux. This assumption is not without exception even in the case of isotropic media[2] and in any case the direct evaluation of the Poynting vector becomes complicated in the more complex class of crystals (e.g. those which possess optical activity). It is therefore worthwhile considering how the ray direction may be obtained independent of the idea of the Poynting vector. In fact, the considerations given below are valid for any type of wave, not necessarily an electromagnetic wave.

As we have seen in Sect. 26, the propagation of waves arising from an arbitrary source distribution in a medium may be represented by a superposition of plane waves. It then follows that the disturbance emanating from a point source may be represented by a series of plane waves, all proceeding from the same origin in various directions, the velocity of propagation along the wave normal being however different for different directions if the medium is anisotropic.

Consider the disposition of the wave fronts after unit time, which will be as shown in Fig. 29. The envelope of the planes is shown by the thick line in the figure, which obviously would form a closed surface in three dimensions. It will

[1] Measured taking the velocity of light as unity.
[2] See e.g., F. Zernicke: J. Opt. Soc. Amer. **47**, 466 (1957).

be noticed that, at a point such as Q, which is not on the envelope, the different waves reaching it have varying phases. On the other hand, at a point like P on the envelope surface, waves having their propagation directions close to that of the tangent plane at P will all have very nearly the same phase, and therefore there will be a concentration of intensity at P. Thus, at time $t=1$, there is a concentration of intensity on the envelope surface, which we may call the *wave surface* at time $t=1$. This surface is defined by the condition that the length of the normal from the origin to a tangent plane is equal to the wave velocity (v_w) along the normal.

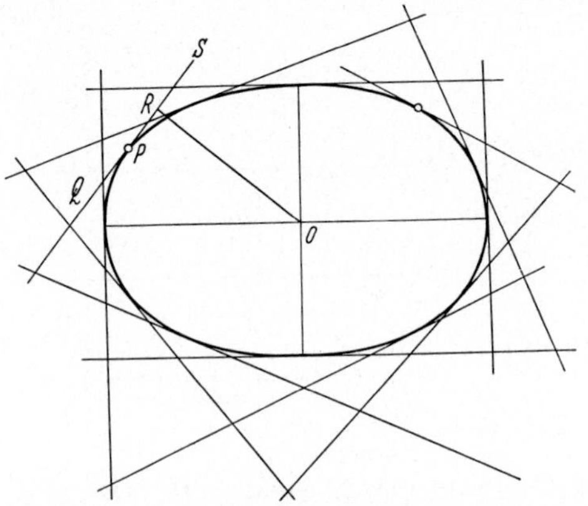

Fig. 29. Construction for obtaining the wave surface. The wave surface is the envelope of the plane waves proceeding in various directions.

We may also plot another surface passing through points, such as R of Fig. 29, i.e., the feet of the normals from the origin to the tangent planes, or the wave fronts at time $t=1$. This surface (Fig. 30a) is called the *wave velocity surface*[1], since the length of the radius vector from the origin to any point on this surface is equal to the wave velocity along that direction.

It is obvious from the construction of Fig. 29 that the shape of the wave surface will be the same at any instant t, only the size increasing proportional to t. So also, it is clear that if we mark a small element ds at P (Fig. 30b), then the marked element would go to the corresponding element ds' at P', and that P' would lie on the line OP produced. We shall call the "ray" direction as that along which a marked portion of the wave surface would proceed. Hence, every radius vector of the wave surface is a ray direction and the distance of its tip from the origin would be proportional to t. Therefore at time $t=1$, the lengths of the radii vectors of the wave surface would be equal to the ray velocity (v_r) along different directions. The wave surface at $t=1$ is thus also the *ray velocity surface*[2], using a terminology similar to the wave velocity surface. It must be noted that the direction of the ray velocity is not normal to the marked element of the wave surface. It is along the radius vector, i.e. along the unit vector $\boldsymbol{\varrho}$ of Fig. 30b. The wave velocity on the other hand is parallel to the normal i.e. along the unit vector $\mathbf{s}$.

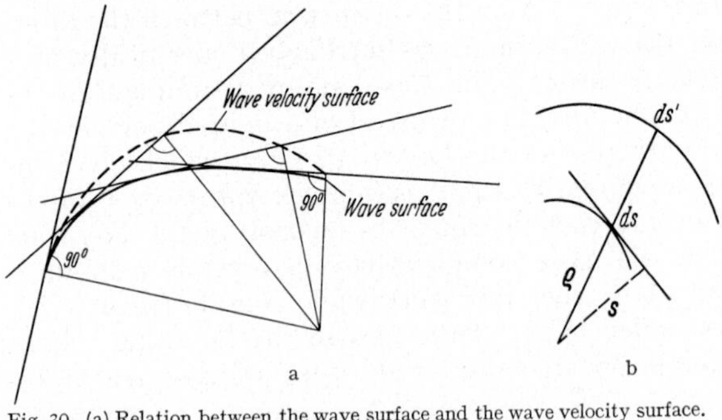

Fig. 30. (a) Relation between the wave surface and the wave velocity surface. (b) Relation between the wave normal $\mathbf{s}$ and the ray direction $\boldsymbol{\rho}$.

It is obvious from the construction shown in Fig. 30a that the wave velocity surface is the "pedal surface" of the ray velocity surface.

[1] This surface is also sometimes called the "normal surface".
[2] Also sometimes called the "ray surface".

28. Light propagation in an anisotropic medium—formulation of the problem. Eq. (26.7) or alternatively its simpler form (26.8) may be regarded as the form which MAXWELL's equations assume for a plane wave field—the properties of the medium not having been introduced in their derivation (except $\boldsymbol{B}=\boldsymbol{H}$). There are however other constitutive relations between the field vectors $\boldsymbol{D}$ and $\boldsymbol{E}$ imposed due to the properties of the medium viz. its particular polarisability characteristics. It is clear from the discussion in the last section that our basic problem reduces to the following: To determine the states of polarisation $\boldsymbol{D}$ of the plane waves that can be propagated along an arbitrary direction Oz in the medium as well as their wave velocities. The reason why only specific plane wave solutions can be obtained is that they have to be consistent with the field equations and the properties of the medium. Since the solutions depend on the relations between $\boldsymbol{D}$ and $\boldsymbol{E}$, these relations completely determine the optical properties of the medium i.e. whether it will be birefringent, optically active, absorbing, etc. We shall deal with these cases individually in the sections that follow.

II. Non-absorbing and non-optically active crystals.

29. Dielectric and index tensors. It has been mentioned earlier that $\boldsymbol{D}$ is a linear vector function of $\boldsymbol{E}$ and this in the most general case can be written as

$$\boldsymbol{D} = [\varepsilon]\,\boldsymbol{E} \tag{29.1}$$

where $[\varepsilon]$ is a tensor of rank two. The tensor $[\varepsilon]$ is called the dielectric tensor. Written explicitly in terms of the three orthogonal axes x, y and z fixed in the medium

$$\left.\begin{aligned} D_x &= \varepsilon_{11} E_x + \varepsilon_{12} E_y + \varepsilon_{13} E_z, \\ D_y &= \varepsilon_{21} E_x + \varepsilon_{22} E_y + \varepsilon_{23} E_z, \\ D_z &= \varepsilon_{31} E_x + \varepsilon_{32} E_y + \varepsilon_{33} E_z. \end{aligned}\right\} \tag{29.2}$$

The tensor $[\varepsilon]$ will vary with the frequency of the incident light. We shall at present confine ourselves to considering the effects for a monochromatic beam.

We shall now show that the dielectric tensor for a non-absorbing optically inactive crystal is symmetric, taking as our starting point POYNTING's theorem which states that at any point of an electromagnetic field the rate of flow of energy is described by the Poynting vector $\boldsymbol{G}$ given by

$$\boldsymbol{G} = c\,(\boldsymbol{E}\times\boldsymbol{H}). \tag{29.3}$$

From MAXWELL's equations, by taking the scalar product of $\boldsymbol{H}$ with (26.3c) and of $\boldsymbol{E}$ with (26.3d), and combining we get

$$-c\,\mathrm{div}\,(\boldsymbol{E}\times\boldsymbol{H}) = (\boldsymbol{E}\cdot\dot{\boldsymbol{D}} + \boldsymbol{H}\cdot\dot{\boldsymbol{H}}). \tag{29.4}$$

The flow of energy into a volume τ through the bounding surface σ is thus

$$-\int \boldsymbol{G}\cdot\boldsymbol{n}\,d\sigma = c\int_\tau \mathrm{div}\,(\boldsymbol{E}\times\boldsymbol{H})\,d\tau = \int_\tau \left[\boldsymbol{E}\cdot\dot{\boldsymbol{D}} + \frac{d}{dt}\left(\frac{1}{2}\boldsymbol{H}^2\right)\right] d\tau \tag{29.5}$$

where $\boldsymbol{n}$ represents the unit normal to the surface element $d\sigma$. This should be equal to the increase in the electric and magnetic energy in the volume plus the energy that may be dissipated. Expressing by $W_e(E)$ and $W_m(H)$ the electric and magnetic energy densities and by W_f the dissipation function appropriate to the medium (representing the rate at which work is performed by the electromagnetic field against dissipative forces), we have

$$-\int \boldsymbol{G}\cdot\boldsymbol{n}\,d\sigma = \frac{d}{dt}\int_\tau (W_e + W_m)\,d\tau + \int_\tau W_f\,d\tau. \tag{29.6}$$

Comparing (29.5) and (29.6) and identifying the magnetic energy density (which should be a function of state of $\boldsymbol{H}$ alone) with $\frac{1}{2}\boldsymbol{H}^2$, we obtain

$$\frac{dW_e}{dt} + W_f = \boldsymbol{E}\cdot\dot{\boldsymbol{D}}.$$

Hence

$$dW_e + W_f dt = \boldsymbol{E}\cdot d\boldsymbol{D}. \tag{29.7}$$

In this chapter we shall only consider non-absorbing crystals for which $W_f = 0$. We then obtain

$$dW_e = \boldsymbol{E}\cdot d\boldsymbol{D}. \tag{29.8}$$

The type of linear vector relationship that can subsist between $\boldsymbol{D}$ and $\boldsymbol{E}$ is now restricted by the condition that W_e is a function of the state, i.e. dW_e should be a perfect differential. We again restrict our attention to media in which $\boldsymbol{D}$ depends on $\boldsymbol{E}$ alone and not on $\partial\boldsymbol{E}/\partial t$ [with the use of complex periodic functions this means, because of (29.1), that the components of the tensor ε_{ij} must all be real and cannot take complex values]. Then

$$dW_e = \sum_i \varepsilon_{ii} E_i dE_i + \sum_{\substack{i \\ i\neq j}}\sum_{j} (\varepsilon_{ij} E_i dE_j + \varepsilon_{ji} E_j dE_i). \tag{29.9}$$

This is a perfect differential only if $\varepsilon_{ij} = \varepsilon_{ji}$ showing that the dielectric tensor must be symmetric. Then

$$dW_e = \tfrac{1}{2}\sum_i\sum_j \varepsilon_{ij}\, d(E_i E_j). \tag{29.10}$$

Integrating the electric energy per unit volume for the particular type of medium considered[1]

$$\left.\begin{aligned} W_e &= \tfrac{1}{2}\sum\sum \varepsilon_{ij} E_i E_j = \tfrac{1}{2} E_i D_i \\ &= \tfrac{1}{2}[\varepsilon]\,\boldsymbol{E}\cdot\boldsymbol{E} = \tfrac{1}{2}\boldsymbol{E}\cdot\boldsymbol{D}. \end{aligned}\right\} \tag{29.11}$$

Hitherto we have expressed $\boldsymbol{D}$ as a vector function of $\boldsymbol{E}$ using the dielectric tensor. If now we take the opposite view and express $\boldsymbol{E}$ as a linear vector function of $\boldsymbol{D}$ then

$$\boldsymbol{E} = [a]\,\boldsymbol{D} \tag{29.12}$$

where $[a]$ is a tensor of the second rank—the index tensor—which must necessarily be symmetric since

$$[a] = [\varepsilon]^{-1}. \tag{29.13}$$

Written explicitly

$$\left.\begin{aligned} E_x &= a_{11} D_x + a_{12} D_y + a_{13} D_z, \\ E_y &= a_{21} D_x + a_{22} D_y + a_{23} D_z, \\ E_z &= a_{31} D_x + a_{32} D_y + a_{33} D_z. \end{aligned}\right\} \tag{29.14}$$

Consequently with $a_{ij} = a_{ji}$ the a_{ij}'s in (29.14) can be obtained in terms of the components of the dielectric tensor by substituting the values of $\boldsymbol{D}$ from (29.2). Thus one obtains

$$a_{ij} = \frac{\varepsilon^{ij}}{|\varepsilon|} \tag{29.15}$$

where ε^{ij} is the minor of ε_{ij} in the determinant $|\varepsilon|$.

---

[1] It is not implied that $W_e = \frac{1}{2}\boldsymbol{E}\cdot\boldsymbol{D}$ for all types of media since it has been assumed that the dielectric tensor is real and that there is no dissipation. The case when the dielectric tensor is complex even in a non-dissipative medium is considered in the section on optically active crystals (Sect. 36) while the general case is met with in Sects. 43 and 50.

Associated with the index tensor $[a]$ we can define a tensor surface without any reference to a co-ordinate system in the following manner. From a chosen origin, lay out radii vectors of length r in all directions, the reciprocal of r^2 being equal to the "magnitude of the tensor property" in that direction, in this case the ratio of the resolved component of $\boldsymbol{E}$ in the direction of $\boldsymbol{D}$ to the magnitude of $\boldsymbol{D}$ which produced it. Thus,

$$\frac{1}{r^2} = \frac{\boldsymbol{D}\cdot\boldsymbol{E}}{D^2} = \frac{\boldsymbol{D}\cdot[a]\,\boldsymbol{D}}{D^2}. \tag{29.15a}$$

If l_1, l_2, l_3 are the direction cosines of the vector $\boldsymbol{D}$ referred to a co-ordinate system and the co-ordinates of the tip of the vector of length r are x, y, z, then

$$\frac{1}{r^2} = \sum_i \sum_j a_{ij} l_i l_j$$

and therefore the equation to the surface traced by the tip of the vector of length r is

$$a_{11}x^2 + a_{22}y^2 + a_{33}z^2 + 2a_{23}yz + 2a_{31}zx + 2a_{12}xy = 1. \tag{29.16}$$

The surface is thus an ellipsoid, and as it is associated with the index tensor it may be called the *index ellipsoid*[1].

It will be noticed from (29.16) that if we denote the vector (x, y, z) by $\boldsymbol{D}_0$ and the corresponding $\boldsymbol{E}$ by $\boldsymbol{E}_0$ then $\boldsymbol{E}_0\cdot\boldsymbol{D}_0 = 1$. This relation can be used to find both the magnitude and direction of $\boldsymbol{E}$ when $\boldsymbol{D}$ is given, by means of a geometric construction on the ellipsoid. This is discussed in Sect. 30.

In the same way, we may associate another ellipsoid, the *Fresnel ellipsoid*, with the dielectric tensor $[\varepsilon]$. The equation to the Fresnel ellipsoid is thus given by

$$\varepsilon_{11}x^2 + \varepsilon_{22}y^2 + \varepsilon_{33}z^2 + 2\varepsilon_{23}yz + 2\varepsilon_{31}zx + 2\varepsilon_{12}xy = 1. \tag{29.17}$$

Thus, we see that the coefficients of the equation to the tensor ellipsoid with respect to any coordinate system are also the components of the tensor with reference to the same coordinate system. It is useful therefore to recall the manner in which the coefficients in the equation to an ellipsoid transform with a transformation of coordinate axes. Let OX, OY, OZ be the coordinate axes taken along the principal axes of the ellipsoid, i.e. for which the equation to the ellipsoid is

$$a_X X^2 + a_Y Y^2 + a_Z Z^2 = 1. \tag{29.18}$$

Then, if we transform to the axes Ox, Oy, Oz whose direction cosines are given by the scheme

	x	y	z
X	α_1	α_2	α_3
Y	β_1	β_2	β_3
Z	γ_1	γ_2	γ_3

we have

$$\begin{aligned} a_{11} &= a_X\alpha_1^2 + a_Y\beta_1^2 + a_Z\gamma_1^2,\\ a_{12} &= a_X\alpha_1\alpha_2 + a_Y\beta_1\beta_2 + a_Z\gamma_1\gamma_2. \end{aligned} \tag{29.19}$$

[1] This is also called by various other names such as the indicatrix, Fletcher ellipsoid and reciprocal ellipsoid.

30. The complete solution of wave propagation: Geometrical method. *α) The index ellipsoid.* By proving that the dielectric tensor is symmetric we have proved that in any non-absorbing non-optically active crystal there exists for a particular wavelength three orthogonal directions OX, OY, OZ called the *principal electric axes* for which

$$\left.\begin{aligned} D_X &= \varepsilon_X E_X, \\ D_Y &= \varepsilon_Y E_Y, \\ D_Z &= \varepsilon_Z E_Z \end{aligned}\right\} \tag{30.1}$$

where ε_X, ε_Y and ε_Z are called the principal dielectric constants. In most cases for discussing the problem of the propagation of waves it is more important to express $\boldsymbol{E}$ as an explicit function of $\boldsymbol{D}$. This can be done by rewriting (30.1) as

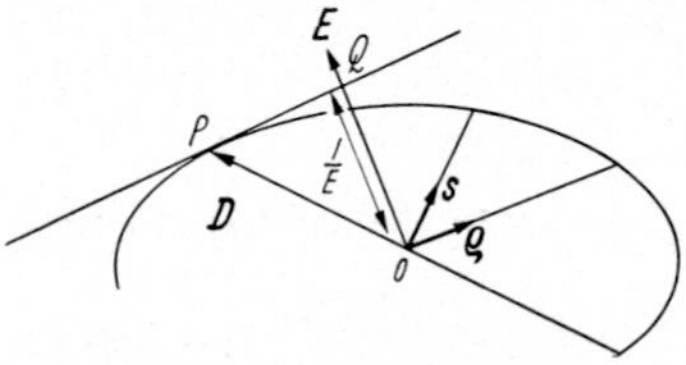

Fig. 31. POINSOT's construction on the index ellipsoid. Given the vibration direction $\boldsymbol{D}$ to be parallel to OP, $\boldsymbol{E}$ is along OQ the perpendicular to the tangent plane at P. Hence the wave is propagated in the plane of OP and OQ, $\boldsymbol{s}$ and $\boldsymbol{\rho}$ being the wave normal and ray directions. If the magnitude of $\boldsymbol{D}$ is OP, then that of $\boldsymbol{E}$ is $1/OQ$. More generally, $|E| = |D|/OP \times OQ$.

$$\left.\begin{aligned} E_X &= a_X D_X, \\ E_Y &= a_Y D_Y, \\ E_Z &= a_Z D_Z \end{aligned}\right\} \tag{30.2}$$

where a_X, a_Y and a_Z are called the principal components of the index tensor and are respectively the reciprocals of the corresponding principal dielectric constants. The electric vector will be parallel to the displacement vector only when the latter is along one of the principal electrical axes. For other directions of the displacement vector, the corresponding directions and magnitude of the electric vector can be obtained by a simple geometric construction from the *index ellipsoid*. This ellipsoid we define by the equation

$$a_X X^2 + a_Y Y^2 + a_Z Z^2 = 1. \tag{30.3}$$

Suppose now we choose the displacement vector $\boldsymbol{D}$ to be equal to the radius vector OP of the ellipsoid, then D_X, D_Y, D_Z are also the coordinates X, Y, Z of the tip of the vector and hence using (30.2) the equation to the ellipsoid can also be written as

$$\boldsymbol{E}\cdot\boldsymbol{D} = 1 = \sum a_X D_X^2 = f, \quad \text{say}. \tag{30.4}$$

The normal to the ellipsoid at the tip of $\boldsymbol{D}$ would have direction cosines proportional to $\frac{\partial f}{\partial X}, \frac{\partial f}{\partial Y}, \frac{\partial f}{\partial Z}$ i.e. to $a_X D_X$, $a_Y D_Y$, $a_Z D_Z$, and is therefore parallel to $\boldsymbol{E}$ from Eq. (30.2). Hence $\boldsymbol{E}$ lies along the perpendicular to the tangent plane of the ellipsoid at the tip of $\boldsymbol{D}$. Further the magnitude of $\boldsymbol{E}$ will be equal to the reciprocal of this perpendicular length since from (30.4) we have

$$\frac{1}{|E|} = D\cos\vartheta. \tag{30.5}$$

By this construction which is known after POINSOT (Fig. 31), if $\boldsymbol{D}$ is the radius vector of the index ellipsoid, then $\boldsymbol{E}$ is the normal from the origin to the corresponding tangent plane. Consequently, given the vector $\boldsymbol{D}$, the plane containing $\boldsymbol{D}$ and $\boldsymbol{E}$ can in general be uniquely determined. From Fig. 27 and Eq. (26.6) we know that a wave can be propagated along a direction perpendicular to $\boldsymbol{D}$, only in the plane of $\boldsymbol{D}$ and $\boldsymbol{E}$. Consequently, given $\boldsymbol{D}$, by virtue of the Poinsot construction there is in general a unique direction of wave propagation inside an anisotropic crystal. This is in sharp contrast to the case of the isotropic solid where the wave can be propagated along any direction perpendicular to $\boldsymbol{D}$ (since the directions of $\boldsymbol{D}$ and $\boldsymbol{E}$ coincide).

The converse problem of determining the orientation of the vector $\boldsymbol{D}$ for any given direction of propagation is of considerable importance in crystal optics. Let us consider the propagation of a wave along an aribtrary direction which we take as the Oz direction. The section of the index ellipsoid by the xy plane will be an ellipse shown in Fig. 32. The vibration of any wave propagated along Oz must be in the plane of this section. It is clear that only that $\boldsymbol{D}$ vibration for which $\boldsymbol{E}$ lies on the $(D_1 z)$ plane can be propagated along Oz. And this happens only when the $\boldsymbol{D}$ vector coincides with the principal radii of the elliptic section. This is a property of any triaxial ellipsoid which can be proved as follows. Let the x axis be taken along the $\boldsymbol{D}$ vibration. We wish to determine the orientation of the x axis for which the above condition i.e. $\boldsymbol{E}$ lies in the DOz plane is satisfied.

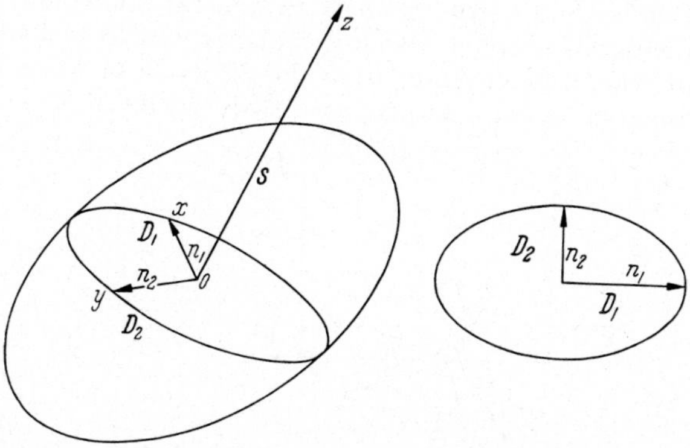

Fig. 32. Given a direction of wave propagation Oz, two waves can be propagated, and these have their $\boldsymbol{D}$ vectors parallel to the principal axes of the central elliptic section of the index ellipsoid perpendicular to Oz. Their refractive indices n_1, n_2 are equal to the principal radii of this section.

If the equation to the ellipsoid is

$$a_{11}x^2 + a_{22}y^2 + a_{33}z^2 + 2a_{12}xy + 2a_{23}yz + 2a_{31}zx = 1 \tag{30.6}$$

the equation to the elliptic section would be

$$a_{11}x^2 + a_{22}y^2 + 2a_{12}xy = 1. \tag{30.7}$$

The normal at any point x, y, z of the ellipsoid has direction cosines proportional to $\frac{\partial f}{\partial x}, \frac{\partial f}{\partial y}, \frac{\partial f}{\partial z}$. Hence the condition that the normal at the tip of the radius vector along the direction should lie in the xz plane is that $\frac{\partial f}{\partial y} = 0$ at $x=0$, $y=0$ i.e.,

$$a_{12} = 0. \tag{30.8}$$

This signifies that the x axis and hence the $\boldsymbol{D}$ vector must be taken along one of the principal axes of the elliptic section. Hence we get the proposition: *Given the direction of the wave normal* **s** *two waves can be propagated with their vibrations linearly polarised along the principal axes of the elliptic section of the index ellipsoid normal to* **s**[1].

It now remains for us to determine the refractive index corresponding to any direction of vibration of the $\boldsymbol{D}$ vector. We have shown in (26.7) that $\boldsymbol{D}$ is equal to the product of n^2 and the projected components of $\boldsymbol{E}$ on $\boldsymbol{D}$ i.e.

$$\frac{1}{n^2} = \frac{D E \cos\vartheta}{D^2} = \frac{\boldsymbol{D}\cdot\boldsymbol{E}}{|D^2|} \tag{30.9}$$

[1] Extremely elegant geometric proofs of this and many theorems in crystal optics using the index ellipsoid have been given in G. Salmon, Analytical Geometry of three dimensions, Dublin 1881.

which from (29.15a) is equal to $1/r^2$, where r is the radius vector of the index ellipsoid. Hence, the refractive index

$$n = r \qquad (30.10)$$

where r is the length of the radius vector of the index ellipsoid[1]. Thus, *for any given direction of the* ***D*** *vector the refractive index is equal to the length of the radius vector of the index ellipsoid drawn parallel to the* ***D*** *vector.* The above results are illustrated in Fig. 32.

The vector $\boldsymbol{E}$ corresponding to any one of the $\boldsymbol{D}$ vibrations is obtained by POINSOT's construction and in general makes an angle with $\boldsymbol{D}$. Consequently the ray direction ϱ, which is coplanar with $\boldsymbol{D}$ and $\mathbf{s}$ but perpendicular to $\boldsymbol{E}$ would in general be different from the direction of wave propagation $\mathbf{s}$. Since for any direction of wave propagation there would in general be two directions of vibra-

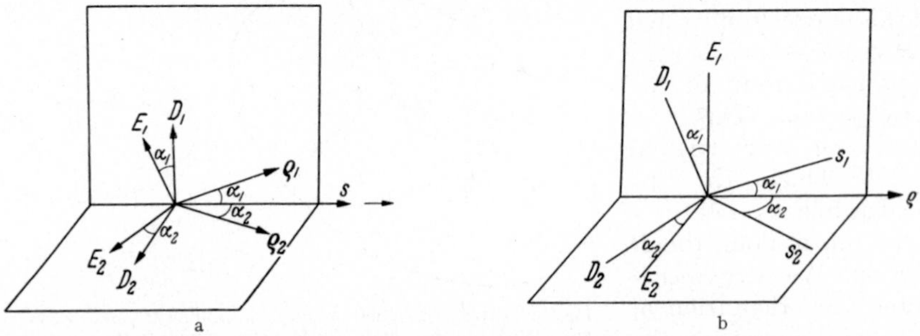

Fig. 33a and b. Relation between ray and wave propagation. (a) For each direction of the wave normal $\boldsymbol{s}$, two waves 1 and 2 are propagated with different ray directions ρ_1 and ρ_2. $\boldsymbol{E}_1, \boldsymbol{D}_1, \boldsymbol{s}, \rho_1$ are coplanar and so are $\boldsymbol{E}_2, \boldsymbol{D}_2, \boldsymbol{s}, \rho_2$. The two planes are perpendicular to each other. (b) Similarly, for every direction of ray propagation ρ there are two directions $\boldsymbol{s}_1$ and $\boldsymbol{s}_2$ of the wave normal and two velocities of ray propagation.

tion, there would also be two directions of ray propagation, respectively in the planes $(\boldsymbol{D}_1, \mathbf{s})$ and $(\boldsymbol{D}_2, \mathbf{s})$ (Fig. 33a). The ray direction corresponding to each one of the $\boldsymbol{D}$ vibrations is parallel to the intersection of the $\boldsymbol{D}, \mathbf{s}$ plane with the tangent plane touching the index ellipsoid at the tip of the corresponding principal axis of the elliptic section (Fig. 31).

Any elliptically polarised vibration can be regarded as the sum of two linearly polarised vibrations along the principal vibration directions of the crystal. Since these two vibrations will be propagated with different velocities, the elliptic vibration cannot in general be transmitted through the crystal without change of form. Hence though we have sought for and obtained only plane polarised solutions it is quite clear that there cannot, in general, be solutions for any other states of polarisation (in transparent, optically inactive crystals).

β) The Fresnel ellipsoid. Just as (29.14) expressing $\boldsymbol{E}$ as an explicit function of $\boldsymbol{D}$ may be described by means of the index ellipsoid so also the relation (29.2) which expresses $\boldsymbol{D}$ as an explicit function of $\boldsymbol{E}$ may be described by the *Fresnel ellipsoid* whose equation is

$$\varepsilon_X X^2 + \varepsilon_Y Y^2 + \varepsilon_Z Z^2 = 1. \qquad (30.11)$$

If the radius vector of this ellipsoid represents in magnitude and direction the $\boldsymbol{E}$ vector, then the equation to the ellipsoid can be written from (29.17) as

$$\boldsymbol{D} \cdot \boldsymbol{E} = 1. \qquad (30.12)$$

Given $\boldsymbol{E}$, the vector $\boldsymbol{D}$ can be obtained from the Fresnel ellipsoid by the POINSOT's construction described in the previous paragraph. Since ϱ the direction of ray

[1] Hence the name *index* ellipsoid for this tensor surface.

propagation is perpendicular to $\boldsymbol{E}$ and it lies in the plane of $\boldsymbol{D}$ and $\boldsymbol{E}$, we get the result that given $\boldsymbol{E}$, we have in general a unique direction of ray propagation. Further $\boldsymbol{E}$ is equal to the product of v_r^2 and the component of $\boldsymbol{D}$ along $\boldsymbol{E}$ [Eq. (26.14)] Hence we can by using all the geometric arguments presented in the previous paragraph show that for a given direction of ray propagation, two $\boldsymbol{E}$ vectors (parallel to the principal axes of the elliptic section of the Fresnel ellipsoid, normal to the ray direction) are propagated with ray velocities equal respectively to the semi-principal axes of the elliptic section (Fig. 33b).

The vector $\boldsymbol{D}$ corresponding to any one of the $\boldsymbol{E}$ vibrations in general makes an angle with $\boldsymbol{E}$. The direction of wave propagation $\mathbf{s}$ lies in the plane of $\boldsymbol{E}$ and $\boldsymbol{\varrho}$ and is perpendicular to $\boldsymbol{D}$ (see Fig. 33b) and would therefore be normally different from the direction of ray propagation. Hence for any direction of ray propagation there would be usually two directions of wave propagation. The wave direction of any one of the $\boldsymbol{E}$ vibrations is the intersection of the $\boldsymbol{E}$, $\boldsymbol{\varrho}$ plane with the tangent plane touching the Fresnel ellipsoid at the tip of the corresponding principal axis of the elliptic section.

From what has been stated above it is clear for every property to be derived from the index ellipsoid there is a corresponding property to be obtained from the Fresnel ellipsoid[1]. It follows that the variables occurring could be written in two rows:

$$\left.\begin{array}{l} \boldsymbol{E}\ \boldsymbol{D}\ \mathbf{s}\ \boldsymbol{\varrho}\ \ v\ \ \ n\ a_X\ a_Y\ a_Z, \\ \boldsymbol{D}\ \boldsymbol{E}\ \boldsymbol{\varrho}\ \mathbf{s}\ \dfrac{1}{v_r}\ \dfrac{1}{n_r}\ \varepsilon_X\ \varepsilon_Y\ \varepsilon_Z. \end{array}\right\} \tag{30.13}$$

Any relation that is valid for the members of one row remains valid when all the corresponding members of the second row are substituted.

31. Analytical solution of wave propagation along an arbitrary direction. We have proved from geometric considerations that given the direction of propagation, all vibration directions transverse to it are not permissible in an anisotropic medium. We have shown that in general, only two directions of vibrations are possible corresponding to two orthogonal states of linear polarisation—these vibration directions and the corresponding refractive indices being determined by the index ellipsoid. We now give a simple analytical proof of the same results. We present this as we shall be extending the same method for the systematic presentation of the features of the propagation of light in a more complex class of crystals.

We may choose the direction Oz of a set of orthogonal coordinate axes Ox, Oy, Oz to be along the direction of propagation. Then $D_z = 0$ as the vibration direction must be perpendicular to the direction of propagation. We wish to find the orientation of the vector $\boldsymbol{D}$ in the x, y plane for which the wave is propagated unchanged. The orientation may be specified by the ratio D_y/D_x. Then the section of the index ellipsoid normal to the direction of propagation lies entirely in the xy plane and is an ellipse with its major and minor axes not coinciding with Ox and Oy. Without loss of generality we may for convenience choose the axes Ox and Oy to be the axes Ox' and Oy' which lie along the principal axes of the ellipse. Then the equation to the ellipse becomes

$$a'_{11} x'^2 + a'_{22} y'^2 = 1. \tag{31.1}$$

[1] It has been remarked in SOMMERFELD's "Optics" [6]. "What is involved here is the same duality that exists in projective geometry between the coordinate spaces of points and planes."

We have already proved in Sect. 29 that the coefficients a_{ij}'s which occur in the equation to the ellipsoid are also the components a_{ij} of the tensor $[a]$ referred to the same axes. By our choice of axes we have made $a'_{12}=0$ and $D_z=0$ and hence Eq. (29.14) which gives the relation between $\boldsymbol{E}$ and $\boldsymbol{D}$ yields

$$\left.\begin{aligned} E_{x'} &= a'_{11} D_{x'}, \\ E_{y'} &= a'_{22} D_{y'}. \end{aligned}\right\} \tag{31.2}$$

Now if n is the refractive index for the wave with the vector $\boldsymbol{D}$ then it follows from Eq. (26.8) that

$$E_{x'} = \frac{1}{n^2} D_{x'}; \quad E_{y'} = \frac{1}{n^2} D_{y'}. \tag{31.3}$$

Combining the two equations (31.2) and (31.3) we have

$$\left.\begin{aligned} \left(\frac{1}{n^2} - a'_{11}\right) D_{x'} &= 0, \\ \left(\frac{1}{n^2} - a'_{22}\right) D_{y'} &= 0. \end{aligned}\right\} \tag{31.4}$$

These two equations must simultaneously be satisfied for wave propagation along the Oz direction.

The two solutions of (31.4) are

$$\left.\begin{aligned} D_{y'} &= 0 \quad \text{for which} \quad \frac{1}{n^2} = a'_{11}, \\ D_{x'} &= 0 \quad \text{for which} \quad \frac{1}{n^2} = a'_{22}. \end{aligned}\right\} \tag{31.5}$$

We get the result that given the direction of wave propagation (a) the direction of vibration of the two $\boldsymbol{D}$ vectors coincide with the direction of the principal axes of the elliptic section of the index ellipsoid normal to the direction of propagation, (b) the refractive indices are equal to the lengths of the major and minor axes, i.e., velocities of propagation along the given direction are proportional to the reciprocal of the two principal axes of the elliptic section. If we define the plane of the $\boldsymbol{D}$ vector and **s** the direction of propagation as the plane of polarisation of the light, we find that all plane waves (monochromatic) travelling in a crystal are completely linearly polarised in directions determined by the major and minor axes of the elliptic section.

32. Crystal symmetry and the index ellipsoid. α) *General considerations.* Since the index tensor is a second order symmetric tensor, it can be defined by six parameters. Correspondingly, the index ellipsoid also requires six parameters for its specification, which may be taken to be the lengths of its three principal axes and three "angle" parameters to specify its orientation with respect to the crystallographic axes. The principal axes of a triaxial ellipsoid are two-fold axes of symmetry and its principal planes are mirror planes of symmetry. It is therefore necessary that if a crystal possesses certain elements of symmetry, the disposition of the optical ellipsoid in the crystal must be in accord with these symmetry operations. The conditions imposed by such elements of symmetry may be readily worked out[1] and may be summarised as in Table 2.

Any combination of these symmetry elements existing in a crystal will lead to the restrictions corresponding to each one of the elements. As a consequence, the crystals occurring in different crystal systems may be classified as in the

[1] See for instance, the article of H. JAGODINSKI in Vol. VII, Part 1 of this Encyclopedia.

Table 2. *Effect of crystal symmetry on the index ellipsoid.*

Element of symmetry	Restriction on index ellipsoid
Centre of inversion ($\bar{1} \equiv i$)	None
2-fold axis (2)	One principal axis parallel to the 2-fold axis
Mirror plane ($\bar{2} \equiv m$)	One principal axis normal to the mirror plane
n-fold axis or n-fold alternating axis with $n \geqq 3$ (n, $\bar{n}$)	One principal axis is parallel to the axis and the two axes in the perpendicular plane are equal, i.e., perpendicular section is a circle

Table 3, according to their optical behaviour[1]. Thus, in a monoclinic crystal, since the orientation of one of the axes is fixed, only 4 parameters are required to specify the index ellipsoid, three to give the magnitudes of the three principal axes and the fourth to specify the azimuth of the major axis in the ac plane with respect to the crystallographic axis a (say). In the other cases, the number may be readily deduced from the data in Table 3.

Table 3. *Optical behaviour of crystals belonging to different crystal systems.*

Crystal system	No. of parameters	Nature and orientation of the optical ellipsoid	Optical behaviour	Variation with wavelength, temperature or isotropic pressure
Triclinic	6	Triaxial, principal axes in general direction	Biaxial, optic axes in general directions	General
Monoclinic (b-axis unique)	4	Triaxial, one principal axis $\parallel b$, other two $\perp b$	Biaxial, optic axial plane either $\parallel$ or $\perp$ to b	Orientation of one principal axis always along b
Orthorhombic	3	Triaxial, all three principal axes along a, b and c	Biaxial, optic axial plane $\parallel$ to ab, bc or ca, acute bisectrix $\parallel$ to one of the crystal axes	No change in orientation, but only in length of principal axes i.e., in α, β, γ (or n_x, n_y, n_z)
Rhombohedral, Tetragonal, Hexagonal (c axis $\parallel$ to 3,4 or 6-fold axis)	2	Uniaxial, spheroid with unique axis parallel to c	Optic axis $\parallel c$	Optic axis always along c, but n_ω and n_ε may vary
Isometric (cubic)	1	Sphere	Isotropic	Always isotropic, but n may change

Obviously the elements of the index tensor would in general vary with the wavelength of light, the temperature of the crystal and also with hydrostatic pressure. The nature of these variations is listed in the last column. The optical axial angle in general varies with these factors in a biaxial crystal, but the plane of the optic axes is not arbitrary except in triclinic crystals.

β) Uniaxial crystals. In crystals belonging to the trigonal, tetragonal and hexagonal systems the index ellipsoid must clearly become an ellipsoid of revolution, the axis of revolution OZ being coincident with the n-fold crystallographic axis

[1] Reference may also be made to the article by C. D. West in "Physical Methods in Chemical Analysis", Ed. Berl, New York 1950, p. 438, wherein he has pointed out the inadequacy of the Hermann-Mauguin (International) or the Schoenflies symbols in connection with crystal optics.

of rotation. The normal to the circular section of the uniaxial ellipsoid viz., the OZ direction is defined as the optic axis. The crystal is termed positive or negative according as the index ellipsoid is a prolate or an oblate spheroid i.e., according as n_ε the refractive index for the $\boldsymbol{D}$-vibration parallel to the optic axis is greater or smaller than n_ω, the refractive index for any vibration perpendicular to the optic axis.

The features of propagation in uniaxial crystals may be obtained by a consideration of the results of the previous section. Referring to Fig. 34a it will be seen that OY will be normal to the ellipsoid at Y, so that the $\boldsymbol{E}$ and $\boldsymbol{D}$ vectors coincide for this direction of vibration as for an isotropic medium. Thus a $\boldsymbol{D}$ vibration parallel to OY can be propagated along any direction lying in the plane

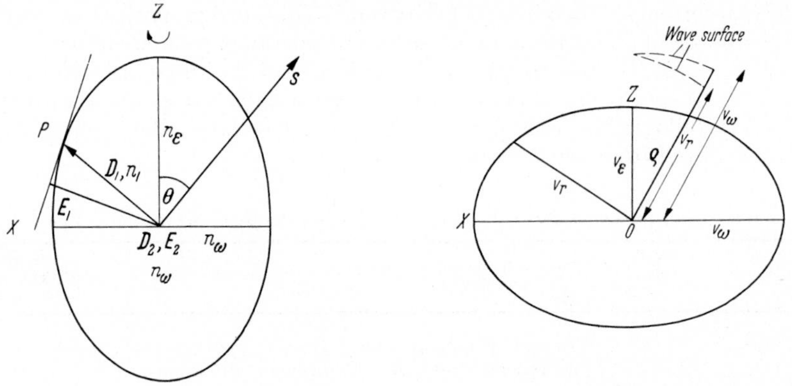

a b

Fig. 34 a and b. Propagation of light in a uniaxial crystal. (a) Section of the index ellipsoid which is an ellipsoid of revolution about OZ. For propagation along $\boldsymbol{s}$, the two $\boldsymbol{D}$ vectors are $\boldsymbol{D}_1$ in the plane of the paper and $\boldsymbol{D}_2$ normal to it. The two refractive indices are $n_1 = OP_1$ and $n_2 = n_\omega$. (b) Section of the Fresnel ellipsoid which is also an ellipsoid of revolution about OZ. The two ray velocities along $\boldsymbol{\rho}$ are v_r and v_ω, which are used for constructing the wave surface.

of the paper. Conversely if we consider an arbitrary direction of wave propagation $\mathbf{s}$ which we may, without loss of generality, suppose to be in the plane of the paper, one of the $\boldsymbol{D}$ vibrations is normal to the principal plane containing the optic axis and the direction of propagation. This is known as the ordinary wave since it has a constant refractive index n_ω and for it the wave normal and the ray direction coincide (since $\boldsymbol{D}$ is parallel to $\boldsymbol{E}$). The second wave—the extraordinary wave—which can be propagated along $\mathbf{s}$ must have its $\boldsymbol{D}$ vibration perpendicular to the first, i.e., lying in the principal plane defined by the optic axis and the direction of propagation. The actual orientation of the vibration is along the radius vector of the ellipsoid drawn perpendicular to $\mathbf{s}$ in the plane of the paper (see Fig. 34a). The extraordinary refractive index n given by the length of this radius vector depends on the inclination ϑ that the direction of propagation makes with the optic axis. The expression for n is readily obtained by writing the equation for the section of the index ellipsoid by the plane of the paper as

$$\frac{\alpha^2}{n_\omega^2} + \frac{\gamma^2}{n_\varepsilon^2} = \frac{1}{r^2} \tag{32.1}$$

where α and γ are the direction cosines of any radius vector of the ellipse. Hence we have

$$\frac{1}{n^2} = \frac{\cos^2\vartheta}{n_\omega^2} + \frac{\sin^2\vartheta}{n_\varepsilon^2}. \tag{32.2}$$

It will be seen from Fig. 34a that for the extraordinary wave, the $\boldsymbol{D}$ vector obtained by POINSOT'S construction does not coincide with $\boldsymbol{D}$. This leads to the most interesting property of this wave, viz., that the ray-direction deviates from the wavenormal, always lying however in the principal plane defined by $\mathbf{s}$ and the optic axis.

Along the optic axis itself any linear vibration lying in the circular section—hence a wave in any state of polarisation—can be propagated unchanged with refractive index n_ω, the ray and the wave normals being also coincident.

The wave surface for a uniaxial crystal may now be obtained by using the fact that it is identical with the ray velocity surface (Sect. 27). The extraordinary *ray velocity* v_r for any direction of ray propagation $\boldsymbol{\varrho}$ (Fig. 34b) in the plane of the paper may be determined from the section of the *Fresnel ellipsoid*. This is done in the same manner as the extraordinary *wave* index corresponding to the wave normal $\mathbf{s}$ has been obtained from the section of the index ellipsoid. Remembering that the lengths of the semi-axes of the Fresnel ellipsoid along OX and OZ are $v_\omega\left(=\frac{1}{n_\omega}\right)$ and $v_\varepsilon\left(=\frac{1}{n_\varepsilon}\right)$ we have corresponding to Eq. (32.2)

$$\frac{1}{v_r^2}=\frac{\varrho_X^2}{v_\omega^2}+\frac{\varrho_Z^2}{v_\varepsilon^2}. \qquad (32.3)$$

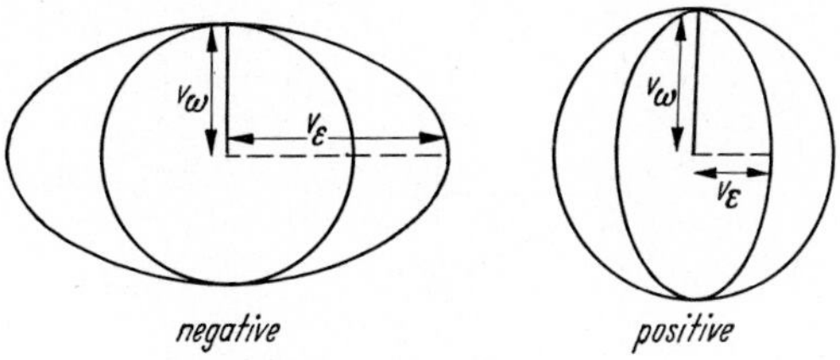

Fig. 35. Wave surfaces of uniaxial crystals. (a) for a negative crystal, (b) for a positive crystal.

The extraordinary ray velocity surface is traced by the tip of the radius vector whose length is equal to the extraordinary ray velocity v_r corresponding to the particular ray direction (see Fig. 34 b). The equation to its section is therefore obtained by setting

$$v_r=r, \quad X=\varrho_X r, \quad Z=\varrho_Z r$$

in Eq. (32.3) giving

$$\frac{X^2}{v_\omega^2}+\frac{Z^2}{v_\varepsilon^2}=1. \qquad (32.4)$$

On the other hand since for all directions of $\boldsymbol{\varrho}$ in the plane of the paper, the $\boldsymbol{E}$ vector perpendicular to the plane of the paper is propagated, the section of the ordinary ray velocity surface is a circle of radius v_ω.

Thus the complete wave surface of a uniaxial crystal consists of a spheroid and a sphere touching at points $Z=\pm v_\omega$. This is illustrated in Fig. 35a and b for positive and negative crystals.

33. Biaxial crystals—singular directions and conical refraction. For crystals of lower symmetry than those considered in the previous section, the index ellipsoid is a triaxial ellipsoid. We shall choose the axes of coordinates OX, OY, OZ such that $n_X<n_Y<n_Z$ where n_X, n_Y, n_Z are the lengths of the principal semi-axes, being also the refractive indices for vibrations parallel to X, Y, Z[1]. The corresponding light velocities are called the principal light velocities being given by

$$v_X^2=a_X=\frac{1}{n_X^2}, \qquad \text{etc.} \qquad (33.1)$$

[1] The three principal refractive indices are often referred to as α, β, γ in the mineralogical literature, $\alpha<\beta<\gamma$.

Considering any direction of propagation, in the XZ plane (Fig. 36) one of the vibrations propagated must be parallel to the Y direction (since the radius vector in that direction meets the surface of the ellipsoid normally), the corresponding refractive index being n_Y. The other vibrations must necessarily lie in the XZ plane, normal to the direction of propagation, having therefore a refractive index n intermediate between n_X and n_Z. As in (32.2) n is given by

$$\frac{1}{n^2} = \frac{\cos^2\vartheta}{n_X^2} + \frac{\sin^2\vartheta}{n_Z^2} \tag{33.2}$$

where ϑ is the inclination of the direction of propagation to the Z axis.

Clearly, there will be two directions ON_1 and ON_2 (Fig. 36) for which n would be equal to n_Y and where the sections normal to these directions would be circular. These directions are called the optic axes (also sometimes called binormals), and they would be symmetrically inclined to the Z direction. The optic axial angle $2V$ is determined by substituting V for ϑ and n_Y for n in Eq. (33.2) giving

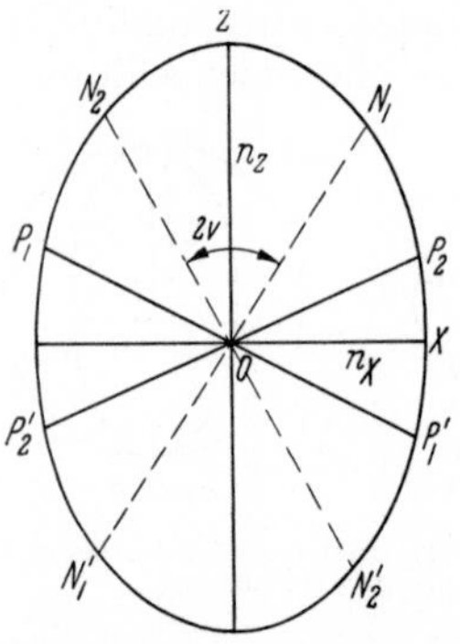

Fig. 36. Central section of the index ellipsoid for a biaxial crystal normal to OY. P_1P_1' and P_2P_2' are the two circular sections of the ellipsoid and the directions N_1ON_1' and N_2ON_2' normal to them are the two optic axes, which lie in this plane.

$$a_Y = a_X \cos^2 V + a_Z \sin^2 V \tag{33.3}$$

or

$$\cos^2 V = \frac{a_Y - a_Z}{a_X - a_Z}, \qquad \sin^2 V = \frac{a_X - a_Y}{a_X - a_Z} \tag{33.4}$$

and

$$\tan^2 V = \frac{a_X - a_Y}{a_Y - a_Z} = \frac{\frac{1}{n_X^2} - \frac{1}{n_Y^2}}{\frac{1}{n_Y^2} - \frac{1}{n_Z^2}}. \tag{33.5}$$

The expressions for $\cos^2 V$ and $\sin^2 V$ could similarly be written in terms of the principal refractive indices.

A crystal is said to be a positive or a negative crystal, according as $2V$ is acute or obtuse, i.e., according as the acute bisectrix coincides with OZ or OX (these directions correspond respectively to the maximum and the minimum refractive index).

Since the section perpendicular to an optic axis is circular, any state of polarisation is capable of being propagated along it with a single refractive index n_Y. The optic axes are therefore sometimes called the axes of isotropy, but actually all directions of the $\boldsymbol{D}$ vibration lying in the circular section are not equivalent as far as the corresponding ray directions are concerned. We have seen that OY lies on the circular section and since OY is also normal to the ellipsoid at Y, the $\boldsymbol{D}$ and $\boldsymbol{E}$ vectors will coincide for this vibration. Hence for a $\boldsymbol{D}$ vibration parallel to OY, the ray direction coincides with the wave normal which in the present case is the optic axis ON_1. However, for a $\boldsymbol{D}$ vibration lying on the circular section perpendicular to OY (i.e. parallel to OP_1, Fig. 37), the $\boldsymbol{E}$ vector obtained by POINSOT's construction would make an angle with the $\boldsymbol{D}$ vector giving rise to a ray direction OR different from ON_1, but lying in the XZ plane. For other directions of the $\boldsymbol{D}$ vector, the deviation between the ray and the wave normal will be less. In fact, it can be shown that as the $\boldsymbol{D}$ vector occupies all possible directions parallel to the radii of the circular section, the corresponding ray directions will describe a cone, the optic axis itself being one of the generators[1].

[1] See G. SALMON: Analytic Geometry of Three Dimensions. Dublin 1881.

This phenomenon is known as the internal conical refraction. Each point of the circle of rays observed with unpolarised light corresponds to a specific direction of vibration of the $\boldsymbol{D}$ vector. The phenomenon is considered in greater detail in Sect. 77.

With an identical treatment, it is clear that the Fresnel ellipsoid will have two circular sections, the normals to which will be the directions of single ray velocity. These are also called the optic bi-radials. These will again lie in the XZ plane symmetrically about the Z axis. To obtain the angle $2V_r$ between them, we note that the principal semi-axes of the Fresnel ellipsoid are $\frac{1}{n_X}, \frac{1}{n_Y}$ and $\frac{1}{n_Z}$ instead of n_X, n_Y and n_Z as is the case of the index ellipsoid. Hence, corresponding to Eq. (33.5), we have

$$\tan^2 V_r = \frac{n_Y^2 - n_X^2}{n_Z^2 - n_Y^2}. \qquad (33.6)$$

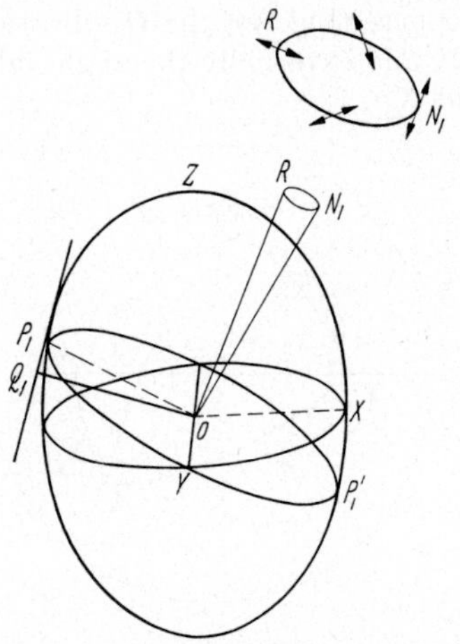

Fig. 37.

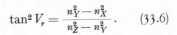

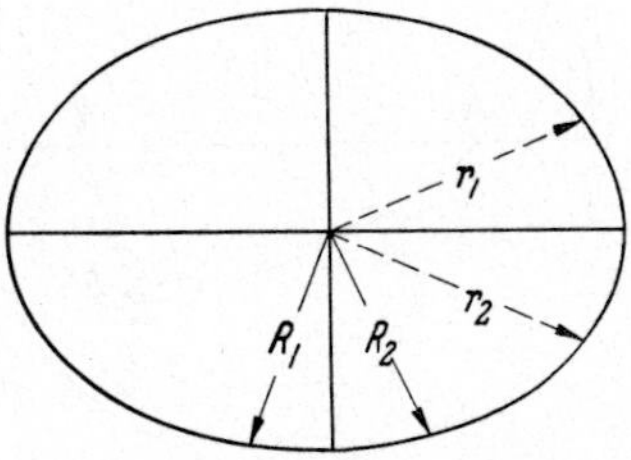

Fig. 38.

Fig. 37. Internal conical refraction. When the vibration direction is along OY, $\boldsymbol{D}$ and $\boldsymbol{E}$ coincide and the ray is along ON_1. When $\boldsymbol{D}$ is along OP_1, in the circular section, $\boldsymbol{E}$ is along OQ_1, and the ray direction is OR. For various other directions of $\boldsymbol{D}$ in the circular section, the ray directions form a cone. The vibration directions for different directions in the cone are marked in the expanded diagram at the top.

Fig. 38. Section of the index ellipsoid normal to a general direction of propagation. $\boldsymbol{R}_1$ and $\boldsymbol{R}_2$ are the traces of the circular section in this plane.

This formula shows that the directions of single ray velocity do not coincide with the optic axes. In the circular section of the Fresnel ellipsoid, as the direction of $\boldsymbol{E}$ varies, one gets different directions of wave propagation for the same direction of ray propagation. This phenomenon is known as the external conical refraction and will be considered again in Sect. 77.

34. Formulation of results in terms of optic axial directions. It is of importance in practice to be able to determine the vibration directions and refractive indices corresponding to any specified direction of wave propagation. Geometrically the problem is to obtain expressions for the orientations and the magnitudes of the principal semi-axes of the elliptic sections in the plane of the wave front (i.e. normal to the direction of wave propagation). The results are more elegantly expressed if the direction of propagation is specified by the angles it makes with the two optic axes rather than by its direction cosines with respect to the principal electric axes.

Let us now consider any direction of wave propagation which we may conveniently take as normal to the plane of the paper (Fig. 38). The central section perpendicular to Oz will be an ellipse and the major and the minor axes of this elliptic section will correspond to the directions of vibrations $\boldsymbol{D}'$ and $\boldsymbol{D}''$ of the waves propagated along Oz. The two circular sections of the index ellipsoid will intersect the elliptic section along $\boldsymbol{R}_1$ and $\boldsymbol{R}_2$; these must be equally inclined to the principal axes of the elliptic section since we must have $R_1 = R_2$. Further since $\boldsymbol{R}_1$ is perpendicular both to Oz and to the optic axial direction ON_1, it must be perpendicular to the plane defined by Oz and ON_1. Similarly $\boldsymbol{R}_2$ is perpendicular to the plane defined by Oz and the other optic axial direction ON_2. The plane N_1Oz and N_2Oz will intersect the elliptic section in $\boldsymbol{r}_1$ and $\boldsymbol{r}_2$ where $\boldsymbol{r}_1$ is perpendicular to $\boldsymbol{R}_1$, and $\boldsymbol{r}_2$ to $\boldsymbol{R}_2$. Hence $\boldsymbol{r}_1$ and $\boldsymbol{r}_2$ must be equally inclined to the principal axes of the elliptic section, or vice versa, the principal axes are the internal and external bisectors of the angle between $\boldsymbol{r}_1$ and $\boldsymbol{r}_2$. Representing the directions by points on a sphere (Fig. 39) the $\boldsymbol{D}$ vibrations propagated along the direction z bisect internally and externally the angle subtended at z by the two optic axial directions N_1 and N_2.

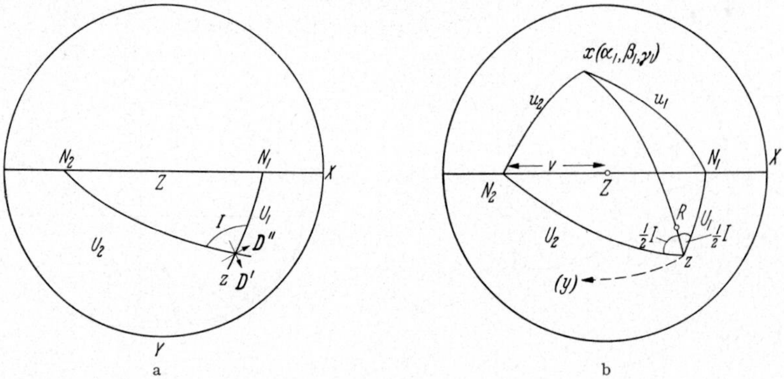

Fig. 39. (a) N_1, N_2, z are the intersections of the optic axes and the direction of propagation with a sphere. The two vibration directions $\boldsymbol{D}'$ and $\boldsymbol{D}''$ for propagation along Oz are the internal and external bisectors of the angle $N_1 z N_2$. (b) Construction for proving Eq. (34.1).

The velocities v' and v'' of the two waves propagated along the arbitrary direction Oz are given by the elegant relations

$$\left.\begin{aligned} v'^2 &= \tfrac{1}{2}(v_X^2 + v_Z^2) + \tfrac{1}{2}(v_X^2 - v_Z^2)\cos(U_2 + U_1) \\ v''^2 &= \tfrac{1}{2}(v_X^2 + v_Z^2) + \tfrac{1}{2}(v_X^2 - v_Z^2)\cos(U_2 - U_1), \end{aligned}\right\} \tag{34.1}$$

where U_1 and U_2 are the respective inclinations that the direction of propagation makes with the optic axes N_1 and N_2.

To prove this we choose our Ox axis such that the xz plane bisects the angles between the planes N_1z and N_2z (Fig. 39b). The x direction is therefore one of the vibration directions $\boldsymbol{D}'$ and the length of the intercept by it is the corresponding refractive index, i.e. we have $v'^2 = a_{11}$ where a_{11} is given by (29.19) in terms of the direction cosines $\alpha_1, \beta_1, \gamma_1$ of Ox. Since the direction cosines of the optic axes are ($\sin V$, 0, $\cos V$) and ($-\sin V$, 0, $\cos V$) the angles u_1 and u_2 which Ox makes with the optic axes are

$$\left.\begin{aligned} \cos u_1 &= \alpha_1 \sin V + \gamma_1 \cos V, & \cos u_2 &= -\alpha_1 \sin V + \gamma_1 \cos V, \\ \cos u_1 - \cos u_2 &= 2\alpha_1 \sin V, & \cos u_1 + \cos u_2 &= 2\gamma_1 \cos V. \end{aligned}\right\} \tag{34.2}$$

We have also from spherical trigonometry

$$\cos u_1 = \sin U_1 \cos \tfrac{1}{2} I, \qquad \cos u_2 = \sin U_2 \cos \tfrac{1}{2} I \tag{34.3}$$

where I is the angle $N_1 \hat{z} N_2$. On account of the expressions for $\sin^2 V$ and $\cos^2 V$ given in (33.4) the first relation of (29.19) can be written as

$$v'^2 = a_{11} = a_Y + (a_X - a_Z)(\alpha_1 \sin^2 V - \gamma_1 \cos^2 V)$$

or because of (34.2) and (34.3)

$$\left.\begin{aligned} v'^2 &= a_Y - (a_X - a_Z)\cos u_1 \cos u_2 \\ &= a_Y - (a_X - a_Z)\sin U_1 \sin U_2 \cos^2 \tfrac{1}{2} I. \end{aligned}\right\} \tag{34.4}$$

Similarly it can be shown that

$$v''^2 = a_Y + (a_X - a_Z)\sin U_1 \sin U_2 \sin^2 \tfrac{1}{2} I. \tag{34.5}$$

Now according to (33.3)

$$\begin{aligned} a_Y &= \tfrac{1}{2}(a_X + a_Z) + \tfrac{1}{2}(a_X - a_Z)\cos 2V \\ &= \tfrac{1}{2}(a_X + a_Z) + \tfrac{1}{2}(a_X - a_Z)(\cos U_1 \cos U_2 + \sin U_1 \sin U_2 \cos I). \end{aligned}$$

Introduction of these in (34.4) and (34.5) leads to the expression (34.1).

From (34.1) we see that[1]

$$v'^2 - v''^2 = (v_X^2 - v_Z^2)\sin U_1 \sin U_2. \tag{34.6}$$

Hence the birefringence for propagation along a direction making angles of U_1 and U_2 with the two optic axes is, approximately

$$\Delta n = K \sin U_1 \sin U_2 \tag{34.7}$$

where K is some constant. When the two optic axes coincide as in a uniaxial crystal $U_1 = U_2 = U$ (say), the formula reduces to

$$\Delta n = K \sin^2 U. \tag{34.8}$$

This may be directly derived from (33.2). These are of importance in the discussion of the interference figures exhibited by uniaxial and biaxial crystals (Sect. 63 *et seq.*).

Since $\boldsymbol{D}$, $\mathbf{s}$ and $\boldsymbol{\varrho}$ lie in a plane, the two ray-normals corresponding to the wave normal z in Fig. 39b must be on the arcs zx and zy respectively. The position of any one of them, for example, the ray R, lying on zx is determined by the condition that zx must also be the internal bisector of the angle subtended by the two optic bi-radials at R since the plane of $\boldsymbol{E}$ and $\boldsymbol{\varrho}$ is also the plane of $\boldsymbol{D}$ and $\mathbf{s}$. This is known as SYLVESTER'S construction. For all the propositions proved in this section, there exist corresponding propositions for rays which can be derived from the Fresnel ellipsoid representation.

35. Wave velocity surface and the wave surface. The wave velocity surface was defined in Sect. 27. The equation to it can be derived from the constitutive equation (26.7), which may be written as follows in terms of the principal electric axes of the medium as co-ordinates axes:

$$D_X = n^2 \left[\frac{D_X}{\varepsilon_X} - s_X (\boldsymbol{E} \cdot \mathbf{s})\right] \tag{35.1}$$

or

$$D_X = - s_X (\boldsymbol{E} \cdot \mathbf{s}) \Big/ \left\{\frac{1}{n^2} - \frac{1}{\varepsilon_X}\right\}. \tag{35.2}$$

---

[1] This relation is usually proved by a method using the wave surface (see, e.g. DITCHBURN), but the above proof of (34.1) and (34.6) due to VOIGT is much simpler. For other elegant proofs, see SALMON'S Analytic Geometry of three dimensions.

Since $\boldsymbol{D}\cdot\mathbf{s}=\sum D_X s_X=0$, we have from the right-hand side of (35.2)

$$\sum s_X^2\Big/\left(\frac{1}{n^2}-\frac{1}{\varepsilon_X}\right)=0 \tag{35.3}$$

or

$$\sum s_X^2/(v^2-v_X^2)=0. \tag{35.4}$$

Since any radius vector $\boldsymbol{r}(x, y, z)$ of the wave velocity surface is equal to the wave velocity $\boldsymbol{v}$ in that direction we may set $\boldsymbol{r}=\boldsymbol{v}$ and $X, Y, Z=s_x r, s_y r, s_z r$ in (35.4) to get the equation to the wave velocity surface, which is

$$\sum X^2/(r^2-v_X^2)=0. \tag{35.5}$$

The ray velocity surface could be obtained in a similar manner from the other constitutive equation (26.14) which may be put in form

$$E_X=\frac{1}{n_r^2}\left[\varepsilon_X E_X-\varrho_X(\boldsymbol{D}\cdot\boldsymbol{\varrho})\right]$$

or

$$E_X=-\varrho_X(\boldsymbol{D}\cdot\boldsymbol{\varrho})/(n_r^2-\varepsilon_X).$$

Since $\boldsymbol{E}\cdot\boldsymbol{\varrho}=0$ we have similar to (35.3) the result

$$\sum \varrho_X^2\Big/\left(\frac{1}{v_r^2}-\frac{1}{v_X^2}\right)=0. \tag{35.6}$$

Since the radius vector $\boldsymbol{r}(x, y, z)$ of the ray velocity surface is equal to the ray velocity v_r along that direction, we thus obtain the equation to the ray velocity surface as

$$\sum X^2 v_X^2/(r^2-v_X^2)=0. \tag{35.7}$$

This is also the equation to the wave surface at $t=1$, which was shown to be identical to the ray velocity surface in Sect. 27.

It may be mentioned that the equations to the wave velocity surface and the ray velocity surface could also be derived from the index ellipsoid and the Fresnel ellipsoid respectively in the following manner. To obtain the former, mark off along a line from an origin O in the direction of wave propagation $\mathbf{s}$, two points P and Q, such that OP and OQ are equal to the two wave velocities, which are given by the *reciprocals* of the major and minor axes of the central section of the index ellipsoid normal to $\mathbf{s}$. The loci of the points P and Q, for all directions of $\mathbf{s}$ in space, would represent the wave velocity surface, which is in general a surface of two sheets. The ray velocity surface (which is the same as the wave surface) could be obtained in a similar manner from the Fresnel ellipsoid, but now OP and OQ are equal to the two ray velocities, which are directly equal to the major and minor axes of its central section normal to $\boldsymbol{\varrho}$. This is only an extension of the method of obtaining the wave surface of a uniaxial crystals discussed in Sect. 32.

The wave surface is also a two-sheeted surface, as would also be evident from its Eq. (35.7), which is of the fourth degree. An idea of its form is best obtained by considering its sections by the principal co-ordinate planes. These sections could also be derived, *ab initio*, by the process illustrated in Fig. 34 for uniaxial crystals, each section therefore consisting of an ellipse and a circle. When making the construction for a biaxial crystal, it must be remembered that the third refractive index for the vibration normal to the paper in Fig. 34 is not equal to one of the other two, so that the circle and the ellipse will not touch each other. In fact it may be shown that, for the section by the YZ plane the circle completely encloses the ellipse; whereas for the XY section, the circle is contained within the ellipse. In the case of the section by the XZ plane however the circle and the ellipse intersect. These are illustrated in Figs. 40a—d. In Fig. 40c the tangent line touching both the circle and the ellipse has been drawn. It can be shown that the plane parallel to the Y axis and containing this line, touches the wave surface along a circle (see SZIVESSY [1]). The perpendiculars ON_1 and ON_2 to these tangent planes are clearly the optic axis, i.e. directions of single wave velocities. Corresponding to one such wave normal ON_1, there are an infinite number of ray directions, lying on a cone obtained by joining the origin

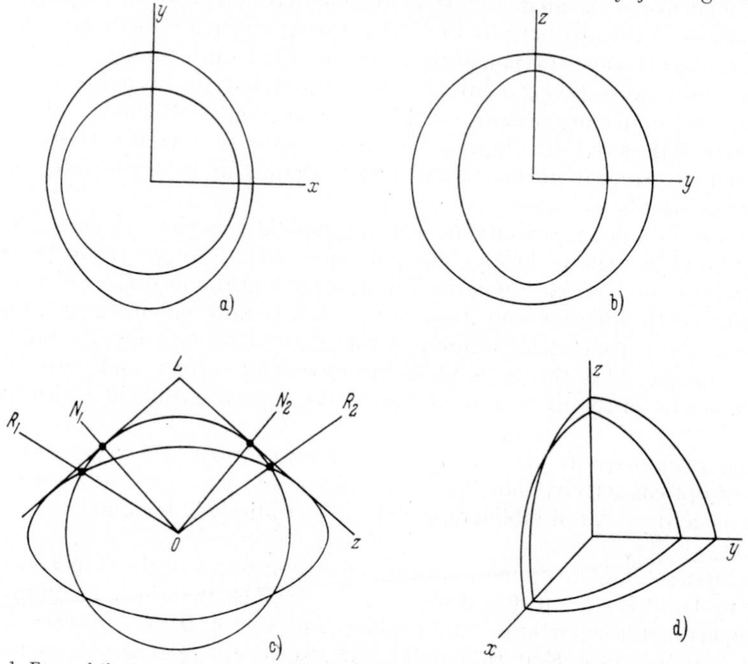

Fig. 40a—d. Form of the wave surface for a biaxial crystal. (a), (b), (c) are the sections by the three co-ordinate planes. (d) is a three-dimensional diagram of one octant.

to the circle of contact. This is the phenomenon of internal conical refraction, which has been discussed in Sect. 33, using the index ellipsoid.

The lines OR_1 and OR_2 joining the origin to the points of intersection of the circle and ellipse in Fig. 40c are the directions of single ray velocity. Each such point is a dimple in the wave surface, through which an infinite number of tangent planes can be drawn. The normals to these tangent planes lie in a cone and represent the possible direction of the wave normal for a ray propagated along the optic biradials OR_1 and OR_2. This corresponds to the phenomenon of external conical refraction already discussed in Sect. 33, using the Fresnel ellipsoid.

The features of light propagation in crystals can be derived not only by the index ellipsoid treatment as described above, but also from the wave surface representation, which is the one that is usually followed. The wave surface representation also finds application in the discussion of the phenomenon of refraction in anisotropic media (see Sect. 58). The two refracted wave fronts are given by the envelopes of the different Huygens wavelets. HUYGENS himself, after introducing the idea of the secondary wavelets applied it to explain the "strange refraction of Iceland spar", assuming with ingenious foresight the correct form of the wave surface for a uniaxial crystal.

III. Non-absorbing optically active crystals.

36. Nature of the dielectric and index tensors. So far, we have discussed the case of non-absorbing, non-optically active crystals, for which the dielectric tensor has real components and is symmetric. In such a crystal, two linearly polarised waves are propagated in any general direction, and in particular directions, namely the optic axes, waves of all states of polarisation are transmitted with the same velocity. The last property is exhibited in all directions by a cubic crystal or an isotropic medium. It is known that some isotropic media exhibit the property of optical activity, i.e. of rotating the plane of polarisation of a linearly polarised wave traversing the medium[1]. The same property is also shown by some cubic crystals, e.g. sodium chlorate and sodium bromate, and by uniaxial (quartz, cinnabar, benzil) and biaxial (cane sugar, Rochelle salt) crystals along their optic axial directions. The phenomenon of optical activity was first discovered by ARAGO[2] in quartz and other crystals in 1811 and later observed by BIOT in liquids and gases.

A theory of optical activity in isotropic media was first given by FRESNEL as early as 1822. The incident plane polarised beam is supposed to be resolved into two opposite circularly polarised components in the medium which are then propagated with different velocities. When they reunite on emergence, the plane of polarisation is rotated on account of the phase difference introduced between the two waves. This theory is phenomenologically correct and corresponds to the special case of the more general theory of the propagation in optically active media.

Some attempts were made in the nineteenth century to develop a structural theory of optical activity, notably by SOHNCKE and REUSCH, but they were not very satisfactory. A full bibliography of these studies will be found in the article by SZIVESSY [*1*].

The first attempt to explain optical activity in terms of the dispersion theory is due to DRUDE ([*3*], p. 400 et seq.). It is obvious that in a medium having the property of a screw axis, the displacement vector $\boldsymbol{D}$ must depend not only on the electric vector $\boldsymbol{E}$ at that point but also on the spatial variation of $\boldsymbol{E}$ ni the neighbourhood. DRUDE therefore assumed for $\boldsymbol{D}$ the form

$$\boldsymbol{D} = \varepsilon \boldsymbol{E} + f \operatorname{curl} \boldsymbol{E}. \tag{36.1}$$

Since

$$\operatorname{curl} \boldsymbol{E} = \frac{1}{c} \frac{\partial \boldsymbol{H}}{\partial t} \quad \text{and} \quad \boldsymbol{H} = \mathbf{s} \times \boldsymbol{E}$$

for an electromagnetic wave in *vacuum*, we have

$$\boldsymbol{D} = \varepsilon \boldsymbol{E} + i \frac{\omega}{c} f (\mathbf{s} \times \boldsymbol{E}). \tag{36.2}$$

Putting

$$i \frac{\omega}{c} f \mathbf{s} = \boldsymbol{G} \tag{36.3}$$

we get

$$\boldsymbol{D} = \varepsilon \boldsymbol{E} + i (\boldsymbol{G} \times \boldsymbol{E}). \tag{36.4}$$

This equation, as will be shown below, agrees with the more general theory, as far as an isotropic medium is concerned. However, DRUDE made a further

---

[1] A full account of this subject of optical activity will be found in the article by J. P. MATHIEU in Vol. XXVIII, p. 333, of this Encyclopedia.

[2] F. ARAGO: OEuvr. Compl., Vol. 10, p. 54. Paris 1858.

assumption that the parameter f and hence the vector $\boldsymbol{G}$ is the same for all directions of propagation; this does not agree with observation.

The form of Eq. (36.4) may also be derived from general phenomenological considerations. If we discard the assumption made in Sect. 29 that the components of the tensor relating the vector $\boldsymbol{D}$ and $\boldsymbol{E}$ are all real, we have the relation

$$\boldsymbol{D} = [\varepsilon]\,\boldsymbol{E} + i\,[\varrho]\,\boldsymbol{E}. \tag{36.5}$$

This implies that $\boldsymbol{D}$ is dependent not only on $\boldsymbol{E}$ but also on $\partial\boldsymbol{E}/\partial t$ (since $\partial/\partial t = i\omega$) and hence (36.5) can be written in the form

$$\boldsymbol{D} = [\varepsilon]\,\boldsymbol{E} - \frac{1}{\omega}\,[\varrho]\,\dot{\boldsymbol{E}}. \tag{36.6}$$

For an infinitesimal change we have

$$d\boldsymbol{D} = [\varepsilon]\,d\boldsymbol{E} + \frac{1}{\omega}\,[\varrho]\,\ddot{\boldsymbol{E}}\,dt.$$

Hence

$$\boldsymbol{E}\cdot d\boldsymbol{D} = \boldsymbol{E}\cdot[\varepsilon]\,d\boldsymbol{E} - \omega\,\boldsymbol{E}\cdot[\varrho]\,\boldsymbol{E}\,dt. \tag{36.7}$$

Comparing Eq. (36.7) with (29.6) and (29.7) we see that the introduction of the imaginary part of the dielectric tensor will generally lead to dissipation unless the second term in (36.7) vanishes identically. This will occur only if $[\varrho]$ is antisymmetric i.e. $\varrho_{ij} = -\varrho_{ji}$. This can be seen more clearly by using the fact that an antisymmetric tensor $\omega[\varrho]$ can be replaced by a vector operator $\boldsymbol{G}\times$ where

$$G_1 = \omega\,\varrho_{23} = -\,\omega\,\varrho_{32};\quad G_2 = \omega\,\varrho_{31} = -\,\omega\,\varrho_{13};\quad G_3 = \omega\,\varrho_{12} = -\,\omega\,\varrho_{21}. \tag{36.8}$$

Then

$$\boldsymbol{D} = [\varepsilon]\,\boldsymbol{E} + i\,\boldsymbol{G}\times\boldsymbol{E}. \tag{36.9}$$

This equation is the same as (36.4) and we shall call $\boldsymbol{G}$ the *gyration vector.*

Integrating Eq. (36.7) we obtain as in the case of an optically inactive medium the electric energy density

$$W_e = \tfrac{1}{2}\,\boldsymbol{E}\cdot[\varepsilon]\,\boldsymbol{E}. \tag{36.10}$$

Thus the antisymmetric tensor $[\varrho]$ does not contribute to the energy density which must be a function of state of $\boldsymbol{E}$. Hence it is not at all necessary that the components of $[\varrho]$ should be the same, independent of the direction of propagation as should be the case with the components of $[\varepsilon]$. As the gyration vector depends on the spatial variation of $\boldsymbol{E}$ in the neighbourhood of a point, it would in general depend on the direction of propagation in an anisotropic crystal. We may take $\boldsymbol{G}$ to be a linear vector function of the wave normal $\boldsymbol{s}$. This has also been obtained from a molecular theory[1] of optical rotatory power. Thus we may write

$$\boldsymbol{G} = [g]\,\boldsymbol{s} \tag{36.11}$$

where the gyration tensor $[g]$ need not necessarily be symmetric. This is in accordance with the molecular theory of Born. It may however be remarked that since the observable rotation is dependent only on $(g_{ij} + g_{ji})$ it would have been sufficient for a phenomenological theory to assume the gyration tensor to be symmetric.

---

[1] M. Born: Z. Physik **8**, 405 (1922).

We shall take Eqs. (36.9) and (36.11) to be the constitutive relations for a transparent optically active medium assuming in addition $\boldsymbol{B}=\boldsymbol{H}$ [1].

37. Refractive index of an optically active crystal [2]. Eq. (36.4) may now be combined with the relation (26.7)

$$\boldsymbol{D} = n^2[\boldsymbol{E} - \mathbf{s}(\boldsymbol{E}\cdot\mathbf{s})] \tag{37.1}$$

for an electromagnetic wave. Suppose the coordinate axes are chosen parallel to the principal axes of the real part of the dielectric tensor. Then, equating the right hand sides of (36.4) and (37.1), we have

$$E_X = [n_X^2 - (1-s_X^2)\,n^2 + E_Y\{(n^2 s_X s_Y + i\,G_Z)\} + E_Z\{n^2 s_Z s_X - i\,G_Y\}] \tag{37.2}$$

and two similar equations. The quantities E_X, E_Y, E_Z may be eliminated from these, giving the following equation for the variation of refractive index with direction:

$$\left.\begin{aligned} n^4(n_X^2 s_X^2 + n_Y^2 s_Y^2 + n_Z^2 s_Z^2) - n^2\{\textstyle\sum n_Y^2 n_Z^2 (s_Y^2 + s_Z^2)\} + n^2(\mathbf{s}\times\boldsymbol{G})^2 + \\ + n_X^2 n_Y^2 n_Z^2 - (n_X^2 G_X^2 + n_Y^2 G_Y^2 + n_Z^2 G_Z^2) = 0. \end{aligned}\right\} \tag{37.3}$$

Although this quadratic equation in n^2 can be exactly solved, the solution may be put in a more tractable, but approximate form, by using the information that the components of $\boldsymbol{G}$ are small compared with those of $[\varepsilon]$. If we denote by n_0' and n_0'' the solutions of (37.3) when $\boldsymbol{G}$ is set equal to zero, then it can be written as

$$(n^2 - n_0'^2)(n^2 - n_0''^2) = g^2 \tag{37.4}$$

where

$$g^2 = \frac{(n_X^2 G_X^2 + n_Y^2 G_Y^2 + n_Z^2 G_Z^2) - n^2(\mathbf{s}\cdot\boldsymbol{G})^2}{n_X^2 s_X^2 + n_Y^2 s_Y^2 + n_Z^2 s_Z^2}. \tag{37.5}$$

Even then, the right-hand side of (37.5) contains the quantity n, which is to be determined. To avoid this difficulty, we put $n_1 = n_2 = n_3$ in Eq. (37.5) only, i.e. we assume that the property of optical activity does not depend on the magnitude of the birefringence, although actually the crystal may be in fact birefringent [3]. Then, g takes the simple form

$$g = \mathbf{s}\cdot\boldsymbol{G} \tag{37.6}$$

and has a fixed value for a given direction of propagation. The two refractive indices for this direction may then be calculated from (37.6) and are

$$\left.\begin{aligned} n'^2 &= \tfrac{1}{2}\left\{n_0'^2 + n_0''^2 + \left|\sqrt{(n_0'^2 - n_0''^2) + 4g^2}\right|\right\} \\ n''^2 &= \tfrac{1}{2}\left\{n_0'^2 + n_0''^2 - \left|\sqrt{(n_0'^2 - n_0''^2) + 4g^2}\right|\right\}, \end{aligned}\right\} \tag{37.7}$$

---

[1] See POCKELS' *Lehrbuch* [2] for an alternative theory where $\boldsymbol{B} \neq \boldsymbol{H}$. In the customary treatments $\boldsymbol{B}$ is set equal to $\boldsymbol{H}$ to avoid excessive complication, although this procedure is considered an approximation. The treatment we have adopted in Sect. 29 and Sect. 36 shows that contrary to what is often supposed, the use of (36.9) and $\boldsymbol{B}=\boldsymbol{H}$, together with POYNTING's theorem, does not lead to any violation of the principle of conservation of energy. However the expression (36.10) which we have derived for energy density is *not* $\frac{1}{2}\boldsymbol{E}\cdot\boldsymbol{D}$ as is assumed at the commencement in the usual treatments. That the electric energy density can differ from $\frac{1}{2}\boldsymbol{E}\cdot\boldsymbol{D}$ for any medium is by itself not a matter of surprise since this is manifestly the case in absorbing crystals. Hence phenomenological considerations by themselves do not require that $\boldsymbol{B}\neq\boldsymbol{H}$. It may be remarked that polarisability theories of optical activity do not appear to lead to any magnetic moment being induced. See BORN [*4*] or e.g. G.N. RAMACHANDRAN: Proc. Ind. Acad. Sci. **33**, 217, 309 (1951).

[2] The treatment in this section follows the conventional method adopted by most treatises, e.g. BORN [*4*], SZIVESSY [*1*]. A more exact solution of the wave equation is given in Sect. 38.

[3] W. VOIGT: Göttinger Nachr. 1903, p. 167.

where we assume that $n_0' > n_0''$. It follows that

$$n'^2 + n''^2 = n_0'^2 + n_0''^2. \tag{37.8}$$

Making use of the above formulae, it is possible to show that the two waves which are propagated corresponding to the principal indices n' and n'' are two opposite ellipses, whose axial ratios $b/a = \varkappa$ are[1]:

$$\varkappa_1 = \frac{n'^2 - n_0'^2}{g}, \qquad \varkappa_2 = \frac{g}{n''^2 - n_0''^2}. \tag{37.9}$$

We have from (37.8)

$$n''^2 - n_0''^2 = -(n'^2 - n_0'^2)$$

so that $\varkappa_1 = -\frac{1}{\varkappa_2}$ showing that the two elliptic vibrations correspond to oppositely polarised states. We shall however show this by other methods.

38. A more exact solution of the wave equation[2]. The approximations which we had to make in the last section can be avoided by the use of the inverse of the dielectric tensor, viz. $[a]$, the index tensor. We have already seen how the use of this tensor, with the associated index ellipsoid, considerably simplifies the discussion of the optical behaviour of non-optically active crystals. When the dielectric tensor is complex and takes the form (36.5), the corresponding equation in terms of the index tensor is

$$\boldsymbol{E} = [a]\,\boldsymbol{D} - i\,\boldsymbol{\Gamma}\times\boldsymbol{D} \tag{38.1}$$

where $\boldsymbol{\Gamma}$ may be called the optical activity vector. Like the gyration vector it will be a function of the direction of propagation being determined by a relation corresponding to (36.11)

$$\boldsymbol{\Gamma} = [\gamma]\,\mathbf{s} \tag{38.2}$$

where $[\gamma]$ is a general nine component tensor which may be called the optical activity tensor. To obtain expressions for the quantities introduced in the present formulation in terms of the dielectric and gyration tensors we may justifiably neglect the squares of the components of $\boldsymbol{G}$ since even their first powers will always be very small compared with the principal values of $[\varepsilon]$ even in crystals whose optical rotation is normally large. Choosing the coordinate axes along the principal electrical axes of the crystal it can then be shown that

$$a_X = \frac{1}{\varepsilon_X} \quad \text{etc.}, \tag{38.3}$$

$$\Gamma_X = \frac{\varepsilon_X\, G_X}{\varepsilon_X\,\varepsilon_Y\,\varepsilon_Z} \quad \text{etc.}, \tag{38.4}$$

$$\gamma_{XY} = \frac{\varepsilon_X\, g_{XY}}{\varepsilon_X\,\varepsilon_Y\,\varepsilon_Z} \quad \text{etc.} \tag{38.5}$$

It may be mentioned that the formulation of the constitutive equation of the medium in the form (38.1), in terms of $[a]$ and $\boldsymbol{\Gamma}$ is as valid as the form (36.4), in terms of $[\varepsilon]$ and $\boldsymbol{G}$. In fact, using the same method as was adopted for $\boldsymbol{G}$ in Sect. 36, we can show that if Eq. (38.1) is valid, then there is no dissipation in the medium. Actually, in discussing the optical behaviour of the medium, the formulation (38.1) in terms of the index tensor and the optical activity vector is the more convenient one, as will be seen below. However,

[1] F. Pockels [2], p. 328; Szivessy [1], pp. 811–813.
[2] S. Pancharatnam: Proc. Ind. Acad. Sci. A **43**, 247 (1956).

both formulations (36.4) and (38.1) are exact and completely valid, although the relations (38.3) to (38.5) between the coefficients in the two formulations are correct only to the first order of magnitude.

If now we choose the coordinate axes such that the z axis is along the wave normal, then $D_z=0$ and we have only two components D_x and D_y. Also from Eq. (37.1) we have the simple relations

$$E_x = v^2 D_x, \quad E_y = v^2 D_y, \quad D_z = 0. \tag{38.6}$$

Since $D_z=0$ we have also from (38.1)

$$\left.\begin{aligned} E_x &= a_{11} D_x + a_{12} D_y + i\Gamma_3 D_y, \\ E_y &= a_{21} D_x + a_{22} D_y - i\Gamma_3 D_x. \end{aligned}\right\} \tag{38.7}$$

Following the same procedure as in Sect. 30 if we now take the x and y axes to be parallel to the principal vibration directions in the absence of optical activity, then

$$a_{12} = 0, \quad a_{11} = v_1^2, \quad a_{22} = v_2^2 \tag{38.8}$$

where v_1 and v_2 are the velocities for the particular direction of propagation in the absence of optical activity (i.e. $\Gamma=0$). Substituting for E_x and E_y from (38.6) we have[1]

$$\left.\begin{aligned} v^2 - v_1^2 &= i\Gamma_3 (D_y/D_x), \\ v^2 - v_2^2 &= i\Gamma_3 (D_x/D_y). \end{aligned}\right\} \tag{38.9}$$

These equations can be solved to give both the principal refractive indices and the polarisation states of the two waves.

The form of the vibration for propagation along Oz is defined by the ratio (D_y/D_x) and may be obtained by eliminating v^2 between the two equations in (38.9) when we obtain

$$\frac{D_y}{D_x} + \frac{D_x}{D_y} = -\frac{i}{\Gamma_3}(v_2^2 - v_1^2) = -\frac{2i}{K}, \quad \text{say.} \tag{38.10}$$

In terms of a general coordinate axis,

$$\Gamma_3 = \mathbf{s}\cdot\boldsymbol{\Gamma} = \gamma, \quad \text{say.} \tag{38.11}$$

Hence

$$K = \frac{2\gamma}{v_2^2 - v_1^2}. \tag{38.12}$$

The two solutions for D_y/D_x are reciprocals of each other and it is also obvious that both should be purely imaginary.

Putting therefore

$$\left(\frac{D_y}{D_x}\right)' = i\tan\vartheta, \quad \left(\frac{D_y}{D_x}\right)'' = -i\cot\vartheta \tag{38.13}$$

in (38.10) we obtain

$$\tan 2\vartheta = K = \frac{2\gamma}{v_2^2 - v_1^2}. \tag{38.14}$$

The two vibrations given by Eq. (38.13) are naturally orthogonal and correspond to oppositely polarised elliptic waves. The ellipses are similar in form though described in opposite senses, the two major axes lying along two perpendicular principal planes.

---

[1] These are practically equivalent to the equations derived in POCKELS [2], p. 328.

If we eliminate (D_y/D_x) between the two equations in (38.9) we obtain the equation for the velocity v of the waves propagated along OZ:

$$(v^2 - v_1^2)(v^2 - v_2^2) = \gamma^2. \tag{38.15}$$

The two solutions of this equation are the two principal velocities v' and v'', which are then given by

$$\left.\begin{aligned} v'^2 &= \tfrac{1}{2}(v_1^2 + v_2^2) - \tfrac{1}{2}\left|\sqrt{(v_1^2 - v_2^2)^2 + 4\gamma^2}\right|, \\ v''^2 &= \tfrac{1}{2}(v_1^2 + v_2^2) + \tfrac{1}{2}\left|\sqrt{(v_1^2 - v_2^2)^2 + 4\gamma^2}\right|. \end{aligned}\right\} \tag{38.16}$$

It follows from this that

$$(v''^2 - v'^2)^2 = (v_2^2 - v_1^2)^2 + 4\gamma^2. \tag{38.17}$$

The wave with velocity v' will be in the state of polarisation $(D_y/D_x)'$, while the velocity v'' corresponds to the state $(D_y/D_x)''$ in Eq. (38.13). This may be verified by substituting the corresponding values in Eq. (38.9)

When $\gamma = 0$ we have from (38.14), $\vartheta = 0$ giving the orthogonal linear vibrations with velocities v_1 and v_2, as should be the case for a non-optically active crystal. The characteristic effect introduced by the parameter γ is best revealed by supposing linear birefringence to be absent i.e. by setting $v_1 = v_2 = v_m$, say, in Eq. (38.13) and (38.17). The former gives $\vartheta = \pi/4$ i.e. the two waves should be circularly polarised in opposite directions, thus theoretically confirming FRESNEL's hypothesis. Thus if there is no birefringence the difference in the refractive indices of the two circular waves is given by

$$\Delta\left(\frac{1}{n^2}\right) = \frac{2}{n^3}(n_r - n_l) = 2\gamma. \tag{38.18}$$

The rotatory power ϱ is related to $n_r - n_l$ by the equation

$$\varrho = \frac{\pi}{\lambda}(n_r - n_l) \tag{38.19}$$

so that

$$\varrho = \frac{\pi}{\lambda} n_m^3 \gamma. \tag{38.20}$$

Eq. (38.20) gives the rotatory power of a crystal to be positive[1] when γ is positive.

The propagation of two circularly polarised waves as described above should occur for instance in an isotropic medium or a cubic crystal for all directions of propagation, and for propagation along the optic axis in birefringent crystals.

In these cases, the medium should actually exhibit circular double refraction. This was first shown to be so by FRESNEL[2] using a combination of quartz prisms. Later, the experiment has also been performed with the cubic crystal, sodium chlorate[3].

39. Method of superposition. A simple way of calculating the combined effect of birefringence and optical activity of a medium is by the method of superposition[4] dealt with in Sect. 5α. Here, we assume the two properties are independent, and that an infinitesimal layer dz of the medium may be considered

[1] This corresponds to a left rotating or laevo-rotatory crystal. In chemical literature, however, ϱ is taken to be positive for a dextro-rotatory crystal. Our convention agrees with the mathematical convention of taking counter-clockwise angles to be positive.

[2] A. FRESNEL: OEuvr. Compl., Vol. 1, p. 731, Paris 1866.

[3] G. MESLIN: C. R. Acad. Sci., Paris **152**, 166 (1911).

[4] For reference to earlier literature, see POCKELS [2], p. 309.

to be made up of two parts, one producing the phase retardation ($d\delta$) due to linear birefringence and the other a rotation ($d\varrho$). The superposition of the two effects is best worked out by means of the Poincaré sphere. The former is a clockwise rotation of the sphere about the axis $X_r Y_r$ (X_r being the slower axis) through an angle $d\delta$, while the latter is a clockwise rotation about a perpendicular axis RL through an angle $2d\varrho$ (see Fig. 41). The combined effect is obviously a clockwise rotation through the angle

$$d\Delta = \sqrt{(d\delta)^2 + (2d\varrho)^2} \tag{39.1}$$

about an axis BB_a in the plane containing $X_r Y_r$ and RL, the latitude 2ϑ of the state B being given by

$$\tan 2\vartheta = -\frac{2d\varrho}{d\delta}. \tag{39.2}$$

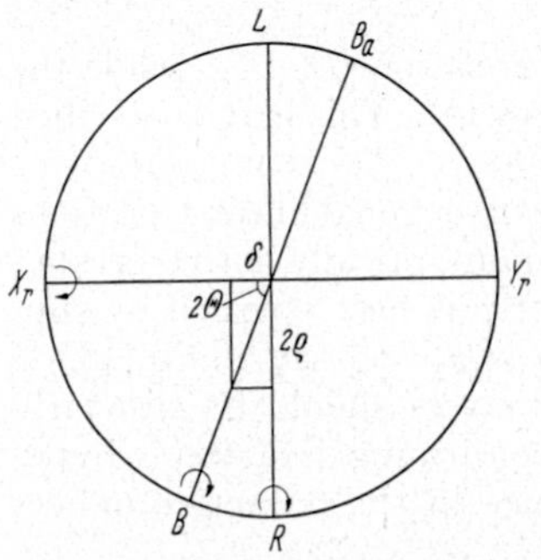

Fig. 41. Superposition of birefringence and optical activity. The ellipses B and B_a are propagated unchanged of which B has the slower velocity.

If δ is the phase retardation per unit length, $= \frac{2\pi}{\lambda}(n_1 - n_2)$ and ϱ is the specific rotation, then

$$\tan 2\vartheta = -\frac{2\varrho}{\delta} \tag{39.3}$$

and per unit thickness the effect on the state of polarisation of the transmitted light is a rotation through an angle

$$\Delta = \sqrt{\delta^2 + (2\varrho)^2}. \tag{39.4}$$

Obviously, the polarisation states of the two beams which are propagated unchanged in the crystal are B and B_a, which represent crossed ellipses, whose axial ratio is $|\tan\vartheta|$.

Further from the results of Sect. 4, Δ represents the relative phase retardation per unit distance between the waves in the state B and B_a the former being the slower wave.

It will be noticed that the results obtained by the method of superposition are closely analogous to those obtained from the exact theory, although they are not exactly equivalent. This may be seen by comparing Eqs. (39.3) and (39.4) with (38.14) and (38.17) respectively.

Since

$$\frac{1}{n'^2} + \frac{1}{n''^2} = \frac{1}{n_1^2} + \frac{1}{n_2^2} \tag{39.5}$$

we may take

$$\frac{1}{2}\left(\frac{n'+n''}{n'^2 n''^2}\right) = \frac{1}{2}\left(\frac{n_1+n_2}{n_1^2 n_2^2}\right) = \frac{1}{n_m^3}, \quad \text{say,} \tag{39.6}$$

where we shall call n_m as the mean refractive index. Then, (38.17) takes the form

$$(n' - n'')^2 = (n_1 - n_2)^2 + (2n_m^3 \gamma)^2. \tag{39.7}$$

If we suppose that

$$\varrho = \frac{\pi}{\lambda} n_m^3 \gamma \tag{39.8}$$

analogous to Eq. (38.20), then we get the result (39.4). Correspondingly, Eq. (38.14) becomes the same as (39.3).

Quite apart from the small approximation involved in (39.6) we have to make the assumption in (39.8) that the medium has a rotation ϱ given by that equation in the direction concerned. It involves in addition to γ the quantity n_m^3 which is not entirely independent of the components of the dielectric tensor. The formal similarity of the results obtained by the use of the superposition method with those from the rigorous theory enables us to use the former method which is much simpler, with the *assumption* that the medium has a "rotatory power" given by Eq. (39.8). We shall use the method of superposition hereafter for working out the theory of the experiments to be described later.

40. Symmetry and optical activity of crystals. The rotatory power of a crystal along any directions is determined by the parameter γ which is given by Eq. (38.11). It turns out that, although γ_{ij} is not symmetric, the expression for γ involves only a *symmetric* combination of the components of the optical activity tensor. Thus combining (38.11) and (38.2)

$$\left.\begin{aligned}\gamma = \gamma_{11} s_1^2 + \gamma_{22} s_2^2 + \gamma_{33} s_3^2 + (\gamma_{23} + \gamma_{32})\, s_2 s_3 + \\ + (\gamma_{31} + \gamma_{13})\, s_3 s_1 + (\gamma_{12} + \gamma_{21})\, s_1 s_2\end{aligned}\right\} \tag{40.1}$$

where s_1, s_2, s_3 are the direction cosines of the wave normal with respect to an arbitrary coordinate system.

If we lay off a radius vector **s** parallel to the direction of propagation such that

$$\frac{1}{r^2} = |\gamma| = |\varrho| \frac{\lambda}{\pi} v_m^3 \tag{40.2}$$

we get the surface of optical rotation. Given this surface we can determine γ for any direction (the sign to be attached being supposed to be marked on the surface). It follows from this that the specific rotation ϱ may be put in the form[1]

$$\varrho = r_{11} s_1^2 + r_{22} s_2^2 + r_{33} s_3^2 + 2 r_{23} s_2 s_3 + 2 r_{31} s_3 s_1 + 2 r_{12} s_1 s_2 . \tag{40.2a}$$

This is a slight approximation because n_m^3 is not a constant, but the subsequent discussion on symmetry does not depend for its validity on this approximation.

Some interesting consequences follow from this regarding the occurrence of optical activity and of its variation with direction in crystals of different symmetry. Thus, if the crystal has a centre of inversion, then applying this operation, a right-handed system of axes is converted into a left-handed one. Referred to the latter, the sign of ϱ is reversed. However, substituting $-s_1, -s_2, -s_3$ for s_1, s_2, s_3 in Eq. (40.2a) the sign of ϱ is unchanged. Both these conditions will be satisfied only if $\varrho = 0$, i.e. there can be no optical activity for centrosymmetric crystals, a result which is in conformity with the corresponding property of molecules.

Thus, of the 32 crystal classes, the specific rotation is zero in all directions in 11 classes, namely $\bar{1}$, $2/m$, mmm, $\bar{3}$, $\bar{3}m$, $4/m$, $4/mmm$, $6/m$, $6/mmm$, $m3$, $m3m$.

Similarly, applying the other symmetry operations for crystals belonging to the remaining 21 points groups, the form of the variation of ϱ with direction can be obtained. Details are omitted[2], but the results are given in Table 4. It will be noticed that the optical activity does not vanish in all directions for a crystal having a symmetry plane of reflection. Optical activity occurs for crystals belonging to 15 classes, but it has actually been observed only in 7 crystal classes, namely 2, 222, 3, 32, 6, 42 and 23. Even among these, measurements are avail-

[1] Unlike the index ellipsoid and the Fresnel ellipsoid, this surface need not be an ellipsoid, but only a central quadric.

[2] These may be found in F. Pockels [2], pp. 313–318; W.A. Wooster: A text-book on crystal physics, pp. 156–160. Cambridge 1949.

Table 4. *Variation of rotatory power ϱ with direction in non-centrosymmetric crystals.*

Crystal system	Crystal class	Expression for ϱ
Triclinic	1	$s_1^2 r_{11} + s_2^2 r_{22} + s_3^2 r_{33} + 2 s_1 s_2 r_{12} + 2 s_2 s_{23} r_{23} + 2 s_3 s_1 r_{31}$
Monoclinic	m	$2 s_3 (s_2 r_{23} + s_1 r_{31})$
	2	$s_1^2 r_{11} + s_2^2 r_{22} + s_3^2 r_{33} + 2 s_1 s_2 r_{12}$
Orthorhombic	222	$s_1^2 r_{11} + s_2^2 r_{22} + s_3^2 r_{33}$
	mm	$2 s_1 s_2 r_{12}$
Rhombohedral	3	$(s_1^2 + s_2^2) r_{11} + s_3^2 r_{33}$
	32	$(s_1^2 + s_2^2) r_{11} + s_3^2 r_{33}$
	$3m$	0
Tetragonal	4	$(s_1^2 + s_2^2) r_{11} + s_3^2 r_{33}$
	42	$(s_1^2 + s_2^2) r_{11} + s_3^3 r_{33}$
	$4mm$	0
	$\bar{4}$	$(s_1^2 - s_2^2) r_{11} + 2 s_1 s_2 r_{12}$
	$\bar{4}2m$	$(s_1^2 - s_2^2) r_{11}$
Hexagonal	6	$(s_1^2 + s_2^2) r_{11} + s_3^2 r_{33}$
	62	$(s_1^2 + s_2^2) r_{11} + s_3^2 r_{33}$
	$6mm$	0
	$\bar{6}$	0
	$6m2$	0
Cubic	23	$(s_1^2 + s_2^2 + s_3^2) r_{11} = r_{11}$
	43	$(s_1^2 + s_2^2 + s_3^2) r_{11} = r_{11}$
	$\bar{4}3m$	0

able only along the optic axes, except for quartz, for which measurements have been made perpendicular to the optic axis (see Sect. 84). It is obvious that the rotatory power along the two optic axes need not be equal in a biaxial crystal—for instance one belonging to the crystal class 2. A typical example is cane sugar for which the rotatory power along the two optic axes are $-1.6°$ and $+5.4°$ per mm.

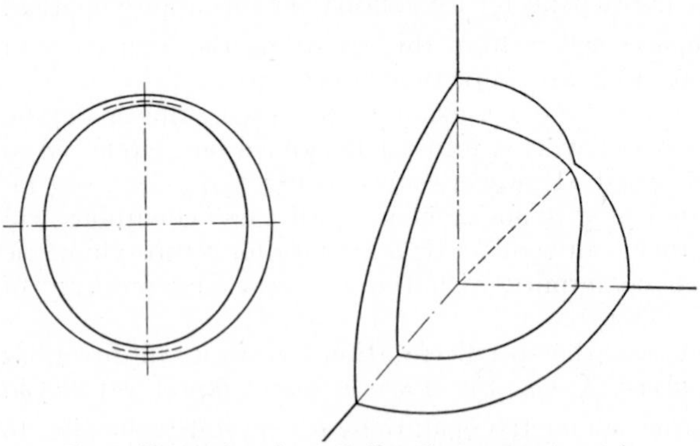

Fig. 42. Wave surface of an optically active transparent crystal.

41. Wave surface in optically active crystals. As was shown in Sect. 38, the refractive indices of the two waves propagated along any direction are only slightly modified by the presence of optical activity. Consequently, the shape of the wave surface is practically the same as in a non-optically active crystal except for directions close to the optic axes. In a non-active crystal, the optic axes are directions of single wave velocity and the two sheets of the wave surface therefore touch along these directions. However, when optical activity is present, two orthogonal circularly polarised waves are propagated along this direction, with slightly differing velocities. The consequent modification of the wave surface is shown schematically in Fig. 42 for both uniaxial and biaxial crystals.

Since the two sheets of the wave surface do not touch along the optic axes, there are no points on the surface, where the tangent plane is singular. Thus internal conical refraction, in the sense of the phenomenon which occurs in non-active crystals, cannot occur here. However, if a slightly divergent pencil is used, it is obvious that the orientation of the tangent planes varies appreciably for the different directions of propagation in the pencil and thus a conical beam emerges from the crystal. The phenomenon has been studied in great detail by VOIGT[1] in cane sugar and tartaric acid.

External conical refraction should also occur readily even in the presence of optical activity.

IV. Absorbing non-optically active crystals.

42. Fundamental equations. For every crystal there are regions of the spectrum in which it exhibits the phenomenon of absorption of electromagnetic radiation. It has long been known in the case of minerals and crystals which absorb visible light that both the intensity and the spectral nature of the absorption depends not only on the direction of propagation but also on the state of polarisation of the incident light. The anisotropy of refractive index (which is present even in the transparent regions) and the anisotropy of absorption are linked to one another by the theory of dispersion, both these phenomena being in their turn related to the ultimate atomistic structure of the crystal. From the point of view of the classical dispersion theory, the motion of the charges giving rise to the polarisation of the medium would be opposed by dissipative forces of an anisotropic nature in the absorbing regions of the spectrum. Thus the polarisation $\boldsymbol{P}$ would not oscillate in phase with the electric intensity $\boldsymbol{E}$. The components of the macroscopic polarisability tensor would therefore be complex. In turn the relation between the vectors $\boldsymbol{D}$ and $\boldsymbol{E}$ would be described by a complex dielectric tensor $[\bar{\varepsilon}]$. We shall not deal with the atomistic causes of the anisotropy in the intensity and the spectral nature of the absorption but only present the phenomenological theory of light propagation in absorbing crystals applicable to one particular frequency.

In an absorbing crystal the propagation of a light wave may be described by two parameters, namely the refractive index n and the absorption coefficient k. Thus the electric vector of a wave propagated along the z direction is given by

$$E_z = E_0\, \mathrm{e}^{-kz}\, \mathrm{e}^{-2\pi i n z/\lambda} \tag{42.1}$$

or

$$E_z = E_0\, \mathrm{e}^{-2\pi i \bar{n} z/\lambda}, \tag{42.2}$$

where $\bar{n}$ is the complex refractive index. Let $\bar{n} = n - i\varkappa$ where $\varkappa$ the *extinction coefficient* is equal to $k\lambda/2\pi$. In an anisotropic crystal both n and $\varkappa$ are functions of the state of polarisation and the variation of both can be expressed by a complex tensor $[\bar{\varepsilon}]$ representing the complex dielectric constant. Just as in the case of non-absorbing crystals, not all waves are propagated without change of form but only those with certain states of polarisation. The method of finding these for a given direction of propagation as well as the corresponding complex refractive indices is closely similar to what was adopted for optically active non-absorbing crystals.

Before however proceeding to discuss the properties of the dielectric tensor we may mention that the absorption in the medium may also arise if the medium has a finite conductivity represented by a tensor $[\sigma]$ in addition to the usual

[1] W. VOIGT: Ann. Phys., Lpz. **18**, 678, 692 (1905). — Phys. Z. **6**, 789 (1905).

dielectric tensor $[\varepsilon]$ relating $\boldsymbol{D}$ and $\boldsymbol{E}$. We shall show that this is formally equivalent to the introduction of a complex dielectric tensor. The current density $\boldsymbol{j}$ and the charge density ϱ (as determined by the equation of continuity) will then be

$$\boldsymbol{j} = [\sigma]\,\boldsymbol{E} \tag{42.3}$$

and

$$\dot{\varrho} = -\operatorname{div}\boldsymbol{j} \quad \text{or} \quad \varrho = \frac{1}{\omega}\operatorname{div}[\sigma]\,\boldsymbol{E}. \tag{42.4}$$

If we introduce these in the MAXWELL's equation (26.1 a) they become formally identical with the MAXWELL's equation (26.3) for a non-conducting medium provided we replace $\boldsymbol{D}$ by $\boldsymbol{D}'$ where

$$D_i' = (\varepsilon_{ij} - i\,\sigma_{ij})\,E_i. \tag{42.5}$$

The solutions for such media will thus be formally equivalent to the more common case of absorbing but non-conducting media in which the relation between $\boldsymbol{D}$ and $\boldsymbol{E}$ is represented by a complex dielectric tensor.

43. The dielectric tensor and the index tensor of absorbing crystals. We may write

$$\boldsymbol{D} = [\bar{\varepsilon}]\,\boldsymbol{E} \tag{43.1}$$

where

$$\bar{\varepsilon}_{ij} = \varepsilon_{ij} - i\,\eta_{ij}. \tag{43.2}$$

If the tensor $[\eta]$ contained an antisymmetric part it would contribute to optical activity as was seen in Sect. 36. To correspond to the case of absorbing non-optically active crystals we shall take $[\varepsilon]$ and $[\eta]$ to be symmetric. We have seen in Sect. 36 that the introduction of the imaginary part of the dielectric tensor leads to a dissipation of energy.

Arguments subsequent to (36.5) may be followed with ϱ replaced by $-i\eta$ and an equation similar to (36.7) may be derived; comparing this with (29.7) we get that the rate of dissipation of energy W_f is given by

$$W_f = \omega\,\boldsymbol{E}\cdot[\eta]\,\boldsymbol{E}. \tag{43.3}$$

If we write

$$\boldsymbol{D} = \boldsymbol{D}_1 - i\,\boldsymbol{D}_2 \tag{43.4}$$

where $\boldsymbol{D}_1$ and $\boldsymbol{D}_2$ are related to $\boldsymbol{E}$ by the real tensors $[\varepsilon]$ and $[\eta]$, then the rate of dissipation of energy is given by $\frac{1}{2}\boldsymbol{E}\cdot\boldsymbol{D}_2$ while the electric energy density will as in transparent optically active crystals be given by $\frac{1}{2}\boldsymbol{E}\cdot\boldsymbol{D}_1$.

It is more convenient to use the complex index tensor and write (43.1) in the form

$$\boldsymbol{E} = [\bar{a}]\,\boldsymbol{D}, \tag{43.5}$$

where

$$[\bar{a}] = [\bar{\varepsilon}]^{-1} \tag{43.6}$$

and

$$\bar{a}_{ij} = a_{ij} + i\,b_{ij}. \tag{43.7}$$

Both the real and imaginary parts of the complex index tensor are tensors of the second rank and could therefore be represented by ellipsoids. The ellipsoid representing the tensor a_{ij} will be called the index ellipsoid as in the previous cases while the ellipsoid representing b_{ij} defines the *absorption ellipsoid*. There is no reason why the principal axes of the index and absorption ellipsoids should coincide, excepting where required by the symmetry of the crystal.

The imaginary part of the complex tensor is usually small compared to unity and to the real part, and therefore it would be sufficient to work up to the first order of magnitude in b_{ij}. To this order of approximation the index and absorption tensors are given by

$$[a] = [\varepsilon]^{-1} \tag{43.8}$$

and

$$[b] = [\varepsilon]^{-1}[\eta][\varepsilon]^{-1}, \tag{43.9}$$

i.e. the principal axes representing $[\varepsilon]$ the dielectric tensor may be taken to coincide with those of the index ellipsoid. However the principal axes of the absorption ellipsoid need not coincide with those of the ellipsoid $[\eta]$ [1].

Along any direction of propagation the nature of the waves propagated depend on the central sections of the index ellipsoid and the absorption ellipsoid normal to the direction of propagation. We shall call the directions of the major and minor axes of the section of the index ellipsoid as the principal directions of linear birefringence and those of the absorption ellipsoid as the principal directions of linear dichroism.

As the magnitude of the dichroism, determined by b_{ij} is usually very small compared with the birefringence, for most directions of propagation it is found that the behaviour of an absorbing anisotropic crystal is closely approximated by the behaviour of non-absorbing crystals. The state of polarisation and the velocities of the two beams propagated along any direction are then determined by the index ellipsoid. We have however the additional property that for any direction of vibration there is an attentuation of the transmitted beam. The extinction coefficient $\varkappa$ is related to the radius vector $1/\sqrt{b}$ of the absorption ellipsoid drawn parallel to the direction of vibration by the equation

$$2\varkappa v^3 = b \tag{43.10}$$

where v is the velocity of propagation for that particular direction of vibration. The above results are exactly true for uniaxial crystals. A behaviour similar to that described in this paragraph was postulated in the early theory of MALLARD[2].

44. Formal solution of the wave equation. The phenomena are however complicated for directions of propagation close to the optic axes in a biaxial crystal. These directions are defined as the normals to the circular sections of the index ellipsoid as in a non-absorbing crystal. If we consider the normal to a circular section of the index ellipsoid in an absorbing crystal, then there is no reason why it should also be normal to the circular section of the absorption ellipsoid. The section of the absorption ellipsoid normal to an optic axis will in general be an ellipse.

Consequently, as will be shown rigorously a little later, two waves can be propagated along an optic axial direction, with different absorption coefficients. There exist however directions along which only one wave is propagated unchanged; there are actually four such directions[3], called *Windungsachsen* or singular axes, two near each of the optic axes, and circular vibrations of one sense is propagated unchanged along two of them and of the other sense along the other two. It is however necessary to work out the full formal solution of

---

[1] As in the case of optically active non-absorbing crystals, here also Eqs. (43.7) and (43.3) are both equally valid. However, the relations between the two tensors given by Eqs. (43.8) and (43.9) are only correct to the first order.

[2] For this and earlier references see SZIVESSY [*1*].

[3] W. VOIGT: Ann. Phys. **9**, 367 (1902).

the wave equation before these and other interesting aspects of absorbing biaxial crystals are discussed.

The complex tensor $\bar{a}_{ij}$ can be brought to the diagonal form by a suitable transformation of axes. Eqs. (44.1) below give the relation between the principal axes $\bar{u}, \bar{v}, \bar{w}$ and the original axes x, y, z. Since $\bar{u}, \bar{v}, \bar{w}$ are complex linear functions of x, y, z, the α_{ij}'s must also be complex. Thus

$$\left.\begin{aligned} \bar{u} &= \bar{\alpha}_{11}\, x + \bar{\alpha}_{12}\, y + \bar{\alpha}_{13}\, z \\ \bar{v} &= \bar{\alpha}_{21}\, x + \bar{\alpha}_{22}\, y + \bar{\alpha}_{23}\, z \\ \bar{w} &= \bar{\alpha}_{31}\, x + \bar{\alpha}_{32}\, y + \bar{\alpha}_{33}\, z\,. \end{aligned}\right\} \tag{44.1}$$

Denote by $\bar{a}_1, \bar{a}_2, \bar{a}_3$ the principal values of the tensor $\bar{a}_{ij}$ so that $E_{\bar{u}} = \bar{a}_1 D_{\bar{u}}$[1].

Referred to the axes $\bar{u}, \bar{v}, \bar{w}$ we have the following equation completely analogous to (26.7) and (37.1):

$$\bar{v}^2 \boldsymbol{D} = \{\boldsymbol{E} - \boldsymbol{s}(\boldsymbol{s}\cdot\boldsymbol{E})\}, \tag{44.2}$$ [2]

$$(\bar{a}_1 - \bar{v}_1^2)\, D_{\bar{u}} = (\boldsymbol{s}\cdot\boldsymbol{E})\, s_{\bar{u}} \tag{44.3}$$

and

$$\frac{s_{\bar{u}}^2}{\bar{a}_1 - \bar{v}^2} = 0\,. \tag{44.4}$$

Formally, therefore, Eq. (44.4) gives the two principal refractive indices, both real and imaginary parts, as well as the principal vibration directions.

45. Simplification of the general solution. The understanding of the phenomena is facilitated by taking one of the axes, say z, along the direction of propagation, and the other two x and y in the perpendicular plane. Then $D_z = 0$ and using a procedure exactly similar to that for a non-absorbing crystal (Sect. 31) and comparing the x and y components of (43.5) with (38.7), we obtain

$$\left.\begin{aligned} \bar{v}^2 D_x &= \bar{a}_{11} D_x + \bar{a}_{12} D_y\,, \\ \bar{v}^2 D_y &= \bar{a}_{12} D_x + \bar{a}_{22} D_y \end{aligned}\right\} \tag{45.1}$$

where D_x and D_y are the complex components of the vibration along x and y. Unlike the case in a non-absorbing crystal it would not in general be possible to choose the coordinate axes OX and OY such that $\bar{a}_{12}$ vanishes, since the principal radii of the elliptic sections of the index and absorption ellipsoids need not coincide.

From (45.1), we have,

$$\left.\begin{aligned} (\bar{v}^2 - \bar{a}_{11}) &= \bar{a}_{12}(D_y/D_x)\,, \\ (\bar{v}^2 - \bar{a}_{22}) &= \bar{a}_{12}(D_x/D_y) \end{aligned}\right\} \tag{45.2}$$

where D_x and D_y are the complex displacements parallel to x and y directions. If we put $D_x/D_y = r$ then r defines the state of polarisation of the wave. Eliminating $\bar{v}^2$ in (45.2)

$$\bar{a}_{12}\left(r - \frac{1}{r}\right) = (\bar{a}_{22} - \bar{a}_{11}) \tag{45.3}$$

or

$$r^2 + \frac{(\bar{a}_{11} - \bar{a}_{22})}{\bar{a}_{12}}\, r - 1 = 0\,. \tag{45.4}$$

[1] The vectors $\boldsymbol{D}$ and $\boldsymbol{E}$ both have complex components in general.

[2] There should be no confusion between the axis $\bar{v}$ and the complex velocity $\bar{v}$ in Eqs. (44.2) to (44.4).

Eliminating r between the two equations, we have for the two velocities,

$$(\bar{v}^2 - \bar{a}_{11})(\bar{v}^2 - \bar{a}_{22}) = \bar{a}_{12}^2. \tag{45.5}$$

It follows from (45.4) that if r' and r'' are the two complex solutions, then

$$r' r'' = -1. \tag{45.6}$$

As may be easily shown from this relation, the two vibrations propagated unchanged along any direction have their major and minor axes crossed but are of the same sense. *They do not correspond to orthogonal states of polarisation unlike the case of an optically active non-absorbing crystal.* The values of r for the two waves and the corresponding refractive indices are given by

$$\left.\begin{aligned} r' &= \frac{1}{2}\frac{(\bar{a}_{22}-\bar{a}_{11})}{\bar{a}_{12}} - \sqrt{\left[\frac{1}{2}\frac{(\bar{a}_{22}-\bar{a}_{11})}{\bar{a}_{12}}\right]^2 + 1}, \\ r'' &= \frac{1}{2}\frac{(\bar{a}_{22}-\bar{a}_{11})}{\bar{a}_{12}} + \sqrt{\left[\frac{1}{2}\frac{\bar{a}_{22}-\bar{a}_{11}}{\bar{a}_{12}}\right]^2 + 1}; \end{aligned}\right\} \tag{45.7}$$

$$\left.\begin{aligned} 1/n'^2 = v'^2 &= \tfrac{1}{2}(\bar{a}_{11}+\bar{a}_{22}) + \sqrt{[\tfrac{1}{2}(\bar{a}_{11}-\bar{a}_{22})]^2 + \bar{a}_{12}^2}, \\ 1/n''^2 = v''^2 &= \tfrac{1}{2}(\bar{a}_{11}+\bar{a}_{22}) - \sqrt{[\tfrac{1}{2}(\bar{a}_{11}-\bar{a}_{22})]^2 + \bar{a}_{12}^2}. \end{aligned}\right\} \tag{45.8}$$

Writing the complex refractive index in the form $\bar{n} = n(1 - i\tau)$ we have $\bar{v}^2 = v^2(1 + 2i\tau)$ neglecting τ^2 and higher powers. Here, n is the refractive index and τ is known as the absorption index. Eq. (45.5) can then be split up into two equations between the real and imaginary parts

$$\left.\begin{aligned} (a_{11} - v^2)(a_{22} - v^2) - a_{12}^2 &= (b_{11} - 2v^2\tau)(b_{22} - 2v^2\tau) - b_{12}^2, \\ (a_{11} - v^2)(b_{22} - 2v^2\tau) + (a_{22} - v^2)(b_{11} - 2v^2\tau) &= 2a_{12}b_{12}. \end{aligned}\right\} \tag{45.9}$$

We shall now consider a few special cases.

46. Special cases. *α) Uniaxial crystals.* For this case both the index and absorption ellipsoids must be ellipsoids of revolution about the common optic axis. Thus, for the arbitrary direction of propagation Oz, the principal axis of the elliptic sections of the index and absorption ellipsoids coincide, lying along and perpendicular to the principal plane containing the direction of propagation and the optic axis. Thus in the treatment of the previous section, it would have been possible to choose axes Ox', Oy', such that $a_{12} = 0$. As for non-absorbing crystals, Eq. (45.1) gives two solutions linearly polarised along the principal planes. For

$$D'_y = 0, \quad \bar{v}^2 = \bar{a}'_{11} \quad \text{or} \quad v^2 = a'_{11}; \quad 2\tau v^2 = b'_{11} \tag{46.1}$$

while for

$$D'_x = 0, \quad \bar{v}^2 = \bar{a}'_{22} \quad \text{or} \quad v^2 = a'_{22}; \quad 2\tau v^2 = b'_{22}. \tag{46.2}$$

This corresponds to the description already given at the end of Sect. 43, the behaviour being similar to that for a non-absorbing crystal, except that the extinction coefficient for each vibration is determined by the absorption ellipsoid from (43.10). The above behaviour becomes true also for certain special directions of propagation in biaxial crystals where the principal planes of linear birefringence and linear dichroism coincide, e.g., along the symmetry planes in orthorhombic crystals.

β) Biaxial crystals—directions appreciably inclined to optic axial directions. For directions that are not too close to the optic axes $(a_{11} - a_{22})$ will be large compared to the absorption parameters, namely $b_{11}, b_{22}, b_{12}, 2v^2\tau$. Then, it follows from (45.9) that

$$1/n'^2 = v'^2 = a_{11}, \quad 1/n''^2 = v''^2 = a_{22} \tag{46.3}$$

and

$$2a_{11}\tau' = b_{11}, \quad 2a_{22}\tau'' = b_{22}$$

giving

$$\tau' = b_{11}/2a_{11}; \quad \tau'' = b_{22}/2a_{22}. \tag{46.4}$$

Also, the corresponding states of polarisation are given by $r' = 0$, $r'' = \infty$ i.e. linear vibrations parallel to x and y axes respectively. The behaviour again obviously corresponds to the situation mentioned at the end of Sect. 43, i.e. the behaviour is similar to that of a non-absorbing crystal, except for the difference in the absorption index between the two propagated waves.

γ) Propagation along optic axes. As with non-absorbing crystals, we shall call the directions normal to the circular sections of the index ellipsoid as the optic axes.

In this case, $a_{11} = a_{22} = a_1$ (say) and a_{12} identically vanishes for any pair of orthogonal directions at right angles to the direction of propagation. We choose that pair for which b_{12} also vanishes, i.e. parallel to the major and minor axes of the corresponding central section of the absorption ellipsoid. Then it follows that

$$1/n'^2 = 1/n''^2 = a_1 \tag{46.5}$$

and

$$\tau' = b_{11}/2a_1, \quad \tau'' = b_{22}/2a_1. \tag{46.6}$$

To find the polarisation states, we may use Eq. (45.3) in which the right hand side is zero, giving the two roots, $r' = 0$, $r'' = \infty$. Here again, two orthogonal linearly polarised waves are transmitted, as in case (α), and they may be regarded as having the same velocity. The two velocities cannot be exactly equal as with non-absorbing crystals, for then every direction of vibration must be possible for this direction of propagation, all of them being propagated with the same velocity. The indices n' and n'' differ to the second order of magnitude of the absorption parameters.

Although two linearly polarised waves are transmitted along directions far away from the optic axes and also exactly along the optic axes, the two waves are in general elliptically polarised in the vicinity of the optic axes. The two waves are not orthogonally polarised and are propagated with different velocities. If the principal constants a_{ij} and b_{ij} are known, then these can be calculated from Eqs. (45.7) and (45.8) but it is easier to do so by applying a method of superposition as we shall show later.

δ) Singular axes. However, there exist directions of single wave velocity in an absorbing crystal, but these do not coincide with the optic axes. From (45.7) and (45.8) it follows that

$$n' = n'' \quad \text{if} \quad [\tfrac{1}{2}(\bar{a}_{11} - \bar{a}_{22})]^2 + \bar{a}_{12}^2 = 0 \tag{46.7}$$

and correspondingly r' and r'' are also equal, both being equal to either to $+i$ or $-i$. Along directions which satisfy Eq. (46.7) therefore the two waves are propagated with the same velocity and are *both* of the same state of polarisation. Thus there is really only *one* wave solution obtained, this wave being either right or left circularly polarised. There are four such directions, called singular axes and they should obviously occur near the optic axes. The exact location of these and the polarisation of the wave propagated along any one are discussed later (Sect. 49).

ε) Idiophanic rings. Unlike transparent crystals, the two waves which are propagated unchanged in form are not of orthogonal states of polarisation in an absorbing crystal. This leads to the interesting result that it is possible to see interference figures (idiophanic rings) namely rings and brushes by using only either a polariser or an analyser (see Sects. 66, 69, 70).

47. Application of the Poincaré sphere. Just as the superposition method gives results which are practically equivalent to those yielded by the rigorous theory

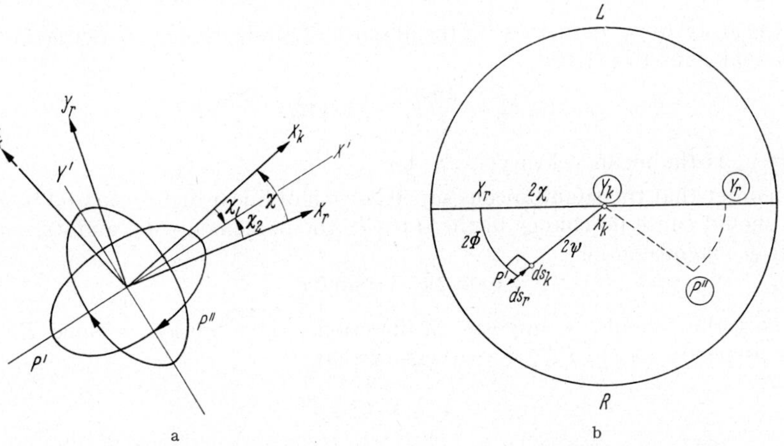

Fig. 43. (a) Section of the index and absorption ellipsoids in an absorbing crystal. X_r, Y_r are the principal axes of refraction and X_k, Y_k are the principal axes of absorption. (b) Poincaré sphere construction for determining the states of polarisation propagated without change (stereographic projection). These are P' and P'' for which the infinitesimal operations of linear birefringence and linear dichroism produce movements ds_r and ds_k which are equal and opposite.

in the case of optically active crystals, this method could be usefully applied to absorbing crystals also[1]. The two properties, which appear superposed in the case of absorbing crystals are linear birefringence and linear dichroism. The elementary operations on the Poincaré sphere corresponding to these two properties have been discussed in Sects. 3, 6 and 7. We shall now consider the superposition of the two.

In Fig. 43a let X_r, Y_r be the principal directions of refraction, representing the major and minor axes of the section of the index ellipsoid, X_r corresponding to the slower wave. Let X_k, Y_k be the principal directions of absorption representing the major and minor axes of the section of the absorption ellipsoid, X_k corresponding to the smaller absorption. Then the effect of birefringence is to rotate the representative point P (of the state of polarisation) about the axis $X_r\,Y_r$ (Fig. 43b) and that of dichroism is to move it towards X_k along the great circle $X_k P Y_k$. If ds_r and ds_k are the movements of P as a result of these operations then the two must be equal and opposite for there to be no change in the state P. In general we shall find that there are two such states P' and P'' as shown in Fig. 43b. Referring to this figure and using Eq. (6.6) the following relations are obvious

$$|ds_r| = \delta \sin 2\varphi; \qquad |ds_k| = k \sin 2\psi \tag{47.1}$$

[1] S. Pancharatnam: Proc. Ind. Acad. Sci. A **42**, 86 (1955).

where 2φ and 2ψ are the angular distances of the representative point P from X_r and X_k respectively and

$$\delta = (\delta_1 - \delta_2); \quad k = (k_2 - k_1) \tag{47.2}$$

where δ_1 and δ_2 are the phase retardations introduced in the absence of dichroism and k_1 and k_2 the absorption coefficients in the absence of linear birefringence[1].

If the major and the minor semi-axes of the sections of the index and absorption elipsoids have the lengths, $1/\sqrt{a_1}$, $1/\sqrt{a_2}$ and $1/\sqrt{b_1}$, $1/\sqrt{b_2}$ then

$$\delta_1 = \frac{2\pi}{\lambda}\frac{1}{\sqrt{a_1}}, \quad \delta_2 = \frac{2\pi}{\lambda}\frac{1}{\sqrt{a_2}} \tag{47.3}$$

and the absorption coefficients in the absence of birefringence are defined by relations analogous to (43.10)

$$2k_1 v_m^3 = \frac{2\pi}{\lambda} b_1, \quad 2k_2 v_m^3 = \frac{2\pi}{\lambda} b_2 \tag{47.4}$$

where v_m is the mean velocity.

In order that the simultaneous superposition of linear dichroism and birefringence should cause no change in the state P, the movements ds_r and ds_k must be equal in magnitude i.e.

$$\delta \sin 2\varphi = k \sin 2\psi. \tag{47.5}$$

Secondly they should be opposite in direction. Since arc ds_k is along PX_k and ds_r is perpendicular to PX_r it is necessary that

$$\widehat{X_r P X_k} = \pi/2$$

or

$$\cos 2\chi = \cos 2\varphi \cos 2\psi \tag{47.6}$$

together with the condition that P will represent a right or left elliptic vibration according as 2φ is positive $\left(0 \text{ to } \frac{\pi}{2}\right)$ or negative $\left(0 \text{ to } -\frac{\pi}{2}\right)$. Both these equations are satisfied when 2φ and 2ψ are changed to $(\pi - 2\varphi)$ and $(\pi - 2\psi)$, thus giving two states $P'(2\varphi', 2\psi')$ and $P''(2\varphi'', 2\psi'')$ indicated in Fig. 43a which are propagated without change of form. Clearly the states P' and P'' have the same latitudes their longitudes differing by π. Hence we arrive at the result also obtained by the electromagnetic theory that the states of polarisation propagated unchanged along any general direction are two *similarly* rotating elliptic vibrations which have their major axes crossed and which have equal ellipticities (Fig. 43b).

The states P' and P'' are fixed by the angular distance 2φ and 2ψ which satisfy the simultaneous Eqs. (47.5) and (47.6). The explicit values of these are obtained by eliminating successively 2φ and 2ψ between these equations and are given by

$$\left.\begin{aligned} k^2\cos^2 2\psi &= \tfrac{1}{2}\left\{(k^2-\delta^2) + \sqrt{(k^2-\delta^2) + 4\delta^2 k^2 \cos^2 2\chi}\right\}, \\ \delta^2\cos^2 2\varphi &= \tfrac{1}{2}\left\{(\delta^2-k^2) + \sqrt{(\delta^2-k^2) + 4\delta^2 k^2 \cos^2 2\chi}\right\}. \end{aligned}\right\} \tag{47.7}$$

The actual latitudes and longitudes of the states can be determined from spherical trigonometry. Referring to Fig. 43a let the inclination of the major axis OX' of one of the ellipses be χ_2 (anticlockwise) with respect to OX_r and χ_1 (clockwise)

[1] The symbol k here introduced differs in sign from that in Sect. 6.

with respect to OX_k. The directions OX' may be determined by the relation

$$\frac{\sin 4\chi_1}{\sin 4\chi_2} = \frac{\delta^2}{k^2} \tag{47.8}$$

and the ratio of the minor to the major axes $\tan \varepsilon$ may be obtained from

$$\sin^2 2\varepsilon = \tan 2\chi_1 \tan 2\chi_2 . \tag{47.9}$$

48. The refractive indices and absorption coefficients of the waves. As in the case of transparent crystals it is convenient to specify the refractive indices and absorption coefficients as functions of the state of polarisation $(2\varphi, 2\psi)$ of the waves.

The alteration in the state of polarisation of a vibration initially in the state X_k to an adjacent state Q (Fig. 44) on travelling through the distance dz may be evaluated by the method of superposition as being entirely due to the operation of birefringence: The infinitesimal arc $X_k Q$ will be equal to $\delta dz \sin 2\chi$ and will be perpendicular to the equator. More properly this alteration in the state of the vibration is connected with the phase retardation $(\delta' - \delta'')\, dz$ between the two waves in the states P' and P'' into which the original vibration will be decomposed. Applying the results of Sect. 4, Eq. (4.9), the relative phase retardation must be equal to the area of the infinitesimal quadrilateral $P'_a X_k P''_a Q$ where P'_a and P''_a are points antipodal to P' and P''. The area of this quadrilateral (being equal to the area of the lune whose angle is contained within the arcs $P' X_k$ and $P' Q$) may be easily shown to be $\delta\, dz \cos 2\varphi'$. Hence we have

$$\delta' - \delta'' = \delta \cos 2\varphi' . \tag{48.1}$$

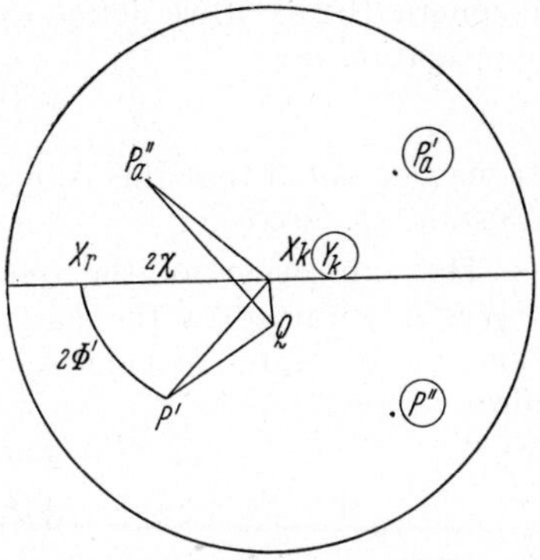

Fig. 44. Construction for determining the phase difference and difference in absorption coefficients of the two waves propagated along any direction.

Alternatively the difference in the refractive indices of the waves is given by

$$(n' - n'') = (n_1 - n_2) \cos 2\varphi' \tag{48.2}$$

where n_1 and n_2 are the refractive indices in the absence of absorption. The state P' for which the value of 2φ (viz. $2\varphi'$) is less than $\pi/2$ is the slower state.

The absorption coefficients k' and k'' of the waves in the states P' and P'' may be easily evaluated from the following considerations. The diminution of intensity $2k\, dz$ which a vibration of unit intensity in state P' suffers on travelling a distance dz arises entirely from the operation of absorption. The X_k and Y_k components of the vibration P' have intensities $\cos^2\psi'$, and $\sin^2\psi'$ respectively; hence the operation of absorption diminishes the intensities of these components by $2k_1\, dz \cos^2\psi'$ and $2k_2\, dz \sin^2\psi'$ respectively. Hence we obtain on addition

$$\left.\begin{aligned} k' &= \tfrac{1}{2}(k_1 + k_2) - \tfrac{1}{2} k \cos 2\psi' , \\ k'' &= \tfrac{1}{2}(k_1 + k_2) + \tfrac{1}{2} k \cos 2\psi' . \end{aligned}\right\} \tag{48.3}$$

These may also be written in the form

$$k', k'' = \tfrac{1}{2}(k_1 + k_2) - \tfrac{1}{2} k \cos 2\psi', 2\psi'' .$$

We have from (48.3)

$$k'' - k' = k \cos 2\psi' . \tag{48.4}$$

The last formula is similar to the expression (48.2) for the difference in the refractive indices. In fact it can be shown, from the symmetry of the operation, that the actual retardations per unit distance δ' and δ'' of the wave will be given by expressions similar to (48.3) i.e.

$$\left.\begin{aligned}\delta' &= \tfrac{1}{2}(\delta_1+\delta_2)+\tfrac{1}{2}\delta\cos 2\varphi',\\ \delta'' &= \tfrac{1}{2}(\delta_1+\delta_2)-\tfrac{1}{2}\delta\cos 2\varphi',\end{aligned}\right\} \tag{48.5}$$

which may be written in the form

$$\delta',\,\delta''=\tfrac{1}{2}(\delta_1+\delta_2)+\tfrac{1}{2}\delta\cos 2\varphi',\,2\varphi''$$

where the value of φ appropriate to the wave in question is to be used.

It can be shown that the states of polarisation of the waves as deduced by the superposition method are identical with those deduced from the electromagnetic theory if we define the mean velocity v_m for the particular direction of propagation as

$$v_m^3=\tfrac{1}{2}(v_1+v_2)\,v_1\,v_2\,. \tag{48.6}$$

It may be noted that this is of the same form as the one used for optically active crystals, cf. (39.6).

The expression for the refractive indices and extinction coefficients of the waves as obtained by the electromagnetic theory may also be expressed as functions of the states of polarisation $(2\varphi, 2\psi)$ of the waves[1]. They then take the form

$$\left.\begin{aligned}v^2 &= \tfrac{1}{2}(a_1+a_2)+\tfrac{1}{2}(a_1-a_2)\cos 2\varphi,\\ 2\varkappa\, v^3 &= \tfrac{1}{2}(b_1+b_2)+\tfrac{1}{2}(b_1-b_2)\cos 2\psi\,.\end{aligned}\right\} \tag{48.7}$$

The difference between these expressions and those deduced by superposition method (48.3) and (48.5) is usually not of much practical significance especially for directions near the optic axis.

β) Approximate formulae. The Poincaré sphere method gives a direct geometric interpretation of the results discussed in Sect. 46. If the birefringence is zero, as along an optic axis, then the polarisation states that are propagated unchanged will be X_k and Y_k i.e. the principal directions of absorption are at right angles to the optic axis. If the birefringence is large, i.e. $\delta \gg k$, then obviously the states of polarisation which are propagated unchanged will be close to X_r and Y_r, i.e. they will be the same as if the crystal had no absorption. This will also be the case if the principal planes of birefringence and dichroism coincide as for a uniaxial crystal. These are identical with the results already deduced in Sect. 46.

For directions not too close to an optic axis we may usually neglect the squares and higher powers of k/δ. Hence from (47.5) the square of $\sin 2\varphi$ may be neglected which means that in Fig. 43 the arc $X_r P'$ is an infinitesimal arc, perpendicular to the equator. Hence we may set

$$\sin 2\varphi = |2\omega|, \qquad \sin 2\psi = \sin|2\chi|$$

which gives the common ellipticity of the two waves to be

$$\omega = -\frac{k}{2\delta}\sin 2\chi\,. \tag{48.8}$$

[1] See Sect. 45.

To this approximation the major and minor axes of the elliptic vibration lie along the principal planes of birefringence and from (48.7) the velocities and absorption coefficients may be determined from the index and absorption ellipsoids as though the waves were linearly polarised.

49. The singular axes. *α) General considerations.* The singular axes also follow very simply from the Poincaré sphere. Since the two states of polarisation are crossed ellipses of the same sense they would become one and the same only when both represent circular vibrations of the same sense i.e. L or R. For example if R is to be propagated unchanged i.e. if state P' of Fig. 43 is to coincide with R the condition that the movement $d s_r$ and $d s_k$ should be oppositely directed will be statisfied only if the arc $X_r X_k$ is a right angle $\left(2\chi = +\frac{\pi}{2}\right)$ since the angle at P' must continue to be a right angle. In this case 2φ and 2ψ are also right angles and the condition that the movements $|d s_r| = |d s_k|$ gives from (47.1) that

$$\delta = k. \tag{49.1}$$

Similarly for $2\chi = -\frac{\pi}{2}$, and $\delta = k$ (see Fig. 45) the left circularly polarised state L alone is propagated unchanged. The same results could also be proved from Eq. (45.8).

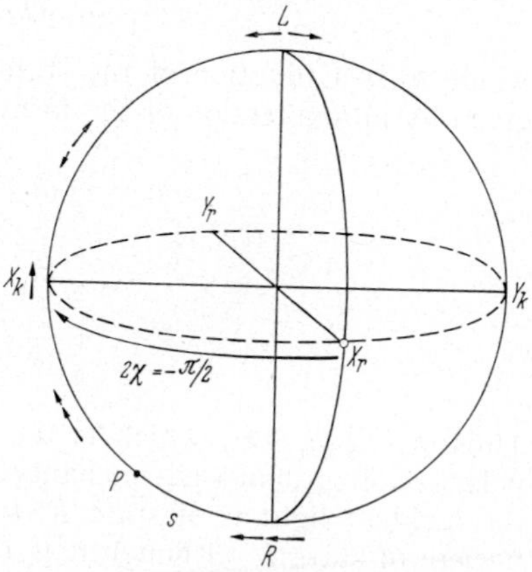

Fig. 45. Propagation of light along a singular axis. Only the state L is propagated unchanged. If the orthogonal state R is incident, it is progressively converted to L via the great circular arc $R X_k L$.

Thus singular axes occur along directions at which the principal planes of absorption and refraction make angles of 45° with each other, the linear birefringence and linear dichroism being equal in magnitude. It will be shown in Sects. 67 and 68 that very close to each one of the optic axes, there exist two singular axes, one on either side of it, propagating respectively right and left circularly polarised waves. It may be noted that a singular axis cannot be designated uniquely as "right circular" or "left circular" unless the direction of propagation is also specified. For example along the same singular axis right circular light is propagated unchanged when traversing it in one direction, left circular light would be propagated unchanged for an opposide direction of travel. This is because the sign of χ changes when Fig. 43a is viewed from the opposite side.

β) Propagation of circularly polarised light along the singular axes. Along any particular singular axis, only circularly polarised light of one sense is propagated without change of state. Let this be the left circular state L (Fig. 45). The question arises as to what would happen if light in the right circular state R is incident exactly in this direction. Voigt[1] suggested, without proof, that it would be totally reflected. However, we obtain an entirely different answer by applying the method of superposition[2]. From Fig. 45 it is seen that for this direction of propagation the movement of the representative point P_k is along the great circle $R X_k L Y_k$. Initially, the effects of birefringence and dichroism are additive until the point X_k is reached; thereafter they are opposite, but the birefringence effect is larger and so the point moves on towards L asymptotically.

[1] W. Voigt: Ann. Phys., Lpz. **2**, 1002 (1908).
[2] S. Pancharatnam: Proc. Ind. Acad. Sci. A **42**, 86 (1955).

Let P be the state of polarisation at depth z inside the crystal, and let arc $\widehat{RP}=s$. Then, the state $s+ds$ at depth $z+dz$ is from (47.1) given by

$$ds = (\delta + k\cos s)\,dz. \tag{49.2}$$

Putting in $\delta = k$ and integrating, we have

$$\tan s/2 = kz. \tag{49.3}$$

Thus, the change from R to X_k i.e. to linear vibration at 45° to the principal planes of refraction, occurs in a smaller distance than would be the case if absorption were absent, while the change from X_k to L requires an infinite distance. The intensity I_k at a depth dz may be similarly calculated. The change dI_z due to the passage through a distance dz is

$$dI_z = -2k_z I_z\,dz \tag{49.4}$$

where k_z is a function of the state of polarisation. In terms of k_1 and k_2 it is given by an expression of the form (48.3)

$$\left.\begin{aligned} k_z &= \frac{1}{2}(k_1+k_2) - \frac{1}{2}k\cos 2\psi \\ &= \frac{1}{2}(k_1+k_2) - \frac{1}{2}k\sin s \\ &= \frac{1}{2}(k_1+k_2) - \frac{k^2 z}{1-k^2z^2}. \end{aligned}\right\} \tag{49.5}$$

Thus, $k_z < \frac{1}{2}(k_1+k_2)$ which is the coefficient of absorption for L, the state of polarisation propagated unchanged. We thus get the surprising result that if the incident light is of state R, then the transmitted intensity is *more* than if it were of state L, although it is L that is propagated unchanged.

Substituting (49.5) in (49.4) we have

$$-\frac{dI_z}{I_z} = (k_1+k_2)\,dz - \frac{2k^2 z}{1+k^2z^2}\,dz. \tag{49.6}$$

If I_0 and I_R are the incident intensity and the intensity transmitted after a thickness z, then

$$\log(I_0/I_R) = (k_1+k_2)\,z - \log(1+k^2z^2). \tag{49.7}$$

For left-circular vibration, we have

$$\log(I_0/I_L) = (k_1+k_2)\,z \tag{49.8}$$

so that the ratio of the two is simply

$$I_R/I_L = 1 + k^2z^2, \tag{49.9}$$

which is always *greater than unity*.

This interesting result has been verified experimentally[1] (Sect. 68).

The result is not really in contradiction with those of the electromagnetic theory. It is true that according to the electromagnetic theory only one *homogeneously* polarised plane wave solution (not two) is obtained for a singular direction. A theoretical approach more general than the one we have adopted in Sect. 26 becomes necessary to establish that other solutions also exist, representing however plane disturbances propagated with a progressive change of polarisation (see Sect. 56).

[1] S. PANCHARATNAM: Proc. Ind. Acad. Sci. A **45**, 1 (1957).

V. Absorbing optically active crystals[1].

50. Formal solution of the wave equation. When both absorption and optical activity are present, then again the relation between $\boldsymbol{E}$ and $\boldsymbol{D}$ takes a form similar to that for an optically active crystal without absorption, viz.

$$\boldsymbol{D} = [\bar{\varepsilon}]\,\boldsymbol{E} + i\,\overline{\boldsymbol{G}}\times\boldsymbol{E}, \qquad \overline{\boldsymbol{G}} = [\bar{g}]\,\mathbf{s}, \tag{50.1}$$

$$\boldsymbol{E} = [\bar{a}]\,\boldsymbol{D} - i\,\overline{\boldsymbol{\Gamma}}\times\boldsymbol{D}, \qquad \overline{\boldsymbol{\Gamma}} = [\bar{\gamma}]\,\mathbf{s}. \tag{50.2}$$

However the tensors $[\bar{\varepsilon}]$ and $[\bar{g}]$ and correspondingly the tensors $[\bar{a}]$ and $[\bar{\gamma}]$ are all complex. Thus $\overline{\boldsymbol{G}}$ and $\overline{\boldsymbol{\Gamma}}$ are complex vectors. We shall use the form (50.2) for further discussion. It is convenient to express the above relations in terms of tensors having real components; these tensors will therefore separately determine the various optical characteristics of the medium. Thus in (50.2) we may substitute

$$[\bar{a}] = [a] + i\,[b] \quad \text{and} \quad [\bar{\gamma}] = [\gamma] + i\,[\beta]. \tag{50.3}$$

We may further substitute

$$\overline{\boldsymbol{\Gamma}} = \boldsymbol{\Gamma} + i\,\boldsymbol{\mathcal{B}} \tag{50.4}$$

with

$$\boldsymbol{\Gamma} = [\gamma]\,\mathbf{s} \quad \text{and} \quad \boldsymbol{\mathcal{B}} = [\beta]\,\mathbf{s} \tag{50.5}$$

where $[a]$ and $[b]$ are the usual index and absorption tensors which occur for example in optically inactive absorbing crystals and which define the index and the absorption ellipsoids. As in the case of transparent optically active crystals. $\boldsymbol{\Gamma}$ is the optical activity vector which for any direction of propagation is determined by the optical activity tensor $[\gamma]$. The new vector $\boldsymbol{\mathcal{B}}$ may be called the vector of circular dichroism being determined for any direction of propagation by the "*tensor of circular dichroism*" $[\beta]$—the reason for this nomenclature will be justified as we proceed.

Taking the direction of the z axis along the wave normal we may proceed as in the case of transparent optically active crystals (Sect. 38). Comparing (38.6) and (38.7) and remembering that in the present case the constants are complex we immediately obtain

$$\left.\begin{aligned} (v^2 - \bar{a}_{11}) &= (\bar{a}_{12} + i\,\bar{\Gamma}_3)\,D_y/D_x\,, \\ (v^2 - \bar{a}_{22}) &= (\bar{a}_{12} - i\,\bar{\Gamma}_3)\,D_x/D_y\,. \end{aligned}\right\} \tag{50.6}$$

If we put $r = D_y/D_x$, then r gives the state of polarisation of the wave. Eliminating r between the two equations we have

$$(\bar{v}^2 - \bar{a}_{11})\,(\bar{v}^2 - \bar{a}_{22}) = (\bar{a}_{12}^2 + \bar{\Gamma}_3^2)\,. \tag{50.7}$$

The solutions of this equation give the complex velocities $\bar{v}'$ and $\bar{v}''$ of the two waves that are propagated along any chosen direction. The two states of polarisation r' and r'' are the roots of the equation

$$(\bar{a}_{12}^2 + i\,\bar{\Gamma}_3)\,r^2 + (\bar{a}_{11} - \bar{a}_{22})\,r - (\bar{a}_{12} - i\,\bar{\Gamma}_3) = 0\,. \tag{50.8}$$

Explicitly written the roots of (50.7) and (50.8) are

$$\bar{v}'^2, \bar{v}''^2 = \tfrac{1}{2}\,(\bar{a}_{11} + \bar{a}_{22}) \pm \sqrt{\{\tfrac{1}{2}\,(\bar{a}_{11} - \bar{a}_{22})\}^2 + (\bar{a}_{12}^2 + \bar{\Gamma}_3^2)} \tag{50.9}$$

[1] S. Pancharatnam: Proc. Ind. Acad. Sci. A **48**, 227 (1958).

and

$$r', r'' = \frac{-\frac{1}{2}(\bar{a}_{11}-\bar{a}_{22}) \pm \sqrt{\{\frac{1}{2}(\bar{a}_{11}-\bar{a}_{22})\}^2 + (\bar{a}_{12}^2 + \bar{\Gamma}_3^2)}}{(\bar{a}_{12}+i\bar{\Gamma}_3)}. \tag{50.10}$$

The task of discussing in greater detail the velocity and absorption coefficients and the state of polarisation of the waves is complicated by the fact that all the coefficients occurring in (50.9) and (50.10) are really complex quantities, namely

$$\bar{a}_{ij} = a_{ij} + i\,b_{ij}, \quad \bar{\Gamma}_3 = \Gamma_3 + i\,\mathcal{B}_3. \tag{50.11}$$

In terms of a general coordinate system

or

$$\left.\begin{aligned} \bar{\Gamma}_3 &= \bar{\boldsymbol{\Gamma}}\cdot\mathbf{s} = \bar{\gamma}, \text{ say,} \\ \Gamma_3 &= \boldsymbol{\Gamma}\cdot\mathbf{s} = \gamma, \text{ say,} \\ \mathcal{B}_3 &= \boldsymbol{\mathcal{B}}\cdot\mathbf{s} = \beta, \text{ say,} \end{aligned}\right\} \tag{50.12}$$

and here γ is the scalar parameter of optical rotation already met with, and β may be called the scalar parameter of circular dichroism for reasons discussed in the next section 51 and $\bar{\gamma}$ is the complex parameter of optical activity.

51. Circular dichroism and its directional variation. By assuming the complete absence of linear birefringence and linear dichroism we can understand the characteristic effect introduced by the parameter $\mathcal{B}_3$. Hence, setting

$$a_{11} = a_{22} = a, \quad a_{12} = 0, \quad b_{11} = b_{22} = b, \quad b_{12} = 0$$

i.e.

$$\bar{a}_{11} = \bar{a}_{22} = \bar{a}; \quad \bar{a}_{12} = 0 \tag{51.1}$$

in Eq. (50.7) and (50.8) we get

$$D_y/D_x = \pm i, \quad v^2 = \bar{a} \pm \bar{\Gamma}_3. \tag{51.2}$$

This means that the waves are right and left circularly polarised and if $\bar{v}_r$ and $\bar{v}_l$ are the complex velocities of the circular waves then

$$\bar{v}_l^2 - \bar{v}_r^2 = 2\bar{\Gamma}_3. \tag{51.3}$$

The complex velocity $\bar{v}$ is related to the actual velocity and the extinction coefficient $\varkappa$ by the relation

$$\bar{v} = \frac{1}{n - i\varkappa} = v(1 + i\varkappa v) \tag{51.4}$$

and when terms containing the squares of the extinction coefficients are of negligible magnitude we get to a high degree of approximation:

$$n_r - n_l = \frac{\gamma}{v_m^3} = \frac{\lambda}{\pi}\varrho, \tag{51.5}$$

$$\varkappa_r - \varkappa_l = \frac{\beta}{v_m^3} = \frac{\lambda}{\pi}\sigma \tag{51.6}$$

where v_m is the mean velocity. Thus, the optical rotation of an absorbing crystal may be considered to be a complex quantity being given by $\bar{\varrho} = \varrho + i\sigma$, where ϱ and σ are related to γ and β by (51.5) and (51.6). The reason why γ and β are termed as the parameters of optical rotation and circular dichroism is now quite evident.

The parameter of optical rotation has been shown to be a quadratic function of the direction cosines of the direction propagation in Sect. 40. The same must be true of the parameter of circular dichroism. If we measure off two radii vectors r_1 and r_2 parallel to the direction of propagation such that their lengths are given by

$$\frac{1}{r_1^2} = |\gamma| = \frac{\lambda}{\pi} |\varrho| v_m^3, \tag{51.7}$$

$$\frac{1}{r_2^2} = |\beta| = \frac{\lambda}{\pi} |\sigma| v_m^3, \tag{51.8}$$

where γ and β denote the parameters for propagation in a general direction, then (51.7) and (51.8) define respectively a surface of optical rotation and a surface of circular dichroism, both of which are central quadrics to a good approximation. Given these surfaces we may determine γ and β for any direction or alternatively the coefficients of circular birefringence and circular dichroism for any direction.

52. Method of superposition.—The use of the Poincaré sphere[1]. It will be noticed that the equations for a general direction of propagation (50.9) and (50.10) are very intractable. We shall now develop the theory of wave propagation in absorbing optically active crystals by making use of the method of superposition. The change in the state of polarisation of a vibration on travelling through a

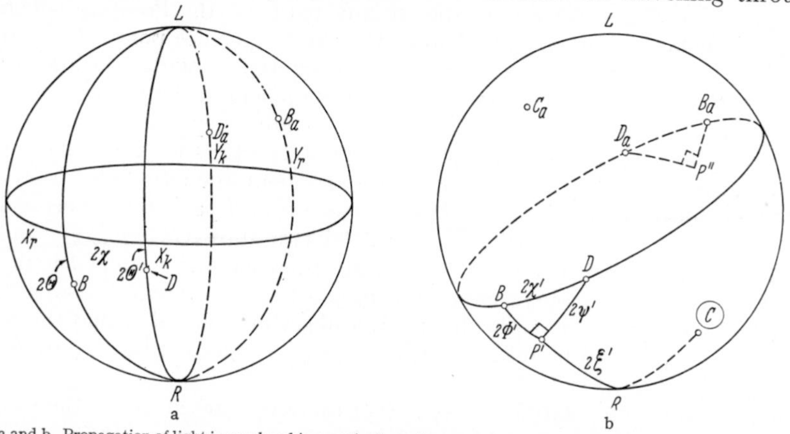

Fig. 46 a and b. Propagation of light in an absorbing, optically active crystal. (a) Linear birefringence about $X_r Y_r$ and circular birefringence about RL compound to yield elliptic birefringence about BB_a. Similarly, linear dichroism about $X_k Y_k$ and circular dichroism about RL compound by the vectorial law to yield elliptic dichroism about DD_a. (b) P', P'' represent states propagated unchanged under the effects of elliptic birefringence (about BB_a) and elliptic dichroism (about DD_a). C is the pole of the great circle through BD.

thickness dz will have to be determined by applying in succession the infinitesimal operations of linear birefringence, linear dichroism, optical activity (i.e. circular birefringence) and circular dichroism. For any particular direction of propagation the first two operations are determined by the sections of the index and absorption ellipsoids according to Eqs. (47.3) and (47.4). The latter two operations are determined respectively from the surfaces of optical rotation and circular dichroism according to Eqs. (51.7) and (51.8). [The mean velocity v_m is defined in Eq. (48.6).]

Referring to Fig. 46a the infinitesimal operations of linear birefringence (rotation δdz about $X_r Y_r$) and of circular birefringence (a rotation $2\varrho\, dz$ about RL) may be compounded by a vectorial law as in the case of transparent optically active crystals. The two operations are together equivalent to a single operation

[1] S. Pancharatnam: Proc. Ind. Acad. Sci. A **46**, 280 (1957).

of elliptic birefringence, a rotation of Δdz about the axis BB_a. The relative phase retardation per unit thickness Δ between the crossed ellipses B and B_a which are propagated unchanged in the absence of absorption, and the latitude 2ϑ of the slower state B, are determined by Eqs. (39.4), (39.2 for transparent optically active crystals.

Similarly it has been shown (Sect. 7) that the infinitesimal operations of linear dichroism (axis $X_k Y_k$) and circular dichroism (axis RL) can be compounded by a vectorial law and may be replaced by the operation of elliptic dichroism. In Fig. 46a, vibrations of two oppositely polarised elliptic states D and D_a (which have the same longitudes as X_k and Y_k respectively) remain unaltered in form under the combined effects of linear and circular dichroism. If ϑ' is the angle of ellipticity of the less absorbed state and K the difference in the absorption coefficient of the vibrations in the state D and D_a then

$$\tan\vartheta' = -2\sigma/K \tag{52.1}$$

$$K = \left|\sqrt{k^2 + (2\sigma)^2}\right| \tag{52.2}$$

where 2σ corresponds to the difference between the absorption coefficients of left and right circular components in the operation of circular dichroism, i.e. $2\sigma = k_L - k_R$ and $k = k_{Y_k} - k_{X_k}$.

Referring to Fig. 46b we may specify any point on the Poincaré sphere by its angular distance 2φ, 2ψ and 2ξ from the three reference points D, B and C which form a right handed set, the point C being at an angular distance of $\pi/2$ from both B and D, the arc BD, which is not in general a right angle, being denoted by $2\chi'$. Since the three direction cosines are not independent, it is sufficient to specify 2φ and 2ψ ,and give merely the sign of 2ξ. Thus we have to superpose only the operations of elliptic birefringence Δ (about the axis BB_a) and of elliptic dichroism K (about the axis DD_a), the two axes BB_a and DD_a being inclined at an angle of $2\chi'$. There will in general be two states $P'(2\varphi', 2\psi')$ and P'' $(2\varphi'', 2\psi'')$ as indicated in Fig. 46b which are propagated unchanged under the combined effects of these operations, 2ξ being positive in both cases. The problem is formally the same as in an optically inactive absorbing crystal so that the results derived in that case can be taken over, provided we replace δ by Δ, k by K, and 2χ by $2\chi'$.

Thus the state of polarisation 2φ, 2ψ of the waves are given by the simultaneous equations analogous to (47.5) and (47.6):

$$\Delta \sin 2\varphi = K \sin 2\psi, \tag{52.3}$$

$$\cos 2\chi' = \cos 2\varphi \cos 2\psi. \tag{52.4}$$

The refractive indices and the absorption coefficients of the waves expressed in terms of these states of polarisation are given by the equations analogous to (48.5) and (48.3).

$$\delta', \delta'' = \tfrac{1}{2}(\delta_1 + \delta_2) \pm \tfrac{1}{2}\Delta \cos 2\varphi'. \tag{52.5}$$

$$k', k'' = \tfrac{1}{2}(k_1 + k_2) \pm \tfrac{1}{2} K \cos 2\psi'. \tag{52.6}$$

Further

$$\delta' - \delta'' = \Delta \cos 2\varphi', \tag{52.7}$$

$$k'' - k' = K \cos 2\psi'. \tag{52.8}$$

The explicit expressions for $\cos 2\varphi$ and $\cos 2\psi$ will be of the form (47.7) with the replacements mentioned above.

For directions of propagation appreciably inclined to the optic axis the effect of linear birefringence predominates over all the other operations and the waves may be regarded as linearly polarised along the principal planes of linear birefringence.

It can be shown that the expressions for the velocities and extinction coefficients of the waves as derived by the electromagnetic theory may also be expressed as functions of the state of polarisation $(2\varphi, 2\psi)$ of the waves[1]. They take a form similar to (52.5) and (52.6) deduced by superposition methods, being for any general direction of propagation given by [cf. (48.7)]

$$v^2 = \tfrac{1}{2}(a_1 + a_2) + \tfrac{1}{2}\sqrt{(a_1 - a_2)^2 + (2\beta)^2}\cos 2\varphi, \tag{52.9}$$

$$2\varkappa v^3 = \tfrac{1}{2}(b_1 + b_2) + \tfrac{1}{2}\sqrt{(b_1 + b_2)^2 + (2\beta)^2}\cos 2\psi. \tag{52.10}$$

For directions not too close to an optic axis the squares and higher powers of ϱ/Δ and K/Δ may be neglected so that from (52.3), $|\cos 2\varphi| \approx 1$. According to (52.9) the velocities may then be determined from the section of the index ellipsoid as though the waves were linearly polarised. Since for such directions $2\psi \approx 2\chi'$ from (52.4), it can be shown from (52.10), using (52.1), that the extinction coefficients of the waves may similarly be determined from the absorption ellipsoid. For directions still closer to the optic axis, the difference between the expression (52.9), (52.10) and those derived bythe superposition methods (52.5) and (52.6) will be entirely negligible, so that the latter may be more conveniently used.

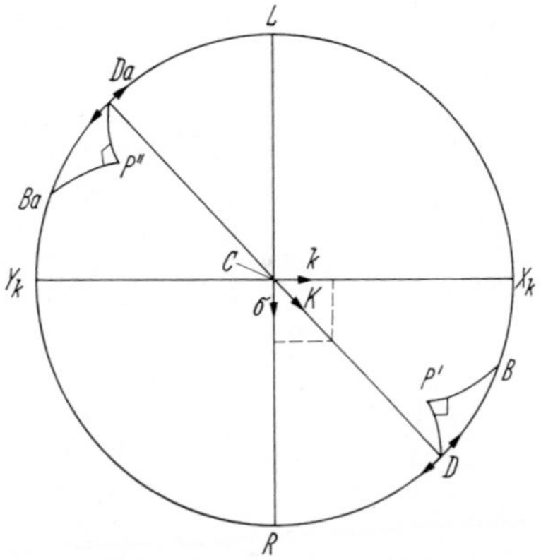

Fig. 47. Propagation in a uniaxial crystal. The great circle through BD is here a meridian of longitude. The states P', P'' which are propagated unchanged also bear a simple geometric relation to one another. The figure also illustrates the vectorial composition of linear and circular dichroism.

For uniaxial crystals the principal planes of linear birefringence and dichroism coincide so that the points B and D (Fig. 47) lie on the same great circle passing through the poles. It will be seen from Fig. 47 that the two ellipses have the same numerical ellipticity though described in opposite senses; and the orientation of the major axes of the two ellipses are obtained from the principal planes of OX_r and OY_r by turning the latter through equal angles in opposite directions. This result has been obtained by Försterling[2] from the electromagnetic theory of propagation in uniaxial crystals. For uniaxial crystals however, the linear dichroism close to the optic axial direction will be weak (being near a circular section of the absorption ellipsoid) while circular dichroism in crystals has always been found to be a weak phenomenon. It is appropriate to remark here that Voigt[3] has made some observations on the so-called liquid crystals which exhibit very strong circular dichroism. However, we shall not deal with them here, for the large circular dichroism and the enormous rotation of the plane of polarisation indicate that these media may not be homogeneous but may on the contrary possess a lamellar structure (De Vries)[4].

---

[1] See Sect. 56.
[2] Försterling: Göttinger Nachr. 1912, p. 207.
[3] W. Voigt: Phys. Z. **17**, 159 (1916).
[4] H. De Vries: Acta crystallogr. **4**, 219 (1951).

As in the case of absorbing inactive crystals, interesting phenomena are to be expected for the class of biaxial crystals showing appreciable linear dichroism along an optic axial direction. In such a case, circular dichroism being a weak phenomenon may be neglected in comparison with linear dichroism. We shall therefore next consider the case when circular dichroism is zero.

53. Biaxial crystals with negligible circular dichroism. *α) General considerations.* In this the constant of elliptic dichroism K has to be replaced by the linear dichroism k. Further the axis DD_a (Fig. 46a) of elliptic dichroism becomes coincident with axis $X_k Y_k$ of linear dichroism. Accordingly Fig. 46b takes the special form shown in Fig. 48.

In this case we have, from (52.4) and (52.7),

$$\cos 2\chi' = \cos 2\varphi' \cos 2\psi' = \frac{\delta}{\Delta} \cos 2\psi'. \tag{53.1}$$

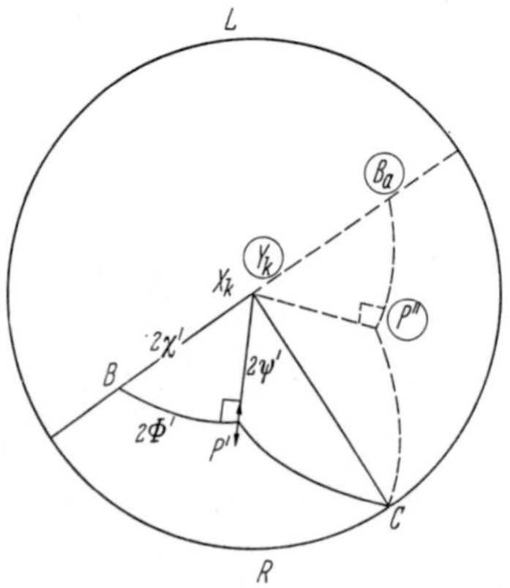

Fig. 48.

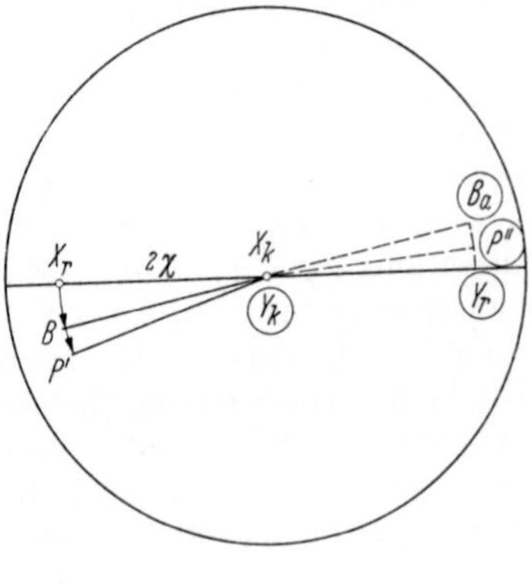

Fig. 49.

Fig. 48. Propagation in a biaxial crystal with no circular dichroism. DD_a of Fig. 46 (b) becomes coincident with $X_k Y_k$.

Fig. 49. Propagation for directions not in the vicinity of the optic axes (no circular dichroism). Each wave has an ellipticity which is the sum of the corresponding ellipticities which would obtain in the absence of absorption and of optical activity.

Here again we note that the two polarised waves in the states P' and P'' that are propagated along any direction are in elliptic states of polarisation whose geometrical forms bear no simple relation to one another, i.e. the major axes of the elliptic vibrations are not in general crossed, their ellipticities are not equal numerically and finally they may or may not be described in the same sense (depending on the direction of propagation). We shall consider only certain special cases.

β) Directions not too near an optic axis. For such directions we may neglect the squares and higher powers of ϱ/Δ and K/Δ. The arcs $X_r B$ and BP' of Figs. 46a and 46b respectively become infinitesimal arcs normal to the plane of the equator, the situation being illustrated in Fig. 49. To this degree of approximation $\Delta \approx \delta$ and $2\chi' \approx 2\chi$ from Eqs. (39.4) and (53.1). From Fig. 49 the directed arc $\widehat{BP'}$ will be equal to 2ε where ε is the common ellipticity of the two waves in the absence of optical activity given by Eq. (48.8) of the section on absorbing inactive crystals. Moreover the directed arc $\widehat{X_r B}$ is equal to 2ϑ where ϑ is the ellipticity of the slower wave in the absence of dichroism (i.e. as in a transparent active crystal). Thus to this degree of approximation the orientations of the major axes are along the principal planes of linear birefringence but the ellipticity for each state now approximates to the sum of the corresponding ellipticities obtaining, in the absence of optical activity and absorption respectively. Thus the ellipticities of P' and P'' are

$$\varepsilon',\ \varepsilon'' = -\frac{k}{2\delta}\sin 2\chi \mp \frac{\varrho}{\delta}. \tag{53.2}$$

As has already been mentioned in the last section the velocities and absorption coefficients may be determined by the usual index and absorption ellipsoid constructions as though the waves are linearly polarised. It may be seen that though the waves are non-orthogonally polarised, the non-orthogonality factor $\cos^2 c$ (where $2c$ is the angular separation of the states on the Poincaré sphere) is the same as in the absence of optical activity. It may also be seen that the waves tend to the form of a linear vibration as δ increases, i.e. as the inclination from the optic axis increases (Sect. 71).

γ) Propagation along an optic axial direction: Two classifications of the general behaviour. Case 1. Linear dichroism $k >$ circular birefringence $|2\varrho|$.

In this case (as will be shown) the waves propagated along the optic axes are actually linearly polarised, the angle between the linear vibrations being different from a right angle. This is illustrated in Fig. 50 for the case when ϱ is positive. The azimuths of the two linear vibrations may be readily calculated remembering that linear birefringence is absent. A linear vibration P initially at an azimuth ψ with respect to OX_k will under the infinitesimal operation of linear dichroism be turned through an angle $\frac{1}{2}k\sin 2\psi\, dz$ towards OX_k, the less absorbed component—as a direct calculation shows. On the other hand, it is turned through an anticlockwise angle $\varrho\, dz$ under the infinitesimal operation of rotation. Since these must be equal and opposite, the azimuths of the states propagated must satisfy the equation

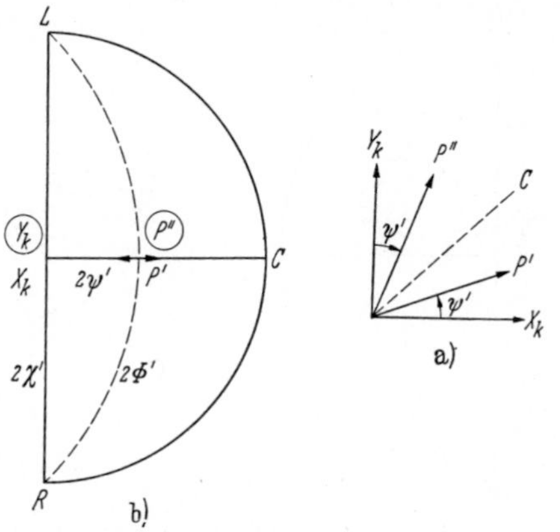

Fig. 50. Propagation along an optic axis. No circular dichroism and $k > |2\varrho|$. Linear states P', P'' are propagated unchanged. The construction is for a left-rotating crystal, i.e. ϱ positive.

$$\sin 2\psi = 2\varrho/k. \tag{53.3}$$

Thus there will be two states at azimuths ψ' and $\frac{\pi}{2} - \psi'$ which are propagated unchanged. These azimuths will be either both positive (0 to $\pi/2$) or both negative $\left(0 \text{ to } -\frac{\pi}{2}\right)$ according as ϱ is positive or negative. The situation is illustrated in the Poincaré sphere drawn for the case when ϱ is positive (Fig. 50). This is the special form which Fig. 46b takes for optic axial directions when linear birefringence is absent i.e. when BB_a coincides with RL and $\Delta = |2\varrho|$. The arc $2\chi'$ in Fig. 46b has become a right angle and from the condition that the angle it subtends at P' should also be a right angle it may be seen geometrically that P' must lie either on the equatorial arc $X_k C$ ($2\varphi = \pi/2$) or on the meridional arc CR ($2\psi = \pi/2$). The latter corresponds to the case when $|2\varrho| > k$ which we shall consider later. The former is the case we are treating at present for which Eq. (53.3) has a solution. The two linearly polarised beams have the same velocity since

$2\varphi' = \pi/2$ in (52.9). They are however propagated with different absorption coefficients given by (52.10)

$$k'' - k' = K \cos 2\psi'. \tag{53.4}$$

The behaviour in this respect is somewhat similar to that for inactive crystals except for the fact that the two linear polarised states are *not* orthogonal.

Case 2. Circular birefringence $|2\varrho| >$ linear dichroism k.

This situation is illustrated in Fig. 51 when ϱ is positive and represents the second of the two cases mentioned in the last paragraph—namely the case when P lies on the meridional arc $CR(2\psi = \pi/2)$. In this case two elliptic vibrations exactly similar in form and orientation but described in opposite senses are propagated. The sense of description of the slower elliptic vibration is the same as that of the slower circular vibration which would be propagated in the absence of dichroism. The major axes of the elliptic vibrations are coincident and make an angle $+\frac{\pi}{4}$ or $-\frac{\pi}{4}$ with reference to OX_k according as ϱ is positive or negative. The numerical value of the ellipticity $|\omega'|$ of the vibrations may be obtained from the Eqs. (52.3) since $2\varphi' = \pi/2 - |2\omega'|$ and $2\psi' = \pi/2$

$$\cos|2\omega'| = k/|2\varrho|. \tag{53.5}$$

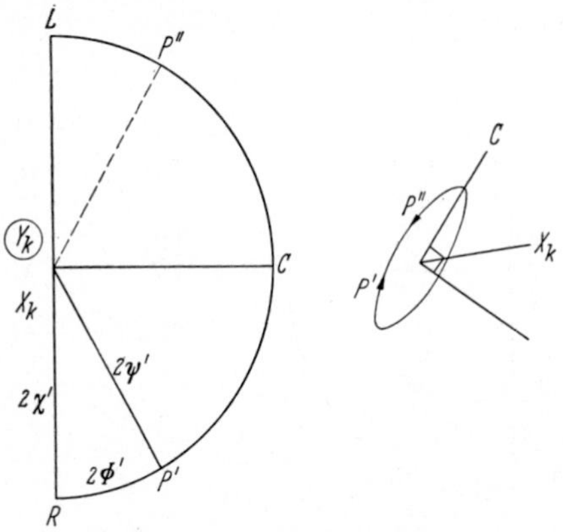

Fig. 51. Same as Fig. 50, but for the case when $|2\varrho| > k$. Two ellipses in opposite senses are propagated unchanged, their ellipticities being equal and their major axes at 45° to X_k.

The two waves have equal absorption coefficients according to (52.8) but they possess different velocities of propagation and the phase retardation which one wave suffers relative to the other per unit distance of propagation is obtained from (52.7) to be

$$\delta' - \delta'' = -2\varrho \sin 2\omega'. \tag{53.6}$$

One can see the parallelism between this and the case of the propagation along the optic axis in transparent optically active crystals. There is however the important difference that, in the present case, the two waves are not circularly but elliptically polarised. This leads to the curious property that the observed rotation of the plane of polarisation along the optic axis depends on the azimuth of the incident linear vibration so that the true rotatory power cannot be obtained without correction for the dichroism. This important correction will be dealt with in Sects. 71β and 72.

54. Propagation in the vicinity of the optic axis. Biaxial crystals with negligible circular dichroism. For directions in the vicinity of an optic axis the linear dichroism and the rotatory power may be regarded constant. Hence for example if $|2\varrho| > k$ along the optic axis, the same holds for directions in its vicinity. The general behaviour even along directions other than the optic axis exhibits a certain similarity to that of transparent optically active crystals or to absorbing inactive crystals according as $|2\varrho| > k$ or $k > |2\varrho|$ along the optic axis itself. Thus, in the former case, there are no singular axes, but in the latter, singular axes do occur in the vicinity of optic axes, just as in absorbing inactive crystals.

Case 1. $|2\varrho| > k$.

We shall first consider the case when the optical activity predominates over linear dichroism. We see from formula (53.2) that the sign of the ellipticity is determined by the second term since it is always numerically greater than the first. Thus the two ellipses will always be described in opposite senses, and the numerical magnitude of the ellipticity for one of the waves will be greater than that for a transparent active crystal, while that for the other will be less by the same amount. Since the formulae (52.5), (52.6) for the states of polarisation are formally similar to those for inactive absorbing crystals (48.5), (48.3) it follows as in that case that the two states P' and P'' of Fig. 48 can become identical, i.e. there will exist a singular axis, only if

$$2\chi' = \pi/2, \quad \Delta = k. \tag{54.1}$$

Since the elliptic birefringence is given by

$$\Delta = \sqrt{\delta^2 + (2\varrho)^2}$$

its minimum value is $|2\varrho|$ which occurs where the birefringence vanishes i.e. along the optic axis itself. Hence if $|2\varrho| > k$, the situation $\Delta = k$ cannot occur for any direction, showing that for such cases (i.e. when $|2\varrho| > k$), there will be *no* singular directions.

Case 2. $k > |2\varrho|$.

Here, we shall first consider a general direction of propagation in the vicinity of the optic axis. The singular axes will be considered in the next section.

We have seen that the principal planes of linear dichroism as well as k and ϱ may be regarded as constant in the neighbourhood of the optic axis. On the other hand the linear birefringence δ increases rapidly with angular distance from the optic axis. Further as we go round the curve $\delta = \text{const}$, i.e. round the optic axis, the principal axes of linear birefringence also turn round rapidly i.e. in the approximate formula (53.2) χ, the inclination of OX_r to OX_k varies rapidly with the azimuth (see for example Sect. 66, Fig. 70a). Hence along these azimuths where the first term becomes numerically equal to the second, one of the waves will be elliptically polarised (with twice the ellipticity obtaining for a transparent active crystal). But the other wave will be linearly polarised. This obviously occurs along directions where

$$\sin 2\chi = \pm |2\varrho|/k. \tag{54.2}$$

Thus when any one of the principal planes of linear birefringence (OX_r or OY_r) is at an azimuth ψ with respect to OX_k, where ψ satisfies the equation

$$\sin 2\psi = 2\varrho/k, \tag{54.3}$$

a linear vibration parallel to that particular principal plane is propagated unchanged.

That the truth of this last statement does not depend on the use of the approximate formula (53.2) is seen directly by applying the method of superposition which gives in fact a simple physical explanation of the phenomenon. A vibration along the principal plane of linear birefringence remains unchanged under the infinitesimal operation of linear birefringence. Further if it is at an azimuth ψ' which satisfies (54.3) it will remain unchanged under the combined effects of the two succeeding operations of linear dichroism and optical rotation, as we have demonstrated in Sect. 53γ. Thus the linear vibration will be propagated unchanged under the superposed effects of all the three operations. It must however be remembered that the second wave propagated along such a direction is elliptically polarised and for directions close to the optic axis, its ellipticity and orientation are different from that derived from the approximate treatment. For these directions, since ψ is a constant, we see from (52.8) that the absorption coefficient of the waves are the same as those propagated along the optic axes.

The results of the previous paragraph leads to the interesting conclusion that in the interference figures observed between crossed polaroids in convergent light, if the polarised vibration is parallel to any one of the vibrations propagated along the optic axis, *true* isogyres are formed occurring in the same position as in a transparent inactive crystal.

55. The singular axes. From Eq. (53.2) we see that the elliptic birefringence increases from a minimum value of $|2\varrho|$ as we move away from the optic axial

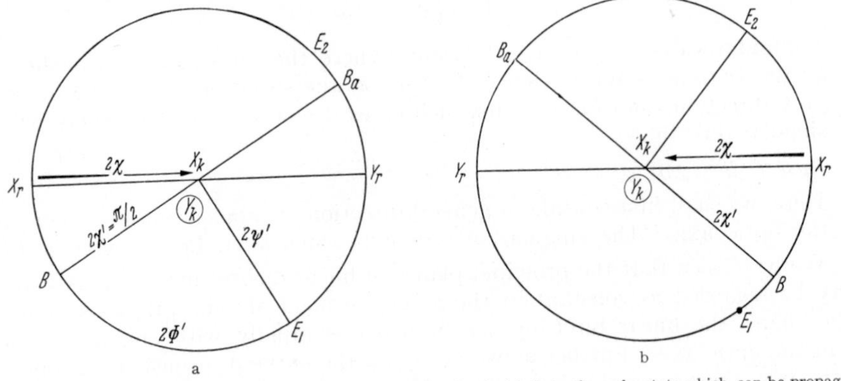

Fig. 52 a and b. Determination of the singular axes, when $k > |2\varrho|$. (a) E_1 is the only state which can be propagated unchanged along one of the singular axes. (b) E_2 is the only state propagated unchanged along the other singular axis associated with the same optic axis. No singular axes occur when $k < |2\varrho|$.

direction. Since $|2\varrho| < k$ there can arise a situation when $\Delta = k$. From Eqs. (54.1) a singular axis will occur if in addition $2\chi' = \pi/2$. In such a case Fig. 48 acquires the form illustrated in Fig. 52a.

Here the arc $\widehat{BX_k}$ has become a right angle and since the angle it subtends at P' must be a right angle, the states P' and P'' both coincide at E_1. Since X_r is on the same longitude as B, the arc $\widehat{X_r X_k}$ is also a right angle, so that the principal planes of linear birefringence and dichroism must make angles of 45° with one another. (The case when $\chi = \pi/4$ and ϱ is positive is illustrated in Fig. 52a.) The major axes of the ellipse will be along the principal plane OY_r of linear birefringence if ϱ is positive, and along OX_r if ϱ is negative. Since $2\varphi' = 2\psi' = \pi/2$, it follows from Eqs. (52.7) and (52.8) that the two refractive indices and the two absorption coefficients become identical in the limiting case. It is seen that along this singular axis only one wave is propagated as in the case of absorbing inactive crystals, but this wave is elliptically polarised.

In the case when $\chi = \pi/4$ and $\Delta = k$ we again get a singular direction where only the elliptically polarised state E_2 (Fig. 52b) is propagated unchanged. This differs only in the sense of its description from the ellipse E_1 which is propagated along the other singular axis associated with the same optic axis. A similar pair of singular axes wil be associated with the other optic axis.

When an elliptic vibration orthogonal to that propagated without change of form along a singular axis is incident in that direction it will not be reflected away, but will be propagated with a progressive change in its state of polarisation towards the state which is propagated unchanged.

VI. The matrix method of solving electro-magnetic equations in anisotropic media[1].

56. The refractive index matrix. *α) Description of the matrix.* The method we have hitherto followed in the previous sections for solving the electromagnetic equations has been to seek homogeneously polarised plane-wave solutions of the customary form (27.4). A limitation of this method is revealed for directions of propagation along singular axes in absorbing crystals where only one such solution is obtained and not two, as is usually the case (see e.g. Sects. 49, 55). Hence the procedure leaves unanswered the question as to what will happen when light in any other state of polarisation is incident in the direction of a singular axis. Though this problem was solved by the method of superposition, it must be capable of being handled directly and more rigorously by the electromagnetic theory. For this purpose we discard the restriction of seeking plane wave solutions of constant polarisation.

We wish to write down the equation to a more general type of plane wave propagated along an arbitrary direction Oz in an anisotropic medium. We however continue to seek solutions for which the time factor is $\exp i\omega t$ so that[2]

$$\frac{\partial \vec{D}}{\partial t} = i\,\omega\,\vec{D} \tag{56.1}$$

and we use the matrix representation of Jones (discussed in Sect. 13) according to which the state of vibration $\vec{D}$ at the plane z would in general be a linear *vector* function of the state at $z=0$ being related by the matrix M of (13.3). The propagation through an infinitesimal distance however is described by the matrix N, the vibration at the plane $z+dz$ being a linear vector function of the vibration at the plane z. In fact by substituting (15.4) in (13.3) and differentiating we have

$$\frac{\partial \vec{D}}{\partial z} = \mathsf{N}\,\vec{D}. \tag{56.2}$$

In order to see the similarity of this equation with that satisfied by the usual plane wave we write (56.2) as

$$\frac{\partial \vec{D}}{\partial z} = -i\,\frac{\omega}{c}\,\mathsf{n}\,\vec{D}. \tag{56.3}$$

This resembles exactly the equation satisfied by the usual type of plane wave of the form (27.4) with the following difference; the refractive index n has been replaced by the refractive index matrix n in order that the same equation may represent the most general plane wave that can be propagated in a homogeneous anisotropic medium. By differentiating (56.3) with respect to t and (56.1) with respect to z we get

$$\frac{\partial^2 \vec{D}}{\partial t^2} = c^2\,\mathsf{n}^{-2}\,\frac{\partial^2 \vec{D}}{\partial z^2}. \tag{56.4}$$

---

[1] R.C. Jones: J. Opt. Soc. Amer. **45**, 126 (1956). — S. Pancharatnam: Proc. Ind. Acad. Sci. A **48**, 227 (1958).

[2] The displacement vector is here written as a two-dimensional vector $\vec{D}$ since it lies on the wave front and it can be described by its x and y components.

This resembles the usual form of the wave equation to a plane disturbance except that the square of the velocity has been replaced by the matrix $c^2 \mathsf{n}^{-2}$. Our problem is to determine the refractive index matrix n or alternatively the matrix n^{-2} satisfying MAXWELL's equations consistent with the properties of the medium.

In Sect. 27 we replaced the operator ∇ by $-i\omega n\mathbf{s}/c$ since solutions of the form (27.4) were sought. More generally $\nabla = \boldsymbol{k}\frac{\partial}{\partial z}$ where $\boldsymbol{k}$ denotes the unit vector along the z-axis (which is here taken as the direction of propagation). The relation obtained by eliminating $\boldsymbol{H}$ between the MAXWELL's equations takes the form (see Sect. 26)

$$\ddot{\boldsymbol{D}} = c^2 \frac{\partial^2}{\partial z^2}\left[\boldsymbol{E} - \boldsymbol{k}(\boldsymbol{k}\cdot\boldsymbol{E})\right] \tag{56.5}$$

and writing the components of this equation we have

$$\ddot{D}_z = 0, \qquad \ddot{D}_x = c^2 \frac{\partial^2 E_x}{\partial z^2}, \qquad \ddot{D}_y = c^2 \frac{\partial^2 E_y}{\partial z^2} \tag{56.6}$$

or

$$\frac{\partial^2 \vec{D}}{\partial t^2} = c^2 \frac{\partial^2 \vec{E}}{\partial z^2}. \tag{56.7}$$

The properties of the medium can be expressed in the form

$$\vec{E} = \mathsf{A}\vec{D} \tag{56.8}$$

where the components of A can be written down by comparison with the complex analogue of (38.7) as follows:

$$\left.\begin{aligned} A_{11} &= \bar{a}_{11}, & A_{12} &= \bar{a}_{12} + i\bar{\Gamma}_3, \\ A_{21} &= \bar{a}_{12} - i\bar{\Gamma}_3, & A_{22} &= \bar{a}_{22}. \end{aligned}\right\} \tag{56.8a}$$

From (56.8) and (56.7) we have

$$\frac{\partial^2 \vec{D}}{\partial t^2} = c^2 \mathsf{A} \frac{\partial^2 \vec{D}}{\partial z^2} \tag{56.9}$$

and comparing with (56.4) we have

$$\mathsf{n}^{-2} = \mathsf{A} \tag{56.10}$$

or

$$\mathsf{n} = \mathsf{A}^{-\frac{1}{2}}. \tag{56.11}$$

Hence if we write (56.8) in the form

$$\vec{D} = \varepsilon\vec{E} \tag{56.12}$$

where

$$\varepsilon = \mathsf{A}^{-1} \tag{56.13}$$

we get the most elegant result[1]

$$\mathsf{n}^2 = \varepsilon \tag{56.14}$$

analogous to the result $n^2 = \varepsilon$ in an isotropic medium. Hence the refractive index matrix n or alternatively the matrix n^{-2} can be determined from (56.10) and (56.11).

Though the wave equations (56.4) and (56.3) describe in general a disturbance propagated with change of polarisation this is not always the case. Clearly they

[1] Only the physically significant square root of the matrices in (56.11) and (56.14) are to be taken. See R.C. JONES: J. Opt. Soc. Amer. **46**, 126 (1956).

We have here considered the case of a homogeneous medium. For the corresponding relation when N is not independent of z see the paper by R.C. JONES quoted above.

reduce to the customary equations satisfied by a homogeneously polarised wave for those *particular* states of $\vec{D}$ for which

$$\mathsf{A}\vec{D} = \bar{v}^2 \vec{D}, \tag{56.15}$$

$$\mathsf{A}^{-\frac{1}{2}}\vec{D} = \bar{n}\vec{D}, \tag{56.16}$$

where $\bar{v}$ is the velocity, $\bar{n}$ the refractive index of the wave. The Eq. (56.15) is usually satisfied for two states $\vec{D}$—the eigen vectors of the matrix A—with two corresponding values of $\bar{v}^2$, the eigenvalues of A; these may be determined as in Sect. 26 since the Eqs. (26.8) previously used are merely the components of the vector equation (56.15), giving thereby the connection with our previous method of solving the electromagnetic equations. Alternatively we could start with Eq. (56.16) and determine the states of polarisation of the waves which should be eigenvectors of the refractive index matrix $\mathsf{n} = \mathsf{A}^{-\frac{1}{2}}$, the corresponding eigenvalues being the complex refractive indices of the waves.

A singular axis represents a special direction for which the matrix A (and correspondingly the refractive index matrix n) has only one eigenvector and correspondingly in this case the matrix itself cannot be reconstructed from a knowledge of its eigenvectors and its eigenvalues but this does not in principle lead to any difficulty in directly determining $\bar{v}^2$ from (56.11). From the present standpoint, along a singular direction, as indeed along any other direction, we can have disturbances propagated with a progressive change in the state of polarisation. The peculiar feature of a singular direction however is that such a disturbance cannot in turn be described as a sum of two plane waves with constant states of polarisation.

Also, while in a general direction, the state of polarisation of the wave undergoes an oscillatory change (the representative point on the Poincaré sphere going around the sphere), along a singular axis it tends asymptotically to the only state propagated unchanged along it.

β) Relationship of the matrix method with the method of superposition. The components of the two-dimensional matrix A are identical with the corresponding components of the three-dimensional matrix $[a]$ relating $\boldsymbol{E}$ to $\boldsymbol{D}$ by $\boldsymbol{E} = [a]\boldsymbol{D}$[1]. Comparing with the complex analogue of (38.7) we may write

$$\mathsf{A} = \mathsf{a} + i\,\mathsf{b} - (\gamma + i\,\beta)\,\mathsf{S}\left(\tfrac{1}{2}\pi\right). \tag{56.17}$$

Here the components of the two-dimensional matrices a and b are identical with the corresponding components of the index and absorption tensors and γ and β are the parameters of optical rotation and circular dichroism in (50.11) and (50.12) and

$$\mathsf{S}\left(\tfrac{1}{2}\pi\right) = \begin{pmatrix} 0 & -1 \\ 1 & 0 \end{pmatrix}, \tag{56.18}$$

the rotation matrix $\mathsf{S}(\beta)$ of (13.6) with $\beta = \frac{1}{2}\pi$.

Our previous procedure has been in effect to determine the refractive index matrix n indirectly by determining the eigenvectors and eigenvalues of the matrix n^{-2}. The refractive index matrix n is also directly given by $\mathsf{A}^{-\frac{1}{2}}$. Though this could be solved exactly, we obtain a direct connection with the method of superposition adopted previously by noting that, when the birefringence is not

---

[1] A corresponding statement cannot be made regarding the relationship between the components of the 2×2 matrix $\boldsymbol{\varepsilon}$ and the components of the three dimensional matrix in $\boldsymbol{D} = [\varepsilon]\boldsymbol{E}$ since $\boldsymbol{E}$ does not lie on the wavefront.

high, we have to the first order of approximation,

$$A^{-\frac{1}{2}} = n - i\,k + \overline{R}\,S(\tfrac{1}{2}\pi) \tag{56.19}$$

where

$$n = a^{-\frac{1}{2}}, \qquad k = \frac{1}{v_m^3}\,b\,, \qquad \overline{R} = \frac{1}{v_m^3}\,\overline{\gamma} = \frac{\lambda}{\pi}\,(\varrho + i\,\sigma) \tag{56.20}$$

[compare with Eq. (51.5)].

Thus we have expressed the refractive index matrix as the sum of symmetric and antisymmetric parts in the form (56.19). This decomposition is very closely related to the splitting of the N matrix into the sum of eight Θ matrices considered in Sect. 15. As has been explained there, such a decomposition is the analytical expression of the method of superposition. It may be remarked that the physical interpretation of the relation (56.20) is the following: the operation of linear birefringence given by n is determined by the section of the index ellipsoid (47.3); the operation of linear dichroism given by k is determined by the section of the absorption ellipsoid by the relation (47.4); the optical rotatory power ϱ and the coefficient of circular dichroism σ are determined from the surfaces of optical rotation and circular dichroism (51.7) and (51.8). With these as postulates the consequences of the method of superposition have been developed using the Poincaré sphere.

The method of superposition as we have adopted is equivalent to solving Eq. (56.16) taking $A^{-\frac{1}{2}}$ to be given by (56.20) and (56.19). Such a procedure can be seen to be formally similar to solving Eq. (56.15) together with (56.17) except that in the latter case we have $\overline{v}$, a, b, $\overline{\gamma}$ occurring in place of $\overline{n}$, n, k, and $\overline{R}$. Hence by following such a replacement scheme, toevery relation derived by the method of superposition we obtain a relation which is exactly the same as that derived from the electromagnetic theory or vice versa[1]. Such a procedure shows that the state of polarisation of the waves derived from the method of superposition must be identical with those given in (50.10) by the electromagnetic theory and hence can be expressed more conveniently by the parameters φ, ψ on the Poincaré sphere. The refractive indices and the absorption coefficients have to be altered from the forms (52.5) and (52.6) to (52.9) and (52.10) so that the results obtained from the electromagnetic theory are also transformed to an elegant form.

C. Optical phenomena in crystalline media.

I. Reflection and refraction at boundaries.

57. General formulation. The laws relating to the phenomena of reflection and refraction can be derived by solving the electromagnetic equations of propagation, subject to the specified boundary condition, and the properties of the two media on either side of the boundary. The subject has been treated in good detail by POCKELS [*2*], DRUDE [*3*] and SZIVESSY [*1*] and therefore only the essential principles will be outlined here.

We shall denote the first medium in which the wave is incident as medium 1 and the second as medium 2. Both of them are supposed to be anisotropic in general. Suppose that the plane of the boundary is the xy-plane and the normal to it is the z-axis. Let the direction of the incident wave normal be in the xz plane making an angle ϑ_0 with Oz. Denote a unit vector along the wave normal

[1] S. PANCHARATNAM: Proc. Ind. Acad. Sci. A **48**, 227 (1958).

by $\mathbf{s}_0$. Let $\mathbf{s}_1$, $\mathbf{s}_2$ be unit vectors of the reflected wave in the first medium and refracted wave in the second medium. Then, the electric vectors in the three waves are given by

$$\left.\begin{aligned} \boldsymbol{E}_0 &= \boldsymbol{A}_0\, e^{2\pi i[\nu t - n_0(\mathbf{s}_0\cdot\boldsymbol{r})]}, \\ \boldsymbol{E}_1 &= \boldsymbol{A}_1\, e^{2\pi i[\nu t - n_1(\mathbf{s}_1\cdot\boldsymbol{r}) + \delta_1]}, \\ \boldsymbol{E}_2 &= \boldsymbol{A}_2\, e^{2\pi i[\nu t - n_2(\mathbf{s}_2\cdot\boldsymbol{r}) + \delta_2]}. \end{aligned}\right\} \tag{57.1}$$

In an anisotropic medium, there would in general be two waves propagated along any direction with two different refractive indices. For the present, we assume that the incident wave is polarised with its state of polarisation corresponding to one of the two waves propagated along that direction. Then, n_0 is unique, but n_1 and n_2 are in general double-valued functions of the direction of propagation. At the boundary, we must have the conditions

$$\left.\begin{aligned} E_{0x} + E_{1x} &= E_{2x}, \qquad H_{0x} + H_{1x} = H_{2x}, \\ E_{0y} + E_{1y} &= E_{2y}, \qquad H_{0y} + H_{1y} = H_{2y}. \end{aligned}\right\} \tag{57.2}$$

It is obvious that these equations would hold for all points (x, y) on the boundary only if the exponential terms are the same in all the three terms, which gives the following conditions:

(a) $\delta_1 = \delta_2 = 0$ or π i.e. if there is a phase change, it can only reverse the amplitude, without producing any phase shift as such;

(b) the vectors $\mathbf{s}_0$, $\mathbf{s}_1$, $\mathbf{s}_2$ and Oz are coplanar, i.e., the reflected and refracted wave normals remain in the plane of incidence, and

(c) if ϑ_0, ϑ_1, ϑ_2 are the angles made by the incident, reflected and refracted wave normals with Oz, then

$$n_0 \sin\vartheta_0 = n_1 \sin\vartheta_1 = n_2 \sin\vartheta_2. \tag{57.3}$$

These laws of reflection and refraction are similar to those for isotropic media, but they differ in important details. Thus, the wave normals of the reflected and refracted waves remain in the plane of incidence, but the corresponding rays need not lie in this plane, as will be shown in the next section. Also, since n_0 is in general not equal to n_1 in an anisotropic medium, the angle of incidence is not equal to the angle of reflection. Further, we should expect to have in general *two* reflected and *two* refracted waves, even when there is only a single incident wave with a definite refractive index. If, however, the incident wave is unpolarised or has a general state of polarisation, this would be split up into two waves in the medium with different refractive indices, and therefore we should expect *four* reflected and *four* refracted waves. We shall denote by A, B the two polarised waves along the incident direction and by P_1, Q_1 and P_2, Q_2 the two polarised waves along the reflected and refracted directions. Then it follows that the directions of propagation of the four waves of each type are given by

$$\left.\begin{aligned} \sin\vartheta_{AP_1} &= \frac{n_{P_1}}{n_A}\sin\vartheta_0, \qquad \sin\vartheta_{AP_2} = \frac{n_{P_2}}{n_A}\sin\vartheta_0, \\ \sin\vartheta_{AQ_1} &= \frac{n_{Q_1}}{n_A}\sin\vartheta_0, \qquad \sin\vartheta_{AQ_2} = \frac{n_{Q_2}}{n_A}\sin\vartheta_0, \\ \sin\vartheta_{BP_1} &= \frac{n_{P_1}}{n_B}\sin\vartheta_0, \qquad \sin\vartheta_{BP_2} = \frac{n_{P_2}}{n_B}\sin\vartheta_0, \\ \sin\vartheta_{BQ_1} &= \frac{n_{Q_1}}{n_B}\sin\vartheta_0, \qquad \sin\vartheta_{BQ_2} = \frac{n_{Q_2}}{n_B}\sin\vartheta_0. \end{aligned}\right\} \tag{57.4}$$

It is obvious that the above laws do not depend on the exact form of the boundary conditions, but follow directly from the condition that the equations must hold for all points on the boundary. If now, the Eqs. (57.2) are applied, one can also obtain relations between the amplitudes of the incident wave and of the reflected and refracted waves. For a definite polarisation of the incident wave, the directions of propagation and states of polarisation of the two reflected and the two refracted waves are first obtained from (57.4). Feeding these data into the four equations (57.2), the amplitudes of the four waves can be solved for in the terms of the amplitude of the incident wave.

If the first medium is isotropic, then there is only one reflected wave and two refracted waves. The reflected wave follows the usual law of reflection as far as direction is concerned, but its intensity and state of polarisation are affected by the anisotropic nature of the second medium. This result has been applied for measuring the optical properties of a crystal from a study of the light reflected from its surface and the theory of the phenomena is discussed in Sect. 60.

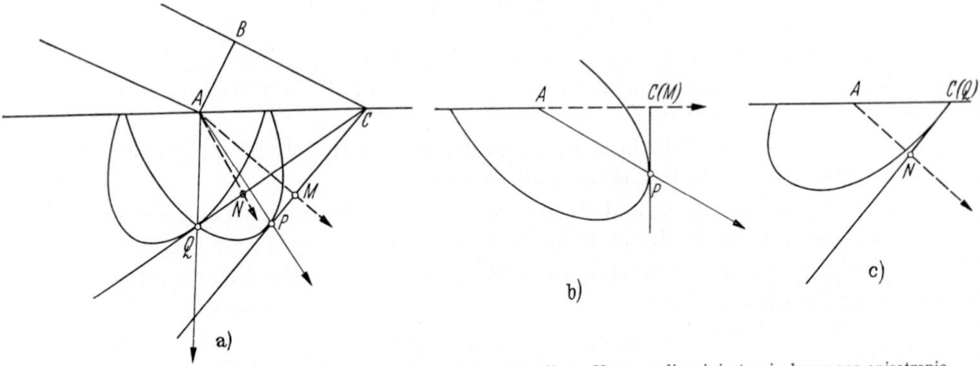

Fig. 53a—c. Total reflection at the boundary of an anisotropic medium. Upper medium is isotropic, lower one anisotropic, AC being the dividing line. (a) Huygens construction for wave propagation in anisotropic medium. AB is the incident wave front and AN and AM represent normals to the waves propagated in the medium. AP and AQ are the ray directions. Two cases when total reflection takes place are illustrated in (b) and (c). (b) When the wave normal (AM) coincides with AC, or (c) when the ray direction (AQ) coincides with AC.

58. HUYGENS' construction and total reflection. Although the relation between the angle of incidence and of reflection or refraction of the wave is formally very simple even in anisotropic crystals, the actual determination of the direction of the reflected or refracted ray is not so straightforward. The method of obtaining this is by a generalisation of the well-known HUYGENS' construction to anisotropic media (see Sect. 27). If we consider the secondary waves radiating from a point A on the boundary into the second medium, then the envelope of the wave at any instant of time will be a surface of two sheets, the so-called wave-surface or ray-surface of Sect. 27. Let AB be the wavefront of the incident plane wave (Fig. 53a), which covers the region AC of the surface, of unit length. Then the incident wave takes a time $t = n_0 \sin\vartheta_0/c$ to reach C after it has reached A. During this interval, the secondary wave from A would have spread out, and its position would be given by the wave surface corresponding to t. The secondary waves from points in between A and C would have spread to intermediate distances proportional to their distance from C and the two resultant refracted wave-fronts would thus be the tangent planes through C to the two sheets of the wave surface. The directions AM and AN perpendicular to these lie in the plane of incidence and give the directions of the wave normals of the two refracted waves. On the other hand, the two ray directions are given by the lines AP, AQ, joining A to the two points where the tangent planes touch the wave surface These do not, in general, lie in the plane of reflection.

A similar situation holds for the reflected waves and rays also, if the first medium is anisotropic. The two reflected wavefronts are parallel to the tangent planes through C to the two sheets of the wave surface radiating from A, after a time t. The ray directions again need not be parallel to the wave normals and may not even lie in the plane of reflection.

An interesting consequence of these is in relation to total internal reflection in anisotropic media when the medium on the other side is isotropic. In Fig. 53a, let n_0 be the refractive index of the isotropic medium, which we may first consider to be greater than all the three principal indices of the crystal. Then, there would in general be two refracted waves in the second medium. Suppose that the angle of incidence is increased. Then the time interval t increases and the size of the wave surface also increases. Thus the point P and Q would approach C and the wave normals AM and AN would also approach the direction AC tangential to the surface of separation.

Considering the point P it is clear that when it reaches the position shown in Fig. 53b, the wave normal AM coincides with AC. For larger angles of incidence, the wave cannot propagate into the second medium and is therefore totally reflected. This condition for total reflection is analogous to that for isotropic media and is given by the condition

$$n_0 \sin \varphi_1 = n_1 \tag{58.1}$$

where, however, n_1 is the *wave* refractive index along the direction AC.

On the other hand, if we consider the point Q, it is clear that when it reaches the point C (Fig. 53c), the refracted wave normal AN is not tangential to the surface of separation, but the ray direction AQ is tangential. For larger angles of incidence, the wave surface with A as origin goes beyond C and so no tangent can be drawn to it from C. In other words, there will be no refracted wave corresponding to this sheet of the wave surface, and there will be total reflection. The critical angle for total reflection is now defined by the condition that the ray is tangential to the surface of separation, i.e.,

$$n_0 \sin \varphi_2 = n_{r_2} \tag{58.2}$$

where now n_{r_2} is the *ray* refractive index along the direction AC.

Thus from the boundary between an isotropic and an anisotropic medium, total reflection may occur if *either* the wave refractive index *or* the ray refractive index satisfies Eq. (58.1) or (58.2). Which one is relevant to a particular situation depends on the shape of the wave surface, and the fact whether the ray or the wave normal is at a smaller angle to the surface, near the critical condition. It is obvious that, if AC coincides with a principal axis, then the ray and the wave normal directions coincide and so the two conditions are equivalent.

If we now denote by n_1 and n_2 the wave or the ray refractive indices, whichever is smaller, for the two sheets of the wave surface along the direction AC, then it follows that

if $n_1 < n_2 < n_0$ there are two critical angles,

if $n_1 < n_0 < n_2$ there is only one critical angle,

the other polarised component being always refracted and if $n_0 < n_1 < n_2$ total reflection does not occur for any angle of incidence in the isotropic medium.

The above results may be used to obtain the principal refractive indices of a crystal from measurement on the critical angles for total reflection from a parallel plate of the crystal[1]. The isotropic medium is chosen such that its refractive index n_0 is larger that the largest index γ of the crystal. The plane of incidence is kept fixed while measurements are made for different settings, rotating the crystal plate in its own plane. Both the indices n_1 and n_2 would then be found to vary between a maximum and minimum over a full rotation of the crystal. It is readily verified that the minimum of n_1 will be α, the maximum of n_2 will be γ, and either the maximum of n_1 or the minimum of n_2 will be β (see Sect. 82ζ for the experimental method).

59. Twin plane reflection phenomenon exhibited by some minerals. α) *Calcite and fascicular gypsum.* The beautiful iridescence displayed by the twin plane reflection in calcite is well known and has been treated in great detail by FRAILICH, OSLOFF, RAYLEIGH[2]. When a distant luminous source is viewed through a rhomb of calcite containing a twin plane, three images of the source may be seen. The central image, which is undeviated, is colourless while the two outer ones display vivid colours. The intensity, the colour and the angular separation of the images are markedly dependent on the direction in the crystal along which the source is viewed.

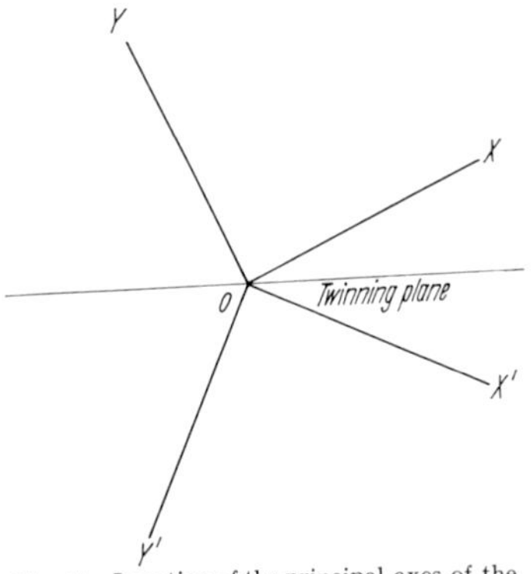

Fig. 54. Location of the principal axes of the index ellipsoid in the symmetry plane in $KClO_3$ twins.

The explanation of this phenomenon is quite simple. When a beam of light traverses a layer of calcite which has on either side of it crystalline matter in different orientations, the incident wave would be both reflected and refracted. Since the medium is birefringent, the incident beam would split into two and associated with each of these, there would be two reflected and refracted beams. Of the four refracted beams possible, two emerge from the twin layer in the same direction as the incident beam in the case of calcite (since it is a uniaxial crystal). Hence for the most general direction of incidence, although there would be four reflected pencils, there occur only three refracted pencils. The central undeviated ray appears in the same direction for all wavelengths, while the dispersion of the refractive indices of calcite manifests itself by the later deviated images being drawn out in the form of spectra.

One can also show that the twin plane reflections actually vanish when the plane of incidence coincides with a plane of symmetry. Fig. 54 represents the location of the principal axes of the index ellipsoid in the symmetry plane, OX and OY referring to the upper side and OX' and OY' to the lower side of a twinning plane. OZ and OZ' coincide and thay are normal to the plane of the paper, coinciding with the two-fold axes. The upper and lower parts being mirror images, the coefficient of reflection at the boundary for a given angle of incidence would be the same whether the incidence is from above or below. But according to the principle of reversibility the reflection coefficient should be of opposite signs according as the wave is incident on one side or the other of the boundary. As these two results are contradictory, the coefficient of reflection should be zero

---

[1] W. H. WOLLASTON: Phil. Trans. Roy. Soc. Lond. **92**, 381 (1802).

[2] See POCKELS' Lehrbuch [2] or WALKER [5] for summary of earlier work. See also C. V. RAMAN and A. K. RAMDAS: Proc. Ind. Acad. Sci. A **40**, 1 (1954).

for all angles of incidence and all states of polarisation when the plane of incidence coincides with the symmetry plane.

An extremely striking variation of the phenomenon described above has been observed[1] in the case of a variety of gypsum. Gypsum is a monoclinic crystal and it is known to have a fibrous modification (satin spar). But another variety, *fascicular gypsum* is found which consists of an aggregate of crystalline rods having their axes of symmetry nearly parallel to each other while the other two axes show a range of variation. Optical studies indicate that in the best specimens the rods can take two orientations, in both of which one of the axes of the index ellipsoid is unchanged, while the two other axes are approximately interchanged.

When such a plate is held close to the eye and a distance source of light is viewed normally through it, a brilliant circle of light is seen and the source of light appears at the centre with an overlaid diffraction pattern of concentric circles. As the plate is slowly tilted away from the normal setting the outer circle enlarges and the inner pattern enlarges first to form a second ring and later as the tilt is increased a third ring appears (Fig. 55a). The intensity over each circle varies considerably. The circles do not display any colours when white light is viewed, suggesting that their origin is due to internal reflection.

Fig. 55a. The circles of internal reflection in fascicular gypsum. Note the source being visible as a bright point on the second circle.

It is well known that if a pencil of rays is incident on an isotropic cylindrical rod in a direction making an angle ϑ with its generator, the reflected rays lie on a right circular cone whose semivertical angle is ϑ and the axis of the cone is parallel to that of the cylinder. The direction of incidence would therefore be a generator of the cone. If now, as in the present case, reflections take place at inter-crystalline boundaries within a birefringent solid, the angles of incidence and reflection need not necessarily be equal as a consequence of the planes of polarisation and the wave velocities being different for the incident and reflected pencils. Hence four cones of rays must emerge from the cylinder. But in the case of fascicular gypsum, since the surface of the plate is normal to the common axis of the index ellipsoids, two of the reflected rays (whose planes of polarisation are perpendicular to each other) would obey the ordinary laws of reflection and would therefore emerge along identical directions. Hence the four reflection cones to be expected in the most general case, degenerate to three. The central one corresponds to the case where the ordinary laws of reflection are obeyed; the direction of incidence being a generator of this cone, the source should appear as a luminous point on it. The first and the third circles correspond respectively to the two cases when the angle of reflection is less than and greater than the angle of incidence.

[1] C.V. RAMAN and A.K. RAMDAS: Proc. Ind. Acad. Sci. A **39**, 153 (1954).

The polarisation characters of the rings may be briefly described as follows: If the incident pencil on entering the plate divides into two pencils with vibrations along two mutually perpendicular directions, (OX and OZ, say) then in the first circle the vibration direction changes from OX to OZ on reflection, while in the third circle it changes from OZ to OX. In the central circle OX remains as OX and OZ as OZ.

The reflecting power at the inter-crystalline boundary would obviously be a function of the azimuth of the incident light, it being zero when the plane of incidence coincides with the plane of symmetry in the crystal. It may be remarked that as this substance has a peculiar preferred orientation it also displays many of the phenomena to be treated in Sect. 61.

β) Iridescence of potassium chlorate. The spectacular iridescence of certain crystals of potassium chlorate ($KClO_3$) when viewed in white light has long been known. Crystals of this substance are strongly birefringent (belonging to the holohedral monoclinic class) and they crystallise in tabular forms. The tablet face (c face) contains the two-fold axis of symmetry with the mirror plane perpendicular to it.

STOKES[1] was the first to recognise that the iridescence had its origin in the reflection of light at twin plane boundaries within the crystal. Rayleigh concluded that a single twin plane layer was quite insufficient to explain the observed effects and postulated that the crystals exhibiting this phenomenon must be polysynthetically twinned parallel to the tablet face causing the medium to be regularly stratified. Hence for a given angle of incidence the intensity of the reflection would be a maximum for wavelengths at which the reflections by successive stratifications reinforce each other because of the agreement in phase. The maximum should therefore be a function of the angle of incidence. This explains the sequence of changes in the colour (the narrow spectral band shifting towards the shorter wavelengths) as the angle of incidence is increased. In all cases however, irrespective of the angle of incidence, the coloured reflection vanishes completely when the plane of incidence coincides with the plane of symmetry in the crystal. The reflections reappear, although feebly when the plane of incidence deviates even slightly from the plane of symmetry. Under these conditions, there would be a rotation of 90° in the plane of polarisation of the incident light. A light wave polarised in the plane of incidence would be reflected as a wave polarised in a perpendicular plane and vice versa. We shall for convenience call this as a reversal of the plane of polarisation.

Since the crystal is highly birefringent other extremely interesting phenomena have been observed by RAMAN and KRISHNAMURTHY[2]. As we have seen previously (Sects. 57, 59α) there would be four reflected streams of light and hence there would be four wavelengths of the maximum intensity in the spectrum, their positions being determined by their respective optical paths; of these four, two would be polarised in the normal manner while the other two would have reversed polarisation. The relative intensities would vary with the angle which the plane of incidence makes with the plane of symmetry. When the angle is small, there would be only two maxima of the latter type while if the angle is large all four would appear with comparable intensities (see Fig. 55b).

When the plane of incidence is perpendicular to the plane of symmetry the total optical paths of the two pencils which emerge after reflection with their

---

[1] For a summary of earlier work see POCKELS [2].

[2] C. V. RAMAN and D. KRISHNAMURTHY: Proc. Ind. Acad. Sci. A **36**, 315—334 (1952); A **38**, 261 (1953).

planes of polarisation rotated would be the same. This can be very simply seen as symmetry permits us to deduce the optical path of one from that of the other by just interchanging the path of the incident and the reflected rays. Therefore for this setting two out of the four maxima of intensity would coincide. It can also be shown that if the alternate layers of the stratifications are of equal thickness then each layer would be related to the one below it by a mirror not only in atomic structure but also in thickness, the optical paths of these two pencils showing reverse polarisation would be the same irrespective of the azimuth of the plane of incidence. This however, would not be the case when the alternate layers are not of equal thickness. Hence the presence of four spectral maxima in any position is an indication of the inequality in the thickness of the alternate layers.

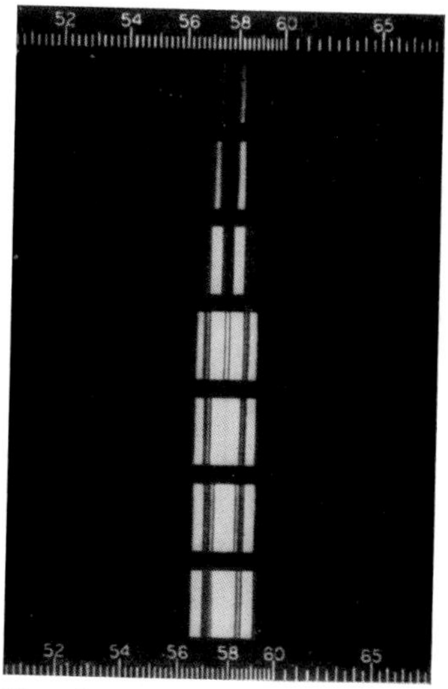

Fig. 55b. Reflection spectra of iridescent potassium chlorate. The angle of incidence of the white light is kept constant and azimuth varied in steps commencing from a setting nearly coinciding with the plane of symmetry and ending with one perpendicular to it. The transition from a doublet to a quartet, thence to a triplet may be noted.

If diffuse *monochromatic* light is allowed to fall on a specimen simultaneously in all directions, the resulting effect would be total reflection in all directions along which all the reflections reinforce each other due to the agreement in their phase. For a particular order of interference such directions will lie on the generators of cones whose cross sections would be circles if the medium is isotropic and ellipses if it is birefringent. In the present case there must be four cones of total reflection of elliptic shape two having the normal type of polarisation and two of the reversed type of polarisation. Each cone will be accompanied by secondary maxima of interference. Such reflection spectra have been observed as bright curves on a dark field when monochromatic source is used. If however, the source is viewed through the crystal, corresponding extinction curves are seen as dark bands on a bright field. The pattern vanishes in the symmetry plane of the crystal and has its maximum clarity in the perpendicular plane. Hence the pattern observed consists of two pairs of crescents with their tips narrowing to sharp points fading off gradually as the symmetry plane is approached. Of the four components of extinction and reflection bands, two are polarised with their vibration direction parallel to the symmetry plane while the other two are perpendicular to it.

60. Reflection at the surface of an absorbing anisotropic crystal. The first medium, from which light is incident on the surface of the anisotropic crystal, is assumed to be isotropic and non-absorbing. The formulae for the intensity and polarisation of the reflected and refracted waves in the case of transparent crystals were derived long ago by MacCullagh and Neumann and they are available in Pockels' Lehrbuch ([*2*], S. 183—211) and Szivessy's article ([*1*], pp. 717—751) and is therefore not given here. The theory has been extended to absorbing crystals by Berek[1], who has also devised several methods of investigating the optical properties of such crystals from a study of the light reflected from their

[1] M. Berek: Z. Kristallogr. **76**, 396 (1931); **77**, 1 (1931); **89**, 125, 144 (1934); **93**, 116 (1936); **96**, 357 (1937). — N. Jb. Min. Geol. Paläont. A **64**, 132 (1931).

surface. It is only possible to discuss some of the more important results obtained in this very interesting series of papers. The original papers may be referred to for the detailed derivations and also for a review of earlier work in this field.

α) Oblique incidence. The general solution of the boundary equations for absorbing media is formally the same as for transparent media, except that the refractive index is complex, and consequently all the quantities involved, such as amplitudes of electric vectors, azimuth of polarisation etc. are also complex. The significance of the complex nature of these quantities is explained below. Complex quantities will be denoted by symbols in bold face italics[1].

As with non-absorbing crystals, there would be, in absorbing crystals also, two refracted waves in general for any angle of incidence, which may be denoted by suffix 1 and 2, the former referring to the faster and the latter to the slower wave. Let i be the angle of incidence in the first medium of refractive index n_0 and let p and s denote the two components parallel and normal to the plane of incidence. If $\boldsymbol{A}$ is the amplitude of the incident wave and $\boldsymbol{R}$ that of the reflected wave, then

$$\left.\begin{aligned} \boldsymbol{R}_p &= \frac{A_p(\boldsymbol{R}_{p_1}\boldsymbol{A}_{s_2} - \boldsymbol{R}_{p_2}\boldsymbol{A}_{s_1}) - A_s(\boldsymbol{R}_{p_1}\boldsymbol{A}_{p_2} - \boldsymbol{R}_{p_2}\boldsymbol{A}_{p_1})}{(\boldsymbol{A}_{p_1}\boldsymbol{A}_{s_2} - \boldsymbol{A}_{p_2}\boldsymbol{A}_{s_1})}, \\ \boldsymbol{R}_s &= \frac{A_p(\boldsymbol{R}_{s_1}\boldsymbol{A}_{s_2} - \boldsymbol{R}_{s_2}\boldsymbol{A}_{s_1}) - A_s(\boldsymbol{R}_{s_1}\boldsymbol{A}_{p_2} - \boldsymbol{R}_{s_2}\boldsymbol{A}_{p_1})}{(\boldsymbol{A}_{p_1}\boldsymbol{A}_{s_2} - \boldsymbol{A}_{p_2}\boldsymbol{A}_{s_1})} \end{aligned}\right\} \tag{60.1}$$

where

$$\left.\begin{aligned} 2\boldsymbol{A}_{ph} &= \frac{\cos\boldsymbol{r}_h\cos\boldsymbol{\delta}_h}{\cos i} + \frac{\sin\boldsymbol{r}_h\cos\boldsymbol{\delta}_h}{\sin i}, \\ 2\boldsymbol{R}_{ph} &= \frac{\cos\boldsymbol{r}_h\cos\boldsymbol{\delta}_h}{\cos i} + \frac{\sin\boldsymbol{r}_h\cos\boldsymbol{\delta}_h}{\sin i}, \\ 2\boldsymbol{A}_{sh} &= \sin\boldsymbol{\delta}_h + \frac{\sin\boldsymbol{r}_k}{\sin i\cos i}\boldsymbol{m}_h, \\ 2\boldsymbol{R}_{sh} &= \sin\boldsymbol{\delta}_h - \frac{\sin\boldsymbol{r}_h}{\sin i\cos i}\boldsymbol{m}_h. \end{aligned}\right\} \tag{60.2}$$

Here, $\boldsymbol{r}_1, \boldsymbol{r}_2$ are the (complex) angles of refraction of the two refracted waves, $\boldsymbol{\delta}$ is the azimuth of polarisation of the refracted wave with respect to the plane of incidence and $\boldsymbol{m}$ stands for

$$\boldsymbol{m}_h = \cos\boldsymbol{r}_h\sin\boldsymbol{\delta}_h + \sin\boldsymbol{r}_h\tan\boldsymbol{\tau}_h, \tag{60.3}$$

where $\boldsymbol{\tau}_h$ is the angle between the ray and the wave normal, which may be obtained in terms of the components of the index tensor and the direction cosines of the wave normal.

The complex nature of the angle of refraction arises from the relation

$$\left.\begin{aligned} n_0\sin i &= \boldsymbol{n}_h\sin\boldsymbol{r}_h \\ &= n_h(1 - i\varkappa_h)\sin\boldsymbol{r}_h. \end{aligned}\right\} \tag{60.4}$$

The complex azimuth of polarisation means that the wave is not linearly, but elliptically polarised. If χ is the azimuth of the linearly polarised wave to which this is brought by a compensator producing a phase difference Δ between the perpendicular and parallel components, then

$$\tan\boldsymbol{\delta} = \tan\chi\, e^{i\Delta}. \tag{60.5}$$

---

[1] Note that this differs from the convention followed in other sections of this article. Further $\varkappa$ is also used in a different sense in this section (see Sect. 45).

Alternatively, if λ is the azimuth of the major axis and ω the ellipticity, i.e., $\tan\omega = b/a$ then λ and ω are related to χ and Δ as follows:

$$\left.\begin{aligned} \cos 2\chi &= \cos 2\omega \cos 2\lambda, \\ \sin\Delta &= \sin 2\omega/\sin 2\chi, \\ \cos\Delta &= \frac{\sin 2\lambda \cos 2\omega}{\sin 2\chi}. \end{aligned}\right\} \tag{60.6}$$

Eq. (60.5) then becomes

$$\tan\boldsymbol{\delta} = \frac{\sin 2\lambda \cos 2\omega + i \sin 2\omega}{1 + \cos 2\lambda \cos 2\omega}. \tag{60.7}$$

β) Normal incidence. In this case, $i = \boldsymbol{r}_1 = \boldsymbol{r}_2 = 0$ and $\boldsymbol{m}_h$ becomes equal to $\sin\boldsymbol{\delta}_h$. The two refracted waves are propagated in the same direction, and therefore the two ellipses have the same axial ratio and sense, but their axes are crossed (see Sects. 42—49). Thus, $\omega_1 = \omega_2$ and $\boldsymbol{\delta}_2 = \frac{\pi}{2} + \boldsymbol{\delta}_1$. Further, there is no particular sense in talking of the parallel or perpendicular component of the incident amplitude, for the plane of incidence is not defined at all for normal incidence. We may therefore take $\boldsymbol{A}_p = A$ the amplitude of the incident linearly polarised wave, and $\boldsymbol{A}_s = 0$.

Putting in these simplifying conditions in (60.1) and (60.2), we obtain

$$\left.\begin{aligned} \frac{\boldsymbol{R}_s}{A} &= \frac{\left(\frac{n_0}{\boldsymbol{n}_2} - \frac{n_0}{\boldsymbol{n}_1}\right)}{\left(1 + \frac{n_0}{\boldsymbol{n}_1}\right)\left(1 + \frac{n_0}{\boldsymbol{n}_2}\right)} \sin 2\boldsymbol{\delta}_1, \\ \frac{\boldsymbol{R}_p}{A} &= -\left\{\frac{1 - \frac{n_0}{\boldsymbol{n}_2}}{1 + \frac{n_0}{\boldsymbol{n}_2}} \sin^2\boldsymbol{\delta}_1 + \frac{1 - \frac{n_0}{\boldsymbol{n}_1}}{1 + \frac{n_0}{\boldsymbol{n}_1}} \cos^2\boldsymbol{\delta}_1\right\}. \end{aligned}\right. \tag{60.8}$$

The ratio of $\boldsymbol{R}_s$ to $\boldsymbol{R}_p$ which gives the complex azimuth of polarisation of the reflected wave, is

$$\frac{\boldsymbol{R}_s}{\boldsymbol{R}_p} = -\frac{\left(\frac{n_0}{\boldsymbol{n}_2} - \frac{n_0}{\boldsymbol{n}_1}\right)\sin 2\boldsymbol{\delta}_1}{1 - \frac{n_0}{\boldsymbol{n}_2}\cdot\frac{n_0}{\boldsymbol{n}_1} + \left(\frac{n_0}{\boldsymbol{n}_2} - \frac{n_0}{\boldsymbol{n}_1}\right)\cos 2\boldsymbol{\delta}_1}. \tag{60.9}$$

If $\boldsymbol{R}$ stands for the resultant amplitude obtained by combining $\boldsymbol{R}_s$ and $\boldsymbol{R}_p$ then

$$\frac{\boldsymbol{R}}{A} = -\sqrt{\left\{\frac{1 - \frac{n_0}{\boldsymbol{n}_2}}{1 + \frac{n_0}{\boldsymbol{n}_2}} \sin\boldsymbol{\delta}_1\right\}^2 + \left\{\frac{1 - \frac{n_0}{\boldsymbol{n}_1}}{1 + \frac{n_0}{\boldsymbol{n}_1}} \cos\boldsymbol{\delta}_1\right\}^2}. \tag{60.10}$$

The most interesting result is that $\boldsymbol{R}_s$ is not zero, i.e., there is a component in the reflected wave which is at right angles to the vibration direction of the polariser. Therefore, the field will not appear dark under crossed polariser and analyser and this phenomenon is known as the "anisotropy effect". The reflecting power under crossed linear analysers is

$$\left.\begin{aligned} \mathfrak{R}_+ = \frac{|\boldsymbol{R}_s|^2}{A^2} &= (\sin^2 2\lambda_1 + \cos^2 2\lambda_1 \sin^2 2\omega_1) \times \\ &\times n_0^2 \frac{n_1^2(1+\varkappa_1^2) + n_2^2(1+\varkappa_2^2) - 2n_1 n_2(1+\varkappa_1\varkappa_2)}{[n_1^2(1+\varkappa_1^2) + 2n_0 n_1 + n_0^2]\,[n_2^2(1+\varkappa_2^2) + 2n_0 n_2 + n_0^2]} \\ &= (\sin^2 2\lambda_1 + \cos^2 2\lambda_1 \sin^2 2\omega_1)\cdot f(n_0, n, \varkappa), \quad \text{say}. \end{aligned}\right\} \tag{60.11}$$

Here, ω_1 is the ellipticity of the two refracted waves, while λ_1 is the azimuth of the faster wave, with reference to the electric vector of the incident wave. It is readily verified that $\mathfrak{R}_+$ is a minimum for $\lambda_1 = 0$ or $\frac{\pi}{2}$ and a maximum for $\lambda_1 = \pm\frac{\pi}{4}$ the two values being

$$\mathfrak{R}_{+\,\min} = f(n_0, n, \varkappa)\sin^2 2\omega_1; \qquad \mathfrak{R}_{+\,\max} = f(n_0, n, \varkappa). \tag{60.12}$$

The ratio of the two gives the ellipticity directly. Thus,

$$\frac{\mathfrak{R}_{+\,\min}}{\mathfrak{R}_{+\,\max}} = \sin^2 2\omega_1 \tag{60.13}$$

and we have here a method of determining the ellipticity of the waves transmitted in any direction in the crystal, purely by observation on light reflected from its surface. The minimum intensity is zero only if there is no absorption. The reflecting power under crossed analysers is identically zero for all azimuths if $\boldsymbol{n}_1 = \boldsymbol{n}_2$ i.e., if the crystal is isotropic, or if the light is incident along the direction of single wave velocity.

The reflecting power $\mathfrak{R} = |\boldsymbol{R}|^2/A^2$ is also of interest. If the ellipticity is zero or small, this is given by

$$\left.\begin{aligned}\mathfrak{R} = \Bigg[&\left\{\frac{(n_2-n_0)^2+n_2^2\varkappa_2^2}{(n_2+n_0)^2+n_2^2\varkappa_2^2}\sin^2\lambda_1 + \frac{(n_1-n_0)^2+n_1^2\varkappa_1^2}{(n_1+n_0)^2+n_1^2\varkappa_1^2}\cos^2\lambda_1\right\} - 4n_0^2\sin^2 2\delta_1 \times \\ &\times \frac{n_1\varkappa_1[n_2^2(1+\varkappa_2^2)-n_0^2] - n_2\varkappa_2[n_1^2(1+\varkappa_1^2)-n_0^2]}{[(n_1+n_0)^2+n_1^2\varkappa_1^2]\,[(n_2+n_0)^2+n_2^2\varkappa_2^2]}\Bigg]^{\frac{1}{2}}.\end{aligned}\right\} \tag{60.14}$$

This is maximum or minimum when $\lambda_1 = 0$ or $\pi/4$ and the two values then correspond to the azimuth of the incident beam parallel to the vibration directions of the two transmitted waves. These are called the uniradial reflecting powers $\mathfrak{R}_1$ and $\mathfrak{R}_2$ and are given by

$$\mathfrak{R}_h = \frac{(n_h-n_0)^2+n_h^2\varkappa_h^2}{(n_h+n_0)^2+n_h^2\varkappa_h^2}, \qquad h = 1, 2. \tag{60.15}$$

The difference between the two,

$$\Delta\mathfrak{R} = \mathfrak{R}_2 - \mathfrak{R}_1 \tag{60.16}$$

may be called the "bireflection" of the section, analogous to the quantities birefringence and dichroism. It is interesting that the uniradial reflecting power and the bireflection (for normal incidence) depend only on the direction of the electric vector and its corresponding refractive index. One may thus talk of the three principal uniradial reflecting powers for the crystal:

$$\mathfrak{R}_\gamma > \mathfrak{R}_\beta > \mathfrak{R}_\alpha.$$

Elegant formulae have been worked by BEREK[1] also for the case when ellipticity is not small. Thus, the ratio of $\boldsymbol{R}_s$ to $\boldsymbol{R}_p$ in (60.9) may be written in the from

$$\frac{\boldsymbol{R}_s}{\boldsymbol{R}_p} = C + iD. \tag{60.17}$$

Consider in particular the settings of the polariser at $\pm\frac{\pi}{4}$ to the fast axis. Then $\lambda_1 = -\frac{\pi}{4}$ and $+\frac{\pi}{4}$ for the two settings and we have from (60.7)

$$\tan\boldsymbol{\delta}_1 = \mp\cos 2\omega + i\sin 2\omega. \tag{60.18}$$

[1] M. BEREK: Z. Kristallogr. 93, 116 (1936).

Putting this in (60.9)

$$\frac{\boldsymbol{R}_s}{\boldsymbol{R}_p} = \frac{1}{\pm \frac{\boldsymbol{n}_2 \boldsymbol{n}_1 - n_0^2}{n_0 (\boldsymbol{n}_1 - \boldsymbol{n}_2)} \cos 2\omega + i \sin 2\omega}. \tag{60.19}$$

Using the absorption coefficient k instead of the absorption index $\varkappa$ we may write

$$\boldsymbol{n}_h = n_h - i\, k_h, \qquad h = 1, 2 \tag{60.20}$$

when we have

$$\frac{\boldsymbol{R}_s}{\boldsymbol{R}_p} = \frac{1}{\pm G \cos 2\omega + i (\sin 2\omega \mp H \cos 2\omega)} \tag{60.21}$$

where

$$\left.\begin{aligned} G &= \frac{1}{n_0} \cdot \frac{n_2 (n_1^2 + k_1^2) - n_1 (n_2^2 + k_2^2) + n_0^2 (n_2 - n_1)}{(n_2 - n_1)^2 + (k_2 - k_1)^2}, \\ H &= \frac{1}{n_0} \frac{k_2 (n_1^2 + k_1^2) - k_1 (n_2^2 + k_2^2) \mp n_0^2 (k_2 - k_1)}{(n_2 - n_1)^2 + (k_2 - k_1)^2}. \end{aligned}\right\} \tag{60.22}$$

Comparing with (60.17)

$$\left.\begin{aligned} \pm G \cos 2\omega &= \frac{C}{C^2 + D^2}, \\ \sin 2\omega \mp H \cos 2\omega &= -\frac{D}{C^2 + D^2}. \end{aligned}\right\} \tag{60.23}$$

Denoting the quantities relating to the two settings of the polariser by the indices I and II, it may be shown that

$$\left.\begin{aligned} \sin 2\omega &= -\frac{1}{2} \left\{ \frac{D_{\mathrm{I}}}{C_{\mathrm{I}}^2 + D_{\mathrm{I}}^2} + \frac{D_{\mathrm{II}}}{C_{\mathrm{II}}^2 + D_{\mathrm{II}}^2} \right\}, \\ G &= \frac{1}{2 \cos 2\omega} \left\{ \frac{C_{\mathrm{I}}}{C_{\mathrm{I}}^2 + D_{\mathrm{I}}^2} - \frac{C_{\mathrm{II}}}{C_{\mathrm{II}}^2 + D_{\mathrm{II}}^2} \right\}, \\ H &= \frac{1}{2 \cos 2\omega} \left\{ \frac{D_{\mathrm{I}}}{C_{\mathrm{I}}^2 + D_{\mathrm{I}}^2} - \frac{D_{\mathrm{II}}}{C_{\mathrm{II}}^2 + D_{\mathrm{II}}^2} \right\}. \end{aligned}\right\} \tag{60.24}$$

For an account of the application of these formula to various crystal symmetries, the original paper should be referred to.

II. Propagation of light in heterogeneous media.

61. Polycrystalline media. Most minerals occur in nature as polycrystalline aggregates, consisting of a great number of optically anisotropic crystallites, variously oriented, firmly adhering to each other to form a coherent solid. It is therefore of importance for the study of the properties of such substances to work out a theory of the propagation of light in polycrystalline aggregates. The optical property of the single crystal, its birefringence, pleochroism, etc. would no doubt play a dominant role in determining the optical characteristics of the aggregate. For example, the greater the birefringence, the greater would be the coefficient of reflection at the intercrystalline boundaries. One could therefore explain the brilliant whiteness of pure marble as due to the strong birefringence of the constituent calcite crystallites. However, it is clear that a simple geometric theory is quite inadequate. For according to it when the crystallites are very small, one should expect the more numerous intercrystalline boundaries to reflect the incident light to a greater extent. Experiment shows the contrary result, namely that the more fine-grained the material is, the more deeply the light penetrates it. This suggests that wave optical principles have to be involked for a better understanding of the optical properties of polycrystalline aggregates.

We present below a theory developed by RAMAN and VISWANATHAN[1] using a very simplified model for introducing random orientation for studying this problem. It is assumed that the crystallites are feebly birefringent, and are in very large numbers, but not numerous enough to completely extinguish the emergent light. To obtain the retardation due to the varying orientations of the individual crystallites, it is assumed that the plate of polycrystalline material consists of crystallites, cubical in shape having a common edge length D completely filling up the available space. The three edges of the cube are assumed to be parallel to the principal axes of the index ellipsoid of the crystallite for which the indices are n_1, n_2, n_3. The varying orientation is introduced in the following manner. The incident light is supposed to be plane polarised with its vibration direction parallel to one set of edges of the cubical blocks, while the effective refractive index may be either n_1, n_2 or n_3 the respective probabilities for these being p_1, p_2 and p_3. One can see that when $p_1=p_2=p_3$ one gets the case of the random orientation of the crystallites while in the case when the p's have different values (provided $p_1+p_2+p_3=1$) one gets the case of a polycrystalline aggregate of any desired preferred orientation. For example $p_1=1$ and $p_2=p_3=0$ is the case of all the crystallites having a common refractive index for a particular direction of vibration while the indices may be different in the perpendicular direction. This case is quite often met with in polycrystalline aggregates. One serious draw-back of these assumptions is that the incident plane polarised disturbance would remain plane polarised in its passage through the plate. In an actual case the incident vibration would be transformed to an elliptic vibration and the parameter describing the ellipticity would alter from crystallite to crystallite. In spite of these serious limitations, these authors have been able to explain many observed phenomena. Finally the assumption has been made that the variation of the amplitude over different areas on the rear face of the plate may be ignored while only changes in the phase are taken into account.

Let the incident wave train be

$$y = e^{\frac{2\pi i}{\lambda}(ct-z)} \tag{61.1}$$

and let there be N cells along the direction of the thickness of the plate. When the wave has passed through k_1 cells of refractive index n_1, k_2 of n_2 and k_3 of n_3 before emerging from the plate, where

$$k_1 + k_2 + k_3 = N, \tag{61.2}$$

the optical path retardation is

$$(k_1 n_1 + k_2 n_2 + k_3 n_3)\, D. \tag{61.3}$$

Now the number of ways in which k_1, k_2 and k_3 cells can be orientated along a row of N cells so as to have refractive indices n_1, n_2 and n_3 is

$$\frac{N!}{k_1!\, k_2!\, k_3!} \tag{61.4}$$

and the probability of occurence of each one of these cases is

$$p_1^{k_1}\, p_2^{k_2}\, p_3^{k_3}. \tag{61.5}$$

Hence the proportion of the total area of the rear surface of the plate from which a wave

$$\exp\left[\frac{2\pi i}{\lambda}\{ct - z - (k_1 n_1 + k_2 n_2 + k_3 n_3)\, D\}\right] \tag{61.6}$$

[1] C.V. RAMAN and K.S. VISWANATHAN: Proc. Ind. Acad. Sci. A **41**, 37 (1955).

emerges is equal to

$$\frac{N!}{k_1!\,k_2!\,k_3!}\,p_1^{k_1}\,p_2^{k_2}\,p_3^{k_3}.$$

Hence the emergent wave is

$$\left.\begin{aligned} y = P \sum_{k_1+k_2+k_3=N} \frac{N!}{k_1!\,k_2!\,k_3!}\,p_1^{k_1}\,p_2^{k_2}\,p_3^{k_3} \times \\ \times \exp\left[\frac{2\pi i}{\lambda}\{c\,t - z - (k_1 n_1 + k_2 n_2 + k_3 n_3)\,D\}\right] \end{aligned}\right\} \tag{61.7}$$

where P is introduced to take into account the loss of intensity of light due to reflections at the intercrystalline boundaries. From the multinomial theorem, (61.7) may be written as

$$y = P\,e^{\frac{2\pi i}{\lambda}(c\,t-z)}\left[p_1\,e^{-\frac{2\pi i}{\lambda}n_1 D} + p_2\,e^{-\frac{2\pi i}{\lambda}n_2 D} + p_3\,e^{-\frac{2\pi i}{\lambda}n_3 D}\right]^N. \tag{61.8}$$

The average refractive index of the medium is

$$n = p_1 n_1 + p_2 n_2 + p_3 n_3; \tag{61.9}$$

hence if we set

$$\nu_1 = (n_2 - n_3), \qquad \nu_2 = (n_3 - n_1), \qquad \nu_3 (n_1 - n_2)$$

we have

$$\left.\begin{aligned} n_1 = n + (p_2\nu_3 - p_3\nu_2), \qquad n_2 = n + (p_3\nu_1 - p_1\nu_3), \\ n_3 = n + (p_1\nu_2 - p_2\nu_1). \end{aligned}\right\} \tag{61.10}$$

Since $d = ND$, substituting (61.10) in (61.8) and expanding in terms of a power series, one obtains

$$y = P\left\{\exp\frac{2\pi i}{\lambda}(c\,t - z) - n\,d\right\} \times \left\{1 - \frac{2\pi^2 D^2}{\lambda^2}\sum p_1(p_2\nu_3 - p_3\nu_2)^2\right\}^N \tag{61.11}$$

neglecting the third and higher powers of $(n_1 - n_2)$, etc. as the birefringence is assumed to be small. Further a little algebra will show that

$$\sum p_1 (p_2\nu_3 - p_3\nu_2)^2 = \sum p_2 p_3 \nu_1^2. \tag{61.12}$$

Hence (61.11) can be rewritten as

$$y = P\,e^{\frac{2\pi i}{\lambda}(c\,t-z)-n\,d}\left\{1 - \frac{1}{N}\,\frac{2\pi^2 D\,d}{\lambda^2}\sum p_2 p_3 \nu_1^2\right\}^N \tag{61.13}$$

$$= P R\,e^{\frac{2\pi i}{\lambda}(c\,t-z-n\,d)} \tag{61.14}$$

where

$$R = e^{-\frac{2\pi^2 D\,d}{\lambda^2}\sum p_1 p_2 \nu_3^2} \quad \text{as } N \text{ is large.} \tag{61.15}$$

The ratio of the intensity of the transmitted light to that of the incident light is given by

$$\frac{I}{I_0} = P^2 R^2 = P^2\,e^{-\frac{4\pi^2 D\,d}{\lambda^2}\{\sum p_2 p_3 (n_2 - n_3)^2\}}. \tag{61.16}$$

If the three axes of the cube have the same probability of being oriented in the direction of the incident light then $p_1 = p_2 = p_3 = \frac{1}{3}$ and (61.16) reduces to

$$\frac{I}{I_0} = P^2 \exp - \frac{8\pi^2 D\,d}{9\,\lambda^2}\left(\sum n_1^2 - \sum n_1 n_2\right). \tag{61.17}$$

RAMAN and VISWANATHAN illustrate the significance of the formula (61.16) by the example that in a plate of alabaster 1 mm thick, taking $\lambda = 5893$ Å and the principal refractive indices of gypsum (the constituent of alabaster) to be $n_1 = 1.520$, $n_2 = 1.523$ and $n_3 = 1.530$, the percentage transmission for $D = 1$, 0.5 and 0.1 μ are respectively 13.5, 37 and 82% thus showing that the plate approaches practically complete transparency as the crystallites approach colloidal dimensions. Also of interest is the case mentioned previously when $p_1 = 1$, $p_2 = p_3 = 0$ i.e., when the crystallites are orientated with a common refractive index along one direction. In such a case for the direction of vibration for the incident light parallel to the common direction, the transmission is complete, while for a perpendicular direction of vibration there would be a considerable attenuation depending on the actual values of the probabilities and the refractive indices for that direction. Since the latter transmission is dependent on the thickness d, if the incident light is unpolarised the state of polarisation of the emergent light would vary with the thickness of the plate. These facts are confirmed in minerals like chalcedony[1]. These substances are very transparent for one particular direction of incident polarised light, while becoming practically opaque for a perpendicular vibration (almost reminiscent of the behaviour of thin tourmaline plates). The polarisation characteristics of the transmitted beam are also well explained by the theory.

The attenuated energy should obviously appear as diffracted radiation in the form of a halo in various directions surrounding the direction of the incident beam. Such a diffusion halo is actually observed in these crystals. According to this theory if the incident light is plane polarised the diffusion halo must also be perfectly plane polarised—a deduction not supported by experiment. This is actually the consequence of some of the simplifying assumptions regarding the orientation of the "cubical" crystallite blocks made in the theory. Experimental observations show that while this theory explains most satisfactorily the intensity and the state of polarisation of the transmitted beam it fails to account for the state of polarisation of the diffracted light.

It may be remarked in this connection that the study of these diffusion haloes by RAMAN[2] and his collaborators have been very fruitful in the understanding of the anisotropic distribution of crystallites in various minerals like moonstone etc.

62. The Christiansen phenomenon in birefringent powders. CHRISTIANSEN[3] in 1884 discovered the beautiful phenomenon that goes after his name. To observe it some powdered isotropic solid like optical glass is put in a flat sided cell and then filled with a liquid whose refractive index is suitably adjusted by either varying its composition or its temperature. Beautiful chromatic effects are observed as the mixture becomes transparent for a restricted region of the spectrum for which the refractive index of the liquid coincides with that of the solid. This phenomenon is often used for the construction of monochromatic filters—particularly in the infrared. CHRISTIANSEN himself failed to observe the phenomenon in birefringent crystals. Recently RAMAN and BHAT[4] have observed this phenomenon using powdered quartz, barium sulphate, calcium sulphate, lithium carbonate, and magnesium fluoride suspendend in suitable liquids. It

---

[1] C.V. RAMAN and A. JAYARAMAN: Proc. Ind. Acad. Sci. A **38**, 199 (1952); A **41**, 1 (1955).—A. JAYARAMAN: Proc. Ind. Acad. Sci. A **38**, 441 (1953).

[2] C.V. RAMAN: Proc. Ind. Acad. Sci. A **37**, 1 (1953).

[3] CHRISTIANSEN: Ann. d. Phys. **23**, 298 (1884); **24**, 439 (1885).

[4] C.V. RAMAN and M.R. BHAT: Proc. Ind. Acad. Sci. A **41**, 61 (1955).

is found that provided the birefringence is small and the material is finely powdered, it is possible to observe the transmission exhibiting brilliant colours. It is also found that the light so transmitted is practically as monochromatic as that observed with isotropic powders. If the incident light is plane polarised the light transmitted is also completely plane polarised. The diffusion halo surrounding the direction of transmitted light however exhibits imperfect polarisation depending on various factors, including the fineness of the powder. Finally the colours of the diffusion halo are markedly different for the two components of the light vibration parallel or perpendicular to that of the incident light. The general features of these observations (except those regarding the state of polarisation of the light of the halo) have been explained by RAMAN and VISWANATHAN[1] by an extension of the theory of the propagation of light in polycrystalline media presented in the last section.

The only difference in the theory is that some of the cubical elements of volume each of edge length D is now considered as filled either by the liquid of refractive index n_l or by the crystallites. We assume that the operative refractive index of any one block may either be n_1, n_2, n_3 with equal probabilities p if it is a crystallite, or n_l (with a probability q) if it is filled with the liquid. Hence

$$3p + q = 1. \tag{62.1}$$

If in the passage of N cells $N-M$ happen to be solid blocks and M liquid blocks then the probability of the occurrence of this event is

$$\frac{N!}{(N-M)!\,M!}\,(3p)^{N-M}\,Q^M \tag{62.2}$$

and again Eq. (61.2) becomes

$$k_1 + k_2 + k_3 = N - M \tag{62.3}$$

and the probability of occurrence of a state in which k_1, k_2 and k_3 cells in a row of $(N-M)$ cells can be oriented in such a manner as to have refractive indices n_1, n_2 and n_3 is

$$\frac{N-M}{k_1!\,k_2!\,k_3!}\left(\frac{1}{3}\right)^{N-M}. \tag{62.4}$$

Following an identical procedure as in the previous derivation we get the ratio of the intensity transmitted to that of the incident radiation to be

$$\frac{I}{I_0} = R^2 = \exp - \frac{4\pi^2 D d}{\lambda^2}\left\{p^2 \sum (n_2 - n_3)^2 + p\,q \sum (n_1 - n_l)^2\right\}. \tag{62.5}$$

This formula reduces to that deduced by RAMAN[2] for an isotropic case.

The formula shows that the effect of birefringence is to diminish the intensity of the transmitted light for all wavelengths and one cannot therefore expect to observe the phenomenon unless the size of the particles is extremely small or the thickness of the cell is reduced to a minimum. When the chromatic effect due to difference in refractive indices is not there, the colour is determined by the factor λ^{-2} (due to scattering by the large particles). However, if the birefringence is not very small, chromatic effects will be observable when the volume occupied by the powder is small compared to the volume of the liquid. All the limitations of the theory mentioned in the last section apply to this case also. Most of the deductions from the theory about the transmitted light have been verified by experiment.

---

[1] C.V. RAMAN and K.S. VISWANATHAN: Proc. Ind. Acad. Sci. A **39**, 55 (1955).
[2] C.V. RAMAN: Proc. Ind. Acad. Sci. A **29**, 381 (1949).

III. Interference phenomena.

a) Transparent crystals.

63. General discussion. *α) Conditions of observation.* The interference phenomena exhibited by crystals in polarised light are very well known and are perhaps the most colourful of phenomena observed in nature. In the case of transparent crystals both a polariser and an analyser are necessary to observe these effects. In this case they arise because every polarised ray incident on the plate splits up into two rays in orthogonal states of polarisation which suffer a relative path retardation on passing through the plate. Pairs of orthogonally polarised rays derived from the same point of the original source will be coherent and can interfere after resolution by an analyser. These interference phenomena are usually observed under two different experimental conditions. In the first case the incident light is very nearly parallel and the eye or the microscope is focussed on the crystalline specimen. If the specimen is a parallel plate it will exhibit a uniform tint over its area since the retardation at all points would be the same. This will not be so in the case of a specimen of varying thickness.

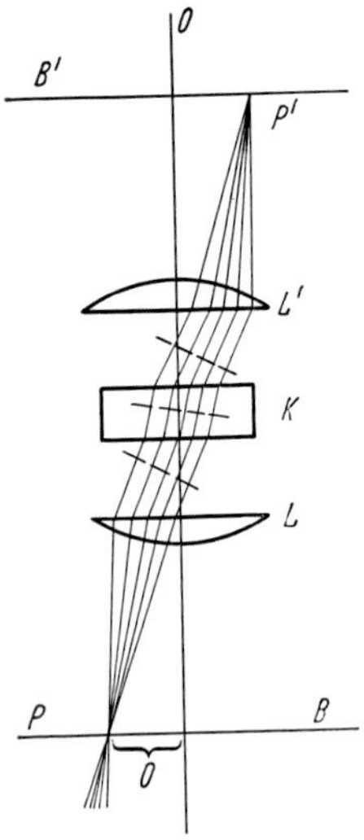

Fig. 56. Schematic diagram of conoscopic arrangement.

The second method of observation is by the use of "convergent light", for example with the aid of the usual conoscopic arrangement given in Fig. 56 [see also Fig. 86b] an extended light source being placed below B. In this case the interference effects occur at infinity i.e., at the focal plane of the lens L'. Each point P' in the focal plane is a focal point of a bundle of parallel rays emerging from the crystal in a particular direction. Since the retardation introduced by the plate varies with direction, the interference phenomenon varies over the field of view. Fig. 57a illustrates one particular ray incident on the crystal which splits into two on entering it, the final rays emerging from the crystal being parallel to the incident ray. The path retardation suffered by each ray should strictly speaking be calculated using the ray velocity. It must be noted that in Fig. 57a any other ray incident on the plate in the same direction would be incoherent with the particular incident ray considered since by reference to Fig. 56 it may be seen that they originate from different points of the original luminous surface. Nevertheless for simplicity we consider the incident ray in Fig. 57a as being normal to the portion of a plane wavefront as in Fig. 57b, the wave normal suffering refraction according to SNELL's law. The path retardation suffered by a parallel wave front on passing through a parallel plate of isotropic medium is $n t \cos r$ where n is the refractive index and r the angle of refraction. In the present case if n_1, n_2 and r_1 and r_2 are respectively the refractive indices and the angles of refraction of the wave normals then the difference in the phase retardation suffered by the two components is

$$\Delta = \frac{2\pi}{\lambda} (n_1 \cos r_1 - n_2 \cos r_2)\, t. \tag{63.1}$$

The equation expresses the fact that Δ depends on the difference in the refractive index as well as the difference in the lengths AL and AN. For normal incidence this is exactly equal to zero and even for oblique incidence, it can be shown that when the birefringence is small the second effect may be neglected in comparison with the first. Then the expression can be written as[1]

$$\Delta = \frac{2\pi}{\lambda} \frac{(n_1 - n_2)}{\cos r} t \tag{63.2}$$

where r is the mean angle of refraction.

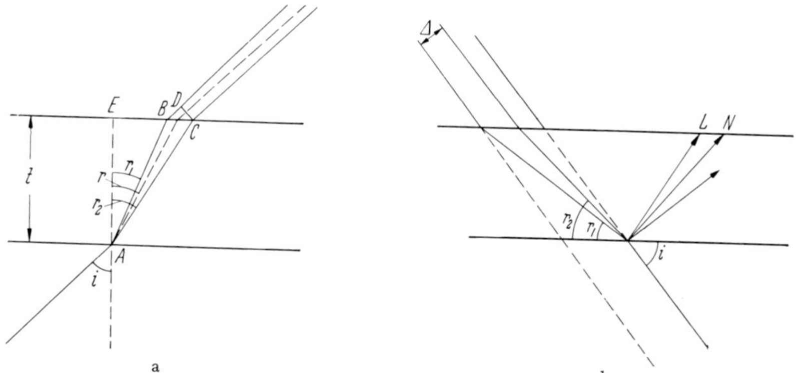

Fig. 57 a and b. The paths of (a) the rays, (b) the wave fronts travelling in a particular direction in a birefringent plate.

β) Interference effects in parallel light. As we have seen above, each point in the conoscopic figure is a focal point of a bundle of parallel rays emerging from the plate in a particular direction. We shall therefore first consider the closely connected problem of the interference effects in parallel light at normal incidence of a transparent crystal cut in any arbitrary direction when examined between an elliptic polariser P and an elliptic analyser A (Fig. 58). Since the crystal is transparent, the incident light of unit intensity will be split into two orthogonally polarised states P_1 and P_2 (in general elliptically polarised), whose intensities will be $\cos^2\alpha_1$ and $\sin^2\alpha_1$ respectively, where $2\alpha_1$ is the angular distance of P from P_1 on the Poincaré sphere. These states suffer a relative phase retardation Δ on passage through the plate, the state P_2 being taken to be the slower beam. The analyser A at $2\alpha_2$ from P_1 transmits fractions $\cos^2\alpha_2$ and $\sin^2\alpha_2$ of these beams; and as we have seen in Sect. 4β, Chap. A, the phase difference between the resolved components will be equal to $(\Delta - \varphi)$ where $-\varphi$ may be described as the phase retardation due to the processes of decomposition and analysation. Here $\varphi = \sphericalangle A P_1 P$ taken to be positive if on looking from P_1 to P_2, an anticlockwise rotation brings arc $\widehat{P_1 P}$ to $\widehat{P_1 A}$ (φ is also equal to $\sphericalangle P P_2 A$). Thus the analyser A transmits two beams of intensities I_1 and I_2 with a phase difference Δ' between them given by

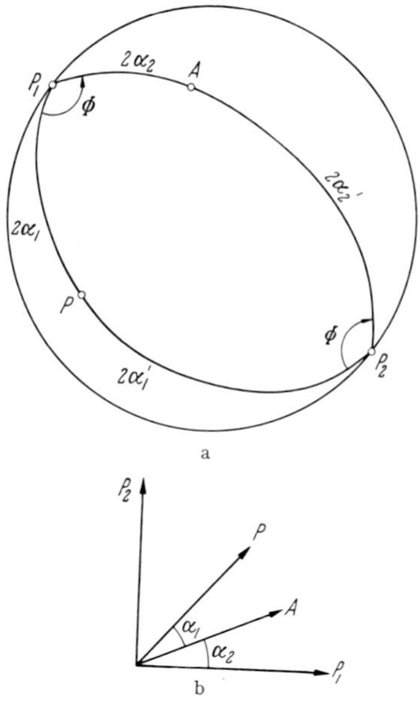

Fig. 58. (a) Poincaré representation for computing the general interference effects in parallel light. P is the polariser, A is the analyser, P_1 and P_2 the two elliptic states propagated unchanged in the crystal, P_2 being the slower state. (b) The case when all the states become linear.

$$I_1 = \cos^2\alpha_1 \cos^2\alpha_2, \quad I_2 = \sin^2\alpha_1 \sin^2\alpha_2, \quad \Delta' = \Delta - \varphi. \tag{63.3}$$

[1] See M. BORN [4], p. 248 or DITCHBURN [8], p. 512.

Being in the same state of polarisation, the intensity obtained by the interference of the resolved components will be

$$I = I_1 + I_2 + 2\sqrt{I_1 I_2}\cos\Delta'. \tag{63.4}$$

This can be written as

$$I = [I_1 + I_2 + 2\sqrt{I_1 I_2}\cos\varphi] - [2\sqrt{I_1 I_2}(\cos\varphi - \cos\Delta')]. \tag{63.5}$$

The first term is the intensity transmitted if $\Delta = 0$ i.e. if the plate were absent and hence must be equal to $\cos^2\frac{1}{2}\widehat{PA}$. Hence

$$I = \cos^2\frac{1}{2}\widehat{PA} - 2\sqrt{I_1 I_2}\sin\frac{1}{2}\Delta\sin\left(\frac{\Delta}{2} - \varphi\right). \tag{63.6}$$

The first term which only depends on the relative orientations of analyser and the polariser is known as the "white term" and does not depend on the wavelength, while the second term gives rise to the "subtraction colours" in white light, since it depends on the retardation introduced by the plate and hence on the wavelength. It may be noticed that when φ is changed to $\varphi - \pi$ the sign of the second term in (63.6) changes; the colour is therefore changed to a complementary hue. The colours will be most vivid when the states of the polariser and analyser are orthogonal to one another when the white term vanishes, i.e. $\varphi = \pi$, and correspondingly the change from the original to the complementary hue will he most striking.

In the particular case when a linear polariser and a linear analyser are used and the medium possesses only linear birefringence, then α_1 and α_2 are the actual (numerical) inclinations of the polariser and analyser to the faster linear state OP_1 (Fig. 58b). Further since the states P and A lie on the same great circle passing through $P_1 P_2$ namely the equator, $\varphi = 0$ or π according as the polariser and analyser are in the same quadrant or in different quadrants. In the general case however φ can take values other than 0 or π. This is true even in the case of linearly birefringent media if the polarising and analysing states are not both linear (or when we are considering the effect of superposed plates). The last mentioned case can also be treated by the same formulae (63.3) and (63.4), since the effect of two such plates on the incident light is that of a single plate showing elliptic birefringence (see Sect. 74).

γ) The phenomena in convergent light. Though the two classes of phenomena in parallel and convergent light present very different appearances, they can be explained on the same broad principles, the basic difference between the two phenomena being in the location of the interference effects. Each point in the convergent light figure corresponds to a definite direction of propagation and the intensity I at a point will be that observed in parallel light for the corresponding direction, being given by formulae (63.3) and (63.4). All the quantities in the formulae vary with the direction.

Considering for example the case of a plate cut approximately normal to the optic axis, as we proceed outwards along directions normal to the curves of constant retardation, the retardation Δ increases rapidly and the corresponding rate of variation of the intensity could usually be taken to be predominantly due to a change in Δ. Interference rings would therefore appear along the directions in which the resolved components transmitted by the analyser are opposed in phase. The curves of minimum intensity will be given by

$$\left.\begin{aligned}\Delta' &= (2n+1)\,\pi,\\ \Delta &= (2n+1)\,\pi + \varphi.\end{aligned}\right\} \tag{63.7}$$

It must be remembered that φ (which represents the phase retardation introduced by the process of decomposition and analysation) is not a constant over the field of view because the states P_1 and P_2 of the waves propagated depend on the direction of propagation. The curves of minimum intensity would therefore, in general, not coincide with the curves of constant retardation.

For a uniaxial crystal or a biaxial crystal of not too small axial angle the curves of minimum intensity could usually be constructed in the following way. *The curve $\Delta = (2n+1)\,\pi$ is drawn and the radii vectors of this curve are increased by amounts corresponding to the additional retardation φ (φ itself depending on the azimuth).* The intensity at any point of the curve of minimum intensity is given by substituting $\Delta' = \pi$ in (63.4) and is

$$I_{\min} = \cos^2(\alpha_1 + \alpha_2) = \cos^2(\alpha_1' + \alpha_2'). \tag{63.8}$$

This is itself not constant over the curve of minimum intensity as the states of vibration of the beams propagated vary with the direction of propagation. The rings appear darkest along zones which have to be determined for each specific problem.

However in the particular case when the polariser and analyser are crossed we have $\varphi = \pm\pi$ and $(\alpha_1+\alpha_2) = \pi/2$. In this case the curves of minmum intensity are perfectly dark and occur along directions for which $\Delta = 2n\pi$ as is also to be expected from physical considerations.

There may also exist lines in the field of view containing directions for which one of the states P_1 or P_2 propagated in the crystal coincides with the state of the polariser (P) or the analyser (A) (i.e. α_1 or $\alpha_2 = 0$). Along these lines and in a narrow band on either side of them, the interference effects would clearly be absent. If now the polariser and analyser are crossed with respect to each other then P and A would coincide with the states P_1 and P_2 and along these zones the intensity would now be zero. These zones are known as isogyres, and it is clear that their position does not depend on the thickness of the crystal but only on the state of polarisation of P and A. If P and A are of the same state then the isogyres will be bright. More generally, if P and A are of different states two sets of isogyres will be observed. For an *approximate* discussion of the interference rings, particularly near the optic axis, the retardation Δ introduced by the plate can be taken to be proportional to the birefringence, the effects due to the variations in the thickness traversed being comparatively negligible.

64. Interference phenomena in inactive crystals. *α) Convergent light figures under crossed nicols.* Consider all directions as passing through the centre of a sphere and defined as points of intersection with the surface (the portion of the spherical surface under consideration can for qualitative purposes be approximated by the plane of the paper). Thus each point on the sphere corresponds to point on the convergent light figure, which corresponds to a particular direction of propagation.

Fig. 59 represents the rings and the isogyres for a uniaxial crystal near the optic axis. The extraordinary ray is polarised in the radial direction. So the isogyres occur along the two perpendicular diameters representing the polarising and analysing states. The curves of constant birefringence are circles given by $\sin^2 W = \text{const}$ [Eq. (34.8)]. Hence the interference rings at $\delta = 2n\pi$ are circles whose radii are proportional to the square root of the natural numbers.

The case of a biaxial crystal where the optic axial angle is large and the plate is cut normal to one optic axis N_1 is illustrated in Fig. 60. The optic axial plane is indicated by the straight line in the diagram and $N_1\,N_2$ contains the z direction.

The vibration direction of the faster wave obtained by the construction given in Sect. 34, Fig. 39a is shown. The lines of like polarisation are again diameters. When the crossed nicols have their planes along and perpendicular to the axial plane, the isogyre lies along the axial plane and when they are turned, the isogyre turns at twice the rate. Thus at the 45° position the isogyre is a vertical brush, though it is slightly curved with the convex side facing the acute bisectrix (Fig. 60). The curves of constant birefringence are, from (34.7) circles $\sin U_1 =$ const and hence the curves of minimum intensity are circles whose radii are proportional to the natural numbers.

In the case of a biaxial crystal cut normal to the actute bisectrix (Fig. 61) the directions of vibration at any point are obtained by bisecting the angle sub-

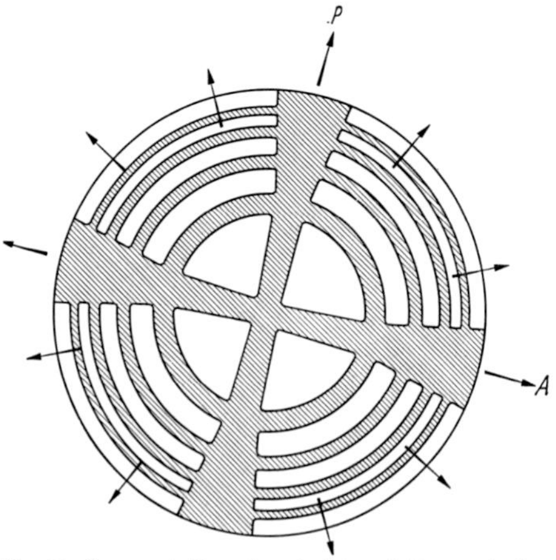

Fig. 59. Conoscopic figure in uniaxial crystal (nonoptically active) in a section normal to the optic axis.

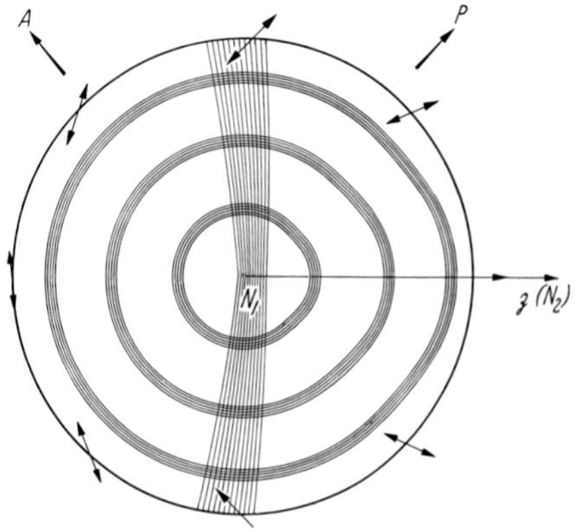

Fig. 60. Conoscopic figure in a biaxial inactive crystal ($2V$ being large) when the plate is cut normal to the optic axis.

tended at the point by the two optic axial directions (Fig. 39a) externally and internally. The internal bisector represents the slower wave in a positive crystal.

The curves of like polarisation are rectangular hyperbolae passing through the optic axes the vibration directions on any point of the hyperbola being parallel to the asymptotes. Conversely for any setting of the crossed nicols the isogyres will be rectangular hyperbolae with the asymptotes parallel to the vibration directions of the polariser and the analyser. The isogyres turn round in a peculiar manner when the crossed polaroids are rotated. The curves of equal birefringence are lemniscates with $\sin u_1 \sin u_2 = \text{const}$ [Eq. (34.7)].

β) The convergent light figures with a linear polariser and a circular analyser. Determination of the optical sign of a crystal. Let us consider the case when the incident light is linearly polarised so that the point P (Fig. 62) on the Poincaré sphere is on the equator and a left circular analyser (which is transparent for left circularly polarised light L) is set after the plate. Such a circular analyser is obtained by a combination of a $\lambda/4$ plate backed by a linear analyser at the suitable azimuth. In this case Fig. 58a gets transformed to Fig. 62 and we have $2\alpha_2 = \frac{\pi}{2}$ and $\varphi = \pm\frac{\pi}{2}$ the upper or lower sign being chosen according as the azimuth ψ of the faster state P_1 $(\alpha_1 = |\psi|)$ with respect to the polariser is positive $\left(0 \text{ to } \frac{\pi}{2}\right)$ or negative $\left(0 \text{ to } -\frac{\pi}{2}\right)$. Thus according to (63.3) the phase difference Δ' between the resolved components transmitted by the analyser is greater or smaller than δ[1] by $\pi/2$ according as the azimuth of the faster state P_1 with respect to the incident vibration is (a) positive $\left(0 \text{ to } \frac{\pi}{2}\right)$ or (b) negative $\left(0 \text{ to } -\frac{\pi}{2}\right)$. Accordingly from (63.7) in the zones given by (a) $\left(\text{i.e. } \psi = 0 \text{ to } +\frac{\pi}{2}\right)$ the curves of minimum intensity occur at $\delta = (2n + \frac{1}{2})\,\pi$ while in the zone (b) they occur at $\delta = (2n + \frac{3}{2})\,\pi$. Thus the curves of minimum intensity shift by quarter of a fringe in opposite directions with respect to the curves $\delta = 2n\pi$, which would be obtained without the $\lambda/4$ plate when the analyser is crossed with respect to the polariser. However the curves are still lemniscates in each of the two zones (a) and (b). The intensity obtained by substituting the relevant quantities in (63.3) and (63.4) is given by

$$I = \tfrac{1}{2}\left[1 - \sin 2\psi \sin \delta\right]. \tag{64.1}$$

Clearly there will be no interference along the zone of directions for which $\psi = 0$.

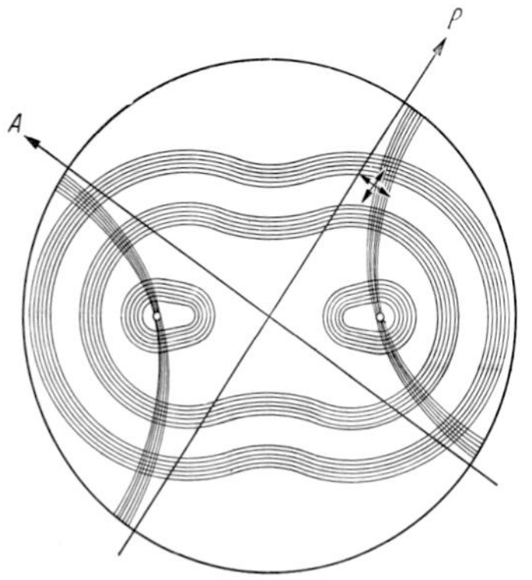

Fig. 61. Conoscopic figure in a biaxial inactive crystal cut normal to the acute bisectrix. The directions of vibration at a point are indicated.

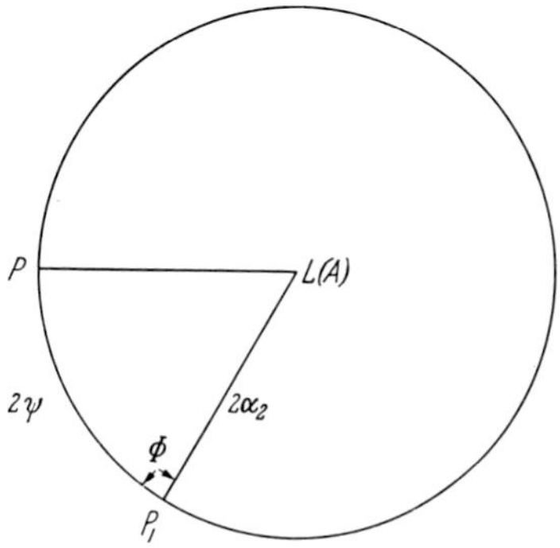

Fig. 62. Poincaré construction for convergent light figures observed in inactive birefringent crystals with a linear polariser P and a left circular analyser $L(A)$.

The shift of the fringes mentioned above may be used to determine the optical sign of a crystal. Consider for example the case illustrated in Fig. 63a, where a biaxial crystal is viewed through a left circular analyser. For any setting of the polariser, for regions in the field of view where the isogyres would normally occur $\psi = \alpha_1 = 0$. Also, for any point in the field of view the vibration direction which internally bisects the angle between the lines proceeding from that point to the two optic axes represents the slower wave if the crystal is optically positive and the faster wave if it is negative. Considering for example the former case, let the polariser be at an azimuth $\pi/4$ with respect to the line joining the acute angle between the optic axes. The convex side of the line of line polarisation will correspond to zone (b) while the concave side to zone (a) mentioned above. Hence the rings would contract on the convex side of the line of like polarisation (the band in Fig. 63a) and expand on the concave side. The reverse would be true if the crystal is optically negative. If however the polariser direction is at $-\frac{\pi}{4}$ then the rings would contract on the concave side and expand on the convex side for an optically positive crystal.

[1] Since the crystal is non-optically active, the relative phase retardation Δ of Sect. 63 is equal to δ.

It may be noticed that from Eq. (63.8) that the intensity at any point of a curve of minimum intensity is $\cos^2\left(\frac{\pi}{4} + |\psi|\right)$ which vanishes only at $\psi = \pm\frac{\pi}{4}$. Hence in the neighbourhood of the optic axes the rings are perfectly dark along an axial plane and they slowly fade away as we approach the curve of like polarisation on crossing which the shift of the ring system occurs.

In the above discussion we have considered the case when a left circular analyser is employed. For this the quarter wave plate is with its fast axis at $\beta = +\frac{\pi}{4}$ with respect to the plane of analysation. We have not specified the actual orientation of the analysing nicol as it is quite immaterial.

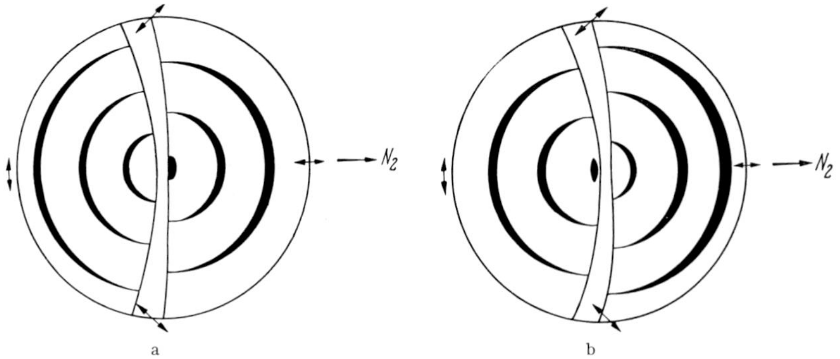

Fig. 63 a and b. Convergent light figure with linear polariser and left circular analyser. (a) Polariser $+\frac{\pi}{4}$ to $N_1 N_2$ and crystal $+ve$ or polariser $-\frac{\pi}{4}$ to $N_1 N_2$ and crystal $-ve$. (b) P at $\frac{\pi}{4}$ to $N_1 N_2$ crystal $-ve$, or P at $-\frac{\pi}{4}$ to $N_1 N_2$ crystal $+ve$.

If a right circular analyser is used the sign of φ (Fig. 62) would change and the intensity at any point of the field would again be given by the same expression (64.1) except that a positive sign should be attached to the second term.

By a similar method the case of a circular polariser with a linear analyser could be treated. It may be remarked that when the polariser and analyser are crossed the effects observed on introducing a $\lambda/4$ plate at 45° above or below the crystal plate are the same.

65. Convergent light figures in transparent optically active crystals. *α) General description of the phenomena.* Transparent optically active crystals in sections normal to the optic axes show a simple rotation of the plane of polarisation. We have seen that this arises because along an optical axial direction, the two waves propagated are circularly polarised in opposite senses, the left circular vibration being propagated with a greater velocity when the rotatory power is positive (laevo rotation for an observer looking at the source). The general treatment given in Sect. 63 β for the colours appearing when a crystal is viewed between a polariser and an analyser is equally applicable to the present case, with $\Delta = 2\varrho$, though for sections of usual thickness, the colour phenomena are only vivid in the case of crystals like quartz which possess considerable optical activity. While in linearly birefringent crystals, the dispersion of birefringence i.e. of $(n_1 - n_2)$ is usually negligible, in quartz the large dispersion of circular birefringence contributes appreciably to the colour phenomenon. This is used in the biquartz —the analogue of the Bravais plate—for a sensitive determination of the azimuth of a linear vibration.

In the biquartz the two halves are of left and right rotating quartz, the rotation for yellow being 90°. When the linear analyser has been set parallel to the incident vibration, the two halves are matched showing the sensitive tint of passage. If the analyser is rotated slightly in one direction the blue component is cut off in one half and the red in the other, causing a noticeable difference in the tints. With large thicknesses of quartz between polariser and analyser along the optic axis, if white light is used, no colours are visible, but the phenomena are still present and the subtraction of colours of different wave lengths can be observed in the channelled spectrum of the transmitted beam. It is interesting to remark that the rotatory dispersion of quartz was used by WOOD[1] to separate the D_1 and D_2 lines of sodium by choosing a suitable thickness of quartz for which the difference in the rotation for the two wavelengths was fairly large and cutting off one of them by a linear analyser.

For directions other than the optic axis the waves propagated are in two orthogonally polarised elliptic states. The major axes of the ellipses lie along the two principal planes of linear birefringence, which are determined by the usual construction for inactive crystals (Sect. 34, Fig. 39a). The ellipticity of the states are given by the equation $\tan|2\omega| = 2\varrho/\delta$, their relative phase retardation per unit distance being given by $\Delta = \sqrt{\delta^2 + (2\varrho)^2}$. In the neighbourhood of an optic axis, if we may regard ϱ as constant, the ellipticity remains the same along the curves of constant linear birefringence. As we proceed away from the optic axis the ellipticity diminishes rapidly and the vibrations tend to become linearly polarised as in an inactive crystal and $\Delta \approx \delta$, since the square of the ellipticity may be neglected.

Thus, in the optic axial figures in convergent light between crossed polaroids, the isogyres appear dark only far away from the optic axis and fade away as the optic axis is approached. However this effect is best observed only in the case of a crystal possessing high optical activity. As we have seen in Sect. 63γ the curves of minimum intensity are perfectly dark and occur at $\Delta = 2n\pi$. If we regard ϱ as constant in the vicinity of an optic axis, the curves of minimum intensity are circles very close to the optic axis and become leminiscates at larger distances.

The optic axial direction itself usually appears bright and it can be extinguished by rotating the analyser with respect to the polariser. Hence the interference figures observed when the analyser is not crossed with respect to the polariser are of more interest here than in the corresponding case in inactive crystals.

β) Interference figures in quartz with linear polariser and analyser in a general setting. In this and the following sections we shall confine ourselves to the interference figures exhibited by quartz although the same treatment may be extended in a straightforward manner to other crystals, uniaxial or biaxial.

For any general setting of the polariser and the analyser the behaviour at the border of the figure should approximate to that of an inactive crystal. We have seen in Sect. 63 that for an inactive crystal the phase difference $-\varphi$ introduced by the processes of decomposition and analysation is 0 or π, the first case obtaining when the polariser and the analyser directions are contained in the same quadrant between the principal planes. Thus, in the acute sector in the field of view defined by the two diameters parallel to the polariser and the analyser vibrations P and A, as also in the acute sector defined by two lines perpendicular to these vibrations, the dark rings occur at $\Delta = 2n\pi$. In the remaining sectors they occur at $\Delta = (2n+1)\pi$. However, the elliptical polarisation of the waves manifests itself as we approach the optic axis and $-\varphi$ is not restricted to the two values 0 or π but varies continuously as we proceed round a

[1] R.W. WOOD [*13*].

circle described about the optic axis. As a consequence, the discontinuity in the ring system is smoothened out and towards the centre ofthe field of view, the rings take the form of squares with rounded corners. The directions at which the corners occur can be discussed using the Poincaré sphere.

Along any direction represented by Q on the convergent light figure (Fig. 64) two crossed elliptic vibrations are propagated. Let the polar coordinates of Q be r, ϑ (where the origin O represents the optic axial direction and OP is parallel to the vibration direction of the polariser). Then, since quartz is a positive crystal, ϑ is also the azimuth of the major axis of the slower vibration P'. Hence if the ellipticity of this slower wave be ε the state P' will be represented on the Poincaré sphere by a point of longitude 2ϑ, while its latitude is numerically equal to 2ε, ε being positive or negative according as the crystal is optically right or left handed. We shall first consider the case of a right handed crystal in which case the point P' lies in the upper hemisphere (Fig. 65a). In what follows the main point to remember is that, as the representative point Q goes round a circle described about the optic axis, the corresponding state on the Poincaré sphere goes round a parallel of latitude. For a general setting A of the analyser we have $\varphi = \sphericalangle PP'A$, and this is positive or negative according as the azimuth ψ of the analyser with respect to OP is negative $\left(0 \text{ to } -\frac{\pi}{2}\right)$ or positive $\left(0 \text{ to } \frac{\pi}{2}\right)$,

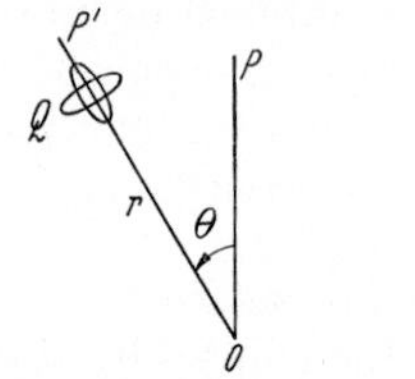

Fig. 64. The origin O represents the optic axial direction. OP is a vertical line. Along any point Q on the convergent light figure the two ellipses propagated for a non-absorbing optically active birefringent crystal are marked.

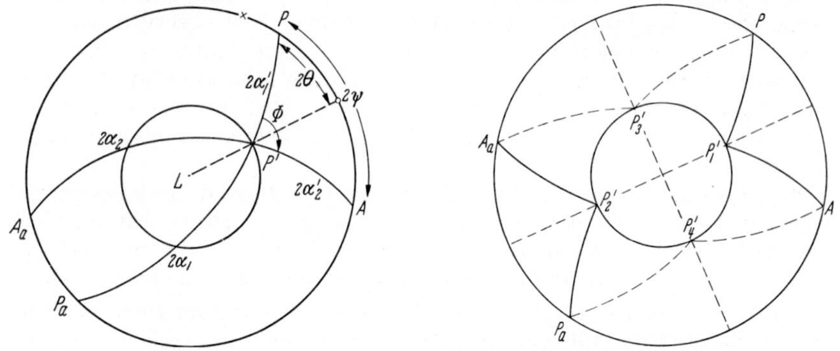

a b

Fig. 65 a and b. Poincaré representations for computing the interference figure obtained in quartz with a linear polariser and analyser in a general setting.

the former case being illustrated in the Fig. 65a. As the analyser is rotated in a clockwise direction, φ increases and the rings will expand according to the construction of the curves of minimum intensity given in Sect. 63γ.

For a fixed setting of P and A, in order to find the orientations of the maximum and minimum radii of the quadratic curves, we have to find the positions at which φ becomes maximum and minimum as P' goes round the small circle. For this we note that $\sphericalangle P_a P' A_a = \sphericalangle P P' A = \varphi$ while $\sphericalangle A_a P' P = \sphericalangle A P' P_a = \pi - \varphi$. The numerical value of φ attains a maximum for the position P_1', P_2' indicated in Fig. 65b for which the azimuths ϑ_1 and ϑ_2 of the major axes bisect internally and externally the acute angle between the polariser and analyser vibration directions. On the other hand, for positions P_3' and P_4' the supplement of $|\varphi|$ attains a maximum value, i.e. $|\varphi|$ attains a minimum value. If the azimuth of the analyser is negative, φ is always positive. Hence to obtain the curve of minimum intensity, we have to draw the circular curves $\Delta=(2n+1)\,\pi$ and increase the radii of the circles by amounts variable with direction. These increments attain their maximum values along the internal and external bisectors of the vibration directions of the polariser and the analyser and their minimum value along directions inclined at $\pi/4$ to the former. The "quadratic curves" in this case are illustrated in Fig. 66. On the other hand, when the analyser azimuth is positive $\left(0 \text{ to } +\frac{\pi}{2}\right.$ with respect to the polariser$\left.\right)$, the greatest contractions from circular form occur along the former set of directions, while the greatest expansions occur along the latter.

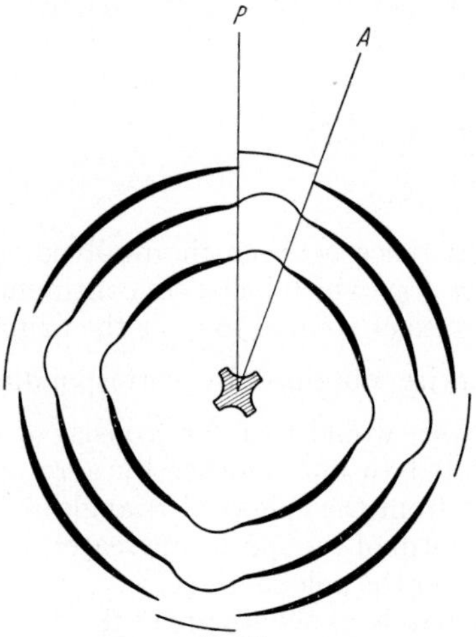

Fig. 66.

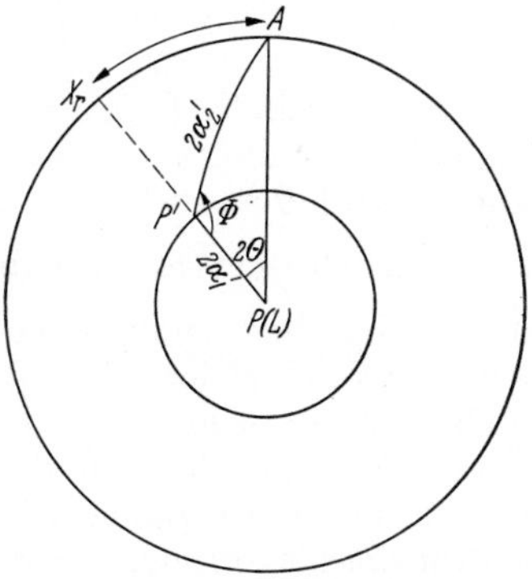

Fig. 67.

Fig. 66. Quadratic curves in basal section of quartz.

Fig. 67. Poincaré representation for intensity transmitted in a basal section of quartz with circular polariser (L) and a linear analyser (A).

The intensity for different points on the curve of minimum intensity is given by

$$I_{\min}=\cos^2\tfrac{1}{2}\,(2\alpha_1'+2\alpha_2'). \tag{65.1}$$

The quantity $(2\alpha_1'+2\alpha_2')$ has also its turning points at P_1', P_2', P_3' and P_4' as P goes round the circle and it can be easily verified that the expression becomes zero at P_3' and P_4' and has a maximum value of $\cos^2 P P_1'$ at P_1' and P_2'. Thus the quadratic curves always appear darkest along the azimuths bisecting internally and externally the angle between the polariser direction and a direction crossed with respect to the analyser. For the same reason, when the optic axis is extinguished, a central cross is formed whose arms point to the dark portions of the quadratic curve.

It may be noticed that only when the analyser is at a positive azimuth with respect to the polariser do the darkest portions occur at the corners of the quadratic curves. Otherwise they occur at the centres of the sides.

All the above discussions apply to a right-handed crystal. For a left handed crystal the point P' will be in the lower hemisphere. It may be readily verified that the figure exhibited at any setting of the polariser and analyser for a left-handed crystal would be the same as that exhibited by a right-handed crystal when the vibration directions of polariser and the analyser are interchanged. In the case of the left handed crystal the rings expand for an anti-clockwise rotation of the analyser. This is contrary to the behaviour of a right handed crystal and may be used for the determination of the sign of the rotatory power.

Corresponding results could be derived for biaxial crystals. The curves of minimum intensity near an optic axis will be elongated in only one direction. At the proper setting of the analyser the optic axis is extinguished by a single bar instead of a cross[1].

γ) Spiral figures in a single basal section of quartz[2]. We shall discuss the case when a left circular polariser represented by P (at L, Fig. 67) is used and a linear analyser (Fig. 64) is set behind a basal section of right handed quartz. As the point P' moves along the small circle in an anticlockwise direction, 2ϑ increases from $0 \to \frac{\pi}{2} \to \pi \to \frac{3\pi}{2} \to 2\pi$ and correspondingly φ ($\sphericalangle PP'A$) increases from $-\pi \to -\frac{\pi}{2} \to 0 \to +\frac{\pi}{2} \to +\pi$.

The curves of minimum intensity are given by (63.7)

$$\varDelta = 2n\pi + (\pi + \varphi). \tag{65.2}$$

Hence along the circle $\varDelta = 2n\pi$ the phase difference between the resolved components falls short of $(2n+1)\pi$ by an angle $(\pi+\varphi)$ which increases continuously with the azimuth ϑ and which in fact becomes exactly equal to *twice* the azimuth at $\vartheta = m\frac{\pi}{4}$. The curves of minimum intensity obtained by correspondingly increasing the radii vectors of the circle $\varDelta = 2n\pi$ would therefore consist of two mutually enwrapping left-handed spirals related to one another by a rotation of π. The expression for φ could be obtained from the spherical triangle $AP'P$ and this expression could be used to study the form of the spirals in greater detail. Close to the optic axis the point P' would be nearer the pole so that $\varphi \approx -(\pi - 2\vartheta)$. Further the linear birefringence varies approximately as the square of the distance r from the optic axis. Hence close to the optic axis the equations to the spirals using (5.2) and (65.2) are given by[3]

$$\varDelta = \sqrt{A r^2 + 4\varrho^2} = 2n\pi + 2\vartheta. \tag{65.3}$$

If the spirals are extrapolated to the origin (where they actually fade away) the common tangent at the origin will be at an azimuth of $-\varrho$ (Fig. 68) [the negative sign has to be attached as the spiral is left handed and at the azimuth $\vartheta = \pi/2$, it passes through the point $\varDelta = \pi/2$].

Towards the border, the figure must tend to the form which we have discussed in the case of inactive crystals (Sect. 63 γ). The transition occurs by way of a non-uniform rate of increase of the arm of the spiral, which manifests itself as kinks along the vertical and horizontal directions. These assume the form of discontinuities towards the border of the figure.

The variation of intensity along the spiral may be studied with sufficient accuracy by considering the variation of $\cos^2(\alpha_1' + \alpha_2')$ [Eq. (65.1)] as P' goes round the small circle, the arc $2\alpha_1'$ being constant. The arc α_2' acquires its minimum value of 2ε at $2\vartheta = 0$ and its maximum value of $\pi - 2\varepsilon$ at $2\vartheta = \pi$. Further the sum $2\alpha_1' + 2\alpha_2'$ lies between the limits $\pi/2$ and π for directions close to an optic axis $\left(\text{where } 2\varepsilon > \frac{\pi}{4}\right)$. Hence the arcs of the spirals appear darkest along the

[1] The observation of a continuous expansion or contraction in the ring system as the analyser is rotated is a very sensitive method of testing for optical activity of a biaxial crystal.

[2] S. PANCHARATNAM: Proc. Ind. Acad. Sci. A **45**, 402 (1957).

[3] Here $\varDelta$ and ϱ refer to the retardation and total rotation for the whole plate and not for unit thickness as in (39.4) or (5.2).

diameter perpendicular to the plane of vibration of the analyser. It must be emphasised that this does not hold at greater angular distances, $2\varepsilon < \frac{\pi}{4}$, so that towards the border of the figure the zones above which the rings appear darkest are 45° to the plane of the analyser as in inactive crystals.

If the polarising state (L) is changed to its opposite state (R) and the analyser is rotated to its orthogonal state there will be no change in the observed figure since φ (in Fig. 67) remains unaltered and $2\alpha_1'$ and $2\alpha_2'$ are changed to their supplements.

We may summarise the above results in a form applicable both to right and left rotating sections of quartz. The hand (left or right) of the spirals observed

Fig. 68.

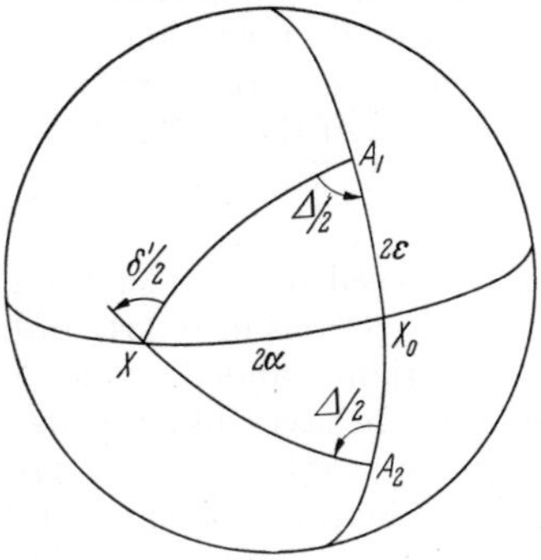

Fig. 69.

Fig. 68. Spiral curves observed in a basal section of quartz with a circular polariser and a linear analyser.

Fig. 69. Airy's spirals. Poincaré representation to prove that in parallel light two equal sections of quartz (first left-handed and the second right-handed) superposed with the corresponding principal planes coinciding, is equivalent to a single optically inactive birefringent plate.

with a circular polariser and a linear analyser is opposite to that of the quartz. When the hand of the circular polariser is opposite to that of the quartz, the common tangent to the spirals at the origin is at an azimuth $-\varrho$ with respect to the analyser vibrations where ϱ is the optical rotation of the basal section measured with the usual sign convention. Close to the optic axis the spirals appear darkest along the diameter normal to the vibration direction of the analyser. A change in the hand of the circular polariser merely rotates the entire figure through a right angle.

From Fig. 67 it is seen that when the polarising and the analysing states are interchanged, only the sign of φ is altered. The same result is obtained by the change of the sign of 2ϑ. Hence the spiral figures exhibited with a linear polariser and a circular analyser may be derived from the figure obtained when the polariser and the analyser are interchanged by reflecting the latter about the plane of vibration of the analyser.

δ) Airy's spirals due to two superposed basal sections of quartz. Let us first consider the case when *parallel* light is incident normally on two superposed sections of quartz, the first being left handed and the second right handed; it is further supposed that both plates are of the same thickness and cut at the same angle to the optic axis, being superposed such that the corresponding principal planes of the two plates are in coincidence.

Referring to Fig. 69, the state of the faster elliptic vibration of ellipticity ε propagated in the first plate is represented by the point A_1 of latitude 2ε. The state of the faster vibration propagated in the second plate will then be represented by the point A_2, which has the same longitude as A_1 but has a latitude -2ε. In order to combine the action of the two successive plates, we construct the isosceles triangle A_1XA_2 as indicated in Fig. 69, the base angles $\sphericalangle A_2A_1X$ and $\sphericalangle XA_2A_1$ being both equal to $\Delta/2$, Δ being the retardation of each plate.

We now apply the theorem for compounding rotations given in Fig. 8 of Sect. 5β. An anticlockwise rotation of the sphere about A_1 through twice the internal angle at A_1 (representing the action of the first plate) followed by an anticlockwise rotation about A_2 through twice the internal angle at A_2 (representing the action of the second plate) is equivalent to a single rotation about the axis X lying on the equator (Fig. 69) through twice the external angle at X. In other words, the combination is equivalent to a single optically inactive birefringent plate of retardation δ', the faster vibration direction being at an azimuth $-\alpha$ with respect to the common principal plane of the quartz plates (containing the major axis of the faster ellipse propagated in each plate). From the spherical triangle A_1XX_0 we have

$$\tan 2\alpha = \tan \tfrac{1}{2}\Delta \sin 2\varepsilon. \tag{65.4}$$

We now proceed to consider the *convergent* light figures exhibited by two superposed basal sections of quartz of equal thickness, the first being left handed and the second right handed. Since for any particular direction of propagation the combination behaves like an inactive crystal between crossed nicols, we should expect the appearance of "isogyres" along the zones where the equivalent planes of the combination coincide with the vibration direction of the polariser and analyser. The "isogyres" would not however take the form of a uniaxial cross since the equivalent principal planes for any particular direction of propagation do not coincide with the principal planes of the individual plates. If the azimuth of any point in the field of view with respect to the vibration direction of the polariser be as usual denoted by ϑ (Fig. 64), then dark isogyres obviously occur where $\vartheta = \alpha$ or $\frac{\pi}{2} + \alpha$ so that the "isogyres" will occur at

$$\tan 2\vartheta = \tan \tfrac{1}{2}\Delta \sin 2\varepsilon. \tag{65.5}$$

This takes the form of four mutually enwrapping left handed spirals[1]. This may be seen particularly for directions close to the axis where, as a first approximation by setting $\sin 2\varepsilon = 1$ in Eq. (65.5) the isogyres would be determined by [see Eq. (65.3)]

$$\Delta = \sqrt{A\, r^2 + 4\varrho^2} = 2n\pi + 4\vartheta. \tag{65.6}$$

These dark curves consist of four left hand spirals, each of which is rotated by 90° with respect to the adjacent one. At the centre the spirals touch two perpendicular lines inclined at an angle $\varrho/2$ (since $\Delta = 2\varrho$ at the optic axis) to the planes polarisation and analysation on the left hand; where ϱ is the rotation of the plane of polarisation produced by any one of the plates.

In addition we have the usual circular curves where the retardation δ' of the equivalent plate is a multiple of 2π and it can be shown from Fig. 69 that these will coincide with the circles $\Delta = 2n\pi$. The sense of description of the AIRY's spiral is reversed when the right handed plate is placed first, because the sign of α in Fig. 69 would then be changed.

b) Absorbing inactive crystals.

66. General introduction. Very remarkable optical phenomena are exhibited by absorbing crystals in the vicinity of the optic axes. Thus BREWSTER discovered

[1] See WALKER [5], p. 368.

long ago that, when an extended source of unpolarised light is viewed through a highly dichroic crystalline plate cut normal to one of the optic axes, two dark brushes—the BREWSTER's brushes—are seen. In the interference between crossed polaroids the dark isogyres do not in general pass through the optic axial directions as they do in the case of transparent crystals. These phenomena can be broadly explained using the approximate theory mentioned in Sect. 43 where the waves propagated along any direction are taken to be linearly polarised. We have seen however that according to the rigorous theory the two waves are really elliptically polarised with non-orthogonal states. Corresponding to this we meet with phenomena which have no parallel whatsoever in the case of transparent crystals. Thus, if the incident light is polarised, then even without an analyser behind the plate, feeble interference phenomena—*the idiophanic rings*—are seen. These arise because the two beams into which the incident light is decomposed along any direction can directly interfere with one another as they are not orthogonally polarised. More striking is the fact that, with an analyser behind the plate, idiophanic interference rings appear even with the incident light completely unpolarised. The explanation of this phenomenon leads us to the concept of the partial coherence between the component non-orthogonal beams into which the incident unpolarised light is split.

We shall not be dealing with the case of uniaxial crystals, because from the demands of symmetry itself the dichroism will necessarily be weak for directions near the optic axis, and hence the phenomena observed are usually not of such great interest. The interference phenomena exhibited by such crystals have been extensively dealt with by SZIVESSY [*1*], POCKELS [*2*].

Consider all directions as passing through the centre of a sphere and defined by their intersections with the spherical surface (Fig. 70a). The regions surrounding the optic axis N_1 which we take as the origin may be approximated by the plane of the paper, the plane $N_1 N_2$ representing the axial plane. We shall be considering the case when the optic axial angle is not very small although the extension to that case is fairly straight forward[1]. N_2 has been enclosed in brackets as it is not capable of being represented in the figure itself.

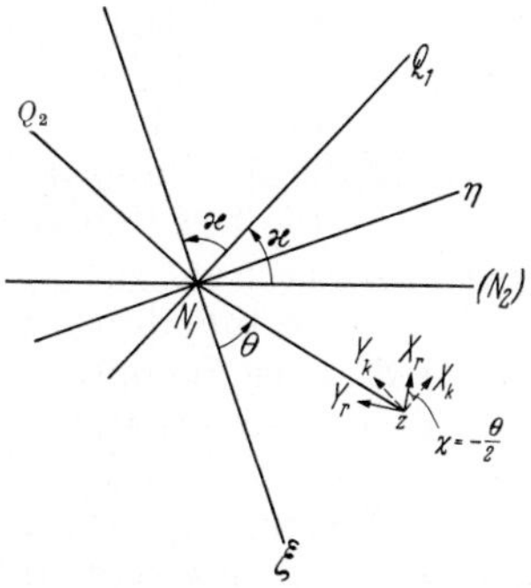

Fig. 70 a. Figure illustrating the different axes to explain convergent light figures in absorbing biaxial crystals. N_1 and N_2 are the optic axes, $N_1 Q_1$, $N_1 Q_2$ the major and minor axes of section of absorption ellipsoid, X_r, Y_r principal planes of linear birefringence, X_k, Y_k principal planes of linear dichroism (parallel to $N_1 Q_1$, $N_1 Q_2$) for a point z; $N_1 \xi$ and $N_1 \eta$ lines along which major and minor axes of sections of index ellipsoid and absorption ellipsoid coincide.

Let $N_1 Q_1$ and $N_2 Q_2$ be the traces of the major and minor axes of the section of the absorption ellipsoid taken normal to the optic axial direction, the angle $Q_1 N_1 N_2$ being denoted by $\varkappa$. These may also be taken to be the principal directions of absorption for any other general point in the small range of directions considered[2]. The principal planes of absorption X_k, Y_k for the point z are parallel to $N_1 Q_1$ and $N_2 Q_2$ and are indicated by dotted lines. On the other hand, the principal planes of linear birefringence vary very rapidly with direction. We have seen in Sect. 34 that for a point of azimuth α with respect to $N_1 N_2$ the slower

[1] S. BOGULOWSKI: Ann. d. Phys. **44**, 1084 (1914).

[2] This will not be the case when the optic axis is near the circular section of the absorption ellipsoid. In such a case the dichroism would be so weak that phenomena of interest will usually be not observable.

vibration direction makes an angle $\frac{\alpha}{2}+\frac{\pi}{2}$ with respect to N_1N_2. (The principal planes of linear birefringence X_r, Y_r are denoted by bold lines for the general point z in the Fig. 70a.) It is therefore clear that the major axes of the sections of the index and absorption ellipsoid will coincide for points on $N_1\xi$, which is at an azimuth $2\mathsf{K}-\pi$ with respect to N_1N_2. We shall choose $N_1\xi$ and the perpendicular direction $N_1\eta$ as the axes of coordinates since the phenomena we are about to discuss exhibit a certain symmetry with respect to these axes.

It may be noted here that as the azimuth of z with respect to $N_1\xi$ is increased, the azimuth of X_r increases at half the rate while X_k remains all the while parallel to N_1Q_1. Hence if ϑ is the azimuth of the point z with respect to $N_1\xi$, χ the angle X_k makes with X_r, then

$$\chi=-\frac{\vartheta}{2}. \tag{66.1}$$

β) Phenomena explicable on the elementary theory. Along the optic axes two waves linearly polarised along the principal axes of linear dichroism N_1Q_1 and N_1Q_2 are propagated, their absorption coefficients k_1 and k_2 being determined by the lengths of these axes. Because of this the optic axial direction does not in general appear extinguished between crossed polaroids (unlike the case of transparent crystals) but shows two extinction positions as the crossed polaroids are rotated together. These positions occur when the vibration directions of the polariser coincides with either N_1Q_1 or N_1Q_2. At other positions of the polariser the incident vibration is split into two linear vibrations which are differentially absorbed and which are propagated with the same velocity. These compound together to form a linear vibration whose plane of polarisation would have turned towards the less absorbed component. The correctness of this explanation is shown by the fact that the optic axial direction can be extinguished by rotating the analyser from the crossed position. In fact it is possible to compute the difference in the absorption coefficients between the two linear vibrations propagated along the optic axis from a measure of this rotation.

We have seen that, for directions not in the vicinity of the optic axis (Sect. 43), the waves may be regarded as linearly polarised as in transparent crystals, with the additional property that they have different absorption coefficients determined by the intercepts that these vibration directions make with the absorption ellipsoid. By assuming that these results continue to hold very close to the optic axes (Mallard theory) an explanation of the phenomenon of *Brewster's brushes* may be given. The clue to the explanation of this phenomenon lies in the fact that in the neighbourhood of the optic axis the vibration direction for any point in the field of view changes rapidly with the azimuth, leading to a corresponding rapid change in the absorption coefficients. With unpolarised light of intensity I_0 incident, the intensity of the emergent light at any point will obviously be

$$I=\frac{I_0}{2}\left(e^{-k' z}+e^{-k'' z}\right) \tag{66.2}$$

where k' and k'' are the absorption coefficients of the two waves propagated along that direction. Since we have already assumed that the section of the absorption ellipsoid does not vary over the range considered, the mean of the absorption coefficients may be considered constant for all directions (in the angular range covered). This follows from the property of any two perpendicular radii of an ellipse. Hence the emergent intensity I is the sum of two terms whose product is a constant. From a well known theorem in algebra it acquires its minimum value when the two terms are equal i.e. $k'=k''$, and its maximum value when the absorption coefficients differ by the maximum extent. The latter will occur for points in the plane $N_1\xi$ since in this case the vibration directions lie along the principal axes of the section of the absorption ellipsoid. On the other hand, the absorption coefficients will be equal (and I will be a minimum) in the plane $N_1\eta$ since the vibration directions will be inclined at 45° to the principal planes of dichroism. This explains the occurrence of two absorption brushes (intensity minima) on either side of the optic axis N_1 lying in the plane. The two brushes do not pass through the optic axis because k' and k'' are practically constant in the vicinity of the optic axis and there is no minimum in that region.

Since for any point on $N_1\xi$ the waves are linearly polarised along N_1Q_1 and N_1Q_2 i.e. the major and minor axes of the section of the absorption ellipsoid, the two waves have the least and the greatest coefficients of absorption for all the points on the line $N_1\xi$. Hence with a polariser or analyser set with its vibration direction parallel to N_1Q_2, a dark brush passing through the optic axis forms in the plane $N_1\xi$, while if the vibration direction is parallel to N_1Q_1 a white brush appears in the same position. Incidentally, this also demonstrates directly the existence of dichroism along the optic axis.

It may be remarked that the above phenomenon will be simplified if N_1N_2 be a plane of symmetry or perpendicular to an axis of symmetry as will occur in an orthorhombic crystal and can sometimes occur in a monoclinic crystal. In this case the principal diameter of the section of the absorption ellipsoid must be along and perpendicular to the axial plane. Then N_1Q_1 will lie on the axial plane. Hence the absorption brushes will lie in a plane perpendicular to the axial plane.

The above simplified theory does not explain some of the important features connected with this phenomenon. For example, when the plate is viewed between crossed polaroids in a general setting it is not the optic axial directions alone that remain unextinguished but the region of non-extinction extends over a finite strip passing through the optic axis. In fact the extinction along the isogyre becomes perfect only at the boundary of the field of view. The isogyres however are perfectly dark for the setting when they pass through the optic axis. These facts by themselves are sufficient to show that while the waves may be linearly polarised for the points on the plane N,ξ, this is not so for any general direction of propagation. Again, the BREWSTER's brushes show incipient traces of interference phenomena. These features can be accounted for only when the elliptical polarisation of the waves propagated along a general direction is taken into account.

67. Results of the detailed theory. According to Sect. 45 except when the principal planes of linear birefringence coincide with those of linear dichroism i.e. except along $N_1\xi$, the waves propagated will be elliptically polarised. The two vibrations have their major axes crossed, possess the same numerical ellipticity and are described in the *same* sense. For directions not too close to the optic axis where the square of the ellipticity may be neglected, the major axes of the ellipses may be taken to lie along the principal planes of linear birefringence, their refractive indices and absorption coefficients being determined as though they were linearly polarised. According to the results of Sect. 48 the common ellipticity of the two waves propagated along any arbitrary direction is given by

$$\varepsilon = -\frac{k}{2\delta}\sin 2\chi \tag{67.1}$$

or

$$\varepsilon = +\frac{k}{2\delta}\sin\vartheta \tag{67.2}$$

from Eq. (66.1). Here k, the superposed linear dichroism, which is taken to be constant over the area of the figure, is therefore equal to the difference in the absorption coefficients $k_2 - k_1$ of the waves propagated along the optic axial directions. The linear birefringence δ on the other hand, unlike k, increases as we move away from the optic axis, being proportional to the angular distance from N_1 (see Sect. 34).

Eq. (67.2) also shows that the sense of description of the ellipses on either side of $N_1\xi$ will be opposite. Further, as we proceed along the circular curve of constant birefringence described about the optic axis, the maximum ellipticity is obtained for points on $N_1\eta$ where the principal planes of linear birefringence and dichroism have the maximum inclination of 45°.

Towards the border, the waves approximate to linear vibrations parallel to the planes of linear birefringence. The continuous transition from this towards waves polarised along principal planes of linear dichroism (along the optic axial direction) is not revealed by the approximate formula given above, which is not applicable for directions close to the optic axis.

We now turn to the rigorous formula (47.5). We may first from simple considerations determine the state of polarisation along $N_1\xi$ and $N_1\eta$. Along the former the waves are rigorously linearly polarised as the principal directions of linear dichroism and linear birefringence coincide. Along $N_1\eta$ however they are inclined at 45° for which $2\chi = -\frac{\pi}{2}$. Substituting this in Eq. (47.5) and considering Fig. 45 we have for $k > \delta$

$$2\varphi = \frac{\pi}{2}$$

which gives

$$\sin 2\psi = \sin 2\varepsilon = \frac{\delta}{k}$$

and for

$$\delta > k, \quad 2\psi = \frac{\pi}{2}$$

giving

$$\sin 2\varphi = \sin 2\varepsilon = \frac{k}{\delta}.$$

Hence when we proceed from the optic axis along $N_1\eta$, the two vibrations, initially polarised along the principal planes of absorption, open out into two right elliptic vibrations and become two identical right circular vibrations at the point C_1 for which the magnitudes of linear dichroism and birefringence become equal. Further on, these split again into two elliptic vibrations, now with their major axes in the principal planes of linear birefringence, tending to the form of two orthogonal linear vibrations at the border of the field of view. A similar behaviour holds for the η axis except that the waves are now left elliptically polarised since $2\chi = +\frac{\pi}{2}$.

Again at the point C_1' for which $k = \delta$, the two elliptic vibrations take the form of one left circular vibration. C_1 and C_1' are the singular axes which are highly characteristic of the behaviour of absorbing crystals. We have already discussed the properties of the singular axes previously (Sect. 55).

For a general direction of propagation the orientation of the major axes and the ellipticities are given by Eqs. (47.7) and (47.8). However their variations over the field of view are somewhat complicated, but have been discussed in some detail by VOIGT[1] whose result we shall quote. These results are summarised in Fig. 70b.

(a) The vibration ellipses of the two waves corresponding to the same direction have constant ratio of axes along circles whose centres lie on the straight line through C_1 and C_1', and whose radii are such that all the circles cut the circles described on $C_1 C_1'$ as diameter orthogonally. The ellipses degenerate to circles at C_1 and C_1' and become straight lines in the ξ axis. The direction of vibration is of opposite sense on the two sides of the ξ axis, though everywhere the same for the two waves.

(b) The orientations of the principal axes of the vibration ellipses is constant along equilateral hyperbolae which pass through C_1 and C_1' (indicated by the dotted lines), the coordinate axes ξ and η being special cases of these hyperbolae. The orientation of the axes of the ellipse corresponding to one segment of one hyperbola is indicated by an arrow corresponding to the principal axis of birefringence. It will be seen that these directions are not constant for the entire hyperbolic branches but that they become rotated through 45° on passing through the points C_1 and C_1' of circular polarisation. The differences in the refractive indices and the absorption coefficients of the waves given by Eqs. (48.3) and (48.5) have also been plotted by VOIGT as a function of direction and he gives the following results.

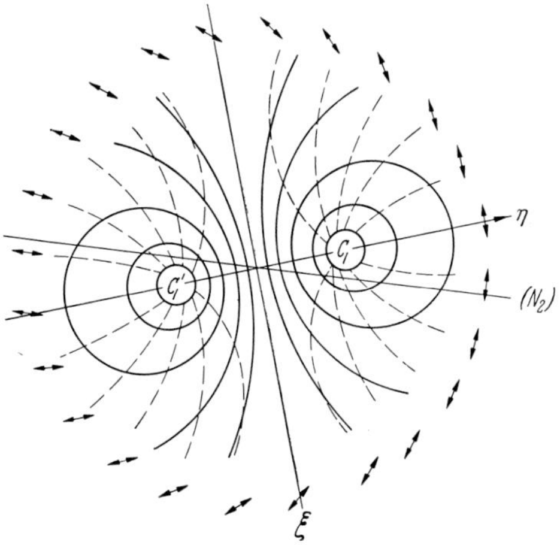

Fig. 70b. Convergent light figure (due to VOIGT) showing the variations of the states of polarisation of the waves for directions of propagation close to an optic axis in an absorbing biaxial crystal cut ⊥ r to one optic axis. C_1 and C_1' are the singular axes associated with this optic axis.

(c) The difference in the refractive indices may be considered constant over ellipses having the points C_1 and C_1' as foci. This difference vanishes along the straight line $C_1 C_1'$ and increases as the ellipses open out. However they are practically circles as the angle between the singular axes is usually extremely small in all cases.

(d) The absorption coefficients k', k'' of the two waves are constant over hyperbolae having their foci at C_1 and C_1'. They have the same value along the straight lines $C_1 C_1'$ and along any hyperbola have values which differ from k_0 by equal amounts of opposite sign, the maximum difference of the absorption occuring along the ξ axis.

68. The singular axes.—Experimental observations on iolite[2]. The existence, even in an inactive crystal, of axes along which a circularly polarised wave is propagated without change is most directly confirmed by observing the convergent light figures between a circular polariser and a crossed circular analyser. Fig. 71a shows the figure observed with iolite, an orthohombic crystal, kept between a left circular polariser and a right circular analyser. The eccentric spot just below the axial plane obviously represents the direction along which the incident left

[1] W. VOIGT: Phil. Mag. **4**, 90 (1902).

[2] S. PANCHARATNAM: Proc. Ind. Acad. Sci. A **42**, 235 (1955); A **45**, 1 (1957).

circular vibration is propagated unchanged and crossed out by the analyser. That along this direction a circular vibration of opposite sense is not transmitted unchanged (as would be the case in a transparent optically active medium) is proved by observing the figure between a right circular polariser and a left circular analyser. This is shown in Fig. 71 b where the other singular axis (above the axial plane) is extinguished.

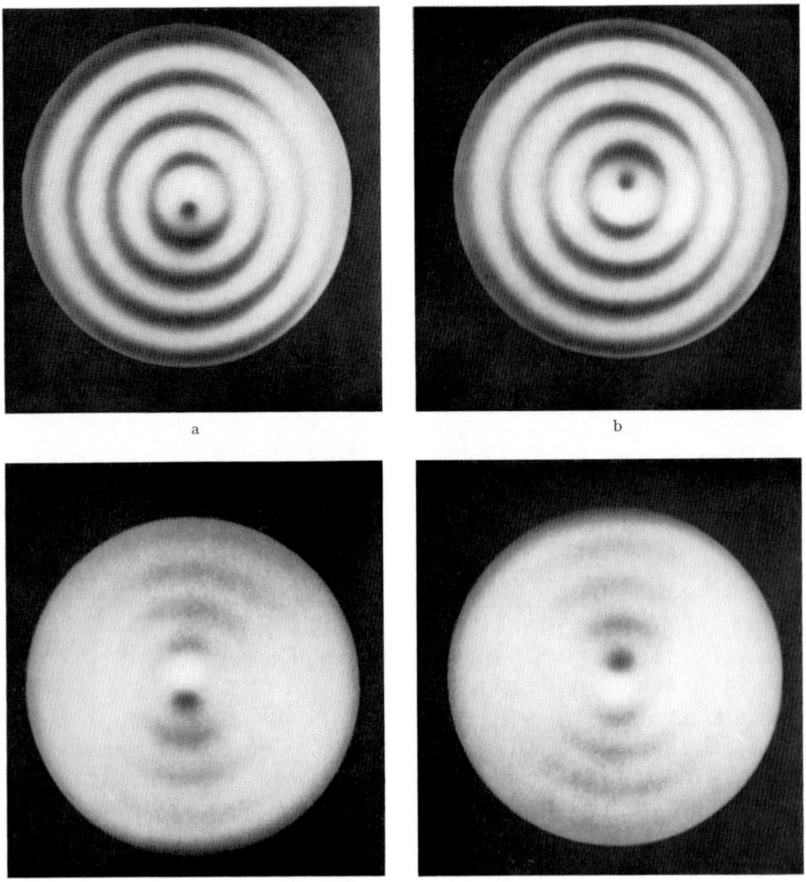

a b c d

Fig. 71 a—d. Optic axial interference figures in convergent light by the absorbing biaxial mineral iolite, the axial plane being horizontal. (a) Left circular polariser and right circular analyser, lower singular axis extinguished. (b) Right-circular polariser and left-circular analyser, upper singular axis extinguished. (c) Left-circular polariser *alone*, dark rings in lower half of figure correspond to bright rings in upper part of figure. Lower singular axis appears darker than the other. (d) Left-circular analyser *alone*; asymmetry with respect to axial plane reversed.

It is possible to show using an elliptic polariser and a crossed elliptic analyser that for any point on the strip joining $C_1 C_1'$ (Fig. 70b), the two waves propagated are: elliptic vibrations of the *same* sense, with their major axes not lying coincident with the principal axes of birefringence, in conformity with the theory. These experiments also show that as the singular axes are approached, the two elliptic vibrations tend to the form of identical circular vibrations.

Since along the singular axis the only wave that can be propagated unchanged is a circular vibration described in one particular sense, the following interesting question arises: What will happen if for example a left circular vibration is incident along a singular axis where only a right circular vibration is propagated unchanged? It had been supposed by VOIGT[1] that the light would be totally reflected, the reflection being partial in practical cases. However the question can be put to test by removing the circular analyser in the arrangement used for Fig. 71 a, but keeping the circular polariser. The result is shown in Fig. 71 c where it will be noted that the upper singular axis where the incident left circular vibration cannot be propagated unchanged actually appears brighter than the lower axis where it can be propagated unchanged, disproving VOIGT's conjecture. The explanation has been considered in Sect. 49. It has been shown that, when left circular vibration is incident in the direction of a singular axis along which only a right circular vibration is propagated unchanged, the incident vibration is propagated into the medium with a progressive change of state of polarisation under the superposed effects of linear birefringence and linear dichroism. Theory also predicts that the state of polarisation which is not propagated unchanged has the smaller absorption coefficient, as is actually observed. The state of polarisation of the emergent light has also been found to be in conformity with theory.

69. Idiophanic rings without an analyser. It will be noticed in Fig. 71 c that feeble interference phenomena are observed even though no analyser has been kept behind the crystal. This is also found to be the case when linear or elliptic polarised light is incident. Such a situation cannot occur if the waves propagated are orthogonally polarised as in transparent crystals, for orthogonally polarised waves (even though coherent) cannot directly interfere unless brought to the same state of polarisation by an analyser. But if the vibrations A and B are non-orthogonal, then B can be resolved into two parts, one of state A and the other in the orthogonal state A_a. The former can interfere with A. Hence the occurrence of interference phenomena without the use of the analyser proves that the waves propagated along a general direction are non-orthogonally polarised. The visibility of the interference phenomenon will however be not very pronounced since the extent of the interference will depend on the non-orthogonality factor. The formula for the interference of two non-orthogonal beams is given by (Sect. 4):

$$I = I_1' + I_2' + 2\sqrt{I_1' I_2'}\cos\tfrac{1}{2}\widehat{AB}\cos\Delta' \qquad (69.1)$$

where $\widehat{AB}$ is the angular separation of the states A and B on the Poincaré sphere. We shall for simplicity confine ourselves to the case when the incident light is left circularly polarised as in Fig. 71 c.

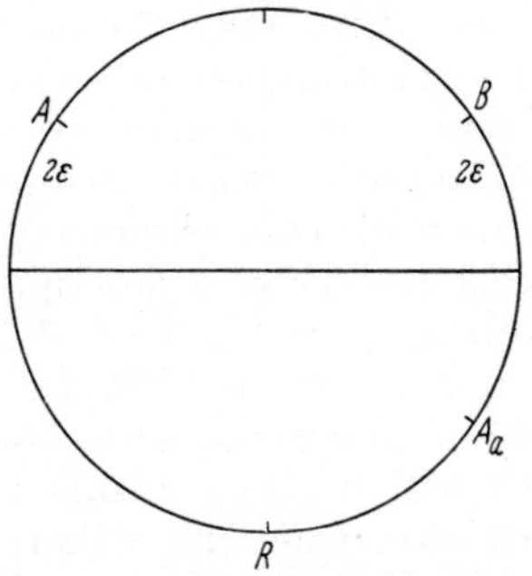

Fig. 72a. Poincaré representation for computing the intensity transmitted for the case of Fig. 71 c.

Two elliptic vibrations A and B propagated along any direction have their major axes crossed and have the same ellipticity ε (which according to the sign convention means that they are described in the same sense). Hence on the Poincaré sphere the longitudes of A and B differ by π but their lattitudes are the same, equal to 2ε as drawn in Fig. 72a.

When the incident vibration of intensity I_0 in the state L is decomposed into two vibrations in the states A and B their intensities I_1 and I_2 are given by

[1] W. VOIGT: Ann. d. Phys. **2**, 1002 (1908).

4.5 and 4.6 as

$$I_1 = I_0 \frac{\sin^2 \frac{1}{2} \widehat{BL}}{\sin^2 \frac{1}{2} \widehat{AB}}, \tag{69.2}$$

$$I_2 = I_0 \frac{\sin^2 \frac{1}{2} \widehat{AL}}{\sin^2 \frac{1}{2} \widehat{AB}}, \tag{69.3}$$

where

$$\widehat{BL} = \widehat{AL} = \frac{\pi}{2} - 2\varepsilon \quad \text{and} \quad \frac{1}{2} \widehat{AB} = \frac{\pi}{2} - 2\varepsilon. \tag{69.4}$$

Their initial phase difference according to formulae 4.14 is 0 or π according as ε is positive or negative (As the three points ABR are coplanar the spherical excess of the triangle ABR is π or 0 according as ε is $-ve$ or $+ve$). The waves have different absorption coefficients and, on emerging from the plate, their intensities I_1' and I_2' being equal to $I_1 e_a^2$ and $I_2 e_b^2$ respectively the relative phase advance Δ' of the first beam over the second is equal to δ or $\pi + \delta$ according as ε is $+ve$ or $-ve$. The minima occur when the phase difference Δ' between the interfering beams is π, 3π etc. In the lower half of the Fig. 71c ε is positive, i.e., the ellipses are left-rotating; hence $\Delta' = \delta$ and therefore minima occur for values $\delta = \pi$, 3π etc. On the other hand, in the upper half of the figure ε is negative and hence $\Delta' = \delta + \pi$. Hence minima occur for $\delta = 0, 2\pi, 4\pi$, etc. The fringes in the lower half of the figure would therefore be shifted by half a fringe width relative to those appearing in the upper half. The fringes in the upper half of the figure should coincide with the fringes observed with crossed polariser and analyser and this may be verified by comparison with Fig. 71b.

There is also an asymmetry in the average intensity distribution. The intensity at any point in the field of view is obtained by substituting the values of I_1', I_2' and Δ' in (69.1) and will be given by

$$I = \frac{I_0}{2(1 + \sin 2\varepsilon)} \left(e_a^2 + e_b^2 + 2 e_a e_b \sin 2\varepsilon \cos \delta\right). \tag{69.5}$$

The expression for I becomes indeterminate for $\varepsilon = -\frac{\pi}{4}$ i.e., along the singular axis where only the right circular vibration can be propagated unchanged. The propagation in this direction has, however, been considered in the last section. When right circular polarised light is used, the sign of the third term in (69.5) has to be changed and the assymmetry about the axial plane will be reversed. This asymmetry of the figure when circular light is used is a clear proof that the sense of description of the ellipses on either side of the axial plane is different.

When linear polarised light is used, the interference figures do not exhibit any asymmetry and the figures are clearest when the incident vibration is either parallel or perpendicular to the axial plane. Further a dark band appears along the axial plane (for orthorhombic crystals like iolite), when the vibration direction of the polariser is set parallel to the vibration direction of the more intensely absorbed wave propagated along the optic axes (i.e. $O\xi$, Fig. 70a).

All these phenomena can be explained by a procedure similar to that adopted for circular polarised light; but we shall not deal with them here. For further details, reference may be made to POCKELS [2], VOIGT[1], PANCHARATNAM[2].

70. Phenomena involving partial coherence. *α) Partial coherence.* Fig. 71d shows that faint interference rings observed when only a left circular analyser

[1] W. VOIGT: Ann. d. Phys. **9**, 367 (1902).
[2] S. PANCHARATNAM: Proc. Ind. Acad. Sci. A **45**, 1 (1957).

is kept behind the plate without any polariser in front. In seeking for an explanation of this occurrence of faint interference rings, even though the incident light is unpolarised, we are led to the subject of partial coherence. As mentioned in Sect. 11, two beams in different states of polarisation are said to be incoherent when they cannot be made to interfere even after being resolved into the same state of vibration by the use of an analyser.

When unpolarised light is incident on a transparent crystal like quartz, and it is viewed through an analyser alone, no interference figures are seen in convergent light. This clearly proves that when unpolarised light is split into two oppositely polarised beams, the component beams are incoherent. Simiarly, the experimental test of the complete coherence of two polarised beams is that interference effects of maximum clarity can be produced by the use of a suitable analyser. Since feeble interference phenomena occur in absorbing crystals, with the use of an analyser alone, it may be concluded that the two non-orthogonally polarised pencils into which an incident unpolarised beam is split, must be regarded as *partially* coherent. As shown in Sect. 11, the general formula for the interference of two partially coherent polarised beams is:

$$I = I_1 + I_2 + 2\gamma\sqrt{I_1 I_2}\cos C\cos\delta, \tag{70.1}$$

where γ is the degree of coherence and $2C$ is the angular separation between the two states on the Poincaré sphere.

The decomposition of unpolarised light into two non-orthogonal vibrations in any two states of polarisation A and B (separated by an angle $2C$ in the Poincaré sphere) may now be analysed. The unpolarised light may be replaced by two incoherent beams each of intensity $\frac{1}{2}I$ in the orthogonally polarised states A and A_a (see for example Fig. 72). The beam in the state of polarisation A_a may in turn be decomposed into two coherent beams in the non-orthogonal states of polarisation B and A. These latter two vibrations will have a phase difference of π, since A_a lies on the greater segment of the great circle through A and B (Sect. 4). Their intensities will be respectively,

$$\tfrac{1}{2}I\operatorname{cosec}^2 C \quad\text{and}\quad \tfrac{1}{2}I\cot^2 C,$$

as may be obtained by substituting $b=\pi$ and $a=\pi-C$ in Eqs. (4.5) and (4.6). Thus in a state of polarisation B, we have a beam of intensity $\frac{1}{2}I\operatorname{cosec}^2 C$, while in the state of polarisation A, we have two incoherent vibrations, which add to give a beam of the same intensity, $\frac{1}{2}I\operatorname{cosec}^2 C$. Of the latter beam, however, an independent fraction comprising of intensity $\frac{1}{2}I\cot^2 C$, and hence forming a fraction $\cos^2 c$, is completely coherent with the other beam and is opposed in phase to it. We may summarise thus—when unpolarised light is split into any two non-orthogonal vibrations, whose states are separated by an angle $2C$ on the Poincaré sphere, the intensities I_1 and I_2 of the component beams, their degree of coherence γ and their effective phase difference φ' are given by

$$I_1 = I_2 = I\operatorname{cosec}^2 C, \qquad \gamma = \cos C, \qquad \varphi' = \pi. \tag{70.2}$$

β) Idiophanic rings with analyser alone. We may apply the results mentioned above to discuss the idiophanic rings presented in unpolarised light by the use of an analyser alone. For the sake of simplicity, we confine our analysis to the case of a left circular analyser, used behind the plate as in obtaining the pattern in Fig. 71d.

The intensities I_1' and I_2' of the two beams in the states A and B emerging along any direction from the crystal plate and their effective phase-difference Δ' are given by (see Fig. 72)

$$I_1' = \tfrac{1}{2} I \frac{1}{\sin^2 \frac{1}{2} \widehat{AB}} e_a^2, \tag{70.3}$$

$$I_2' = \tfrac{1}{2} I \frac{1}{\sin^2 \frac{1}{2} \widehat{AB}} e_b^2, \tag{70.4}$$

$$\Delta' = \delta + \varphi_1 = \delta + \pi. \tag{70.5}$$

If I_1'' and I_2'' be the resolved components of the beam transmitted by the analyser, and Δ'' the phase-difference between these components, then

$$I_1'' = I_1' \cos^2 \tfrac{1}{2} \widehat{AL}, \tag{70.6}$$

$$I_2'' = I_2' \cos^2 \tfrac{1}{2} \widehat{BL}, \tag{70.7}$$

$$\Delta'' = \Delta' + \varphi_2, \tag{70.8}$$

where φ_2 may be called the phase-difference introduced in the process of analysation. These resolved components, although in the same state of polarisation, are partially coherent, their degree of coherence γ being $\cos \frac{1}{2} \widehat{AB}$. The intensity at any point in the field of view is therefore obtained from the general interference formula (70.1), by substituting the value of the degree of coherence $\gamma = \cos \frac{1}{2} \widehat{AB}$ and by putting $\cos C = 1$, (as the two resolved components on passing through the analyser are in the same state of polarisation); thus

$$I = I_1'' + I_2'' + 2 \sqrt{I_1'' I_2''} \cos \widehat{AB} \cos \Delta''. \tag{70.9}$$

Now the phase-difference φ_2 introduced by analysation will be equal to 0 or π, according as L lies on the smaller or the greater segment of the great circle through A and B, i.e. according as ε is positive or negative. Hence in the upper half of the figure, where the ellipses propagated are rightrotating, minima occur at $\delta = \pi$, 3π etc., while in the lower half of the figure they occur at $\delta = 2\pi$, 4π etc., being shifted by half a fringe-width.

The intensity at any point in the field of view is obtained by substituting in (70.9) from (70.6) to (70.8) and (70.3) to (70.5) using (69.4):

$$I = \frac{I_0}{2(1 - \sin 2\varepsilon)} (e_a^2 + e_b^2 - 2 e_a e_b \sin 2\varepsilon \cos \delta). \tag{70.10}$$

Thus, the idiophanic rings with a left circular polariser are not the same as with a left circular analyser, but should be the same as with a right circular analyser, as may be seen from the fact that (70.10) goes over into (69.5) when 2ε is replaced by -2ε. However, it is found that the idiophanic rings with a *linear* analyser alone at a particular setting are exactly the same as those presented with a linear polariser alone kept at the same setting. It can be shown that this is a particular consequence of the fact that the two waves propagated along any direction are two crossed ellipses, having the same ellipticity and decribed in the same sense. This, however, is not the case in optically active absorbing crystal (vide Sects. 71 to 73).

It may be shown that the interference effects observed with the polariser P alone have the same visibility as those observed with (a) a polariser P_a alone, (b) an analyser of state P alone and (c) an analyser of state P_a alone. In the former case, the interfering beams are completely coherent, but the extent of their interference is limited because of the non-orthogonality of the two waves propagated in the crystal. In the latter case, the interfering beams transmitted by the analyser are in the same state of polarisation, but they are only partially coherent, the degree of coherency being determined by the identical non-orthogonality factor.

γ) Phenomena with partially circular-polarised light. In Sect. 11, it is shown that when two non-orthogonally polarised beams are mixed together incoherently, the result is a partially polarised beam. Hence, it should be possible for the converse phenomenon to occur under certain conditions. That is, for partially polarised incident light, it may so happen that the non-orthogonally polarised beams (into which the incident light is split) may be completely incoherent for some particular direction, so that near this region no interference effects should be observed, *even if the beams are resolved by an analyser.* This effect has been observed in iolite by PANCHARATNAM[1] with the incident light partially circularly polarised—say, left-circularly polarised light.

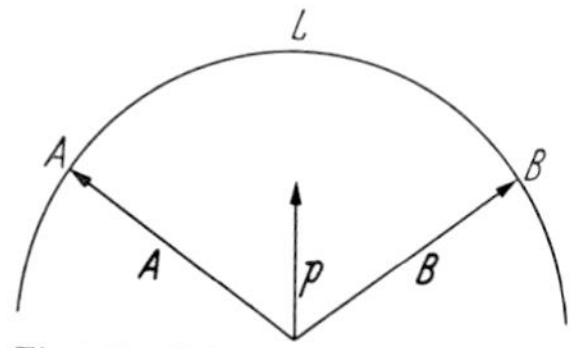

Fig. 72b. Poincaré representation for computing the case discussed in Sect. 70γ (illustrated in Fig. 73).

If the degree of polarisation be p, the incident light will be represented by a Poincaré vector of length p directed towards L (Fig. 72b). If the component completely polarised beams $\boldsymbol{A}$ and $\boldsymbol{B}$ are to be completely incoherent, then the following two equations must hold.

$$I\boldsymbol{p} = I_1\boldsymbol{A} + I_2\boldsymbol{B}, \qquad (70.11)$$

$$I = I_1 + I_2. \qquad (70.12)$$

Since $\boldsymbol{p}$ must be contained in the acute angle between A and B, such a resolution can occur only when the ellipticity ε is positive i.e., on the side of the axial plane where the ellipses propagated are left rotating. From symmetry, the intensities I_1 and I_2 of the component beams are equal to one another and hence equal to $\frac{1}{2}I$ from Eq. (70.12). Substituting this in Eq. (70.11), and resolving the vectors along $\boldsymbol{p}$, we see that such an incoherent resolution can occur only when

$$\sin 2\varepsilon = p. \qquad (70.13)$$

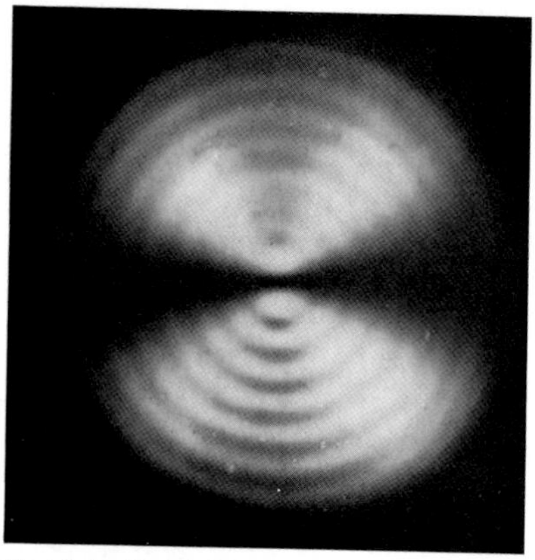
Fig. 73. Incident light partially left circularly polarised and linear analyser with vibration direction vertical. In the upper half of the figure the ring system fades away near the second and third rings and reappears further with a shift of half a fringe.

As we proceed outwards from the optic axis in a direction perpendicular to the axial plane (on the side of the axial plane where ε is positive), the ellipticity varies and near a particular region where condition (70.13) is satisfied, the visibility of the interference effect should become negligible. For other directions, the resolved beams will be partially coherent; the region defined by (70.13) is a particular case where the degree of coherence vanishes and on crossing which the effective phase difference changes by π. This behaviour is confirmed by experimental observation (Fig. 73).

When partially plane polarised light with the plane of polarisation of the polarised part at 45° to the axial plane is incident on a plate of iolite and it is

[1] S. PANCHARATNAM: Proc. Ind. Acad. Sci. A **45**, 1 (1957).

viewed through a circular analyser, a beautiful spiral has been observed[1]. The sense of the spiral does not depend on whether a right or a left circular analyser is used, but it changes sign when the azimuth of maximum polarisation is rotated by 90°. The phenomenon is also observed when the incident light is completely polarised, but the spirals are not so continuous. It can be shown that as in the case of transparent optically active crystals, the spirals arise because the sum of the phase differences introduced in the processes of decomposition and analysation increases continuously with the azimuth.

c) Absorbing optically active crystals.

71. Phenomena along the optic axis when dichroism is weak. *α) General description of the phenomena.* Little experimental work appears to have been done on the optical behaviour of crystals belonging to this class. However in one particular case, namely in amethystine quartz, which has an absorption in the yellow green region, extensive observations, though of a qualitative nature, have been reported[2] agreeing in detail with the theory presented in Sects. 50 to 55. The observations have been made with intensely coloured sectors of amethyst[3], carefully selected so as to exclude certain extraneous complicating features (such as twinning etc.) which are very often found in this substance. Such sectors, unlike quartz, are biaxial with the c axis of quartz appearing as the acute bisectrix. They show a pronounced dichroism near the axial directions, the elliptic section of the absorption ellipsoid having its major and minor axes lying respectively parallel and perpendicular to the axial plane.

In blue light, which is practically outside the absorption range, the dichroism is negligible and the interference figures observed between crossed polaroids are as in transparent optically active crystals, the isogyres not penetrating to the optic axial directions. The axial directions can however be extinguished by rotating the analyser from the crossed position, the rotation of the plane of polarisation thus measured agreeing with that for colourless quartz.

In red light, which is on the other side of the absorption maximum, the same sector exhibits a weak dichroism and the phenomena observed correspond to the case when the optical activity predominates over dichroism i.e. $|2\varrho| > k$, a case which has been dealt with in Sects. 53, 54. Here again the axial directions are not perfectly extinguished by isogyres when observed between crossed polaroids (Fig. 74a). They can be extinguished by rotating the analyser (Fig. 74b) but the rotation of the plane of polarisation thus measured is found to depend on the azimuth of the incident linear vibration. This proves that the waves propagated along the optic axis cannot be circularly polarised as in transparent active crystals. According to Sect. 53 the waves propagated along the axial directions should be elliptically polarised, the elliptic vibrations being exactly similar in form and orientation but described in opposite senses. (The major axes of the ellipse should be coincident, making an angle $\pm\frac{\pi}{4}$ with respect to the axial plane according as ϱ is $+ve$ or $-ve$.) This was verified to be true by viewing the crystal between crossed elliptic analysers (Sect. 21 δ). In the present case the principal planes of the quarter wave plates are set at 45° to the axial plane. Thus the principal axes of the incident elliptic vibration are at 45° to the axial plane. As the

[1] For a discussion of this and other phenomena see S. PANCHARATNAM: Proc. Ind. Acad. Sci. A **45**, 1 (1957).

[2] S. PANCHARATNAM: Proc. Ind. Acad. Sci. A **46**, 280 (1957); A **47**, 201, 210 (1958).

[3] The photographs illustrating thus section have been taken with right rotating amethyst. Correspondingly much of the discussion and figures refer to right rotating specimens.

ellipticity is altered by turning the crossed polaroids, it is observed that there are two settings of the coupled polaroids (symmetrically situated with respect to the principal planes of the $\lambda/4$ plates) where the optic axial directions are completely extinguished, confirming the view that the two waves propagated along this direction are elliptically polarised. Fig. 74c illustrates one such position, where the major axis makes an angle of $-45°$. ϱ in this case is negative.

β) Measurement of the optical rotatory power in the presence of weak dichroism. The variation of the rotation of the plane of polarisation with azimuth of the incident vibration may be explained by using the results of Sect. 53. The plane vibration is resolved into two elliptic vibrations which are propagated with different velocities but with the same absorption coefficient. These have to be

a

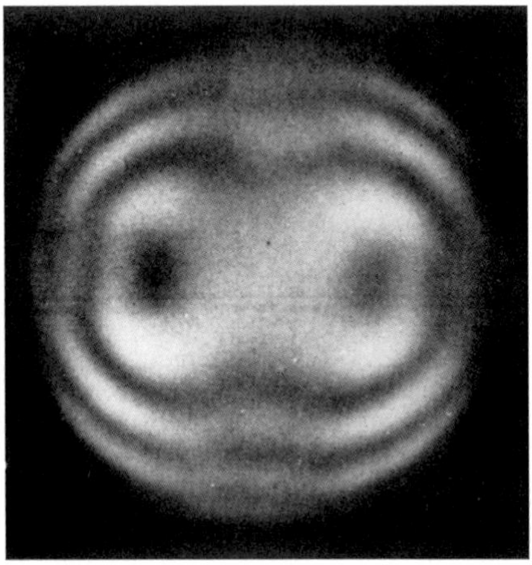

b

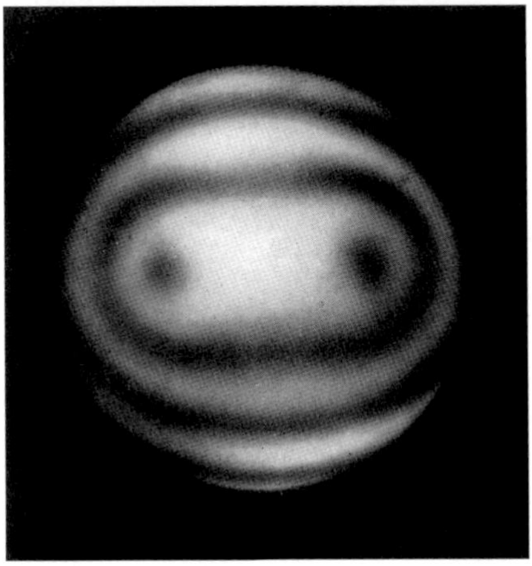

c

Fig. 74a—c. Biaxial interference figures exhibited by amethyst quartz in red light ($2\varrho < k$). (a) Between crossed polaroids with the polariser and analyser direction at 45° to the axial plane. The optic axial direction is not extinguished. (b) The analyser rotated to extinguish the optic axial direction. (The crystal is rotated to keep the polariser and analyser symmetrically oriented with respect to the axial plane.) (c) Optic axial directions extinguished between an elliptic polariser and a crossed elliptic analyser.

compounded after emergence from the plate. The actual rotatory power may be calculated from the measured rotations α_1 and α_2 observed with the incident vibration lying respectively parallel and perpendicular to the major axes of the ellipses propagated along the optic axis. In the former case the incident vibration represented by a point M (on the equator) Fig. 75 will be decomposed into two vibrations in states A and B which have the same longitudes as M. Since M is equidistant from A and B, and it lies on the arc AB itself, the intensities of the component beams will be equal and their initial phase difference will be zero [according to Eq. (4.10)]. The waves, on emerging from the plate, will have a phase difference φ, but will still be of equal intensity because of the equality of their absorption coefficients. Hence they will compound to give a vibration whose state will again be equidistant from A and B i.e. a linear vibration represented by a point C_1 on the equator. If ε_1' be the area of the triangle $C_{1a}BA$ where C_{1a} is a point opposite to C_1 then $\frac{1}{2}\varepsilon_1' = \pi - \varphi$. The spherical excess of the right angled triangle $C_{1a}BM$ is given by

$$\tan \tfrac{1}{4}\varepsilon' = \tan\omega \tan \tfrac{1}{2}(\pi - 2\alpha_1) \tag{71.1}$$

and so

$$\cot \tfrac{1}{2}\varphi = \tan\omega \cot\alpha_1 . \tag{71.2}$$

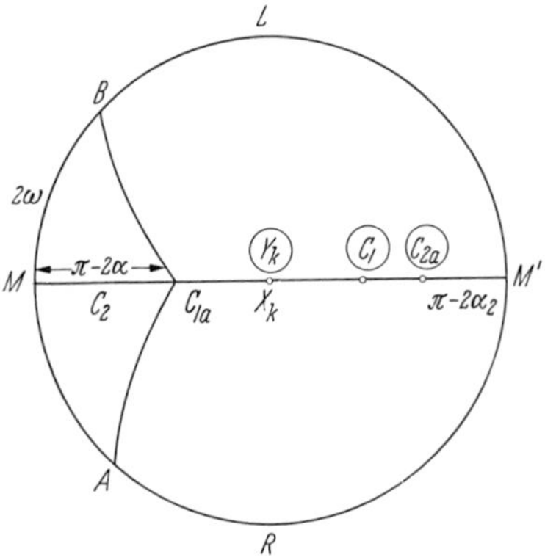

Fig. 75.

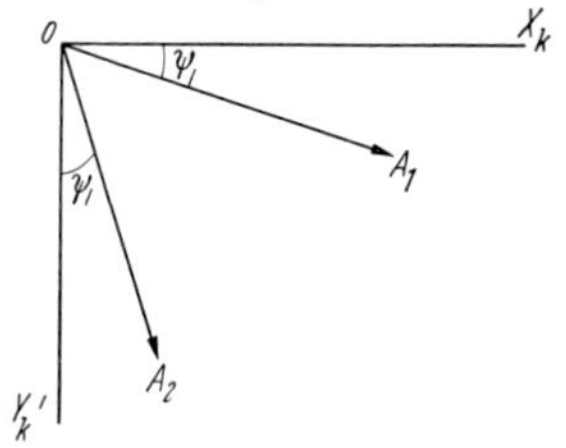

Fig. 76 a.

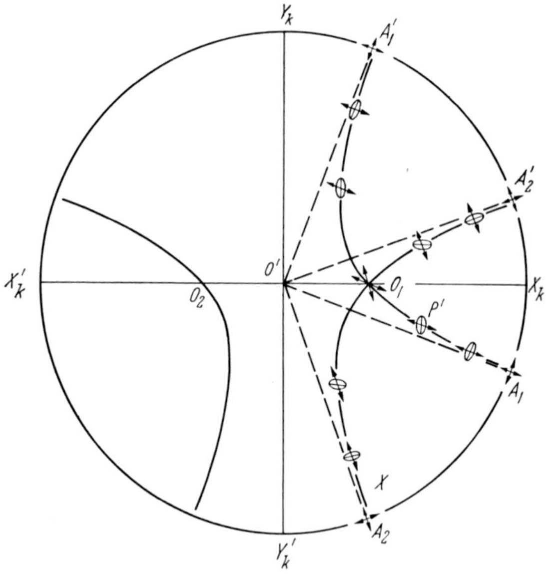

Fig. 76 b.

Fig. 75. The Poincaré sphere representation for explaining the apparent variation of optical rotation with the azimuth of the incident vibration in a biaxial crystal showing weak dichroism.

Fig. 76 a. Plate cut normal to an optic axis along which waves are propagated linearly polarised in non-orthogonal states A_1 and A_2.

Fig. 76 b. Convergent light figure depicting the variations of the states of polarisation of the waves for directions of propagation for particular zones in the field of view. O_1 and O_2 are the optic axes along which two non-orthogonal linearly polarised vibrations are propagated unchanged.

On the other hand if the azimuth of the incident vibration is parallel to the minor axis, it is represented by the state M'. The two initial vibrations A and B into which it is split will have an initial phase difference of $-\pi$ and a final phase difference of $\varphi - \pi$. The corresponding linear vibration obtained by composition being in the state C_2. Hence φ should be equal to half the spherical excess of the triangle $C_{2a}AB$ where C_{2a} is the point opposite to C_2. Proceeding as before

$$\tan \tfrac{1}{2}\varphi = \tan\omega \tan\alpha_2 . \tag{71.3}$$

From (71.2) and (71.3) we get

$$\tan^2\omega = \frac{\tan\alpha_1}{\tan\alpha_2} \tag{71.4}$$

and

$$\tan^2\varphi = \tan\alpha_1 \tan\alpha_2 . \tag{71.5}$$

From (71.5) we can calculate the relative phase advance φ gained by the faster wave on passage through the plate. The relative phase difference per unit path (φ/d) is not directly equal to $|2\varrho|$ since the waves are not circularly polarised but is related to it by equation

$$|\varrho| = \frac{1}{2}\,\frac{\varphi}{d}\Big/\sin|2\omega|. \tag{71.6}$$

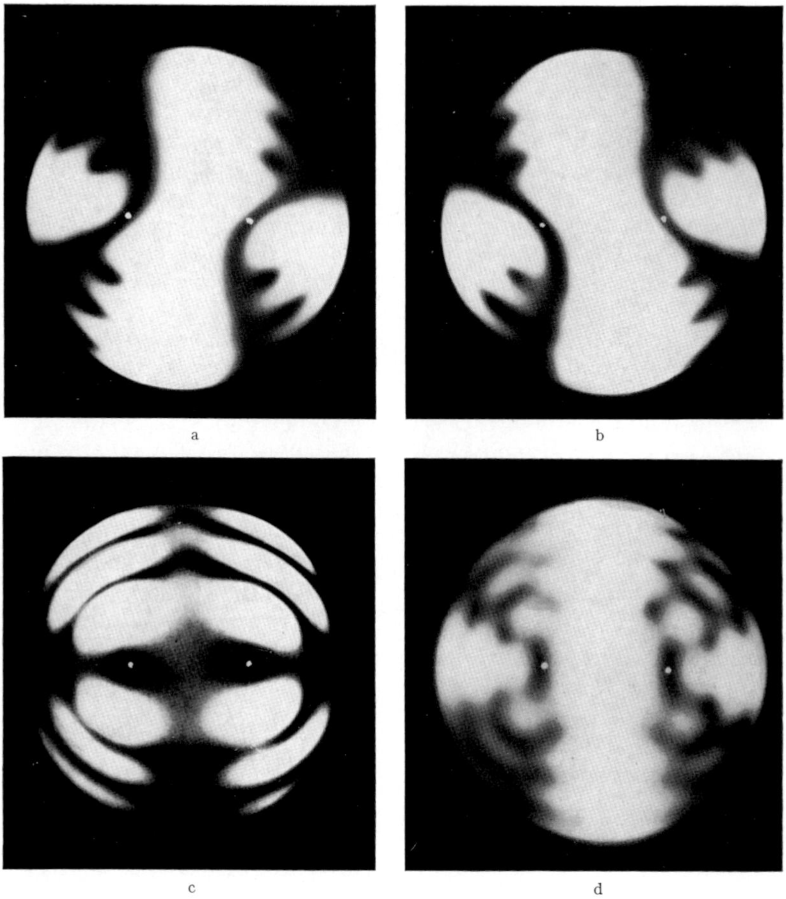

Fig. 77 a—d. Convergent light figures in amethyst quartz. (a) and (b) show the only two settings between crossed polaroids for which genuine isogyres passing through the optic axial directions are observed. The polariser and analyser settings are parallel to $O'A_1$ and $O'A_2$ of Fig. 76(b). (c) and (d). The optic axial directions crossed by turning the analyser from the crossed position. The polariser and analyser make equal angles ($\pm 59°$, $\pm 84\frac{1}{2}°$) with the axial plane.

The numerical ellipticity $|\omega|$ of the vibration propagated along the optic axis which is to be substituted in (71.6) can be determined from (71.4) or may be determined directly from the observations with the elliptic polariser and crossed elliptic analyser, described above. In the case of amethyst rough measurements show that the ellipticities determined by these two methods are practically the same. Further the optical rotation determined is also of the order of rotation in quartz.

72. Phenomena along the optic axis when dichroism is strong. The same sectors of amethyst which exhibit the phenomena (described in the last section) associated with weak dichroism can be used to study the case when $k > |2\varrho|$ by using a wavelength which lies in the heart of the absorption band. In fact, the dichroism for yellow light is so large that even the phenomenon of optical activity can be only inferred indirectly. When the convergent light figures are observed between crossed polaroids the optic axes in general are not extinguished. However there are two settings of the incident vibrations for which genuine isogyres are observed passing unmodified through the optic axes (Fig. 77a and b). This has a certain resemblance to the phenomenon observed in inactive absorbing crystals. But in this case the two settings of the incident vibrations are *not* at right angles but are equally inclined to the line drawn at 45° to the axial plane. Thus the waves propagated along the optic axes are not two orthogonal linearly polarised waves as in inactive absorbing crystals, but are linearly polarised along two non-orthogonal directions OA_1 and OA_2 (Fig. 76). This agrees with the deductions from theory in Sect. 53γ.

For any general setting of the incident vibration it is always found possible to extinguish the optic axial direction by rotating the analyser from the crossed position (Fig. 77c and d). This shows that the two waves cannot differ in their velocities but only in their absorption coefficient. The incident linear vibration will then be decomposed into two non-orthogonal vibrations in states P' and P'' according to the parallelogram law. After being differentially absorbed the vibrations emerging from the plate may be compounded (again by the parallelogram law) to yield a linear vibration whose azimuth would always have turned towards the less attenuated state P'. Hence by noting the settings of the polariser and the corresponding setting of the analyser at which the optic axis is extinguished, a simple calculation based on the above explanation enables the difference in the absorption coefficients $(k''-k')$ of the waves propagated along the axial direction to be estimated. The linear dichroism can be determined from the formula

$$k''-k' = k\cos 2\psi_1 \tag{72.1}$$

and the optical rotatory power could be obtained from the formula

$$\tfrac{1}{2}k\sin 2\psi_1 = \varrho. \tag{72.2}$$

Here again approximate measurements show that the rotatory power of amethyst is practically the same as that of uniaxial quartz.

73. Other phenomena in the vicinity of the optic axis. α) *Formation of isogyres.* We have seen in Sect. 72 (Fig. 77a and b) that the optic axial direction appears extinguished between crossed polaroids when the vibration direction of the polariser is parallel to either $O'A_1$ or $O'A_2$ (Fig. 76b). Consider for example the former position. It is not the optic axial directions alone that are extinguished but all points on a dark isogyre, one branch of which coincides with A_1OA_1'. The isogyre would have occurred in the same position even in a transparent optically inactive crystal. Hence for any point on the isogyre one of the principal planes of linear birefringence lies parallel to $O'A_1$. For such a direction, a vibration parallel to $O'A_1$ will therefore remain unchanged for an infinitesimal operation of linear birefringence. The same vibration also remains unaltered under the combined effects of the two succeeding operations of linear dichroism and optical rotation. (This is proved by the fact that it is propagated unchanged along the optic axial direction where these two factors alone exist. It may be remembered that the factors of linear dichroism and optical rotation are regarded as constant over the field of view.) Hence for all points on the hyperbolic arc $A_1O_1A_1'$ one of the waves is linearly polarised parallel to $O'A_1$, thus explaining the formation of isogyre when the polariser vibration is parallel to $O'A_1$. By the same argument for any point on the hyperbolic arc $A_2O_1A_2'$ one of the waves is linearly polarised parallel to $O'A_1$, thus explaining the formation of the isogyre when the polariser vibration is parallel to $O'A_1$. By the same argument for any point on the hyperbolic arc $A_2O_1A_2'$ one of the waves is linearly polarised parallel to $O'A_2$. Hence when the polariser vibration is parallel to $O'A_2$ a second set of isogyres, one branch of which coincides with $A_2O_1A_2'$ should be formed. This is in accordance with experiment. Fig. 77 shows that one wave is linearly polarised for any point on $A_1O_1A_1'$ and $A_2O_1A_2'$. The other wave is elliptically polarised approximating to a linear vibration at the border of the figure. Qualitative observations with an elliptic polariser and a crossed elliptic analyser have confirmed these and other predictions of theory.

β) The singular axes. We have seen that singular axes occur where the principal planes of linear birefringence and linear dichroism are inclined at 45° to one another and where Δ becomes equal to k (Sect. 55). It can be shown that they are located on either side of the optic axis along a line drawn perpendicular to the axial plane. Two singular axes are associated with each optic axis. The wave propagated unchanged along any singular axis is elliptically polarised. This and other properties have been discussed in Sect. 55. Using a suitable elliptic polariser and a crossed elliptic analyser, two singular directions, one associated with each optic axis can be extinguished at a time.

γ) Observations with polariser and analyser alone. It is clear that with a polariser alone set in front of the plate the optic axial direction O_1 will appear darkest when the polariser vibration is parallel to $O'A_2$ i.e., to the vibration direction of the more heavily absorbed wave propagated along the optic axis. The absorption coefficient of all the plane polarised waves propagated along the points on $A_2O_1A_2'$ is the same since their direction of vibration makes the same angle with OX_k, OY_k. Hence a pair of brushes appear at the same setting of the polariser, passing through the two optic axes (one of the brushes being coincident with A_2OA_2'). The phenomenon is akin to the appearance of brushes in the case of absorbing inactive crystals when the polariser vibration is set along the more strongly absorbed linear vibration propagated along the optic axis. However, as A_1 and A_2 are not orthogonal (unlike the case in the inactive absorbing crystals) the setting of the polaroid at which the optic axis appears darkest becomes different when the polaroid is placed behind the plate and used as an analyser. In this case the analyser vibration has to be parallel to $O'A_1'$ so that it will be crossed with respect to the less absorbed linear vibration OA_1, propagated along the optic axis. At the same setting of the analyser the less absorbed wave propagated along any direction on the hyperbolic arc $A_1O_1A_1'$ is also crossed out—since it is also linearly polarised parallel to $O'A_1$. Hence a pair of hyperbolic brushes are formed (one of which coincides with $A_1O_1A_1'$). Very simple arguments show that the intensity of the brush observed in this case is the same as that observed with the polariser alone with its vibration parallel to $O'A_2$.

It may be noted that in the two cases, not only do the settings (of the polaroid) at which the brushes occur differ, but also the positions of the brushes themselves.

Idiophanic rings also appear when the crystal plate is viewed with a polariser alone or an analyser alone. The reasons for their appearance are broadly the same as those in the case of the inactive absorbing crystals (Sect. 68) and may be traced to the fact that the two waves that are transmitted along any direction are non-orthogonally polarised. These can be analysed using the general principles outlined in Sect. 68 to 70. The effects presented with a linear polariser alone are in general not the same as those observed with a linear analyser alone at the same setting (except for certain special settings). This again proves that the non-orthogonally polarised waves propagated along a general direction cannot be of the special type obtaining in inactive absorbing crystals.

δ) Brewster's brushes. For directions not too close to an optic axis the squares of the ellipticity of the waves may be neglected even if the first powers of these quantities may not be negligible. For such directions we have already seen that the absorption coefficients of the waves will practically be the same as in the absence of optical activity. To this degree of approximation the formation and the position of the BREWSTER'S brushes may be treated as for inactive absorbing crystals. It may however be remarked that since the optic axial angle in amethyst is small the discussion for the position of the BREWSTER'S brushes given in Sect. 66β (for iolite) for large optic axial angles must be correspondingly modified.

IV. Passage of light through birefringent plates.

74. General theory. The study of the passage of light through a system of birefringent plates is of particular interest in two applications, namely the theory of compensators and of birefringent filters. The general theory may be readily worked out in terms of the Poincaré representation, following the methods outlined in Sect. 5β.

The complete solution in the important case when all the plates exhibit ordinary linear birefringence forms one of the oldest applications[1] of the Poincaré sphere but may be briefly described not only because of its elegance but because analytical discussions of the problem are still not uncommon. Let $\delta_1, \delta_2 \ldots \delta_n$ be the phase retardations introduced by the constituent plates, the orientation of the fast axes being represented by the points $A_1, A_2 \ldots A_n$ on the equator, the arc $A_{m+1} A_m$ being denoted by $2\vartheta_m$ (see Fig. 78). Consider the solid pyramidal figure obtained by joining the centre 0 of the sphere to the vertices of a spherical polygon $A_1 A_2' A_3' \ldots A_n' A'$ drawn as indicated such that the angle at A_m is $(\pi - \delta_m)$ and the side is equal to $2\vartheta_m$. The angle $\pi - \delta$ at A' and the adjacent sides $A_m' A_{m+1}'$ are automatically determined by constructing the polygon. We have to combine successive rotations $\delta_1, \delta_2, \ldots, \delta_n$ about the equatorial radii $A_1 O, A_2 O, \ldots A_n O$. This will cause the pyramidal figure to be rolled on the equator, the vertices $A_2', A_3', \ldots, A_n', A'$ of the polygon being in succession brought to coincide with $A_2, A_3, \ldots, A_n A$, the figure coming to rest with $A_n' A'$ resting on the equatorial arc $A_n A$. The final orientation of the pyramidal figure could equally well have been produced by the following two successive operations: (a) an anticlockwise rotation 2ϱ about the polar diameter through the arc $A' A$ which is the excess of 2π over the sum of the sides of the polygon, and (b) a clockwise rotation δ about the axis AO where arc $A A_n$ is equal to the side 2ϑ of the polygon.

Thus the combination is equivalent to an optically active plate of rotation ϱ followed by an ordinary birefringent plate of retardation δ, the orientation of the slow axis being determined by the angle 2ϑ. It is more convenient (using the formulae of spherical trigonometry) to determine 2ϱ, δ and 2ϑ by drawing the polar polygon (Fig. 78b) $B_0 B_1 B_2 \ldots B_n$ such that the sides $\overset{\frown}{B_{m-1} B_m} = \delta_m$ and the angle $\sphericalangle B_{m-1} B_m B_{m+1} = \pi - 2\vartheta_m$. We then have $\delta = \overset{\frown}{B_n B_0}$ and $2\vartheta = \sphericalangle B_{n-1} B_n B_0$ while 2ϱ is the spherical excess or area of the polygon—thus determining completely the two optical elements to which the combination is equivalent.

[1] H. POINCARÉ: Théorie Math. de la lumière, Vol. II, p. 266. Paris 1892.

If the n plates in the system are all non-dichroic, then the effect of each plate is to rotate the point representing the state of polarisation on the Poincaré sphere through an angle δ_i about some axis. If this operation is denoted by $R_i(\delta_i)$, the resultant is again a rotation

$$R(\delta) = R_1(\delta_1) \dots R_i(\delta_i) \dots R_n(\delta_n). \tag{74.1}$$

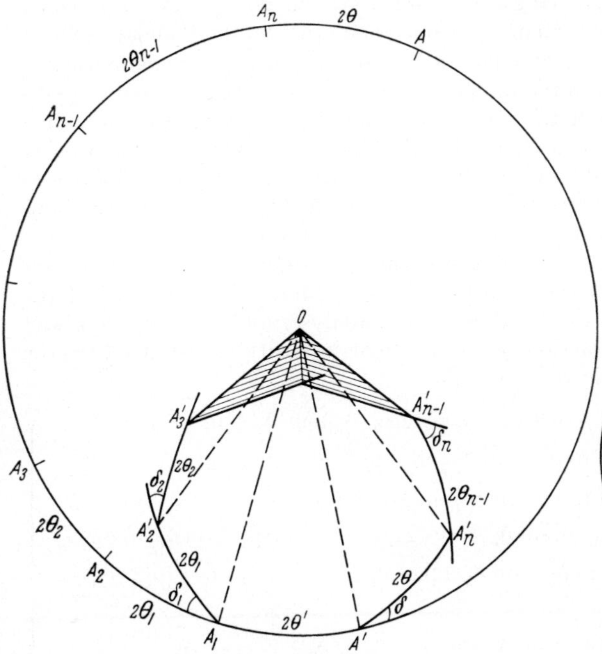

Fig. 78 a.

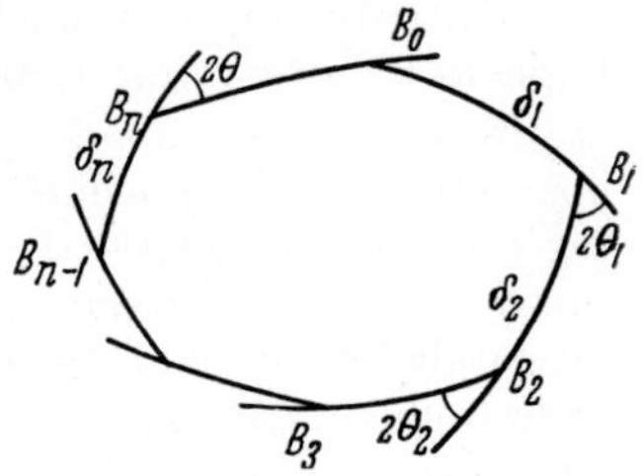

Fig. 78 b.

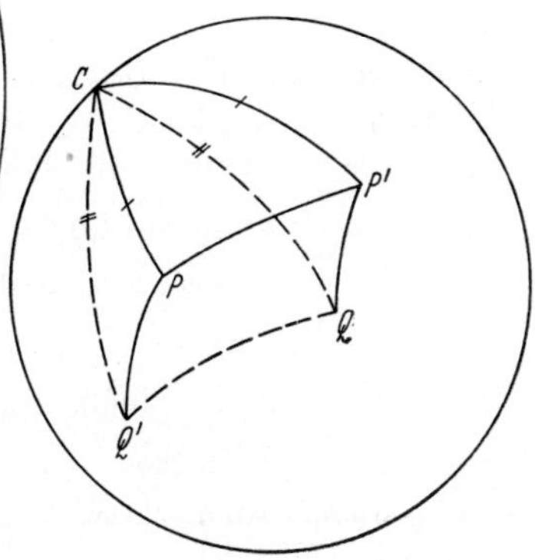

Fig. 79.

Fig. 78 a and b. Poincaré representation to calculate the effect of a series of linear birefringent plates.

Fig. 79. The Poincaré representation showing the effect of reversing the direction of the light beam on the intensity transmitted by an optical system.

Thus, the whole system is equivalent to a single plate exhibiting both optical activity and linear birefringence, of appropriate thickness, or to a combination of two plates, one of which exhibits pure circular birefringence, while the other has only pure linear birefringence and is oriented at a suitable azimuth[1]. If now light traverses the system in the reverse direction, then the resultant operator is

$$R_n(-\delta_n) \dots R_i(-\delta_i) \dots R_1(-\delta_1) = [R(\delta)]^{-1} = R(-\delta). \tag{74.2}$$

This result is, of course, true only if the optical activity present is natural, not of the magneto-optic type.

A consequence of this result is that if the system is placed between a polariser and an analyser, then the fraction of the intensity transmitted by the system is the same when light traverses it either way, for all azimuths of the polariser and analyser. If P is the state of the incident beam (Fig. 79) and Q that of the

[1] This result has been proved by the matrix method by H. Hurwitz jr. and R.C. Jones: J. Opt. Soc. Amer. **31**, 493 (1941). Some of the results proved below have also been obtained by a modification of this method, using quaternions, by H.Y. Hsü, M. Richartz and Y.K. Liang: J. Opt. Soc. Amer. **37**, 99 (1947).

analyser, then the transmitted intensity in the first case is $\cos^2 \frac{1}{2} \widehat{P'Q}$, while in the second case, it is $\cos^2 \frac{1}{2} \widehat{PQ'}$. It is obvious from the diagram that the arcs $\widehat{P'Q}$ and $\widehat{PQ'}$ are equal, making the two intensities equal. The transmitted intensities are however unequal if the system of plates is alone reversed, keeping polariser and analyser unchanged. If the polariser and analyser are crossed, then the transmitted intensity is unchanged even when the system alone is reversed, which happens because P and Q are then antipodal to each other on the Poincaré sphere.

Since rotations about non-coincident axes are in general non-commutative operators, it is not possible to interchange the order of two plates without affecting the state of polarisation of the emergent beam. If, however, two successive plates have their principal planes parallel (the fast directions of the two may be parallel or at right angles), then they may be interchanged. This follows at once from the fact that the corresponding rotations in Poincaré space are about the same axis, but may be of the same or opposite senses.

The particular case of three doubly refracting plates kept between a polariser and analyser is of interest in the theory of compensators. The azimuth of the polariser is taken to be zero, and let those of the analyser and of the three plates be $\varphi, \gamma_1, \gamma_2, \gamma_3$. Then, the fraction of the incident intensity transmitted by the system is τ_3 given by the following formula:

$$\left.\begin{aligned}
\tau_3 = {} & \cos^2\varphi + 4\sin 2\gamma_1 \sin 2(\varphi-\gamma_3)\cos 2(\gamma_2-\gamma_1)\cos 2(\gamma_3-\gamma_2)\sin^2\delta_1/2\sin^2\delta_2/2\sin^2\delta_3/2 + \\
& + \sin 2\gamma_1 \sin 2(\varphi-\gamma_1)\sin^2\delta_1/2 + \sin 2\gamma_2 \sin 2(\varphi-\gamma_2)\sin^2\delta_2/2 + \\
& + \sin 2\gamma_3 \sin 2(\varphi-\gamma_3)\sin^2\delta_3/2 - \sin 2\gamma_1 \sin 2(\varphi-\gamma_3)\left[\cos 2(\gamma_2-\gamma_1)\sin^2\delta_1/2 \times\right. \\
& \times \sin\delta_2\sin\delta_3 + \sin^2\delta_2/2\sin\delta_3\sin\delta_1 + \left.\cos 2(\gamma_3-\gamma_2)\sin^2\delta_3/2\sin\delta_1\sin\delta_2\right] + \\
& + 2\left[\sin 2\gamma_1\sin 2(\varphi-\gamma_2)\sin\delta_1/2\sin\delta_2/2\{\cos\delta_1/2\cos\delta_2/2 - \cos 2(\gamma_2-\gamma_1)\times\right. \\
& \times \sin\delta_1/2\sin\delta_2/2\} + \\
& + \sin 2\gamma_2\sin 2(\varphi-\gamma_3)\sin\delta_2/2\sin\delta_3/2\{\cos\delta_2/2\cos\delta_3/2 - \cos 2(\gamma_3-\gamma_2)\times \\
& \times \sin\delta_2/2\sin\delta_3/2\} + \\
& + \sin 2\gamma_3\sin 2(\varphi-\gamma_1)\sin\delta_3/2\sin\delta_1/2\{\cos\delta_3/2\cos\delta_1/2 - \cos 2(\gamma_1-\gamma_3)\times \\
& \left.\times \sin\delta_3/2\sin\delta_1/2\}\right].
\end{aligned}\right\}$$

For two plates and a single plate, these reduce to the expressions[1]:

$$\left.\begin{aligned}
\tau_2 = {} & \cos^2\varphi + \sin 2\gamma_1\sin 2(\varphi-\gamma_1)\sin^2\delta_1/2 + \sin 2\gamma_2\sin 2(\varphi-\gamma_2)\sin^2\delta_2/2 + \\
& + 2\sin 2\gamma_1\sin 2(\varphi-\gamma_2)\sin\delta_1/2\sin\delta_2/2\{\cos\delta_1/2\cos\delta_2/2 - \cos 2(\gamma_2-\gamma_1)\sin\delta_1/2\sin\delta_2/2\};
\end{aligned}\right\}$$

$$\tau_1 = \cos^2\varphi + \sin 2\gamma_1\sin 2(\varphi-\gamma_1)\sin^2\delta_1/2. \tag{74.5}$$

We shall not consider the applications of these formulae further here.

If some of the plates in the system are also linearly dichroic (these may be called as partial polarisers), then the following theorems hold[2]:

(a) A system consisting of any number of partial polarisers and circularly birefringent plates is equivalent to a combination of two elements, one a partial polariser and the other a circularly birefringent plate.

(b) A system consisting of any number of (linearly or circularly) birefringent plates and partial polarisers is equivalent to a system containing four elements—two linearly birefringent plates, a partial polariser and a circularly birefringent plate.

[1] H.G. JERRARD: J. Opt. Soc. Amer. **38**, 35 (1948).
[2] For a proof see H. HURWITZ jr. and R.C. JONES: J. Opt. Soc. Amer. **31**, 493 (1941).

75. Birefringent filters. An interesting application of the propagation of light through birefringent crystals and the interference phenomena exhibited in polarised light is to the design of narrow-band filters for obtaining monochromatic light. The device, which is known as the birefringent filter, was first invented by LYOT[1], although one was constructed independently by OHMAN[2]. The filter is mainly used for astrophysical purposes. A detailed account of the theory and practical details have been given by LYOT[3] and more recently by EVANS[4].

Suppose monochromatic light is incident normally on a uniformly thick birefringent plate of thickness t. If the polariser and analyser are kept parallel, at an angle of 45° to the principal planes of the plate, then it follows from (69.5) that the transmitted intensity is just $\cos^2\frac{1}{2}\delta$ where $\delta=\frac{2\pi}{\lambda}(n'-n'')\,t=\frac{2\pi}{\lambda}\mu t$. If we put $\frac{\mu t}{\lambda}=N$, say, which may be called the order of interference, then the transmission is $\tau_1=\cos^2\pi N$. If continuous radiation is used, the order of interference would vary with wavelength and one thus obtains sinusoidal fringes with minimum intensity zero in the spectrum of the transmitted light. The fringe width is given by

$$\Delta\lambda=\frac{\lambda}{N}\,\frac{1}{\frac{\lambda}{\mu}\frac{\partial\mu}{\partial\lambda}-1}. \tag{75.1}$$

Suppose now a second crystal of twice the thickness as the first is placed after the above system with its principal planes parallel to the first crystal and is backed by an analyser parallel to the other two analysers. Then the intensity transmitted by the system is

$$\tau_2=\cos^2\pi N\cos^2 2\pi N. \tag{75.2}$$

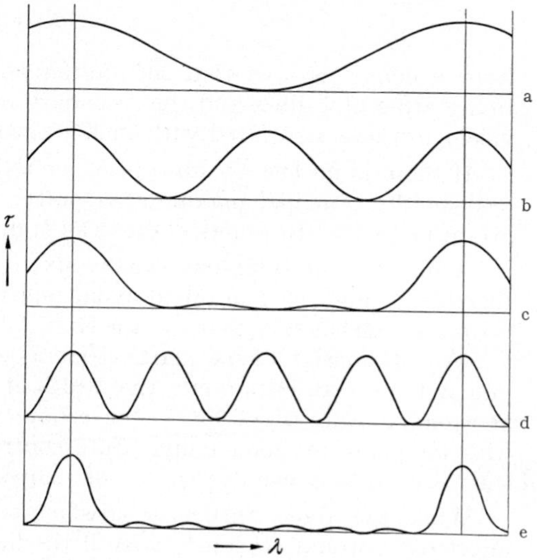

Fig. 80. Transmission curves for birefringent filters. (a) One element of thickness t. (b) One element of thickness $2t$. (c) Two elements t and $2t$. (d) One element $4t$. (e) Three elements t, $2t$ and $4t$.

The transmission curves for τ_1 and τ_2 are given in Fig. 80 from which it will be seen that there is appreciable transmission only near the maxima of τ_1. Further elements, composed of crystal plates of thickness $2^r t$ backed by polarisers, may be added, and the effect will be to make the principal maxima sharper, while at the same time suppressing the transmission in between them. If there are l such elements, the transmission of the filter is

$$\tau=\cos^2\pi N\ldots\cos^2(\pi\,2^r N)\ldots\cos^2(\pi\,2^{l-1}N). \tag{75.3}$$

This expression can be put in a more elegant form as follows. Expressing the cosines in terms of exponential functions and substituting πN by the

[1] B. LYOT: C. R. Acad. Sci., Paris **197**, 1593 (1933).
[2] Y. OHMAN: Nature, Lond. **141**, 157, 291 (1938).
[3] B. LYOT: Ann. Astrophys. **7**, 31 (1944).
[4] J.W. EVANS: J. Opt. Soc. Amer. **39**, 229 (1949).

symbol ϑ

$$\begin{aligned}\sqrt{\tau} &= \frac{e^{i\vartheta}+e^{-i\vartheta}}{2}\cdots\frac{e^{i2^r\vartheta}+e^{-i2^r\vartheta}}{2}\cdots\frac{e^{i2^{l-1}\vartheta}+e^{-i2^{l-1}\vartheta}}{2}\\ &= \frac{1}{2^l}\{e^{i\vartheta\Sigma 2^{r-1}}\}\left\{1+e^{-i2\vartheta}+e^{-i4\vartheta}+\cdots+e^{-\sum_1^l 2^r\vartheta}\right\}\\ &= \left\{\frac{e^{i\vartheta(2^l-1)}}{2^l}\,\frac{1-e^{-i2\vartheta 2^l}}{1-e^{-i2\vartheta}}\right\}\\ &= \frac{1}{2^l}\,\frac{\sin 2^l\vartheta}{\sin\vartheta}.\end{aligned}$$

Hence,

$$\tau = \left[\frac{\sin 2^l\pi N}{2^l\sin\pi N}\right]^2 \qquad (75.4)$$

from which it is seen that an interference filter composed of plates is similar to a grating of 2^l lines and the secondary maxima have relative intensities equivalent to those associated with such a grating.

If there is no loss by absorption or reflection, then the transmission at the peak of the principal maximum is unity. Theoretically, therefore, there is no loss of intensity. In practice, the peak transmission is of the order of 30 to 40%.

A birefringent filter has usually six to eight elements, which are cemented together or immersed in oil to avoid multiple reflections. A typical example is the one which has been in use at the High Altitude Laboratory at Climax, Colorado, U.S.A.[1]. It consists of six quartz elements with $N=23$, $t_1=1.677$ mm, $t_6=53.658$ mm and the peak has an effective width of 4 Å centered on the H_α line (6563 Å), at a temperature of 35.5° C[2]. Since both the thickness and birefringence vary with temperature, good temperature control is required. For quartz, the peak shifts by -0.66 Å per degree rise of temperature in the red region.

While the above theory is satisfactory for normal incidence, the order of interference would obviously vary if the light traverses the filter at an angle to the normal. The theory of such effects has been considered and it has been possible to design filters having a much wider field of view than the simple type described above. The principle is essentially to split each element into two or three parts and to choose the material and orientation of these parts in such a way that the variations in N are compensated as far as possible. Details of these may be obtained from EVANS' review mentioned above[3].

It would obviously be a great advantage if the transmission peak of a birefringent filter can be adjusted. Control of temperature has been suggested and attempted by LYOT, but it is not very satisfactory. An alternative method is to vary the thickness of each element, which may be made as a pair of wedges as in the Soleil or Babinet compensator. A third method will be to have a phase shifter capable of introducing a path retardation of upto one wavelength. This may be either of the photoelastic or electro-optic type[4]. A one-Ångström passband filter has been constructed using ammonium dihydrogen phosphate (ADP),

---

[1] J.W. EVANS: J. Opt. Soc. Amer. **39**, 229 (1949).

[2] Other designs for a Lyot filter are given by A.B. GILVARG and A.B. SEVERNYI: J. Tech. Phys. USSR. **19**, 997 (1949) and by L. BERTI: Nuovo Cim. **9**, 304 (1953).

[3] Methods of reducing the stray light are discussed by R.G. GIOVANELLI and J.T. JEFFRIES: Austral. J. Phys. **7**, 254 (1954).

[4] B.H. BILLINGS: J. Opt. Soc. Amer. **37**, 738 (1947).

which has a birefringence five times that of quartz[1]. For a 1 Å band-pass filter, the thickest plate would have to be nearly 24 cm thick, if made of quartz. With ADP, a thickness five times less would be sufficient, but the tolerances are also more severe (±0.6 micron). By using mica corrector plates, the tolerances are made less critical. The filter consists of seven elements and the thicker elements are split in order to increase the angular field of view to 1°. The filter is temperature controlled to work at (40±0.05)°C and is also equipped with a Sénarmont compensator at each end, in order that the pass band may be adjusted, over a range of about 3 Å.

An entirely different type of birefringent filter in which all the plates are of the same thickness, but their principal planes are rotated with respect to one another has also been proposed[2].

V. Miscellaneous topics.

76. HAIDINGER's rings in birefringent crystals. The interference rings observed between plane parallel surfaces under diffuse monochromatic illumination are of great importance in view of their practical applications in the construction of spectroscopes of high resolving power. These rings were first observed by HAIDINGER in mica. Mica being a double refracting substance there should be two systems of rings superposed on each other due to the beams that are polarised at right angles to each other. This superposition causes regions of maximum and minimum visibility in the field of view. This was first noted by RAYLEIGH[3] in 1909 and this phenomenon was investigated in great detail by CHINMAYANANDAM[4]. Later very beautiful photographs of this phenomenon have been published by other authors[5].

For an isotropic medium the path difference δ between the two interfering rays is $\delta = 2nt\cos r$ where t is the thickness of the plate and n is the refractive index and the dark rings appear when

$$\delta = 2nt\cos r = k\lambda. \qquad (76.1)$$

In the case of a birefringent crystal the incident ray is split into two rays polarised along and perpendicular to the principal vibration directions. And in a mica plate where the acute bisectrix is practically normal to the plate there would be two sets of fringes which satisfy respectively equations

$$\left.\begin{aligned} \delta_1 &= 2n_1 t\cos r_1 = n\lambda, \\ \delta_2 &= 2n_2 t\cos r_2 = m\lambda \end{aligned}\right\} \qquad (76.2)$$

where n and m are integers. The points of minimum visibility will correspond to the case when the dark rings of one set fall on the points which correspond to the bright rings of the second set i.e., when

$$\left.\begin{aligned} \delta_1 &= N\lambda, \\ \delta_2 &= (M+\tfrac{1}{2})\lambda \end{aligned}\right\} \qquad (76.3)$$

[1] B.H. BILLINGS, S. SAGE and W. DRAISIN: Rev. Sci. Instrum. **22**, 1009 (1951).
[2] I. SOLE: Czech. J. Phys. **4**, 53 (1954).
[3] Lord RAYLEIGH: Phil. Mag. **12**, 489 (1906).
[4] T.K. CHINMAYANANDAM: Proc. Roy. Soc. Lond., Ser. A **95**, 177 (1919).
[5] A.H. PFUND: J. Opt. Soc. Amer. **32**, 383 (1942). — B.H. BILLINGS: J. Opt. Soc. Amer. **35**, 570 (1945).

where $(N-M)$ is an integer. Hence a line of minimum visibility satisfies the condition that the respective orders of the rings of two sets have a constant difference $N-(M+\frac{1}{2})$. Hence the curve of minimum visibility is given by the equation

$$p = 2t(n_1 \cos r_1 - n_2 \cos r_2) \tag{76.4}$$

which is the equation for the isochromatic lines in a convergent polarised light for a plate of thickness $2t$ [see Eq. (63.1)]. This has been verified by experiment. It must be mentioned that this analogy between the lines of minimum visibility and the isochromatic lines in convergent polarised light is applicable only to the case of crystals with the surface perpendicular to the axes of optical symmetry and not to crystals cut in any random manner. Fig. 81 illustrates the Moiré or scalar fringes observed.

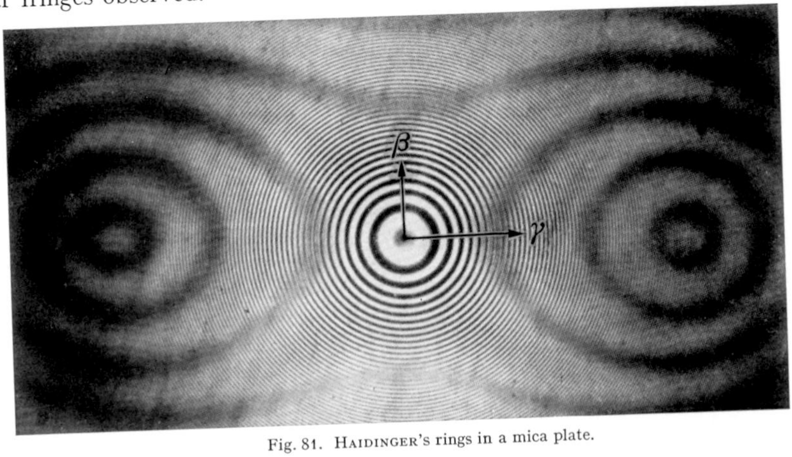

Fig. 81. HAIDINGER's rings in a mica plate.

CHINMAYANANDAM has discussed in detail the two cases when the optic axial angle is large and small. In the case of a plate of calcite (uniaxial crystal) cut normal to the optic axis n will assume two values n_ω the ordinary index for the vibration at right angles to the plane of incidence and n'_ε given by

$$n'_\varepsilon = [n_\varepsilon n_\omega / (n_\varepsilon^2 \cos^2 r + n_\omega^2 \sin^2 r)^{\frac{1}{2}}]. \tag{76.5}$$

Hence the two sets of interference rings will be given by

$$\left.\begin{aligned} 2t\, n_\omega \cos r_\omega &= n\lambda, \\ \frac{2t\, n_\varepsilon n_\omega \cos r_\varepsilon}{[n_\varepsilon^2 \cos^2 r_\varepsilon + n_\omega^2 \sin^2 r_\varepsilon]^{\frac{1}{2}}} &= m\lambda \end{aligned}\right\} \tag{76.6}$$

where the subscript ω refers to the ordinary ray and ε to the extraordinary ray. The patterns will be independent of each other and a single linear polariser will extinguish a large part of two opposite quadrants of the circles.

In viewing these fringes when the plates are not perfectly parallel BILLINGS found that the technique developed by RAMAN and RAJAGOPALAN[1] proves invaluable. They showed that the effects of irregularity in the specimen could be effectively removed by using a very small section of the plate.

---

[1] C. V. RAMAN and V. S. RAJAGOPALAN: J. Opt. Soc. Amer. **29**, 413 (1939). — Phil. Mag. **29**, 508 (1940).

77. Conical refraction. *α) General.* The phenomenon of internal conical refraction was first observed in aragonite by HUMPHREY LLOYD[1]. But it may be very much more conveniently observed with naphthalene[2] for which the angle of the cone is 13°44′ as compared to 1°52′ in aragonite; so much so that the conical refraction can be exhibited in the same way as ordinary birefringence is by viewing a line of print through an appropriately cut crystal plate. To observe it conveniently a plate cut approximately normal to one of the optic axes is kept on the Federov stage. The lower face is covered with a screen with a very small aperture. With parallel light incident from below a suitable adjustment of the stage enables the circle of light to be seen through the microscope which is withdrawn so that its focal plane lies above the crystal. The simple explanation of this phenomenon has already been consideredin Sect. 33 using the index ellipsoid and in Sect. 35 using the wave surface. According to these results when the wave normal of the pencil entering the crystal is along the optic axial direction, there are not just two ray normals but an infinite number, lying in a cone with the optic axis as a generator. Since the wave normals are practically perpendicular to the second surface, they experience no refraction and the emerging pencil of rays is not a cone but a hollow cylinder (Fig. 82a). This may be easily verified by raising the microscope when it is found that there is practically no increase in the diameter of the ring of light. Further with the analyser above the microscope, the polarisation at each point is what is to be expected from the explanation given in Sect. 33 if we consider all directions of linear vibration to be equally probable in unpolarised light.

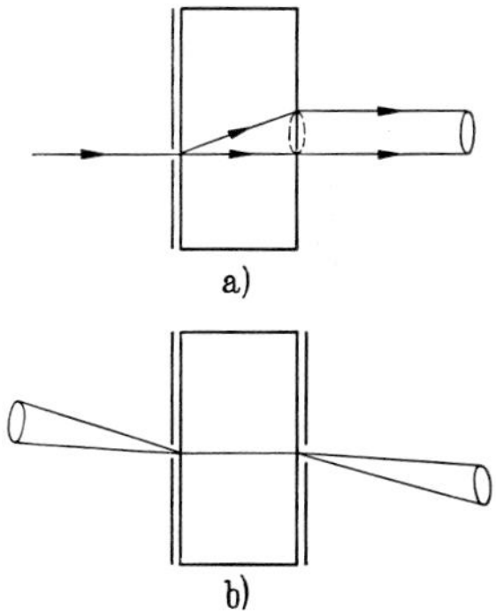

Fig. 82. Schematic diagrams for observing (a) internal conical refraction (b) external conical refraction.

To observe the external conical refraction however, an extended source of light is used and both the upper and the lower surfaces of the crystal are covered up except for small apertures situated at the ends of the axis of single ray velocity. In this case the emergent pencil forms a divergent cone as may be seen from the expansion of the ring of light when the microscope is raised (Fig. 82b). Both from the Fresnel ellipsoid and the wave surface we have seen that, when the direction of the ray normal is along the direction of single ray velocity, there are an infinite number of wave normals forming a cone with the optic biradial as one of the generators. Nevertheless this simple explanation is not quite adequate. For example, according to it, while internal conical refraction is shown only when the wave normal is *exactly* coincident with the optic axis, for any slight deviation ordinary double refraction should ensue. It is true that, when the wave-normal is quite far from the optic axial direction, two points of light are seen near two diametrically opposite points on the circle of conical refraction. When the wavenormal is gradually brought towards the optic axis these two points are drawn out into the form of two circular arcs, one approaching the circle of conical refraction from the interior and the other from the exterior, the intensity at any point on the two arcs at the same time diminishing; when the setting is exact they run together to form a ring of light. Further, POGGENDORF and HAIDINGER under better conditions have observed two concentric

[1] See SZIVESSY [*1*], POCKELS [*2*] for earlier literature.

[2] C.V. RAMAN, V.S. RAJAGOPALAN and T.M.K. NEDUNGADI: Nature, Lond. **147**, 262 (1941).

rings of light separated by a fine line, the Poggendorf dark circle actually corresponding to the directions where we should expect true conical refraction according to the elementary explanation.

The simple explanation of this phenomenon given by VOIGT[1] is along the following lines. We have to take into account the fact that we are concerned with a pencil of rays with a finite divergence, any limitation even of a plane wave-front leads in fact to such a divergence. Representing directions by corresponding points on the surface of the sphere, the small region in the vicinity of the optic axis may be approximated by the plane of the paper in Fig. 83.

Here N_1 and R_1 represent the optic axis and the optic biradial, N_1R_1 being the axial plane. Let the direction of P, the wave-normal close to the optic axis be specified by its polar coordinates r, φ with respect to the optic axis and let the corresponding directions of the ray normal be specified by R, Φ measured with respect to the optic biradial R_1. The principal planes S_1P and S_2P corresponding to the wave normal P are obtained by bisecting internally and externally the angle between PN_1 and the horizontal line PN_2 which proceeds to the other optic axis N_2. Hence it may easily be shown that S_1P is inclined at an angle $\frac{\pi}{2}+\frac{\varphi}{2}$ to the axial plane, the other plane S_2P being at right angles. The points of intersection of these two lines with a line through R_1 parallel to N_1P will be the direction of the ray normals S_1 and S_2 corresponding to the wave normal P. This may be verified from the fact that S_1P bisects the angle between S_1R_1 and S_1R_2 where R_2 is the other biradial (Sect. 33). Then by a little geometry it may be shown that $R_1S_1=R_1N_1+r$ and $R_1S_2=R_1N_1-r$. Thus the polar coordinates R, Φ of the two ray normals will be $(\chi+r)$, π and $(\chi-r)$, $(\varphi+\pi)$, where $\chi=R_1N_1$ the semi-angle of conical refraction. For directions appreciably inclined to the optic axis a small change in the direction of the wave normal will cause a corresponding small change in the directions of the ray normals so that a pencil of incident wave normals will emerge without appreciable change of divergence. Even for this case the distortion of the bundle of rays due to astigmatism is well known (STOKES[2]). On the other hand in the present case a small change $r\,d\varphi$ in the direction of the wave normal causes appreciable changes $(\chi+r)\,d\varphi$ and $(\chi-r)\,d\varphi$ in the position of the ray normal S_1 and S_2. This lateral extension is not compensated for by a radial contraction, a small change dr causing an equal change dR in the position of the ray normals. If we consider a pencil of wave normals about the optic axis we will obtain a ring of ray normals *containing* the circle of conical refraction. The portion of the incident pencil having the divergence $r\,dr\,d\varphi$ will give rise to two sets of ray normals with large divergences $(\chi+r)\,d\varphi\,dr$ and $(\chi-r)\,d\varphi\,dr$. Since energy must be conserved the intensity will be reduced by the factor $\approx r/\chi$. As r tends to zero the

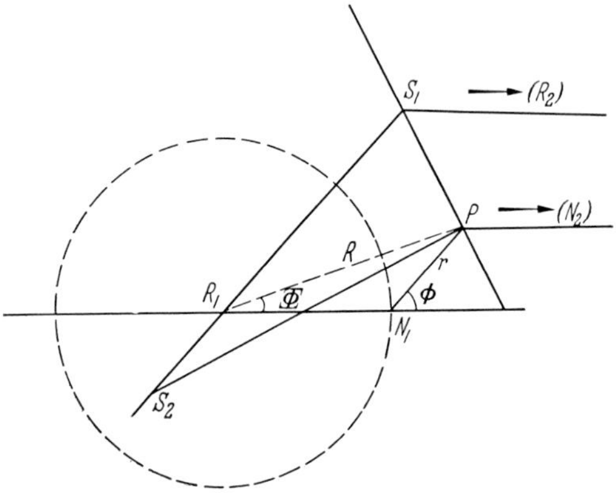

Fig. 83. Figure illustrating the simple explanation of the Poggendorf circle. N_1, N_2 optic axial directions (binormals); R_1, R_2 directions of the biradials.

[1] W. VOIGT: Phys. Z. **6**, 673, 818 (1905).

[2] C. G. STOKES: Sci. Pap. Cambridge **5**, 6.

intensity tends to zero, so that the exact circle of conical refraction is a region of vanishing intensity. It is also clear that the vibration direction at any point of the ring is parallel to the line joining that point to the optic axis.

β) Observations in naphthalene[1]. It is indeed remarkable that the above geometric theory is able to explain most of the general features of the phenomenon considering that the wave optical principles on which the very concept of the ray for directions of singularity can be justified have to be critically examined. It is therefore to be expected that the wave optical principles would furnish a deeper understanding of the subject. For example similar arguments based on geometrical optics could be used to explain the phenomenon of external conical refraction and in this case one would get an infinite concentration of energy along the axis of single ray velocity which would be physically inadmissible.

In any case, as RAMAN has emphasised, the practical method of observing the conical refraction ties up the subject with the question of aberration of images viewed through biaxial plates. This is particularly the case with the arrangement usually regarded as demonstrating internal conical refraction wherein an illuminated pinhole is viewed and focussed through a crystal plate by means of a microscope or magnifying lens. Since the pinhole is backed by an extended source of light, the phenomenon corresponds to neither the internal nor external conical refraction. The phenomenon in this case has been extensively investigated by RAMAN and his collaborators and we shall describe some of these results. Using naphthalene it is found that the Poggendorf circle is an ultrafocal phenomenon *completely disappearing* in the position of best focus, the image being then a single circular ring that is extremely sharp. It is well known (WALKER [5]) that there are no fewer than four distinct positions of best focus for an image viewed through a biaxial plate these being determined by the principal radii of curvature of each of the two sheets of the wave surface. The image exhibits astigmatism being drawn out perpendicular to the principal planes of curvature, one of the principal radii of curvature of the wave surface is infinite along the circle of contact. In the case of crystals for which the angle of internal and external conical refraction are nearly the same, as is the case with most crystals including naphthalene, the other radius of curvature is practically constant at all points on the circle and changes only slowly as we move away from the circle along the wave surface either towards or away from the conical point. Accordingly the astigmatism of the rays emerging from the crystal gives rise to a particularly simple form of image viz., a sharply focussed circular ring of the same diameter as the circle in which the wave surface makes contact with the second face of the crystal. When the microscope is raised, the Poggendorf circle develops and when it is focussed on the second surface of the plate, a luminous point is observed at the centre of the field of view *showing the converse of the Poggendorf phenomenon*, namely the intense concentration of energy along the axis of single ray velocity. In fact with the microscope focussed on the second surface, the field of view exhibits as it were an illuminated picture of the wave surface of two sheets, their intersection appearing as an intensely luminous point and the circle of contact made by the tangent plane as a dark ring. The dark circle and the luminous central point can be traced to a considerable distance behind the crystal. The luminous point is in effect an image of an original pinhole. This remarkable phenomenon that a biaxial crystal cut normal to the direction of single ray velocity can form an erect image of a luminous source was first observed by RAMAN[2] with aragnoite

[1] C.V. RAMAN, V.S. RAJAGOPALAN and T.M.K. NEDUNGADI: Proc. Ind. Acad. Sci. A **14**, 221 (1941).

[2] C.V. RAMAN: Nature, Lond. **107**, 747 (1921).

though it is better displayed with naphthalene. The image is in continuous focus and can be seen at great distances from the crystal plate.

We have seen that for crystals having the angles of internal and external conical refraction nearly equal, a position of perfect focus can be obtained in which the Poggendorf circle vanishes. This is not the case in aragonite. A remarkable photograph taken with a specimen of this substance appears in RAMAN's[1] paper with the microscope adjusted to as near a perfect focus as possible where the two circles actually intersect!

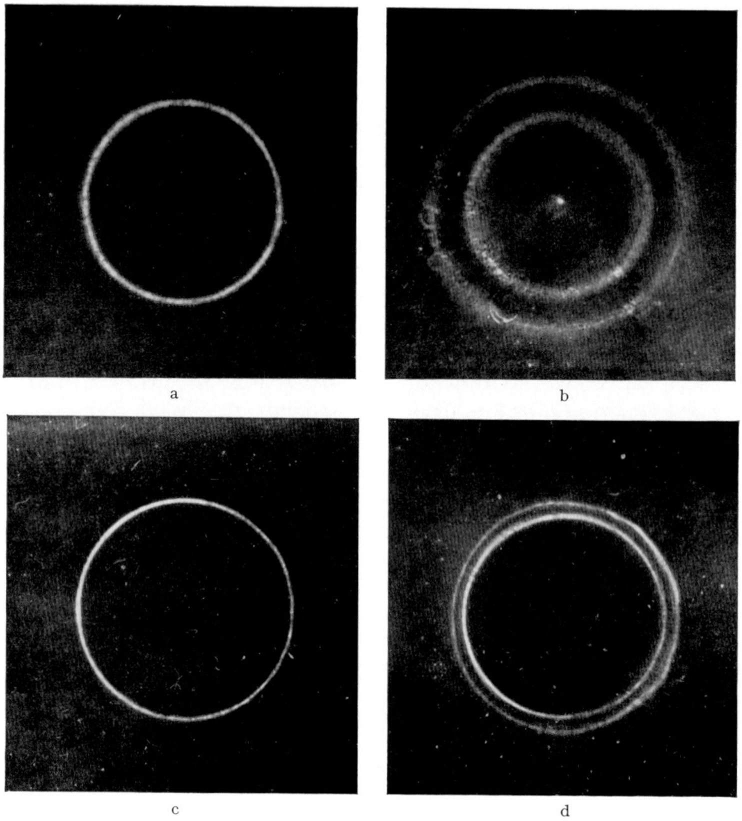

Fig. 84 a—d. Conical refraction in naphthalene. (a) Hollow cone of external conical refraction. (b) Cylinder of internal conical refraction. (Note the intense central spot which corresponds to the inverse of the Poggendorf phenomena.) (c) Image of source seen in focus. Poggendorf circle not present. (d) Poggendorf circle appears when image of source is out of focus.

78. Dispersion in birefringent crystals. Effects of dispersion on the optic axial figures. Since the refractive index is a function of the wavelength of the incident light, we shall briefly discuss the effects of dispersion with wavelength on the convergent light phenomena.

In uniaxial crystals, although the magnitudes of ω and ε may vary with wavelength, the direction of the optic axis remains the same. There are a few uniaxial crystals which become isotropic at a particular wavelength. Of special interest is the case of the positive uniaxial crystal benzil whose birefringence progressively decreases as one goes from red to blue[2]. In fact at $\lambda = 4900$ Å the crystal becomes

[1] C. V. RAMAN: Current Sci. **11**, 44 (1942).
[2] W. M. D. BRYANT: J. Amer. Chem. Soc. **65**, 96 (1943).

isotropic and for still smaller wavelengths the crystal becomes negative. Since benzil is an optically active crystal the investigation of the shape of the gyration surface when the index surface is a sphere would be of the greatest interest.

In the case of biaxial crystals, the variations in the principal refractive indices with wavelength may cause considerable changes in the optic axial angle—dispersion of the optic axes—which may even be accompanied by changes in the optic axial plane itself (crossed axial dispersion). In the case of monoclinic and

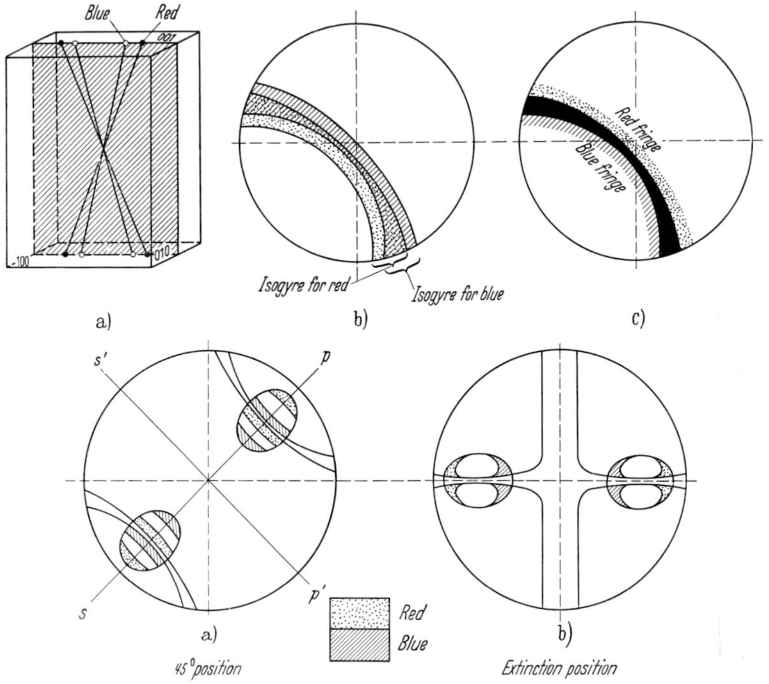

Fig. 85a. (a) Dispersion of optic axes in crystals. Orthorhombic crystals. (b) Monoclinic crystals. (c) Triclinic crystals

triclinic crystals for different wavelengths the orientation of the optical ellipsoid, may itself alter with respect to the crystallographic axes (dispersion of the bisectrices).

In orthorhombic crystals, the axes of the index ellipsoid coincide with the crystallographic axes since the optic axial plane contains α and γ, the acute bisectrix must be parallel to a, b or c axis. The bisectrices would therefore not change with wavelength and the interference figures would be symmetrical with respect to two planes that are at right angles to each other, their line of intersection being a bisectrix (Fig. 85a).

In monoclinic crystals one of the axes of the indicatrix (α, β or γ) must coincide with the unique b axis, hence three cases are possible. When the b axis coincides with the β axis the plane of the optic axis (plane of α and γ) coincides with the symmetry plane. The optic axial figures (with different wavelength) are no longer symmetrical with respect to a plane at right angles to the plane of the optic axes. When β and the acute bisectrix lie in the symmetry plane and the third axis coincides with the crystallographic axis b, the plane of the optic axis will lie at right angles to the symmetry plane. This is called the Horizontal Dispersion.

Finally when the acute bisectric coincides with the crystallographic b axis, there is no dispersion of the bisectrix and the figure has a twofold axis of symmetry about the acute bisectrix. Fig. 85b illustrates these cases.

In the case of triclinic crystals the optic axial figure will show an unsymmetrical figure as the three vibration axes are dispersed (Fig. 85c).

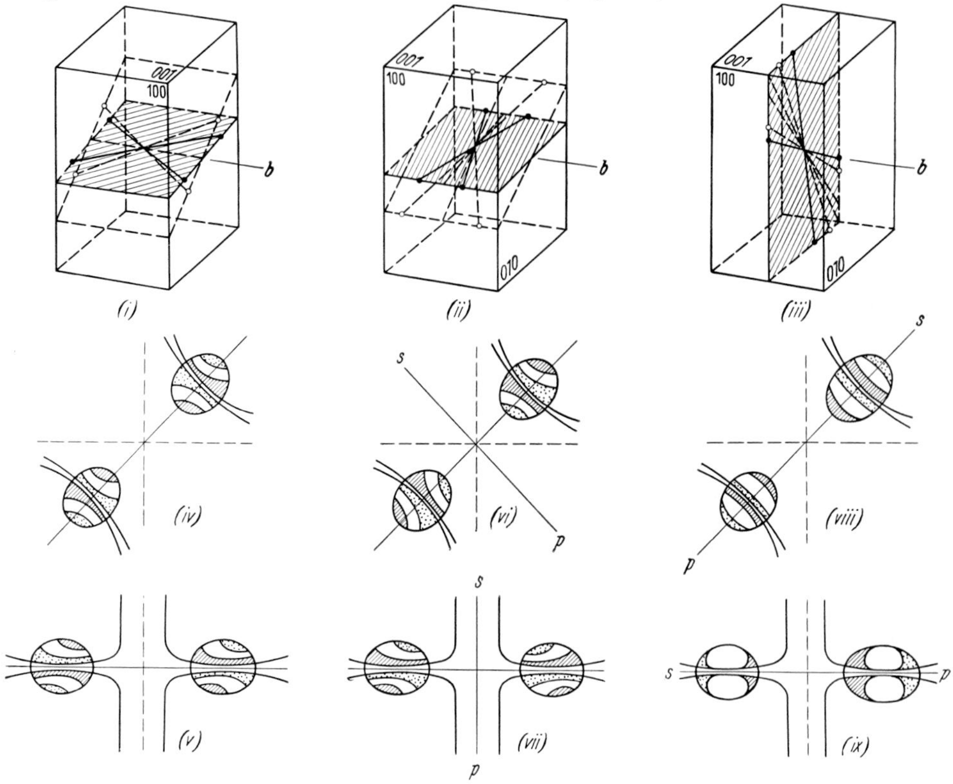

Fig. 85b. Dispersion of optic axes in monoclinic crystal.

The plane of the optic axes contains the longest and the shortest axes of the index ellipsoid. In certain crystals the principal refractive indices vary so uniquely with wavelength that very peculiar effects arise. For example if in a particular

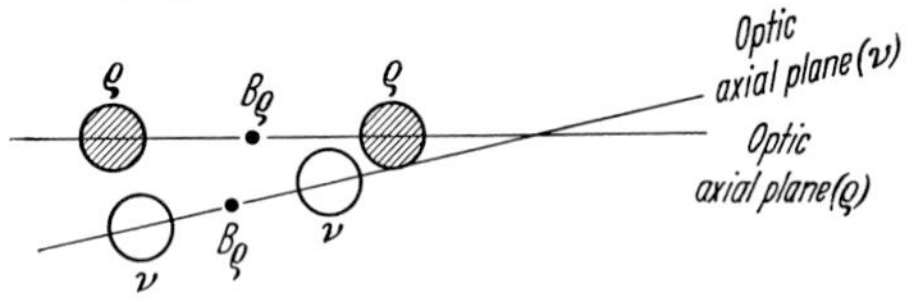

Fig. 85c. Dispersion of optic axes in triclinic crystals.

crystal $n_1 < n_2 < n_3$ (where the subscripts 1, 2, 3 correspond to the principal axes of the index ellipsoid, then the optic axial plane would be the $n_1\, n_3$ plane. As the wavelength of the incident light is changed if for a particular wavelength if $n_1 = n_2$ then the crystal becomes uniaxial while for a still further change of wavelength if $n_2 < n_1$ then the plane of the optic axes would get rotated to the $n_2 n_3$ plane. The famous case that is often quoted to illustrate this phenomenon of crossed axial dispersion is that of the orthorhombic crystal brookite where the optic axial plane for red light is parallel to (001), the crystal becomes uniaxial for λ 5550 and the plane rotates to (010) for lower wavelengths. Again the case of saccharo lactone ($C_6H_{10}O_5$), an orthorhombic crystal which is also optically active and which exhibits this phenomenon, is of great interest.

It may also be remarked that in many crystals (particularly those having low birefringence) the dispersion actually causes a change in the optical sign of the crystal[1].

D. Experimental techniques in crystal optics.

79. The polarising microscope[2]. The polarising or the petrographic microscope is an invaluable instrument for optical research and in recent years its application has been extended to many fields of investigation. It was originally constructed for the examination of rock sections and its design has undergone many changes because of its varying uses. Stripped to its essentials, the polarising microscope differs from an ordinary microscope in that it possess a revolving graduated stage, a polarising device below and another above this stage. A removable auxiliary lens (called the Bertrand-Amici lens) is present between the upper polarising device and the eyepiece. Fig. 86a represents the median section of a typical polarising microscope.

The polarising microscope is used in two ways. When the Bertrand-Amici lens is not inserted, the optical system magnifies any object on the stage and the microscope acts as an orthoscope. The paths of the light rays for this arrangement is given in Fig. 86a. If however the Bertrand lens is inserted, it brings the eyepiece into focus on a focal plane of the objective, thus bringing the entire optical system to a focus at infinity. This enables one to observe simultaneously all the bundles of parallel rays which pass in various directions through a plate placed on the stage. This is known as the conoscopic arrangement and is used for the examination of interference phenomena exhibited by crystals in "convergent light". To make the convergence of the light entering the crystal large enough, a converger can be introduced above the condensing lens. The paths of the light rays for the conoscopic arrangement is given in Fig. 86b.

Some microscopes are provided with means for bringing the axis of rotation of the stage and the optical axis of the instrument into coincidence. This is essential if the crystal is to remain at the intersection of the cross wire when the stage is rotated. But this difficulty is avoided in most microscopes by having a mechanism for rotating the polariser and analyser simultaneously, with the crystal on the stage remaining stationary. The polarising microscope is provided with all the diaphragms and stops to be found in ordinary microscopes. In addition there is a substage adjustable diaphragm below or above the polariser which can decrease the convergence of the incident light and is particularly useful in the measurement of the refractive index of a crystal by the Becke method. Another adjustable diaphragm in the upper tube helps to isolate the interference figures in tiny crystals. This diaphragm if it is to be really effective for this purpose, must be situated where the real image of the crystal is formed.

---

[1] See W. M. D. BRYANT and J. MITCHELL: J. Amer. Chem. Soc. **63**, 511 (1941); **65**, 96 128 (1943). See also A. E. H. TUTTON [*12*].

[2] Several excellent treatises some of which are listed below are available which describe the different parts and accessories of a polarising microscope. They also give full accounts of the different uses described in this and the following section. F. E. WRIGHT: Methods of Petrographic Microscopic Research. 1911. — A. JOHANNSEN [*10*]. — H. ROSENBUSCH and E. A. WULFING: Mikroskopische Physiographie der Mineralogie und Gesteine. 1924. — N. H. HARTSHORNE and A. STUART [*11*].

The eyepiece of the microscope can be replaced by oculars of other special types for the measurement of different optical characters under the microscope. These oculars amongst others include the scale, net grating, screw micrometer and planimeter oculars for the measurements of lengths and area, the ocular

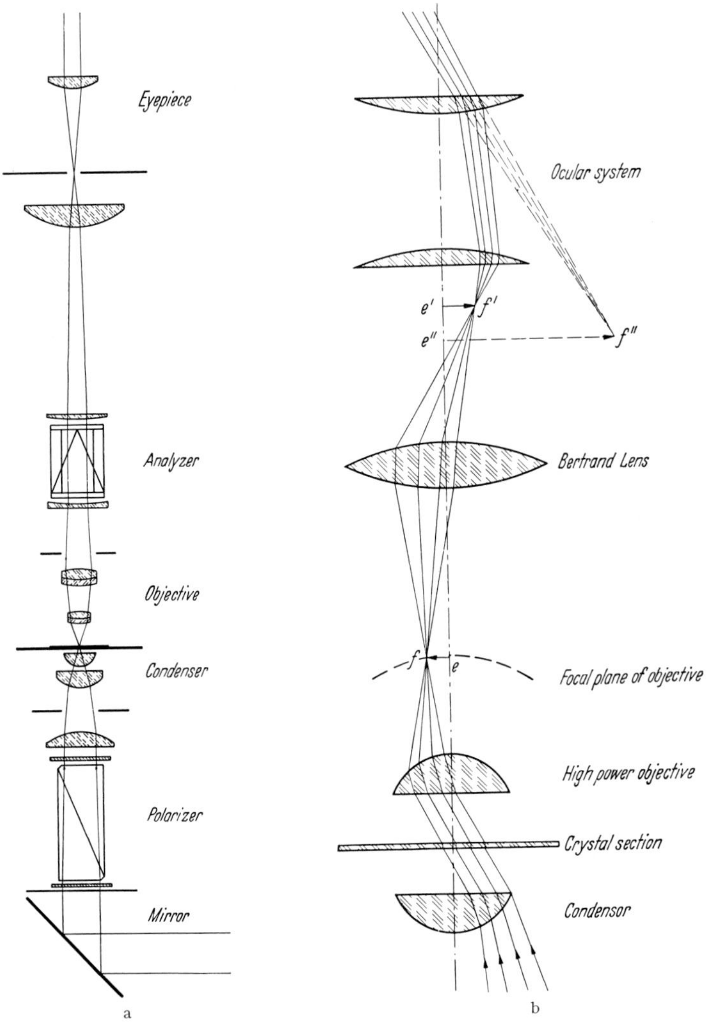

Fig. 86. The polarising microscope. (a) Light rays for orthoscopic arrangement. (b) Light rays for the conoscopic arrangement.

goniometer for measurement of edge angles, Bertrand half shadow ocular (which is actually a rotating biquartz (65α)] for determining the exact position of extinction, ocular compensators of the quartz wedge and the Babinet types for the measurement of small and large retardations, the dichroiscope ocular for estimating the pleochroism and so on. The microscope has also recesses for the insertion of quarter-wave and full wave undulation plates, quartz wedge, Berek compensator, etc. for the determination of the optical sign and birefringence of crystals.

Additional devices are used sometimes for mounting the crystal or the slide on the stage of the microscope. The *mechanical stage* is used for varying the position of the slide on the stage and is very popular with the mineralogists as the movement of the slide can be adjusted to a nicety. The *rotation apparatus* (e.g., the Miers stage goniometer or its simpler modification) is most useful in the determination of the optical characters of a crystal for different orientations. Most of these devices involve the fixing of the crystal on a rotatable support which in its turn can be attached to the revolving stage. The crystal can be immersed in a liquid of the appropriate refractive index when necessary. The most versatile of this type of rotation apparatus is the Federov Universal Stage or its modification by EMMONS (Sect. 82 δ).

The microscope has usually linear polarising and analysing devices (either nicols or polaroids). By the introduction of retardation plates at the proper positions the microscopes can be converted for observations with circular or elliptic polarised light (Sect. 21 δ). Achromatic quarter wave plates that have been devised[1,2] should prove quite useful in this respect.

Normally the microscope has its tube axis vertical but it is capable of being set with its axis horizontal. Such a setting is found to be very convenient for the study of stress optic and thermo-optic behaviour of crystals.

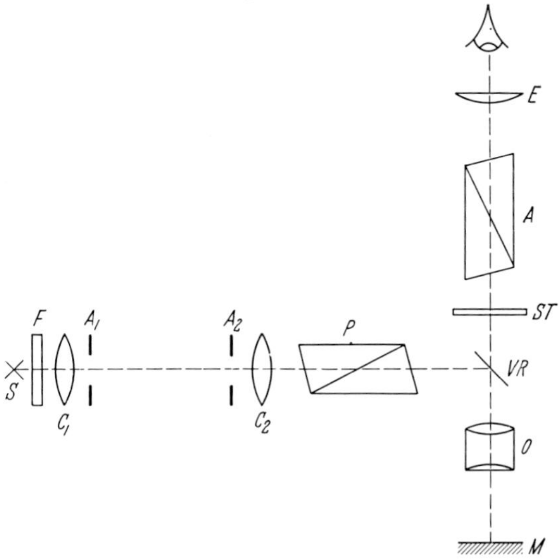

Fig. 87. Schematic diagram of reflecting polarising microscope. S = source, F = filter, A_1, A_2 = apertures, C_1, C_2 = condensers, P = polariser, VR = vertical reflector, O = objective, M = metal specimen, ST = sensitive tint, A = analyser, E = eypiece.

80. Polarising microscope for reflected light[3]. It is obvious that the microscope described above can only be used for the studies of light transmitted by the specimens. Since the important investigations of JAMIN[4] and DRUDE[5] on the problem of the reflection of light by conducting and non-conducting materials, it has been realised that a polarising microscope for reflected light could be put to significant use particularly in metallography. Since the pioneering work of KÖNIGSBERGER[6] and BEREK (see Sect. 60) in this field, various types of reflection polarising microscopes have been designed but only recently have these designs been perfected. The most convenient set up for a reflection polarising microscope is given in Fig. 87.

It is customary to replace the nicols shown in Fig. 87 by polaroid sheets when visual observations are made. Owing to the anomalies that are likely to arise

[1] G. DESTRIAU and J. PROUTEAU: J. Phys. Radium **10**, 53 (1949).
[2] S. PANCHARATNAM: Proc. Ind. Acad. Sci. A **41**, 130, 137 (1955).
[3] Several review articles on this subject have appeared which may be consulted for the details of this important instrument, e.g. B.W. MOTT: The Microscopy of Metals. London 1953. — G.K.T. CONN and F.G. BADSHAW: Polarised Light in Metallography. London 1952. B.W. MOTT and H.R. HAINES: Research **4**, 24, 63 (1951). — B.W. MOTT and S. FORD: Research **6**, 396 (1953).
[4] P. JAMIN: Ann. Phys. **19**, 296 (1847).
[5] P. DRUDE: Wied. Ann. Phys. Chem. **32**, 584 (1887); **36**, 532, 865 (1889); **39**, 481 (1890).
[6] J. KÖNIGSBERGER: J. Zentr. Min. 1901, 195; 1908, 565; 1909, 245; 1910, 712.

due to the pressure and strains in the lenses etc., the analyser and polariser are placed as close to the vertical reflector as possible. Considerable research is being done to get rid of this anomaly[1]. A further source of error is the ellipticity and the rotation of the plane of polarisation introduced by the vertical reflector. A large part of these errors have been reduced by coating the reflecting surface of the glass plate with a highly refracting material like zinc sulphide and the other side with magnesium fluoride to reduce the effect of internal reflection inside the glass.

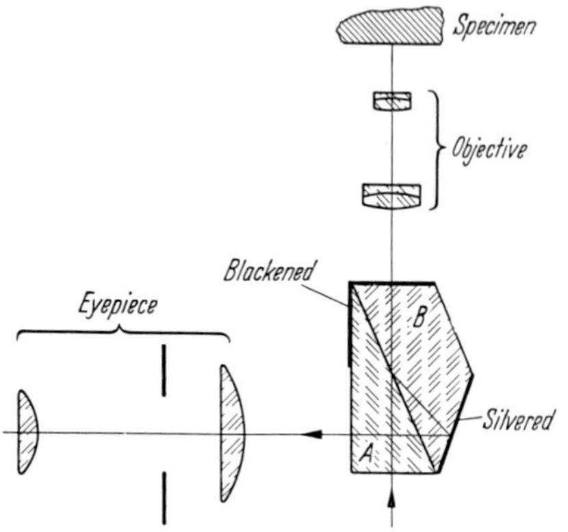

a

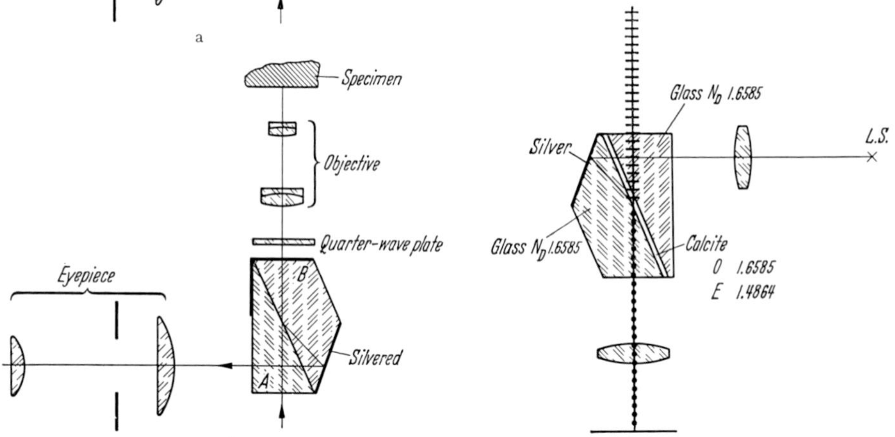

b c

Fig. 88 a—c. Foster polarising vertical illuminator. (a) Dark field illumination. (b) Bright field illumination. (c) A modification of the Foster prism.

Since most observations are made between crossed polarisers, these difficulties have been avoided in some microscopes by the use of the Foster prism[2] and its principle is illustrated in Fig. 88a. It consists of a calcite rhomb which is split and recemented with material of the same refractive index as the extraordinary ray so that the ordinary ray is totally reflected (exactly as in a nicol prism) and absorbed on the blackened surface. The plane polarised extraordinary ray is transmitted to the specimen and unless a change in the polarisation occurs at reflection no light reaches the eyepiece. The unit therefore serves as a polariser, vertical reflector and analyser all combined. The correctness of the angle of the prism and the strain-free nature of the cementing medium are important factors for making the microscope efficient. A bright field illumination can be obtained by inserting a $\lambda/4$ plate between the objective lens and the prism (Fig. 88b).

In another polarising vertical illuminator (Fig. 88c), the reduction of the aperture of the objective present in the first prism is avoided. Unpolarised light passes through a lens and enters the glass prism passing through a thin calcite plate

[1] See for example B. W. Mott and H. R. Haines: Proc. Phys. Soc. Lond. B **66**, 302 (1953).

[2] L. V. Foster: J. Opt. Soc. Amer. **28**, 124, 127 (1938).

and is reflected at the silvered surface of the calcite plate where a part of it vibrating in a plane perpendicular to the plane of incidence is reflected to the objective. The other part is transmitted and absorbed at the lower part of the entering face, which is blackened. The light reflected by the specimen passes back through the objective and no light will be transmitted unless it is depolarised by the specimen. There will be complete polarisation in all parts of the field since the reflecting surface is the polariser and it is inclined at an angle sufficient to include the angular field of the microscope.

While the Foster prisms are a very great improvement over other types of polarisers in reflection microscopes, its chief disadvantage lies in that the condition for crossed polarisers cannot be varied. The microscope can be used for conoscopic observation by the use of an auxiliary lens.

81. The shearing interference microscopes. When a wave is incident on a birefringent crystal plate placed between two polaroids, the two wavefronts emerging

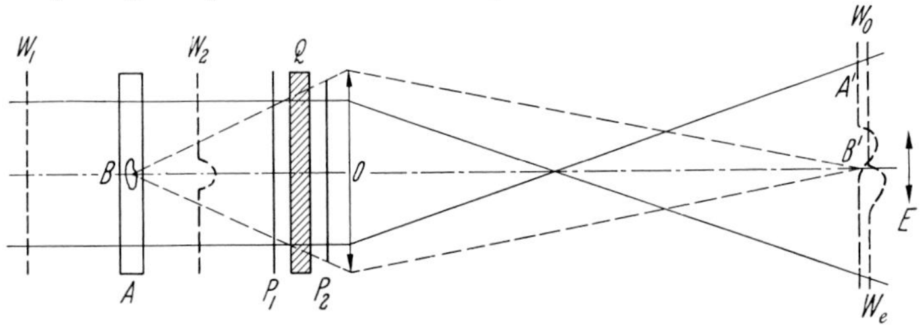

Fig. 89. Schematic diagram illustrating the principles of a shearing microscope.

from the system are in a position to interfere (see Sect. 63). This property has been made use of in the design of certain microscopes for making objects which are actually transparent but with a refractive index slightly differing from that of the surrounding media, visible. We present only the most elementary ideas about these microscopes and follow the treatment given by FRANÇON. For greater details the articles by FRANÇON[1], INGLESTAM[2] and the references given therein may be consulted.

The basic principles of the shearing interference microscope can be made clear from Fig. 89. The object A is transparent with a region B whose refractive index varies from that of the surrounding medium. This introduces a phase change and the incident wavefront W_1 gets distorted to the form W_2. The light then passes through the birefringent system, P_1 and P_2 being two polarisers and Q a birefringent crystal. The lens which can either be placed before or after the birefringent system produces an image at B'. The distorted wavefront W_2 is doubled to W_o and W_e by the birefringent system and, because of the polarisers P_1 and P_2, these waves are coherent and are in a position to interfere. If the doubling is comparatively large then the two wavefronts can be pictured as in Fig. 90a.

In the regions (a), (c) and (e) where there is not much distortion of the wavefronts the path difference between the two wavefronts would be a constant given by Δ and due to the interference between the two wavefronts the illumination in these regions would be the same.

However in the regions (b) and (d), where there is a considerable distortion of the wavefront, the situation would be entirely different. If δ is the maximum

[1] M. FRANÇON: J. Opt. Soc. Amer. **47**, 528 (1957).

[2] E. INGLESTAM: J. Opt. Soc. Amer. **47**, 536 (1957). See also Vol. XXIV of this Encyclopedia.

path difference variation due to B then the maximum path difference between W_o and W_e at (b) would be $(\delta - \Delta)$ whereas it would be $(\delta + \Delta)$ at (d). Hence due to interference effects the illumination at (b) and (d) would be different from that of the background and the object would become visible but it would necessarily be doubled. This doubling effect would be of no consequence if the object B is completely isolated from other objects. However such a situation rarely arises and it is usually arranged that the doubling is actually quite small with respect to the width of the object (see Fig. 90b). Here again in regions (a) and (d) where the path difference is the same the illumination is the same but in regions (b) and (c) where the path difference changes the object becomes visible. If d is the lateral doubling, the path difference Δ' in the region (b) having a slope d is given by $\Delta' = \alpha d$ if the two wavefronts are in phase (i.e. if $\Delta = 0$). If however, the two wavefronts are not in phase the path difference in the region (b) is $\Delta' = \alpha d - \Delta$ and in the region (c) it is $\Delta' = \alpha d + \Delta$. The object B therefore becomes visible.

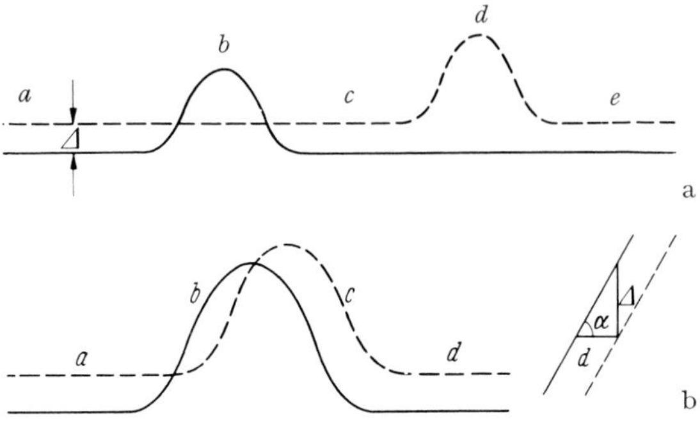

Fig. 90 a and b. The doubling of the wave front in a shearing microscope. (a) Large doubling. (b) Small doubling.

The first method of total doubling obviously corresponds to introducing a path difference in a manner similar to phase contrast microscopy. The second method obviously gives a differential method.

JAMIN[1] was the first to construct a polarisation interferometer while it was first applied to a microscope by LEBEDEFF[2]. JAMIN used two identical uniaxial crystal plates (calcite) cut at 45° to the axis and oriented in the same way. A half wave plate placed at 45° between the two calcite plates converts the ordinary and extraordinary waves in the first plate into the extraordinary and ordinary waves respectively in the second plate. There is therefore a compensation of path differences in the two plates and observations can be made in white light. The object is placed *between* the two plates when there is doubling. The disadvantages of this system are that (1) a calcite plate has to be introduced between the specimen and the objective and (2) the half wave plate is usually correct only for a narrow spectral range, (3) the system may not be useful for large macroscopic objects where large crystal plates have to be used.

All these disadvantages have been avoided in the arrangement suggested by FRANÇON where the two crystalline plates (made of quartz) are crossed—the axis of the second plate makes an angle of 45° with the plane of Fig. 91a and the projection of the axis is shown as a dotted line. The rays inside the plates are also shown. While EO is in the plane of the paper, OE is not in the plane but is parallel to EO. The adaptation of this to a microscope is shown in Fig. 91b, the part $O_2 P_1 Q_1 Q_2 P_2 O_3$ forming the interference eye piece which may be used with any microscope it may be remarked that the unit $Q_1 Q_2$ when it has a large birefringence can be used for total doubling and from the hues present, a very accurate estimate of the optical thickness of the object can be made. When the

[1] JAMIN: C. R. Acad. Sci., Paris **67**, 814 (1868).
[2] LEBEDEFF: Rev. d. Opt. **9**, 385 (1930).

doubling is small the eye piece can be used with great advantage to observe objects with slight differences in refractive indices. Since the doubling used is quite small there is not too much loss of sensitivity. Using similar principles differential refractometers have been made for measuring extremely small changes in the refractive indices[1].

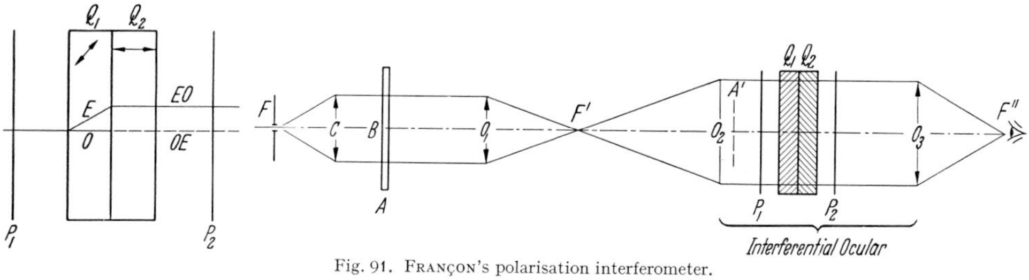

Fig. 91. FRANÇON's polarisation interferometer.

82. Measurement of the refractive index[2]. *α) Immersion technique.* With the aid of the polarising microscope many of the optical constants can be measured for crystals. We shall not describe all the techniques nor the experimental details, which are given in standard textbooks on the polarising microscope. We shall content ourselves by describing some of the procedures.

The refractive indices of crystals are usually determined by the immersion method. The basic principle of the method is that when a transparent crystal is immersed in a liquid having the same refractive index it becomes invisible. This will occur accurately only for one wavelength at a time, as the dispersion of the refractive index of the solid and the liquid may differ. The immersion medium employed is usually a liquid[3] and in rare cases a solid[4]. The variation in the refractive index of the medium to attain exact equality with that of the crystal is obtained by varying the relative proportions of two miscible liquids[5], or by varying the temperature of the liquid[6] or by varying the wavelength of observation[7] or by varying both.

A complete list of miscible liquids and the methods of determining their refractive indices are given in most standard works on petrographic microscopy. The last three methods given above make use of the property that the variation of refractive index with wavelength or temperature of a liquid is in general much greater than that of a solid.

Two methods are used to distinguish whether the refractive index of a crystal is higher or lower than that of the immersion medium.

(a) *The Becke method* or the method of parallel illumination: With a high power objective if the crystal is sharply focussed and if the objective is slightly *raised*, a bright line (Becke line) will appear near the border and will move into the substance having the *higher* refractive index. On depressing the tube the phenomenon is reversed.

---

[1] E. INGLESTAM: J. Opt. Soc. Amer. **47**, 536 (1957). — R. BARER: J. Opt. Soc. Amer. **47**, 545 (1957).

[2] See article by C.D. WEST: Physical Methods in Chemical Analysis, Ed. G. BERL, New York 1950 and the references given therein.

[3] F.E. WRIGHT: The methods of Petrographic Microscopic Research. Carnegie Inst. Publ. No. 158, 1917.

[4] E.S. LARSEN and H. BERMAN: Microscopic determination of non-opaque numerals. Bull. Geol. Survey, U.S.A. No. 848 (1934).

[5] See for example JOHANNSEN [*10*].

[6] MERWIN and E.S. LARSEN: Amer. J. Sci. (4), **34**, 42 (1912).

[7] R.C. EMMONS: Amer. Mineral. **13**, 504 (1928).

(b) *The Van der Kolk*[1] or the method of oblique illumination: If one-half of the incident light is cut off by inserting a card between the condenser and the stage then a shadow appears on the *same* side of the crystal as that on which the screen is inserted if the substance has a *greater* refractive index than the medium. There are many methods of obtaining this inclined illumination but perhaps one of the most sensitive methods is that given by SAYLOR[2] in which two light stops are used, one at the focal plane of the objective and the other above the low power component of the condenser. The limit of accuracy of the immersion method is usually about 0.002 while with temperature control it could be increased to 0.0005. However, recently using the Saylor technique the accuracy has been greatly increased to 0.00003 for optical glasses[3]. It may also be remarked that for identification purposes measurements are usually made in white light.

For optically isotropic crystals refractive index measurements can be made in unpolarised light, the isotropy being detected by the fact that crystals show no restoration between crossed polarisers for all orientations.

The determination of the ordinary refractive index (ω) for uniaxial crystals presents no difficulty; the indicatrix being a spheroid ω is one of the principal refractive indices of every section. The measurement is made with the incident light having its vibration parallel to the appropriate principal vibration direction in the crystal section. For very accurate determination, a section perpendicular to the optic axis, showing no restoration should be used. The principal extraordinary index ε for a crystal lying on a slide with its 3, 4 or 6 fold axis (i.e. optic axis) horizontal, can be measured directly using incident light with its vibration parallel to this axis. However many uniaxial crystals are of such a shape that the optic axis is never horizontal. Then the crystals are broken and the two principal indices for a series of specimens are determined. It will be found that while one refractive index (ω) is always the same, the other continuously varies. The limiting value (either maximum of minimum depending on the optical sign of the crystal) of the other index gives the value of ε. It is best to make measurements on crystal grains that show the highest polarisation colours.

For biaxial crystals also, advantage is usually taken of the morphological relationship between the crystal axes and the axes of the index ellipsoid. It may be possible, under favourable circumstances using a simple rotation apparatus, to determine all the three indices for crystals belonging to the orthorhombic or monoclinic classes. In the former class all the principal axes can be determined from the morphology, while in the second at least one principal axis of the crystal can be determined from the morphology.

In many crystals the refractive index γ is so high that it cannot be determined by immersion techniques. A simple and accurate method for finding γ has been given by WOOD and AGLIFFE[4], when the directions of the three principal axes can be obtained from morphology. The crystal is mounted on the needle of a rotation apparatus so that β is parallel to the axis of rotation and the optic axial plane (containing α, γ) is normal to the axis of rotation. It must be possible with this mounting to determine α, β directly by the immersion methods with the plane of the incident polariser in that of the optic axial plane. The crystal

---

[1] For a simple explanation and also the pit-falls in making measurements see R. C. EVANS and N. F. M. HENRY: Min. Mag. **26**, 267 (1942).
[2] SAYLOR: J. Res. Nat. Bur. Stand. **15**, 277 (1935).
[3] A. CONRAD, FAICK and B. FONOROFF: J. Opt. Soc. Amer. **34**, 530 (1944).
[4] R. G. WOOD and S. H. AGLIFFE: Phil. Mag. (7) **21**, 324 (1936).

is now immersed in liquids of successively greater refractive index and it is rotated until a match is obtained. If n is the refractive index of the liquid, then

$$\frac{1}{n^2} = \frac{1}{\gamma^2} + \left(\frac{1}{\alpha^2} - \frac{1}{\gamma^2}\right)\cos^2\vartheta \tag{82.1}$$

where ϑ is the angle through which the α direction has to be rotated to get a match. Plotting the known values of $1/n^2$ against $\cos^2\vartheta$ one can get to a fair accuracy an extrapolated value of γ.

β) *Measurements with convergent light figures.* When the principal axes of a crystal cannot be determined from the morphology, the help of convergent light figures have to be resorted to. Sections giving centred interference figures which show the principal refractive indices are listed in Table 5.

Table 5.

Figure	Optical sign	Indices shown
Acute bisectrix	$+$	α, β
Acute bisectrix	$-$	β
Obtuse bisectrix	$+$	β
Obtuse bisectrix	$-$	α, β
Optic normal	$+ve$ or $-ve$	α
Single optic axis	$+ve$ or $-ve$	β

Hence using the usual immersion techniques the refractive indices could be determined.

From a knowledge of the refractive indices the optic axial angle can be calculated. Also from a knowledge of two of the indices and the optic axial angle the third index can be computed from Eqs. (33.5) and (33.6)

$$\left.\begin{aligned} \cos^2 V(\alpha) &= \frac{\gamma^2(\beta^2-\alpha^2)}{\beta^2(\gamma^2-\alpha^2)}, \\ \cos^2 V(\gamma) &= \frac{\alpha^2(\gamma^2-\beta^2)}{\beta^2(\gamma^2-\alpha^2)} \end{aligned}\right\} \tag{82.2}$$

where $2V(\alpha)$ is the acute axial angle for a negative crystal (Sect. 83β) and $2V(\gamma)$ that for a positive crystal. The optic axial angle is also an important constant for a crystal and its determination is useful for identification purposes. It must be remembered that the angle between the axes which is observed under the microscope is $2E$, the apparent optic axial angle after refraction which is different from the real optic axial angle $2V$ inside the crystal. The relation between $2E$ and $2V$ is given by

$$\sin E = \beta \sin V \tag{82.3}$$

where β is the intermediate refractive index of the substance.

It is easiest to measure the optic axial angle when both the *metalopes* i.e., the "eyes" of the convergent light figure appear in the field of view. Under the usual conditions of observation (using the Bertrand Amici lens) several factors contribute to make the measurement of the optic axial angle inaccurate. The primary figure at the principal focus of the objective is formed on a curved surface which is observed in an orthographic projection by the eye. The isogyres may be so diffuse that the exact point of emergence of the optic axis cannot be found accurately. The simplest method of determining the optic axial angle is by MALLARD's method. The distance between the melatopes is measured with a micrometer ocular and E is calculated from the formula

$$D = K \sin E \tag{82.4}$$

where K is the MALLARD'S constant depending on the lens system, tube length etc. D is determined by using a specimen of known optic axial angle under identical conditions. V is evaluated from the formula (82.3) for which graphical methods have also been developed.

SLAWSON[1] has devised a method for measuring the angle between the melatopes by using a variable diaphragm placed at the focal plane of the objective. This can be calibrated to give the angular distance between the centre of the field to any point on the interference figure. This method is found to be better than MALLARD'S method, as all the errors due to length of the tube, position of the lenses etc. are automatically eliminated.

When the apparent optic axial angle $2E$ is near about 90°, for a section normal to the bisectrix the two melatopes will be outside the field of view. MICHEL LEVY, WRIGHT, DANA and JOHANNSEN [*10*] have evolved methods for estimating the optical axial angle under these conditions. In optic axial sections when only the isogyre is visible, it is possible to estimate the value of $2V$ from the curvature of this isogyre. In large random crystal sections it is most convenient to measure the optic axial angles directly on a universal stage.

It is quite obvious that for many of these measurements it is necessary to observe the convergent light figures in small crystal grains. When the grains are comparatively large they can be isolated by using the iris diaphragm of the tube. But perhaps the most satisfactory method is that due to JOHANNSEN. When a small auxiliary lens (which is actually a spherical globule produced by heating a fine glass fibre in a flame) is held closely above the crystal grain and viewed between crossed nicols, the interference figure is clearly seen. The use of a converger is also not essential. For convenience the fibre with the globular lens at its end may be fixed by means of wax to the stage so that it lies in the centre of the field slightly above the slide, which may then be moved around to bring the different grains beneath the lens.

γ) A method for determining the refractive indices of small crystals using a simple rotation apparatus. We give here a simple method developed by JOEL[2] by which using only one crystal, whatever be its habit, it is possible to get both the orientation of indicatrix and also the magnitudes of the principal axes at the same time. One of the important advantages of this method is that it uses only a simple rotation apparatus.

The crystal is mounted on a glass fibre at the end of a very simple one-circle goniometer which can be fitted on to a microscope stage and which enables one to rotate the crystal about the horizontal axis. A glass slide may be adjusted such that the crystal may be completely immersed in a drop of liquid of suitable refractive index. Now when the crystal is in a given position (on a polarising microscope with the nicols crossed in parallel light), on rotating the nicols together, two extinctions are observed which correspond to the major and the minor axes of the section of the index ellipsoid by the plane of the microscope stage. For each position φ of the goniometer there are two extinction directions ϑ_1 and ϑ_2 perpendicular to each other. These extinctions may be represented on a stereographic projection where $\varphi = 0$ corresponds to the primitive great circle and $\vartheta = 0$ corresponds to the polariser vibration parallel to the rotation axis. The goniometer is rotated successively by small angles and the corresponding values of ϑ_1 and ϑ_2 are plotted, each φ value corresponding to a great circle with the axis of rotation on the line of intersection (Fig. 92a). During a complete rotation of

[1] C. B. SLAWSON: Amer. J. Mineral. **19**, 25 (1934).
[2] N. JOEL: Miner. Mag. **29**, 206 (1950); **29**, 602 (1951).

the indicatrix about its fixed but arbitrary axis, it is clear that every vector in it will at some time or other come into the horizontal plane. Hence it is possible to bring into the horizontal plane each one of the three axes in its turn.

As each axis of an ellipsoid is a twofold axis, every central section that contains one of the three axes has this as the axis of symmetry. For example as γ along the Z axis is the longest vector in the ellipsoid it must be the longest vector of any ellipse containing it and hence will be the major axis of that ellipse. Same argument applies to the X axis, α being the smallest refractive index. Hence it follows that when each of the three axes comes to the horizontal plane it corresponds to an extinction direction and the points X, Y, or Z therefore lie on the curves of the extinction direction. The axes can be located if the position of one of them could be determined. This could be easily done by finding that

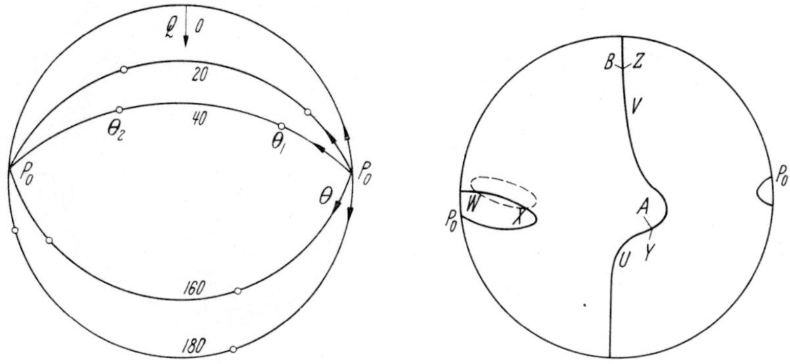

Fig. 92a and b. Stereographic projection showing JOEL's method for determining the refractive indices using a simple rotation apparatus.

vibration direction for which the refractive index is a maximum or a minimum. For this a drop of suitable liquid of known refractive index is used to immerse the crystal. By successive rotations of the crystal and setting it for extinction each time and using the Becke line technique it is possible to determine the direction of vibration for which the refractive indices of the crystal and the liquid are the same. It is now easy to discover the directions of rotation of the goniometer for which the refractive index increases (or decreases) and by changing the immersing liquid it is possible [usually within two or three attempts] to get the vibration direction when the refractive index is a maximum (say). This corresponds to the point Z. A great circle is drawn with Z as the pole and the points of intersection of the direction of "extinction curve" with this arc is the probable position of the X and Y axes. The choice of these axes is usually quite unambiguous. For details and the mathematical treatment of the method the original references may be consulted. The possibility of determining the principal axes of the indicatrix directly by graphical method from the extinction curves have been discussed by JOEL and GARAY COCHEA[1]. The procedure as before consists of drawing the curve for the extinction direction which consists of two distinct parts—an equitorial branch and a polar branch. (It is better to immerse the crystal in a liquid having approximately the mean refractive index of the crystal when plotting the extinction curves.) The next step consists of determining the spherical triangle XYZ for which each side is a quadrant, the two of whose vertices lie on the equitorial curve. Taking two points on the equitorial curve

[1] N. JOEL and I. GARAY COCHEA: Acta crystallogr. **10**, 399 (1957).

the pole of the great circle passing through these is marked. Taking a series of such points the locus of the pole is drawn (Fig. 92b). The locus intersects the extinction curves at two points one of which corresponds to the axis of the index ellipsoid.

Two great circles can be drawn with these points as the pole. Each great circle intersects the equatorial part of the extinction curve at two points. We therefore have two spherical triangles one of which corresponds to the "true" indicatrix. In order to know which is the "true" one and which the "ghost", it is sufficient to remember that one of the vertices of the "ghost" triangle is 90° away from P_0, the goniometer axis. Hence it would be easily possible to distinguish the "ghost" triangle UVW from the "true" triangle XYZ.

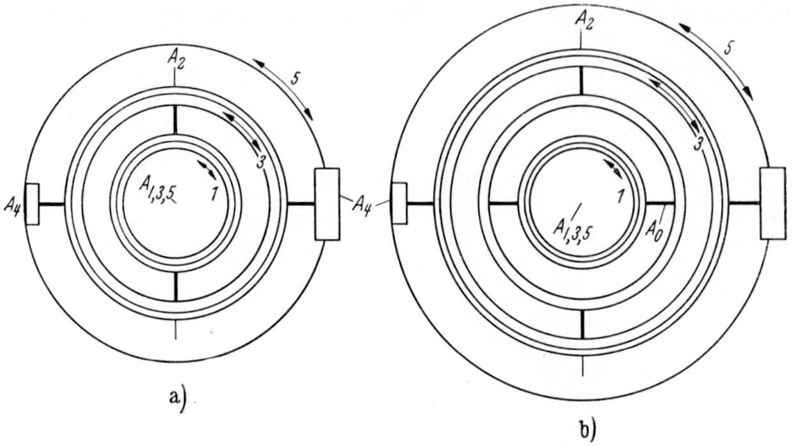

Fig. 93. (a) The four axes of the Federov stage. (b) The five axes of the Emmons stage.

δ) The universal stage[1]. This is an instrument which helps to orientate a single crystal grain by rotation about a number of axes that are mutually perpendicular. This is particularly useful in the identification of a single grain by optical means. The important principle underlying the method of examining crystals on a universal stage is the recognition of the optical symmetry planes. For example a uniaxial crystal may be recognised by the infinite symmetry planes parallel to the optic axis and one symmetry plane perpendicular to it. A biaxial crystal on the other hand is recognised by the three mirror planes of optical symmetry the intersections of which define the three principal axes of the triaxial ellipsoid, which are themselves two-fold axes of optical symmetry. The biaxial crystal has also two optic axes. These symmetry planes can be readily recognised by a simple procedure using the universal stage. The Federov stage has four axes of rotation while its improved version by EMMONS[2] has five axes. Fig. 93 give the arrangement of the axes of rotation in both the Federov and the Emmons stages.

The axes $A_1 A_3$ and A_5 are parallel to the axis of the microscope (the last i.e. A_5 is the microscope stage itself) when the other axes are in the zero position, A_2 is a N-S axis and A_4 is an E-W axis. The Emmons stage differs from that of Federov in that there is an extra E-W axis which is usually denoted by A_0, so that the same nomenclature can be used for both stages. This extra axis

[1] A good summary of the techniques using the universal stage is available in the monograph by P. R. J. NAIDU: 4-axes universal stage. Madras 1958.

[2] R. C. EMMONS: Amer. J. Mineral. **14**, 441 (1929).

considerably reduces the labour of determining each symmetry plane separately and then finding the angular coordinates of the line of intersection by the stereographic projection method. But we shall not give the routine process by which the optical indicatrix of a single grain is recognised and measured using the phenomenon of extinction.

ε) The prism method. The well known minimum deviation method can be used for the measurement of the refractive indices of anisotropic crystals also. In the case of uniaxial crystals a single prism will enable both ω and ε to be determined provided it be cut so that either the refracting edge is parallel to the optic axis or else perpendicular to it, with the optic axis lying in the plane bisecting the refracting angle. In the case of biaxial crystals, two of the three refractive indices can be obtained from a prism (60° say) in which the plane bisecting the refracting angle contains two of the principal axes of the index ellipsoid with one of these parallel to the refracting edge. Hence one requires at least two prisms to determine the three refractive indices. The making of these prisms with the principal axes of the indicatrix in specified direction becomes more and more complex as we proceed from orthorhombic (where the crystallographic axes coincide with the axes of the optical ellipsoid) to triclinic where there is no relation between the two sets of axes[1].

ζ) Total reflection method. If the crystal has one polished surface then perhaps the most convenient method of determining the three principal refractive indices is by the method of total internal reflection using an instrument corresponding to the Pulfrich refractometer[2]—the crystal having a lower refractive index than the adjacent medium. When the crystal is put in optical contact with the prism on the hemisphere of the refractometer two critical edges are seen (which are linearly polarised). When the crystal is rotated in the plane of its surface the critical edges move and the four extreme positions of the two edges are noteds Since the crystal is being rotated about a random axis all the arguments presented in Sect. 82γ in connection with JOEL's method hold. Hence the maximum and minimum values correspond to α and γ while one of the two inner extremalt corresponds to β. The ambiguity in β can be resolved by making measuremens. on another non-parallel section of the crystal. When no other section is avilable the method used is the following[3].

Where the crystal has been rotated into the position giving the maximum reading γ the other shadow edge provides a second reading say R. If the reading associated with α is r and if φ is the angle between the position at which these occur then

$$\cos^2\varphi = \frac{\alpha^2\gamma^2(\beta^2 - r^2)(\beta^2 - R^2)}{r^2 R^2(\beta^2 - \alpha^2)(\beta^2 - \gamma^2)}\,. \tag{82.5}$$

From this the approximate value of β can be computed, and the extremal corresponding to β recognized. Other methods using a polarising cap have also been suggested.

83. Measurement of birefringence. *α) The determination of the "fast" and "slow" axes in a crystal plate possessing only linear birefringence.* These correspond to the principal axes of the elliptic section of the index ellipsoid normal to the direction of observation and are also the two privileged directions of vibration in a crystal plate. It is worthwhile remembering that the "fast" axis corresponds

[1] For details of the experimental methods see SZIVESSY [*1*] or A.E.H. TUTTON [*12*].
[2] For a detailed description of the various refractometers see TUTTON [*12*].
[3] E. J. BINBAGE and B.W. ANDERSON: Min. Mag. **26**, 246 (1942).

to that direction of vibration which has the lower refractive index (minor axis) and the "slow" axis to that with the higher refractive index (major axis).

When a crystal plate is observed between simultaneously rotated crossed polarisers, there are two positions, perpendicular to each other, where one gets complete crossing. These happen only when the direction of vibration of the incident light coincides with one of the two privileged directions of the crystal plate. In all other positions the crystal exhibits polarisation colours, which arise due to the phase difference introduced by the crystal between the two waves that travel inside it (see Sects. 63 and 64). The colours are most vivid when the incident vibration is at 45° to the privileged directions of the vibrations of the crystal. For this setting colour charts giving the polarisation colours for different values of phase retardation are available and are usually referred to as the Newtonian scale of colours. If now a birefringent plate or wedge of known optical characteristics is placed above or below the crystal with its principal vibration direction coinciding with those of the crystalline plate, the colours seen through the combination change. If for example the "fast" axis of the test plate coincides with that of the crystal plate, the phase difference between the two emerging beams increases and the interference colours will rise in the Newtonian colour scale. If on the other hand, the "fast" axis of one coincides with the "slow" axis of the other, the interference colours will fall in the Newtonian scale. The test devices used are usually (a) a mica $\lambda/4$ retardation plate, (b) a full wave retardation plate made of gypsum or (c) a simple quartz wedge. These can be introduced in a slot in the microscope tube but care must be taken to see that they are in a proper orientation with respect to the crystal plate. The $\lambda/4$ plate is more useful for examining crystals of relatively high retardation while the full wave plate is more suitable for the study of specimens with low birefringence.

β) Determination of the optical sign of a crystal. A uniaxial crystal is "positive" (+) if $\varepsilon > \omega$ i.e., the index ellipsoid is a prolate spheroid and is negative (—) if $\varepsilon < \omega$. A biaxial crystal is positive if γ is the acute bisectrix and is negative if α is the acute bisectrix. If one gets the appropriate crystal sections it will be possible to determine the optical sign directly by measuring the refractive indices. The optical character can be easily determined by making observations on the interference figures. The determination of the sign finally resolves itself to finding (a) whether the radial or tangential directions is faster in uniaxial crystals and (b) whether in the acute interference figure the vibration in the optic normal direction (β) is faster or slower than that in the line joining the melatopes in biaxial crystals. This can be done by the insertion of a $\lambda/4$, a full wave retardation plate or a quartz wedge, at the proper angle. Fig. 94 gives the effect of a quartz wedge on a centred uniaxial or biaxial figure.

The problem however is more complicated when the melatopes are not in the field of view but many of the text books mentioned earlier give excellent diagrams showing the actual movements of the fringes and these should prove useful in such cases. The theory of these phenomena has been dealt with in detail in Sect. 64.

γ) The measurement of birefringence. The birefringence introduced by any crystalline plate can be accurately determined by compensating it by a graduated quartz wedge compensator or a Babinet compensator which have been dealt with in detail in Sect. 21. The former, which has a graduated scale etched on its surface, usually gives the path difference directly in 10^{-7} cm. Both these require special oculars with a cap analyser. The compensator that is now very popular with microscopists is the *Berek compensator* which can be introduced in the tube above the objective and which does not require a cap analyser or any special ocular. A plate of calcite about 0.1 mm thick is cut normal to the optic axis and mounted on a rotating axis in a metal holder. A calibrated drum controlling the rotation

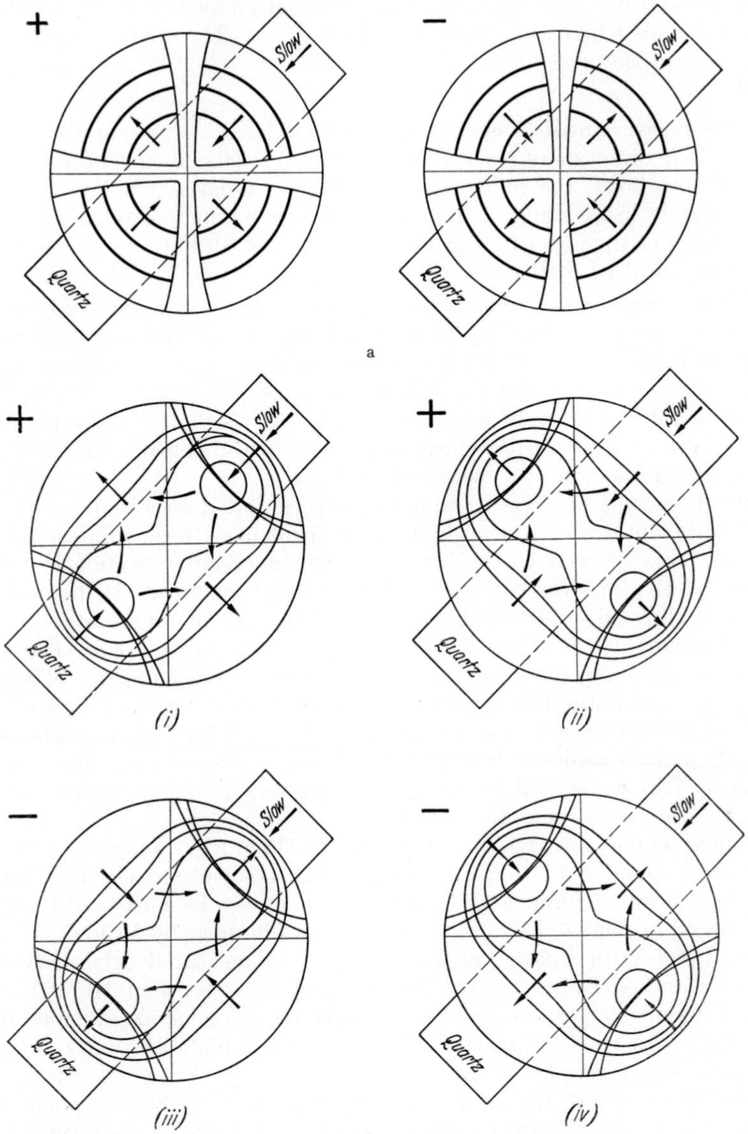

b

Fig. 94 a and b. Effect of a quartz wedge on the interference figures due to $+ve$ and $-ve$ crystals. (a) Uniaxial. (b) Biaxial.

measures the angular position of the calcite plate. To determine the birefringence with this instrument, the crystal plate on the stage is rotated so that the trace of the vibration of the fast ray is parallel to the trace of the slow ray in the inclined plate of the compensator. The angle through which the calcite plate is rotated to reach compensation measures the path difference produced by the crystal plate. The Berek, the Babinet and the quartz wedge compensators can also be used effectively in the determination of the sign of the crystal.

The dispersion of birefringence with wavelength can be measured from the channeled spectrum observed in the beam transmitted by a crystal placed between crossed polaroids when white light is incident on it. This method has been used with success in the measurement of the dispersion of the stress birefringence in crystal[1].

84. The measurement of optical rotation. *α) Along the optic axis.* In a cubic crystal for any direction of propagation, or in a birefringent crystal for directions along the optic axes, the rotation of the plane of polarisation can be measured very accurately using some of the well known techniques of polarimetry. Very good accounts of the experimental methods are given in various review articles[2]. We shall not deal with them here.

β) Along directions other than the optic axes. The effect observed would be the result of superposing the effects of optical rotation and birefringence (Sect. 39). Most of the measurements that have been made are confined to the case of quartz (a uniaxial crystal) and that too for directions perpendicular to the optic axis. We shall therefore deal only with this specific case, although the same methods can be directly applied for the measurement of optical rotation along any direction in either a uniaxial or a biaxial crystal.

From the results of Sects. 38 and 39 one sees that if on a plate of quartz cut parallel to the optic axis, a linear vibration is incident with the vibration direction parallel or perpendicular to the optic axis, the emergent vibration is not linear (as in an inactive birefringent crystal), but is slightly elliptic. If the ratio of the axes of this ellipse is b/a, then the emergent light may be represented by a point on the Poincaré sphere whose latitude is 2ω, where $\tan\omega = b/a$. The angle ω would be a maximum for a thickness corresponding to a *half wave plate* and for such a plate ω_m has been measured to be 13′ by VOIGT[3] for the D line of sodium (for propagation perpendicular to the optic axis). This measurement alone is quite sufficient to compute the optical rotation of quartz perpendicular to the optic axis. This comes out to be half the rotatory power along the optic axis but the rotation is of the opposite sign.

The next important experiment is that of WEVER[4] who, using a 60° prism with its edge parallel to the optic axis, actually separated the two privileged vibrations transmitted unchanged along any direction. He measured the ellipticities of the vibrations and confirmed the values obtained by VOIGT.

Later the rotatory power of quartz has been measured accurately by two groups of workers, BRUHAT and GRIVET[5], and SZIVESSY and MÜNSTER[6], using slightly different techniques and we shall describe the general principles of these two methods. In both the methods a plane parallel plate of quartz cut parallel to the optic axis is employed.

In the first method, the plate is placed between crossed linear polarisers and rotated till a minimum of intensity is transmitted. This is what BRUHAT *et al.* call the azimuth of minimum. Next a Nakamura biplate is introduced in front of the analysing nicol. It is found that the two halves do not show equality.

[1] E.G. COKER and L.N.G. FILON: A Treatise on Photoelasticity. Cambridge 1957.

[2] W. HELLER: Physical methods in organic chemistry, Ed. WEISSBERGER. New York: Interscience Publ. 1949.

[3] W. VOIGT: Göttinger Nachr. 1903, p. 155. — Ann. d. Phys. **18**, 645 (1905).

[4] F. WEVER: Jb. Phil. Fak. Univ. Göttingen **2**, 206 (1920).

[5] G. BRUHAT and R. GRIVET: J. Phys. Radium **6**, 12 (1935).

[6] CL. MÜNSTER and G. SZIVESSY: Phys. Z. **36**, 101 (1935).

The plate is again rotated in its own plane till the two halves of the Nakamura plate show an equality of intensity. This position is called the azimuth of equality. Now the total birefringence of the plate is measured using any of the well known methods. These three measurements are sufficient to compute the rotation perpendicular to the optic axis.

The theory of the method can be understood by referring to Figs. 95 a and 95 b. Let P be the linear incident vibration. The effect of the crystal plate of thickness t, possessing both birefringence and optical activity would be a rotation $t\Delta' = \Delta$ about the axis EOF where the latitude of E i.e. 2ϑ is given by

$$\tan 2\vartheta = \frac{2t\varrho'}{t\delta'} = \frac{2\varrho}{\delta} \tag{84.1}$$

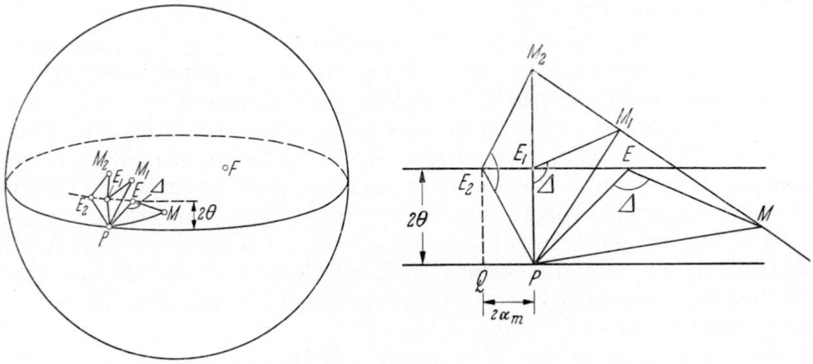

a b

Fig. 95 a and b. Poincaré representation to explain BRUHAT's method of determining the optical rotation of quartz normal to the optic axis.

where ϱ' is the rotatory power in the absence of birefringence and δ' is the birefringence in the absence of rotation. The total birefringence

$$t\Delta' = t\sqrt{\delta^2 + (2\varrho)^2} = \frac{t\delta'}{\cos 2\vartheta} = \frac{\delta}{\cos 2\vartheta} \tag{84.2}$$

and since the ellipticity of the emergent ellipse is small, one could take

$$2\vartheta \approx \frac{2\varrho}{\delta} \quad \text{and} \quad \Delta \approx \delta. \tag{84.3}$$

The incident state P would therefore be brought to the elliptic state M. The effect of rotating the plate in its own plane would be to move the point E along a small circle whose latitude is 2ϑ. Since the ellipticities are small the portion of the Poincaré sphere could be approximated to a plane and this is shown in Fig. 95 b. For any general setting of the plate (axis of rotation EF) the intensity transmitted by the analyser is

$$I = \sin^2 \tfrac{1}{2}\,\widehat{PM} \tag{84.4}$$

and since $\widehat{PM} = 2\widehat{PE}\sin\frac{\Delta}{2}$, I would be a minimum when $\widehat{PE}$ is a minimum. This will occur when E is at E_1 (latitude 2ϑ) on the same meridian as P. Hence, at the azimuth of minimum, the ellipses that are *propagated unchanged* correspond to E_1 and the opposite ellipse F_1. (It may however be noted that the ellipse *emerging* from the crystal actually corresponds to M_1.) Now when a Nakamura plate is used in front of the analysing nicol the two halves will not be equal.

The crystal plate will have to be rotated in its own plane and the two halves will become equal only when the emerging vibration M_2 is on the same meridian as P so that E now occupies the position E_2.

Now

$$PM_2 = 4\vartheta \tag{84.5}$$

and since E_1 lies on PM_2 the azimuth of equality E_2 differs from the azimuth of minimum E_1 by an angle $2\alpha_m$ given by (from the triangle PM_2E_2)

$$2\alpha_m = 2\vartheta \cot\frac{\Delta}{2}. \tag{84.6}$$

Here the approximation is made that the length of the small circular arc $E_1E_2 =$ the great circular arc $\widehat{PQ}$.

Since both Δ (measured using a compensator), and α_m are experimentally determined, ϑ can be calculated and hence ϱ can be computed from (84.3).

BRUHAT and GRIVET using this technique have measured the optical rotation of quartz perpendicular to the optic axis for a series of wavelengths from $\lambda =$ 5461 Å to $\lambda = 2537$ Å. They used an accurate photoelectric method for measuring the azimuths of minimum. For the exact experimental procedure and the estimation of errors the original paper may be consulted. The value obtained for $\varrho_\perp/\varrho_\parallel$ was -0.51 for $\lambda = 5461$ Å which increased to -0.57 for $\lambda = 2537$ Å. These results confirm not only the values obtained by VOIGT and WEVER but also their finding that the sign of the rotation perpendicular to the optic axis is opposite to that parallel to the optic axis.

In the second method due to SZIVESSY and MÜNSTER, the azimuth of minimum is first determined using crossed linear polarisers. Then instead of a Nakamura biplate, a birefringent half shade (Bravais plate of small retardation) is introduced before the final analyser. This consists of two birefringent plates of exactly equal thicknesses but with their slow and fast axes interchanged. Hence the two halves show equality only when *linearly* polarised light is incident on it (see Sect. 20γ). The quartz plate (cut parallel to the optic axis) is rotated in its own plane till the Bravais double plate shows equality of intensity (i.e. plane polarised light is emergent from the crystal). When the polariser and analyser are crossed there are two positions in a complete rotation of the crystal plate in which the emergent light is linearly polarised. The situation is illustrated in Fig. 96, the point P representing the incident light on the equator is brought back to M_3 on the equator by a rotation about E_3OF_3 where the latitude of E_3 is 2ϑ.

From the triangle PE_3S, $\widehat{PS} = 2\alpha$ the angle through which plate is turned from the azimuth of minimum to get a linear vibration emergent from it and $\widehat{E_3S} = 2\vartheta$ and hence

$$\tan 2\alpha = \sin 2\vartheta \tan\frac{\Delta}{2}. \tag{84.7}$$

Measuring the total birefringence $t\Delta'$, the value of ϑ can be determined from which ϱ can be computed. It may be remarked that in the paper by SZIVESSY and MÜNSTER the formula is expressed in terms of $k = \tan\vartheta$.

Using this method, $\varrho_\perp$ for different wavelengths have been measured and the value -0.45 was obtained for $\varrho_\perp/\varrho_\parallel$, a value differing by about 10% from that of BRUHAT and GRIVET.

From Sect. 40 we know that the optical rotation power is determined by the symmetric tensor which can be represented by the equation [cf. Eq. (40.1)]

$$\gamma'_{11}\varkappa_1^2 + \gamma'_{22}\varkappa_2^2 + \gamma'_{33}\varkappa_3^2 + 2\gamma'_{23}\varkappa_2\varkappa_3 + 2\gamma'_{31}\varkappa_3\varkappa_1 + 2\gamma'_{12}\varkappa_1\varkappa_2 = \pm 1 \tag{84.8}$$

where $\varkappa_1, \varkappa_2, \varkappa_3$ correspond to the axes of coordinates. The sign in the right is to be so chosen that the surface is real. In optically uniaxial crystals the gyration surface represented by (84.8) is a surface of revolution[1] about the optic axes. If the axial system $(\varkappa_1, \varkappa_2, \varkappa_3)$ is so chosen that $\varkappa_1$ is along the optic axis, then $\gamma'_{ik}=0$ for $i \neq k$, $\gamma'_{22}=\gamma'_{33}$ and if we put $\gamma'_{11}=\gamma'_a$ and $\gamma'_{22}=\gamma'_{33}=\gamma'_s$ and $\varkappa_1=a$ and $\varkappa_2^2+\varkappa_3^2=s^2$ Eq. (84.8) reduces to

$$\gamma'_a a^2 + \gamma'_s s^2 = \pm 1. \tag{84.9}$$

Since in quartz γ'_s and γ'_a are of opposite signs, the rotation surface has the shape of two conjugate hyperboloids of revolution about the optic axis.

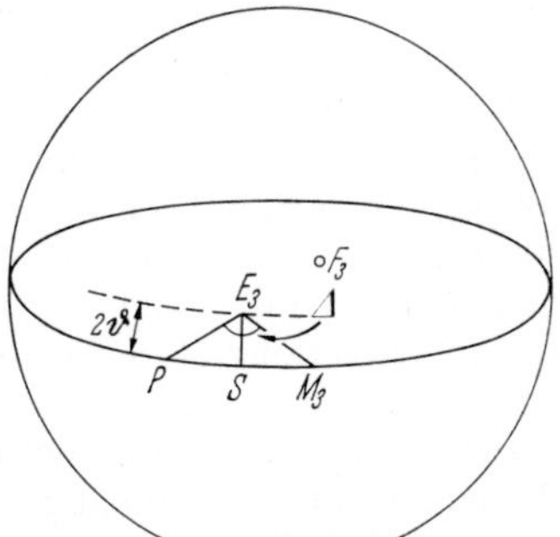

Fig. 96. Poincaré representation showing SZIVESSY's method of measuring the optical rotation of quartz normal to the optic axis.

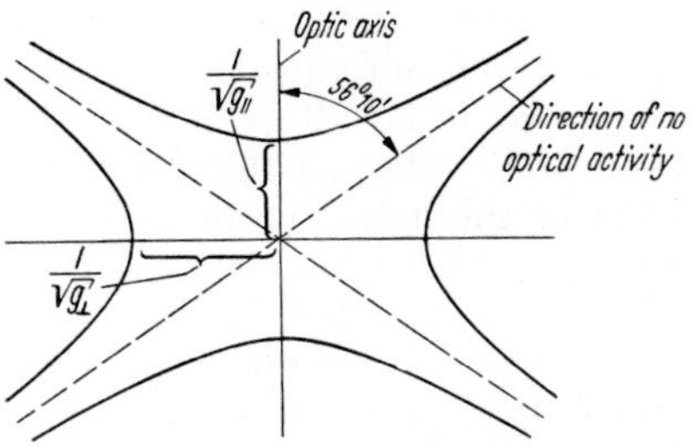

Fig. 97. The section of the optical activity surface parallel to the optic axis in quartz.

The lines of the common asymptotic cone make with the optic axis an angle $\bar{\beta}$ given by

$$\tan^2\bar{\beta} = -\gamma'_a/\gamma'_s. \tag{84.10}$$

The meridonial section of the surface is shown in Fig. 97. The optical activity in a direction making an angle β with the optic axis is given by

$$\gamma_G = \gamma'_a \cos^2\beta + \gamma'_s \sin^2\beta$$

where γ_G is the scalar parameter of gyration and here obviously γ'_a and γ'_s are the measure of the activity along and perpendicular to the optic axis. Since $\gamma'_s/\gamma'_a = \varrho_\perp/\varrho_\parallel = -0.45$ the scalar parameter would be given by

$$\gamma_G = -\frac{n_\omega \varrho_\parallel \lambda}{\pi}(\cos^2\beta - 0.45\sin^2\beta) \tag{84.11}$$

where n_ω is the ordinary refractive index.

Since the ratio of $\varrho_\perp/\varrho_\parallel$ is practically independent of wavelength it follows that a plate cut at 56° 10′ to the optic axis [from Eq. (76.10)] behaves as an inactive crystal.

SZIVESSY and MÜNSTER have established by experiments that a quartz plate whose normal makes an angle 56° 10′ with the optic axis behaves like an optically inactive plate over the entire spectral region for a parallel beam of light at normal incidence, thus confirming the predictions of theory. These authors have therefore advocated that in making Soleil compensators and certain other half shades, sections of quartz at 56° 10′ to the optic axis must be used if the measurements are to be free from errors.

γ) *Along the optic axis in the presence of dichroism:* This has been dealt with in detail in Sects. 71β and 72.

[1] This is not true for the tetragonal tetartohedral and tetragonal hemihedral classes.

E. Variation of properties due to external influences.

85. General considerations. The external influences that could affect the optical properties of a crystal could take the form of a *scalar* (e.g., temperature or hydrostatic pressure), or a *vector* (e.g., electric field, magnetic field etc.) or a *tensor* (a stress, strain etc.). The general effect of these external influences would be to alter the optical parameters determining the propagation of light in a crystal.

These can for convenience be classified into those that relate to the refractive, the gyratory or the absorptive properties of the crystals. The parameters that are usually chosen for the complete description of the effect of external influences on crystals are the components of the index, gyration and absorption tensors. In what follows we shall be referring mostly to refractive properties (i.e., the changes in the index tensor) as a large amount of experimental and theoretical work has been concentrated on this aspect of the subject. The methods indicated can however be equally well applied to the case of the gyration and the absorption tensors. The effect of the external agent would therefore be to alter each component of the index tensor a_{ij} by a small amount Δa_{ij}. This would physically correspond to the alteration of the magnitudes and directions of the principal axes of the index ellipsoid.

One could to a first degree of approximation assume that the changes induced in the optical parameters are proportional to the magnitude of the scalar or are a homogeneous linear function of the components of the vector or the tensor. In such a case using the matrix notation we can write

$$\left.\begin{aligned} &\text{(a)} \quad [\Delta a_{ij}] = [c_{ij}]\, S && (S \text{ is a scalar}), \\ &\text{(b)} \quad [\Delta a_{ij}] = [c_{ij,k}]\, A_k && (A_k \text{ is a vector}), \\ &\text{(c)} \quad [\Delta a_{ij}] = [c_{ij,kl}]\, B_{kl} && (B_{kl} \text{ is a tensor of the second rank}) \end{aligned}\right\} \tag{85.1}$$

and so on. From a knowledge of the nature of the tensor whose components are Δa_{ij} and also the nature of S, A_k or B_{kl} one can determine the type of the tensors c_{ij}, $c_{ij,k}$ or $c_{ij,kl}$.

For example since $[a_{ij}]$ is a symmetric tensor of rank two, $[\Delta a_{ij}]$ would also be a symmetric tensor. Hence $[c_{ij}]$ must be 3×3 symmetric tensor having therefore 6 independent components. However $[c_{ij,k}]$ must be a tensor of rank 3 but symmetric in i and j. Hence its elements can be written in the form of a 6×3 matrix with 18 components. If B_{kl} is a symmetric tensor of rank two as in the classical case of homogeneous stress or strain then $[c_{ij,kl}]$ would be a tensor of rank 4 but symmetric in i and j and k and l. Hence its independent elements can be represented by a 6×6 matrix with 36 distinct constants for the most general case. It is to be noted that $c_{ij,kl}$ is *not* symmetric for an interchange of (ij) and (kl), since these indices refer to entirely different properties of the medium, e.g. optical and elastric properties. That this had been overlooked by POCKELS in his classical studies in photo-elasticity was pointed out by BHAGAVARTAM (see Sect. 92 below). The number of independent constants in all cases would be reduced by any symmetry in the crystal.

If however the changes of the optical parameters are quadratic functions of the vector or tensor components we have

$$\left.\begin{aligned} &\text{(a)} \quad [\Delta a_{ij}] = [c_{ijkl}]\, A_k A_l, \\ &\text{(b)} \quad [\Delta a_{ij}] = [c_{ijklmn}]\, B_{kl} B_{mn} \end{aligned}\right\} \tag{85.2}$$

and so on. In these cases also, the nature of the matrix describing the change may be computed. It may be remarked that, except in a very few substances, the quadratic effect is usually a second order effect. The changes in the optical properties which we are discussing do not relate to those associated with transformations of crystal structures due to external influences.

I. Variation with temperature.

86. Changes in refractive indices and the optic axial angle. α) In the most general case the number of constants necessary to describe the changes in the constants of the index tensor $[a_{ij}]$ due to an alteration in the temperature is six and Δa_{ij} can be written as

$$\Delta a_{ij} = k_{ij} \Delta t \tag{86.1}$$

where Δt is the rise in temperature. It is convenient to choose the principal axes of the index ellipsoid as the axes of coordinates. These coincide with the crystallographic axes for cubic, tetragonal (trigonal, hexagonal) and orthorhombic crystals. Hence for all these classes $k_{ij}(i \neq j) = 0$. The effect of temperature would therefore be to alter the magnitude of the principal axes of the index ellipsoid without any change in their orientation. In monoclinic crystals one of the principal axes will continue to coincide with the unique axis, while the other two may change their orientation, remaining all the while in the symmetry plane. In triclinic crystals the temperature would affect the orientation and magnitude of all the three axes of the index ellipsoid. The number of constants necessary to describe the effect of temperature in different crystal classes is given below.

Cubic	Tetragonal Trigonal Hexagonal	Orthorhombic	Monoclinic unique axis *o y*	Triclinic
$\begin{vmatrix} k_{11} & 0 & 0 \\ 0 & k_{11} & 0 \\ 0 & 0 & k_{11} \end{vmatrix}$	$\begin{vmatrix} k_{11} & 0 & 0 \\ 0 & k_{11} & 0 \\ 0 & 0 & k_{33} \end{vmatrix}$	$\begin{vmatrix} k_{11} & 0 & 0 \\ 0 & k_{22} & 0 \\ 0 & 0 & k_{33} \end{vmatrix}$	$\begin{vmatrix} k_{11} & 0 & k_{13} \\ 0 & k_{22} & 0 \\ k_{13} & 0 & k_{33} \end{vmatrix}$	$\begin{vmatrix} k_{11} & k_{12} & k_{13} \\ k_{12} & k_{22} & k_{23} \\ k_{13} & k_{23} & k_{33} \end{vmatrix}$

It is quite obvious that in the last three cases there would be an alteration in the optic axial angle due to temperature. This can be computed using Eq. (82.2).

Perhaps the most interesting phenomenon connected with thermo-optics is the Mitscherlish phenomenon. When a plate of gypsum which at room temperature is a positive biaxial crystal is heated, the optic axial angle goes on diminishing and at about 90° C, for λ 5893, the crystal becomes uniaxial. Above this temperature the crystal again becomes biaxial, but with its optic axial plane rotated through a right angle. It has been shown in Sect. 33 that the optic axial plane in any biaxial crystal is that which contains the directions of the minimum and maximum principal refractive indices (namely γ and α, where $\gamma > \beta > \alpha$). The condition necessary for exhibiting the Mitscherlisch penomenon in any biaxial crystal is that two of the principal refractive indices must be close to each other (say $n_2 = \beta \approx n_1 = \alpha$) and $\frac{d\alpha}{dt} > \frac{d\beta}{dt}$. In such a case at some particular temperature n_2 could become equal to α, making the crystal uniaxial. At higher temperatures n_1 may become greater than n_2 so that n_2 becomes α and n_1 becomes β and the axial plane would be now that containing n_2 and n_3. This phenomenon *of crossed axial dispersion* can be most spectacularly exhibited in the case of crystals in which all the three refractive indices are very close to each other, for in such a case the optic axial angle would be large. This phenomenon has been observed in many crystals but special mention[1] may be made of $CsSeO_4$ in which within

[1] A.E.H. TUTTON [*12*].

the narrow range of 0 to 250° C each of the three axes of the index ellipsoid becomes in turn the acute bisectrix. It must be remembered that in the case of monoclinic and triclinic crystals this effect is accompanied by the rotation of the axes of the index ellipsoid with respect to the crystallographic axes due to thermal expansion effects.

Very few investigations have been made of the variation of the absorption or gyration tensor surfaces with temperature in a general biaxial crystal. Most of these studies have been confined to isotropic or uniaxial crystals. In the latter case the observations have been restricted to directions parallel to the optic axis.

Experimental methods. Very few measurements of the actual constants have been made for crystals of symmetries lower than orthorhombic. For crystals for which there is no rotation of the axes of the index ellipsoid, we have

$$a_{ii} = \frac{1}{n_i^2}\,.$$

Hence

$$k_{ii} = \frac{\Delta a_{ii}}{\Delta t} = -\frac{2}{n_i^3}\,\frac{d n_i}{d t}\,. \tag{86.2}$$

The temperature coefficient of refractive index of a solid can be evaluated from the measurements of the refractive index of the substance at different temperatures by the well known prism method. The various details of the technique can be obtained elsewhere[1-3]. The disadvantages and the limitations of this method are obvious. The requirement of the experimental specimen in bulk, the maintenance of these large non-conducting specimens at uniform temperatures, the making of prisms from crystals that exhibit a layer structure are some of the problems one is confronted with. Since the magnitude of dn/dt is of the order of 10^{-5}, the prism has to be heated by 100° C to alter its refractive index by one unit in the third place of decimals. Hence the accuracy of the method is also not very high.

A much simpler way of measuring dn/dt is provided by the interference method[4] where it is evaluated from the measurements of the shift with temperature of the interference fringes formed between the two surfaces of the crystal, fashioned in the form of a plate. Either Newtonian fringes or Haidinger fringes can be used. In both cases, for normal incidence the bright fringes satisfy the relation

$$2 n_i l = N \lambda, \tag{86.3}$$

where n_i is the refractive index, l the thickness of the crystal and λ is the wavelength and N an integer. On varying the temperature the fringes will move past a reference mark on the crystal. If ΔN is the number of fringes crossing this mark for a temperature change Δt then

$$2\frac{\Delta n_i}{\Delta t}\, l + 2 n_i \frac{\Delta l}{\Delta t} = \lambda \frac{\Delta N}{\Delta t} \tag{86.4}$$

giving

$$\frac{d n_i}{d t} = \frac{\lambda}{2l}\,\frac{\Delta N}{\Delta t} - n_i \alpha_i \tag{86.5}$$

---

[1] Martens: In Vol. VI of Winkelmann's Handbuch der Physik, 1906.
[2] W. S. Rodney and R. J. Spindler: J. Res. Nat. Bur. Stand. **49**, 253 (1952).
[3] Szivessy [*1*].
[4] See for example G.N. Ramachandran: Proc. Ind. Acad. Sci. A **25**, 266 (1947).

where l is the length of the specimen and α_i is the coefficient of linear expansion along the direction of propagation of light. By this method, knowing α_i one can obtain the value of dn_i/dt with respect to vacuum. The shift of the fringes can be determined either visually or photographically. It must be mentioned that even though $\Delta N/\Delta t$ may be determined to within 1%, the value of dn/dt can usually be obtained only to an accuracy of 5%, as the major contribution to the path retardation change usually arises due to the thermal expansion. The application of this method to birefringent crystals is obvious.

For the measurement of the variation of optical activity with temperature, the method consists of measuring the rotations of the crystal at various temperatures using the well known visual, photographic or photoelectric polarimeters[1]. A fair amount of experimental data on the thermo-optic behaviour of crystals has accumulated. These and a list of references on this subject may be found elsewhere[2].

Phenomenological atomistic theories have been proposed to explain the thermal variation of refractive index[3] and the thermal variation of optical activity in crystals[4]. We shall not deal with these here. But for a list of references on this subject reference 2 (footnote below) may be consulted.

II. Electro-optics.

87. Phenomenological theory. When a crystal is placed in an electric field, there would be an alteration of the distribution of the electric charges of the atoms and molecules, which constitute the crystal. These alterations in the charges which give rise to the opposing polarisation field would affect the optical properties of the medium. It should be possible in principle to develop a consistent picture of these electro-optical effects purely from an atomistic standpoint. But in this section we shall present the simple phenomenological theory of electro-optics.

The changes in the optical properties of the medium can be, as has been shown in Sect. 85, best expressed as changes in the constants of the index ellipsoid. With respect to any set of co-ordinate axes, the equation to the index ellipsoid could be written as

$$a_{11}x^2 + a_{22}y^2 + a_{33}z^2 + 2a_{23}yz + 2a_{31}zx + 2a_{12}xy = 1. \qquad (87.1)$$

If one assumes that the constants of the undeformed crystals are represented by a_{ij}^0 and those of the electrically stressed crystal by a_{ij} then to a first degree of approximation it could be assumed that $\Delta a_{ij}[= a_{ij} - a_{ij}^0]$ can be expressed as homogeneous linear function of the components of either (a) the electric polarisation or (b) the electric field. The three components of the polarisation field P_1, P_2, P_3 and the electric field E_1, E_2, E_3 along the principal electric axes are related by the following equations, if one neglects second order effects.

$$P_i = \frac{\varepsilon_i - 1}{4\pi} E_i \qquad (i = 1, 2, 3) \qquad (87.2)$$

[1] See e.g. the article by W. HELLER, Physical Methods in Organic Chemistry, Ed. WEISSBERGER. New York: Interscience 1949.

[2] See article by S. RAMASESHAN, K. VEDAM and R. S. KRISHNAN, in: Progress of Crystal Physics, Vol. 1, Ed. R. S. KRISHNAN. Madras 1958.

[3] G. N. RAMACHANDRAN: Proc. Ind. Acad. Sci. A **25**, 266 (1947).

[4] S. CHANDRASEKHAR: Proc. Ind. Acad. Sci. A **39**, 290 (1954).

where ε_i's are the principal dielectric constants of the substance. We therefore have (writing the six components of the index tensor as $a_1, a_2, \dots, a_6$)

$$\Delta a_i = a_i - a_i^0 = -\sum_j \varrho_{ij} P_j, \qquad \begin{pmatrix} j = 1, 2, 3 \\ i = 1 \text{ to } 6 \end{pmatrix} \tag{87.3}$$

or

$$\Delta a_i = a_i - a_i^0 = \sum_j r_{ij} E_j, \qquad \begin{pmatrix} j = 1, 2, 3 \\ i = 1 \text{ to } 6 \end{pmatrix} \tag{87.4}$$

written explicitly in terms of the components of the polarisation field Eq. (87.3) becomes

$$\left.\begin{aligned} a_{11} - a_{11}^0 &= -\left[\varrho_{11} P_1 + \varrho_{12} P_2 + \varrho_{13} P_3\right], \\ a_{22} - a_{22}^0 &= -\left[\varrho_{21} P_1 + \varrho_{22} P_2 + \varrho_{23} P_3\right], \\ a_{33} - a_{33}^0 &= -\left[\varrho_{31} P_1 + \varrho_{32} P_2 + \varrho_{33} P_3\right], \\ a_{23} - a_{23}^0 &= -\left[\varrho_{41} P_1 + \varrho_{42} P_2 + \varrho_{43} P_3\right], \\ a_{31} - a_{31}^0 &= -\left[\varrho_{51} P_1 + \varrho_{52} P_2 + \varrho_{53} P_3\right], \\ a_{12} - a_{12}^0 &= -\left[\varrho_{61} P_1 + \varrho_{62} P_2 + \varrho_{63} P_3\right], \end{aligned}\right\} \tag{87.5}$$

and in terms of the components of the electric field, Eq. (87.4) becomes

$$\left.\begin{aligned} a_{11} - a_{11}^0 &= \left[r_{11} E_1 + r_{12} E_2 + r_{13} E_3\right], \\ a_{22} - a_{22}^0 &= \left[r_{21} E_1 + r_{22} E_2 + r_{23} E_3\right], \\ a_{33} - a_{33}^0 &= \left[r_{31} E_1 + r_{32} E_2 + r_{33} E_3\right], \\ a_{23} - a_{23}^0 &= \left[r_{41} E_1 + r_{42} E_2 + r_{43} E_3\right], \\ a_{31} - a_{31}^0 &= \left[r_{51} E_1 + r_{52} E_2 + r_{53} E_3\right], \\ a_{12} - a_{12}^0 &= \left[r_{61} E_1 + r_{62} E_2 + r_{63} E_3\right], \end{aligned}\right\} \tag{87.6}$$

and the two sets of constants ϱ_{ij} and r_{ij} are related as

$$r_{ij} = \frac{\varepsilon_j - 1}{4\pi} \varrho_{ij}. \tag{87.7}$$

It must be mentioned that although ϱ_{ij}'s are of greater theoretical importance for the development of atomistic theories, the constants r_{ij} are the ones that are most readily obtained experimentally. It is therefore customary to measure the constants r_{ij} and then compute the values of ϱ_{ij} from a knowledge of the dielectric properties of the crystal. We shall call the constants r_{ij} as the electro-optic constants.

From Eqs. (87.5) and (87.6) we find that in the most general case, the number of electro-optic constants that can exist is 18. However, if one uses the principle that all expressions involving any physical constant of a crystal should be invariant when any symmetry operation of the crystal is applied, one can find the number of electro-optic constants for the different crystal classes. The detailed methods of computation have been given elsewhere[1,2]. When this is done one finds that there are only twenty groups (all non-centro-symmetric) for which there are suviving constants. *These are also the groups that exhibit piezoelectricity.* The surviving constants for these 20 groups have been listed in Table 6. All classes not listed have $r_{ij}=0$. The subscripts indicate the independent values

[1] S. BHAGAVANTAM: Acta crystallogr. **5**, 591 (1952).
[2] W. CADY: Piezoelectricity. New York: McGraw-Hill 1946.

of the coefficients. Since crystals that exhibit the electro-optic phenomenon are also piezo-electric, we must take into account the changes in the optical property caused by stresses or strains induced by the latter phenomenon. We know that in a free crystal only strains can develop while in a clamped crystal only stresses can develop. Hence the changes Δa_{ij} in the coefficients of the index ellipsoid due to both the electro-optic and the photoelastic effect (induced by the piezo-

Table 6. *Electro-optic constants surviving in the different point groups.*

Triclinic

$C_1 = 1$, 18 constants

$$\begin{array}{ccc} r_{11} & r_{12} & r_{13} \\ r_{21} & r_{22} & r_{23} \\ r_{31} & r_{32} & r_{33} \\ r_{41} & r_{42} & r_{43} \\ r_{51} & r_{52} & r_{53} \\ r_{61} & r_{62} & r_{63} \end{array}$$

Monoclinic

$C_2 = 2$, 8 constants

$$\begin{array}{ccc} 0 & 0 & r_{13} \\ 0 & 0 & r_{23} \\ 0 & 0 & r_{33} \\ r_{41} & r_{42} & 0 \\ r_{51} & r_{52} & 0 \\ 0 & 0 & r_{63} \end{array}$$

$C_s = m$, 10 constants

$$\begin{array}{ccc} r_{11} & r_{12} & 0 \\ r_{21} & r_{22} & 0 \\ r_{31} & r_{32} & 0 \\ 0 & 0 & r_{43} \\ 0 & 0 & r_{53} \\ r_{61} & r_{62} & 0 \end{array}$$

Orthorhombic

$D_2 = 222$, 3 constants

$$\begin{array}{ccc} 0 & 0 & 0 \\ 0 & 0 & 0 \\ 0 & 0 & 0 \\ r_{41} & 0 & 0 \\ 0 & r_{52} & 0 \\ 0 & 0 & r_{63} \end{array}$$

$C_{2v} = mm$, 5 constants

$$\begin{array}{ccc} 0 & 0 & r_{13} \\ 0 & 0 & r_{23} \\ 0 & 0 & r_{33} \\ 0 & r_{42} & 0 \\ r_{51} & 0 & 0 \\ 0 & 0 & 0 \end{array}$$

Tetragonal

$S_4 = \bar{4}$, 3 constants

$$\begin{array}{ccc} 0 & 0 & r_{13} \\ 0 & 0 & r_{13} \\ 0 & 0 & r_{33} \\ 0 & r_{51} & 0 \\ r_{51} & 0 & 0 \\ 0 & 0 & 0 \end{array}$$

$C_4 = 4$, 4 constants

$$\begin{array}{ccc} 0 & 0 & r_{13} \\ 0 & 0 & r_{13} \\ 0 & 0 & r_{33} \\ r_{41} & r_{51} & 0 \\ r_{51} & -r_{41} & 0 \\ 0 & 0 & 0 \end{array}$$

$D_{2d} = \bar{4}2m$, 3 constants

$$\begin{array}{ccc} 0 & 0 & 0 \\ 0 & 0 & 0 \\ 0 & 0 & 0 \\ r_{41} & 0 & 0 \\ 0 & r_{52} & 0 \\ 0 & 0 & r_{63} \end{array}$$

$D_4 = 422$, 1 constant

$$\begin{array}{ccc} 0 & 0 & 0 \\ 0 & 0 & 0 \\ 0 & 0 & 0 \\ r_{41} & 0 & 0 \\ 0 & -r_{41} & 0 \\ 0 & 0 & 0 \end{array}$$

$C_{4v} = 4mm$, 4 constants

$$\begin{array}{ccc} 0 & 0 & r_{13} \\ 0 & 0 & -r_{13} \\ 0 & 0 & 0 \\ r_{41} & -r_{51} & 0 \\ r_{51} & r_{41} & 0 \\ 0 & 0 & r_{63} \end{array}$$

Trigonal

$C_3 = 3$, 6 constants

$$\begin{array}{ccc} r_{11} & -r_{22} & r_{13} \\ -r_{11} & r_{22} & r_{13} \\ 0 & 0 & r_{33} \\ r_{41} & r_{51} & 0 \\ r_{51} & -r_{41} & 0 \\ -2r_{22} & -2r_{11} & 0 \end{array}$$

$D_3 = 32$, 2 constants

$$\begin{array}{ccc} r_{11} & 0 & 0 \\ -r_{11} & 0 & 0 \\ 0 & 0 & 0 \\ r_{41} & 0 & 0 \\ 0 & -r_{41} & 0 \\ 0 & -2r_{11} & 0 \end{array}$$

$C_{3v} = 3m$, 4 constants

$$\begin{array}{ccc} 0 & -r_{22} & r_{13} \\ 0 & r_{22} & r_{13} \\ 0 & 0 & r_{33} \\ 0 & r_{51} & 0 \\ r_{51} & 0 & 0 \\ -2r_{22} & 0 & 0 \end{array}$$

Hexagonal

$C_{3h} = \bar{6}$, 2 constants

$$\begin{array}{ccc} r_{11} & -r_{22} & 0 \\ -r_{11} & r_{22} & 0 \\ 0 & 0 & 0 \\ 0 & 0 & 0 \\ 0 & 0 & 0 \\ -2r_{22} & -2r_{11} & 0 \end{array}$$

$D_{3h} = \bar{6}m2$, 1 constants

$$\begin{array}{ccc} r_{11} & 0 & 0 \\ -r_{11} & 0 & 0 \\ 0 & 0 & 0 \\ 0 & 0 & 0 \\ 0 & 0 & 0 \\ 0 & -2r_{11} & 0 \end{array}$$

$C_6 = 6$, 4 constants

$$\begin{array}{ccc} 0 & 0 & r_{13} \\ 0 & 0 & r_{13} \\ 0 & 0 & r_{23} \\ r_{41} & r_{51} & 0 \\ r_{51} & -r_{41} & 0 \\ 0 & 0 & 0 \end{array}$$

$D_6 = 622$, 1 constant

$$\begin{array}{ccc} 0 & 0 & 0 \\ 0 & 0 & 0 \\ 0 & 0 & 0 \\ r_{41} & 0 & 0 \\ 0 & -r_{41} & 0 \\ 0 & 0 & 0 \end{array}$$

$C_{6v} = 6mm$, 4 constants

$$\begin{array}{ccc} 0 & 0 & r_{13} \\ 0 & 0 & r_{13} \\ 0 & 0 & r_{33} \\ 0 & r_{51} & 0 \\ r_{51} & 0 & 0 \\ 0 & 0 & 0 \end{array}$$

Cubic

$T = 23$, 1 constant

$$\begin{array}{ccc} 0 & 0 & 0 \\ 0 & 0 & 0 \\ 0 & 0 & 0 \\ r_{41} & 0 & 0 \\ 0 & r_{41} & 0 \\ 0 & 0 & r_{41} \end{array}$$

$T_d = \bar{4}3m$, 1 constant

$$\begin{array}{ccc} 0 & 0 & 0 \\ 0 & 0 & 0 \\ 0 & 0 & 0 \\ r_{41} & 0 & 0 \\ 0 & r_{41} & 0 \\ 0 & 0 & r_{41} \end{array}$$

electric effect) can be expressed in terms of the electric field and the stresses or strains in the crystal. Hence

$$\Delta a_i = \sum_{j=1}^{3} r_{ij} E_j + \sum_{k=1}^{6} q_{ik} X_k, \tag{87.8}$$

$$\Delta a_i = \sum_{j=1}^{3} r'_{ij} E_j + \sum_{k=1}^{6} p_{ik} x_k. \tag{87.9}$$

where X_k and x_k are the components of the stress and strain respectively and q_{ik} and p_{ik} are the stress optic and the strain optic coefficients (see Sect. 91). r_{ij} and r'_{ij} are the electro-optic coefficients for a clamped and a free crystal. The relations (87.8) and (87.9) are not independent as

$$x_k = \sum_{k=1}^{6} s_{kj} X_j + \sum_{k=1}^{6} d_{jk} E_j \tag{87.10}$$

where s_{kj} and d_{jk} are the elastic and piezo electric constants. Substituting Eq. (87.10) and (87.9) we have

$$\Delta a_i = \sum_{j=1}^{3} \left(r'_{ij} + \sum_{k=1}^{6} p_{ik} d_{jk}\right) E_j + \sum_{j=1}^{6} \left[\sum_{k=1}^{6} p_{ik} s_{kj}\right] X_j. \tag{87.11}$$

Comparing Eqs. (87.8) and (87.11) we have [see (91.10)]

$$q_{ij} = \sum_{k=1}^{6} p_{ik} s_{kj}, \tag{87.12}$$

$$r_{ij} = r'_{ij} + \sum_{k=1}^{6} p_{ik} d_{jk}. \tag{87.13}$$

One can see clearly that r'_{ij} is the electro-optic coefficient associated with the direct effect of the electrical field on the optical constants while r_{ij} is the electro-optic coefficient which represents the total effect of the electric field on the constants of the index ellipsoid. In the early stages of experimentation it was thought that the electro-optic effect was just a secondary effect of the piezo-electric deformation (i.e. $r'_{ij}=0$). The classical experiments of POCKELS[1] were the first to establish the existence of r'_{ij}, the direct effect of the electric field in the atomic polarisability.

88. Changes in the optical behaviour of a crystal due to the electric field[2]. The next problem that we shall consider will be the relative dispositions of the index ellipsoids of the undeformed crystal and the electrically deformed crystal. If we choose the principal axes OX_0, OY_0, OZ_0 of the index ellipsoid as the axes of co-ordinates, then the equation to the index ellipsoid is

$$a_{11}^0 x_0^2 + a_{22}^0 y_0^2 + a_{33}^0 z_0^2 = 1 \tag{88.1}$$

and that of the deformed crystal with respect to the same axis is

$$a_{11} x_0^2 + a_{22} y_0^2 + a_{33} z_0^2 + 2a_{23} y_0 z_0 + 2a_{31} z_0 x_0 + 2a_{12} x_0 y_0 = 1 \tag{88.2}$$

and consequently in Eqs. (87.5) and (87.6)

$$a_{ij} - a_{ij}^0 = a_{ij} \qquad (\text{for } i \neq j). \tag{88.3}$$

Referring Eq. (88.2) to the principal axes OX', OY', OZ' of the ellipsoid we have

$$a'_{11} x^2 + a'_{22} y^2 + a'_{33} z^2 = 1 \tag{88.4}$$

[1] POCKELS [2].

[2] See B.H. BILLINGS: J. Opt. Soc. Amer. **39**, 797 (1949).

and the direction cosines relating the two sets of axes may be described by the matrix (88.4a) where α_1 is the cosine of the angle between OX_0 and OX' and so on.

$$\begin{array}{c|ccc} & X' & Y' & Z' \\ \hline X_0 & \alpha_1 & \alpha_2 & \alpha_3 \\ Y_0 & \beta_1 & \beta_2 & \beta_3 \\ Z_0 & \gamma_1 & \gamma_2 & \gamma_3 \end{array} \tag{88.4a}$$

From a knowledge of the r_{ij} these direction cosines can be computed (see also Sect. 93 on photoelasticity) from which the magnitudes of a'_{ii} of the index ellipsoid after deformation can be computed from the formulae

$$\left.\begin{aligned} a'_{11} &= a_{11}\alpha_1^2 + a_{22}\alpha_2^2 + a_{33}\alpha_3^2 + 2a_{23}\alpha_2\alpha_3 + 2a_{31}\alpha_3\alpha_1 + 2a_{12}\alpha_1\alpha_2, \\ a'_{22} &= a_{11}\beta_1^2 + a_{22}\beta_2^2 + a_{33}\beta_3^2 + 2a_{23}\beta_2\beta_3 + 2a_{31}\beta_3\beta_1 + 2a_{12}\beta_1\beta_2, \\ a'_{33} &= a_{11}\gamma_1^2 + a_{22}\gamma_2^2 + a_{33}\gamma_3^2 + 2a_{23}\gamma_2\gamma_3 + 2a_{31}\gamma_3\gamma_1 + 2a_{12}\gamma_1\gamma_2. \end{aligned}\right\} \tag{88.5}$$

The data available in electro-optics are extremely meagre and in no case has the measurements been extended to cases of monoclinic or triclinic crystals where the principal axes of the index ellipsoid do not coincide with the crystallographic axes. We shall present some typical cases to exemplify the methods of computation.

In the case of the point group $\bar{4}2m$ or D_{2d} to which a large number of signette electric crystals belong, the number of surviving constants is two, viz. $r_{41}=r_{52}$ and r_{63}. The crystals belonging to this class are uniaxial and so $a_{11}^0 = a_{22}^0$ giving

$$\left.\begin{aligned} a_{11} - a_{11}^0 &= 0, & a_{22} - a_{22}^0 &= 0, & a_{33} - a_{33}^0 &= 0, \\ a_{23} &= r_{41} E_x, & a_{31} &= r_{41} E_y, & a_{12} &= r_{63} E_z. \end{aligned}\right\} \tag{88.6}$$

Hence the crystal becomes biaxial with the axis of the index ellipsoid rotated with respect to those of the original ellipsoid. We shall consider the case of the field being parallel to OZ in which case $E_x = E_y = 0$. Here $a_{23} = a_{31} = 0$ and the equation to the index ellipsoid reduces to

$$a_{11}^0 (x^2 + y^2) + a_{33}^0 z^2 + 2r_{63} E_z xy = 1. \tag{88.7}$$

From this one can conclude that OZ' and OZ_0 coincide and the x and the y axes rotate in the XY plane. This gives

$$\gamma_1 = \gamma_2 = \alpha_3 = \beta_3 = 0 \tag{88.8}$$

and since the rotation is in a plane

$$-\alpha_2 = \beta_1, \quad \alpha_1 = \beta_2. \tag{88.9}$$

From the matrix given in (88.4) we have

$$x' = \alpha_1 x + \beta_1 y, \quad y' = \alpha_2 x + \beta_2 y. \tag{88.10}$$

Substituting the values from Eqs. (88.8) and (88.9) we get

$$x' = \alpha_1 x - \alpha_2 y, \quad y' = \alpha_2 x + \alpha_1 y. \tag{88.11}$$

Introducing these in Eq. (88.7) of the index ellipsoid,

$$2r_{63} (\alpha_1^2 - \alpha_2^2) E_z xy = 0. \tag{88.12}$$

Hence, if ϑ is the angle of rotation,

$$\cos 2\vartheta = 0 \quad \text{or} \quad \vartheta = \pm \frac{\pi}{4}. \tag{88.13}$$

The angle of rotation of the x and y axes is independent of the field. Since the unstressed crystal is uniaxial one can observe the uniaxial figures along the Z_0 axis. On putting on the electric field, since OZ_0 and OZ' coincide, the circles become ovals, the major and minor axes of the ovals being at 45° to the crystallographic axes. The lengths of the two axes of the ovals change with the field, while its direction remains constant.

Substituting the values of the direction cosines in Eq. (88.5) we get

$$\left.\begin{aligned} a'_{11} &= a^0_{11} - r_{63} E_z, \\ a'_{22} &= a^0_{11} + r_{63} E_z, \\ a'_{33} &= a^0_{33}. \end{aligned}\right\} \tag{88.14}$$

If n_ω and n_ε are the ordinary and extraordinary refractive indices

$$a^0_{11} = \frac{1}{n^2_\omega}, \qquad a^0_{33} = \frac{1}{n^2_\varepsilon}, \tag{88.15}$$

or

$$a'_{11} - a^0_{11} = \Delta a_1 = -\frac{2\Delta n}{n^3_\omega} = -r_{63} E_z. \tag{88.16}$$

Therefore the change in refractive index is given by

$$\Delta n = \tfrac{1}{2} n^2_\omega r_{63} E_z \tag{88.17}$$

which gives

$$\left.\begin{aligned} n'_x &= n_\omega + \tfrac{1}{2} n^3_\omega r_{63} E_z, \\ n'_y &= n_\omega - \tfrac{1}{2} n^3_\omega r_{63} E_z, \\ n'_z &= n_\varepsilon. \end{aligned}\right\} \tag{88.18}$$

The birefringence of plane waves propagated along these axes will be

$$\left.\begin{aligned} B'_x &= n'_y - n'_z = n_\omega - n_\varepsilon - \tfrac{1}{2} n^3_\omega r_{63} E_z, \\ B'_y &= n'_z - n'_x = n_\omega - n_\varepsilon + \tfrac{1}{2} n^3_\omega r_{63} E_z, \\ B'_z &= n'_x - n'_y = n^3_\omega r_{63} E_z \end{aligned}\right\} \tag{88.19}$$

and finally the angle $2V$ between the optic axes is obtained from (33.5) or (82.2) to be

$$\tan 2V = 2 n_\omega \sqrt{\frac{2 r_{63} E_z}{n^2_\varepsilon - n^2_\omega}}. \tag{88.20}$$

The rotation of the axes when the field is parallel to X or Y can be computed in the same way. For this case

$$a^0_{11}(x^2 + y^2) + a^0_{33} z^2 + 2 r_{41} E_x yz = 1, \tag{88.21}$$

i.e., OX_0 and OX' coincide and the rotation ξ of the axis in the yz plane is given by

$$\tan 2\xi = -\frac{2 r_{41} E_x}{a^0_{33} - a^0_{11}}. \tag{88.22}$$

For the trigonal class 32 (D_3) to which quartz belongs the independent constants that survive are two, viz. r_{11}, r_{41}, with $r_{21} = -r_{11}$, $r_{11} - r_{22} = r_{62}$ and $r_{32} = -r_{43}$. and hence a field perpendicular to the optic axis is only effective in changing the optical parameters and since $a^0_{11} = a^0_{22}$ for this class also

$$\left.\begin{aligned} a_{11} - a^0_{11} = r_{11} E_x; \quad a_{22} - a^0_{11} = - r_{11} E_x; \quad a_{33} - a^0_{33} = 0, \\ a_{23} = r_{41} E_x; \quad a_{31} = - r_{41} E_y; \quad a_{12} = - r_{11} E_z, \end{aligned}\right\} \tag{88.23}$$

the crystal becomes biaxial with a rotation of the axes.

For the orthorhombic class 222 (D_2 or V) to which Rochelle salt belongs (above the Curie temperature) there are only three constants r_{41}, r_{52}, r_{63} giving

$$\left.\begin{aligned} a_{11} - a^0_{11} = 0; \quad a_{22} - a^0_{22} = 0; \quad a_{33} - a^0_{33} = 0, \\ a_{23} = r_{41} E_x; \quad a_{31} = r_{52} E_y; \quad a_{12} = r_{63} E_z. \end{aligned}\right\} \tag{88.24}$$

89. Experimental methods. The experimental methods in electro-optics consist by and large of the measurement of the birefringence induced in a crystal plate due to the electric field and determining the electro-optic constants using formulae of the type (88.19). For the measurement of the birefringence the compensator methods mentioned in Sect. 2 can be used. In most investigations the Sénaramont or the Babinet compensator have been used. A variation of this method[1] is to place the crystal between two plane polarisers parallel to each other, with a half-wave plate after the crystal. The electric field is increased till an extra half-wave retardation is introduced. At this position the emergent light is crossed by the second analyser. This position can be accurately determined either by the use of a half shade device in front of the analyser or by a photo-electric cell.

Some of the constants can be accurately determined from the measurement of the optic axial angle[2,3] and using formulae of the type given in Eq. (88.20). The method has proved quite satisfactory in the case of tetragonal seignette crystals.

In the case of certain directions where the retardation is large even in the absence of the field, other methods have been resorted to. One is to fashion a wedge of very small angle (a few minutes of arc) so as to get a small number of "Babinet fringes" between crossed polarisers. From the measurement of the shift of the fringes with electric field the induced birefringence can be computed[4].

Another novel method[1] is based on the measurement of the rotation of the axis of the index ellipsoid induced by the field by electronic means. If Δ is the retardation of the plate, and if ϑ is the inclination of the fast axis of the plate with respect to the initial polariser, the intensity transmitted through the system is

$$\frac{I}{I_0} = \frac{1}{2} + \frac{1}{2} \sin^2 \pi \Delta \sin 4\alpha$$

where $\Delta = \frac{n_\omega - n_\varepsilon}{\lambda}$ (for a uniaxial crystal) is a rapidly varying function with wavelength. For a sufficiently thick crystal, by using a broad continuous source, $\sin^2 \pi \Delta$ can be replaced by its mean value $\frac{1}{2}$ which gives

$$\frac{I}{I_0} = \frac{1}{2} + \frac{1}{4} \sin 4\alpha .$$

To detect this small modulation, an alternating voltage is applied to the crystal and the intensity detected by a sharply tuned amplifier. Knowing α, the electro-optic constant can be computed from a formula of the type (88.20).

[1] R.O. Carpenter: J. Opt. Soc. Amer. **40**, 225 (1950).
[2] B.H. Billings: J. Opt. Soc. Amer. **39**, 797, 802 (1949).
[3] Pockels [2].
[4] B. Zwicker and P. Scherrer: Helv. phys. Acta **16**, 214 (1943).

The following are some of the important crystals in which the linear electro-optic effect has been studied: $NaClO_3$, $NaBrO_3$, ZnS, CuCl, KH_2PO_4, KD_2BO_4 and similar seignette electric crystals, quartz and Rochelle salt.

The applications to which the electro-optic phenomena have been put are multifarious. Of particular interest are the tuneable interference filters in which the narrow band of transmitted colour can be altered by changing the birefringence of the crystals in these systems by adjusting the electric field[1]. Electro-optic crystals have been used as light valves for which there are many uses[2]. One of the optical problems in connection with these applications is that the angular field of the light shutter is limited by the natural retardation. Some practical methods of diminishing this natural retardation have been suggested[3]. One is to put another non-electro-optic crystal of opposite sign in series with the crystal excited by the electric field. Another is to use two identical crystals with a 90° optical rotator placed between them. The use of ZnS and CuCl crystal plates (which are cubic) have also been suggested[4].

One of the important experimental problems in electro-optics is that of the electrodes. When the direction of propagation of light is perpendicular to the electric field, electrodes of either silver or gold either directly evaporated on to the crystal or spliced on by a thin layer of liquid, like glycerine or oleic acid, is found to work very well. In the case of the direction of propagation and the electric field being parallel the problem is more complicated. Thin layers of liquids, or semitransparent layers of gold have been tried. But a promising material is a commercially available thin conducting transparent layer of stannous oxide which has been found very satisfactory[5]. The electrical and optical problems associated with these types of electrodes have been ennumerated by BILLINGS. Evaporated grid and ring electrodes have now been proved quite suitable, particularly in the use of electro-optic crystals as light shutters[6].

III. Magneto-optics[7].

90. Faraday rotation in solids. *α) Isotropic substances.* When a transparent substance is placed in a magnetic field, it rotates the plane of polarisation of the light traversing it along the lines of force. This is known as the Faraday effect. It differs from natural optical activity in that the sense of the rotation depends on the direction of the magnetic field and not just on the direction in which light passes through the medium. The rotation is proportional to the thickness of the material traversed and the magnetisation intensity. For a diamagnetic medium the magnetisation intensity is almost equal to the applied magnetisation and so if it is placed in a uniform magnetic field the rotation is

$$\alpha = V H L \cos\vartheta \tag{90.1}$$

where L is the total length of the specimen, H the magnetic field, ϑ the angle which the magnetic field makes with the direction of light propagation in the

[1] B.H. BILLINGS: J. Opt. Soc. Amer. **41**, 966 (1951).

[2] E. BURSTEIN, J.W. DAVISSON, P.L. SMITH and J.E. DEHNEL: J. Opt. Soc. Amer. **41**, 288 (1951).

[3] B.H. BILLINGS: J. Opt. Soc. Amer. **42**, 12 (1952).

[4] C.D. WEST: J. Opt. Soc. Amer. **43**, 335 (1953).

[5] B.H. BILLINGS: J. Opt. Soc. Amer. **39**, 802 (1949).

[6] J.G. JELATIS: J. Opt. Soc. Amer. **43**, 335 (1953).

[7] For detailed discussion see the article by W. SCHÜTZ in: Handbuch der Experimentalphysik, Vol. 16. 1936. — For other references and experimental data see article by S. RAMASESHAN and V. SIVARAMAKRISHNAN: Progress in Crystal Physics, Vol. 1, Ed. R.S. KRISHNAN. Madras 1958.

medium. V is the Verdet constant which represents the rotation per unit length per unit magnetic field.

Experiments on the velocity of light in isotropic media have definitely established that the Faraday rotation in an isotropic medium owes its origin to the fact that plane polarised light splits up into two circular vibrations which are propagated with different velocities in a magneto-optic medium. The rotation is given by the Fresnel formula

$$V = \frac{\pi \nu}{c} (n_- - n_+) \tag{90.2}$$

where n_- and n_+ are the refractive indices of the two circular components for the light frequency ν and c is the velocity of light. The measurement of the Faraday rotation in an isotropic medium is quite a straightforward process and in fact most of the data available in the literature relate to isotropic substances.

β) Magneto-optic rotation and birefringence. Even the measurement of magneto-optic rotation in isotropic solids is made very much more complicated by the fact that most of these substances show a small residual birefringence which would vitiate the results of measurements unless corrected for. It must be remembered that when the magneto-optic rotation is measured in a solid with a small amount of birefringence using a conventional apparatus, what is determined is the position of the major axis of the emergent elliptic vibration with respect to the plane of polarisation of the incident light. This could be called the apparent rotation ψ. One should therefore be in a position to compute the value of true rotation from the measured value of ψ.

The theory of magnetic rotation in anisotropic media has been the subject of a series of experimental and theoretical investigations. A medium exhibiting magneto-optic rotation behaves similarly to one possessing natural optical activity. The only difference is that the sense of rotation is different for opposite directions of travel in the former case while it is the same in the case of optical activity. So long as one is interested in the propagation of light in a particular direction the theory of propagation of light in an optically active medium can be applied *in toto*, and used to evaluate the results in the case of magneto-optic rotation when birefringence is present. When plane polarised light is incident on an anisotropic medium placed in a magnetic field it splits up (as in the case of optical rotation) into two elliptic vibrations of opposite senses lying crossed to each other which travel with different velocities. The two being coherent, they combine at every point to produce an elliptic vibration whose major axis is rotated with respect to the plane of polarisation of the incident light. The magnitude of this rotation and the ellipticity of the emergent vibration are determined by the thickness of the crystal, its birefringence and its magneto-optic rotation. Hence the use of the Poincaré sphere representation would prove ideal for the evaluation of the magneto-optic rotation in a birefringent medium.

CHAUVIN[1] measured the rotation in directions slightly away from the optic axis of calcite with the incident light polarised along a principal direction. With increasing magnitude of birefringence the apparent rotation (which was actually the azimuth of the emergent elliptic vibration with respect to the incident plane polarised vibration) not only diminished in magnitude but actually reversed in sign and exhibited several reversals in sign. This observation can be explained from a simple geometric construction on the Poincaré sphere. Assuming ϱ (the magneto-optic rotation) to be a constant and δ (the birefringence) to increase

[1] M. CHAUVIN: C. R. Acad. Sci., Paris **102**, 972 (1886). See also WIENER: Wied. Ann. **1**, 35 (1888). For further references see reference quoted previously.

continuously the inclination 2ϑ of the axis of rotation of the Poincaré sphere continuously decreases since $2\varrho/\delta$ is continuously decreasing while $\Delta = \sqrt{\delta^2 + (2\varrho)^2}$ the total phase retardation increases. Hence the final state of polarisation executes a spiral shown in Fig. 98. The azimuth λ of the major axis decreases from ϱ, reverses sign and oscillates with several reversals of sign finally tending to zero as it should for a purely birefringent crystal.

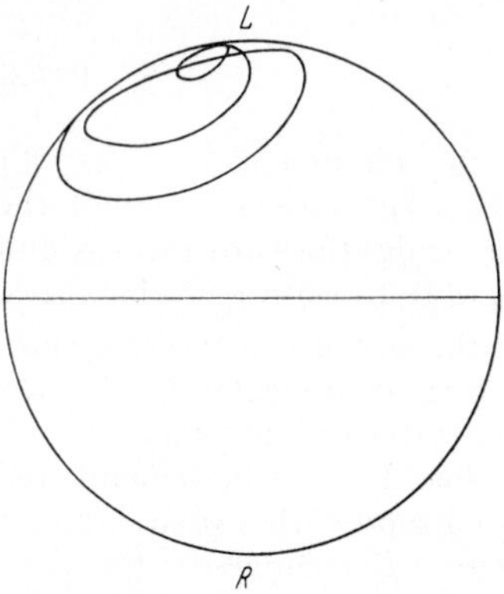

Fig. 98. Poincaré representation showing the variation of the azimuth ψ (apparent magneto-optic rotation) in calcite for directions of propagation away from the optic axes.

In principle the evaluation of the Faraday rotation in an anisotropic medium reduces to the accurate determination of the constants of the emergent ellipse when the magnetic field is on and off. RAMACHANDRAN and RAMASESHAN[1] have made a detailed investigation regarding the exact methods involved. The general method of determining the true rotation in the presence of birefringence is the following. Linearly polarised light is allowed to fall on the medium at an azimuth α to the principal directions and one measures the apparent rotation ψ by means of a half-shade at the analyser end and the ratio of the axes ($\tan\omega$) of the emergent ellipse by a suitable method. From this both δ and 2ϱ can be calculated from the formulae

$$\tan 2\gamma = [\cos 2\alpha - \cos 2\omega \cos 2(\alpha + \psi)]/\sin 2\omega, \tag{90.3}$$

$$\cos\Delta = -[(1 - \cos 2\omega \cos 2\psi)/(1 - \cos^2 2\gamma \cos^2 2\alpha)], \tag{90.4}$$

$$\delta = \Delta \cos 2\gamma, \quad 2\varrho = \Delta \sin 2\gamma. \tag{90.5}$$

This method may be used when neither δ nor 2ϱ can be measured independently. But in Faraday effect studies the birefringence δ can be measured. Then the true rotation can be deduced from a measurement of ψ alone. When both 2ϱ and δ are small from (90.3), (90.4) and (90.5) it follows that

$$\text{if } \alpha = 0 \text{ or } 90^\circ \quad 2\psi_0 = 2\varrho\left(1 - \frac{\delta^2}{3!}\right) \tag{90.6}$$

and

$$\text{if } \alpha = 45^\circ \qquad 2\psi_{45} = 2\varrho\left(1 + \frac{\delta^2}{3}\right), \tag{90.7}$$

the error in using these approximations is less than 1% so long as δ and 2ϱ are less than 30°. From these two equations one gets

$$\varrho = \tfrac{1}{3}(2\psi_0 + \psi_{45}). \tag{90.8}$$

This equation is correct to the third order in δ. This is an extremely convenient method of eliminating the effect of birefringence without measuring its value when both 2ϱ and δ are small.

In fact this method can be used to make accurate measurements of the Faraday effect in isotropic solids which show residual strain. Fortunately most specimens grown from melt or solution exhibit a preferred axis of strain and the method suggested by Eq. (90.8) is of great utility in the accurate measurement of the Verdet constant[2].

[1] G.N. RAMACHANDRAN and S. RAMASESHAN: J. Opt. Soc. Amer. **49**, 42 (1952).
[2] S. RAMASESHAN and V. SIVARAMAKRISHNAN: J. Ind. Inst. Sci. **38**, 228 (1956).

The mean value of ψ over a range $-\frac{\pi}{2}$ to $\frac{\pi}{2}$ is given by

$$2\psi_m = 2\varrho\left(1 + \frac{\delta^2}{12}\right). \tag{90.9}$$

It may be mentioned that the procedure may be reversed and this method may be used with profit to measure the small birefringence introduced due to artifical stresses in isotropic media[1]. It has actually been used to measure the stress-optic constants in glasses[2].

It may be mentioned in this connection that RAMACHANDRAN and RAMASESHAN have proved several theorems (using the Poincaré sphere) which are extremely useful when actual experiments are made on magneto-optic rotation. Thus, when birefringence is present, the observed value of the apparent rotation is very sensitive to small variations in the value of α, the angle between the plane of the linear incident vibration and the principal axis of the specimen. However if measurements are made for opposite directions of the magnetic field and the mean is taken, as is usually the practice, then the errors arising due to variations (is missellings) in α are practically eliminated. This result is of interest in connection with measurement of magneto-optic rotation when residual birefringence is present. In such a case the principal axes are never exactly the same throughout the specimen and they usually exhibit a variation of 5 to 10°. Consequently it is very important to eliminate the errors arising from the variation in α.

γ) Faraday rotation in anisotropic media. In an anisotropic medium the measurement of the magneto-optic rotation along the optic axis is similar to that in an isotropic solids and in the few cases of anisotropic solids that have been investigated, the measurements have been confined to the propagation along the optic axis. However, in spite of the practical difficulties rotations have been measured for directions slightly inclined to the optic axis in calcite[3] and alumina[4]. The analysis of the results using the procedures mentioned in the last section indicates that within the limits of experimental error no sensible change could be detected in the Verdet constant for these small inclinations. VOIGT[5] has considered the problem of the variation of the Verdet constant with direction from another point of view. Using the simple electron theory and the concept of the anisotropic polarisability tensor he has shown that in certain types of monoclinic crystals in which the optic axes lie in the plane of symmetry, the magneto-optic rotation along the two optic axes may be different for the same applied field. Physically this arises because in such crystals, in spite of the fact that the refractive indices along the two optic axes are the same, the arrangement and orientation of the molecules in the path of the light would in general be considerably different. This was experimentally confirmed by VOIGT in the case of cane sugar when he discovered that the magneto-optic rotation along the two axes are significantly different. This is not surprising as the natural optical activity along the two optic axes in this substance are actually of different signs.

VOIGT also foresaw the possibility of the Verdet constant varying with direction in paramagnetic anisotropic crystals, where, due to the perceptible magnetisability, the external field causes internal fields of different strengths in different

---

[1] S. RAMASESHAN and V. CHANDRASEKHARAN: Current Sci. **20**, 150 (1951).
[2] S. RAMASESHAN: Proc. Ind. Acad. Sci. A **34**, 32 (1951).
[3] M. CHAUVIN: C. R. Acad. Sci., Paris **102**, 972 (1886).
[4] S. RAMASESHAN: Proc. Ind. Acad. Sci. A **34**, 97 (1951).
[5] W. VOIGT: Phys. Z. **9**, 585 (1908).

directions. This effect was experimentally demonstrated by BECQUEREL[1] who showed in an ingenious experiment this variation of the Verdet constant with direction in anisotropic paramagnetic crystals.

IV. Photoelasticity[2].

91. Photoelastic constants. We shall consider only the phenomenological theory of photoelasticity of solids in this article. This is based on the following two assumptions.

1. In a homogeneously deformed solid, all the laws of propagation of light derived for homogeneous anisotropic media are valid. The effect of the deformation is only to alter the parameters contained in these laws of propagation.

2. When the strain is within elastic limits, the variation of an optical parameter of the solid due to the deformation can be expressed as a homogeneous linear function of the six stress components $X_x, Y_y, Z_z, Y_z, Z_x, X_y$ or the six strain components $x_x, y_y, z_z, y_z, z_x, x_y$.

The first assumption means that the effect of the deformation only leads to a change in the magnitudes and directions of the principal axes of the optical ellipsoid of a solid. The second assumption is a generalisation of the experimentally observed BREWSTER's law, according to which the magnitude of the double refraction induced by stress in an isotropic solid is proportional to the stress.

We shall represent the six stress components $X_x, Y_y, Z_z, Y_z, Z_x, X_y$ by $X_1, X_2, \ldots, X_6$. The six strain components $x_x, y_y, z_z, y_z, z_x, x_y$ are similarly denoted by $x_1, x_2, \ldots, x_6$.

The stress is taken as positive when compressional and negative when extensional. The strain however is considered positive for extension and negative for compression. The stress and the strain components are related by the following equations[3].

$$X_i = -c_{ij}\, x_j; \qquad x_i = -s_{ij}\, X_j \tag{91.1}$$

where the c_{ij} are called the elastic constants and the s_{ij} the elastic moduli of the substance[4].

These two types of constants are related to each other by the following equations:

$$\sum_{j=1}^{6} c_{ij}\, s_{ij} = 1 \quad \text{and} \quad \sum_{j=1}^{6} c_{ij}\, s_{kj} = 0 \qquad \text{if } i \neq k. \tag{91.2}$$

Since X_i and x_i have 6 components each, the tensor c_{ij} (and s_{ij}) have 36 components each in general. In the classical theory of elasticity, these tensors are symmetric in i and j, so that

$$c_{ij} = c_{ji}; \qquad s_{ij} = s_{ji} \tag{91.3}$$

and there are only 21 independent constants of each type for the crystals of lowest symmetry.

According to the recent ideas of RAMAN[5] and LAVAL the stress and strain tensors are both not symmetric tensors for a general deformation, so that X_i, x_i have 9 com-

[1] J. BECQUEREL: Z. Physik **52**, 342 (1929). — Le Radium **5**, 116, 238 (1908).

[2] For an article on photoelasticity, mainly written from the point of view of its engineering applications, cf. H. T. JESSOP, in Vol. VI of this Encyclopedia.

[3] A. E. H. LOVE: Mathematical Theory of Elasticity.

[4] The two sets c_{ij} and s_{ij} are also called by some authors as elastic stiffness coefficients and compliance coefficients.

[5] C. V. RAMAN: Proc. Ind. Acad. Sci. A **42**, 1 (1955). — C. V. RAMAN and K. S. VISWANATHAN: Proc. Ind. Acad. Sci. A **42**, 51 (1955). — C. V. RAMAN and D. KRISHNAMURTHI: Proc. Ind. Acad. Sci. A **42**, 111 (1955). — J. LAVAL: C. R. Acad. Sci., Paris **232**, 1947 (1951). — Y. LE CORRE: C. R. Acad. Sci., Paris **236**, 1903 (1953).

ponents each and the tensors c_{ij} and s_{ij} should have 81 components in general. However, they are symmetric in the indices referring to stress and strain, i.e., $c_{ij}=c_{ji}$ and $s_{ij}=s_{ji}$ so that there are only 45 independent components. The consequences of this theory for photoelasticity have not been worked out, and so we shall not be considering it further in this article.

It is necessary now to choose a proper optical property of the medium that alters with stress or strain to represent its photoelastic behaviour. As has been shown in the previous chapters, the most satisfactory optical parameter would be the index tensor $[a]$ connecting $\boldsymbol{D}$ and $\boldsymbol{E}$. In the case of a non-optically active medium,

$$\boldsymbol{E} = [a]\,\boldsymbol{D} \tag{91.4}$$

and the equation to the index ellipsoid is

$$a_{11}\,x^2 + a_{22}\,y^2 + a_{33}\,z^2 + 2a_{23}\,y\,z + 2a_{31}\,z\,x + 2a_{12}\,x\,y = 1 \tag{91.5}$$

where a_{ij} are the components of the tensor $[a]$ with respect to the co-ordinate axes chosen. We shall denote the value of a_{ij} in the undeformed crystal by a_{ij}^0 and if it changes to a_{ij} on deformation, then the change $\Delta a_{ij}=(a_{ij}-a_{ij}^0)$ can be expressed as a homogeneous linear function of the stress or strain-components. Denoting a_{11}, a_{22}, a_{33}, a_{23}, a_{31}, a_{12} by a_1 to a_6, we may write the changes in the optical parameters in terms of the strain components as

$$\Delta a_i = a_i - a_i^0 = \sum_j p_{ij}\,x_j, \qquad (i,j = 1 \text{ to } 6) \tag{91.6}$$

and in terms of the stress components as

$$\Delta a_i = a_i - a_i^0 = \sum - q_{ij}\,X_j, \qquad (i,j = 1 \text{ to } 6). \tag{91.7}$$

Written out in full, these equations take the form:

in terms of the strain components as

$$\left.\begin{aligned}
a_{11} - a_{11}^0 &= p_{11}\,x_x + p_{12}\,y_y + p_{13}\,z_z + p_{14}\,y_z + p_{15}\,z_x + p_{16}\,x_y,\\
a_{22} - a_{22}^0 &= p_{21}\,x_x + p_{22}\,y_y + p_{23}\,z_z + p_{24}\,y_z + p_{25}\,z_x + p_{26}\,x_y,\\
a_{33} - a_{33}^0 &= p_{31}\,x_x + p_{32}\,y_y + p_{33}\,z_z + p_{34}\,y_z + p_{35}\,z_x + p_{36}\,x_y,\\
a_{23} - a_{23}^0 &= p_{41}\,x_x + p_{42}\,y_y + p_{43}\,z_z + p_{44}\,y_z + p_{45}\,z_x + p_{46}\,x_y,\\
a_{31} - a_{31}^0 &= p_{51}\,x_x + p_{52}\,y_y + p_{53}\,z_z + p_{54}\,y_z + p_{55}\,z_x + p_{56}\,x_y,\\
a_{12} - a_{12}^0 &= p_{61}\,x_x + p_{62}\,y_y + p_{63}\,z_z + p_{64}\,y_z + p_{65}\,z_x + p_{66}\,x_y,
\end{aligned}\right\} \tag{91.8}$$

and in terms of the stress components as

$$\left.\begin{aligned}
a_{11} - a_{11}^0 &= -\left[q_{11}\,X_x + q_{12}\,Y_y + q_{13}\,Z_z + q_{14}\,Y_z + q_{15}\,Z_x + q_{16}\,X_y\right],\\
a_{22} - a_{22}^0 &= -\left[q_{21}\,X_x + q_{22}\,Y_y + q_{23}\,Z_z + q_{24}\,Y_z + q_{25}\,Z_x + q_{26}\,X_y\right],\\
a_{33} - a_{33}^0 &= -\left[q_{31}\,X_x + q_{32}\,Y_y + q_{33}\,Z_z + q_{34}\,Y_z + q_{35}\,Z_x + q_{36}\,X_y\right],\\
a_{23} - a_{23}^0 &= -\left[q_{41}\,X_x + q_{42}\,Y_y + q_{43}\,Z_z + q_{44}\,Y_z + q_{45}\,Z_x + q_{46}\,X_y\right],\\
a_{31} - a_{31}^0 &= -\left[q_{51}\,X_x + q_{52}\,Y_y + q_{53}\,Z_z + q_{54}\,Y_z + q_{55}\,Z_x + q_{56}\,X_y\right],\\
a_{12} - a_{12}^0 &= -\left[q_{61}\,X_x + q_{62}\,Y_y + q_{73}\,Z_z + q_{64}\,Y_z + q_{65}\,Z_x + q_{66}\,X_y\right].
\end{aligned}\right\} \tag{91.9}$$

The negative sign in Eq. (91.9) arises because of the convention that positive strain corresponds to negative stress. The constants p_{ij} are called the elasto-optic constants, while q_{ij} are called the piezo-optic constants. When either is to be referred to, we shall use the term photoelastic constant. They are also sometimes referred to as strain-optic and stress-optic constants. The thirty-six constants p_{ij} or q_{ij} completely define the photoelastic behaviour of a crystal when subjected to known stresses or strains.

The constants p_{ij} and q_{ij} are related as follows:

$$p_{ij}=\sum_{k=1}^{6} q_{ik}c_{jk}; \qquad q_{ij}=\sum_{k=1}^{6} p_{ik}s_{jk}, \qquad i,j=1 \text{ to } 6) \tag{91.10}$$

where c_{jk} and s_{jk} are the elastic constants and elastic moduli respectively.

Table 7. *The number of optical, elastic and photoelastic constants in the 32 crystal classes.*

Crystal system.	Photo elastic class	Crystal class	Symmetry operation	Constants		
				Optical	Elastic	Photo-Elastic
Triclinic	I	$C_1 - 1$	E	6	21	36
		$C_i - \bar{1}$	E, i	6	21	36
Monoclinic	II	$C_s - m$	E, σ_h	4	13	20
		$C_2 - 2$	E, C_2	4	13	20
		$C_{2h} - 2/m$	E, C_2, i, σ_h	4	13	20
Orthorhombic	III	$C_{2v} - mm$	$E, C_2\sigma_v, \sigma_v'$	3	9	12
		$D_2 - 222$	E, C_2, C_2', C_2''	3	9	12
		$D_{2h} - mmm$	$E, C_2, C_2', C_2'' i, \sigma_h, \sigma_v, \sigma_v'$	3	9	12
Tetragonal	IV	$C_4 - 4$	$E, 2C_4, C_2$	2	7	10
		$S_4 - \bar{4}$	$E, 2S_4, C_2$	2	7	10
		$C_{4h} - 4/m$	$E, 2C_4, C_2, i, 2S_4, \sigma_h$	2	7	10
	V	$C_{4v} - 4mm$	$E, 2C_4, C_2, 2\sigma_v, 2\sigma_v'$	2	6	7
		$D_{2d} - \bar{4}2m$	$E, C_2, C_2', C_2'', \sigma_v, 2S_4, \sigma_v'$	2	6	7
		$D_4 - 422$	$E, 2C_4, C_2, 2C_2, 2C_2'$	2	6	7
		$D_{4h} - 4/mmm$	$E, 2C_4, C_2, 2C_2, 2C_2'$ $i, 2S_4, \sigma_h, 2\sigma_v, 2\sigma_v'$	2	6	7
Trigonal	VI	$C_3 - 3$	$E, 2C_3$	2	7	12
		$S_6 - \bar{3}$	$E, 2C_3, i, 2S_6$	2	7	12
	VII	$C_{3v} - 3m$	$E, 2C_3, 3\sigma_v$	2	6	8
		$D_3 - 32$	$E, 2C_3, 3C_2$	2	6	8
		$D_{3d} - \bar{3}m$	$E, 2C_3, 3C_2, i, 2C_6, 3\sigma_v$	2	6	8
Hexagonal	VIII	$C_6 - 6$	$E, 2C_6, 2C_3, C_2$	2	5	8
		$C_{3h} - \bar{6}$	$E, 2C_3, \sigma_h, 2S_3$	2	5	8
		$C_{6h} - 6/m$	$E, 2C_6, 2C_3, C_2$ $i, 2S_6, 2S_3, \sigma_h$	2	5	8
	IX	$D_{3h} - \bar{6}m2$	$E, 2C_3, 3C_2, \sigma_h, 2S_3, 2\sigma_v$	2	5	6
		$C_{6v} - 6mm$	$E, 2C_6, 2C_3, C_2, 3\sigma_v, 3\sigma_v'$	2	5	6
		$D_6 - 622$	$E, 2C_6, 2C_3, C_2, 3C_2, 3C_2$	2	5	6
		$D_{6h} - 6/m2m$	$E, 2C_6, 2C_3, C_2, 3C_2, 3C_2$ $i, 2S_6, 2S_3, \sigma_h, 3\sigma_v, 3\sigma_v'$	2	5	6
Cubic	X	$T - 23$	$E, 3C_2, 8C_3$	1	3	4
		$T_h - m3$	$E, 3C_2, 8C_3, i, 3\sigma, 8S_6$	1	3	4
	XI	$T_d - \bar{4}3m$	$E, 8C_3, 3C_2, 6\sigma, 6S_4$	1	3	3
		$O - 432$	$E, 8C_3, 3C_2, 6C_2, 6C_4$	1	3	3
		$O_h - m3m$	$E, 8C_3, 3C_2, 6C_2, 6C_4$ $i, 8C_6, 3\sigma, 6\sigma, 6S_3$	1	3	3
Isotropic solids	Spherical symmetry			1	2	2

The various p_{ij} and q_{ij} are experimentally determinable, the methods for which are given in Sects. 98 and 99. However the piezo-optic constants (q_{ij}) can be determined more directly by experiment, although the elasto-optic constants (p_{ij}) are more significant from the theoretical point of view. Hence it is usual to determine the former experimentally and make use of values of the elastic constants of the crystal to determine the values of the latter.

92. Number of photoelastic constants in relation to symmetry of the crystal. Unlike in the case of elastic constants, the tensors p_{ij} and q_{ij} are not symmetric in i and j and consequently the number of constants in the general case is 36. This number would however be less for crystals possessing various elements of symmetry. This is so because all expressions involving the photoelastic constants should be invariant when each of the symmetry operations is applied. Consequently, it would be possible to derive relationships between some of the 36 photoelastic constants[1] and the number of independent constants is thus reduced.

The number of surviving optical, elastic and photoelastic constants are given in Table 7.

Pockels found that the 32 point group can be classified into 9 classes according to the number and nature of the surviving photoelastic constants. This has been shown to be erroneous by Bhagavantam[2] who showed that the 32 point groups can be classified into 11 classes. These 11 classes are the same as the so-called Laue-symmetry groups[3] and are what one would obtain if an additional symmetry of inversion is introduced. This symmetry is possessed both by the elastic and optical properties of a crystal, which do not change their magnitude when the direction of the stress and of light propagation are reversed.

The surviving constants in these 11 groups are listed in Table 8.

93. Changes in the optical behaviour of a crystal due to deformation. *α) General formulae.* One of the important problems in this subject is to know the changes in the magnitudes and orientation of the principal axes of the optical ellipsoid of a crystal for various types of deformation. When the q_{ij} or p_{ij} are completely known, these changes can be computed. In this section, we shall derive the formulae for the general case. The formulae appear complicated, but the principle of deriving them is simple and in practice only special directions of stress and observation are employed, for which the formulae reduce to comparatively elementary expressions.

Let OX_0, OY_0 and OZ_0 be the principal axes of the optical ellipsoid of the crystal in the undeformed state. The equation to the ellipsoid would then be

$$a_{11}^0 x_0^2 + a_{22}^0 y_0^2 + a_{33}^0 z_0^2 = 1. \tag{93.1}$$

On deforming the crystal the altered ellipsoid is given by the following equation, referred to the same axes $OX_0 Y_0 Z_0$

$$a_{11} x_0^2 + a_{22} y_0^2 + a_{33} z_0^2 + 2a_{23} y_0 z_0 + 2a_{31} z_0 x_0 + 2a_{12} x_0 y_0 = 1. \tag{93.2}$$

Let the principal axes of this ellipsoid be along OX', OY', OZ'. Referred to these axes of co-ordinates, the equation to the altered ellipsoid becomes

$$a_{11}' x'^2 + a_{22}' y'^2 + a_{33}' z'^2 = 1. \tag{93.3}$$

[1] The technique of working these out is discussed by Jagodzinski, in Vol. VII/1 of this Encyclopedia.

[2] S. Bhagavantam: Proc. Ind. Acad. Sci. A **16**, 359 (1942). — Acta crystallogr. **5**, 591 (1952).

[3] International Tables for X-ray crystallography, Vol. I, p. 30. Birmingham: Kynoch Press 1952.

Table 8.

I. First group: Triclinic system—36 coefficients.

p_{11}	p_{12}	p_{13}	p_{14}	p_{15}	p_{16}	q_{11}	q_{12}	q_{13}	q_{14}	q_{15}	q_{16}
p_{21}	p_{22}	p_{23}	p_{24}	p_{25}	p_{26}	q_{21}	q_{22}	q_{23}	q_{24}	q_{25}	q_{26}
p_{31}	p_{32}	p_{33}	p_{34}	p_{35}	p_{36}	q_{31}	q_{32}	q_{33}	q_{34}	q_{35}	q_{36}
p_{41}	p_{42}	p_{43}	p_{44}	p_{45}	p_{46}	q_{41}	q_{42}	q_{43}	q_{44}	q_{45}	q_{46}
p_{51}	p_{52}	p_{53}	p_{54}	p_{55}	p_{56}	q_{51}	q_{52}	q_{53}	q_{54}	q_{55}	q_{56}
p_{61}	p_{62}	p_{63}	p_{64}	p_{65}	p_{66}	q_{61}	q_{62}	q_{63}	q_{64}	q_{65}	q_{66}

II. Second group: Monoclinic system—20 coefficients.

p_{11}	p_{12}	p_{13}	0	0	p_{16}	q_{11}	q_{12}	q_{13}	0	0	q_{16}
p_{21}	p_{22}	p_{23}	0	0	p_{26}	q_{21}	q_{22}	q_{23}	0	0	q_{26}
p_{31}	p_{32}	p_{33}	0	0	p_{36}	q_{31}	q_{32}	q_{33}	0	0	q_{36}
0	0	0	p_{44}	p_{45}	0	0	0	0	q_{44}	q_{45}	0
0	0	0	p_{54}	p_{55}	0	0	0	0	q_{54}	q_{55}	0
p_{61}	p_{62}	p_{63}	0	0	p_{66}	q_{61}	q_{62}	q_{63}	0	0	q_{66}

III. Third group: Orthorhombic system—12 coefficients.

p_{11}	p_{12}	p_{13}	0	0	0	q_{11}	q_{12}	q_{13}	0	0	0
p_{21}	p_{22}	p_{23}	0	0	0	q_{21}	q_{22}	q_{23}	0	0	0
p_{31}	p_{32}	p_{33}	0	0	0	q_{31}	q_{32}	q_{33}	0	0	0
0	0	0	p_{44}	0	0	0	0	0	q_{44}	0	0
0	0	0	0	p_{55}	0	0	0	0	0	q_{55}	0
0	0	0	0	0	p_{66}	0	0	0	0	0	q_{66}

IV. Fourth group: Tetragonal system—10 coefficients.

p_{11}	p_{12}	p_{13}	0	0	p_{16}	q_{11}	q_{12}	q_{13}	0	0	q_{16}
p_{12}	p_{11}	p_{13}	0	0	$-p_{16}$	q_{12}	q_{11}	q_{13}	0	0	$-q_{16}$
p_{31}	p_{31}	p_{33}	0	0	0	q_{31}	q_{31}	q_{33}	0	0	0
0	0	0	p_{44}	p_{45}	0	0	0	0	q_{44}	q_{45}	0
0	0	0	$-p_{45}$	p_{44}	0	0	0	0	$-q_{45}$	q_{44}	0
p_{61}	$-p_{61}$	0	0	0	p_{66}	q_{61}	$-q_{61}$	0	0	0	q_{66}

V. Fifth group: Tetragonal system—7 coefficients.

p_{11}	p_{12}	p_{13}	0	0	0	q_{11}	q_{12}	q_{13}	0	0	0
p_{12}	p_{11}	p_{13}	0	0	0	q_{12}	q_{11}	q_{13}	0	0	0
p_{31}	p_{31}	p_{33}	0	0	0	q_{31}	q_{31}	q_{33}	0	0	0
0	0	0	p_{44}	0	0	0	0	0	q_{44}	0	0
0	0	0	0	p_{44}	0	0	0	0	0	q_{44}	0
0	0	0	0	0	p_{66}	0	0	0	0	0	q_{66}

VI. Sixth group: Trigonal system—12 coefficients.

p_{11}	p_{12}	p_{13}	p_{14}	$-p_{25}$	p_{62}	q_{11}	q_{12}	q_{13}	q_{14}	$-q_{25}$	$2q_{62}$
p_{12}	p_{11}	p_{13}	$-p_{14}$	p_{25}	$-p_{62}$	q_{12}	q_{11}	q_{13}	$-q_{14}$	q_{25}	$-2q_{62}$
p_{31}	p_{31}	p_{33}	0	0	0	q_{31}	q_{31}	q_{33}	0	0	0
p_{44}	$-p_{41}$	0	p_{44}	p_{45}	p_{52}	q_{41}	$-q_{41}$	0	q_{44}	q_{45}	$2q_{52}$
$-p_{52}$	p_{52}	0	$-p_{45}$	p_{44}	p_{41}	$-q_{52}$	q_{52}	0	$-q_{45}$	q_{44}	$2q_{41}$
$-p_{62}$	p_{62}	0	p_{25}	p_{14}	$p_{11}-p_{12}/2$	$-q_{62}$	q_{62}	0	q_{25}	q_{14}	$q_{11}-q_{12}$

VII. Seventh group: Trigonal system—8 coefficients.
Hemimorphic, Enantiomorphic, Holohedral

p_{11}	p_{12}	p_{13}	p_{14}	0	0	q_{11}	q_{12}	q_{13}	q_{14}	0	0
p_{12}	p_{11}	p_{13}	$-p_{14}$	0	0	q_{12}	q_{11}	q_{13}	$-q_{14}$	0	0
p_{31}	p_{31}	p_{33}	0	0	0	q_{31}	q_{31}	q_{33}	0	0	0
p_{41}	$-p_{41}$	0	p_{44}	0	0	q_{41}	$-q_{41}$	0	q_{44}	0	0
0	0	0	0	p_{44}	p_{41}	0	0	0	0	q_{44}	$2q_{41}$
0	0	0	0	p_{14}	$p_{11}-p_{12}/2$	0	0	0	0	q_{14}	$q_{11}-q_{12}$

Table 8. (Continued).

VIII. Eighth group: Hexagonal system—8 coefficients.

$$
\begin{array}{cccccc}
p_{11} & p_{12} & p_{13} & 0 & 0 & -p_{61} \\
p_{12} & p_{11} & p_{13} & 0 & 0 & p_{61} \\
p_{31} & p_{31} & p_{33} & 0 & 0 & 0 \\
0 & 0 & 0 & p_{44} & p_{45} & 0 \\
0 & 0 & 0 & -p_{45} & p_{44} & 0 \\
p_{61} & -p_{61} & 0 & 0 & 0 & p_{11}-p_{12}/2
\end{array}
\qquad
\begin{array}{cccccc}
q_{11} & q_{12} & q_{13} & 0 & 0 & -2q_{61} \\
q_{12} & q_{11} & q_{13} & 0 & 0 & 2q_{61} \\
q_{31} & q_{31} & q_{33} & 0 & 0 & 0 \\
0 & 0 & 0 & q_{44} & q_{45} & 0 \\
0 & 0 & 0 & -q_{45} & q_{44} & 0 \\
q_{61} & -q_{61} & 0 & 0 & 0 & q_{11}-q_{12}
\end{array}
$$

IX. Ninth group: Hexagonal system—6 coefficients.

$$
\begin{array}{cccccc}
p_{11} & p_{12} & p_{13} & 0 & 0 & 0 \\
p_{12} & p_{11} & p_{13} & 0 & 0 & 0 \\
p_{31} & p_{31} & p_{33} & 0 & 0 & 0 \\
0 & 0 & 0 & p_{44} & 0 & 0 \\
0 & 0 & 0 & 0 & p_{44} & 0 \\
0 & 0 & 0 & 0 & 0 & p_{11}-p_{12}
\end{array}
\qquad
\begin{array}{cccccc}
q_{11} & q_{12} & q_{13} & 0 & 0 & 0 \\
q_{12} & q_{11} & q_{13} & 0 & 0 & 0 \\
q_{31} & q_{31} & q_{33} & 0 & 0 & 0 \\
0 & 0 & 0 & q_{44} & 0 & 0 \\
0 & 0 & 0 & 0 & q_{44} & 0 \\
0 & 0 & 0 & 0 & 0 & q_{11}-q_{12}
\end{array}
$$

X. Tenth group: Cubic system—4 coefficients.

$$
\begin{array}{cccccc}
p_{11} & p_{12} & p_{13} & 0 & 0 & 0 \\
p_{13} & p_{11} & p_{12} & 0 & 0 & 0 \\
p_{12} & p_{13} & p_{11} & 0 & 0 & 0 \\
0 & 0 & 0 & p_{44} & 0 & 0 \\
0 & 0 & 0 & 0 & p_{44} & 0 \\
0 & 0 & 0 & 0 & 0 & p_{44}
\end{array}
\qquad
\begin{array}{cccccc}
q_{11} & q_{12} & q_{13} & 0 & 0 & 0 \\
q_{13} & q_{11} & q_{12} & 0 & 0 & 0 \\
q_{12} & q_{13} & q_{11} & 0 & 0 & 0 \\
0 & 0 & 0 & q_{44} & 0 & 0 \\
0 & 0 & 0 & 0 & q_{44} & 0 \\
0 & 0 & 0 & 0 & 0 & q_{44}
\end{array}
$$

XI. Eleventh group: Cubic system—3 coefficients.

$$
\begin{array}{cccccc}
p_{11} & p_{12} & p_{12} & 0 & 0 & 0 \\
p_{12} & p_{11} & p_{12} & 0 & 0 & 0 \\
p_{12} & p_{12} & p_{11} & 0 & 0 & 0 \\
0 & 0 & 0 & p_{44} & 0 & 0 \\
0 & 0 & 0 & 0 & p_{44} & 0 \\
0 & 0 & 0 & 0 & 0 & p_{44}
\end{array}
\qquad
\begin{array}{cccccc}
q_{11} & q_{12} & q_{12} & 0 & 0 & 0 \\
q_{12} & q_{11} & q_{12} & 0 & 0 & 0 \\
q_{12} & q_{12} & q_{11} & 0 & 0 & 0 \\
0 & 0 & 0 & q_{44} & 0 & 0 \\
0 & 0 & 0 & 0 & q_{44} & 0 \\
0 & 0 & 0 & 0 & 0 & q_{44}
\end{array}
$$

XII. Isotropic solids—2 coefficients.

Let the direction cosines of OX', OY', OZ' referred to the system $OX_0\, Y_0, Z^0$ be given by the following scheme:

$$
\begin{array}{c|ccc}
 & X' & Y' & Z' \\
\hline
X_0 & \alpha_1 & \alpha_2 & \alpha_3 \\
Y_0 & \beta_1 & \beta_2 & \beta_3 \\
Z_0 & \gamma_1 & \gamma_2 & \gamma_3
\end{array}
\tag{93.4}
$$

One has now to determine the magnitudes of $\alpha_i, \beta_i, \gamma_i$ and a'_{11}, a'_{22} and a'_{33} in terms of the stress optic coefficients and the principal values a^0_{11}, a^0_{22} and a^0_{33} of the undeformed crystal.

Referred to the old co-ordinate axes, we have the six relations

$$
\left.\begin{aligned}
a_{ii} &= a'_{11}\,\alpha_i^2 + a'_{22}\,\beta_i^2 + a'_{33}\,\gamma_i^2 \qquad (i = 1, 2, 3)\,, \\
a_{ij} &= a'_{11}\,\alpha_i\,\alpha_j + a'_{22}\,\beta_i\,\beta_j + a'_{33}\,\gamma_i\,\gamma_j \quad (i, j = 1, 2, 3)
\end{aligned}\right\}
\tag{93.5}
$$

where the a_{ii} and a_{ij} are known in terms of a^0_{ii} and the photoelastic constants.

There are in addition six relations between the direction cosines in (93.4) of the form:

$$
\alpha_i\,\alpha_j + \beta_i\,\beta_j + \gamma_i\,\gamma_j = \delta_{ij} \quad (i, j) = 1, 2, 3 \tag{93.6}
$$

where

$$\delta_{ij} = 0 \quad (i \neq j)$$

and

$$= 1 \quad (i = j).$$

From the twelve equations in (93.5) and (93.6), the twelve unknown quantities namely the three principal values of the index tensor a'_{11}, a'_{22}, a'_{33} and the nine direction cosines $\alpha_i, \beta_i, \gamma_i$ can be determined in terms of the stress-optic coefficients.

It is convenient to express the transformation of $OX_0 Y_0 Z_0$ to $OX'\,Y'\,Z'$ by the following angles. We shall represent the co-ordinate axes by the points X_0, Y_0, Z_0 and X', Y', Z' at which they intersect a sphere of unit radius drawn with the origin as centre. Let the great circle passing through Z_0 and Z' intersect the great circles passing through $X_0\,Y_0$ and $X'\,Y'$ at T_0 and T'. Let $\widehat{X_0 T_0} = \psi$, $\widehat{X T'} = \varphi$ and $\widehat{Z Z_0} = \vartheta$. The direction cosines $\alpha_i, \beta_i, \gamma_i$ are related to ψ, ϑ, φ by the following equations:

$$\left.\begin{aligned}
\alpha_1 &= -\cos\varphi\cos\psi\cos\vartheta - \sin\varphi\sin\psi,\\
\beta_1 &= -\sin\varphi\cos\psi\cos\vartheta + \cos\varphi\sin\psi,\\
\gamma_1 &= \cos\psi\sin\vartheta,\\
\alpha_2 &= -\cos\varphi\sin\psi\cos\vartheta + \sin\varphi\cos\psi,\\
\beta_2 &= -\sin\varphi\sin\psi\cos\vartheta - \cos\varphi\cos\psi,\\
\gamma_2 &= \sin\varphi\sin\psi,\\
\alpha_3 &= \cos\varphi\sin\vartheta, \quad \beta_3 = \sin\varphi\sin\vartheta, \quad \gamma_3 = \cos\vartheta.
\end{aligned}\right\} \tag{93.7}$$

Substituting these in the 12 equations (93.5) and (93.6), the values of ψ are obtained as the three roots of the equation.

$$\left.\begin{aligned}
&\tan^3\psi\{a_{23}(a_{31}^2 - a_{12}^2) + a_{31}a_{12}(a_{22} - a_{33})\} + \\
&+\tan^2\psi\{a_{31}(a_{11}-a_{33})(a_{22}-a_{33}) - a_{23}a_{12}(2a_{11}-a_{22}-a_{33}) - a_{31}(2a_{23}^2 - a_{31}^2 - a_{12}^2)\} + \\
&+\tan\psi\{a_{23}(a_{22}-a_{11})(a_{11}-a_{33}) - a_{31}a_{12}(2a_{22}-a_{11}-a_{33}) - a_{23}(2a_{31}^2 - a_{23}^2 - a_{12}^2)\} + \\
&+a_{12}a_{23}(a_{11} - a_{33}) + a_{31}(a_{23}^2 - a_{12}^2) = 0.
\end{aligned}\right\} \text{(9}$$

There is however an ambiguity in the solution, since $\tan\psi$ is the same both for ψ and $\pi + \psi$ but the effect is only a reversal of the appropriate axis, and the two are equivalent. Knowing ψ, ϑ and φ can be obtained from

$$\tan 2\vartheta = \frac{a_{31}\sin\psi - a_{23}\cos\psi}{\frac{1}{2}(a_{22} - a_{11})\sin 2\psi + a_{12}\cos 2\psi}, \tag{93.9}$$

$$\left.\tan 2\varphi = \frac{\cos\vartheta\{(a_{11} - a_{22})\sin 2\psi - 2a_{12}\cos 2\psi\} + 2\sin\vartheta\{a_{23}\cos\psi - a_{31}\sin\psi\}}{[\cos^2\vartheta\{a_{11}\cos^2\psi + a_{22}\sin^2\psi - a_{33} + a_{12}\sin 2\psi\} - \sin 2\vartheta\{a_{23}\sin\psi + a_{31}\cos\psi\} + a_{12}\sin 2\psi - a_{11}\sin^2\psi - a_{22}\cos^2\psi + a_{33}]}.\right\} \tag{93.10}$$

The values of $\alpha_i, \beta_i, \gamma_i$ are calculated using (93.7) and hence a'_{11}, a'_{22}, a'_{33} are obtained from the relations:

$$a'_{ii} = a_{11}\alpha_i^2 + a_{22}\beta_i^2 + a_{33}\gamma_i^2 + 2a_{23}\beta_i\gamma_i + 2a_{31}\gamma_2\alpha_i + 2a_{12}\alpha_i\beta_i. \tag{93.11}$$

β) Special cases. Simpler relations can be obtained from the equations of the last paragraph in the case of biaxial crystals with not too small birefringence, i.e., when $\Delta a_{11}, \Delta a_{22}, \Delta a_{33}, \Delta a_{23}, \Delta a_{31}, \Delta a_{12}$ are very much smaller than $a_{11}^0 - a_{22}^0$, $a_{22}^0 - a_{33}^0$ and $a_{33}^0 - a_{11}^0$. Then it follows that

$$\alpha_1, \beta_2, \gamma_3 \approx 1; \tag{93.12}$$

$$\beta_3 = -\gamma_2 = \frac{\Delta a_{23}}{a_{22} - a_{33}}; \quad \gamma_1 = -\alpha_3 = \frac{\Delta a_{31}}{a_{33} - a_{11}}; \quad \alpha_2 = -\beta_1 = \frac{\Delta a_{12}}{a_{11} - a_{22}}. \tag{93.13}$$

The transformation of axes from $OX_0Y_0Z_0$ to $OX'Y'Z'$ is then equivalent to three rotations through angles Φ_x, Φ_y, Φ_z about the three axes of the undeformed crystal, the values of which are given by

$$\tan 2\Phi_x = \frac{2\Delta a_{23}}{a_{22} - a_{23}}, \qquad \tan 2\Phi_y = \frac{2\Delta a_{31}}{a_{33} - a_{11}}, \qquad \tan 2\Phi_3 = \frac{2\Delta a_{12}}{a_{11} - a_{22}}. \tag{93.14}$$

By a proper combination of the three individual rotations Φ_x, Φ_y and Φ_z, one obtains the total rotation which the principal axes of a crystal experience on deformation. In biaxial crystals, Φ_x, Φ_y and Φ_z are in general small and hence to a first degree of approximation the order of the successive rotations does not matter. In uniaxial crystals the rotation about the optic axis would be finite (as $a_{11} - a_{22} \approx a_{12}$), while Φ_x, Φ_y will be small. In such cases, the rotation about the optic axis must be carried out first.

94. Optical behaviour under hydrostatic pressure. In this case, $X_x = Y_y = Z_z$ ($= p$ say) and $X_y = Y_z = Z_x = 0$. Introducing these in Eq. (91.9) we have

$$\left.\begin{aligned} \Delta a_1 &= -(q_{11} + q_{12} + q_{13})\, p, \\ \Delta a_2 &= -(q_{21} + q_{22} + q_{23})\, p, \\ \Delta a_3 &= -(q_{31} + q_{32} + q_{33})\, p, \\ \Delta a_4 &= -(q_{41} + q_{42} + q_{43})\, p, \\ \Delta a_5 &= -(q_{51} + q_{52} + q_{53})\, p, \\ \Delta a_6 &= -(q_{61} + q_{62} + q_{63})\, p. \end{aligned}\right\} \tag{94.1}$$

If the values of q_{ij} are known, then the behaviour of the crystal ander hydrostatic pressure can be deduced. From the equations given above one finds that the right hand side of the last three equations are equal to zero for all crystal classes, excepting those belonging to the triclinic and monoclinic systems. This is true in spite of the fact that in certain groups such as 4, 5, 6, 8 (Table 8) cross-coefficients of the type q_{41}, q_{51} are present. In crystals of the monoclinic and triclinic systems, the principal axes experience a rotation under a hydrostatic pressure. However, in no case is the crystal symmetry altered and the isotropic, uniaxial or biaxial nature is always retained.

95. Effect of unidirectional stresses. If a stress P acts in any arbitrary direction having direction cosines l, m, n with respect to the chosen crystallographic axes, then the stress components are given by

$$\left.\begin{aligned} X_1 = l^2 P, \quad X_2 = m^2 P, \quad X_3 = n^2 P, \quad X_4 = mn\, P, \\ X_5 = nl\, P, \quad X_6 = lm\, P. \end{aligned}\right\} \tag{95.1}$$

If these values of the stress components are substituted in the fundamental photoelastic equations, then the orientation of the optical ellipsoid of the deformed crystal can be calculated by the method indicated in the Sect. 93.

It is very seldom that one would require the constants of the optical ellipsod for an arbitrary stress direction. Some special cases of interest are discussed below. For instance, it is possible to distinguish between the different photoelastic classes by a study of the tilt, if any, of the principal planes when the stress is along one of the principal axes of the optical ellipsoid.

We shall consider in particular a crystal not belonging to the monoclinic or the triclinic system, in which the stress is along OX, and calculate the tilt of the axes of the elliptic section when the direction of observation is OY or OZ. Since the stress is along OX, all components except X_1 are zero. Thus

$$\left.\begin{aligned} a_{11}-a_{11}^0 &= -q_{11}X_1, & a_{23} &= -q_{41}X_1,\\ a_{22}-a_{22}^0 &= -q_{12}X_1, & a_{31} &= -q_{51}X_1,\\ a_{33}-a_{33}^0 &= -q_{13}X_1, & a_{12} &= -q_{61}X_1. \end{aligned}\right\} \tag{95.2}$$

The section of the deformed ellipsoid normal to OZ and OY are

$$\left.\begin{aligned} a_{11}x^2+a_{22}y^2+2a_{12}xy &= 1,\\ a_{11}x^2+a_{33}z^2+2a_{31}zx &= 1. \end{aligned}\right\} \tag{95.3}$$

The tilt of the axes in the two cases are respectively

$$\tan 2\vartheta_1 = \frac{2a_{12}}{a_{11}-a_{22}} = \frac{2q_{61}}{q_{11}-q_{12}}, \tag{95.4}$$

and

$$\tan 2\vartheta_2 = \frac{2a_{31}}{a_{11}-a_{33}} = \frac{2q_{51}}{q_{11}-q_{13}}. \tag{95.5}$$

Such tilts in the axes can occur only when either $q_{61}\neq 0$ or $q_{51}\neq 0$. A tilting occurs for both directions of observations only for crystals belonging to the point groups 3 and $\bar{3}$.

It is quite obvious that this gives a simple method for distinguishing crystals belonging to different photoelastic classes in the trigonal, tetragonal and hexagonal systems.

β) In the case of cubic crystals also, it is possible to distinguish between the two photoelastic classes by means of a similar observation. Thus, if the stress direction is equally inclined to OX and OY (making an angle of $+45°$ with OX) and the direction of observation OZ, then a tilt will be observed only in the classes T and T_h[1].

In this case

$$X_1 = X_2 = X_6 = \frac{P}{2}$$

and

$$X_3 = X_4 = X_5 = 0. \tag{95.6}$$

The equation to the optical ellipsoid of the deformed crystal is

$$a_{11}x^2 + a_{22}y^2 + a_{33}z^2 + 2a_{12}yx = 0 \tag{95.7}$$

and its section normal to OZ is

$$a_{11}x^2 + a_{22}y^2 + 2a_{12}xy = 0 \tag{95.8}$$

where

$$\left.\begin{aligned} a_{11} &= a_{11}^0 - \tfrac{1}{2}(q_{11}+q_{12})P,\\ a_{22} &= a_{22}^0 - \tfrac{1}{2}(q_{13}+q_{11})P,\\ a_{12} &= -\tfrac{1}{2}q_{44}P. \end{aligned}\right\} \tag{95.9}$$

---

[1] S. BHAGAVANTAM and D. SURYANARAYANA: Proc. Ind. Acad. Sci. A **26**, 97 (1947). — Nature, Lond. **162**, 740 (1948).

The magnitude of the major and minor axes of the elliptic section are given by

$$a'_{11} = a_{11}\cos^2\vartheta + a_{22}\sin^2\vartheta + 2a_{12}\sin\vartheta\cos\vartheta$$

and

$$a'_{22} = a_{11}\sin^2\vartheta + a_{22}\cos^2\vartheta - 2a_{12}\sin\vartheta\cos\vartheta$$

and the difference

$$a'_{11} - a'_{22} = (a_{11} - a_{22})\cos 2\vartheta + 2a_{12}\sin 2\vartheta .$$

Thus

$$\tan 2\vartheta = \frac{2a_{12}}{a_{11} - a_{22}} = \frac{2q_{44}}{q_{12} - q_{13}} . \tag{95.10}$$

For the photoelastic class No. 11, comprising of crystal classes T_d, O and O_h, $q_{12} = q_{13}$ and therefore $\vartheta = 45°$, and one of the principal axes coincides with pressure direction. For the other class No. 10, composed of T and T_h crystal classes $q_{12} \neq q_{13}$ and so the principal planes are tilted with respect to the direction of pressure. The magnitude of the tilt is $(\vartheta - 45°)$, where $\tan 2\vartheta$ is given by (86.10).

Such a tilt has in fact been observed in a number of crystals belonging to the crystal classes T and T_h and this elegant method has been used to distinguish crystals that belong to and T and T_h classes from those of the T_d, O and O_h classes[1].

γ) In the case of isotropic solids, there are only two piezo-optic constants and under unidirectional stress the solid becomes uniaxial with the optic axial parallel to the direction of stress. The deformed solid behaves like either a positive or negative uniaxial crystal according as $(q_{11} - q_{12})$ is $-ve$ or $+ve$.

96. Behaviour of cubic crystals. For crystals belonging to the T_d, O and O_h classes, the number of independent constants is three, i.e. q_{11}, q_{12} and q_{44} and Eq. (91.9) becomes:

$$\left.\begin{aligned} a_{11} - a^0 &= -\left[(q_{11} - q_{12})X_1 + q_{12}(X_1 + X_2 + X_3)\right],\\ a_{22} - a^0 &= -\left[(q_{11} - q_{12})X_2 + q_{12}(X_1 + X_2 + X_3)\right],\\ a_{33} - a^0 &= -\left[(q_{11} - q_{12})X_3 + q_{12}(X_1 + X_2 + X_3)\right],\\ a_{23} = -q_{44}X_4, \quad & a_{31} = -q_{44}X_5, \quad a_{12} = -q_{44}X_6, \end{aligned}\right\} \tag{96.1}$$

where $a^0_{11} = a^0_{22} = a^0_{33} = a^0$, the value for the undeformed crystal. Consequently, the stressed crystal becomes biaxial in general. Although the birefringence for any direction of propagation is proportional to the stress, it is interesting that the optic axial angle $2V$ depends only on the direction of the pressure and is independent of its magnitude. The value of $2V$ is given by

$$\sin^2 V = \frac{a'_{11} - a'_{22}}{a'_{11} - a'_{33}}, \tag{96.2}$$

where $\frac{1}{\sqrt{a'_{11}}}$, $\frac{1}{\sqrt{a'_{22}}}$, $\frac{1}{\sqrt{a'_{33}}}$ are the principal refractive indices. It is readily seen that $(a'_{11} - a'_{22})$ and $(a'_{11} - a'_{33})$ are homogeneous linear functions of the stress components, so that their ratio and hence the optic axial angle is independent of the magnitude of the stress. The orientation of the optic axial plane depends on the ratio $\chi = q_{44}/q_{11} - q_{12}$ and one may classify crystals belonging to this photoelastic class into four types according to the magnitude and sign of this quantity:

(i) $\chi > 1$, (ii) $0 < \chi < 1$, (iii) $-1 < \chi < 0$, (iv) $\chi < -1$.

[1] S. Bhagavantam and D. Suryanarayana: Proc. Ind. Acad. Sci. A **26**, 97 (1947). — Nature, Lond. **162**, 740 (1948).

The optical behaviour of the four types for various stress directions parallel to the cubic and dodecahedral planes have been worked out by POCKELS[1].

Cubic crystals belonging to T and T_h classes. The phenomena in these cases become more complicated as the number of surviving constants is four, i.e. q_{11}, q_{12}, q_{13} and q_{44}. These crystals therefore become biaxial even for compression along a cubic axis. Thus, if P is the magnitude of the stress along the x-axis,

$$\left.\begin{aligned} a_{11} - a^0 &= -q_{11} P, \\ a_{22} - a^0 &= -q_{12} P, \\ q_{33} - a^0 &= -q_{13} P, \\ a_{23} = a_{31} &= a_{12} = 0. \end{aligned}\right\} \tag{96.3}$$

It is obvious from these equations that the principal axes of the optical ellipsoid coincide with the cubic axes of the crystal. The optic axes occur in the XOZ plane if $q_{12} > q_{13}$, and the axial angle is given by

$$\sin^2 V = \frac{q_{12} - q_{13}}{q_{11} - q_{13}}.$$

Here again, one notices that the optic axial angle is independent of the magnitude of the pressure. This can be proved to be true for any direction of pressure in this photoelastic class also.

The only direction of pressure for which the crystal becomes uniaxial is when it is parallel to a cube diagonal [111]; for all other pressure directions it becomes biaxial. This is because these are the only directions in the crystal which have a symmetry axis of order greater than two. Of particular interest is the fact that for stress along the dodecahedral direction, the crystal becomes biaxial as in the previous case, but with one important difference. No principal axis of the deformed ellipsoid coincides with the direction of stress. (Again this is because this direction is not a two fold axis in crystal class T and T_h.) It must however be remembered that this angle between the axis of the optical ellipsoid and the pressure direction can only be detected experimentally when observations are made along proper directions. For example when the stress is along a dodecahedral direction [110] and observations along a cubic axis [001], then the major axis of the elliptic section normal to [001] is tilted with respect to the stress direction by an angle ϑ given by

$$\tan 2\vartheta = \frac{2 q_{44}}{q_{12} - q_{13}}. \tag{96.4}$$

However for the same stress direction, if the observation is along $[1\bar{1}0]$ the major axis of the elliptic section coincides with the stress direction.

In these crystals, if the stress is along one of the cubic axes (OX), the birefringence observed for directions of observation OY and OZ are different, these being proportional to $(q_{11} - q_{12})$ and $(q_{11} - q_{13})$. Thus, we get the interesting result that in a cubic crystal, for which the three axes are equivalent in the unstressed state, the stress birefringence for pressure along OX is different for observation along the other two cubic axes OY and OZ. However, the equivalence of the three cubic axes under the operations of a three-fold axis along the cube diagonal is seen from the fact that stress along OX and observation

[1] F. POCKELS [2]. A summary of the photoelastic behaviour of cubic crystals is also given by types I and II. G. SZIVESSY [1].

along OY is equivalent to stress along OY and observation along OZ and to stress along OZ and observation along OX. Similarly, the other three combinations of stress and observation directions are equivalent.

97. Behaviour of uniaxial crystals. In cubic crystals it is found that a pressure along any trigonal or tetragonal axis of symmetry makes the crystal optically uniaxial with the pressure direction as the unique axis; a pressure applied along any other axis makes the crystal biaxial[1]. This rule is found to be valid for uniaxial crystals also. From the Table 6, it is seen that for a unidirectional pressure along the Z axis since $q_{43}=q_{53}=q_{63}=0$ there will be no rotation of the axes. And as $q_{23}=q_{13}$ the principal components of the index tensor a_1 and a_2 of the deformed crystal will be the same. For any other direction of pressure these two constants will not be the same, showing that for any unidirectional pressure a uniaxial crystal becomes biaxial unless the pressure direction coincides with the optic axis. If the pressure direction is perpendicular to the optic axis (i.e. OZ_0) and if it is parallel to OX_0 then the optic axial angle exhibited by the deformed crystal is given by

$$\sin^2 V = \left\{ \left| \frac{q_{11}-q_{12}}{\frac{1}{n_\omega^2}-\frac{1}{n_\varepsilon^2}} \right| P \right\} \tag{97.1}$$

where n_ω and n_ε are the ordinary and extraordinary indices of refraction. Unlike in cubic crystals the optic axial angle is proportional to the square root of the pressure. For all crystals excepting these belonging to group V of Table 7 the acute bisectric of the deformed crystal will *not* coincide with the optic axes of the undeformed crystal but would be rotated by an angle determined by the first two equations of (93.14). Further if $q_{11}<q_{12}$ the optic axial plane is parallel to the pressure direction for a positive uniaxial crystal and perpendicular to the pressure direction for a negative uniaxial crystal. For $q_{11}>q_{12}$ the behaviour would be just the opposite.

98. Experimental methods. The photoelastic constants of a crystal can be evaluated from observations in specimens of suitable orientation of the absolute and relative retardations induced by stress. These retardations arise firstly due to the change in the refractive indices due to the photoelastic effect and secondly the change in the thickness of the specimens caused by the stress. The magnitude of the last effect must be known before the photoelastic constants can be computed from the observed values of the retardations. We shall briefly mention the various methods available for measuring the retardation before dealing with the methods of computation.

The crystal specimen is subjected to a *uniform* unidirectional stress and the relative retardation produced between rays with electric vectors parallel and perpendicular to the stress is measured by any of the compensator methods. The Babinet compensator has proved by far the most useful instrument for these measurements. Recently a magneto-optic method (see Sect. 90) has been evolved for measuring small birefringence usually encountered in photoelastic experiments and the method is particularly useful for the measurement of the dispersion of the photoelastic constants with wavelength. This method consists of measuring the decrease of the apparent Faraday rotation with stress and is normally applicable to cubic crystals.

The absolute retardation measurements can be made using two identical crystals in a Jamin interferometer, one being subjected to a longitudinal stress

[1] S. Bhagavantam and D. Suryanarayana: Proc. Ind. Acad. Sci. A **26**, 97 (1947).

while the other is not[1]. Another extremely accurate method for determination of the retardation has been described[2]. Light passes through three specimens each placed in front of a slit. A precise exploration of the Fraunhofer pattern with and without the central crystal stressed yields an accurate measure of the variation of the optical path of the central beam. Another convenient method[3] is to measure the shift with stress of the Newtonian fringes formed between two surfaces of the crystal specimen.

For a pressure change ΔP, if ΔN fringes cross a fiducial mark in the crystal, then the change in refractive index

$$\frac{\Delta n_i}{\Delta P} = \frac{\lambda}{2l}\,\frac{\Delta N}{\Delta P} - n_i\,\frac{\Delta L}{\Delta P} \tag{98.1}$$

where in the last term $\frac{1}{L}\,\frac{\Delta L}{\Delta P}$ represents the elastic modulus along the direction of propagation. ΔN and ΔP can be measured very accurately. However, in general the experimental position in photoelasticity is quite unsatisfactory, as in most of the methods of measurements the major part of the path retardation arises due to the change in thickness of the specimen. These changes cannot be accurately found out as the elastic constants are not precisely known.

We shall now take the case of an orthorhombic crystal to exemplify the computation[4]. Here

$$\left.\begin{aligned} a_{11} - a_{11}^0 &= -\,(q_{11} X_x + q_{12} Y_y + q_{13} Z_z)\,,\\ a_{22} - a_{22}^0 &= -\,(q_{21} X_x + q_{22} Y_y + q_{23} Z_z)\,,\\ a_{33} - a_{33}^0 &= -\,(q_{31} X_x + q_{32} Y_x + q_{33} Z_z)\,. \end{aligned}\right\} \tag{98.2}$$

and

$$a_{23} = -\,q_{44}\,,\,Y_z, \qquad a_{31} = -\,q_{55}\,Z_x, \qquad a_{12} = -\,q_{66} X_y$$

and the strains etc. are given by

$$\left.\begin{aligned} x_x &= -\,(s_{11} X_x + s_{12}\,Y_y + s_{13}\,Z_z)\,,\\ y_y &= -\,(s_{21} X_x + s_{22}\,Y_y + s_{23}\,Z_z)\,,\\ z_z &= -\,(s_{31} X_x + s_{32}\,Y_y + s_{33}\,Z_z)\,,\\ y_z &= -\,s_{44}\,Y_z, \quad z_x = -\,s_{55}\,Z_x, \quad x_y = -\,s_{66}\,Y_x, \end{aligned}\right\} \tag{98.3}$$

and along any direction making direction cosines l, m, n with the axes, the dilatation is given by

$$\frac{\Delta L}{L} = x_x l^2 + y_y m^2 + z_z n^2 + y_z m n + z_x n l + x_y l m \tag{98.4}$$

for a unidirectional stress along x,

$$\left.\begin{aligned} a_{11} - a_{11}^0 &= -\,q_{11}\,P_x\,,\\ a_{22} = a_{22}^0 &= -\,q_{21}\,P_x\,,\\ a_{33} - a_{33}^0 &= -\,q_{31}\,P_x\,, \end{aligned}\right\} \tag{98.5}$$

since $a_{11}^0 = 1/n_x^2$, $a_{22}^0 = 1/n_y^2$ and $a_{33}^0 = 1/n_z^2$ for observation along the z axis for light with electric vector parallel to the direction of pressure

$$\Delta n_x = \frac{n_x^3\,q_{11}\,P_x}{2} \tag{98.6}$$

[1] R. EPPENDAHL: Ann. d. Phys. **61** (4), 591 (1920).
[2] B. VITTOZ: Helv. phys. Acta **26**, 400 (1954).
[3] G.N. RAMACHANDRAN: Proc. Ind. Acad. Sci. A **25**, 208 (1947).
[4] K. VEDAM: Proc. Ind. Acad. Sci. A **34**, 161 (1951).

and for the localised fringe method described, the retardation for one fringe shift is

$$\lambda / P_x^{\parallel} t = n_x^3 q_{11} - 2 n_x s_{13} \tag{98.7}$$

where $P_x^{\parallel}$ is the pressure (in dynes-cm²) necessary to bring about one fringe shift for light vibrating parallel to the direction of pressure. Similarly

$$\lambda / P_x^{\perp} t = n_y^3 q_{21} - 2 n_y s_{13} \tag{98.8}$$

for light vibrating perpendicular to the direction of pressure and relative retardation when measured with a Babinet compensator is

$$\frac{\lambda}{2t}\left[\frac{1}{P_x^{\parallel}} - \frac{1}{P_x^{\perp}}\right] = \frac{1}{2}\left(n_x^3 q_{11} - n_y^3 q_{21}\right) + s_{13}\left(n_y - n_x\right). \tag{98.9}$$

The factor of 2 being due to the fact that the light travels through the crystal only once when the Babinet method is used and not twice as in the fringe method.

β) Optically active medium. We shall consider the case of a cubic crystal possessing optical activity for which this method has been worked out[1]. If light of any state of polarisation represented by P on the Poincaré sphere (Fig. 99) is incident on the unstressed crystal (of thickness t), the emergent light will be in the state P_2 obtained by a rotation about the axis LR by an angle $2\varrho t$ where ϱ is the optical rotation per unit length of the crystal. If now the crystal is stressed, the emergent light would be represented by a point Q obtained by rotation of

$$\Delta = t\sqrt{\delta^2 + (2\varrho)^2} \tag{98.10}$$

about an axis SS' which makes an angle φ with LR given by

$$\tan\varphi = \frac{\delta}{2\varrho} \tag{98.11}$$

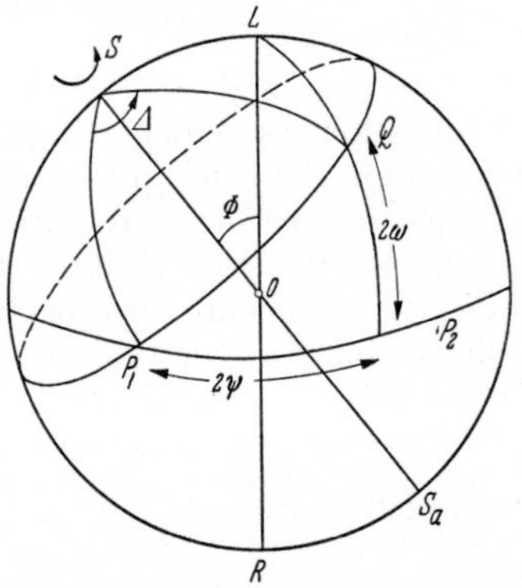

Fig. 99. Poincaré representation to compute the state of the beam emerging from an optically active crystal which has been strained.

where δ is the birefringence introduced in the plate due to the stress. If now we are able to measure the state of vibration of the emergent vibration, then Δ can be easily computed, from which δ can be calculated since 2ϱ is known. The analytical expression when P is any general vibration is rather complicated but the problem can be solved graphically on a stereographic projection with the aid of a Wulff net.

However when the incident vibration is linearly polarised the analytical expressions are comparatively simple. If the major axis of the emergent elliptic vibration makes an angle ψ with the vibration direction of incident light and if the axial ratio b/a is given by $\tan\omega = b/a$ then

$$\tan\varphi = \frac{\sin 2\omega}{\cos 2\alpha - \cos 2\omega \cos 2(\alpha + \psi)}, \tag{98.12}$$

$$\cos\Delta = 1 - \frac{1 - \cos 2\omega \cos 2\psi}{1 - \sin^2\varphi \cos^2\alpha} \tag{98.13}$$

where α is the inclination of the plane of vibration of the incident light to one of the principal vibration directions of the crystal: ψ and α can be directly deter-

[1] G. N. RAMACHANDRAN and V. CHANDRASEKHARAN: Proc. Ind. Acad. Sci. A **33**, 199 (1952).

mined using a Babinet compensator. In addition it is necessary to determine the principal vibration directions of the rotating birefringent crystal. This can be done by determining the azimuth of minimum, the method due to BRUHAT (see Sect. 84) using crossed nicols. The azimuth at which the transmitted intensity is a minimum gives the principal vibration direction. This method is not accurate unless $2\varrho/\delta$ is small. Otherwise the minimum is not marked. However the use of the analysers described in Sect. 21 would be of great help. Knowing α, ψ and ω it is possible to compute both Δ and φ.

The birefringence introduced may be calculated from the formula (98.10) or from the equation

$$\delta = \Delta \sin\varphi .$$

For $2\alpha = 0$ or $\pi/2$ formulae (98.12) and (98.13) reduce to

$$\left.\begin{aligned} \underline{2\alpha = 0} \qquad & \tan\varphi = \sin 2\omega/1 - \cos 2\omega \cos 2\psi , \\ & \sin\Delta = \cos 2\omega \sin 2\psi/\cos\varphi , \\ \underline{2\alpha = \pi/2} \qquad & \tan\varphi = \tan 2\omega/\sin 2\psi , \\ & \cos\Delta = \cos 2\omega/\cos 2\psi . \end{aligned}\right\} \tag{98.14}$$

Another extremely simple method of determining the birefringence is to determine the ellipticity of the elliptic vibration that is propagated without any change in the stressed optically active crystal. The experimental method is identical with the technique described in Sect. 71 for the measurement of optical activity in the presence of absorption using an elliptic polariser and a crossed elliptic analyser. If the ratio of the axes of the ellipse is given by B/A then

$$\tan\frac{1}{2}\left(\frac{\pi}{2} - \varphi\right) = \frac{B}{A}$$

and

$$\delta = 2\varrho \tan\varphi . \tag{98.15}$$

Using these techniques, by stressing the crystals along [100] and making observations along [010] and [001], $q_{11} - q_{12}$ and $q_{11} - q_{13}$ were determined and by stressing the crystal along [111] and making observations along [$1\bar{1}0$] and [$11\bar{2}$], q_{44} was determined for sodium chlorate a crystal which belongs to the T class.

99. Ratio of the photoelastic constants in cubic crystals using ultrasonics. MUELLER[1] has developed an elegant method for measuring the ratio of the elasto-optic constants in cubic crystals by studying the optical characteristics of the light diffracted by ultrasonic waves passing through a single crystal. The details of the theory are beyond the scope of this article but we shall mention only the physical basis of the method. RAMAN and NATH[2] have given a very satisfactory theory of the diffraction of light by ultrasonic waves in a liquid. The theory is based on the simple concept that the changes in phase due to changes in the refractive index at each point of the liquid due to sound field, has the effect of corrugating the wave-front of a plane parallel light wave incident on it in the transverse direction. In liquids it can be easily shown that if the incident light is polarised all the components of the light diffracted by the ultrasonic waves have the same polarisation as the incident light. However in the case of a cubic crystal the case is slightly different. Under the influence of the strains in the

[1] H. MUELLER: Z. Kristallogr. A **99**, 122 (1938).

[2] C.V. RAMAN and N. NATH: Proc. Ind. Acad. Sci. A **2**, 406 (1935).

solid every volume element in the crystal becomes *birefringent* and for light travelling in the z direction the birefringence can be characterised by the index ellipse which is the section of the index ellipsoid normal to the z axis. The ellipse has its axial direction at an angle ϑ and $90+\vartheta$ with the x axis where $\tan 2\vartheta = \frac{2a_{12}}{a_{11}-a_{22}}$ (Sect. 95). But the important point is that these directions do not vary in time and are also the same for every volume element for a *cubic crystal*. Hence if the incident light is at any arbitrary polarisation, its amplitude can be resolved into two components E_{I} and E_{II} along the major and the minor axes of the index ellipse. Hence two diffraction patterns with different amplitudes are obtained if the Raman-Nath theory is applied to the case of solids. Since both these amplitudes originate from the same incident light by diffraction on the same elastic wave, they must be coherent and consequently the two resultant amplitudes must be added vectorially to get the resultant vibration. The result can be stated as follows. For plane polarised incident light all diffraction orders produced by a progressive sound wave in an optically isotropic solid are plane polarised. However, the direction of polarisation is different for different orders and differs from that of the incident light. In the case of birefringent crystals for any general direction the diffracted light is in general elliptically polarised. By measuring the rotation of the plane of polarisation of the light in the different orders with respect to the light in the zeroth order it is possible to evaluate the ratio of the elasto-optic constants in isotropic solids and cubic crystals. This method has been extended to the case of cubic crystals which possess optical activity[1].

Acknowledgement.

The authors wish to record their most grateful thanks to Dr. S. PANCHARATNAM of the Raman Research Institute, Bangalore, India, without whose unstinting co-operation this article could not have been written.

General references.

[1] SZIVESSY, G.: Kristalloptik. In GEIGER and SCHEEL's Handbuch der Physik, Vol. 20, pp. 635—904. Berlin: Springer 1928.
[2] POCKELS, F.: Lehrbuch der Kristalloptik. Leipzig 1906.
[3] DRUDE, P.: Theory of Optics. London: Longmans & Green 1829.
[4] BORN, M.: Optik. Berlin: Springer 1933.
[5] WALKER, J.: Analytical Theory of Light. Cambridge 1904.
[6] SOMMERFELD, A.: Optics. New York: Academic Press 1954.
[7] BRUHAT, G., and A. KASTLER: Optique. Paris: Masson & Cie. 1954.
[8] DITCHBURN, R.V.: Light. London: Blackie & Son 1955.
[9] SCHULTZ, H.: Handbuch der Experimentalphysik, Vol. 18. Leipzig 1928.
[10] JOHANNSEN, A.: Manual of Petrographic Methods. New York-Toronto-London: McGraw-Hill 1918.
[11] HARTSHORNE, N.H., and A. STUART: Crystals and the Polarising Microscope. London: Arnold 1950.
[12] TUTTON, A.E.H.: Crystallography and Practical Crystal Measurements. London: Macmillan 1911.
[13] WOOD, R.W.: Physical optics. New York: Wiley 1949.

[1] K. VEDAM and G.N. RAMACHANDRAN: Proc. Ind. Acad. Sci. A **34**, 240 (1951).

Theorie der Beugung.

Von

H. Hönl, A. W. Maue und K. Westpfahl.

Mit 143 Figuren.

1. Einführung und historische Übersicht. Aufs große und ganze gesehen lassen sich in der Theorie der Beugung *drei* verschiedene Entwicklungsstufen unterscheiden:

1) Die herkömmliche Theorie der Lichtbeugung ist bekanntlich eine der großen Leistungen Fresnels (1818), der erstmals das bis dahin rein geometrisch verstandene Huygenssche Prinzip (1690) (Enveloppen-Konstruktion) mit dem Youngschen Prinzip der Interferenz (1801) verband. Tatsächlich gibt das „*Huygens-Fresnelsche Prinzip*" von den historisch bekannten Beugungserscheinungen vollkommene Rechenschaft. Diese Entwicklung findet etwa in dem Werke von Schwerd (1835)[1] ihren Abschluß, worin das Ergebnis der Fresnelschen Theorie dahin zusammengefaßt ist, „daß die Undulationstheorie die Beugungserscheinungen eben so zuverlässig vorhersagt, wie die Gravitationstheorie die Bewegung der Himmelskörper". Der Vergleich der Fresnelschen Theorie mit der Gravitationstheorie Newtons scheint von unserm heutigen Standpunkt auch darin treffend, als die Grundlagen der Beugungstheorie damals theoretisch ebenso wenig geklärt waren als diejenigen der Gravitationstheorie und doch in beiden Fällen eine vorzügliche Annäherung an die Erfahrung erreicht wurde.

2) Eine exakte Fassung des Huygensschen Prinzips gelang erstmalig Helmholtz (1859), der gezeigt hat, daß dieses auf eine Integralumformung hinausläuft (ähnlich wie in der Potentialtheorie), welche das Feld v in einem Aufpunkt P aus den Werten des Feldes (und seiner Normalen-Ableitungen $\partial v/\partial n$) auf einer beliebigen, den Aufpunkt P umhüllenden *geschlossenen Fläche* zu berechnen gestattet:

$$v(P) = -\frac{1}{4\pi}\oint\left\{v\,\frac{\partial}{\partial n}\left(\frac{e^{ikr_{PQ}}}{r_{PQ}}\right) - \frac{\partial v}{\partial n}\,\frac{e^{ikr_{PQ}}}{r_{PQ}}\right\} d\sigma_Q. \tag{1.1}$$

Bei der Anwendung dieser strengen Integralformel — sie wird in der deutschen Literatur meist (unhistorisch) als „*Huygens-Kirchhoffsches Prinzip*" bezeichnet[2] — auf das Problem der Beugung an beliebigen Körpern machte Kirchhoff (1882) in seiner Beugungstheorie weiterhin willkürliche, theoretisch nicht weiter unterbaute Annahmen, so daß seine (sowohl die Fresnelschen wie die Fraunhoferschen Beugungserscheinungen umfassende) Beugungstheorie wiederum doch nur Näherungscharakter besitzt. Praktisch führt die Kirchhoffsche Beugungstheorie über die Fresnelsche Theorie nicht hinaus.

[1] F. M. Schwerd: Die Beugungserscheinungen aus den Fundamentalgesetzen der Undulationstheorie entwickelt. Mannheim 1835.

[2] Während Helmholtz stationäre Wellenfelder untersucht, legt Kirchhoff seiner Beugungstheorie die allgemeine zeitabhängige Ausbreitungsgleichung für Wellenfelder zugrunde; sein Ausdruck für das Huygenssche Prinzip ist daher komplizierter gebaut als der Helmholtzsche.

Das Kirchhoffsche Verfahren besteht bekanntlich darin, daß man die (über das Unendliche geschlossene) Hüllfläche der der Strahlungsquelle abgewandten Seite des beugenden Körpers eng anschmiegt, die in (1.1) vorgesehene Integration aber nur über denjenigen Teil der Hüllfläche erstreckt, der nicht im geometrischen Schatten des Körpers liegt („Öffnung") und dort die Werte v_0 und $\partial v_0/\partial n$ einsetzt, die dem von der Anwesenheit des Körpers unbeeinflußten Primärfeld zukommen. KIRCHHOFF glaubte, die sich so ergebende Formel *(„Kirchhoffsches Integral")* durch die Annahme begründen zu können, daß erstens v und $\partial v/\partial n$ auf der Rückseite des Körpers nahezu verschwinden und zweitens in der Öffnung durch die Anwesenheit des Körpers nicht wesentlich beeinflußt werden. Diese Annahmen sind jedoch in sich *widerspruchsvoll* (aus der ersten würde bereits das identische Verschwinden von v im ganzen Raume folgen); sie werden daher von dem Kirchhoffschen Integral bei Annäherung an die Hüllfläche auch *nicht reproduziert.* Es erhebt sich damit die Frage, welchem physikalischen Problem die durch das Kirchhoffsche Integral gegebene Lösung der Wellengleichung (unabhängig von der heuristischen Herleitung KIRCHHOFFs) korrespondiert. In dieser Hinsicht ist von RUBINOWICZ (1917) darauf hingewiesen worden, daß die Kirchhoffsche Lösung *nicht* einem *Randwertproblem,* sondern einem *Sprungwertproblem* entspricht, wobei die Unstetigkeiten des *geometrisch-optischen Feldes* an der *Schattengrenze* durch entgegengesetzt gleiche Unstetigkeiten des Kirchhoffschen Integrals, erstreckt über den *Schattenkegel,* ausgeglichen werden. In ähnlicher Weise hat KOTTLER (1923) die Kirchhoffsche Lösung als ein Sprungwertproblem charakterisiert, wobei die Sprungwerte beim Hindurchtreten durch einen (unendlich dünnen) *„schwarzen Schirm"* als vorgegeben zu betrachten sind[1]. Sowohl in der Akustik als auch in der Maxwellschen Theorie ist der beugende Körper jedoch nur durch ein *Randwertproblem* zu erfassen.

Ferner ist zu betonen, daß die Kirchhoffsche Theorie (im Grenzfall *kleiner* Wellenlängen) nur für das Fernfeld — und auch dort nur in der Nähe der Schattengrenze — brauchbar ist. Daß sie in der Nähe der beugenden Körper versagt, hängt wesentlich damit zusammen, daß die Kirchhoffsche Lösung sich im Sinne von YOUNG (1801) als Superposition von Kugelwellen auffassen läßt, die von der Randlinie der Öffnung ausgehen (MAGGI 1888, RUBINOWICZ 1917). Diese Linie wirkt also bei KIRCHHOFF als zusätzliche Strahlungsquelle, was zu unzulässigen Feldsingularitäten führt.

In neuerer Zeit ist von KELLER (1953) eine *geometrische Beugungstheorie* entwickelt worden, die die geometrische Optik durch die Konzeption *„gebeugter Strahlen"* heuristisch erweitert. Mit ihrer Hilfe läßt sich das geometrisch-optische Feld durch Beugungsterme korrigieren, die der *asymptotischen Lösung* des Randwertproblems für *kleine* Wellenlängen entsprechen. Diese Theorie hängt eng mit einer von BRAUNBEK (1950) vorgeschlagenen Verbesserung der Kirchhoffschen Theorie zusammen.

Eine strenge Fassung des Huygensschen Prinzips analog der Helmholtzschen Formel (1.1) läßt sich nach LARMOR (1903) und KOTTLER (1923) auch für elektromagnetische Wellenfelder angeben.

3) Erst durch die Arbeiten von POINCARÉ (1892) und SOMMERFELD (1896) ist deutlich geworden, daß es sich bei dem Beugungsproblem der elektromagnetischen Strahlungsfelder um ein reguläres *Randwertproblem* der mathematischen Physik handelt. In allgemeiner Auffassung liegt die Aufgabe vor, die Lösung

[1] Eine eingehende Darstellung der Kirchhoffschen Theorie findet man bei B.B. BAKER und E.T. COPSON: The Mathematical Theory of Huygens Principle, 2. Aufl., Oxford 1950, sowie A. RUBINOWICZ: Die Beugungswelle in der Kirchhoffschen Theorie der Beugung. Warschau 1957.

der Maxwellschen Gleichungen zu finden, die an der Oberfläche des beugenden Körpers bestimmte Rand- bzw. Grenzbedingungen erfüllen; hinzu tritt ferner eine „*Ausstrahlungsbedingung*“ (Sommerfeld 1912), welche bewirkt, daß die gesamte von der (im Endlichen oder Unendlichen gelegenen) Strahlungsquelle gelieferte Energie, abgesehen von einer etwaigen Absorption im beugenden Körper (bei endlicher Leitfähigkeit σ), ins Unendliche abgestrahlt wird. Besitzt die Oberfläche des beugenden Körpers Kanten, so ist das Problem noch durch eine „*Kantenbedingung*“ zu ergänzen (Meixner 1948), die dafür sorgt, daß die ausgestrahlte Energie nur von den vorgegebenen Strahlungsquellen geliefert wird (und nicht die Kanten zusätzlich noch „strahlen“). Die beugenden Körper können an sich beliebige Gestalt besitzen aus beliebigem (durch die Konstanten ε, μ, σ charakterisierten) Material gebildet sein. Die Lösung des Randwertproblems umfaßt dann die als Reflexion, Brechung, Absorption und Beugung beschriebenen Phänomene in einheitlicher Weise.

Was die Abgrenzung des Problemkreises betrifft, so wollen wir uns in diesem Artikel auf „*ideale Leiter*“ ($\sigma \to \infty$) beschränken, auf deren Oberfläche die Tangentialkomponente der elektrischen Feldstärke verschwindet. Diese im Rahmen der Maxwellschen Theorie sinnvolle Idealisierung gibt das Verhalten einiger Metalle (etwa Kupfer) bei den in der Mikrowellentechnik üblichen Frequenzen sehr gut wieder; allerdings gibt es gerade im eigentlichen optischen Frequenzbereich auch bei den besten Leitern Phänomene, die nur durch die Annahme einer endlichen Leitfähigkeit erklärt werden können (z.B. in der Mieschen Theorie der Farberscheinungen an kolloidalen Lösungen). Sowohl bei den historischen Beugungsversuchen als auch bei der modernen Antennentechnik beanspruchen die unendlich dünnen „*Schirme*“ ein besonderes Interesse; sie können im Rahmen der Maxwellschen Theorie als Unstetigkeitsflächen des Feldes charakterisiert werden. Außer Betracht bleiben außerdem die elektromagnetischen *Eigenschwingungen* von Hohlräumen und Hohlleitern, obwohl Öffnungen in solchen Gebilden (Schlitzantennen) zu Beugungsproblemen führen, die mit den hier behandelten eng zusammenhängen[1].

Hinsichtlich der Formulierung des *Randwertproblems der strengen Beugungstheorie* lassen sich im wesentlichen drei verschiedene *Zugänge* unterscheiden:

a) Methode der Flächenströme. Der Poincarésche Gedanke läßt sich folgendermaßen formulieren: Die einfallende Welle induziert auf der Oberfläche der beugenden Körper *Flächenströme*, die ihrerseits die Ausstrahlung des Beugungsfeldes verursachen. Hierbei wird die Verteilung des Flächenstromes einerseits durch die *primäre* Welle, andererseits durch die von sämtlichen Elementen der Oberfläche einander zugestrahlten *Sekundärwellen* reguliert. Diese Betrachtungsweise führt zur Aufstellung einer Integralgleichung für die Verteilung des Flächenstromes (Maue 1949). Bei Kenntnis dieser Verteilung läßt sich das Gesamtfeld mit Hilfe der strengen Fassung des Huygensschen Prinzips durch ein Integral über die *Oberfläche des beugenden Körpers* darstellen, was sich dahingehend deuten läßt, daß von jedem Stromelement sekundäre Kugelwellen ausgehen, die sich zum Beugungsfeld superponieren (*„Huygens-Poincarésches Prinzip“*)[2]. Das

[1] Über Hohlleiterprobleme s. N. Markuvitz: Waveguide Handbook, New York 1951; H. Zuhrt: Elektromagnetische Strahlungsfelder, Berlin 1953; F. Borgnis u. C. Papas: Randwertprobleme der Mikrowellenphysik, Berlin 1955, sowie in Bd. XVI dieses Handbuches; G. Goubau: Elektromagnetische Wellenleiter und Hohlräume, Stuttgart 1955.

[2] Es läßt sich allgemein zeigen, daß bei ebenen Schirmen stets auch eine Formulierung möglich ist, wonach die sekundären Kugelwellen von Elementen der Öffnung ausgehen (Bethe 1944); beide Formulierungen sind mathematisch äquivalent. Demgemäß wäre es sinnvoll, zwischen einem „Huygens-Poincaréschen Prinzip“ und einer *strengen* Fassung des „Huygens-Fresnelschen Prinzips“ zu unterscheiden (im Gegensatz zur historischen Fassung des letzteren Prinzips).

eigentliche *mathematische* Problem ist also hier die Ermittlung der Flächenströme.

Mittels der physikalischen Konzeption der Flächenströme in Verbindung mit der Theorie der linearen Operatoren ist es CL. MÜLLER[1] gelungen, die *allgemeine Theorie des Beugungsproblems* zu einem gewissen Abschluß zu bringen, d.h. Eindeutigkeits- und Existenzbeweise für die Lösungen zu führen. Dadurch erreicht die Theorie der Beugung eine der Potentialtheorie vergleichbare innere Geschlossenheit; hinsichtlich der verfügbaren Methoden zur expliziten strengen Lösung spezieller Beugungsprobleme steht sie allerdings noch weit hinter dieser zurück.

Für die induzierten Flächenströme liefert der *statische Grenzfall* (sehr *große Wellenlänge*, verglichen mit einer charakteristischen Körperabmessung a) einen geeigneten Ausgangspunkt, um eine Entwicklung nach *steigenden* Potenzen des Parameters $\varepsilon = ka$ (k Wellenzahl) zu gewinnen. Dieses Verfahren benutzt die elektrostatischen Potentiale der Beugungsanordnung und paßt sie in sukzessiven Schritten dem dynamischen Problem an (BOUWKAMP 1949). Der erste Schritt dieses Störungsverfahrens geht auf RAYLEIGH (1897) zurück.

Eine geeignete Methode, einen *größeren Frequenzbereich* zu überbrücken, knüpft an die Möglichkeit an, ein *Variationsproblem* zu formulieren, dessen Extremale der Flächenstrom ist (LEVINE und SCHWINGER 1948). Auf diese Weise können die Näherungsmethoden der Variationsrechnung (insbesondere das Ritzsche Verfahren) für die Beugungstheorie fruchtbar gemacht werden. Wesentlich ist ferner, daß sich die Fernfeldamplitude in eine „*stationäre Form*" bringen läßt, so daß schon relativ willkürlich gewählte Flächenströme zu einem qualitativ richtigen Fraunhoferschen Beugungsbild für den gesamten Frequenzbereich führen. In quantitativer Hinsicht hängt das Verfahren von der Genauigkeit ab, mit der man sich die Kenntnis des Flächenstroms nach der einen oder anderen Methode verschafft hat.

Für *kleine Wellenlängen* ($\varepsilon \gg 1$) lassen sich, ausgehend von der Integralgleichung für den Flächenstrom, Korrekturen zur Feldverteilung der *geometrischen Optik* berechnen. Hierbei handelt es sich um eine Darstellung der Lösung des Randwertproblems durch *asymptotische* Reihen nach *fallenden* (gebrochenen) Potenzen des Parameters ε. Diese Darstellungen haben bei ebenen Schirmen (LEVINE 1955, WESTPFAHL 1959) einen anderen Charakter als bei konvexen Körpern (FOCK 1946, FRANZ und DEPPERMANN 1952). Bei letzteren kann das Beugungsfeld als Folge der tangentialen Wellenabstrahlung von „*Kriechströmen*" gedeutet werden, die längs der glatten Oberfläche der Körper in den geometrischen Schattenbereich hineinfließen.

b) Fourier-Methode. Einen weiteren Zugang zur strengen Theorie der Beugung (der bisher im wesentlichen nur für ebene Schirme entwickelt worden ist) eröffnet die Methode der Fourier-Darstellung des Wellenfeldes. Dabei können die Fourier-Komponenten direkt als Amplituden der nach den verschiedenen Richtungen ausgehenden ebenen Wellen des „*Fraunhoferschen Beugungsfeldes*" — einschließlich inhomogener Wellen — gedeutet werden (CLEMMOW 1951, HÖNL 1952). Das System simultaner *(dualer)* Integralgleichungen für die Fourier-Amplituden, das man durch Anwendung der Rand- und Stetigkeitsbedingung erhält, hat zudem eine besonders einfache Gestalt (sowohl für skalare als auch für vektorielle Felder). Der analytische Zusammenhang mit der Methode von POINCARÉ ergibt sich aus der Fourier-Transformation der Flächenströme sowie der Fourier-

[1] Zusammengefaßt in der Monographie von CL. MÜLLER: Grundlagen der mathematischen Theorie elektromagnetischer Schwingungen, Berlin 1957.

Darstellung der Kugelwellen, wobei die Fourier-Komponenten des Flächenstroms unmittelbar das Fraunhofersche Fernfeld ergeben.

Auch Sommerfelds berühmte Behandlung der Beugung an der Halbebene — historisch das erste Beispiel einer strengen Lösung eines Beugungsproblems — nimmt den Weg über das Fourier-Integral. Allerdings wird hierbei die Fourier-Amplitude durch die Forderung bestimmt, daß die Lösung erst auf einer *zweiblättrigen Riemannschen Fläche* eindeutig sein soll; die Randbedingung auf dem Schirm läßt sich dann nach dem Sommerfeldschen Spiegelungsprinzip erfüllen. Die Auffindung der Lösung erfolgt bei Sommerfeld auf heuristischem Wege, während hierbei die Methode der dualen Integralgleichungen in systematischer Weise zum Ziel führt.

c) Die Separationsmethode und das Wiener-Hopf-Verfahren. Die „klassische" (schon auf Fourier zurückgehende) Methode zur Behandlung von Randwertaufgaben besteht darin, solche krummlinigen Koordinaten einzuführen, daß die Oberfläche des beugenden Körpers mit einer der Koordinatenflächen zusammenfällt. Diese Methode ist jedoch auf diejenigen Fälle beschränkt, in denen sich die betreffende Differentialgleichung in den der Körperform angepaßten Koordinaten *separieren* läßt. (Für die Separation kommen allenfalls Koordinaten in Frage, deren Koordinatenflächen ein System von Flächen zweiter Ordnung bilden.) Die Methode führt im allgemeinen auf Reihen nach *höheren transzendenten Funktionen*. Die numerische Auswertung ist daher daran gebunden, in welchem Umfange Tabellen für diese Funktionen verfügbar sind. Hierbei ist die Zahl der bei den Reihenentwicklungen zu berücksichtigenden Glieder von der Größenordnung des Parameters $\varepsilon = k a$ (die Reihen nach steigenden *Potenzen* von ε konvergieren hingegen sehr viel schlechter). Für die Behandlung des an die geometrische Optik anschließenden Grenzfalls ist es jedoch möglich, die Reihen so umzutransformieren, daß sie gerade für $\varepsilon \gg 1$ sehr rasch konvergieren (Transformation von Watson 1918); man gelangt auf diese Weise wieder zu den oben erwähnten „*Kriechwellen*".

Einer der wesentlichsten Fortschritte in der Theorie der Randwertaufgaben besteht in der *Kombination* der Separationsmethode mit einer auf Wiener und Hopf (1931) zurückgehenden Anwendung *funktionentheoretischer Methoden*. Damit lassen sich Probleme lösen, in denen nur *einseitig* ins Unendliche reichende *Teile* von Zylinderflächen (zweiten Grades) ins Spiel kommen, deren *Kanten* in einer Ebene senkrecht zu den Erzeugenden des Zylinders liegen. Der einfachste hierher gehörige Fall ist die Halbebene (ein Problem, das sich jedoch auch vollständig separieren läßt). Kompliziertere Anwendungsbeispiele sind die aus Parallelplatten oder Kreisrohren (verschwindender Dicke) gebildeten Wellenleiter, die ein *offenes* Ende haben. Wesentlich ist dabei, daß die Randbedingung nur auf einem Teil einer Koordinatenfläche vorgegeben ist, auf dem komplementären Teil dieser Fläche dagegen eine Stetigkeitsforderung. Das in Rede stehende, von Schwinger sowie Copson (1946) entwickelte Verfahren besteht nun darin, mit Hilfe einer Integraltransformation geeignete neue Feldgrößen einzuführen, für die die Rand- und Stetigkeitsbedingungen Funktionalgleichungen ergeben, die durch die Methode von Wiener und Hopf gelöst werden können[1]. (Man kann dies Verfahren auch als eine Methode zur Auflösung der Integralgleichung für den Flächenstrom auf den offenen Wellenleitern auffassen.)

---

[1] Eine zusammenfassende Darstellung der Methode sowie eine große Zahl durchgerechneter Beispiele findet man in der Monographie von B. Noble: Methods based on the Wiener-Hopf-Technique for the Solution of Partial Differential Equations. London-New York-Paris-Los Angeles: Pergamon Press 1958.

In Teil A werden die Grundlagen und allgemeinen Methoden der Beugungstheorie unter möglichst einheitlichen Gesichtspunkten zusammengestellt[1]. Teil B greift aus der großen Zahl der in der Literatur behandelten Beugungsprobleme einige wenige einfache aber *typische* Fälle heraus. Es sind dies die Beugung an der Halbebene, am Spalt, an der Kreisscheibe, am Kreiszylinder und an der Kugel[2].

A. Grundlagen und allgemeine Methoden.

I. Grundlagen.

a) Maxwellsche Gleichungen, Grenzbedingungen und Bezeichnungen.

2. Maxwellsche Gleichungen und Randwerte. Der natürliche Ausgangspunkt für unsere Betrachtungen sind die Maxwellschen elektrodynamischen Feldgleichungen

$$\left.\begin{aligned} \operatorname{rot}\mathfrak{E} + \dot{\mathfrak{B}} &= 0, \qquad \operatorname{div}\mathfrak{B} = 0\,, \\ \operatorname{rot}\mathfrak{H} - \dot{\mathfrak{D}} &= \mathfrak{j}, \qquad \operatorname{div}\mathfrak{D} = \varrho \end{aligned}\right\} \tag{2.1}$$

mit der bekannten Bedeutung der Feldvektoren $\mathfrak{E}, \mathfrak{B}$; $\mathfrak{H}, \mathfrak{D}$ und der Strom-Ladungsbeziehung (Kontinuitätsgleichung)

$$\dot{\varrho} + \operatorname{div}\mathfrak{j} = 0\,. \tag{2.2}$$

Setzt man, wie in der Optik üblich, *monochromatische* Wellenfelder d.h. *rein periodische* Zeitabhängigkeit mit dem im folgenden fortbleibenden Zeitfaktor $\exp(-i\omega t)$ voraus, so folgt aus (2.1) mit $\mathfrak{D} = \varepsilon\mathfrak{E}$, $\mathfrak{B} = \mu\mathfrak{H}$, $\mathfrak{j} = \sigma\mathfrak{E}$

$$\operatorname{rot}\mathfrak{E} = i\,\omega\,\mu\,\mathfrak{H}, \qquad \operatorname{rot}\mathfrak{H} = -\,i\,\omega\,\varepsilon\,\mathfrak{E} + \mathfrak{j}\,. \tag{2.1a}$$

Die beiden Divergenzbedingungen von (2.1) sind dann bei Beachtung von Gl. (2.2) von selbst erfüllt.

Es werde ferner vorausgesetzt, daß in ein den ganzen Feldraum erfüllendes Medium von *konstanter* skalarer Permeabilität μ_0 und Dielektrizitätskonstante ε_0 beliebig gestaltete „*ideale*" (elektrische) *Leiter* ($\sigma \to \infty$) eingebettet seien. Gebiete von idealer Leitfähigkeit (im folgenden beugende Körper genannt), sind im Innern *feldfrei*, andernfalls würde $\mathfrak{j} \to \infty$ streben (wir können hier auch von „*idealer Reflexion*" sprechen). Auf ihrer Oberfläche (S) steht die elektrische Feldstärke senkrecht; daher haben wir die Randbedingung

$$[\mathfrak{n}\,\mathfrak{E}] = 0 \quad \text{auf } (S), \tag{2.3}$$

wobei $\mathfrak{n}$ die (äußere) Normale der Oberfläche sein möge.

[1] Frühere zusammenfassende Darstellungen: H. Batman: Elektrical and Optical Wave Motion, Cambridge 1915; P. Epstein: Enzyklopädie der mathematischen Wissenschaften, Bd. V, 3 Art. 24, Leipzig 1919; A. Sommerfeld, in Ph. Frank u. R. v. Mises: Die Differential- und Integralgleichungen der Mechanik und Physik, Bd. 2, 1. u. 2. Aufl. Kap. 13 u. 20, Braunschweig 1927 u. 1934; Vorlesungen über theoretische Physik, Bd. 4, Wiesbaden 1950; G. Wolfsohn: Handbuch der Physik, Bd. XX, Kap. 7, Berlin 1928; J.A. Stratton: Electromagnetic Theory, New York 1941; B.B. Baker u. E.T. Copson: l. c.; G. Toraldo di Francia: Electromagnetic Waves, New York 1955; W. Franz: Theorie der Beugung elektromagnetischer Wellen, Berlin-Göttingen-Heidelberg: Springer 1957; M. Born u. E. Wolf: Principles of Optics. London-New York-Paris-Los Angeles: Pergamon Press 1959; R.W.P. King u. T.T. Wu: The Scattering and Diffraction of Waves, Cambridge, Mass., 1959.

[2] Ein sehr umfangreicher Nachweis der in der neueren Literatur behandelten Beugungsprobleme bei C. J. Bouwkamp: Progr. Phys. **17**, 35—100 (1954); W. Franz, l. c. Zur vollständigen Übersicht vergleiche man die einschlägigen Kurzreferate in den Mathematical Reviews (seit 1940).

Ideale Leiter können außer durch $\sigma\to\infty$ unter Umständen auch durch $\varepsilon\to\infty$, $\mu\to 0$ charakterisiert werden. Gelegentlich werden wir rein fiktiv auch Körper von der entgegengesetzten Eigenschaft $\mu\to\infty$, $\varepsilon\to 0$ annehmen *(ideale „magnetische“ Leiter)* und für ihre Oberfläche (L) die *Randbedingung* (s. Fig. 1):

$$[\mathfrak{n}\,\mathfrak{H}] = 0 \quad \text{auf } (L). \tag{2.3a}$$

Während metallische Körper für nicht zu hohe Frequenzen idealer elektrischer Leitfähigkeit sehr nahe kommen, gibt es für ideale magnetische Leiter bisher keine physikalische Realisierung (s. jedoch Ziff. 26).

Es erweist sich bei den Überlegungen dieses allgemeinen Teils als zweckmäßig, alle Längen in Vielfachen der zur Kreisfrequenz ω gehörigen Wellenlänge λ zu messen, die durch

$$k = \omega\sqrt{\varepsilon_0\mu_0} = \frac{2\pi}{\lambda} \tag{2.4}$$

definiert ist *(k = Wellenzahl)*; $(\varepsilon_0\mu_0)^{-\frac{1}{2}}$ ist die Ausbreitungsgeschwindigkeit in dem betrachteten Medium. Wir beseitigen demnach unnötige Faktoren, indem wir die Transformation $k\,\mathfrak{r}\to\mathfrak{r}$ ($\mathfrak{r}$ = Ortsvektor) benutzen. Ferner soll künftig unter $\mathfrak{H}$ die mit dem *„Wellenwiderstand“* $\sqrt{\mu_0/\varepsilon_0}$ multiplizierte magnetische Feldstärke verstanden werden: $\sqrt{\mu_0/\varepsilon_0}\,\mathfrak{H}\to\mathfrak{H}$. $\mathfrak{E}$ und $\mathfrak{H}$ sind dann *dimensionsgleich* und Gl. (2.1a) nimmt ihre einfachste Gestalt an $\left(\frac{1}{\omega\varepsilon_0}\,\mathfrak{j}\to\mathfrak{j}\right)$:

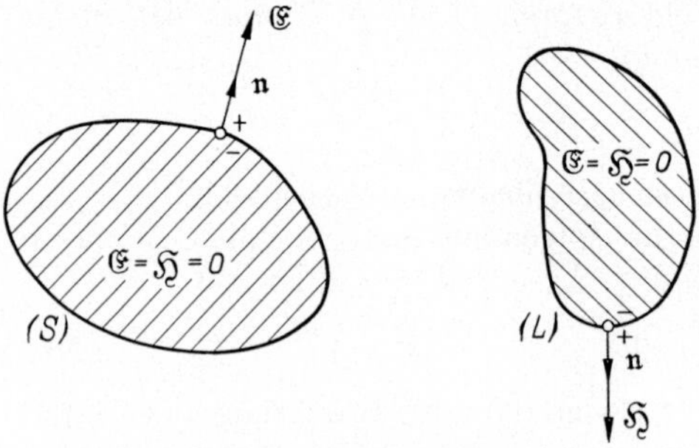

Fig. 1. Idealer *elektrischer* (S) und idealer *„magnetischer“* Leiter (L) im elektromagnetischen Feld.

$$\left.\begin{aligned} \operatorname{rot}\mathfrak{E} &= i\,\mathfrak{H},\\ \operatorname{rot}\mathfrak{H} &= -\,i\,\mathfrak{E} + \mathfrak{j}. \end{aligned}\right\} \tag{2.1b}$$

Bezüglich der elektrischen Stromdichte $\mathfrak{j}$ bemerken wir, daß sie als vorgegeben zu betrachten ist und die Rolle der Strahlungsquelle spielt, d.h. der Quelle des zeitlichen Mittelwerts des Poyntingschen Vektors $[\operatorname{div}\overline{\mathfrak{S}} = -\,\frac{1}{2}\operatorname{Re}(\mathfrak{j}\,\mathfrak{E}^*)$; vgl. Ziff. 16]. Die Ladungsdichte ist aus der Kontinuitätsgleichung $\operatorname{div}\mathfrak{j} - i\varrho = 0$ zu entnehmen. In der Beugungstheorie werden als Quellen meistens nur im Endlichen oder Unendlichen vorgegebene Punktsingularitäten (Kugelwellen oder ebene Wellen) betrachtet. Wir wollen daher durchweg $\mathfrak{j} = 0$ voraussetzen (wenn nichts anderes vereinbart wird), müssen dabei aber die (Energie liefernden) Feldsingularitäten im Auge behalten.

3. Sprungwerte. Im folgenden werden wir häufig davon Gebrauch machen, daß sich aus den längs einer Fläche (Normale $\mathfrak{n}$) gegebenen *Tangentialkomponenten* der Feldvektoren die zugehörigen *Normalkomponenten* unmittelbar durch die Maxwellschen Gleichungen berechnen lassen. Aus

$$[\mathfrak{n}\,\mathfrak{E}] = \mathfrak{L}, \qquad [\mathfrak{n}\,\mathfrak{H}] = \mathfrak{J} \tag{3.1}$$

(wobei $\mathfrak{L}$ und $\mathfrak{J}$ beliebige stetige Vektoren *in* der Fläche seien, d.h. sie sollen jeweils in der Tangentialebene im betrachteten Flächenpunkt liegen und sind nur in den Punkten der Fläche definiert) folgt nämlich mit Hilfe von (2.1b)

$$(\mathfrak{n}\,\mathfrak{E}) = i\,(\mathfrak{n}\,[\nabla\,\mathfrak{H}]) = -\,i\,(\nabla[\mathfrak{n}\,\mathfrak{H}]) = -\,i\,\widehat{\operatorname{div}}\,\mathfrak{J}, \tag{3.2a}$$

da $[\nabla \mathfrak{n}] = 0$ (falls $\mathfrak{n}$ stetig ist, d.h. also die Fläche *keine* Knicke bzw. Kanten hat). Entsprechend folgt

$$(\mathfrak{n}\,\mathfrak{H}) = i\,\widehat{\mathrm{div}}\,\mathfrak{L}. \tag{3.2b}$$

Die Bildung der „*Divergenz*“ $\widehat{\mathrm{div}}$ ist hierbei als Operation *in* der Fläche aufzufassen, bei der nur in der Fläche gelegene Nachbarpunkte des betrachteten Flächenpunktes mit der Normale $\mathfrak{n}$ ins Spiel kommen (s. weiter unten).

In ähnlicher Weise kann man Flächen betrachten, auf denen sich, wenn man durch sie hindurchtritt, die Feldvektoren *sprunghaft* ändern. Unterscheidet man eine *positive* und eine *negative* Seite der Fläche (positiv sei diejenige, von der die Normale *wegweist*, s. Fig. 2), so ist $\mathfrak{E}_+ - \mathfrak{E}_-$ der „*Sprung*“ der elektrischen Feldstärke (entsprechend für $\mathfrak{H}$). Sei nunmehr der *Sprung* der Tangentialkomponenten

$$[\mathfrak{n}, \mathfrak{E}_+ - \mathfrak{E}_-] = \mathfrak{L}, \qquad [\mathfrak{n}, \mathfrak{H}_+ - \mathfrak{H}_-] = \mathfrak{J} \tag{3.3}$$

gegeben, so folgt wieder mit Hilfe von (2.1b) der *Sprung der Normalkomponenten*:

$$\left.\begin{aligned} (\mathfrak{n}, \mathfrak{E}_+ - \mathfrak{E}_-) &= -i\,\widehat{\mathrm{div}}\,\mathfrak{J}, \\ (\mathfrak{n}, \mathfrak{H}_+ - \mathfrak{H}_-) &= i\,\widehat{\mathrm{div}}\,\mathfrak{L}. \end{aligned}\right\} \tag{3.3a}$$

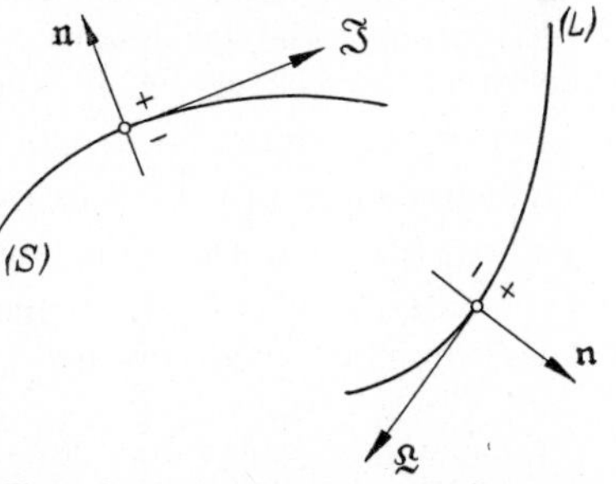

Fig. 2. Durch unendlich dünne *elektrische* und „*magnetische*“ Leiter gebildete Sprungflächen (S) und (L).

Insbesondere erleidet die Tangentialkomponente von $\mathfrak{H}$ beim Hindurchtreten durch die Oberfläche eines idealen Leiters den Sprung $[\mathfrak{n}\,\mathfrak{H}]_+ = \mathfrak{J}$ (da sein Inneres feldfrei ist, vgl. Fig. 1); $\mathfrak{J}$ ist nach den Maxwellschen Gln. (2.1b) der *elektrische Oberflächenstrom*, da $[\mathfrak{n}\,\mathfrak{H}]$ der zum *Flächenwirbel* entartete Wirbel von $\mathfrak{H}$ ist. Die Tangentialkomponente von $\mathfrak{E}$ ist gemäß (2.3) stetig und damit auch die Normalkomponente von $\mathfrak{H}$. Andererseits erleidet die Normalkomponente von $\mathfrak{E}$ nach (3.3a) den Sprung $(\mathfrak{n}\,\mathfrak{E})_+ = -i\,\widehat{\mathrm{div}}\,\mathfrak{J}$; dies ist die *Oberflächenladung* η des Leiters, die also mit $\mathfrak{J}$ durch die *Kontinuitätsgleichung* $\widehat{\mathrm{div}}\,\mathfrak{J} - i\eta = 0$ verbunden ist. Entsprechend fließt auf der Oberfläche des magnetischen Leiters der „*magnetische Flächenstrom*“ $\mathfrak{L} = [\mathfrak{n}\,\mathfrak{E}]_+$, und es ist dort die „*magnetische Flächenladung*“ $(\mathfrak{n}\,\mathfrak{H})_+ = i\,\widehat{\mathrm{div}}\,\mathfrak{L}$ vorhanden[1]. Schrumpfen die körperlichen Gebilde der Fig. 1 zu den flächenhaften Gebilden von Fig. 2 zusammen, so entstehen „*Schirme*“ (S) bzw. (L), auf denen die Flächenströme $[\mathfrak{n}, \mathfrak{H}_+ - \mathfrak{H}_-] = \mathfrak{J}$ bzw. $[\mathfrak{n}, \mathfrak{E}_+ - \mathfrak{E}_-] = \mathfrak{L}$ fließen. Diese Schirme sind also als *berandete* Flächenstücke aufzufassen, zu deren *beiden* Seiten die Randbedingung $[\mathfrak{n}\,\mathfrak{E}] = 0$ bzw. $[\mathfrak{n}\,\mathfrak{H}] = 0$ zu erfüllen ist. Schirme (S) können durch dünne Metallfolien (deren Dicke klein gegen die Wellenlänge ist) realisiert werden. Andererseits besitzen die *Löcher* in *ebenen* Metallfolien (S) in gewissem Sinne die Eigenschaft der Schirme (L) (s. Ziff. 26; die Bezeichnung S bzw. L soll auf *Schirm* bzw. *Loch* hinweisen)[2].

[1] Die differentialgeometrischen und topologischen Eigenschaften solcher Flächenströme werden in der Monographie von Cl. Müller: Grundprobleme der mathematischen Theorie elektromagnetischer Schwingungen, Berlin 1957, ausführlich behandelt.

[2] Zur phänomenologischen Erfassung einer selektiven *Absorption* wird in letzter Zeit häufig eine sog. *Impedanz-Randbedingung* zugrunde gelegt (d.h. eine homogene lineare Beziehung zwischen den Tangentialkomponenten von $\mathfrak{E}$ und $\mathfrak{H}$ mit einer komplexen frequenzabhängigen Konstanten). Da diese Konzeption auch für unendlich dünne Schirme sinnvoll ist, ergibt sich von hier aus die Möglichkeit, auch den sog. „schwarzen Schirm“ — den die ältere Theorie der Beugung durch ein hypothetisches Sprungwertproblem zu beschreiben suchte, vgl. Ziff. 29 und 30 — durch ein physikalisch sinnvolles Randwertproblem zu erfassen. Zur Impedanz-Randbedingung vgl. man G.A. Grunberg: Phys. Rev. **63**, 185 (1943); J. Bazer u. S.N. Karp: N.Y. Univ. Res. Rep. No. EM-46 (1952); B. Friedman u. W.E. Williams: N.Y. Univ. Res. Rep. No. EM-99 (1954); S.N. Karp u. F. Karal: N.Y. Univ. Res. Rep. No. EM-116 (1958); No. EM-124 (1959); No. EM-146 (1960).

Wir bemerken noch, daß eine sprunghafte Änderung der Tangentialkomponenten von $\mathfrak{E}$ bzw. $\mathfrak{H}$ längs einer Fläche auch mit flächenhaft verteilter *Magnetisierung* $\mathfrak{m}$ bzw. *elektrischer Polarisation* $\mathfrak{p}$, in Zusammenhang gebracht werden kann:

$$[\mathfrak{n}, \mathfrak{E}_+ - \mathfrak{E}_-] = i\,\mathfrak{m}, \qquad [\mathfrak{n}, \mathfrak{H}_+ - \mathfrak{H}_-] = -i\,\mathfrak{p}. \tag{3.3b}$$

Bezüglich unserer Bezeichnung bemerken wir folgendes: Den Ortsvektor des *Aufpunktes* bezeichnen wir durchgehend mit $\mathfrak{r}$, denjenigen des *Integrationspunktes* mit $\mathfrak{r}'$. Ein Ortsvektor, der den Punkt einer *Fläche* mit der Normalen $\mathfrak{n}$ beschreibt, sei durch $\hat{\mathfrak{r}}$ charakterisiert (entsprechend sei $\hat{\mathfrak{r}}'$ der Ortsvektor eines Flächenpunktes mit der Normalen $\mathfrak{n}'$); Volumen- bzw. Flächenelement sollen mit $d\mathfrak{r}$ bzw. $d\hat{\mathfrak{r}}$ bezeichnet werden (gelegentlich auch mit $d\tau$ bzw. $d\sigma$, wenn keine Integrationsvariablen geschrieben werden). Ferner sei die Projektion eines beliebigen Feldvektors $\mathfrak{A}$ in die Tangentialebene einer Fläche im Punkte $\hat{\mathfrak{r}}$ durch $\hat{\mathfrak{A}}$ bezeichnet; $(\mathfrak{n}\,\hat{\mathfrak{A}}) = 0$. Insbesondere soll neben dem dreidimensionalen symbolischen Vektor ∇ (Nabla) auch der zweidimensionale Operator $\hat{\nabla}$ verwendet werden: $(\mathfrak{n}\,\hat{\nabla}) = 0$. Demgemäß werden wir alle mit $\hat{\nabla}$ gebildeten zweidimensionalen Differentiationsprozesse mit einem Dach ($\hat{}$) versehen z.B. $(\hat{\nabla}\,\mathfrak{J}) = \widehat{\mathrm{div}}\,\mathfrak{J}$. Schließlich schreiben wir abkürzend

$$\left\{\frac{\partial}{\partial n}\,\varphi(\mathfrak{r})\right\}_{\mathfrak{r}=\hat{\mathfrak{r}}} = \frac{\partial\varphi(\hat{\mathfrak{r}})}{\partial n}.$$

b) Das ebene (zylindrische) Beugungsproblem und die Separation der Maxwellschen Gleichungen.

4. Das ebene (zylindrische) Problem. Sind die beugenden Körper *Zylinder*, die durch Parallelen zur y-Achse eines kartesischen Koordinatensystems erzeugt werden und werden nur Strahlungsquellen betrachtet, deren Bestimmungsstücke nicht von y abhängen (Zylinderwellen oder ebene Wellen, deren Ausbreitungsrichtung parallel zur xz-Ebene ist), so sind alle Ebenen senkrecht zur y-Achse physikalisch gleichwertig und die Feldvektoren demnach von y unabhängig $(\partial/\partial y = 0)$. Die Maxwellschen Gleichungen zerfallen dann in *zwei unabhängige* Systeme für die Komponenten $\mathfrak{E}_y$, $\mathfrak{H}_x$, $\mathfrak{H}_z$ einerseits und $\mathfrak{H}_y$, $\mathfrak{E}_x$, $\mathfrak{E}_z$ andererseits. Die hinsichtlich der *elektrischen* Feldstärke parallel oder senkrecht zur y-Achse *polarisierten* Komponenten der Strahlung sind also unabhängig voneinander und können getrennt behandelt werden. Wir unterscheiden diese beiden Polarisationsfälle als *p*- und *s-Fall.*

Für den p- bzw. s-Fall erhalten wir aus (2.1b) (in kartesischen Koordinaten)

$$(p\text{-Fall}) \qquad \mathfrak{E} = (0, v, 0), \qquad \mathfrak{H} = i\left(\frac{\partial v}{\partial z}, 0, -\frac{\partial v}{\partial x}\right) \tag{4.1p}$$

bzw.

$$(s\text{-Fall}) \qquad \mathfrak{H} = (0, v, 0), \qquad \mathfrak{E} = -i\left(\frac{\partial v}{\partial z}, 0, -\frac{\partial v}{\partial x}\right), \tag{4.1s}$$

wobei v in beiden Fällen der *Wellengleichung*

$$\Delta v + v = 0 \qquad \left(\Delta = \frac{\partial^2}{\partial x^2} + \frac{\partial^2}{\partial z^2}\right) \tag{4.2}$$

zu genügen hat.

Die Randbedingung (2.3) überträgt sich auf v in der Form

$$v = 0 \ \textit{auf}\ (S) \quad \text{im } p\text{-Fall} \tag{4.3p}$$

bzw.

$$\frac{\partial v}{\partial n} = 0 \text{ auf } (S) \quad \text{im } s\text{-Fall}, \tag{4.3 s}$$

letzteres wegen (4.1 s); dabei bedeutet (S) die Schnittkurve der beugenden Zylinder mit der xz-Ebene und $\mathfrak{n}$ ihre nach außen gerichtete Normale. Die Randbedingung (2.3a) lautet jetzt: $\partial v/\partial n = 0$ bzw. $v = 0$, sie bedeutet also hier einfach eine *Vertauschung von p- und s-Fall.*

Das *ebene* elektromagnetische Beugungsproblem kann somit auf die *skalare* akustische Beugungstheorie zurückgeführt werden[1]. Die Randwerte $v = 0$ bzw. $\partial v/\partial n = 0$ entsprechen hierbei den Randbedingungen für die Oberfläche eines „*schallweichen*“ bzw. „*schallharten*“ Körpers. Wir werden die skalare Theorie gelegentlich auch für *räumliche* Beugungsprobleme betrachten, d. h. Lösungen der Differentialgleichung

$$\varDelta v + v = 0 \qquad \left(\varDelta = \frac{\partial^2}{\partial x^2} + \frac{\partial^2}{\partial y^2} + \frac{\partial^2}{\partial z^2}\right) \tag{4.4}$$

unter der Randbedingung (4.3 p) bzw. (4.3 s), wobei (S) nun die Oberfläche eines beliebigen Körpers sein kann. Der Kürze halber soll auch dann noch von p- bzw. s-Fall gesprochen werden, obwohl sich die beiden Fälle jetzt natürlich nicht mehr durch ihre Polarisationsrichtung unterscheiden, sondern durch die Randbedingung für die Wellenfunktion v (Geschwindigkeitspotential).

Die Möglichkeit, das ebene elektromagnetische Beugungsproblem bei beliebiger Polarisation auf *zwei* voneinander *unabhängige*, der Wellengleichung genügende *skalare* Funktionen zurückzuführen, bedeutet eine wesentliche *Vereinfachung* der analytischen Situation, die wir als *Separation der Maxwellschen Gleichungen* (Entkopplung der Komponenten, auch hinsichtlich der Randbedingung) bezeichnen wollen.

5. Über allgemeine Separation. Es soll nun untersucht werden, ob sich die Maxwellschen Gleichungen, auch bei allgemeineren (nicht zylindrischen) Körperformen separieren lassen.

Zunächst läßt sich aus (2.1b) $\mathfrak{H}$ oder $\mathfrak{E}$ eliminieren, was auf die „*Vektorwellengleichung*“

$$\operatorname{rot}\operatorname{rot}\mathfrak{E} - \mathfrak{E} = 0\,, \qquad \operatorname{rot}\operatorname{rot}\mathfrak{H} - \mathfrak{H} = 0 \tag{5.1}$$

führt. Diese ist zufolge der Identität rot rot = grad div $-\varDelta$, wobei $\varDelta$ der Laplace-Operator (4.4) ist, äquivalent mit der Gleichung

$$\varDelta\mathfrak{E} + \mathfrak{E} = 0, \qquad \varDelta\mathfrak{H} + \mathfrak{H} = 0 \tag{5.2}$$

und der *Nebenbedingung*

$$\operatorname{div}\mathfrak{E} = 0, \qquad \operatorname{div}\mathfrak{H} = 0. \tag{5.2a}$$

Es genügt also, $\mathfrak{E}$ oder $\mathfrak{H}$ als Lösung von (5.1) bzw. (5.2) und (5.2a) unter der Randbedingung (2.3) oder (2.3a) zu bestimmen und dann das Feld durch $\mathfrak{H} = -i \operatorname{rot}\mathfrak{E}$ oder $\mathfrak{E} = i \operatorname{rot}\mathfrak{H}$ zu ergänzen. Somit läßt sich also jedes elektromagnetische Beugungsproblem auf *drei* skalare Funktionen (die drei *kartesischen* Komponenten von $\mathfrak{E}$ oder $\mathfrak{H}$) zurückführen, die der Wellengleichung (4.4) genügen. Diese sind jedoch *nicht* voneinander unabhängig, sondern im allgemeinen über (5.2a) und die Randbedingung *gekoppelt*.

Die Kopplung durch die Randbedingung läßt sich vermeiden, wenn man ein System von Koordinatenflächen so einführt, daß die Oberfläche (S) des beugenden Körpers selbst zu einer dieser Flächen wird. Die drei Scharen von Koordinaten-

[1] Vgl. Bd. XI dieses Handbuches.

flächen seien durch die Parameter ξ_i ($i=1, 2, 3$) bestimmt, die Oberfläche (S) sei durch $\xi_1=\text{const}=\xi_0$ gegeben. Der Ortsvektor $\mathfrak{r}$ ist dann Funktion der Flächenparameter: $\mathfrak{r}=\mathfrak{r}(\xi_1, \xi_2, \xi_3)$; die ξ_i seien insbesondere *orthogonale* Koordinaten:

$$\left(\frac{\partial \mathfrak{r}}{\partial \xi_i} \frac{\partial \mathfrak{r}}{\partial \xi_j}\right) = s_i^2 \delta_{ij}. \tag{5.3}$$

Es spannen also die Vektoren $\partial\mathfrak{r}/\partial\xi_i$ in jedem Punkte des Raumes ein orthogonales Dreibein auf und die Komponenten von $\mathfrak{E}$ in Richtung dieser Vektoren sollen mit $\mathfrak{E}_i$ bezeichnet werden:

$$\mathfrak{E}_i = \frac{1}{s_i}\left(\frac{\partial \mathfrak{r}}{\partial \xi_i}, \mathfrak{E}\right),$$

entsprechend

$$\mathfrak{H}_i = \frac{1}{s_i}\left(\frac{\partial \mathfrak{r}}{\partial \xi_i}, \mathfrak{H}\right). \tag{5.4}$$

Die Randbedingung (2.3) lautet jetzt einfach

$$\mathfrak{E}_2 = \mathfrak{E}_3 = 0 \quad \text{für} \quad \xi_1 = \xi_0. \tag{5.5}$$

Schreibt man nun aber die Maxwellschen Gln. (2.1b) für die Komponenten $\mathfrak{E}_i$ und $\mathfrak{H}_i$ in den Koordinaten ξ_i an, so ist es im allgemeinen *nicht* möglich, durch Eliminierung der anderen Komponenten Differentialgleichungen für jeweils nur *eine* Komponente $\mathfrak{E}_i$ oder $\mathfrak{H}_i$ aufzustellen. Die Aufhebung der Kopplung über die Randbedingung bringt also eine unauflösliche Kopplung über die Differentialgleichungen mit sich.

Bromwich[1] hat jedoch gezeigt, daß bei Einschränkung der zuzulassenden Koordinatensysteme durch die Bedingungen

$$s_1 = 1, \qquad \frac{\partial}{\partial \xi_1}\left(\frac{s_2}{s_3}\right) = 0 \tag{5.6}$$

zwei „entkoppelte" skalare Potentiale Π_1 und Π_2 eingeführt werden können, die der verallgemeinerten Wellengleichung

$$\left(\varDelta - \frac{1}{s_2 s_3}\frac{\partial(s_2 s_3)}{\partial \xi_1}\frac{\partial}{\partial \xi_1} + 1\right)\Pi_{1,2} = 0 \tag{5.7}$$

genügen und aus denen sich die Lösung der Maxwellschen Gln. (2.1b) in der Form

$$\left.\begin{aligned}
\mathfrak{H}_1^{(1)} &= 0, & \mathfrak{E}_1^{(1)} &= \frac{1}{s_2 s_3}\left[\frac{\partial}{\partial \xi_2}\left(\frac{s_3}{s_2}\frac{\partial \Pi_1}{\partial \xi_2}\right) + \frac{\partial}{\partial \xi_3}\left(\frac{s_2}{s_3}\frac{\partial \Pi_1}{\partial \xi_3}\right)\right],\\
\mathfrak{H}_2^{(1)} &= -\frac{i}{s_3}\frac{\partial \Pi_1}{\partial \xi_3}, & \mathfrak{E}_2^{(1)} &= -\frac{1}{s_2}\frac{\partial^2 \Pi_1}{\partial \xi_1 \partial \xi_2},\\
\mathfrak{H}_3^{(1)} &= \frac{i}{s_2}\frac{\partial \Pi_1}{\partial \xi_2}, & \mathfrak{E}_3^{(1)} &= -\frac{1}{s_3}\frac{\partial^2 \Pi_1}{\partial \xi_1 \partial \xi_3},
\end{aligned}\right\} \tag{5.8a}$$

$$\left.\begin{aligned}
\mathfrak{H}_1^{(2)} &= -\frac{1}{s_2 s_3}\left[\frac{\partial}{\partial \xi_3}\left(\frac{s_2}{s_3}\frac{\partial \Pi_2}{\partial \xi_3}\right) + \frac{\partial}{\partial \xi_2}\left(\frac{s_3}{s_2}\frac{\partial \Pi_2}{\partial \xi_2}\right)\right], & \mathfrak{E}_1^{(2)} &= 0,\\
\mathfrak{H}_2^{(2)} &= \frac{1}{s_2}\frac{\partial^2 \Pi_2}{\partial \xi_1 \partial \xi_2}, & \mathfrak{E}_2^{(2)} &= \frac{i}{s_3}\frac{\partial \Pi_2}{\partial \xi_3},\\
\mathfrak{H}_3^{(2)} &= \frac{1}{s_3}\frac{\partial^2 \Pi_2}{\partial \xi_1 \partial \xi_2}, & \mathfrak{E}_3^{(2)} &= -\frac{i}{s_2}\frac{\partial \Pi_2}{\partial \xi_2}
\end{aligned}\right\} \tag{5.8b}$$

[1] T. J. I'A Bromwich: Phil. Mag. **38**, 143 (1919). Siehe auch R. L. Lamont: Wave Guides, S. 17ff. London 1942.

ableiten läßt, wobei das vollständige Feld durch die Überlagerung

$$\mathfrak{E} = \mathfrak{E}^{(1)} + \mathfrak{E}^{(2)}, \qquad \mathfrak{H} = \mathfrak{H}^{(1)} + \mathfrak{H}^{(2)} \tag{5.9}$$

gewonnen wird.

Die durch (5.6) bewirkte Einschränkung der Koordinatensysteme, in denen die Bromwichsche Separation der Maxwellschen Gleichungen möglich ist, hat CL. MÜLLER[1] differentialgeometrisch untersucht. Es ergibt sich, daß die Koordinatenflächen $\xi_1 = \text{const}$ entweder *Kugeln* oder planparallele *Ebenen* sind, die zugelassenen Koordinaten sind also entweder Kugel- oder allgemeine Zylinderkoordinaten. Für Zylinderprobleme haben wir die Separation schon in Ziff. 4 durchgeführt. Eine ähnlich einfache Behandlung wie dort ist also sonst nur noch für die Beugung an der Kugel möglich. Diese Methode hat erstmals G. MIE[2] für die Behandlung der Farberscheinungen an kolloidalen Lösungen (mikroskopisch kleine kugelförmige Teilchen) angewandt. Die hier dem Verfahren von BROMWICH entsprechenden Potentiale Π_1 und Π_2 sind von DEBYE eingeführt worden (*Debyesche Potentiale*, s. weiter unten).

Schon beim Ellipsoid ist die Separation der Maxwellschen Gleichungen im allgemeinen *nicht* mehr vollständig durchführbar, wie der Versuch von F. MÖGLICH[3] zeigt (vgl. auch Ziff. 153).

Auch die Lösung der Wellengleichung bereitet Schwierigkeiten bezüglich der Erfüllung der Randbedingung. Diese lassen sich überwinden, wenn die *Wellengleichung* ihrerseits in den Koordinaten ξ_i *separierbar* ist, d.h., falls durch den Ansatz $v(\xi_1, \xi_2, \xi_3) = \Phi_1(\xi_1)\, \Phi_2(\xi_2)\, \Phi_3(\xi_3)$ die in den ξ_i geschriebene Wellengleichung in drei *gewöhnliche* Differentialgleichungen für die $\Phi_i(\xi_i)$ aufgespalten werden kann. Dies ist bekanntlich nur für Flächen zweiten Grades der Fall, bzw. für deren Entartungen (z.B. Kreisscheibe).

6. Die Debyeschen Potentiale. Wir legen ein System von Kugelkoordinaten r, ϑ, φ zugrunde und betrachten ein spezielles Feld, bei dem die radiale Komponente $\mathfrak{H}_r$ des Magnetfeldes identisch null ist. Dann gilt nach (2.1 b) $\text{rot}_r\, \mathfrak{E} = 0$, d.h. die tangentialen, in den Kugelflächen liegenden Komponenten von $\mathfrak{E}$ sind aus einem Potential ableitbar:

$$\mathfrak{E}_{\text{tang}} = -\,\text{grad}_{\text{tang}}\, U. \tag{6.1}$$

Führen wir nun den Vektor *(Hertzscher Vektor)*

$$\mathfrak{Z} = \mathfrak{E} + \text{grad}\, U \tag{6.2}$$

ein, so beschreibt

$$\mathfrak{E} = \text{rot}\,\text{rot}\,\mathfrak{Z}, \qquad \mathfrak{H} = -\,i\,\text{rot}\,\mathfrak{Z} \tag{6.3}$$

bei Beachtung von Gl. (5.1) das vorgegebene Feld. $\mathfrak{Z}$ ist wegen (6.1) radial gerichtet. Wir dürfen daher unter Einführung eines Skalars Π ohne Beschränkung der Allgemeinheit ansetzen

$$\mathfrak{E} = \text{rot}\,\text{rot}\,(\mathfrak{r}\Pi), \qquad \mathfrak{H} = -\,i\,\text{rot}\,(\mathfrak{r}\Pi). \tag{6.4}$$

Der Ansatz befriedigt eine der beiden Maxwellschen Gleichungen (2.1 b) identisch, die andere fordert

$$\text{rot}\,\text{rot}\,\text{rot}\,(\mathfrak{r}\Pi) = \text{rot}\,(\mathfrak{r}\Pi) \tag{6.5}$$

---

[1] CL. MÜLLER: Abh. math. Sem. Hamburg **16**, 95 (1949). Siehe auch D.E. SPENCE: J. Appl. Phys. **22**, 286 (1951); P.M. MORSE u. H. FESHBACH: Methods of Theoretical Physics. New York 1953.

[2] G. MIE: Ann. d. Phys. **25**, 377 (1908).

[3] F. MÖGLICH: Ann. d. Phys. **83**, 609 (1927).

oder, hiermit gleichbedeutend,

$$\operatorname{rot}\operatorname{rot}(\mathfrak{r}\Pi) = \mathfrak{r}\Pi + \operatorname{grad} V \tag{6.6}$$

mit willkürlichem V. Setzen wir speziell

$$V = \operatorname{div}(\mathfrak{r}\Pi) - 2\Pi, \tag{6.7}$$

so geht (6.6) in die Wellengleichung

$$\Delta\Pi + \Pi = 0 \tag{6.8}$$

über.

Dieselbe Betrachtung unter Vertauschung der Rolle von elektrischem und magnetischem Feld läßt sich für ein Feld mit verschwindender Radialkomponente $\mathfrak{E}_r$ des elektrischen Feldes durchführen. Denken wir uns schließlich ein beliebiges Feld aus zwei Feldern der betrachteten Art aufgebaut, so gelangen wir zu dem allgemein gültigen Ansatz

$$\left.\begin{aligned} \mathfrak{E} &= \operatorname{rot}\operatorname{rot}(\mathfrak{r}\Pi_1) + i\operatorname{rot}(\mathfrak{r}\Pi_2) \\ \mathfrak{H} &= -i\operatorname{rot}(\mathfrak{r}\Pi_1) + \operatorname{rot}\operatorname{rot}(\mathfrak{r}\Pi_2). \end{aligned}\right\} \tag{6.9}$$

Π_1 und Π_2 sind die *Debyeschen Potentiale* und genügen der Wellengleichung

$$\Delta\Pi_i + \Pi_i = 0 \qquad (i = 1, 2). \tag{6.10}$$

Die Debyeschen Potentiale haben in der Theorie der Beugung an der Kugel[1] und an der Kreisscheibe[2] Anwendung gefunden (vgl. Ziff. 152).

7. Hertzscher Vektor für den ebenen Schirm. Bei der Methode von BROMWICH werden die $\partial\mathfrak{r}/\partial\xi_i$ als *stetige* Vektoren behandelt. Sollen jedoch die Koordinatenflächen auch Körperoberflächen mit *Kanten* angepaßt werden, so ändern die entsprechenden $\partial\mathfrak{r}/\partial\xi_i$ an der Kante *sprunghaft* ihre Richtung. Als zusätzliche Schwierigkeit erweist sich hier die Tatsache, daß es bei beugenden Körpern mit scharfen Kanten eine *Mannigfaltigkeit* von Lösungen des Randwertproblems der Maxwellschen Gleichungen gibt, die sich im wesentlichen durch ihr *singuläres Verhalten* an der *Kante* unterscheiden. Es läßt sich jedoch zeigen, daß aus diesen Lösungen eine *eindeutig* ausgewählt werden kann, wenn man fordert, daß die Feldenergiedichte in der Umgebung der Kante räumlich integrierbar sein soll (*Meixnersche Kantenbedingung*, s. Ziff. 22).

Ohne hier näher auf die Kantenbedingung einzugehen, behandeln wir die Beugung an einem *ebenen Schirm* beliebiger Gestalt (berandetes Ebenenstück) mit Hilfe des *Hertzschen* Vektors (6.3). In diesem Falle kann der Hertzsche Vektor parallel zur Schirmebene gewählt werden und besitzt dann nur *zwei Komponenten*. Man gelangt zu dieser Darstellung, wenn man sich das Vektorpotential, mit dem der Hertzsche Vektor nach Gl. (6.3) im wesentlichen identisch ist, in bekannter Weise als Integral über die Stromverteilung ermittelt denkt (s. Ziff. 53). Dabei wird die gebeugte Welle durch den Strom im Beugungsschirm und die einfallende Welle durch einen im Unendlichen befindlichen elektrischen Dipol erzeugt, dessen Schwingungsrichtung ebenfalls parallel zum Schirm angenommen werden kann.

---

[1] P. DEBYE: Ann. Phys. (4) **30**, 57 (1909). Zur Ableitung aus einem radial gerichteten Hertzschen Vektor vgl. A. SOMMERFELD, in PH. FRANK u. R. v. MISES: Die Differential- und Integralgleichungen der Mechanik und Physik, 2. Aufl., S. 790, Braunschweig 1935; E. T. HANSON: Phys. Rev. **47**, 139 (1935); Physics **7**, 460 (1936); J. Appl. Phys. **8**, 284 (1937); A. NISBET: Proc. Roy. Soc. Lond. A **231**, 260 (1955); W. FRANZ: Theorie der Beugung elektromagnetischer Wellen, Ziff. 9, Springer: Berlin, Göttingen, Heidelberg 1957.

[2] J. MEIXNER: Z. Naturforsch. **3**a, 506 (1948).

Wir untersuchen die Randbedingung am Schirm (S). Die Schirmebene sei die xy-Ebene. Mit $\mathfrak{Z} = (\mathfrak{Z}_x, \mathfrak{Z}_y, 0)$ und der durch

$$\frac{\partial \mathfrak{Z}_x}{\partial x} + \frac{\partial \mathfrak{Z}_y}{\partial y} + \Phi = 0 \tag{7.1}$$

eingeführten Abkürzung Φ lautet dann die *Randbedingung* $\mathfrak{E}_{\text{tang}} = 0$ nach (6.3) mit Rücksicht darauf, daß $\mathfrak{Z}$ der Wellengleichung

$$\Delta \mathfrak{Z} + \mathfrak{Z} = 0 \tag{7.2}$$

genügt

$$\left.\begin{aligned} \mathfrak{E}_x &= \mathfrak{Z}_x - \frac{\partial \Phi}{\partial x} = 0\,, \\ \mathfrak{E}_y &= \mathfrak{Z}_y - \frac{\partial \Phi}{\partial y} = 0 \end{aligned}\right\} \quad \mathit{auf}\ (S)\,. \tag{7.3}$$

Elimination von $\mathfrak{Z}_x$ und $\mathfrak{Z}_y$ aus (7.1) und (7.3) liefert für Φ auf (S) die Bedingung

$$\frac{\partial^2 \Phi}{\partial x^2} + \frac{\partial^2 \Phi}{\partial y^2} + \Phi = 0 \qquad \mathit{auf}\ (S)\,. \tag{7.4}$$

Φ hat dabei die Bedeutung des skalaren Potentials; Gl. (7.1) ist die *Lorentz-Konvention*. Durch die Gln. (7.1) bis (7.4) ist die Separation der Maxwellschen Gleichungen für den ebenen Schirm gelungen; allerdings ist das Problem noch nicht eindeutig definiert, sondern es muß zu (7.4) noch eine *Randbedingung für* Φ auf dem Rande von (S) (Schirmkante) hinzutreten. Diese ergibt sich aus der Kantenbedingung (Ziff. 25 und 54).

Bei der oben behandelten Separationsmethode ist das gesuchte Feld als spezielle Lösung einer oder mehrerer Differentialgleichungen definiert, die gewissen Zusatzbedingungen (Rand-, Ausstrahlungs-, Kantenbedingung) genügen. Bei direkter Inangriffnahme des Problems haben wir zunächst die allgemeine Lösung der Differentialgleichung aufzusuchen und diese dann nachträglich den Zusatzbedingungen anzupassen. Dieser direkte Lösungsweg ist zweifellos insofern unbefriedigend, als man sich zunächst mit der großen Mannigfaltigkeit der Lösungen der Differentialgleichungen auseinanderzusetzen hat, von denen für das Beugungsproblem dann schließlich nur eine einzige in Betracht kommt. Diesen Nachteil vermeidet man ganz oder teilweise, wenn man das Beugungsproblem statt in der ursprünglichen differentiellen Fassung mit Hilfe von Integralgleichungen (vgl. Abschn. III) formuliert. Die Integralgleichungen enthalten nämlich die Zusatzbedingungen insgesamt oder teilweise bereits implicite, so daß man es entweder von vornherein nur mit einer einzigen Lösung zu tun hat oder zumindest die zunächst aufzusuchende Lösungsmannigfaltigkeit von Anfang an stark eingeschränkt ist.

Trotz dieser Nachteile ist die direkte Lösungsmethode aus verschiedenen Gründen von Bedeutung. Erstens ist die Lösung einer Differentialgleichung eine prinzipiell leichtere Aufgabe als die einer Integralgleichung. Zweitens gibt es eine ganze Reihe von speziellen Beugungsproblemen, die bisher nur auf dem direkten Wege behandelt worden sind. Drittens ist es, wenn man bis zu genauen numerischen Ergebnissen vordringen will, wichtig, Tafeln spezieller Funktionen benutzen zu können. Die bekannten speziellen Funktionen sind aber im allgemeinen als Lösungen von Differentialgleichungen definiert.

c) Das Huygenssche Prinzip und das Kirchhoffsche Integral.

Es ist eine bemerkenswerte Eigenschaft der Lösungen der Maxwellschen Gleichungen bzw. der Wellengleichung, daß sich die Werte der Feldfunktionen in irgendeinem regulären Aufpunkt $\mathfrak{r}$ als *Oberflächenintegrale* über beliebige, den

Aufpunkt einhüllende geschlossene Flächen darstellen lassen. Diese Eigenschaft ist die Grundlage für die strenge Fassung des *Huygensschen Prinzips* der Elementarwellen.

c 1) Skalare Fassung

8. Huygenssches Prinzip. Wir bilden den „*Greenschen Vektor*“

$$\mathfrak{B}(\mathfrak{r},\mathfrak{r}') = v(\mathfrak{r}')\,\mathrm{grad}'\,G(\mathfrak{r}-\mathfrak{r}') - \mathrm{grad}'\,v(\mathfrak{r}')\,G(\mathfrak{r}-\mathfrak{r}'), \tag{8.1}$$

wobei $v(\mathfrak{r})$ irgendeine reguläre Lösung der *Wellengleichung* (4.2) bzw. (4.4) bedeute. $G(\mathfrak{r}-\mathfrak{r}')$ sei die „*Greensche Funktion des unbegrenzten Raumes*“ mit der Eigenschaft

$$(\Delta + 1)\,G(\mathfrak{r}-\mathfrak{r}') = -\,\delta(\mathfrak{r}-\mathfrak{r}'), \tag{8.2}$$

wobei

$$\delta(\mathfrak{r}-\mathfrak{r}') = 0 \quad \text{für} \quad \mathfrak{r} \neq \mathfrak{r}', \qquad \int\limits_T \delta(\mathfrak{r}-\mathfrak{r}')\,d\mathfrak{r}' = \begin{cases} 1 & \textit{für } \mathfrak{r} \textit{ innerhalb } T \\ 0 & \textit{für } \mathfrak{r} \textit{ außerhalb } T, \end{cases} \tag{8.2a}$$

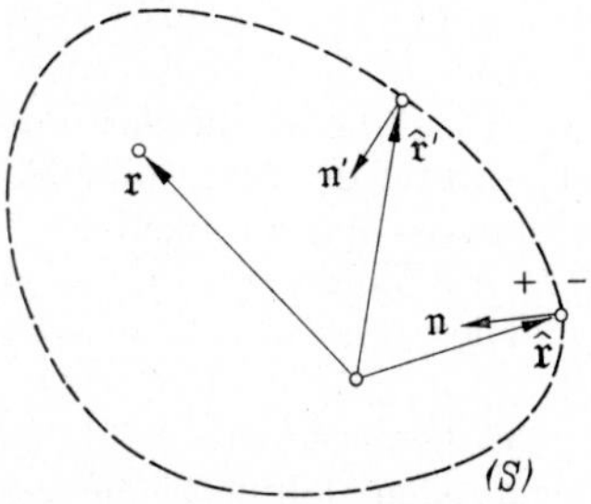

Fig. 3. Zum Huygensschen Prinzip für einen durch (S) begrenzten *endlichen* (quellenfreien) Feldraum.

für *beliebige* Raumbereiche T [$\delta(\mathfrak{r}-\mathfrak{r}')$ ist die dreidimensionale *Diracsche δ-Funktion*]. $G(\mathfrak{r}-\mathfrak{r}')$ ist *symmetrische* Funktion der Raumpunkte $\mathfrak{r}$ und $\mathfrak{r}'$, sie hängt nur von deren Abstand $|\mathfrak{r}-\mathfrak{r}'| = R$ ab. Die Stelle $\mathfrak{r} = \mathfrak{r}'$ entspricht einer „*Einheitsquelle*“ d.h. es gilt die mit (8.2a) [in Verbindung mit (8.2)] äquivalente Beziehung

$$\oint (\mathrm{grad}'\,G(\mathfrak{r}-\mathfrak{r}')\,\mathfrak{n}')\,d\hat{\mathfrak{r}}' = -1 \tag{8.2b}$$

für eine beliebige den Punkt $\mathfrak{r}$ umschließende auf $\mathfrak{r}$ zusammenschrumpfende Integrationsfläche mit der nach außen gerichteten Normale $\mathfrak{n}$.

Eine *explizite* die „*Ausstrahlungsbedingung*“ (Ziff. 17) erfüllende Form der *Greenschen Funktion* ist

$$\left.\begin{aligned} &G(\mathfrak{r}-\mathfrak{r}') = \frac{1}{4\pi}\,\frac{e^{i|\mathfrak{r}-\mathfrak{r}'|}}{|\mathfrak{r}-\mathfrak{r}'|} \\ \text{mit}\quad &|\mathfrak{r}-\mathfrak{r}'| = R = \sqrt{(x-x')^2+(y-y')^2+(z-z')^2} \end{aligned}\right\} \tag{8.3}$$

im *räumlichen Fall:* $\mathfrak{r} = (x, y, z)$ bzw.

$$\left.\begin{aligned} &G(\mathfrak{r}-\mathfrak{r}') = \frac{1}{4\pi}\int\limits_{-\infty}^{\infty} \frac{e^{i\sqrt{R^2+y^2}}}{\sqrt{R^2+y^2}}\,dy = \frac{i}{4}\,H_0^{(1)}(|\mathfrak{r}-\mathfrak{r}'|) \\ \text{mit}\quad &|\mathfrak{r}-\mathfrak{r}'| = R = \sqrt{(x-x')^2+(z-z')^2} \end{aligned}\right\} \tag{8.3a}$$

im *zylindrischen Fall:* $\mathfrak{r} = (x, z)$. Sie entspricht einer vom Punkt $\mathfrak{r}'$ ausgehenden *Kugel-* bzw. *Zylinderwelle (Punkt- bzw. Linienquelle)*. Die Divergenz des Vektors $\mathfrak{B}$ ist nach (8.1) und (8.2)

$$\mathrm{div}'\,\mathfrak{B}(\mathfrak{r},\mathfrak{r}') = v\,\Delta' G - G\,\Delta' v = -\,v(\mathfrak{r})\,\delta(\mathfrak{r}-\mathfrak{r}'); \tag{8.4}$$

integriert man daher (8.4) bezüglich $\mathfrak{r}'$ über irgendein räumliches Gebiet mit der Begrenzung (S) und der nach innen gerichteten Normalen $\mathfrak{n}$ (s. Fig. 3), so erhält man nach dem *Gaußschen Integralsatz*, falls von (S) keine Singularität *(Strahlungsquelle)* und Unstetigkeit *(beugender Körper)* von v eingeschlossen wird (alle auf den Integrationspunkt $\mathfrak{r}'$ bezüglichen Größen und Operationen sind mit einem

Strich versehen):

$$\left.\begin{matrix} v(\mathfrak{r}) \\ 0 \end{matrix}\right\} = \oint\limits_S \left\{ v(\hat{\mathfrak{r}}') \frac{\partial}{\partial n'} - \frac{\partial v(\hat{\mathfrak{r}}')}{\partial n'} \right\} G(\mathfrak{r} - \hat{\mathfrak{r}}')\, d\hat{\mathfrak{r}}'. \tag{8.5}$$

Diese Schreibweise soll bedeuten, daß das Oberflächenintegral den Wert $v(\mathfrak{r})$ oder 0 hat, je nachdem ob $\mathfrak{r}$ *innerhalb* oder *außerhalb* (S) liegt. [Um die Anwendung des Gaußschen Satzes zu ermöglichen, denke man sich die δ-Funktion in (8.4) zunächst durch eine schmale kontinuierliche Zacke ersetzt, die man nach Ausführung der Integration unendlich schmal werden läßt.]

Formel (8.5) ist ein exakter Ausdruck für das *Huygenssche Prinzip*[1]: Jedes Wellenfeld $v(\mathfrak{r})$ kann im Regularitätsgebiet durch Überlagerung von *Kugelwellen* (e^{iR}/R) mit der „*Belegungsdichte*" $-\frac{\partial v(\hat{\mathfrak{r}})}{\partial n}$ und „*Dipolwellen*" $\left(\frac{\partial}{\partial n}\frac{e^{iR}}{R}\right)$ mit der Belegungsdichte $v(\hat{\mathfrak{r}})$ erzeugt werden, die von einer den Aufpunkt $\mathfrak{r}$ *umhüllenden geschlossenen*, im übrigen aber *beliebigen* Fläche (S) ausgehen. Der Sachverhalt ist demnach komplizierter als die elementare (Fresnelsche) Fassung des Huygensschen Prinzips vermuten ließ. Außerhalb (S) löschen sich die „*Sekundärwellen*" *aus*.

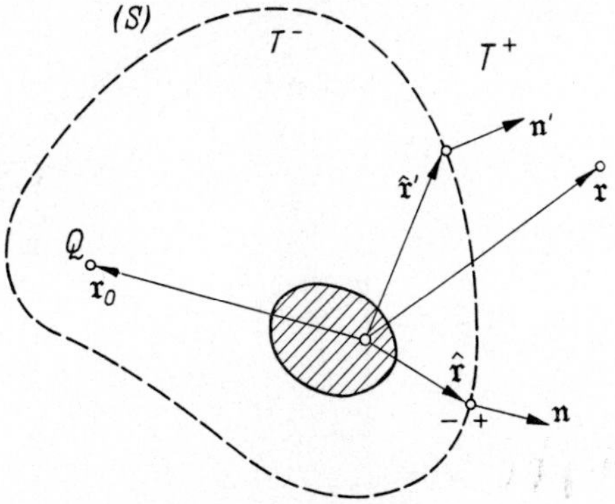

Fig. 4. Zum Huygensschen Prinzip für einen durch (S) nach innen begrenzten *unendlichen* (quellenfreien) Feldraum.

Die Wahl von (S) ist topologisch weitgehend willkürlich. (S) kann insbesondere auch in *zwei* geschlossene Flächen (S) und ($\overline{S}$) zerfallen, von denen die äußere Fläche ($\overline{S}$) die innere Fläche (S) einhüllt. (S) möge ihrerseits alle vorhandenen Strahlungsquellen und beugenden Körper umschließen. Läßt man nun ($\overline{S}$) allseitig ins Unendliche wandern (Limes einer Kugelfläche mit $r \to \infty$), so liefert ($\overline{S}$) keinen Beitrag, falls v der Ausstrahlungsbedingung genügt (vgl. Ziff. 17). In diesem Falle gilt also Gl. (8.5) mit der Abänderung, daß das Integral über (S) den Wert $v(\mathfrak{r})$ oder 0 liefert, je nachdem ob $\mathfrak{r}$ *außerhalb* oder *innerhalb* (S) liegt, wobei die Normale jetzt in das *Äußere* von (S) weist. Endlich kann auch (S) ins Unendliche reichen, wobei nur maßgebend ist, daß die Fläche (S) noch immer die vorhandenen Quellen Q und beugenden Körper von einem von solchen freien Raumteil trennt; wir wollen diesen den „*quellenfreien*" T^+ Raum nennen; die Flächennormale $\mathfrak{n}$ soll stets nach ihm hin, d.h. aus dem Raumteil T^- *mit Quellen* herausweisen (s. Fig. 4). Überschreitet man die Grenze (S) von der Seite des quellenfreien Raumteils gegen den Raumteil mit Quellen, so erleidet der Wert des Integrals (8.5) den Sprung $v(\hat{\mathfrak{r}})$, da das Integral in letzterem verschwindet; ebenso ist der Sprung der Normalableitung von (8.5) gleich $\frac{\partial v(\hat{\mathfrak{r}})}{\partial n}$.

9. Funktionaler Zusammenhang der Randwerte. Da eine reguläre Lösung $v(\mathfrak{r})$ der Wellengleichung in einem Gebiet mit der Berandung (S) im allgemeinen bereits *eindeutig* bestimmt ist, wenn auf (S) *entweder* $v(\hat{\mathfrak{r}})$ *oder* $\frac{\partial v(\hat{\mathfrak{r}})}{\partial n}$ willkürlich vorgegeben wird (vgl. Ziff. 20), so *muß zwischen den beiden Randwerten* $v(\hat{\mathfrak{r}})$ und $\frac{\partial v(\hat{\mathfrak{r}})}{\partial n}$ *ein allgemeiner funktionaler Zusammenhang bestehen.* Um ihn zu finden, lassen wir

[1] Sie wurde zuerst von H. v. HELMHOLTZ abgeleitet. J. Math. **57**, 7 (1859). — G. KIRCHHOFF verallgemeinerte sie für beliebige Zeitabhängigkeit der Wellenfunktion. Ann. Phys. **18**, 663 83).

den Aufpunkt $\mathfrak{r}$ in (8.5) gegen die Fläche (S) rücken, wir wollen uns dabei (S) sowohl von der positiven wie von der negativen Seite her nähern und bezeichnen diesen Grenzübergang durch $\lim \mathfrak{r} \to \hat{\mathfrak{r}} \pm 0$ (die Verhältnisse sind in Fig. 3 bzw. 4 dargestellt). Das Integral in (8.5) ist eine Lösung der Wellengleichung, die im Raumteil T^- dann und nur dann verschwindet, wenn $v(\hat{\mathfrak{r}})$ bzw. $\frac{\partial v(\hat{\mathfrak{r}})}{\partial n}$ die *zusammengehörigen Werte* sind, die irgendeine in T^+ quellenfreie Lösung $v(\mathfrak{r})$ der Wellengleichung bzw. deren Normalableitung annimmt, wenn $\mathfrak{r}$ sich der Fläche (S) von der *positiven* Seite her nähert. Im Raumteil T^+ stellt das Integral dann $v(\mathfrak{r})$ dar. Mit den Abkürzungen

$$v_+(\hat{\mathfrak{r}}) = \varphi(\hat{\mathfrak{r}}), \qquad \left(\frac{\partial v(\hat{\mathfrak{r}})}{\partial n}\right)_+ = \psi(\hat{\mathfrak{r}}) \tag{9.1}$$

erhält also (8.5) die Gestalt

$$\left.\begin{matrix} v(\mathfrak{r}) \\ 0 \end{matrix}\right\} = \oint_S \left\{\varphi(\hat{\mathfrak{r}}')\frac{\partial}{\partial n'} - \psi(\hat{\mathfrak{r}}')\right\} \cdot G(\mathfrak{r} - \hat{\mathfrak{r}}')\, d\hat{\mathfrak{r}}', \tag{9.1a}$$

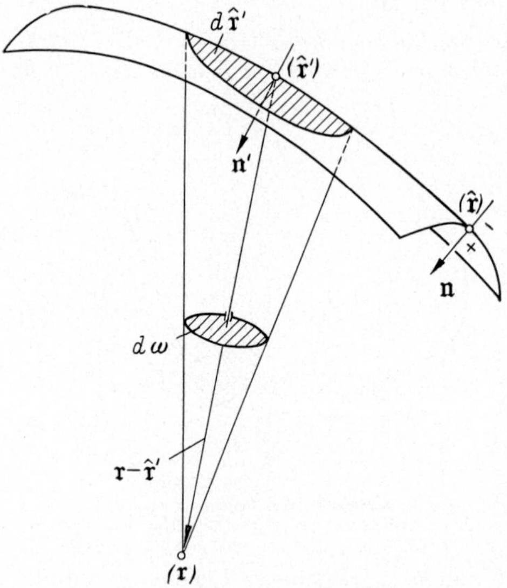

Fig. 5. Zur Definition des räumlichen Winkels.

je nachdem ob $\mathfrak{r}$ in T^+ oder T^- liegt. Wir berechnen nun zunächst den Grenzwert

$$\lim_{\mathfrak{r} \to \hat{\mathfrak{r}} \pm 0} \int_S \varphi(\hat{\mathfrak{r}}') \frac{\partial}{\partial n'} G(\mathfrak{r} - \hat{\mathfrak{r}}')\, d\hat{\mathfrak{r}}', \tag{9.2}$$

wobei es auf die Bedeutung von $\varphi(\hat{\mathfrak{r}})$ hier nicht ankommt und wir von der Fläche (S) voraussetzen wollen, daß sie überall eine Tangentialebene besitzt. Grenzt man um den Flächenpunkt $\hat{\mathfrak{r}}$ herum ein sehr kleines Flächenstück (S_0) ab, so kann man dort für $\mathfrak{r} \to \hat{\mathfrak{r}}$ die Greensche Funktion $G(\mathfrak{r} - \hat{\mathfrak{r}}') = \frac{\exp(i|\mathfrak{r} - \hat{\mathfrak{r}}'|)}{4\pi|\mathfrak{r} - \hat{\mathfrak{r}}'|}$ durch ihren „*statischen Wert*“ $\frac{1}{4\pi|\mathfrak{r} - \hat{\mathfrak{r}}'|}$ ersetzen und erhält

$$\left.\begin{aligned} &\lim_{\mathfrak{r} \to \hat{\mathfrak{r}} \pm 0} \int_S \varphi(\hat{\mathfrak{r}}') \frac{\partial}{\partial n'} G(\mathfrak{r} - \hat{\mathfrak{r}}')\, d\hat{\mathfrak{r}}' \\ &= \frac{1}{4\pi} \lim_{\mathfrak{r} \to \hat{\mathfrak{r}} \pm 0} \int_{S_0} \varphi(\hat{\mathfrak{r}}') \frac{\partial}{\partial n'} \frac{1}{|\mathfrak{r} - \hat{\mathfrak{r}}'|}\, d\hat{\mathfrak{r}}' + \int_{S - S_0} \varphi(\hat{\mathfrak{r}}') \frac{\partial}{\partial n'} G(\hat{\mathfrak{r}} - \hat{\mathfrak{r}}')\, d\hat{\mathfrak{r}}'. \end{aligned}\right\} \tag{9.2'}$$

Dabei haben wir den Grenzübergang $\lim \mathfrak{r} \to \hat{\mathfrak{r}} \pm 0$ beim zweiten Term rechts unter dem Integral ausführen können, da dort $\partial G/\partial n'$ überall stetig und endlich ist. Nun bedeutet

$$\frac{\partial}{\partial n'} \frac{1}{|\hat{\mathfrak{r}} - \hat{\mathfrak{r}}'|}\, d\hat{\mathfrak{r}}' = \frac{(\mathfrak{n}', \hat{\mathfrak{r}} - \hat{\mathfrak{r}}')}{|\mathfrak{r} - \hat{\mathfrak{r}}'|^3}\, d\hat{\mathfrak{r}}' = d\omega(\mathfrak{r}, \hat{\mathfrak{r}}') \tag{9.3}$$

den *räumlichen Winkel*, unter dem das Flächenelement $d\hat{\mathfrak{r}}'$ von $\mathfrak{r}$ aus erscheint (s. Fig. 5); daher können wir den in (9.2') geforderten Grenzwert leicht ausführen:

$$\lim_{\mathfrak{r} \to \hat{\mathfrak{r}} \pm 0} \int_{S_0} \varphi(\hat{\mathfrak{r}}') \frac{\partial}{\partial n'} \frac{1}{|\mathfrak{r} - \hat{\mathfrak{r}}'|}\, d\hat{\mathfrak{r}}' = \pm 2\pi\, \varphi(\hat{\mathfrak{r}}_0), \tag{9.3'}$$

wobei $\hat{\mathfrak{r}}_0$ ein Punkt auf (S_0) ist. Lassen wir nun (S_0) auf den Punkt $\hat{\mathfrak{r}}$ zusammenschrumpfen, so ergibt sich aus (9.2′)

$$\lim_{\mathfrak{r}\to\hat{\mathfrak{r}}\pm 0} \int\limits_S \varphi(\hat{\mathfrak{r}}') \frac{\partial}{\partial n'} G(\mathfrak{r}-\hat{\mathfrak{r}}')\, d\hat{\mathfrak{r}}' = \pm \frac{1}{2} \varphi(\hat{\mathfrak{r}}) + \fint\limits_S \varphi(\hat{\mathfrak{r}}') \frac{\partial}{\partial n'} G(\hat{\mathfrak{r}}-\hat{\mathfrak{r}}')\, d\hat{\mathfrak{r}}'. \quad (9.2'')$$

Dabei ist das uneigentliche Integral rechts offensichtlich als *Hauptwert* aufzufassen ($\lim S_0 \to 0$), was wir durch $\fint$ angedeutet haben. Auf ganz entsprechende Weise ergibt sich der folgende Grenzwert

$$\lim_{\mathfrak{r}\to\hat{\mathfrak{r}}\pm 0} \frac{\partial}{\partial n} \int\limits_S \psi(\hat{\mathfrak{r}}')\, G(\mathfrak{r}-\hat{\mathfrak{r}}')\, d\hat{\mathfrak{r}}' = \mp \frac{1}{2} \psi(\hat{\mathfrak{r}}) + \fint\limits_S \psi(\hat{\mathfrak{r}}') \frac{\partial}{\partial n} G(\hat{\mathfrak{r}}-\hat{\mathfrak{r}}')\, d\hat{\mathfrak{r}}' \quad (9.4)$$

für beliebige auf (S) stetige Funktionen $\psi(\hat{\mathfrak{r}})$. Ferner existieren die Grenzwerte

$$\lim_{\mathfrak{r}\to\hat{\mathfrak{r}}\pm 0} \frac{\partial}{\partial n} \int \varphi(\hat{\mathfrak{r}}') \frac{\partial}{\partial n'} G(\hat{\mathfrak{r}}-\hat{\mathfrak{r}}')\, d\hat{\mathfrak{r}}'$$

nicht ohne weiteres; ihre Differenz verschwindet jedoch stets. Solche Grenzwerte werden in Ziff. 47, 48 und 76 näher untersucht; wir wollen sie hier der Kürze halber durch

$$\frac{\partial}{\partial n} \fint \varphi(\hat{\mathfrak{r}}') \frac{\partial}{\partial n'} G(\hat{\mathfrak{r}}-\hat{\mathfrak{r}}')\, d\hat{\mathfrak{r}}'$$

bezeichnen. Mit (9.2″) und (9.4) folgen also für das Integral (9.1a) die folgenden Grenzwerte

$$\lim_{\mathfrak{r}\to\hat{\mathfrak{r}}\pm 0} \oint\limits_S \{\cdots\}\, d\hat{\mathfrak{r}}' = \pm \frac{1}{2} \varphi(\hat{\mathfrak{r}}) + \fint\limits_S \left\{\varphi(\hat{\mathfrak{r}}') \frac{\partial}{\partial n'} - \psi(\hat{\mathfrak{r}}')\right\} G(\hat{\mathfrak{r}}-\hat{\mathfrak{r}}')\, d\hat{\mathfrak{r}}', \quad (9.5\text{a})$$

$$\lim_{\mathfrak{r}\to\hat{\mathfrak{r}}\pm 0} \frac{\partial}{\partial n} \oint\limits_S \{\cdots\}\, d\hat{\mathfrak{r}}' = \pm \frac{1}{2} \psi(\hat{\mathfrak{r}}) + \frac{\partial}{\partial n} \fint\limits_S \left\{\varphi(\hat{\mathfrak{r}}') \frac{\partial}{\partial n'} - \psi(\hat{\mathfrak{r}}')\right\} G(\hat{\mathfrak{r}}-\hat{\mathfrak{r}}')\, d\hat{\mathfrak{r}}'. \quad (9.5\text{b})$$

Nach den vorangegangenen Bemerkungen müssen nun die Grenzwerte $\lim \mathfrak{r} \to \hat{\mathfrak{r}} - 0$ verschwinden, während die Grenzwerte $\lim \mathfrak{r} \to \hat{\mathfrak{r}} + 0$ die Werte (9.1) liefern sollen. Aus beiden Bedingungen folgt übereinstimmend

$$\left.\begin{aligned} \frac{1}{2} \varphi(\hat{\mathfrak{r}}) &= \fint\limits_S \left\{\varphi(\hat{\mathfrak{r}}') \frac{\partial}{\partial n'} - \psi(\hat{\mathfrak{r}}')\right\} G(\hat{\mathfrak{r}}-\hat{\mathfrak{r}}')\, d\hat{\mathfrak{r}}', \\ \frac{1}{2} \psi(\hat{\mathfrak{r}}) &= \frac{\partial}{\partial n} \fint\limits_S \left\{\varphi(\hat{\mathfrak{r}}') \frac{\partial}{\partial n'} - \psi(\hat{\mathfrak{r}}')\right\} G(\hat{\mathfrak{r}}-\hat{\mathfrak{r}}')\, d\hat{\mathfrak{r}}'. \end{aligned}\right\} \quad (9.6)$$

Dies ist der gesuchte allgemeine funktionale Zusammenhang für die Randwerte der Lösungen der Wellengleichung und ihrer Normalableitungen.

Zur Lösung einer (inneren oder äußeren) *Randwertaufgabe* wird man die Fläche (S) mit (der inneren oder äußeren Seite) derjenigen Fläche zusammenfallen lassen, auf der die Randwerte aus physikalischen Gründen vorgegeben sind. Man erkennt nun aus (9.6) auch sofort, daß z.B. nur *entweder* der Randwert $\varphi(\hat{\mathfrak{r}})$ *oder* $\psi(\hat{\mathfrak{r}})$ willkürlich vorgegeben werden kann. Der jeweils andere Randwert ist dann zufolge (9.6) durch eine Integraltransformation mit dem vorgegebenen verknüpft. Gibt man etwa $\psi(\hat{\mathfrak{r}})$ willkürlich vor: $\psi(\hat{\mathfrak{r}}) = \psi_0(\hat{\mathfrak{r}})$ *(Neumannsche Randwertaufgabe)*, so ist damit $\varphi(\hat{\mathfrak{r}})$ durch (9.6) festgelegt, und zwar ist es mit Hilfe der inhomogenen *Fredholmschen Integralgleichung zweiter Art*

$$-\frac{1}{2} \varphi(\hat{\mathfrak{r}}) + \fint\limits_S \varphi(\hat{\mathfrak{r}}') \frac{\partial}{\partial n'} G(\hat{\mathfrak{r}}-\hat{\mathfrak{r}}')\, d\hat{\mathfrak{r}}' = \oint\limits_S \psi_0(\hat{\mathfrak{r}}')\, G(\hat{\mathfrak{r}}-\hat{\mathfrak{r}}')\, d\hat{\mathfrak{r}}' \quad (9.7\text{a})$$

oder mit Hilfe der *Integrodifferentialgleichung*

$$\frac{\partial}{\partial n} \oint_S \varphi(\hat{\mathfrak{r}}') \frac{\partial}{\partial n'} G(\hat{\mathfrak{r}} - \hat{\mathfrak{r}}')\, d\hat{\mathfrak{r}}' = \frac{1}{2} \psi_0(\hat{\mathfrak{r}}) + \oint \psi_0(\hat{\mathfrak{r}}') \frac{\partial}{\partial n} G(\hat{\mathfrak{r}} - \hat{\mathfrak{r}}')\, d\hat{\mathfrak{r}}' \qquad (9.7\,\text{b})$$

zu berechnen. (Das Ableitungssymbol $\partial/\partial n$ darf hier nicht ohne weiteres unter das Integral genommen werden, da sonst der Integrand für $\hat{\mathfrak{r}}' \to \hat{\mathfrak{r}}$ so stark singulär wird, daß das Integral nicht mehr existiert; durch eine partielle Integration läßt sich jedoch eine Ableitung auf φ abwälzen; vgl. Ziff. 48 und 76.) *Das Huygenssche Prinzip ist daher erst in Verbindung mit der Auflösung einer Integralgleichung zur Lösung einer Randwertaufgabe geeignet.*

Wird die geschlossene Fläche (S) zu einem (beiderseitig überspannten) berandeten Flächenstück zusammengedrückt („*Schirm*"), so steht nur die Gl. (9.7b) zur Verfügung (Ziff. 47). In der Theorie der Beugung handelt es sich meistens um *homogene Randwertaufgaben* (*Verschwinden* von v oder $\partial v/\partial n$ auf der Oberfläche des Körpers), dafür wird eine Singularität im Feldgebiet zugelassen *(einfallende Welle)*.

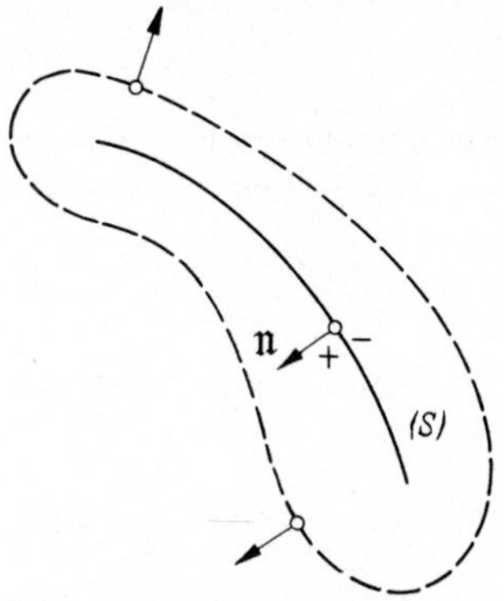

Fig. 6. Ausschluß einer Sprungfläche aus dem Feldraum.

10. Sprungwertproblem. Trägt man in das Integral (9.1a) *sowohl* für $\varphi(\hat{\mathfrak{r}})$ *als auch* für $\psi(\hat{\mathfrak{r}})$ *willkürliche* Werte $\varphi_0(\hat{\mathfrak{r}})$ und $\psi_0(\hat{\mathfrak{r}})$ ein, so entsteht eine Lösung der Wellengleichung von der Gestalt

$$v(\mathfrak{r}) = \int_S \left\{\varphi_0(\hat{\mathfrak{r}}') \frac{\partial}{\partial n'} - \psi_0(\hat{\mathfrak{r}}')\right\} G(\mathfrak{r} - \hat{\mathfrak{r}}')\, d\hat{\mathfrak{r}}', \qquad (10.1)$$

die wir wegen ihrer Bedeutung für die *Kirchhoffsche Beugungstheorie* (Abschn. IIa) als *Kirchhoffsches Integral* bezeichnen wollen. Hier sind aber die Größen φ_0 bzw. ψ_0 *nicht* mehr die Randwerte, die v bzw. seine Normalableitung bei Annäherung an (S) von der positiven Seite her annimmt, noch verschwindet (was damit gleichbedeutend wäre) v auf der negativen Seite (und damit in T^-), da die *willkürlich* vorgegebenen Werte im allgemeinen nicht in dem funktionalen Zusammenhang (9.6) stehen werden.

Mit Hilfe der Grenzwerte (9.2″) und (9.4) sieht man jedoch unmittelbar, daß die Größen φ_0 bzw. ψ_0 den *Sprung* bedeuten, den die Lösung v bzw. deren Normalableitung erleidet, wenn man durch die Fläche (S) von der positiven nach der negativen Seite hindurchtritt:

$$\varphi_0(\hat{\mathfrak{r}}) = (v)_+ - (v)_-, \qquad \psi_0(\hat{\mathfrak{r}}) = \left(\frac{\partial v}{\partial n}\right)_+ - \left(\frac{\partial v}{\partial n}\right)_-. \qquad (10.2)$$

Man sieht leicht ein, daß (S) in Gl. (10.1) auch eine beliebige *nicht* geschlossene Fläche (berandetes Flächenstück) sein kann (s. Fig. 6). Sind nämlich längs einer solchen die Sprungwerte (10.2) beliebig vorgegeben, während v sonst überall regulär sei und im Unendlichen der *Ausstrahlungsbedingung* genüge, so hat man bei der Integration von Gl. (8.4) über den ganzen Raum *beide Seiten* der Sprungfläche (S) mit zur Oberfläche des Bereiches zu zählen. Andererseits liefert die unendlich ferne Feldbegrenzung zufolge der Ausstrahlungsbedingung keinen Beitrag. Die Integration von (8.4) führt also über den Gaußschen Satz unmittelbar auf (10.1). Ferner ist eine Lösung der Wellengleichung, die beim Durchtritt durch eine Fläche (S) die vorgegebenen Sprungwerte (10.2) besitzen soll (sonst aber überall regulär und im Unendlichen der Ausstrahlungsbedingung unterworfen ist) durch diese Daten *eindeutig* definiert. Gäbe es nämlich zwei verschiedene Lösungen $v^{(1)}$

und $v^{(2)}$ mit den gleichen Sprungwerten (10.2), die beide der Ausstrahlungsbedingung genügen, so ist die Differenz $w = v^{(1)} - v^{(2)}$ im ganzen Raum regulär und erfüllt im Unendlichen die Ausstrahlungsbedingung. Integriert man Gl. (8.4) mit $v = w$ über den ganzen Raum, so ergibt sich also $w \equiv 0$. Das Sprungwertproblem ist also im Gegensatz zur Randwertaufgabe eine leicht zu lösende „*Summationsaufgabe*". Es können dabei die Sprungwerte (10.2) des Funktionswertes *und* der Normalableitung *simultan* auf der gleichen Fläche (S) oder je auf verschiedenen Flächen vorgegeben werden; sie werden durch das Kirchhoffsche Integral (10.1) *reproduziert.*

Andererseits benötigt man zur Darstellung einer Lösung v der Wellengleichung durch ihre *Randwerte* $v(\hat{\mathfrak{r}})$ bzw. $\frac{\partial v(\hat{\mathfrak{r}})}{\partial n}$ auf (S) — die die beliebig vorgegebenen Randwerte *reproduziert* — die zur *Fläche* (S) *gehörige Greensche Funktion der ersten bzw. zweiten Art*[1]. Diese besitzt dieselbe Singularität, wie die Greensche Funktion des freien Raumes (8.2) bis (8.3a); genügt jedoch auf (S) der entsprechenden *homogenen* Randbedingung. Ihre explizite Darstellung ist also mit der Lösung des Beugungsproblems identisch.

11. Beziehung zwischen Sprungwertaufgabe und Randwertaufgabe. Um diese Beziehung hier kurz zu beleuchten, fassen wir etwa die *Greensche Funktion zweiter Art* für den Außenraum ins Auge: Gesucht eine Lösung der Wellengleichung $(\Delta + 1)\, v(\mathfrak{r}) = -\delta(\mathfrak{r} - \mathfrak{r}_0)$, die auf der Außenseite der geschlossenen (glatten) Fläche (S) der Randbedingung $\partial v/\partial n = 0$ genüge [und im Unendlichen die Ausstrahlungsbedingung befriedige; $\mathfrak{r}_0$ sei ein beliebiger Punkt außerhalb (S)]. Das singuläre Verhalten im Punkte $\mathfrak{r}_0$ ist das gleiche wie dasjenige der Greenschen Funktion des freien Raumes (Kugelwelle), die wir hier mit $v_0(\mathfrak{r})$ bezeichnen wollen. Bei Anwendung der Integralformel (9.1a) ist das quellenfreie Raumgebiet T^+ der Außenraum von (S) abzüglich einer kleinen Kugel um $\mathfrak{r}_0$. Die Oberfläche der letzteren liefert den Beitrag $v_0(\mathfrak{r})$, so daß wegen $\psi(\hat{\mathfrak{r}}) = \left(\frac{\partial v}{\partial n}\right)_+ = 0$ folgt (äußere Normale)

$$v(\mathfrak{r}) = v_0(\mathfrak{r}) + \oint_S \varphi(\hat{\mathfrak{r}}') \frac{\partial}{\partial n'} G(\mathfrak{r} - \hat{\mathfrak{r}}')\, d\hat{\mathfrak{r}}'. \tag{11.1}$$

Die Größe $\varphi(\hat{\mathfrak{r}}) = v_+(\hat{\mathfrak{r}})$ ist dabei zufolge (9.5a) durch die Fredholmsche Integralgleichung

$$\frac{1}{2}\varphi(\hat{\mathfrak{r}}) - \oint_S \varphi(\hat{\mathfrak{r}}') \frac{\partial}{\partial n'} G(\hat{\mathfrak{r}} - \hat{\mathfrak{r}}')\, d\hat{\mathfrak{r}}' = v_0(\hat{\mathfrak{r}}) \tag{11.2}$$

definiert (die wir in Abschn. IIId näher untersuchen werden). Das durch (11.1) gegebene Feld verschwindet dann im Inneren von (S) identisch; $\varphi(\hat{\mathfrak{r}})$ ist zugleich der Sprung, den v beim Hindurchtreten durch (S) (von außen nach innen) erleidet.

Versucht man nun die Integralgleichung (11.2) mit Hilfe *wiederholter Iteration (Neumannsche Reihe)* zu lösen, so erhält man in nullter Näherung $\varphi^0(\hat{\mathfrak{r}}) = 2v_0(\hat{\mathfrak{r}})$. Mit andern Worten ersetzt man also den unbekannten Sprung $\varphi = v_+ - v_-$ durch $2v_0$ und erhält so über (11.1) die Lösung der entsprechenden *Sprungwertaufgabe*. In nullter Näherung ergibt sich also eine Lösung nach Art der *Kirchhoffschen Beugungstheorie*; vgl. Ziff. 30.

In ihrer ursprünglichen Fassung ersetzt diese Theorie jedoch das Randwertproblem durch das Sprungwertproblem $v_+ - v_- = v_0$ *und* $(\partial v/\partial n)_+ - (\partial v/\partial n)_- = \partial v_0/\partial n$ beim Durchtritt durch (S). Außerdem werden diese Sprungwerte nicht

[1] Siehe etwa A. Sommerfeld: Vorlesungen über theoretische Physik, Bd. IV, S. 203, Wiesbaden 1950.

auf der ganzen (geschlossenen) Fläche (S) gefordert, sondern auf demjenigen (berandeten) Teil (S'), der im Sinne der *geometrischen Optik* von der einfallenden Welle v_0 „*beleuchtet*" wird (s. Fig. 7). Die Kirchhoffsche Lösung lautet also

$$v_K(\mathfrak{r}) = v_0(\mathfrak{r}) + \int\limits_{S'} \left\{ v_0(\hat{\mathfrak{r}}') \frac{\partial}{\partial n'} - \frac{\partial v_0(\hat{\mathfrak{r}}')}{\partial n'} \right\} G(\mathfrak{r} - \hat{\mathfrak{r}}')\, d\hat{\mathfrak{r}}'. \tag{11.3}$$

Sie kann aber — da es sich im wesentlichen um den Fluß eines quellenfreien Vektors handelt, vgl. Ziff. 30 — auch in der Form

$$v_K(\mathfrak{r}) = v_0'(\mathfrak{r}) + \int\limits_{S''} \left\{ v_0(\hat{\mathfrak{r}}') \frac{\partial}{\partial n'} - \frac{\partial v_0(\hat{\mathfrak{r}}')}{\partial n'} \right\} G(\mathfrak{r} - \hat{\mathfrak{r}}')\, d\hat{\mathfrak{r}}' \tag{11.3'}$$

geschrieben werden. Dabei bedeutet (S'') eine beliebige Fläche, die durch Deformation aus (S') bei *festgehaltenem Rande* hervorgegangen ist (s. Fig. 7); ferner ist $v_0'(\mathfrak{r}) = v_0(\mathfrak{r})$ für $\mathfrak{r}$ außerhalb des von (S') und (S'') berandeten Gebietes und $=0$ innerhalb dieses Gebietes. $v_0(\mathfrak{r})$ kann nämlich innerhalb dieses Gebietes mit Hilfe der Helmholtzschen Formel (8.5) durch ein Flächenintegral über (S') und (S'') mit nach innen weisender Normale dargestellt werden; das Flächenintegral über (S') kompensiert aber gerade das entsprechende Integral in (11.3) wegen der entgegengesetzten Normalenrichtung, so daß das Integral über (S'') in (11.3') übrigbleibt. Die Kirchhoffsche Lösung (11.3) hat also mit der Lösung der ursprünglichen Randwertaufgabe (11.1) und (11.2) nichts mehr zu tun. Andererseits vermag sie sich dem *geometrisch optischen* Grenzfall anzupassen; läßt man nämlich (S'') mit der „*Schattengrenze*" (Sg) zusammenfallen, so stellt $v_0'(\mathfrak{r})$ gerade die durch die geometrische Optik geforderte Feldverteilung dar. Das Flächenintegral in (11.3') stellt dann eine Korrektur im Sinne der Wellenoptik dar, indem es die Unstetigkeiten des Feldes v_0' nach Maßgabe der Wellengleichung stetig ausgleicht. Dieses Integral erleidet ja beim Hindurchtreten durch die *Schattengrenze* (Sg) zufolge (10.2) gerade den Sprung $v_0(\hat{\mathfrak{r}})$ bzw. $\frac{\partial v_0(\hat{\mathfrak{r}})}{\partial n}$.

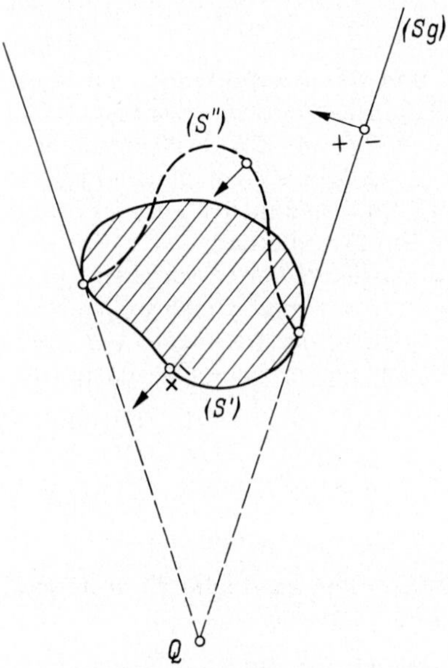

Fig. 7. Zum Vergleich von Randwert- und Sprungwertproblem.

c 2) Elektromagnetische Fassung.

12. Vektorielles Huygenssches Prinzip. Da es sich beim vektoriellen Problem um die Lösung eines simultanen Systems von Vektor-Differentialgleichungen handelt, haben wir in Analogie zu (8.1) einen „*Huygensschen Tensor*" $\boldsymbol{\Phi}(\mathfrak{r}, \mathfrak{r}')$ zu bilden, dessen *Tensor-Divergenz* überall verschwindet, bis auf eine „*Einheitsquelle*" für $\mathfrak{r} \to \mathfrak{r}'$. Dieses allgemeine Schema[1] soll hier aber zunächst nicht entwickelt werden; man kommt auf einem kleinen Umweg auch mit dem Vektor-

[1] Siehe z.B. W. Franz: Z. Naturforsch. **3**a, 500 (1948). — H. Levine u. J. Schwinger: Comm. Pure Appl. Math. **3**, 355 (1950).

kalkül zum Ziel[1]. Dementsprechend bilden wir statt eines Tensors den Vektor

$$\left.\begin{aligned}\mathfrak{W}(\mathfrak{r},\mathfrak{r}') &= [\mathfrak{G}(\mathfrak{r}-\mathfrak{r}')\,\mathrm{rot}'\,\mathfrak{E}(\mathfrak{r}')] - [\mathfrak{E}(\mathfrak{r}')\,\mathrm{rot}'\,\mathfrak{G}(\mathfrak{r}-\mathfrak{r}')]\\ &+ \mathfrak{G}(\mathfrak{r}-\mathfrak{r}')\,\mathrm{div}'\,\mathfrak{E}(\mathfrak{r}') - \mathfrak{E}(\mathfrak{r}')\,\mathrm{div}'\,\mathfrak{G}(\mathfrak{r}-\mathfrak{r}')\,.\end{aligned}\right\} \tag{12.1}$$

Hier sei $\mathfrak{E}$ eine reguläre Lösung der Maxwellschen Gleichungen (2.1b), also auch der Vektorwellengleichung (5.1). Ferner sei

$$\mathfrak{G}(\mathfrak{r}-\mathfrak{r}') = \mathfrak{a}\,G(\mathfrak{r}-\mathfrak{r}') \tag{12.2}$$

mit willkürlichem *konstantem Hilfsvektor* $\mathfrak{a}$ und der *skalaren Greenschen Funktion G des freien Raumes* aus (8.2). Beachtet man (2.1b) und setzt man (12.2) in (12.1) ein, so folgt nach bekannten Regeln:

$$\left.\begin{aligned}\mathfrak{W} &= i\,[\mathfrak{a}\,\mathfrak{H}]\,G - (\mathfrak{a}\,\mathfrak{E})\,\nabla' G\\ &+ \mathfrak{a}(\mathfrak{E}\,\nabla' G) - \mathfrak{E}(\mathfrak{a}\,\nabla' G)\,.\end{aligned}\right\} \tag{12.1'}$$

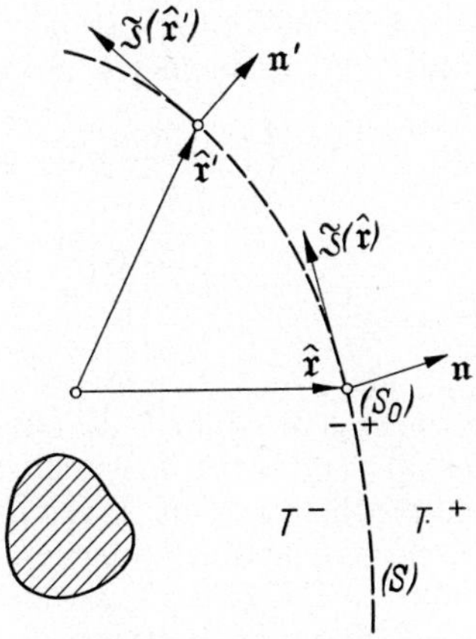

Fig. 8. Zur elektromagnetischen Fassung des Huygensschen Prinzips.

Für die Divergenz von (12.1) erhält man ferner

$$\left.\begin{aligned}\mathrm{div}'\,\mathfrak{W} &= \mathfrak{E}\,\mathrm{rot}'\,\mathrm{rot}'\,\mathfrak{G} -\\ &-\mathfrak{G}\,\mathrm{rot}'\,\mathrm{rot}'\,\mathfrak{E} - (\mathfrak{E}\,\nabla')\,\mathrm{div}'\,\mathfrak{G}\,,\end{aligned}\right\} \tag{12.3}$$

falls man von den Identitäten

$$\mathrm{div}\,[\mathfrak{A}\,\mathfrak{B}] = (\mathfrak{B}\,\mathrm{rot}\,\mathfrak{A}) - (\mathfrak{A}\,\mathrm{rot}\,\mathfrak{B})\,,$$

$$(\nabla\mathfrak{A})\,\mathfrak{B} = \mathfrak{B}\,\mathrm{div}\,\mathfrak{A} + (\mathfrak{A}\,\nabla)\,\mathfrak{B}$$

Gebrauch macht und $\mathrm{div}\,\mathfrak{E} = 0$ beachtet. Mit Hilfe von (8.2) folgt nun

$$\left.\begin{aligned}\mathrm{rot}'\,\mathrm{rot}'\,\mathfrak{G} &= (\mathfrak{a}\,\nabla')\,\nabla' G - \mathfrak{a}\,\Delta' G\\ &= (\mathfrak{a}\,\nabla')\,\nabla' G + \mathfrak{a}\,G + \mathfrak{a}\,\delta(\mathfrak{r}-\mathfrak{r}')\,.\end{aligned}\right\} \tag{12.4}$$

Dies und (5.1) in (12.3) eingesetzt liefert schließlich

$$\mathrm{div}'\,\mathfrak{W}(\mathfrak{r},\mathfrak{r}') = \big(\mathfrak{a}\,\mathfrak{E}(\mathfrak{r})\big)\,\delta(\mathfrak{r}-\mathfrak{r}')\,. \tag{12.3'}$$

Wir berechnen nun noch die Projektion von $\mathfrak{W}$ auf die Normale $\mathfrak{n}$ einer Fläche (S), über die wir sogleich integrieren werden, und erhalten aus (12.1')

$$(\mathfrak{n}\,\mathfrak{W}) = -\big(\mathfrak{a},\, i\,[\mathfrak{n}\,\mathfrak{H}] + [[\mathfrak{n}\,\mathfrak{E}]\,\nabla'] + (\mathfrak{n}\,\mathfrak{E})\,\nabla'\big)\,G\,. \tag{12.5}$$

Die Integration von (12.3') über irgendeinem räumlichen, bezüglich $\mathfrak{E}$ quellenfreien Bereich mit der Hülle (S) und der *inneren* Normale $\mathfrak{n}$ liefert nach dem Gaußschen Satz:

$$\left.\begin{matrix}\big(\mathfrak{a}\,\mathfrak{E}(\mathfrak{r})\big)\\ 0\end{matrix}\right\} = -\oint_S \big(\mathfrak{n}'\,\mathfrak{W}(\mathfrak{r},\mathfrak{r}')\big)\,d\,\hat{\mathfrak{r}}'\,, \tag{12.6}$$

je nachdem ob $\mathfrak{r}$ innerhalb oder außerhalb (S) liegt. Die Fläche (S) kann hier wieder weitgehend deformiert werden; wesentlich ist nur, daß sie einen bezüglich $\mathfrak{E}$ *quellenfreien* Raumteil T^+ vom Raumteil mit Quellen T^- *vollständig trennt* (s. Fig. 8). Die Normale $\mathfrak{n}$ muß stets in den Raum T^+ weisen. Gl. (12.6) gilt dann, je nachdem $\mathfrak{r}$ in T^+ oder T^- liegt. Da sich zufolge (12.5) auch das rechtsstehende Flächenintegral als skalares Produkt mit dem konstanten willkürlichen Vektor $\mathfrak{a}$

[1] Wir folgen im wesentlichen der Darstellung von J. A. STRATTON: Electromagnetic Theory, S. 468. New York-Toronto-London 1941.

schreiben läßt, müssen die links und rechts in Gl. (12.6) mit der Hilfsgröße $\mathfrak{a}$ multiplizierten vektoriellen Faktoren einander gleich sein:

$$\left.\begin{matrix}\mathfrak{E}(\mathfrak{r})\\0\end{matrix}\right\} = \oint_S \{i[\mathfrak{n}'\,\mathfrak{H}(\hat{\mathfrak{r}}')] + [[\mathfrak{n}'\,\mathfrak{E}(\hat{\mathfrak{r}}')]\,\nabla'] + (\mathfrak{n}'\,\mathfrak{E}(\hat{\mathfrak{r}}'))\,\nabla'\}\,G(\mathfrak{r}-\hat{\mathfrak{r}}')\,d\hat{\mathfrak{r}}', \qquad (12.6')$$

je nachdem $\mathfrak{r}$ innerhalb oder außerhalb (S) liegt. Da der Operator ∇' hier nur an G angreift, so können wir ihn durch $-\nabla$ ersetzen und vor das Integral ziehen:

$$\left.\begin{matrix}\mathfrak{E}(\mathfrak{r})\\0\end{matrix}\right\} = i\oint_S [\mathfrak{n}'\,\mathfrak{H}(\hat{\mathfrak{r}}')]\,G(\mathfrak{r}-\hat{\mathfrak{r}}')\,d\hat{\mathfrak{r}}' + \operatorname{rot}\oint_S [\mathfrak{n}'\,\mathfrak{E}(\hat{\mathfrak{r}}')]\,G(\mathfrak{r}-\hat{\mathfrak{r}}')\,d\hat{\mathfrak{r}}' - \operatorname{grad}\oint_S (\mathfrak{n}'\,\mathfrak{E}(\hat{\mathfrak{r}}'))\,G(\mathfrak{r}-\hat{\mathfrak{r}}')\,d\hat{\mathfrak{r}}', \qquad (12.6\text{a})$$

je nachdem $\mathfrak{r}$ innerhalb oder außerhalb (S) liegt. Genau die gleiche Überlegung führt für die magnetische Feldstärke zu der Gleichung

$$\left.\begin{matrix}\mathfrak{H}(\mathfrak{r})\\0\end{matrix}\right\} = \oint_S \{-i[\mathfrak{n}'\,\mathfrak{E}(\hat{\mathfrak{r}}')] + [[\mathfrak{n}'\,\mathfrak{H}(\hat{\mathfrak{r}}')]\,\nabla'] + (\mathfrak{n}'\,\mathfrak{H}(\hat{\mathfrak{r}}'))\,\nabla'\}\,G(\mathfrak{r}-\hat{\mathfrak{r}}')\,d\hat{\mathfrak{r}}', \qquad (12.7)$$

$$= -i\oint_S [\mathfrak{n}'\,\mathfrak{E}(\hat{\mathfrak{r}}')]\,G(\mathfrak{r}-\hat{\mathfrak{r}}')\,d\hat{\mathfrak{r}}' + \operatorname{rot}\oint_S [\mathfrak{n}'\,\mathfrak{H}(\hat{\mathfrak{r}}')]\,G(\mathfrak{r}-\hat{\mathfrak{r}}')\,d\hat{\mathfrak{r}}' - \operatorname{grad}\oint_S (\mathfrak{n}'\,\mathfrak{H}(\hat{\mathfrak{r}}'))\,G(\mathfrak{r}-\hat{\mathfrak{r}}')\,d\hat{\mathfrak{r}}', \qquad (12.7\text{a})$$

je nachdem $\mathfrak{r}$ innerhalb oder außerhalb (S) liegt. Die Gln. (12.6′), (12.6a) bzw. (12.7), (12.7a) können als *vektorielle Fassung* des Huygensschen *Prinzips* angesprochen werden: Das Feld $\mathfrak{E}(\mathfrak{r})$, $\mathfrak{H}(\mathfrak{r})$ läßt sich durch ein Flächenintegral darstellen, genommen über eine beliebige, $\mathfrak{r}$ einhüllende, geschlossene Fläche (S), falls die Tangential- und Normalkomponenten des darzustellenden Feldes längs (S) *bekannt* sind. Da sich nun die Normalkomponenten durch die Tangentialkomponenten ausdrücken lassen (Ziff. 2), so müssen sich die Normalkomponenten aus (12.6), (12.7) eliminieren lassen. Um dies hier durchzuführen, bemerken wir, daß die Anwendung der Operation i rot auf (12.7) mit Hilfe partieller Integration [Stokesscher Satz; ein Linienintegral tritt dabei nicht auf, da die Fläche (S) *geschlossen* ist] — und Anwendung der Maxwellschen Gleichungen auf die Größen unter dem Integral — die rechte Seite von (12.6′) liefert. [Entsprechend führt die Operation $-i$ rot Gl. (12.6′) in Gl. (12.7) über.] Das durch (12.6′), (12.7) dargestellte Feld genügt also in der Tat den Maxwellschen Gleichungen; bilden wir daher von (12.6a) bzw. (12.7a) die Rotation, so verschwindet der Gradient und wir erhalten

$$\left.\begin{aligned}\left.\begin{matrix}\mathfrak{E}(\mathfrak{r})\\0\end{matrix}\right\} &= \operatorname{rot}\oint_S [\mathfrak{n}'\,\mathfrak{E}(\hat{\mathfrak{r}}')]\,G(\mathfrak{r}-\hat{\mathfrak{r}}')\,d\hat{\mathfrak{r}}' + i\operatorname{rot}\operatorname{rot}\oint_S [\mathfrak{n}'\,\mathfrak{H}(\hat{\mathfrak{r}}')]\,G(\mathfrak{r}-\hat{\mathfrak{r}}')\,d\hat{\mathfrak{r}}',\\ \left.\begin{matrix}\mathfrak{H}(\mathfrak{r})\\0\end{matrix}\right\} &= \operatorname{rot}\oint_S [\mathfrak{n}'\,\mathfrak{H}(\hat{\mathfrak{r}}')]\,G(\mathfrak{r}-\hat{\mathfrak{r}}')\,d\hat{\mathfrak{r}}' - i\operatorname{rot}\operatorname{rot}\oint_S [\mathfrak{n}'\,\mathfrak{E}(\hat{\mathfrak{r}}')]\,G(\mathfrak{r}-\hat{\mathfrak{r}}')\,d\hat{\mathfrak{r}}',\end{aligned}\right\} \qquad (12.8)$$

je nachdem, ob $\mathfrak{r}$ innerhalb oder außerhalb (S) liegt.

In dieser symmetrischen Form des Huygensschen Prinzips treten die Normalkomponenten der Feldvektoren unter dem Integral *nicht* mehr auf. Sie ergibt sich auch direkt bei Anwendung des Formalismus des *Greenschen Tensors*, den wir nun skizzieren wollen[1]. Zunächst bemerken wir, daß der Operator rot rot vor den

[1] Vgl. W. Franz: l. c. sowie Theorie der Beugung elektromagnetischer Wellen. Berlin: Springer 1957. — H. Severin: Z. Physik **129**, 426 (1951). — F.E. Borgnis u. C.H. Papas: Randwertprobleme der Mikrowellenphysik, S. 251. Berlin: Springer 1955. — R.D. Kodis: J. Soc. Indust. Appl. Math. **2**, 89 (1954).

Flächenintegralen in (12.8) durch (grad div + 1) ersetzt werden darf [wegen rot rot = grad div − $\varDelta$ und weil die Integrale der Wellengleichung $(\varDelta + 1)\cdots = 0$ genügen, falls $\mathfrak{r}$ nicht auf (S) liegt]. Dieser Operator läßt sich aber als symbolischer *Tensor* $\nabla\nabla + \mathbf{1}$ schreiben (dabei soll der erste Term das *dyadische* Produkt der beiden Vektoren ∇ bedeuten, während $\mathbf{1}$ den *Einheitstensor* bezeichnen möge). Gehen wir mit diesem Operator unter das Integral, so entsteht der sog. „*Greensche Tensor des freien Raumes*"

$$\boldsymbol{\Gamma}(\mathfrak{r}, \mathfrak{r}') = -(\nabla\nabla + \mathbf{1})\, G(\mathfrak{r} - \mathfrak{r}') = -\frac{1}{4\pi}(\nabla\nabla + \mathbf{1})\frac{e^{i|\mathfrak{r}-\mathfrak{r}'|}}{|\mathfrak{r}-\mathfrak{r}'|}. \tag{12.9}$$

Mit seiner Hilfe läßt sich nämlich die erste Formel (12.8) folgendermaßen schreiben

$$\left.\begin{matrix}\mathfrak{E}(\mathfrak{r})\\ 0\end{matrix}\right\} = \oint_S \{[\mathfrak{n}'\,\mathfrak{E}(\hat{\mathfrak{r}}')]\cdot \mathrm{rot}\,\boldsymbol{\Gamma}(\mathfrak{r}, \hat{\mathfrak{r}}') - i\,[\mathfrak{n}'\,\mathfrak{H}(\hat{\mathfrak{r}}')]\cdot\boldsymbol{\Gamma}(\mathfrak{r}, \hat{\mathfrak{r}}')\}\, d\hat{\mathfrak{r}}', \tag{12.8a}$$

je nachdem $\mathfrak{r}$ innerhalb oder außerhalb (S) liegt. Der zweite Term wurde oben verifiziert; zur Umformung des ersten Terms haben wir die Beziehung verwendet

$$\mathfrak{A}\cdot \mathrm{rot}\,\boldsymbol{\Gamma} = [\mathfrak{A}\,\mathrm{grad}\,G] = -\mathrm{rot}\,(\mathfrak{A}\,G) \tag{12.10}$$

für einen beliebigen konstanten Vektor $\mathfrak{A}$. Sie läßt sich mit Hilfe von (12.9) leicht verifizieren, indem man (12.9) vektoriell mit ∇ multipliziert: wegen $[\nabla\nabla] = 0$ folgt dann $\mathrm{rot}\,\boldsymbol{\Gamma} = [\nabla\,\mathbf{1}]\,G = [\mathrm{grad}\,G\,\mathbf{1}]$, also $\mathfrak{A}\cdot\mathrm{rot}\,\boldsymbol{\Gamma} = [\mathfrak{A}\,\mathrm{grad}\,G]$.

Ersetzen wir in (12.8a) noch $i\mathfrak{H}$ durch rot $\mathfrak{E}$, so folgt

$$\mathrm{rot}\,\boldsymbol{\Gamma} = -\mathrm{rot}'\,\boldsymbol{\Gamma}$$

$$\left.\begin{matrix}\mathfrak{E}(\mathfrak{r})\\ 0\end{matrix}\right\} = \oint_S \{\mathrm{rot}'\,\boldsymbol{\Gamma}(\mathfrak{r}, \hat{\mathfrak{r}}')\cdot[\mathfrak{n}'\,\mathfrak{E}(\hat{\mathfrak{r}}')] - [\mathfrak{n}'\,\mathrm{rot}'\,\mathfrak{E}(\hat{\mathfrak{r}}')]\cdot\boldsymbol{\Gamma}(\mathfrak{r}, \hat{\mathfrak{r}}')\}\, d\hat{\mathfrak{r}}', \tag{12.8b}$$

je nachdem $\mathfrak{r}$ innerhalb oder außerhalb (S) liegt. In dieser Form läßt sich jede innerhalb (S) quellenfreie Lösung der homogenen Gleichung

$$\mathrm{rot}\,\mathrm{rot}\,\mathfrak{E} - \mathfrak{E} = 0$$

mit Hilfe ihrer *Tangential*komponenten von $\mathfrak{E}$ und rot $\mathfrak{E}$ auf (S) darstellen und zwar in vollständiger Analogie zur *Helmholtzschen Formel* (8.5), die das entsprechende skalare Problem betrifft.

Gl. (12.8b) läßt sich daher auch auf einem direkten Wege ableiten (der unserer Ableitung der Helmholtzschen Formel genau entspricht): Der „*Huygenssche Tensor*"

$$\boldsymbol{\Phi}(\mathfrak{r}, \mathfrak{r}') = [\mathfrak{E}(\mathfrak{r}')\,\boldsymbol{\Gamma}(\mathfrak{r}, \mathfrak{r}')] - [\mathrm{rot}'\,\mathfrak{E}(\mathfrak{r}')\,\boldsymbol{\Gamma}(\mathfrak{r}, \mathfrak{r}')] \tag{12.11}$$

ist *divergensfrei* bis auf eine δ-artige Singularität für $\mathfrak{r} = \mathfrak{r}'$:

$$\nabla'\cdot\boldsymbol{\Phi}(\mathfrak{r}, \mathfrak{r}') = \mathfrak{E}(\mathfrak{r})\,\delta(\mathfrak{r} - \mathfrak{r}'). \tag{12.12}$$

Dies folgt — wie man leicht bestätigt — mit Hilfe der Gleichung $\mathrm{rot}\,\mathrm{rot}\,\mathfrak{E} - \mathfrak{E} = 0$ aus der *Differentialgleichung des Greenschen Tensors*

$$\mathrm{rot}\,\mathrm{rot}\,\boldsymbol{\Gamma}(\mathfrak{r}, \mathfrak{r}') - \boldsymbol{\Gamma}(\mathfrak{r}, \mathfrak{r}') = -\mathbf{1}\delta(\mathfrak{r} - \mathfrak{r}') \tag{12.13}$$

[wegen der Symmetrie des Greenschen Tensors (12.9) kann man die auf $\boldsymbol{\Gamma}$ wirkenden Differentiationen nach $\mathfrak{r}$ unter Vorzeichenumkehr in solche nach $\mathfrak{r}'$ verwandeln].

Mit (12.9) gleichwertig ist übrigens die Differentialgleichung

$$(\varDelta + 1)\,\boldsymbol{\Gamma}(\mathfrak{r}, \mathfrak{r}') = (\nabla\nabla + \mathbf{1})\,\delta(\mathfrak{r} - \mathfrak{r}') \tag{12.13a}$$

unter der aus (12.13) folgenden Nebenbedingung

$$\nabla \cdot \boldsymbol{\Gamma}(\mathfrak{r}, \mathfrak{r}') = \nabla \delta(\mathfrak{r} - \mathfrak{r}'). \tag{12.13b}$$

In der Tat zeigt man leicht, daß die Gln. (12.13a, b) die der Ausstrahlungsbedingung genügende Lösung (12.9) besitzen.

Integriert man nun den Vektor (12.12) bezüglich $\mathfrak{r}'$ über ein Volumen mit der Oberfläche (S), so erhält man mit Hilfe des Gaußschen Satzes unmittelbar die Formel (12.8b), da der Vektor $\mathfrak{n}' \cdot \boldsymbol{\Phi}$ mit dem Integranden in (12.8b) identisch ist.

Denjenigen Vektor $\mathfrak{H}$, der mit $\mathfrak{E}$, Gl. (12.8b), zusammen die Maxwellschen Gleichungen (2.1b) befriedigt, erhält man durch $\mathfrak{H} = -i \operatorname{rot} \mathfrak{E}$:

$$\left.\begin{aligned} \left.\begin{matrix}\mathfrak{H}(\mathfrak{r})\\ 0\end{matrix}\right\} &= \oint_S \{[\mathfrak{n}'\,\mathfrak{H}(\hat{\mathfrak{r}}')] \cdot \operatorname{rot} \boldsymbol{\Gamma}(\mathfrak{r}, \hat{\mathfrak{r}}') + i\,[\mathfrak{n}'\,\mathfrak{E}(\hat{\mathfrak{r}}')] \cdot \boldsymbol{\Gamma}(\mathfrak{r}, \hat{\mathfrak{r}}')\}\, d\hat{\mathfrak{r}}' \\ &= \oint_S \{\operatorname{rot}' \boldsymbol{\Gamma}(\mathfrak{r}, \hat{\mathfrak{r}}') \cdot [\mathfrak{n}'\,\mathfrak{H}(\hat{\mathfrak{r}}')] - [\mathfrak{n}' \operatorname{rot}' \mathfrak{H}(\hat{\mathfrak{r}}')] \cdot \boldsymbol{\Gamma}(\mathfrak{r}, \hat{\mathfrak{r}}')\}\, d\hat{\mathfrak{r}}' \end{aligned}\right\} \tag{12.8c}$$

je nachdem $\mathfrak{r}$ innerhalb oder außerhalb (S) liegt.

Die *physikalische Bedeutung* des Greenschen Tensors liegt darin, daß er dem *körperlichen Stromelement* $\mathfrak{j}(\mathfrak{r}')\, d\mathfrak{r}'$ am Orte $\mathfrak{r}'$ die elektrische Feldstärke

$$d\mathfrak{E}(\mathfrak{r}) = -i\,\mathfrak{j}(\mathfrak{r}') \cdot \boldsymbol{\Gamma}(\mathfrak{r}, \mathfrak{r}')\, d\mathfrak{r}' \tag{12.14}$$

am Orte $\mathfrak{r}$ zuordnet, bzw. dem *Flächenstromelement* $\mathfrak{J}(\hat{\mathfrak{r}}')\, d\mathfrak{r}'$ die Feldstärke

$$d\mathfrak{E}(\mathfrak{r}) = -i\,\mathfrak{J}(\hat{\mathfrak{r}}') \cdot \boldsymbol{\Gamma}(\mathfrak{r}, \hat{\mathfrak{r}}')\, d\hat{\mathfrak{r}}'. \tag{12.14a}$$

Die zugehörige magnetische Feldstärke ist

$$\left.\begin{aligned} & d\mathfrak{H}(\mathfrak{r}) = \mathfrak{j}(\mathfrak{r}') \cdot \operatorname{rot} \boldsymbol{\Gamma}(\mathfrak{r}, \mathfrak{r}')\, d\mathfrak{r}' \\ \text{bzw.}\quad & d\mathfrak{H}(\mathfrak{r}) = \mathfrak{J}(\hat{\mathfrak{r}}') \cdot \operatorname{rot} \boldsymbol{\Gamma}(\mathfrak{r}, \hat{\mathfrak{r}}')\, d\hat{\mathfrak{r}}'. \end{aligned}\right\} \tag{12.14b}$$

Die aus der Darstellung (12.9) leicht abzuleitende *Symmetriebeziehung*

$$\boldsymbol{\Gamma}(\mathfrak{r}, \mathfrak{r}') = \boldsymbol{\Gamma}(\mathfrak{r}', \mathfrak{r}) = \boldsymbol{\Gamma}^{\dagger}(\mathfrak{r}, \mathfrak{r}') = \boldsymbol{\Gamma}^{\dagger}(\mathfrak{r}', \mathfrak{r}) \tag{12.15}$$

($\boldsymbol{\Gamma}^{\dagger}$ ist der zu $\boldsymbol{\Gamma}$ *adjungierte* Tensor) enthält das *Reziprozitätstheorem* elektromagnetischer Strahlungsfelder.

13. Funktionaler Zusammenhang zwischen den Randwerten der Tangentialkomponenten von $\mathfrak{E}$ und $\mathfrak{H}$. Da eine Lösung der Maxwellschen Gleichungen bereits eindeutig bestimmt ist, wenn auf dem Rande (S) *entweder* die Tangentialkomponente von $\mathfrak{E}$ *oder* $\mathfrak{H}$ willkürlich vorgegeben wird, vgl. Ziff. 20, so muß zwischen diesen beiden Größen ein allgemeiner funktonaler Zusammenhang bestehen, der sich hier wieder ergibt, wenn wir in (12.8) $\mathfrak{r}$ von T^+ oder T^- herkommend auf (S) rücken lassen ($\lim \mathfrak{r} \to \hat{\mathfrak{r}} \pm 0$, s. Fig. 8). Wir führen zunächst die Abkürzungen

$$[\mathfrak{n}\,\mathfrak{E}(\hat{\mathfrak{r}})]_+ = \mathfrak{L}(\hat{\mathfrak{r}}), \qquad [\mathfrak{n}\,\mathfrak{H}(\hat{\mathfrak{r}})]_+ = \mathfrak{J}(\hat{\mathfrak{r}}) \tag{13.1}$$

ein, und betrachten die Integrale (12.8) in der Form

$$\left.\begin{aligned} \left.\begin{matrix}\mathfrak{E}(\mathfrak{r})\\ 0\end{matrix}\right\} &= \operatorname{rot} \oint_S \mathfrak{L}(\hat{\mathfrak{r}}')\, G(\mathfrak{r} - \hat{\mathfrak{r}}')\, d\hat{\mathfrak{r}}' + i \operatorname{rot}\operatorname{rot} \oint_S \mathfrak{J}(\hat{\mathfrak{r}}')\, G(\mathfrak{r} - \hat{\mathfrak{r}}')\, d\hat{\mathfrak{r}}', \\ \left.\begin{matrix}\mathfrak{H}(\mathfrak{r})\\ 0\end{matrix}\right\} &= \operatorname{rot} \oint_S \mathfrak{J}(\hat{\mathfrak{r}}')\, G(\mathfrak{r} - \hat{\mathfrak{r}}')\, d\hat{\mathfrak{r}}' - i \operatorname{rot}\operatorname{rot} \oint_S \mathfrak{L}(\hat{\mathfrak{r}}')\, G(\mathfrak{r} - \hat{\mathfrak{r}}')\, d\hat{\mathfrak{r}}'. \end{aligned}\right\} \tag{13.2}$$

Zunächst berechnen wir etwa den Grenzwert von

$$\Big[\mathfrak{n} \operatorname{rot} \int_S \mathfrak{J}(\hat{\mathfrak{r}}')\, G(\mathfrak{r} - \hat{\mathfrak{r}}')\, d\hat{\mathfrak{r}}'\Big] = \Big[\mathfrak{n}\big[\nabla \int_S \mathfrak{J}\, G\, d\hat{\mathfrak{r}}'\big]\Big] = \nabla\Big(\mathfrak{n} \int_S \mathfrak{J}\, G\, d\hat{\mathfrak{r}}'\Big) - (\mathfrak{n}\nabla) \int_S \mathfrak{J}\, G\, d\hat{\mathfrak{r}}' \tag{13.3}$$

für $\mathfrak{r}\to\hat{\mathfrak{r}}\pm 0$; dabei bedeute $\mathfrak{n}$ die Normale von (S) im Punkte $\hat{\mathfrak{r}}$, $\mathfrak{J}(\hat{\mathfrak{r}}')$ sei ein zunächst beliebiger stetiger in den Punkten von (S) definierter Vektor, der jeweils *parallel* zur *Tangentialebene* von (S) im Punkte $\hat{\mathfrak{r}}'$ sein soll. Nähert sich nun $\mathfrak{r}$ einem Flächenpunkt $\hat{\mathfrak{r}}$, so läßt sich der Beitrag der Umgebung (S_0) von $\hat{\mathfrak{r}}$ leicht bestimmen. Dazu wählen wir (S_0) so klein, daß es durch den entsprechenden Bereich der Tangentialebene in $\hat{\mathfrak{r}}$ ersetzt werden kann; da nun $\mathfrak{J}$ in dieser Tangentialebene liegt, $\mathfrak{n}$ hingegen auf ihr senkrecht steht, so liefert (S_0) zum ersten Term der rechten Seite von (13.3) keinen Beitrag. Andererseits haben wir den Beitrag von (S_0) zum zweiten Term bereits in Gl. (9.3′) berechnet, daher erhält man jetzt

$$\left.\begin{aligned}\lim_{\mathfrak{r}\to\hat{\mathfrak{r}}\pm 0}&\left[\mathfrak{n}\,\mathrm{rot}\int_S \mathfrak{J}(\hat{\mathfrak{r}}')\,G(\mathfrak{r}-\hat{\mathfrak{r}}')\,d\hat{\mathfrak{r}}'\right]\\ &=\pm\tfrac{1}{2}\mathfrak{J}(\hat{\mathfrak{r}})+\left[\mathfrak{n}\,\mathrm{rot}\,⨍_S \mathfrak{J}(\hat{\mathfrak{r}}')\,G(\hat{\mathfrak{r}}-\hat{\mathfrak{r}}')\,d\hat{\mathfrak{r}}'\right]\\ &=\pm\tfrac{1}{2}\mathfrak{J}(\hat{\mathfrak{r}})-⨍_S[\mathfrak{n}\,[\mathfrak{J}(\hat{\mathfrak{r}}')\,\mathrm{grad}\,G(\hat{\mathfrak{r}}-\hat{\mathfrak{r}}')]]\,d\hat{\mathfrak{r}}';\end{aligned}\right\}\quad(13.4)$$

dabei ist das Integral wieder als *Hauptwert* aufzufassen. Ferner sind die Grenzwerte der Form $\lim\limits_{\mathfrak{r}\to\hat{\mathfrak{r}}\pm 0}\mathrm{rot}\,\mathrm{rot}\int \mathfrak{J}(\hat{\mathfrak{r}}')\,G(\mathfrak{r}-\hat{\mathfrak{r}}'\,d\hat{\mathfrak{r}}'$, die wir in Ziff. 54, 55 und 77 behandeln werden (falls sie existieren), einander gleich: wir wollen sie durch $-\mathrm{rot}⨍[\mathfrak{J}(\hat{\mathfrak{r}}')\,\mathrm{grad}\,G(\hat{\mathfrak{r}}-\hat{\mathfrak{r}}')]\,d\hat{\mathfrak{r}}'$ abkürzen. Mit Hilfe der Grenzwerte (13.4) ergibt sich also aus den Formeln (13.2) sowohl im $\lim \mathfrak{r}\to\hat{\mathfrak{r}}-0$ als auch im $\lim\mathfrak{r}\to\hat{\mathfrak{r}}+0$ bei Beachtung von (13.1) der *allgemeine funktionale Zusammenhang*

$$\left.\begin{aligned}\tfrac{1}{2}\mathfrak{L}(\hat{\mathfrak{r}})&=-⨍\!\!\!\!\oint_S[\mathfrak{n}\,[\mathfrak{L}(\hat{\mathfrak{r}}')\,\mathrm{grad}\,G(\hat{\mathfrak{r}}-\hat{\mathfrak{r}}')]]\,d\hat{\mathfrak{r}}'\\ &\quad-i\left[\mathfrak{n}\,\mathrm{rot}⨍\!\!\!\!\oint_S[\mathfrak{J}(\hat{\mathfrak{r}}')\,\mathrm{grad}\,G(\hat{\mathfrak{r}}-\hat{\mathfrak{r}}')]\,d\hat{\mathfrak{r}}'\right],\\ \tfrac{1}{2}\mathfrak{J}(\hat{\mathfrak{r}})&=-⨍\!\!\!\!\oint_S[\mathfrak{n}\,[\mathfrak{J}(\hat{\mathfrak{r}}')\,\mathrm{grad}\,G(\hat{\mathfrak{r}}-\hat{\mathfrak{r}}')]]\,d\hat{\mathfrak{r}}'\\ &\quad+i\left[\mathfrak{n}\,\mathrm{rot}⨍\!\!\!\!\oint_S[\mathfrak{L}(\hat{\mathfrak{r}}')\,\mathrm{grad}\,G(\hat{\mathfrak{r}}-\hat{\mathfrak{r}}')]\,d\hat{\mathfrak{r}}'\right]\end{aligned}\right\}\quad(13.5)$$

für die Tangentialkomponenten (13.1) der durch die Maxwellschen Gleichungen verknüpften elektrischen und magnetischen Feldstärke eines beliebigen [innerhalb einer Fläche (S) bzw. in T^+ quellenfreien] elektromagnetischen Strahlungsfeldes längs der beliebigen geschlossenen Fläche (S) im Feldraum. Er läßt sich dahingehend interpretieren, daß sich jedes in T^+ quellenfreie Strahlungsfeld $\mathfrak{E}(\mathfrak{r})$, $\mathfrak{H}(\mathfrak{r})$ dort durch die Strahlung von auf (S) fließenden elektrischen und magnetischen Flächenströmen, die durch (13.5) verknüpft sind, ersetzen läßt. Nach außen bzw. in den Raumteil T^- strahlen diese Ströme *nicht*. Diese Interpretation nimmt jedoch erst dann konkrete physikalische Gestalt an, wenn (S) mit der Oberfläche eines gegebenen Körpers zusammenfällt.

14. Elektromagnetisches Sprungwertproblem. Die Gln. (13.5) zeigen wieder, daß auf (S) nur etwa $[\mathfrak{n}\mathfrak{E}]$ oder $[\mathfrak{n}\mathfrak{H}]$ willkürlich vorgegeben werden darf. Setzt man jedoch für *beide* Größen $\mathfrak{L}$ und $\mathfrak{J}$ in Gl. (13.2) *willkürliche* in der *Fläche* (S) liegende Vektoren $\mathfrak{L}_0(\hat{\mathfrak{r}})$ und $\mathfrak{J}_0(\hat{\mathfrak{r}})$ ein [d.h. solche Vektoren, die parallel zur jeweiligen Tangentialebene von (S) in $\hat{\mathfrak{r}}$ sind], so ergibt sich eine Lösung der Maxwellschen Gleichungen in der Gestalt

$$\left.\begin{aligned}\mathfrak{E}(\mathfrak{r})&=\mathrm{rot}\int_S \mathfrak{L}_0(\hat{\mathfrak{r}}')\,G(\mathfrak{r}-\hat{\mathfrak{r}}')\,d\hat{\mathfrak{r}}'+i\,\mathrm{rot}\,\mathrm{rot}\int_S \mathfrak{J}_0(\hat{\mathfrak{r}}')\,G(\mathfrak{r}-\hat{\mathfrak{r}}')\,d\hat{\mathfrak{r}}',\\ \mathfrak{H}(\mathfrak{r})&=\mathrm{rot}\int_S \mathfrak{J}_0(\hat{\mathfrak{r}}')\,G(\mathfrak{r}-\hat{\mathfrak{r}}')\,d\hat{\mathfrak{r}}'-i\,\mathrm{rot}\,\mathrm{rot}\int_S \mathfrak{L}_0(\hat{\mathfrak{r}}')\,G(\mathfrak{r}-\hat{\mathfrak{r}}')\,d\hat{\mathfrak{r}}',\end{aligned}\right\}\quad(14.1)$$

die mit Hilfe des *Greenschen Tensors* auch in der Form

$$\left.\begin{aligned}\mathfrak{E}(\mathfrak{r}) &= \int\limits_S \{\mathfrak{L}_0(\hat{\mathfrak{r}}') \cdot \operatorname{rot} \boldsymbol{\Gamma}(\mathfrak{r}, \hat{\mathfrak{r}}') - i\,\mathfrak{J}_0(\hat{\mathfrak{r}}') \cdot \boldsymbol{\Gamma}(\mathfrak{r}, \hat{\mathfrak{r}}')\}\, d\hat{\mathfrak{r}}', \\ \mathfrak{H}(\mathfrak{r}) &= \int\limits_S \{\mathfrak{J}_0(\hat{\mathfrak{r}}') \cdot \operatorname{rot} \boldsymbol{\Gamma}(\mathfrak{r}, \hat{\mathfrak{r}}') + i\,\mathfrak{L}_0(\hat{\mathfrak{r}}') \cdot \boldsymbol{\Gamma}(\mathfrak{r}, \hat{\mathfrak{r}}')\}\, d\hat{\mathfrak{r}}'\end{aligned}\right\} \tag{14.1'}$$

geschrieben werden können. Hier kann (S) eine beliebige *nicht* notwendig geschlossene Fläche sein. In der Tat ist (14.1), (14.1′) auch für nicht geschlossene Flächen (S) eine Lösung der Maxwellschen Gleichungen (2.1b), wie man direkt mit Hilfe der Umformung

$$\operatorname{rot}\operatorname{rot} \int \mathfrak{J}(\hat{\mathfrak{r}}')\, G(\mathfrak{r} - \hat{\mathfrak{r}}')\, d\hat{\mathfrak{r}}' = (\operatorname{grad}\operatorname{div} + 1) \int \mathfrak{J}(\hat{\mathfrak{r}}')\, G(\mathfrak{r} - \hat{\mathfrak{r}}')\, d\hat{\mathfrak{r}}'$$

bestätigen kann. Die Größen $\mathfrak{L}_0$ bzw. $\mathfrak{J}_0$ sind jetzt nicht mehr die Randwerte sondern die *Sprungwerte*, die die Tangentialkomponenten der elektrischen bzw. magnetischen Feldstärke beim Hindurchtreten durch (S) von der positiven nach der negativen Seite erleiden [es sei denn $\mathfrak{L}_0$ und $\mathfrak{J}_0$ stehen in dem Zusammenhang (13.5), der bewirkt, daß die Integrale in T^- verschwinden]:

$$\mathfrak{L}_0(\hat{\mathfrak{r}}) = [\mathfrak{n}, \mathfrak{E}_+ - \mathfrak{E}_-], \qquad \mathfrak{J}_0(\hat{\mathfrak{r}}) = [\mathfrak{n}, \mathfrak{H}_+ - \mathfrak{H}_-]. \tag{14.2}$$

Dies folgt unmittelbar durch Berechnung der Grenzwerte von (14.1) zu beiden Seiten der Fläche (S) mit Hilfe von Gl. (13.4).

Mit Hilfe des Huygensschen Prinzips (12.8) bis (12.8c) läßt sich auch leicht zeigen, daß durch Vorgabe der beiden *Sprungwerte* (14.2) und unter Zuhilfenahme der vektoriellen Ausstrahlungsbedingung (Ziff. 18) eine Lösung der Maxwellschen Gleichungen *eindeutig* definiert ist; die Unstetigkeitsfläche (S) ist dabei wieder durch eine sich ihr beiderseits anschmiegende Hülle aus dem Feldgebiet auszuschließen. Die Formeln (14.1) bzw. (14.1′) stellen also das genaue elektromagnetische Analogon des Kirchhoffschen Integrals (10.1) dar[1].

15. Die historische Entwicklung der Lösung des elektromagnetischen Sprungwertproblems hat einen Umweg gemacht[2]. Das vektorielle Huygenssche Prinzip in der Form (12.8) wurde von Lorentz[3] auf Grund seines Reziprozitätstheorems angedeutet und von Larmor[4] mit Hilfe physikalischer Überlegungen gewonnen. Später hat Tedone[5] das Prinzip in der Gestalt (12.6′), (12.7) abgeleitet. Mit Hilfe dieser Form, die immer wieder in der Literatur auftauchte[6], ist es aber schwierig, die Lösung des *Sprungwertproblems* für *berandete* Flächenstücke zu erhalten; bei diesem können ja nur die Sprungwerte der *Tangentialkomponenten* von $\mathfrak{E}$ und $\mathfrak{H}$ vorgegeben werden (im vorstehenden mit $\mathfrak{L}_0$ und $\mathfrak{J}_0$ bezeichnet), während die Sprungwerte der Normalkomponenten daraus mit Hilfe der Maxwellschen Gleichungen berechnet werden müssen (Ziff. 3). Ferner genügen die Flächenintegrale rechterhand in (12.6′), (12.7) — auf berandete Flächen angewandt — *nicht* mehr den Maxwellschen Gleichungen. Man überzeugt sich in der Tat leicht (durch Umformung mit Hilfe des Stokesschen

[1] Vgl. auch W. Franz: Proc. Phys. Soc. Lond. **63**, 925 (1950). — L. de Broglie: Problemes de propagation guides des ondes electromagnetiques. Paris 1951.

[2] Vgl. dazu die Darstellung in B. B. Baker and E. T. Copson: The Mathematical Theory of Huygens' Principle, S. 102ff. Oxford 1950.

[3] H. A. Lorentz: Nederl. Akad. Wet., Verslag Afd. Natuurk. **4**, 176 (1884).

[4] J. Larmor: Proc. Lond. Math. Soc. **1**, 1 (1903).

[5] O. Tedone: Atti Accad. Naz. Lincei, Rend., Ser. V, **26**, 286 (1917). Tedone behandelt das Problem für eine beliebige Zeitabhängigkeit, während wir stets nur zeitlich rein periodische Fälle betrachten.

[6] Vgl. W. v. Ignatowsky: Ann. Phys. **23**, 875 (1907); **25**, 99 (1908). Weitere Literatur bei C. J. Bouwkamp: Progr. Phys. **17**, 35 (1954) (§ 5).

Satzes), daß die Operation $i\,\mathrm{rot}$ — auf (12.7) angewandt — jetzt nur bis auf ein *Linienintegral* über den Rand von (S) in Gl. (12.6′) übergeht {für $[\mathfrak{n}\mathfrak{E}]$ und $[\mathfrak{n}\mathfrak{H}]$ hat man sich jetzt die vorgegebenen *Sprungwerte* $\mathfrak{L}_0$ und $\mathfrak{J}_0$ eingesetzt zu denken, für $(\mathfrak{n}\mathfrak{E})$ und $(\mathfrak{n}\mathfrak{H})$ die daraus nach Ziff. 3 zu berechnenden Sprungwerte $-i\,\widehat{\mathrm{div}}\,\mathfrak{J}_0$ und $i\,\widehat{\mathrm{div}}\,\mathfrak{L}_0$}. Um daher für berandete Flächen Lösungen der Maxwellschen Gleichungen zu erhalten, muß man zu (12.6′) und (12.7) entsprechende Linienintegrale hinzufügen. Diese wurden erstmals von KOTTLER[1] abgeleitet und durch auf dem *Rande sitzende „elektrische und magnetische Linienladungen“* gedeutet. Die von KOTTLER angegebenen Randintegrale lassen sich jedoch mit Hilfe des Stokeschen Satzes in Flächenintegrale verwandeln. Dies führt — wie FRANZ[2] gezeigt hat — genau wieder auf die Gln. (14.1). Das Abspalten von Randintegralen von Gl. (14.1) ist jedoch im allgemeinen unzweckmäßig, da dadurch der Charakter von (S) als *Sprungfläche* für die Werte der *Tangentialkomponenten der Feldvektoren* verwischt wird.

Wählt man andererseits die Sprungwerte $\mathfrak{L}_0$ und $\mathfrak{J}_0$ als Tangentialkomponenten irgendeiner speziellen Lösung $\mathfrak{E}_0$, $\mathfrak{H}_0$ der Maxwellschen Gleichungen: $\mathfrak{L}_0=[\mathfrak{n}\mathfrak{E}_0]$ und $\mathfrak{J}_0=[\mathfrak{n}\mathfrak{H}_0]$, so lassen sich die Flächenintegrale (14.1) *vollständig* in *Randintegrale* überführen, da der Tensor $\boldsymbol{\Phi}$ im wesentlichen quellenfrei ist (Ziff. 32). Dies erlaubt zwar eine anschauliche Interpretation *(Youngsches Prinzip)*, dabei bleibt allerdings offen, wie Sprungflächen mit den genannten Eigenschaften zu realisieren sind. *Reale Sprungflächen* für die Tangentialkomponente des *magnetischen* Vektors stellen ideal leitende (unendlich dünne) Schirme sowie die Oberflächen ideal leitender Körper dar (Flächenstrom, vgl. Abschn. III a2 und III d1). Das Abspalten von Randintegralen (die bei Annäherung des Aufpunktes gegen einen Randpunkt *divergieren*) führt hier zu einer allgemeinen Einschränkung des Flächenstromes (*Kantenbedingung*, vgl. Ziff. 55).

Zusammenfassend betonen wir, daß die Helmholtzsche Formel (8.5) und ihr elektromagnetisches Analogon (12.8), (12.8b), (12.8c) eine in *Strenge gültige* mathematische Formulierung des Huygensschen Prinzips darstellen. Das Kirchhoffsche Integral (10.1) bzw. seine elektromagnetische Fassung (14.1), (14.1′) liefern andererseits eine Lösung der Wellengleichung bzw. der Maxwellschen Gleichungen, die längs einer gegebenen Fläche die vorgegebenen *Sprungwerte* des *Funktionswerts und der Normalableitung* bzw. der *Tangentialkomponenten der Feldvektoren* $\mathfrak{E}$, $\mathfrak{H}$ besitzt. Die Lösung ist in beiden Fällen bei Hinzunahme der Ausstrahlungsbedingung (Ziff. 18) eindeutig.

d) Über Eindeutigkeit, Ausstrahlungs- und Kantenbedingung.

Ist das Feld allseitig durch einen Leiter auf einen *endlichen* Raumbereich beschränkt (Hohlleiter), so stellen sich (bei homogenener Randbedingung) *Eigenschwingungen* ein, d.h. es gibt nur für eine *diskrete* Folge von Werten der Frequenz ω bzw. der Wellenzahl k Lösungen unseres Randwertproblems. Diese Eigenlösungen sind als *stehende Wellen* zu interpretieren, die durch Reflexion am Rande des Feldgebiets zustande kommen.

Reicht das Feld jedoch allseitig ins Unendliche — dieser Fall liegt ja gerade bei den Beugungsproblemen vor — so müssen wir die Forderung stellen, daß eine Reflexion („Echo“) aus dem Unendlichen ausbleibt. Es genügt also nicht allein — wie in der Potentialtheorie — ein hinreichendes Verschwinden im Unendlichen zu fordern, sondern die von den (im endlichen gelegenen) Feldquellen ge-

[1] F. KOTTLER: Ann. Phys. **71**, 457 (1923). Siehe auch I. A. STRATTON u. L. I. CHU: Phys. Rev. **56**, 99 (1939).

[2] W. FRANZ: Z. Physik **125**, 563 (1949).

lieferte Energie muß ins Unendliche *abgestrahlt* werden *(Ausstrahlungsbedingung)* unter Ausschluß von Einstrahlung aus dem Unendlichen. Die Energiestromdichte *(Poyntingscher Vektor)* muß also in großer Entfernung von den Quellen und beugenden Körpern überall nach *außen* gerichtet sein. Wir werden sehen, daß diese heuristisch physikalische Forderung zugleich hinreichend und notwendig ist, um im allgemeinen die mathematische *Eindeutigkeit* des Problems zu erzwingen.

16. Behandlung quadratischer Feldgrößen. Bei der Betrachtung der Energiestromdichte $\mathfrak{S} = [\mathfrak{E}\,\mathfrak{H}]$ bzw. der Energiedichte $w = \frac{1}{2}(\mathfrak{E}^2 + \mathfrak{H}^2)$ treten die Produkte bzw. Quadrate der Feldkomponenten auf, so daß man zu ihrer reellen Darstellung übergehen muß. Da wir uns jedoch nur für den zeitlichen Mittelwert dieser Größen interessieren, können wir auch hier mit komplexen Feldvektoren rechnen, wenn wir folgende Regel beachten: Bezeichnet $\mathfrak{A}_\nu = |\mathfrak{A}_\nu|\, e^{i(\Phi_\nu - \omega t)}$ eine komplexe Feldkomponente, $\widehat{\mathfrak{A}}_\nu = |\mathfrak{A}_\nu| \cos(\Phi_\nu - \omega t)$ (vorübergehend) ihren Realteil (reelle Feldkomponente), so berechnet sich der zeitliche *Mittelwert* des Produktes zweier *reeller* Feldkomponenten $\widehat{\mathfrak{A}}_\nu$ und $\widehat{\mathfrak{A}}_\mu$ wie folgt[1]

$$\left.\begin{aligned}\frac{\omega}{2\pi}\int_0^{\frac{2\pi}{\omega}} \widehat{\mathfrak{A}}_\nu \widehat{\mathfrak{A}}_\mu\, dt &= \frac{\omega}{2\pi} |\mathfrak{A}_\nu|\,|\mathfrak{A}_\mu| \int_0^{\frac{2\pi}{\omega}} \cos(\Phi_\nu - \omega t)\cos(\Phi_\mu - \omega t)\, dt \\ &= \frac{1}{2}|\mathfrak{A}_\nu|\,|\mathfrak{A}_\mu| \cos(\Phi_\nu - \Phi_\mu) = \frac{1}{2}\operatorname{Re}\{\mathfrak{A}_\nu \mathfrak{A}_\mu^*\}.\end{aligned}\right\} \tag{16.1}$$

Wir wollen diesen (reellen) Mittelwert mit $\overline{\mathfrak{A}_\nu \mathfrak{A}_\mu}$ bezeichnen und erhalten somit

$$\overline{\mathfrak{A}_\nu \mathfrak{A}_\mu} = \tfrac{1}{2}\operatorname{Re}\{\mathfrak{A}_\nu \mathfrak{A}_\mu^*\}. \tag{16.2}$$

Verstehen wir also wie bisher unter $\mathfrak{E}$ und $\mathfrak{H}$ *komplexe* Vektoren (mit der Zeitabhängigkeit $e^{-i\omega t}$), so folgt in verständlicher Schreibweise

$$\left.\begin{aligned}&\overline{\mathfrak{S}} = \overline{[\mathfrak{E}\,\mathfrak{H}]} = \tfrac{1}{2}\operatorname{Re}[\mathfrak{E}\,\mathfrak{H}^*] = \tfrac{1}{4}\{[\mathfrak{E}\,\mathfrak{H}^*] + [\mathfrak{E}^*\,\mathfrak{H}]\}\\ &\qquad \textit{(zeitlicher Mittelwert der Energiestromdichte)},\\ &\overline{w} = \tfrac{1}{4}(\mathfrak{E}\,\mathfrak{E}^* + \mathfrak{H}\,\mathfrak{H}^*)\\ &\qquad \textit{(zeitlicher Mittelwert der Feldenergiedichte)}.\end{aligned}\right\} \tag{16.3}$$

Aus den Maxwellschen Gleichungen (2.1b) folgt nun in bekannter Weise

$$\operatorname{div}\overline{\mathfrak{S}} = \overline{w}_0; \tag{16.4}$$

dabei ist $\overline{w}_0 = -\frac{1}{2}\operatorname{Re}(\mathfrak{j}\,\mathfrak{E}^*)$ die im Zeitmittel von den Feldquellen (Strömen) gelieferte Energie. Für ein quellenfreies elektromagnetisches Feld ($\mathfrak{j} = 0$) ist also der zeitliche Mittelwert der Energiestromdichte quellenfrei, wie es sein muß.

Für das zweidimensionale Problem ($\partial/\partial y = 0$) ergibt sich sowohl im p- wie im s-Fall mit Hilfe der Gln. (4.1 p, s) für das Zeitmittel der Energiestromdichte

$$\overline{\mathfrak{S}} = \frac{i}{4}(v \operatorname{grad} v^* - v^* \operatorname{grad} v) = \frac{1}{2}\operatorname{Im}\{v^* \operatorname{grad} v\}. \tag{16.5}$$

Da v und v^* der Wellengleichung (4.1) genügen, so kann man wieder leicht bestätigen, daß $\overline{\mathfrak{S}}$ quellenfrei ist. Für den zeitlichen Mittelwert der Energiedichte ergibt sich hier

$$\overline{w} = \tfrac{1}{4}(|v|^2 + |\operatorname{grad} v|^2). \tag{16.6}$$

[1] Der Stern * bedeutet den Übergang zur konjugiert komplexen Größe.

Auch im dreidimensionalen Fall ($\partial/\partial y \neq 0$) haben die Ausdrücke (16.5) und (16.6) eine (akustisch modifizierte) Bedeutung.

d 1) Die Ausstrahlungsbedingung.

Nach diesen Vorbereitungen wollen wir nun dazu übergehen, die Ausstrahlungsbedingung zu formulieren und wählen dazu den zuerst von A. SOMMERFELD[1] eingeschlagenen, anschaulichen Weg über das Huygenssche Prinzip.

17. Die skalare Ausstrahlungsbedingung. Wir stellen das skalare Problem voran, wenden daher Gl. (8.5) auf eine Fläche an, die aus den beiden geschlossenen Flächen (S) und $(\bar{S})$ bestehe, so daß (S) alle Feldquellen (Quellen des Pointingschen Vektors) und beugenden Körper umschließe, während $(\bar{S})$ eine Kugelfläche sei, deren Radius r' nach Unendlich strebe [der Koordinatenursprung liege in dem von (S) umschlossenen Gebiet]. Wir wollen untersuchen, welchen Bedingungen v zu unterwerfen ist, damit das Flächenintegral über $(\bar{S})$ *verschwindet* (das Unendliche soll *keinen* Beitrag zum Feld liefern):

$$\lim_{r'\to\infty} \oint_{\bar{S}} \left\{ v(\hat{\mathfrak{r}}') \frac{\partial}{\partial r'} - \frac{\partial v(\hat{\mathfrak{r}}')}{\partial r'} \right\} G(\mathfrak{r} - \hat{\mathfrak{r}}')\, r'^2\, d\omega' = 0 \tag{17.1}$$

($d\omega$ = Flächenelement der Einheitskugel). Setzen wir hier für $G(\mathfrak{r} - \hat{\mathfrak{r}}')$ die Darstellung $\frac{1}{4\pi} \exp \frac{iR}{R}$, Gl. (8.3), mit $R = |\mathfrak{r} - \hat{\mathfrak{r}}'| \to r'$ ein, so folgt

$$\lim_{r'\to\infty} \left\{ \oint_{\bar{S}} r' \left(\frac{\partial v}{\partial r'} - i v \right) e^{ir'} d\omega' + \oint_{\bar{S}} v\, e^{ir'} d\omega' \right\} = 0. \tag{17.1 a}$$

Es ist also hinreichend, zu fordern

$$\lim_{r\to\infty} r \left(\frac{\partial v}{\partial r} - i v \right) = 0 \tag{17.2}$$

und

$$r v \textit{ beschränkt für } r \to \infty. \tag{17.2a}$$

Gl. (17.2) ist die nach SOMMERFELD benannte *Ausstrahlungsbedingung*, Gl. (17.2a) die „*Endlichkeitsbedingung*". Beide Gleichungen sollen auf allen Radien, d.h. gleichmäßig für alle Polarwinkel ϑ, φ gelten. Wie RELLICH[2] gezeigt hat, ist (17.2a) als zusätzliche Forderung allerdings *überflüssig*, denn sie ist automatisch erfüllt, wenn (17.2) gilt. Integrieren wir (17.2) mit Hilfe von (17.2a), so folgt asymptotisch

$$v(\mathfrak{r}) \to A(\vartheta, \varphi) \frac{e^{ir}}{r} \quad \text{für } r \to \infty \tag{17.2b}$$

mit beliebiger Amplitude $A(\vartheta, \varphi)$ (Integrationskonstante). Die Ausstrahlungsbedingung besagt also, daß jedes Wellenfeld sich im Unendlichen wie eine *ausstrahlende Kugelwelle* $\exp[i(r - \omega t)]/r$ (mit einer aus dem jeweiligen speziellen Problem zu bestimmenden Richtungsverteilung) verhalten muß.

Bei *ebenen* Problemen haben wir für die Greensche Funktion des freien Raumes die Darstellung $\frac{i}{4} H_0^1(R)$, Gl. (8.3a), zu verwenden, die asymptotisch in die Form $G(\mathfrak{r} - \hat{\mathfrak{r}}') \to \sim \exp(ir')/\sqrt{r'}$ übergeht, so daß man auf demselben Wege wie oben zu der Ausstrahlungsbedingung

$$\lim_{r\to\infty} \sqrt{r} \left(\frac{\partial v}{\partial r} - i v \right) = 0; \quad r v \text{ beschränkt für } r \to \infty \tag{17.3}$$

[1] A. SOMMERFELD: Jber. dtsch. Math.-Ver. **21**, 309 (1912).
[2] F. RELLICH: Jber. dtsch. Math.-Ver. **53**, 57 (1943).

bzw.

$$v(\mathfrak{r}) \to A(\varphi)\,\frac{e^{ir}}{\sqrt{r}} \qquad \text{für } r \to \infty \tag{17.3a}$$

gelangt.

18. Die vektorielle Ausstrahlungsbedingung. Bevor wir nun die Ausstrahlungsbedingung mit der Energiestromdichte in Zusammenhang bringen, soll das elektromagnetische Problem betrachtet werden. Hierzu greifen wir auf das vektorielle Huygenssche Prinzip (12.6′), (12.7) zurück und verlangen wieder, daß die Fläche $(\overline{S})$ keinen Beitrag liefert, falls das Feldgebiet durch die beiden Flächen (S) und $(\overline{S})$ begrenzt wird. Zunächst folgt aus Gl. (8.3) asymptotisch für $r' \to \infty$

$$\nabla' G(\mathfrak{r}-\hat{\mathfrak{r}}') \to -\left(i - \frac{1}{r'}\right)\mathfrak{e}'\,G(\mathfrak{r}-\hat{\mathfrak{r}}') \qquad \text{für } r' \to \infty, \tag{18.1}$$

wobei $\mathfrak{e}$ die nach außen gerichtete Normale von $(\overline{S})$ ist (vgl. Fig. 9). Der Beitrag von $(\overline{S})$ zu Gl. (12.6′) lautet daher

$$\left.\begin{aligned}&\oint\limits_{\overline{S}}\left\{i\,[\mathfrak{e}'\,\mathfrak{H}] + [[\mathfrak{e}'\,\mathfrak{E}]\,\mathfrak{e}']\left(i-\frac{1}{r'}\right) + (\mathfrak{e}'\,\mathfrak{E})\,\mathfrak{e}'\left(i-\frac{1}{r'}\right)\right\}G(\mathfrak{r}-\hat{\mathfrak{r}}')\,d\hat{\mathfrak{r}}'\\ &\qquad = \oint\limits_{\overline{S}}\left\{i\,[\mathfrak{e}'\,\mathfrak{H}] + \left(i-\frac{1}{r'}\right)\mathfrak{E}\right\}G(\mathfrak{r}-\hat{\mathfrak{r}}')\,d\hat{\mathfrak{r}}'.\end{aligned}\right\} \tag{18.2}$$

Da dies für $r' \to \infty$ verschwinden soll:

$$\lim_{r'\to\infty}\left\{i\oint\limits_{\overline{S}} r'\left([\mathfrak{e}'\,\mathfrak{H}] + \mathfrak{E}\right)e^{ir'}\,d\omega' - \oint\limits_{\overline{S}}\mathfrak{E}\,e^{ir'}\,d\omega'\right\} = 0,$$

ist also hinreichend zu fordern

$$\lim_{r\to\infty} r\left(\mathfrak{E} + [\mathfrak{e}\,\mathfrak{H}]\right) = 0; \qquad r\,\mathfrak{E} \text{ beschränkt für } r \to \infty. \tag{18.3}$$

Ganz entsprechend folgt mit Hilfe von (12.7)

$$\lim_{r\to\infty} r\left(\mathfrak{H} - [\mathfrak{e}\,\mathfrak{E}]\right) = 0; \qquad r\,\mathfrak{H} \text{ beschränkt für } r \to \infty. \tag{18.3a}$$

Dies sind sie „*elektromagnetischen Ausstrahlungsbedingungen*", wie sie von CL. MÜLLER[1] formuliert worden sind. Aus ihnen folgt zunächst, daß die Normalkomponenten $(\mathfrak{e}\,\mathfrak{E})$ und $(\mathfrak{e}\,\mathfrak{H})$ ($\mathfrak{e}$ = Einheitsvektor in Richtung von $\mathfrak{r}$) asymptotisch *stärker* verschwinden als die Tangentialkomponenten: *das Fernfeld ist rein transversal; die Tangentialkomponenten von elektrischer und magnetischer Feldstärke haben den gleichen absoluten Betrag.* Die Integration der Ausstrahlungsbedingungen (18.3), (18.3a) ergibt

$$\left.\begin{aligned}\mathfrak{E}(\mathfrak{r}) &\to \left\{[\mathfrak{e}\,\mathfrak{P}(\mathfrak{e})] + [\mathfrak{e}\,[\mathfrak{e}\,\mathfrak{M}(\mathfrak{e})]]\right\}\frac{e^{ir}}{r},\\ \mathfrak{H}(\mathfrak{r}) &\to \left\{[\mathfrak{e}\,[\mathfrak{e}\,\mathfrak{P}(\mathfrak{e})]] - [\mathfrak{e}\,\mathfrak{M}(\mathfrak{e})]\right\}\frac{e^{ir}}{r}\end{aligned}\right\} \text{ für } r \to \infty. \tag{18.4}$$

Das elektromagnetische Fernfeld hat also die Gestalt eines Strahlungskomplexes, der sich als allgemeine Multipolstrahlung interpretieren läßt. $\mathfrak{P}(\mathfrak{e})$ und $\mathfrak{M}(\mathfrak{e})$ sind nur von den Polarwinkeln ϑ, φ abhängige Vektoren, die aus dem jeweiligen speziellen Problem bestimmt werden müssen.

---

[1] CL. MÜLLER: Abh. dtsch. Akad. Wiss. Nr. 3 (1950). Siehe auch A. E. HEINS u. S. SILVER: Proc. Cambridge Phil. Soc. **51**, 149 (1955).

19. Der Energiestrom im Unendlichen; der Satz von Rellich. Wir berechnen nun den mittleren Energiestrom durch die unendlich ferne Fläche $(\bar{S})$. Für den skalaren Fall folgt mit Hilfe von (16.5) und der Ausstrahlungsbedingung (17.2)

$$\oint_{\bar{S}} (\mathfrak{e}\,\bar{\mathfrak{S}})\,d\sigma = \frac{i}{4}\oint_{\bar{S}}\left(v\,\frac{\partial v^*}{\partial r} - v^*\,\frac{\partial v}{\partial r}\right) r^2\,d\omega = \frac{1}{2}\oint_{\bar{S}} v\,v^*\,r^2\,d\omega\,. \tag{19.1}$$

Andererseits folgt aus (16.3) und der elektromagnetischen Ausstrahlungsbedingung (18.3), (18.3a)

$$\left.\begin{aligned}\oint_{\bar{S}} (\mathfrak{e}\,\bar{\mathfrak{S}})\,d\sigma &= \tfrac{1}{4}\oint_{\bar{S}}\{([\mathfrak{e}\,\mathfrak{E}]\,\mathfrak{H}^*) - (\mathfrak{E}^*\,[\mathfrak{e}\,\mathfrak{H}])\}\,r^2\,d\omega\\ &= \tfrac{1}{4}\oint_{\bar{S}}\{(\mathfrak{E}\,\mathfrak{E}^*) + (\mathfrak{H}\,\mathfrak{H}^*)\}\,r^2\,d\omega\\ &= \tfrac{1}{2}\oint_{\bar{S}}(\mathfrak{E}\,\mathfrak{E}^*)\,r^2\,d\omega = \tfrac{1}{2}\oint_{\bar{S}}(\mathfrak{H}\,\mathfrak{H}^*)\,r^2\,d\omega\,.\end{aligned}\right\} \tag{19.2}$$

Wie man aus diesen Gleichungen erkennt, sorgt die Ausstrahlungsbedingung also in der Tat dafür, daß die Energieströmung im Unendlichen *nach außen* gerichtet ist (positiv definite Integranden).

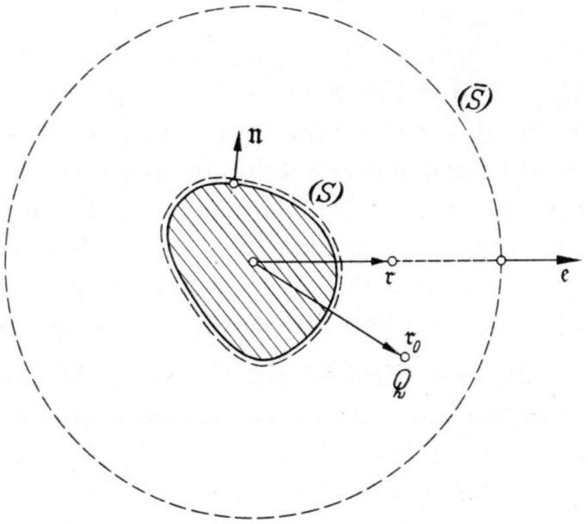

Fig. 9. Zum Eindeutigkeitsbeweis.

Die Abnahme des Feldes mit $1/r$ wie sie in (17.2b) bzw. (18.4) zum Ausdruck kommt, hat ihren physikalischen Grund darin, daß der Energiestrom (19.1) bzw. (19.2) durch alle Kugelflächen $r = \text{const}$ derselbe sein muß, falls diese Flächen nur alle Quellen und beugenden Körper umhüllen, denn es kann zwischen zwei solchen Flächen keine Energie entstehen oder versickern. Aus (17.2b) und (19.1) bzw. (18.4) und (19.2) erkennt man aber unmittelbar, daß der Energiestrom asymptotisch von r unabhängig ist. Bei Ausstrahlungsphänomenen ist daher ganz allgemein eine stärkere Feldabnahme wie $1/r$ nicht möglich (im Gegensatz zu statischen Problemen): *Jedes Feld, das stärker als $1/r$ zu Null geht, verschwindet identisch im ganzen Raum.*

Dieser Satz von Rellich (l. c.) soll im folgenden analytisch näher erläutert werden. Wir gehen auf das Helmholtzsche Integral (8.5) zurück, legen die Randbedingung $v = 0$ auf den beugenden Körpern (S) zugrunde und wählen die Integrationsfläche so, daß sie sich deren Oberflächen eng anschmiegt. Im Unendlichen begrenzen wir das Feldgebiet wieder durch die Fläche $(\bar{S})$ (s. Fig. 9). Diese liefert keinen Beitrag (zufolge der Ausstrahlungsbedingung), daher folgt

$$v(\mathfrak{r}) = -\oint_{S}\frac{\partial v(\hat{\mathfrak{r}}')}{\partial n'}\,G(\mathfrak{r} - \hat{\mathfrak{r}}')\,d\hat{\mathfrak{r}}'\,. \tag{19.3}$$

Hier können wir G in eine Reihe

$$\left.\begin{aligned} G(\mathfrak{r} - \hat{\mathfrak{r}}') &= \frac{e^{ir}}{4\pi r}\sum_{\nu=0}^{\infty}\frac{g_\nu(\mathfrak{e},\hat{\mathfrak{r}}')}{r^\nu}\\ g_0 &= e^{-i(\mathfrak{e}\hat{\mathfrak{r}}')}\end{aligned}\right\} \tag{19.4}$$

entwickeln (wobei die g_ν nicht von r abhängen), die für alle r absolut und gleichmäßig konvergiert, für die die Kugeln $r=\text{const}$ die beugenden Körper und Quellen Q im Inneren enthalten. Damit folgt aus (19.3)

$$\left.\begin{aligned} v(\mathfrak{r}) &= \frac{e^{ir}}{r}\sum_{\nu=0}^{\infty}\frac{v_\nu(\mathfrak{e})}{r^\nu} \\ \text{mit}\qquad v_\nu(\mathfrak{e}) &= -\frac{1}{4\pi}\oint\limits_S \frac{\partial v(\hat{\mathfrak{r}}')}{\partial n'}\, g_\nu(\mathfrak{e},\hat{\mathfrak{r}}')\, d\hat{\mathfrak{r}}'. \end{aligned}\right\} \tag{19.3a}$$

Mit Hilfe der Wellengleichung (4.1) läßt sich nun eine *Rekursionsformel* für die winkelabhängigen Größen $v_\nu(\mathfrak{e})$ ableiten[1], aus der folgt, daß alle v_ν verschwinden, wenn v_0 verschwindet. Das ist aber gerade der Satz von Rellich.

Für elektromagnetische Probleme erhalten wir für die Randbedingung $[\mathfrak{n}\mathfrak{E}]=0$ auf (S) auf einem ganz entsprechenden Wege aus den Franzschen Formeln (12.8)

$$\left.\begin{aligned} \mathfrak{E}(\mathfrak{r}) &= i\,\mathrm{rot}\,\mathrm{rot}\oint\limits_S [\mathfrak{n}'\,\mathfrak{H}(\hat{\mathfrak{r}})]\, G(\mathfrak{r}-\hat{\mathfrak{r}}')\, d\hat{\mathfrak{r}}', \\ \mathfrak{H}(\mathfrak{r}) &= \mathrm{rot}\oint\limits_S [\mathfrak{n}'\,\mathfrak{H}(\hat{\mathfrak{r}}')]\, G(\mathfrak{r}-\hat{\mathfrak{r}}')\, d\hat{\mathfrak{r}}'. \end{aligned}\right\} \tag{19.5}$$

Hier können wir wieder die Entwicklung (19.4) einsetzen und erhalten dann Reihen der Form (19.3a), deren Glieder nur dann nicht sämtlich verschwinden, wenn das erste Glied von Null verschieden ist: Auch elektromagnetische Ausstrahlungslösungen können nicht stärker als $1/r$ zu Null gehen. Dies folgt schon daraus, daß jede *kartesische* Feldkomponente der Wellengleichung (4.4) genügt.

Ganz analog läßt sich schließlich zeigen, daß keine Ausstrahlungslösung der *zweidimensionalen* Wellengleichung (4.2) stärker als $1/\sqrt{r}$ verschwinden darf, da hier die Flächen konstanter Energieströmung Zylinder (vom Umfang $2\pi r$) sind.

20. Der Eindeutigkeitsbeweis. Klassifizierung von Beugungsproblemen. Nachdem wir die Energieverhältnisse im Unendlichen durch die Ausstrahlungsbedingung festgelegt haben, ist es leicht, die *Eindeutigkeit* der Lösung des Beugungsproblems zu beweisen. Sie ergibt sich unmittelbar durch Anwendung des Energiesatzes.

Beim skalaren Beugungsproblem suchen wir eine Funktion v, die

I. *der Wellengleichung* $\Delta v + v = 0$ *bei vorgegebener Feldsingularität der Ergiebigkeit* $\mathrm{div}\,\overline{\mathfrak{S}} = W_0\,\delta(\mathfrak{r}-\mathfrak{r}_0)$,

II. *der Randbedingung* $v=0$ *oder* $\partial v/\partial n = 0$ *auf* (S),

III. *der Ausstrahlungsbedingung* (17.2) *genügt.*

Integrieren wir nun die Quelldichte $\mathrm{div}\,\overline{\mathfrak{S}}$ mit $\overline{\mathfrak{S}}$ aus Gl. (16.5) über das gesamte Feldgebiet mit den Begrenzungen (S) und $(\bar{S})$ (s. Fig. 9), so folgt mit Hilfe des Gaußschen Satzes und Gl. (19.1)

$$W_0 = \frac{1}{2}\lim_{r\to\infty}\oint\limits_{\bar{S}} v\,v^*\,r^2\,d\omega. \tag{20.1}$$

Der beugende Körper (S) tritt in dieser Gleichung explizit nicht mehr in Erscheinung, seine Oberfläche liefert *infolge der Randbedingung keinen Beitrag.* Dies muß so sein, da sie Energie weder emittieren noch absorbieren darf. Nehmen wir nun an, es gäbe zwei Lösungen $v^{(1)}$ und $v^{(2)}$ unseres Beugungsproblems I—III,

[1] Vgl. A. Sommerfeld: Vorlesungen über theoretische Physik, Bd. VI, S. 194. Wiesbaden 1947. — Siehe auch W. Magnus: Jber. dtsch. Math.-Ver. **52**, 177 (1942).

so hat das Differenzfeld $v = v^{(1)} - v^{(2)}$ die Ergiebigkeit $W_0 = 0$, daher muß in (20.1) das Integral verschwinden. Dies ist nur möglich, falls v *stärker* als $1/r$ im Unendlichen verschwindet; nach dem Satz von RELLICH muß daher v identisch verschwinden. Damit ist die Eindeutigkeit $v^{(1)} = v^{(2)}$ bewiesen.

Ist an Stelle der homogenen Randbedingung II die allgemeinere Randbedingung:

$$\text{IIa.} \quad v = \varphi_0 \quad \textit{oder} \quad \frac{\partial v}{\partial n} = \psi_0 \text{ auf } (S)$$

vorgegeben (mit gegebenen Funktionen φ_0, ψ_0), so genügt das *Differenzfeld* $v^{(1)} - v^{(2)}$ der Randbedingung II. Daraus läßt sich wie oben die Eindeutigkeit des Randwertproblems I, IIa, III, beweisen, was wir in Ziff. 9 bereits benutzt haben.

Das vektorielle Beugungsproblem ist mit Hilfe der Daten

I'. $\mathfrak{E}$, $\mathfrak{H}$ *genügen den Maxwellschen Gleichungen* (2.1b) *mit vorgegebener Feldsingularität der Ergiebigkeit* $\operatorname{div} \overline{\mathfrak{S}} = W_0 \delta(\mathfrak{r} - \mathfrak{r}_0)$ (*oder vorgegebener Stromdichte* $\mathfrak{j}$).

II'. $\mathfrak{E}$ *genügt der Randbedingung* $[\mathfrak{n}\mathfrak{E}] = 0$ *auf* (*S*) (*oder* $\mathfrak{H}$ *der Randbedingung* $[\mathfrak{n}\mathfrak{H}] = 0$);

III'. $\mathfrak{E}$, $\mathfrak{H}$ *genügen der Ausstrahlungsbedingung* (18.3, 3a)

zu lösen. Der Gaußsche Satz, angewandt auf den Vektor $\overline{\mathfrak{S}}$, Gl. (16.3), liefert hier mit Hilfe von (19.2)

$$W_0 = \tfrac{1}{4} \lim_{r \to \infty} \oint_{S} \{(\mathfrak{E}\mathfrak{E}^*) + (\mathfrak{H}\mathfrak{H}^*)\} r^2 \, d\omega. \tag{20.2}$$

Da das Differenzfeld zweier möglicher Lösungen des Problems I'—III' wieder quellenfrei ist, folgt auch hier aus (20.2) sofort die Eindeutigkeit, da kein elektromagnetisches Feld im Unendlichen stärker als $1/r$ verschwinden kann, es sei denn, es verschwindet identisch. Die tiefer liegende Frage nach der *Existenz* von Lösungen unseres Beugungsproblems wurde von H. WEYL und CL. MÜLLER im Anschluß an die Integralgleichungstheorie der Beugung eingehend erörtert; s. dazu Ziff. 77, 81 und 82.

Es ergibt sich nun auch unmittelbar, daß es bei Beugungsproblemen *keine* singularitätenfreien Lösungen der (homogenen) Wellengleichung bzw. der Maxwellschen Gleichungen gibt, also *keine* Eigenschwingungen der Beugungsanordnung (im Gegensatz zu den Randwertaufgaben bei endlich begrenztem Feldgebiet: Hohlleiterprobleme). In der Tat ist die Feldenergie

$$\overline{W} = \tfrac{1}{4} \int (|v|^2 + |\operatorname{grad} v|^2) \, d\tau \quad \text{bzw.} \quad \overline{W} = \tfrac{1}{4} \int (\mathfrak{E}\mathfrak{E}^* + \mathfrak{H}\mathfrak{H}^*) \, d\tau$$

(die Integration hat über das gesamte Feldgebiet zu erfolgen) beim Beugungsproblem *unendlich* groß. Man erkennt dies daran, daß die rechte Seite von (19.1) bzw. (19.2) asymptotisch (sagen wir von $r = \bar{r}$ ab) unabhängig von r ist; wir haben aber die rechte Seite von (19.1) bzw. (19.2) noch über r von $\bar{r}$ bis ∞ zu integrieren, um den Beitrag des Fernfeldes zur Feldenergie zu erhalten. Dieser divergiert aber. Von dieser unendlichen Feldenergie haben wir uns vorzustellen, daß sie während des (unendlich langdauernden) Einschwingungsvorganges im Raum verteilt wurde, bis sich der von uns allein betrachtete *stationäre* Zustand eingestellt hat.

Wenn das Feldgebiet *nicht*, wie bisher angenommen wurde, *allseitig* ins Unendliche reicht, sondern sich auch die beugenden Körper bis ins Unendliche erstrecken und einen Teil davon einnehmen (Halbröhren), so muß die Ausstrahlungsbedingung so abgeändert werden, daß sie sich nur auf den Teil des Unendlichen bezieht, der nicht von beugenden Körpern besetzt ist. Rellich[1] und Jones[2] haben Kriterien für die Gestalt der Halbröhren im Unendlichen entwickelt, um zu entscheiden, ob nur Ausstrahlungslösungen ($\overline{W}\to\infty$) vorhanden sind, die für alle Werte der Frequenz ω bzw. Wellenzahl k möglich sind (*kontinuierliches* Eigenwertspektrum), oder ob auch oder nur Eigenschwingungen ($\overline{W}<\infty$) existieren (für die die möglichen Werte der Wellenzahl k ein *diskretes* Spektrum bilden).

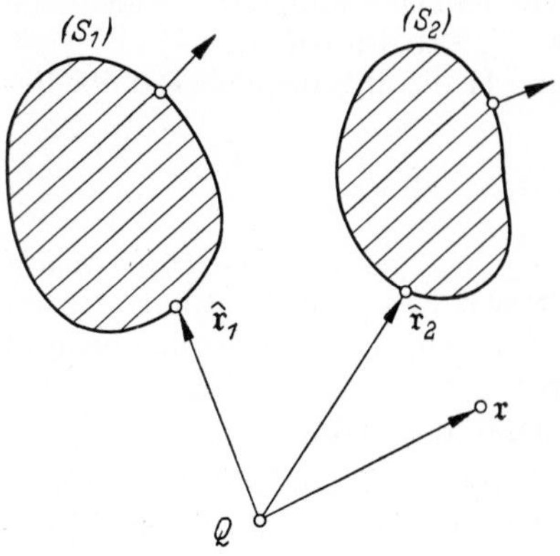

Fig. 10a. Anordnung der Leiter im „*Streufall*".

Wir wollen einer einfachen Ausdrucksweise zuliebe folgende Fallunterscheidung einführen:

a) „*Streufall*": die beugenden („streuenden") Körper liegen ganz im Endlichen (s. Fig. 10a).

b) „*Beugungsfall*": die beugenden Körper reichen teilweise ins Unendliche, das Eigenwertspektrum ist jedoch rein kontinuierlich (Eigenschwingungen sollen hier außer Betracht bleiben, s. Fig. 10b).

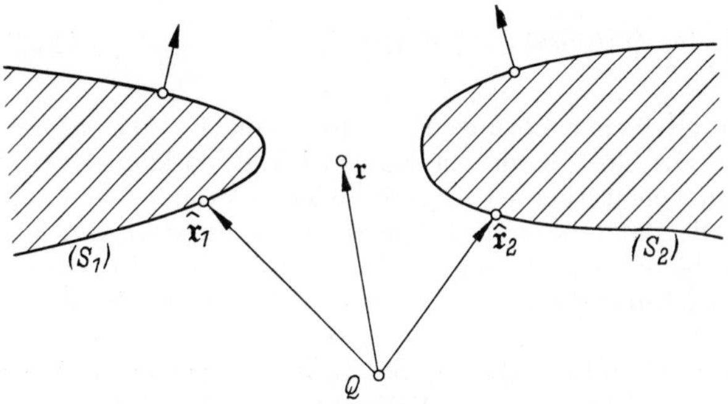

Fig. 10b. Anordnung der Leiter im „*Beugungsfall*".

Bei den uns hauptsächlich interessierenden *ebenen Schirmen* hängen Streu- und dazu komplementärer Beugungsfall über das *Babinetsche Theorem* zusammen (Ziff. 27).

Wenn die Feldquelle ins Unendliche rückt, ist die Ausstrahlungsbedingung so abzuändern, daß sie der aus vorgegebener Richtung einfallenden ebenen Welle Rechnung trägt[3].

d2) Die Kantenbedingung.

In den bisherigen Betrachtungen wurde stillschweigend angenommen, daß die Oberflächen der beugenden Körper keine *Kanten* (Linien, längs denen die Oberflächennormale *unstetig* ist) besitzen. Tritt dieser Fall jedoch ein, so haben wir an den Kanten *Feldsingularitäten* zu gewärtigen, etwa analog der *Spitzenwirkung* der Elektrostatik.

Besonders scharfe Kanten besitzen insbesondere die *Beugungsschirme*, die als unendlich dünn, d.h. als berandete Flächenstücke behandelt werden. Bouwkamp[4] hat wohl als erster nachgewiesen, daß es für ebene Beugungsschirme eine *Vielzahl* von Lösungen gibt, die sämtlich den Bedingungen I—III genügen

[1] F. Rellich: Jber. dtsch. Math.-Ver. **53**, 157 (1943). — Studies and Essays presented to R. Courant 1948, S. 329.

[2] D. S. Jones: Proc. Cambridge Phil. Soc. **49**, 668 (1953).

[3] Vgl. dazu D. S. Jones: Proc. Cambridge Phil. Soc. **48**, 733 (1952).

[4] C. J. Bouwkamp: Physica, Haag **12**, 467 (1946).

und die sich im wesentlichen durch den Charakter ihrer Singularität am Rand des Schirmes voneinander unterscheiden.

21. Die Bedeutung der Kantenbedingung. In der Tat läßt sich unser oben gegebener Eindeutigkeitsbeweis nicht ohne weiteres auf Körper mit Kanten ausdehnen. Er läßt aber leicht erkennen, durch welche zusätzliche Forderung sich auch hier die Eindeutigkeit erzwingen läßt: Gl. (20.1) bzw. (20.2), die zum Ausdruck bringt, daß die von den Feldquellen gelieferte Energie vollständig ins Unendliche abgestrahlt wird, beruht auf der Anwendung des Gaußschen Satzes, die nur für singularitätenfreie Felder möglich ist. Wir müssen also die Kanten der beugenden Objekte mit ringwulstartigen Flächen umgeben, deren Radius ϱ (s. Fig. 11) wir nach Anwendung des Gaußschen Satzes nach Null streben lassen. Der Beitrag dieser Ringwülste muß im Limes $\varrho \to 0$ *verschwinden*. Andernfalls träte nämlich in den Gln. (20.1), (20.2) noch ein zusätzlicher, von den Kanten herrührender Term auf, der bedeuten würde, daß die Kanten Energie *abstrahlen* (die gemeinsam mit der von den Feldquellen gelieferten Energie W_0 ins Unendliche zerstreut wird) bzw. *absorbieren* (so daß nur die Differenz zwischen W_0 und dieser absorbierten Energie ins Unendliche ausgestrahlt wird). *Beides ist auszuschließen.* Mit dieser zusätzlichen Forderung *(Kantenbedingung)* bleibt also die Gültigkeit der Gln. (20.1), (20.2) auch für *Objekte mit Kanten* bestehen. Daher folgt auch für diese, genau wie oben die Eindeutigkeit des Beugungsproblems.

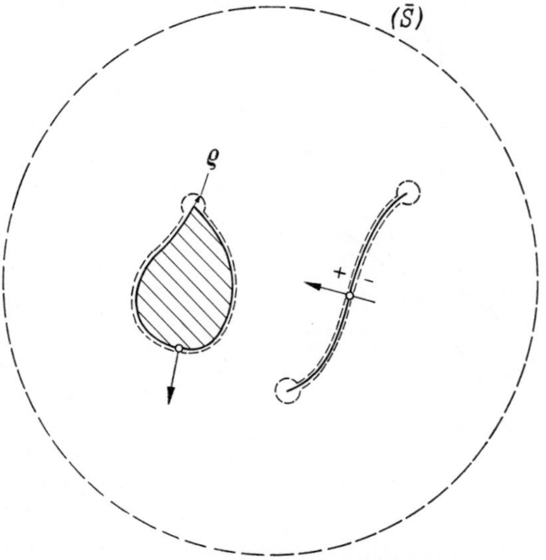

Fig. 11. Zur Formulierung der Kantenbedingung.

Wir kommen somit zu der Feststellung, daß die Daten I—III bzw. I′—III′ durch die Forderung ergänzt werden müssen:

IV. *v bzw.* $\mathfrak{E}$, $\mathfrak{H}$ *haben der Kantenbedingung zu genügen.*

Diese kann, wie sich zeigen wird, noch verschiedene analytische Formen annehmen. Wir werden jedoch jede auf die Kanten des beugenden Objektes bezügliche Forderung, die die Eindeutigkeit des Beugungsproblems garantiert, als Kantenbedingung bezeichnen.

Zur *analytischen* Formulierung der Kantenbedingung wollen wir uns auf den Fall der extrem scharfen Kante beschränken, wie er bei berandeten Flächenstücken vorliegt. Bei diesen ändert sich die Richtung der Normalen längs des Randes beim Übergang von der Oberseite (+) zur Unterseite (—) des Schirmes sprunghaft um π. Zunächst läßt sich allgemein sagen, daß die (bezüglich des Ringwulstes) normale Komponente des Pointingschen Vektors $\overline{\mathfrak{S}}$ im Limes $\varrho \to 0$ nur schwächer als ϱ^{-1} singulär werden darf:

$$\lim_{\varrho \to 0} \varrho\, \overline{\mathfrak{S}}_n = \tfrac{1}{4} \lim_{\varrho \to 0} \varrho\, \{[\mathfrak{E}\, \mathfrak{H}^*] + [\mathfrak{E}^*\, \mathfrak{H}]\}_n = 0, \tag{21.1}$$

damit die Kante *nicht strahlt* (das Flächenelement des Ringwulstes ist nämlich $\sim \varrho$).

Es bleibt nun noch die Frage zu klären, wie sich diese Singularität auf die Komponenten der Feldvektoren verteilt. Wir zerlegen diese in ihre Komponenten *parallel* und *senkrecht zur Kante* und konstruieren dazu in jedem Randpunkt ein orthogonales Dreibein aus den drei Einheitsvektoren $\mathfrak{t}$ [$=$Tangentenvektor der Randkurve (C) des Schirms $= y$-Achse], $\mathfrak{n}$ ($=$Normalenvektor des Schirmes in der Umgebung des betrachteten Kantenelements $= z$-Achse) und $\mathfrak{s} = [\mathfrak{t}\,\mathfrak{n}]$ ($= x$-Achse) (s. Fig. 12), dann lautet die Zerlegung:

$$\mathfrak{E}_x = (\mathfrak{s}\,\mathfrak{E}), \quad \mathfrak{E}_y = (\mathfrak{t}\,\mathfrak{E}), \quad \mathfrak{E}_z = (\mathfrak{n}\,\mathfrak{E}) \quad \text{oder} \quad \mathfrak{E}_{\parallel} = \mathfrak{E}_y, \quad \mathfrak{E}_{\perp} = (\mathfrak{E}_x, \mathfrak{E}_z); \tag{21.2}$$

entsprechend für $\mathfrak{H}$. Wie wir unten zeigen werden, sind die Parallelkomponenten $\mathfrak{E}_{\parallel}$ und $\mathfrak{H}_{\parallel}$ stets *endlich* (oder sie verschwinden). Das singuläre Verhalten der $\perp$-Komponenten $\mathfrak{E}_{\perp}$ und $\mathfrak{H}_{\perp}$ wird also durch die Kantenbedingung (21.1) auf $\varrho^{-\alpha}$, $\alpha < 1$ eingeschränkt.

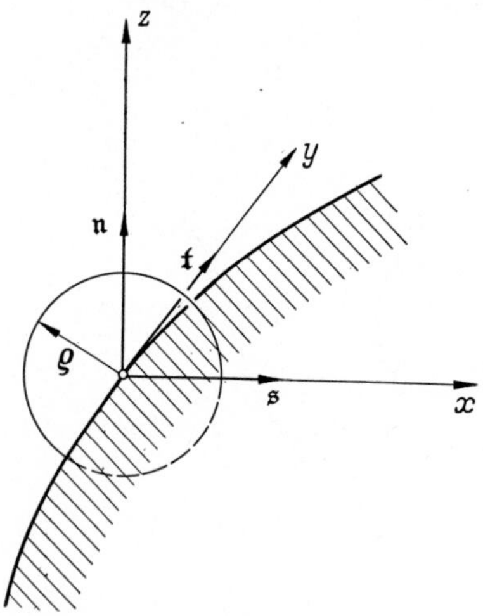

Fig. 12. Lokales Koordinatensystem für ein Kantenelement.

22. Die Meixnersche Form der Kantenbedingung. An Stelle der Forderung (21.1), daß die Kanten nicht strahlen dürfen (d.h. daß der Energie*strom* durch die die Kanten umgebende Ringwulstfläche im Limes $\varrho \to 0$ verschwindet), verlangt Meixner[1], daß die Feldenergie*dichte* $\overline{w}$ in der Umgebung der Kante räumlich integrierbar ist (endliche Feldenergie in endlichen Raumgebieten). Da das Volumelement einen Faktor ϱ enthält, dürfen also die Feldstärkequadrate nur wie $\varrho^{-2\alpha}$, $\alpha < 1$ an der Kante singulär werden. Dies führt für die Komponenten der Feldstärken auf die gleiche Bedingung wie oben.

Der Wert des Exponenten α läßt sich nach Meixner[2] dadurch gewinnen, daß man für die Feldkomponenten in der Umgebung der Kante *Potenzreihen* in ϱ ansetzt und diese in die Maxwellschen Gleichungen einführt. Auf Grund der *Randbedingung für den vollkommen leitenden Schirm* ($\mathfrak{E}_{\text{tang}} = 0$) gelangt man dann zu dem Ergebnis, daß nur *halbzahlige* Potenzen von ϱ auftreten können. Damit wird der oben eingeführte Exponent zu $\alpha = \frac{1}{2}$ festgelegt. Ferner ergibt sich, daß die Feldstärken bezüglich des (den Umlauf um die Kante messenden) Winkels φ die Periode 4π haben, d.h. erst bei *zweimaligem* Umlaufen der Schirmkante ihren Ausgangswert wieder annehmen. Das Ergebnis läßt sich auch so interpretieren, daß man für die Erfüllung der Randbedingung an unendlich dünnen ideal leitenden Schirmen *zweiwertige* Lösungen der Maxwellschen Gleichungen braucht, wie sie von Sommerfeld[3] in die Beugungstheorie eingeführt worden sind (Ziff. 28).

23. Potentialtheoretische Betrachtung. Wir gelangen nach Maue[4] einfacher zum gleichen Ergebnis indem wir die Umgebung eines beliebigen Kantenpunktes so klein wählen, daß in ihrem Bereich der Schirm als eben und die Randkurve als geradlinig angesehen werden kann, ferner seien ihre Abmessungen klein gegen die Wellenlänge. Innerhalb dieses kleinen Bereiches dürfen wir die Variabilität des

[1] J. Meixner: Z. Naturforsch. **3**a, 506 (1948).
[2] J. Meixner: Ann. d. Phys. **6**, 2 (1949).
[3] A. Sommerfeld: Math. Ann. **47**, 317 (1896). — Proc. Lond. Math. Soc. **28**, 395 (1897).
[4] A.-W. Maue: Z. Physik **126**, 601 (1949).

Feldes parallel zur Kante vernachlässigen und uns auf die Diskussion des uns interessierenden Feldverhaltens in einer zur Kante senkrechten Ebene beschränken; ferner genügt es, statt der Wellengleichung bzw. der Maxwellschen Gleichungen die Potentialgleichung $\Delta v = 0$ zugrunde zu legen. Die Fragestellung reduziert sich somit auf ein zweidimensionales statisches Problem.

Wählen wir den Schirm als xy-Ebene und die Kante als y-Achse, so ergeben sich in der xz-Ebene die in Fig. 13 dargestellten geometrischen Verhältnisse. Die Randbedingung II lautet im p- bzw. s-Fall bei Benutzung von Polarkoordinaten ϱ, φ in der Zeichenebene

$$(p) \quad v = 0 \quad \text{bzw.} \quad (s) \; \frac{\partial v}{\partial \varphi} = 0 \quad \text{für} \quad \varphi = 0, 2\pi \tag{23.1}$$

und die zugehörige allgemeine [die Randbedingung (23.1) befriedigende] Lösung der Potentialgleichung bei zunächst willkürlicher Singularität im Nullpunkt:

$$\left.\begin{aligned} &(p) \quad v = \sum_{\nu=1}^{\infty} \left(a_\nu \varrho^{\frac{\nu}{2}} + b_\nu \varrho^{-\frac{\nu}{2}}\right) \sin \frac{\nu\varphi}{2}, \\ \text{bzw.} \\ &(s) \quad v = \sum_{\nu=1}^{\infty} \left(a_\nu \varrho^{\frac{\nu}{2}} + b_\nu \varrho^{-\frac{\nu}{2}}\right) \cos \frac{\nu\varphi}{2} + a_0 + b_0 \ln \varrho. \end{aligned}\right\} \tag{23.2}$$

Wir denken uns nun vorübergehend auch die Werte von (p) v bzw. (s) $\partial v/\partial \varrho$ auf dem Umfang eines beliebigen Kreises um den Nullpunkt vorgegeben, der also zusammen mit dem Schirm einen geschlossenen Bereich abgrenzt (in Fig. 13 gestrichelt umrandet), in dem v — zunächst bei abgerundeter Kante und daher auch im interessierenden Grenzfall einer scharfen Kante — *eindeutig*[1] festgelegt ist (erste bzw. zweite Randwertaufgabe der Potentialtheorie). Um die vorgeschriebenen Randwerte auf dem Kreisumfang (die man sich als Fourier-Reihe dargestellt denke) zu erzielen, genügt es aber offenbar, die Koeffizienten a_ν in Gl. (23.2) verfügbar zu haben. Wir schließen hieraus, daß die mit den Koeffizienten b_ν versehenen Glieder wegen ihres singulären Charakters auszuschließen, die b_ν also gleich null zu setzen sind. Andernfalls wäre die Lösung nicht eindeutig. Das Verhalten von v an der Kante ist durch die ersten nicht verschwindenden Glieder der Entwicklung (23.2) gegeben und ist demnach

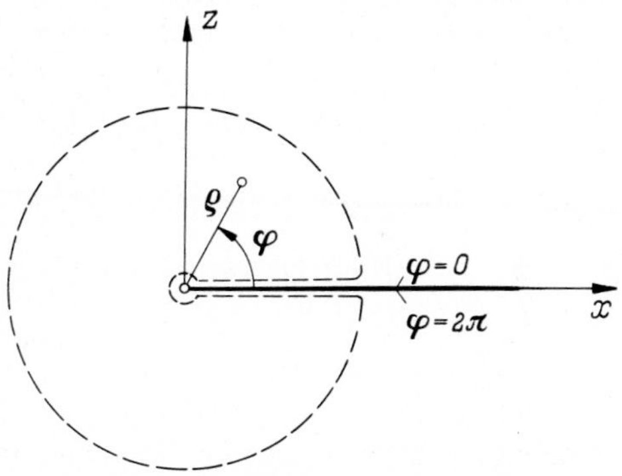

Fig. 13. Lokales Koordinatensystem in einer Ebene senkrecht zum Kantenelement.

$$(p) \quad v \sim \varrho^{\frac{1}{2}} \sin \frac{\varphi}{2} \quad \text{bzw.} \quad (s) \quad v \sim \text{const} + \varrho^{\frac{1}{2}} \cos \frac{\varphi}{2}, \quad \text{für } \varrho \to 0. \tag{23.3}$$

Den höheren Entwicklungsgliedern in (23.2) kommt keine Bedeutung zu, da die Ersetzung der Wellen- durch die Potentialgleichung nur in erster Näherung möglich ist. Gl. (23.3) stellt die *Kantenbedingung* für das *skalare* Problem bei der Beugung an Flächenstücken (Beugungsschirmen) dar. Etwas einfacher läßt sich diese Kantenbedingung als Forderung der *Endlichkeit von* v an der Kante formulieren (s. unten) und ist in dieser Gestalt auch für keilförmige Kanten zutreffend.

[1] Im Falle (s) bis auf eine additive Konstante.

Wir spalten nun das elektromagnetische Feld lokal (in der Umgebung der betrachteten Stelle der Kante) in zwei verschieden polarisierte Felder auf (p-Fall und s-Fall im Sinne von Ziff. 4). Beim ersten schwingt der elektrische, beim zweiten der magnetische Vektor parallel zur Kante, also bei Benutzung der Bezeichnungsweise von Ziff. 21 und den Fig. 12 und 13 parallel zur y-Achse, und ist mit der skalaren Funktion v zu identifizieren. Wir können daher die *Kantenbedingung* (23.3) direkt übernehmen und haben mit Rücksicht auf (4.1 p) bzw. (4.1 s)

$$\mathfrak{E}_y \sim \varrho^{\frac{1}{2}} \sin\frac{\varphi}{2}, \qquad \mathfrak{H}_y \sim \text{const} + \varrho^{\frac{1}{2}} \cos\frac{\varphi}{2}, \qquad \text{für } \varrho \to 0. \tag{23.3a}$$

Für das Feld in der Normelebene zur Kante ergibt sich aus (23.3a) mit Hilfe der Maxwellschen Gleichungen (2.1b) d.h. hier (4.1 p, s)

$$\mathfrak{E}_x, \mathfrak{H}_z \sim \varrho^{-\frac{1}{2}} \sin\frac{\varphi}{2}; \qquad \mathfrak{E}_z, \mathfrak{H}_x \sim \varrho^{-\frac{1}{2}} \cos\frac{\varphi}{2}, \qquad \text{für } \varrho \to 0. \tag{23.3b}$$

Diese Feldkomponenten werden demnach an der Kante wie $\varrho^{-\frac{1}{2}}$ *unendlich*. Ferner erleiden sie (infolge der Winkelabhängigkeit) einen (unendlich großen) *Sprung*, wenn man die Kante in der Ebene des Schirmes überquert. Für das Verhalten des *Flächenstromes* im Beugungsschirm ergibt sich aus dem Sprung der Tangentialkomponenten des Magnetfeldes

$$\mathfrak{J}_x \sim \varrho^{\frac{1}{2}}, \qquad \mathfrak{J}_y \sim \varrho^{-\frac{1}{2}} \quad \text{für } \varrho \to 0, \tag{23.4}$$

d.h. die Stromdichte senkrecht bzw. parallel zur Kante wird am Rande null bzw. unendlich (vgl. auch Ziff. 55)[1].

Wir werfen nun noch einmal einen Blick auf das *skalare* zweidimensionale Problem und können hier (21.1) mit Hilfe von (16.5) in der Form

$$\lim_{\varrho \to 0} \varrho\,(v \operatorname{grad} v^* - v^* \operatorname{grad} v) = 0 \tag{23.5a}$$

schreiben. Mit (23.5a) gleichwertig sind offenbar die *beiden* Forderungen

v sei überall endlich und stetig einschließlich des Schirmrandes (23.5b)

und

$$\lim_{\varrho \to 0} \varrho \operatorname{grad} v = 0. \tag{23.5c}$$

Nun sahen wir oben, daß die Ränder der Schirme zu *Verzweigungslinien* der Beugungsfunktionen werden. Bei *zweidimensionalen* Problemen handelt es sich also um Verzweigungs*punkte*; in diesen kann die verzweigte Wellenfunktion v in der Gestalt

$$v = \sum_{\nu=0}^{\infty} A_\nu\, J_{\nu/\mu}(\varrho)\, e^{i\frac{\nu}{\mu}\varphi}$$

entwickelt werden (Analogon zur Puiseuxschen Entwicklung der Funktionentheorie in einem Verzweigungspunkt, $J_{\nu/\mu}$ ist die Bessel-Funktion vom Index ν/μ). Dabei ist vorausgesetzt, daß v im Verzweigungspunkt ($\varrho = 0$; Kante) *keine* Unendlichkeitsstelle hat und daß dort μ Riemannsche Blätter zusammenhängen. Beachtet man, daß sich die Bessel-Funktion $J_{\nu/\mu}(\varrho)$ für kleine ϱ wie $\varrho^{\nu/\mu}$ verhält,

[1] Mehr vom mathematischen Standpunkt wird die Kantenbedingung im akustischen und elektromagnetischen Falle in mehreren Arbeiten von D. S. Jones eingehend diskutiert: Quart. J. Mech. Appl. Math. **3**, 420 (1950); **5**, 363 (1952); Proc. Lond. Math. Soc. (3) **2**, 440 (1952). Vgl. auch E. T. Copson: Proc. Roy. Soc. Lond. A **202**, 177 (1950); J. Meixner: New York Univ. Res. Rep. No. EM-72 (1954); A. E. Heins u. S. Silver: Proc. Cambridge Phil. Soc. **51**, 149 (1955); **54**, 131 (1958).

so folgt, daß v für $\varrho \to 0$ *endlich* bleibt (wie vorausgesetzt), $\partial v/\partial \varrho$ jedoch *divergiert*, aber nur so schwach, daß der Limes (23.5 c) verschwindet[1]. Daher ist also (23.5 c) *eine Folge* der Endlichkeit von v und kann als zusätzliche Forderung *fortfallen*. Die Anzahl der im Verzweigungspunkt zusammenhängenden Blätter wird durch die allgemeine Kantenbedingung (23.5 a) *nicht* festgelegt; sie ergibt sich erst durch Anwendung der Randbedingung für den ideal leitenden Schirm (s. oben) zu $\mu = 2$. Diese Überlegungen lassen sich auch auf den dreidimensionalen skalaren Fall erweitern[2].

24. Kantenbedingung und Separation der Variablen. Um schließlich den Zusammenhang mit der Separationsmethode (Ziff. 5) zu überblicken, diskutieren wir das die Verhältnisse an der Kante eines Beugungsschirms charakterisierende zweidimensionale Potentialproblem von diesem Standpunkt aus. In der zur Kante senkrechten Ebene (xz-Ebene von Fig. 13) verwenden wir *parabolische* Koordinaten ξ, η (vgl. Fig. 14). Der Zusammenhang mit den kartesischen Koordinaten ist durch

$$x = \frac{\eta^2 - \xi^2}{2}, \qquad z = \xi\eta \tag{24.1}$$

und der Variabilitätsbereich durch

$$0 \leqq \xi < \infty, \quad -\infty < \eta < \infty \tag{24.2}$$

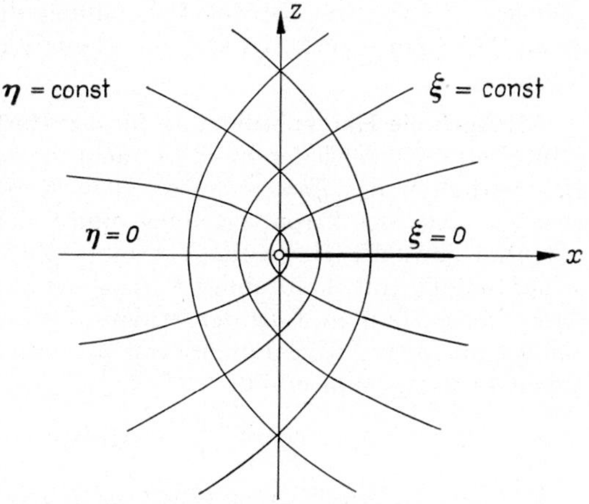

Fig. 14. Parabolische Koordinaten in der Umgebung eines Kantenelements.

gegeben. Auf dem Schirm gilt $\xi = 0$, an der Kante ist $\xi = \eta = 0$. Die Potentialgleichung lautet

$$\frac{\partial^2 v}{\partial \xi^2} + \frac{\partial^2 v}{\partial \eta^2} = 0, \tag{24.3}$$

und die Randbedingung II wird

$$(p) \quad v = 0 \quad \text{bzw.} \quad (s)\ \frac{\partial v}{\partial \xi} = 0 \quad \text{für } \xi = 0. \tag{24.4}$$

Durch Separation der Variablen

$$v(\xi, \eta) = f_1(\xi)\ f_2(\eta) \tag{24.5}$$

entsteht aus (24.3)

$$f_1'' + \lambda f_1 = 0, \qquad f_2'' - \lambda f_2 = 0. \tag{24.6}$$

Beide Differentialgleichungen sind singularitätenfrei, ihre Lösungen daher als Potenzreihen nach ξ bzw. η darstellbar. Man gewinnt damit v in der allgemeinen Gestalt

$$v = \text{const} + a\xi + b\eta + \cdots \tag{24.7}$$

und bei Verwendung der Randbedingung (24.4)

$$(p) \quad v \sim \xi; \quad (s) \quad v \sim \text{const} + \eta \quad \textit{bei} \quad \xi = \eta = 0, \tag{24.4a}$$

---

[1] Vgl. A. Sommerfeld: Vorlesungen über theoretische Physik, Bd. IV, S. 278. Wiesbaden 1950.

[2] A. Sommerfeld: Proc. Lond. Math. Soc. **28**, 405 (1897).

was wegen des Zusammenhanges mit den Polarkoordinaten ϱ, φ

$$\xi = \varrho^{\frac{1}{2}} \sin\frac{\varphi}{2}, \quad \eta = \varrho^{\frac{1}{2}} \cos\frac{\varphi}{2} \tag{24.1a}$$

mit Gl. (23.3) übereinstimmt. Die Kantenbedingung ist also *automatisch* erfüllt.

Dieser Sachverhalt steht scheinbar im Widerspruch mit unserer früheren Feststellung der Notwendigkeit, die Kantenbedingung zusätzlich zu den Randbedingungen zu fordern. Diese Notwendigkeit entfällt jedoch nur dann, wenn wir die Differentialgleichung in Koordinaten ξ, η, die der Form des beugenden Körpers angepaßt sind, durch *Separationsansatz* lösen oder die gesuchte Lösung aus so gewonnenen Lösungen aufbauen, die *bereits einzeln* der Randbedingung genügen. Gehen wir bei der Behandlung des skalaren Beugungsproblems in dieser Weise vor, so erübrigt sich eine gesonderte Diskussion der Kantenbedingung tatsächlich.

25. Auch die Kantenbedingung für den Hertzschen Vektor des ebenen Schirms (Ziff. 7) ergibt sich wieder durch Betrachtung der Umgebung eines Kantenpunktes. Das Verhalten des *Flächenstromes* $\mathfrak{J}$ in Kantennähe ist dann durch Gl. (23.4) gegeben. Aus der Stromverteilung ergibt sich in bekannter Weise das Vektorpotential bzw. der Hertzsche Vektor (s. Ziff. 53). Da wir uns nur für die Art seiner Singularität (halbzahlige Potenz von ϱ) an der Kante interessieren, können die weiter entfernten Teile der Stromverteilung, die nur reguläre Beiträge (ganzzahlige, nicht negative Potenz von ϱ) zum Vektorpotential liefern, außer Betracht bleiben. Man erhält:

$$\left.\begin{aligned} \mathfrak{Z}_x &\sim \varrho^{\frac{3}{2}} \sin\frac{3\varphi}{2} + \textit{reguläre Glieder}, \\ \mathfrak{Z}_y &\sim \varrho^{\frac{1}{2}} \sin\frac{\varphi}{2} + \textit{reguläre Glieder} \end{aligned}\right\} \textit{für } \varrho \to 0. \tag{25.1}$$

Die *Kantenbedingung* (25.1) läßt sich auch in vereinfachter Form unter Verzicht auf die Angabe der Winkelabhängigkeit aussprechen. Bezeichnen wir wieder, um von der speziellen Koordinatenwahl frei zu werden, die zur Kante senkrechte bzw. parallele Komponente von $\mathfrak{Z}$ mit $\mathfrak{Z}_\perp$ bzw. $\mathfrak{Z}_\parallel$, so lautet (25.1) vereinfacht:

$$\left.\begin{aligned} \mathfrak{Z}_\perp &\sim \varrho^{\frac{3}{2}} + \textit{reguläre Glieder} \\ \mathfrak{Z}_\parallel &\sim \varrho^{\frac{1}{2}} + \textit{reguläre Glieder} \end{aligned}\right\} \textit{für } \varrho \to 0. \tag{25.2}$$

Vom Standpunkt der der Form der Kante angepaßten parabolischen Koordinaten ξ, η, Gl. (24.1), ergeben sich die folgenden Verhältnisse. Durch Separation der Wellen- bzw. Potentialgleichung erhält man $\mathfrak{Z}_\perp$ und $\mathfrak{Z}_\parallel$ analog zu Gl. (24.7) als Potenzreihe in ξ, η. Da ξ und η nach Gl. (24.1a) proportional zu $\varrho^{\frac{1}{2}}$ sind, entsprechen die Produkte mit gerader Anzahl von Faktoren ξ, η den regulären Gliedern in (25.2) und die ungeradzahligen den singulären. Somit ist die zweite Forderung (25.2) von selbst erfüllt. Zusätzlich ist nur noch das Fehlen des Gliedes $\varrho^{\frac{1}{2}}$, d.h. der in ξ, η linearen Glieder, in der ersten Gl. (25.2) zu verlangen. Es muß also gelten

$$\frac{\partial \mathfrak{Z}_\parallel}{\partial \xi} = \frac{\partial \mathfrak{Z}_\parallel}{\partial \eta} = 0 \quad \textit{für} \quad \xi = \eta = 0, \tag{25.3}$$

womit der Kantenbedingung genüge getan ist.

e) Das Babinetsche Theorem.

Die Lösungen der Maxwellschen Gleichungen ebenso wie die der Wellengleichung besitzen einfache Symmetrieeigenschaften, wenn im Raum auf irgend eine Weise eine Ebene ausgezeichnet ist. Eine solche Symmetrieebene liegt z.B. vor, wenn ein Teil (S) der Ebene $z=0$ mit einem unendlich *dünnen ideal leitenden Schirm* bedeckt ist. Wir bezeichnen den zu (S) komplementären Bereich der Ebene $z=0$ als *Loch* (L) und wollen annehmen, daß aus dem Halbraume $z<0$ eine Welle v_0 bzw. $\mathfrak{E}_0$, $\mathfrak{H}_0$ auf den Schirm auftreffe (d.h. die Feldsingularität soll im Halbraum $z<0$ liegen). Hier sind nun zunächst wie in Ziff. 20 zwei Fälle zu unterscheiden.

26. Unterscheidung zwischen Streu- und Beugungsfall bei ebenen Schirmen. *α) Der Schirm (S) liege ganz im endlichen.* Es wird dann *vor* und *hinter* dem Schirm in großer Entfernung von ihm im wesentlichen das Feld der einfallenden Welle herrschen, während die Wirkung des Schirmes als eine nach beiden Seiten ausgehende Störung beschrieben werden kann, die wir als „*Streuung*" bezeichnen wollen. Ist nun $\mathfrak{n}$ die Schirmnormale (in Richtung der positiven z-Achse; s. Fig. 15), so wollen wir den Ortsvektor $\mathfrak{r}$ in eine zur Ebene $z=0$ parallele Komponente $\hat{\mathfrak{r}}$ und die zu ihr senkrechte $\mathfrak{n}z$ zerlegen: $\mathfrak{r}=\hat{\mathfrak{r}}+\mathfrak{n}z$. Entsprechend sollen die Feldvektoren zerlegt werden. Infolge der *Symmetrieeigenschaften der Streuung* (bezüglich der Ebene $z=0$) können wir nun für das Streuproblem folgenden Ansatz machen (das obere Vorzeichen gilt jeweils für $z>0$, das untere für $z<0$):

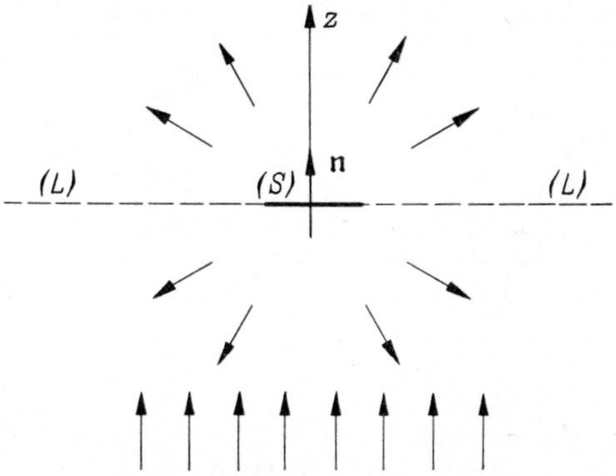

Fig. 15. Zur *Streuung* am ebenen Schirm.

p-Fall; $v=0$ auf (S):

$$v(\mathfrak{r}) = v_0(\mathfrak{r}) + v_S(\hat{\mathfrak{r}}, \pm z), \qquad z \gtrless 0; \tag{26.1p}$$

s-Fall; $\partial v/\partial z = 0$ auf (S):

$$v(\mathfrak{r}) = v_0(\mathfrak{r}) \pm v_S(\hat{\mathfrak{r}}, \pm z), \qquad z \gtrless 0; \tag{26.1s}$$

elektromagnetischer Fall; $[\mathfrak{n}\mathfrak{E}]=0$ *auf* (S):

$$\left.\begin{aligned} \mathfrak{E}(\mathfrak{r}) &= \mathfrak{E}_0(\mathfrak{r}) + \widehat{\mathfrak{E}}_S(\hat{\mathfrak{r}}, \pm z) \pm \mathfrak{E}_S^{\perp}(\hat{\mathfrak{r}}, \pm z),\\ \mathfrak{H}(\mathfrak{r}) &= \mathfrak{H}_0(\mathfrak{r}) \pm \widehat{\mathfrak{H}}_S(\hat{\mathfrak{r}}, \pm z) + \mathfrak{H}_S^{\perp}(\hat{\mathfrak{r}}, \pm z) \end{aligned}\right\} \quad z \gtrless 0. \tag{26.2}$$

Der durch den Index S gekennzeichnete *Streuterm* kann dabei als eine jeweils nur für $z>0$ definierte Funktion betrachtet werden. Das Streufeld im Raume $z<0$ ergibt sich daraus durch „*Spiegelung*" an der Ebene $z=0$. Im p-Fall erzwingt nämlich die Randbedingung $v=0$ ein in z *symmetrisches* Streufeld; im s-Fall die Randbedingung $\partial v/\partial z=0$ ein in z *antisymmetrisches*. Schließlich haben wir im elektromagnetischen Fall eine Zerlegung der Feldvektoren in ihre zum Schirm parallelen und senkrechten Komponenten vorgenommen und beachtet, daß sich $\mathfrak{E}_S$ infolge der Randbedingung $[\mathfrak{n}\mathfrak{E}]=0$ wie ein *polarer* Vektor spiegelt; $\mathfrak{H}_S$ muß sich dann wie ein *axialer* Vektor spiegeln (s. Fig. 16)[1].

Da nun die *Streufelder* zufolge der Wellengleichung bzw. der Maxwellschen Gleichungen beim Hindurchtreten durch das Loch (L) *stetig* sein müssen, so

[1] Der Begriff der „Spiegelung" ist hier cum grano salis zu verstehen; so hätte man bei der Randbedingung $[\mathfrak{n}\mathfrak{H}]=0$ auf (S) $\mathfrak{E}$ als axialen und $\mathfrak{H}$ als polaren Vektor zu spiegeln.

folgt aus (26.1 *p, s*) bzw. (26.2)

$$(p\text{-}Fall) \qquad \frac{\partial v_S(\hat{\mathfrak{r}})}{\partial z} = 0, \quad \hat{\mathfrak{r}} \text{ auf } (L); \tag{26.3p}$$

$$(s\text{-}Fall) \qquad v_S(\hat{\mathfrak{r}}) = 0, \quad \hat{\mathfrak{r}} \text{ auf } (L); \tag{26.3s}$$

$$(\text{elektromagnetischer } Fall) \qquad \mathfrak{E}_S^{\perp}(\hat{\mathfrak{r}}) = \widehat{\mathfrak{H}}_S(\hat{\mathfrak{r}}) = 0, \quad \hat{\mathfrak{r}} \text{ auf } (L). \tag{26.4}$$

Diese Stetigkeit kann jedoch für das Hindurchtreten durch den Schirm (*S*) nicht gefordert werden, da dort die Feldgleichungen nicht mehr gelten. Der sich aus (26.1 *p, s*) und (26.2) ergebende *Sprung beim Hindurchtreten durch* (*S*):

$$\left(\frac{\partial v}{\partial z}\right)_+ - \left(\frac{\partial v}{\partial z}\right)_- = 2\left(\frac{\partial v_S}{\partial z}\right)_+, \tag{26.5p}$$

$$v_+ - v_- = 2(v_S)_+ \tag{26.5s}$$

$$\left.\begin{aligned} (\mathfrak{n}, \mathfrak{E}_+ - \mathfrak{E}_-) &= 2(\mathfrak{n}\,\mathfrak{E}_S)_+, \\ [\mathfrak{n}, \mathfrak{H}_+ - \mathfrak{H}_-] &= 2[\mathfrak{n}\,\mathfrak{H}_S]_+ \end{aligned}\right\} \tag{26.6}$$

ist als elektrischer *Flächenstrom* bzw. als elektrische *Flächenladung* zu interpretieren, durch die man sich die Streufelder erzeugt denken kann (vgl. Abschn. IIIa). Aus (26.3 *p, s*) erkennt man, daß das Streufeld auf (*L*) die jeweils „*andere*" Randbedingung erfüllt, wie das Gesamtfeld auf (*S*). Zufolge (26.4) kann man ferner sagen, daß die Öffnung (*L*) auf das elektromagnetische *Streufeld* wie ein *idealer magnetischer Leiter* wirkt (vgl. Ziff. 2). Die Stetigkeitsbedingungen (26.3 *p, s*) und (26.4) übertragen sich auf das Gesamtfeld (26.1 *p, s*) und (26.2) in der Form

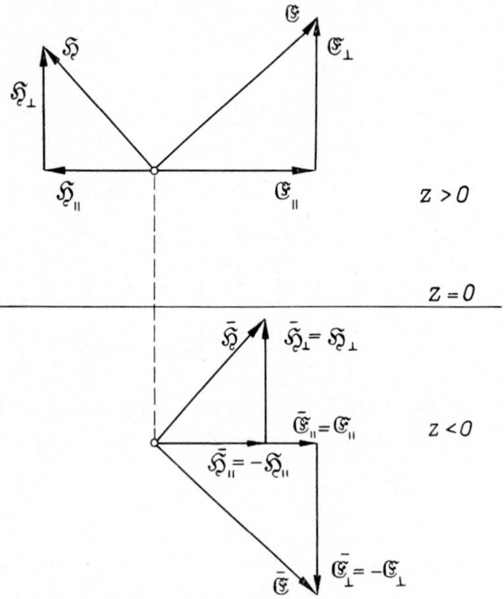

Fig. 16. Spiegelung der Feldvektoren bei Vorhandensein einer Symmetrieebene $z = 0$.

$$(p\text{-}Fall) \qquad \frac{\partial v(\hat{\mathfrak{r}})}{\partial z} = \frac{\partial v_0}{\partial z}, \quad \hat{\mathfrak{r}} \text{ auf } (L) \tag{26.3'p}$$

$$(s\text{-}Fall) \qquad v(\hat{\mathfrak{r}}) = v_0, \quad \hat{\mathfrak{r}} \text{ auf } (L) \tag{26.3's}$$

$$(\text{elektromagnetischer } Fall) \qquad (\mathfrak{n}\,\mathfrak{E}) = (\mathfrak{n}\,\mathfrak{E}_0); \quad [\mathfrak{n}\,\mathfrak{H}] = [\mathfrak{n}\,\mathfrak{H}_0] \quad \text{auf } (L). \tag{26.4'}$$

Die Tangentialkomponente der magnetischen Feldstärke sowie die Normalkomponente der elektrischen Feldstärke nehmen also in der Öffnung (*L*) *in Strenge die Werte der einfallenden Welle an.*

β) Die Öffnung (*L*) *liege ganz im Endlichen.* Hier ist es zweckmäßiger von demjenigen (ungestörten) Feld auszugehen, das sich einstellt, wenn die Öffnung (*L*) nicht vorhanden ist, also von dem Feld, das sich aus einfallender und (unter der entsprechenden Randbedingung auf der *ganzen* Ebene $z = 0$) *reflektierter Welle* zusammensetzt (s. Fig. 17). Das Loch (*L*) verursacht dann eine Störung dieses Feldes, die wir als „*Beugungswelle*" bezeichnen wollen und die wiederum die entsprechenden Symmetrieeigenschaften bezüglich der Ebene $z=0$ besitzen muß. Wir machen demgemäß folgenden Ansatz

p-Fall $v=0$ *auf* (S)

$$v(\mathfrak{r}) = \left\{\begin{array}{lr} v_B(\hat{\mathfrak{r}}, +z), & z>0 \\ v_0(\mathfrak{r}) - v^0(\mathfrak{r}) + v_B(\hat{\mathfrak{r}}, -z), & z<0 \end{array}\right\} \tag{26.6p}$$

s-Fall $\partial v/\partial z=0$ *auf* (S)

$$v(\mathfrak{r}) = \left\{\begin{array}{lr} v_B(\hat{\mathfrak{r}}, +z), & z>0 \\ v_0(\mathfrak{r}) + v^0(\mathfrak{r}) - v_B(\hat{\mathfrak{r}}, -z), & z<0 \end{array}\right\} \tag{26.6s}$$

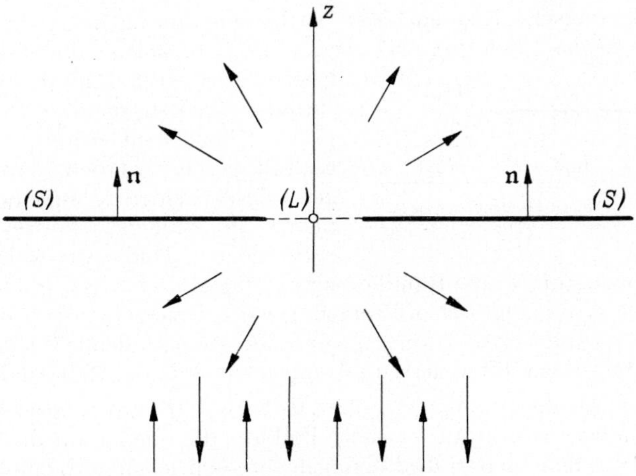

Fig. 17. Zur *Beugung* am ebenen Schirm.

elektromagnetischer Fall $[\mathfrak{n}\,\mathfrak{E}]=0$ *auf* (S)

$$\left.\begin{array}{l} \mathfrak{E}(\mathfrak{r}) = \left\{\begin{array}{lr} \hat{\mathfrak{E}}_B(\hat{\mathfrak{r}}, +z) + \mathfrak{E}_B^{\perp}(\hat{\mathfrak{r}}, +z), & z>0 \\ \mathfrak{E}_0(\mathfrak{r}) + \mathfrak{E}^0(\mathfrak{r}) + \hat{\mathfrak{E}}_B(\hat{\mathfrak{r}}, -z) - \mathfrak{E}_B^{\perp}(\hat{\mathfrak{r}}, -z), & z<0 \end{array}\right. \\ \mathfrak{H}(\mathfrak{r}) = \left\{\begin{array}{lr} \hat{\mathfrak{H}}_B(\hat{\mathfrak{r}}, +z) + \mathfrak{H}_B^{\perp}(\hat{\mathfrak{r}}, +z), & z>0 \\ \mathfrak{H}_0(\mathfrak{r}) + \mathfrak{H}^0(\mathfrak{r}) - \hat{\mathfrak{H}}_B(\hat{\mathfrak{r}}, -z) + \mathfrak{H}_B^{\perp}(\hat{\mathfrak{r}}, -z), & z<0, \end{array}\right. \end{array}\right\} \tag{26.7}$$

dabei haben wir die „*reflektierte Welle*"

$$v^0(\mathfrak{r}) = v_0(\hat{\mathfrak{r}}, -z) \tag{26.8}$$

bzw.

$$\left.\begin{array}{l} \mathfrak{E}^0(\mathfrak{r}) = -\hat{\mathfrak{E}}_0(\hat{\mathfrak{r}}, -z) + \mathfrak{E}_0^{\perp}(\hat{\mathfrak{r}}, -z), \\ \mathfrak{H}^0(\mathfrak{r}) = \hat{\mathfrak{H}}_0(\hat{\mathfrak{r}}, -z) - \mathfrak{H}_0^{\perp}(\hat{\mathfrak{r}}, -z) \end{array}\right\} \tag{26.9}$$

eingeführt, die zusammen mit der einfallenden Welle auf der ganzen Ebene $z=0$ die Randbedingung $v_0 - v^0 = 0$, $\frac{\partial}{\partial z}(v_0 + v^0) = 0$ bzw. $[\mathfrak{n}, \mathfrak{E}_0 + \mathfrak{E}^0] = (\mathfrak{n}, \mathfrak{H}_0 + \mathfrak{H}^0) = 0$ erfüllt.

Für die Beugungsfelder (Index B) — die ebenfalls als nur für $z>0$ definierte Funktionen betrachtet werden können — ergibt sich nun wieder aus den durch die Feldgleichungen erzwungenen Stetigkeitsforderungen beim Hindurchtreten durch die Öffnung (L):

$$(p\text{-}Fall)\qquad \frac{\partial v(\hat{\mathfrak{r}})}{\partial z} = \frac{\partial v_B(\hat{\mathfrak{r}})}{\partial z} = \frac{\partial v_0}{\partial z}, \quad \hat{\mathfrak{r}}\ auf\ (L); \tag{26.10p}$$

$$(s\text{-}Fall)\qquad v(\hat{\mathfrak{r}}) = v_B(\hat{\mathfrak{r}}) = v_0, \quad \hat{\mathfrak{r}}\ auf\ (L); \tag{26.10s}$$

(elektromagnetischer Fall)

$$(\mathfrak{n}\,\mathfrak{E}) = (\mathfrak{n}\,\mathfrak{E}_B) = (\mathfrak{n}\,\mathfrak{E}_0), \quad [\mathfrak{n}\,\mathfrak{H}] = [\mathfrak{n}\,\mathfrak{H}_B] = [\mathfrak{n}\,\mathfrak{H}_0] \quad auf\ (L). \tag{26.11}$$

Ein prinzipieller Unterschied zwischen „*Streu-*" und „*Beugungsproblem*" besteht selbstverständlich nicht; auf der Grenze zwischen beiden liegt beispielsweise die Beugung (bzw. Streuung) an der Halbebene.

27. Das Babinetsche Theorem. Wir betrachten nun nacheinander zwei zueinander *komplementäre* Schirme (S_1) und (S_2), d.h. solche die sich zur *vollen* Ebene $z=0$ ergänzen. Es ist dann die Öffnung (L_1) kongruent zu (S_2) und ebenso (L_2) kongruent zu (S_1) (s. Fig. 18). Es soll gezeigt werden, daß die Lösungen dieser beiden komplementären Probleme in einfacher Weise auseinander hervorgehen. Und zwar wollen wir beim skalaren Problem auf (S_1) die Randbedingung $\partial v/\partial z = 0$ fordern, auf (S_2) hingegen $v=0$. Beim elektromagnetischen Problem legen wir zunächst die Randbedingung $[\mathfrak{n}\,\mathfrak{E}]=0$ auf (S_1) und $[\mathfrak{n}\,\mathfrak{H}]=0$ auf (S_2) zugrunde (die einfallende Welle sei beidemal die *gleiche*). Die so charakterisierten Lösungen sollen in der Reihenfolge, in der sie oben eingeführt wurden, mit $v_s^{(S_1)}$, $v_p^{(S_2)}$ bzw. $\mathfrak{E}^{(S_1)}$, $\mathfrak{H}^{(S_1)}$; $\breve{\mathfrak{E}}^{(S_2)}$, $\breve{\mathfrak{H}}^{(S_2)}$ bezeichnet werden. Die unteren Indices weisen auf s- und p-Fall hin, die oberen auf die Schirme, auf denen die entsprechenden Randbedingungen vorgeschrieben sind. Zufolge der Randbedingung gilt also im skalaren Fall

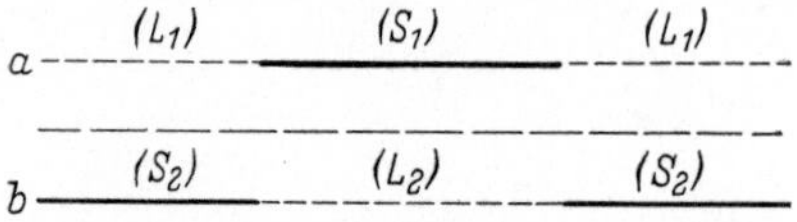

Fig. 18. Zum Babinetschen Theorem bei ebenen Schirmen [a und b komplementäre Schirme].

$$\frac{\partial v_s^{(S_1)}}{\partial z} = 0 \quad auf\ (S_1); \qquad v_p^{(S_2)} = 0 \quad auf\ (S_2); \tag{27.1}$$

andererseits gilt zufolge der Stetigkeitsbedingungen (26.3′p, s) oder (26.10p, s)

$$\frac{\partial v_p^{(S_2)}}{\partial z} = \frac{\partial v_0}{\partial z} \quad auf\ (L_2); \qquad v_s^{(S_1)} = v_0 \quad auf\ (L_1). \tag{27.1'}$$

Da nun (S_1) zu (L_2) und ebenso (S_2) zu (L_1) kongruent ist, folgt durch Addition und Subtraktion der entsprechenden Gln. (27.1) und (27.1′)

$$\left.\begin{aligned} \frac{\partial}{\partial z}\{v_s^{(S_1)} \pm v_p^{(S_2)}\} &= \pm\frac{\partial v_0}{\partial z} \quad && auf\ (S_1), \\ v_s^{(S_1)} \pm v_p^{(S_2)} &= v_0 && auf\ (S_2). \end{aligned}\right\} \tag{27.2}$$

Ganz entsprechend erhält man im vektoriellen Fall

$$\left.\begin{aligned} [\mathfrak{n},\, \mathfrak{E}^{(S_1)} \pm \breve{\mathfrak{E}}^{(S_2)}] &= \pm[\mathfrak{n}\,\mathfrak{E}_0] \quad && auf\ (S_1), \\ [\mathfrak{n},\, \mathfrak{H}^{(S_1)} \pm \breve{\mathfrak{H}}^{(S_2)}] &= [\mathfrak{n}\,\mathfrak{H}_0] && auf\ (S_2). \end{aligned}\right\} \tag{27.3}$$

Ein Lösungssystem der entsprechenden Feldgleichungen, das dieses gemischte Randwertproblem (27.2) bzw. (27.3) löst, läßt sich aber sofort angeben, nämlich das folgende

$$\left.\begin{aligned} v_s^{(S_1)} + v_p^{(S_2)} &= v_0, \\ v_s^{(S_1)} - v_p^{(S_2)} &= v^0 \end{aligned}\right\} \tag{27.4}$$

bzw.

$$\left.\begin{aligned} \mathfrak{E}^{(S_1)} + \breve{\mathfrak{E}}^{(S_2)} &= \mathfrak{E}_0; \qquad \mathfrak{H}^{(S_1)} + \breve{\mathfrak{H}}^{(S_2)} = \mathfrak{H}_0 \\ \mathfrak{E}^{(S_1)} - \breve{\mathfrak{E}}^{(S_2)} &= \mathfrak{E}^0; \qquad \mathfrak{H}^{(S_1)} - \breve{\mathfrak{H}}^{(S_2)} = \mathfrak{H}^0, \end{aligned}\right\} \tag{27.5}$$

dabei bedeutet v^0 bzw. $\mathfrak{E}^0$, $\mathfrak{H}^0$ wieder die *reflektierte Welle* aus Gl. (26.8) bzw. (26.9). Die Eindeutigkeit der so gefundenen Lösungen ist gesichert, wenn sie die *Ausstrahlungs-* und *Kantenbedingung* erfüllen und die vorgeschriebenen Singularitäten besitzen. Fällt die Primärwelle v_0 bzw. $\mathfrak{E}_0$, $\mathfrak{H}_0$ wie bisher aus dem Raume $z<0$ ein, so ist die jeweils erste Lösung (27.4) bzw. (27.5) (mit dem $+$-Zeichen) nur für $z>0$ brauchbar, da sich für $z<0$ die Singularität als doppelt so groß wie die der einfallenden Welle ergeben müßte. Andererseits ist die jeweils zweite Lösung (mit dem $-$-Zeichen) nur für $z<0$ zu verwenden, da sie wegen der Singularität der reflektierten Welle für $z>0$ hier nicht brauchbar ist (andererseits ist die reflektierte Welle für $z<0$ *singularitätenfrei*, wie es auch die *Differenz* der Lösungen der komplementären Probleme sein muß). Setzt man voraus, daß jede der Lösungen für sich der Ausstrahlungs- und Kantenbedingung genügt, so ergibt sich *eindeutig*

$$\left.\begin{aligned} v_s^{(S_1)} + v_p^{(S_2)} &= v_0 \qquad \textit{für } z>0, \\ v_s^{(S_1)} - v_p^{(S_2)} &= v^0 \qquad \textit{für } z<0, \end{aligned}\right\} \tag{27.4'}$$

bzw.

$$\left.\begin{aligned} \mathfrak{E}^{(S_1)} + \breve{\mathfrak{E}}^{(S_2)} &= \mathfrak{E}_0; \qquad \mathfrak{H}^{(S_1)} + \breve{\mathfrak{H}}^{(S_2)} = \mathfrak{H}_0 \qquad \textit{für } z>0, \\ \mathfrak{E}^{(S_1)} - \breve{\mathfrak{E}}^{(S_2)} &= \mathfrak{E}^0; \qquad \mathfrak{H}^{(S_1)} - \breve{\mathfrak{H}}^{(S_2)} = \mathfrak{H}^0 \qquad \textit{für } z<0. \end{aligned}\right\} \tag{27.5'}$$

Die Gln. (27.4′) bzw. (27.5′) zeigen, wie die Lösungen der komplementären Randwertprobleme auseinander hervorgehen; sie werden als *Babinetsches Theorem* bezeichnet[1]. Ein Theorem unter diesem Namen war schon der heuristischen Fresnel-Kirchhoffschen Theorie bekannt; dort bezieht es sich auf die Beugung an zwei beliebig gekrümmten Schirmen, die sich gegenseitig zu einer geschlossenen Fläche ergänzen und ist nahezu trivial, da die Beugung in dieser Theorie als reiner Kanteneffekt angesehen werden kann (abgesehen von geometrisch optischen Termen; vgl. dazu Ziff. 32, 33). Das eben abgeleitete Theorem dagegen bezieht sich auf die *strengen Lösungen der Randwertprobleme für komplementäre Bereiche einer Ebene.* Es läßt sich zu einem umfassenderen „*Äquivalenztheorem*" verallgemeinern — bei dem *mehrere* Ebenen ins Spiel kommen — wenn man das *Schwartzsche Spiegelungsprinzip* (für die analytische Fortsetzung in Bereiche mit gemeinsamer gradliniger Begrenzung) heranzieht[2].

Gl. (27.4′) ist unmittelbar auf die uns hier interessierenden Randwertprobleme anwendbar. Andererseits ist man bisher an der Lösung $\breve{\mathfrak{E}}^{(S_2)}$, $\breve{\mathfrak{H}}^{(S_2)}$ für den „ideal magnetisch leitenden" Schirm (S_2) nicht interessiert. Man kann jedoch — da die Maxwellschen Gleichungen (2.1b) gegenüber der Substitution $\mathfrak{E}\to\mathfrak{H}$, $\mathfrak{H}\to-\mathfrak{E}$ *invariant* sind — durch

$$\hat{\mathfrak{E}}^{(S_2)} = -\breve{\mathfrak{H}}^{(S_2)}, \qquad \hat{\mathfrak{H}}^{(S_2)} = \breve{\mathfrak{E}}^{(S_2)} \tag{27.6}$$

zu einer andern Lösung der Maxwellschen Gleichungen übergehen, die jetzt auf (S_2) die physikalisch interessante Randbedingung $[\mathfrak{n}\,\mathfrak{E}]=0$ befriedigt. Allerdings liefert dann $\hat{\mathfrak{E}}^{(S_2)}$, $\hat{\mathfrak{H}}^{(S_2)}$ die Lösung dieses Randwertproblems für die „*vertauschte*"

[1] Für den skalaren Fall vgl. C. J. Bouwkamp: Diss. Groningen 1941; für den elektromagnetischen H. G. Booker: J. Inst. Electr. Engrs. Pt. III A, **93**, 620 (1946). — E. T. Copson: Proc. Roy. Soc. Lond. **186**, 100 (1946); **202**, 277 (1950). — J. Meixner: Z. Naturforsch. **1**, 496 (1946); **3**a, 506 (1948). — A.-W. Maue: Z. Naturforsch. **4**a, 393 (1949).

[2] S. N. Karp u. W. E. Williams: N. Y. Univ. Res. Rep. No. EM-83 (1955).

einfallende Welle $\widehat{\mathfrak{E}}_0 = -\mathfrak{H}_0$, $\widehat{\mathfrak{H}}_0 = \mathfrak{E}_0$. [Für eine ebene linear polarisierte einfallende Welle bedeutet diese Vertauschung eine Drehung der Polarisationsrichtung um $\pi/2$.] Das Babinetsche Theorem lautet jetzt bei Beachtung von (27.6)

$$\left.\begin{aligned} \mathfrak{E}^{(S_1)} + \widehat{\mathfrak{H}}^{(S_2)} &= \mathfrak{E}_0, \quad \mathfrak{H}^{(S_1)} - \widehat{\mathfrak{E}}^{(S_2)} = \mathfrak{H}_0 \quad \text{für } z > 0, \\ \mathfrak{E}^{(S_1)} - \widehat{\mathfrak{H}}^{(S_2)} &= \mathfrak{E}^0, \quad \mathfrak{H}^{(S_1)} + \widehat{\mathfrak{E}}^{(S_2)} = \mathfrak{H}^0 \quad \text{für } z < 0. \end{aligned}\right\} \tag{27.5''}$$

Da (S_1) und (S_2) komplementäre Bereiche der vollen Ebene $z=0$ sind, so ist nach der Bezeichnungsweise von Ziff. 26 das eine der zugehörigen Randwertprobleme ein Streu-, das andere ein Beugungsproblem. Nehmen wir etwa an, daß (S_1) endlich begrenzt ist, so wollen wir — unter Abänderung der Bezeichnungsweise — die zugehörige Lösung des Streuproblems mit einem oberen Index (S) versehen, während wir der Lösung des komplementären Beugungsproblems den oberen Index (L) geben. Diese Indices sollen auf „*Schirm*" und „*Loch*" hinweisen, wobei jetzt aber (S) und (L) nicht komplementäre sondern *kongruente* ebene Bereiche sein sollen. Das Babinetsche Theorem (27.4′) bzw. (27.5″) nimmt also jetzt für den Zusammenhang von *Streu-* und *komplementärem Beugungsproblem* folgende Gestalt an

$$\left.\begin{aligned} v_s^{(S)} + v_p^{(L)} &= v_0 \quad \text{für } z > 0, \\ v_s^{(S)} - v_p^{(L)} &= v^0 \quad \text{für } z < 0 \end{aligned}\right\} \tag{27.7}$$

$$\left.\begin{aligned} \mathfrak{E}^{(S)} + \widehat{\mathfrak{H}}^{(L)} &= \mathfrak{E}_0, \quad \mathfrak{H}^{(S)} - \widehat{\mathfrak{E}}^{(L)} = \mathfrak{H}_0 \quad \text{für } z > 0, \\ \mathfrak{E}^{(S)} - \widehat{\mathfrak{H}}^{(L)} &= \mathfrak{E}^0, \quad \mathfrak{H}^{(S)} + \widehat{\mathfrak{E}}^{(L)} = \mathfrak{H}^0 \quad \text{für } z < 0. \end{aligned}\right\} \tag{27.8}$$

Man beachte, daß bei einer Zerlegung des Streuproblems in einfallende und gestreute Welle — vgl. (26.1 p, s) bzw. (26.2) — das komplementäre Beugungsproblem aus (27.7) bzw. (27.8) automatisch in der Form resultiert, die wir oben als zweckmäßig erkannten. Es ergibt sich so nämlich eine Zerlegung des Beugungsproblems in einfallende, reflektierte und gebeugte Welle für $z<0$, während im Halbraum $z>0$ die gebeugte Welle allein auftritt; vgl. (26.6 p, s) bzw. (26.7).

Hat man also etwa eine (der Kantenbedingung genügende) Lösung des Streuproblems gefunden, so ergibt sich aus dem Babinetschen Theorem (27.7), (27.8) unmittelbar die (der Kantenbedingung genügende) Lösung des komplementären Beugungsproblems. Trotzdem werden wir im folgenden häufig Streu- und Beugungsprobleme nebeneinander behandeln, um die dabei auftretenden physikalischen Gesichtspunkte hervortreten zu lassen.

f) Die Methode der verzweigten Lösungen von Sommerfeld.

Sommerfeld[1] hat gezeigt, daß man in der Beugungstheorie von der Vorstellung *mehrblättriger Riemannscher Räume* (im Sinne der Funktionentheorie) Gebrauch machen kann.

28. Spiegelung von verzweigten Lösungen der Wellengleichung und der Maxwellschen Gleichungen. Wir betrachten einen zweiblättrigen Riemannschen Raum, dessen beide Blätter längs eines Flächenstückes (S) der Ebene $z=0$ miteinander zusammenhängen, derart, daß man aus dem vorderen $(z<0)$ bzw. hinteren $(z>0)$ Halbraum des einen Blattes durch (S) hindurch in den hinteren bzw. vorderen

[1] A. Sommerfeld: Math. Ann. **47**, 317 (1896). — Ph. Frank u. R. v. Mises: Differential- und Integralgleichungen der Mechanik und Physik, Bd. II, Kap. 13. bzw. 20. Braunschweig 1927 bzw. 1934. — A. Sommerfeld: Vorlesungen über theoretische Physik, Bd. IV, § 38. Wiesbaden 1950.

Halbraum des anderen Blattes gelangt. Das eine der beiden Blätter identifizieren wir mit dem wirklichen „physikalischen“ Raum, das andere nennen wir den „mathematischen“ Raum. Die Randkurve (C) von (S) ist Verzweigungslinie.

Es sei $u(x, y, z)$ eine zweideutige — im zweiblättrigen Riemannschen Raum eindeutige — Lösung der Wellengleichung $\Delta v + v = 0$, die die Ausstrahlung einer in einem Punkte Q des „physikalischen“ Raumes befindlichen Quelle beschreibt und im Unendlichen beider Blätter der *Ausstrahlungsbedingung* genügt. Durch „*Spiegelung*“ von u an der Fläche (S) entsteht eine neue Lösung $\bar{u}$ der Wellengleichung, die einer Quelle im Spiegelpunkte $\overline{Q}$ von Q entspricht, der dem „mathematischen“ Raume angehört[1]. Sind u und $\bar{u}$ bekannt, so läßt sich die Lösung v des durch eine Lichtquelle in Q und einen Schirm in (S) definierten Beugungsproblems sofort angeben. Sie ist gegeben durch den [längs (S) aufgeschnittenen] „physikalischen“ Zweig von $u - \bar{u}$ bzw. $u + \bar{u}$, wenn auf (S) die Randbedingung $v = 0$ bzw. $\partial v/\partial n = 0$ vorgeschrieben ist, und besitzt außer der Quelle in Q keine weitere Singularität, da $\overline{Q}$ nicht dem „physikalischen“ Raume angehört. Die Erhaltung der Strahlungsenergie innerhalb des „physikalischen“ Raumes kommt dabei anschaulich dadurch zustande, daß die von Q aus durch (S) hindurch in den „mathematischen“ Raum abgestrahlte Energie dem „physikalischen“ Raum von $\overline{Q}$ aus in gleichem Betrage wieder zugestrahlt wird.

Das Verfahren ist auch auf elektromagnetische Wellen anwendbar. Die zweideutige elektromagnetische Welle $\mathfrak{E}$, $\mathfrak{H}$, die das Feld einer im „physikalischen“ Raume gelegenen Lichtquelle Q beschreibt, gehe durch „*Spiegelung*“ an (S) in $\overline{\mathfrak{E}}$, $\overline{\mathfrak{H}}$ über. Im einzelnen gilt dabei mit Rücksicht auf den axialen Charakter von $\mathfrak{H}$

$$\begin{aligned}
\overline{\mathfrak{E}}_x(x, y, z) &= \mathfrak{E}_x(x, y, -z), & \overline{\mathfrak{H}}_x(x, y, z) &= -\mathfrak{H}_x(x, y, -z)\\
\overline{\mathfrak{E}}_y(x, y, z) &= \mathfrak{E}_y(x, y, -z), & \overline{\mathfrak{H}}_y(x, y, z) &= -\mathfrak{H}_y(x, y, -z)\\
\overline{\mathfrak{E}}_z(x, y, z) &= -\mathfrak{E}_z(x, y, -z), & \overline{\mathfrak{H}}_z(x, y, z) &= \mathfrak{H}_z(x, y, -z),
\end{aligned}$$

ferner die Festsetzung, daß sich „physikalischer“ und „mathematischer“ Zweig von $\mathfrak{E}$, $\mathfrak{H}$ und $\overline{\mathfrak{E}}$, $\overline{\mathfrak{H}}$ wechselseitig entsprechen. Mit der Randbedingung $\mathfrak{E}^{\text{tang}} = 0$ auf dem ideal leitenden Schirm (S) erhält man als Lösung des Beugungsproblems den „physikalischen“ Zweig von $\mathfrak{E} - \overline{\mathfrak{E}}$, $\mathfrak{H} - \overline{\mathfrak{H}}$.

Besondere Beachtung erfordert das *singuläre Verhalten* einer zweiwertigen Lösung der Wellengleichung bzw. der Maxwellschen Gleichungen an der Verzweigungslinie (C). Bei der Festlegung der Lösung durch Randbedingungen — insbesondere der oben erwähnten Lösung u bzw. $\mathfrak{E}$, $\mathfrak{H}$ durch die Quelle Q und die Ausstrahlungsbedingung im Unendlichen — hat die Zulassung einer solchen singulären Linie gegenüber der überall regulären einwertigen Lösung — d.i. im obigen Beispiel: der einfachen von Q ausgehenden Kugelwelle — eine Unbestimmtheit zur Folge, über die verfügt werden muß, um die Lösung eindeutig zu machen. Die erforderliche Zusatzbedingung ist die *Kantenbedingung* (vgl. Ziff. 21), die das singuläre Verhalten einschränkt und eine Ausstrahlung der singulären Linie ausschließt. Sie fordert die *Endlichkeit* von u auf (C) bzw. die *quadratische Integrierbarkeit* von $\mathfrak{E}$ und $\mathfrak{H}$ in der Umgebung von (C). Bedeutet ϱ den Abstand eines Punktes von der Kurve (C), so läßt sich das Verhalten der Lösung noch genauer durch die Bedingung (23.3), (23.3a, b)

$$u,\ \mathfrak{E}_{\parallel},\ \mathfrak{H}_{\parallel} \lesssim \text{const}, \qquad \mathfrak{E}_{\perp},\ \mathfrak{H}_{\perp} \lesssim \varrho^{-\frac{1}{2}} \quad \text{für } \varrho \to 0$$

[1] Der hier benutzte Spiegelungsbegriff ist selbstverständlich mit dem in Ziff. 26 verwendeten nicht identisch. Dort handelte es sich um eine Spiegelung im schlichten Raum, hier gelangt man durch Spiegelung in ein anderes Raumexemplar.

beschreiben. Die Indices $\|$ und $\perp$ kennzeichnen dabei die Komponenten von $\mathfrak{E}$, $\mathfrak{H}$ parallel und senkrecht zu (C) im betrachteten Kurvenpunkt.

29. Mehrfach verzweigte Lösungen. Ergänzend sei noch auf die Lösungen der Wellengleichung (bzw. der Maxwellschen Gleichungen im elektromagnetischen Falle, für den die folgenden Betrachtungen entsprechend gelten) im mehrblättrigen, allgemein p-blättrigen, Riemannschen Raum eingegangen. Die einzelnen Blätter mögen auch jetzt durch das Flächenstück (S) miteinander zusammenhängen, jedes Blatt mit dem nächstfolgenden, das letzte wieder mit dem ersten. Es sei u_p die von einer Quelle Q im ersten („physikalischen") Blatt ausgestrahlte p-wertige Welle mit den einzelnen Zweigen $u_p^{(i)}$ $(i=1$ bis $p)$. u_p hat die einfache Eigenschaft

$$u_p^{(1)} + u_p^{(2)} + \cdots + u_p^{(p)} = u_1,$$

worin u_1 die einwertige Lösung, also die einfache von Q ausgehende Kugelwelle, bedeutet. Das Ergebnis folgt aus dem Umstand, daß die linksseitige Summe jedenfalls einwertig ist, sich beim Durchgang durch (S) regulär verhält und die Quelle Q als einzige Singularität besitzt. Vorausgesetzt ist dabei, daß die Randlinie (C) *nicht strahlt*, also u_p der Kantenbedingung genügt. Aus der Kantenbedingung folgt jetzt als Verhalten der Lösung in der Nähe von (C) unter Einbeziehung des elektromagnetischen Falles:

$$u,\ \mathfrak{E}_{\|},\ \mathfrak{H}_{\|} \lesssim \text{const}, \qquad \mathfrak{E}_{\perp},\ \mathfrak{H}_{\perp} \lesssim \varrho^{1/p-1} \qquad \text{für } \varrho \to 0.$$

Die Welle $u_p^{(1)}$ kann zur Darstellung der Beugung an einem „schwarzen Schirm" (S) verwendet werden, der die auffallende Strahlung verschluckt[1]. Vorder- und Rückseite des „schwarzen Schirms" sind dabei als Öffnungen des „physikalischen" Raumes nach dem $p-1$-blättrigen „mathematischen" Raume hin veranschaulicht, was an die physikalische Realisierung des schwarzen Körpers durch ein Loch in einem Hohlraum erinnert. Ein strenger Sinn kommt diesen Vorstellungen und der Welle $u_p^{(1)}$ allerdings nicht zu, da die Eigenschaft „schwarz" nicht als Randbedingung faßbar ist und die ganze Problemstellung daher weitgehend unbestimmt bleibt.

Im Rahmen der *strengen* Theorie der Beugung an ebenen Schirmen spielen mehrwertige Lösungen mit $p>2$ keine Rolle; doch haben sie bei der Beugung am Keil (vgl. Ziff. 114) Anwendung gefunden.

II. Heuristische Methoden.

Eine strenge allgemeine Theorie der Beugung (als Randwertproblem der Maxwellschen Gleichungen aufgefaßt) hat konsequenterweise vom Huygensschen Prinzip in Verbindung mit der das Randwertproblem charakterisierenden *Integralgleichung* auszugehen. Wir werden dieses Programm, soweit es bisher durchgeführt worden ist, in Abschnitt III darstellen. Es ist jedoch für den gegenwärtigen Stand der Beugungstheorie charakteristisch, daß sie in der Praxis noch immer auf die Heranziehung heuristischer — aus der physikalischen Anschauung hervorgegangener — Methoden nicht verzichten kann, obwohl eine strenge Begründung dieser Methoden teilweise noch aussteht, ja — wie bei der Kirchhoffschen Beugungstheorie — gar nicht zu erwarten ist.

Die älteste dieser Methoden — die auf Kirchhoff zurückgeht — ist so allgemein bekannt, daß wir uns auf die Darstellung ihrer wesentlichsten Merkmale beschränken können (Abschn. IIa). Sie ersetzt das Randwertproblem durch ein Sprungwertproblem, wobei die Sprungfläche noch weitgehend deformiert werden

[1] Vgl. dazu W. Voigt: Kompendium der theoretischen Physik, Bd. 2, S. 768. Leipzig 1896. — Göttinger Nachr. **1899**, 1. — A. Sommerfeld: Z. Math. Phys. **46**, 11 (1901).

kann. Dadurch ist sie von außerordentlicher Geschmeidigkeit; ihre Rechtfertigung kann jedoch immer erst nachträglich durch Vergleich mit dem Experiment oder mit der in besonders einfachen Fällen möglichen strengen Lösung erfolgen. Die Kirchhoffsche Theorie läßt sich auch im Sinne des noch wesentlich älteren *Th. Youngschen Prinzips* als reiner *Kanteneffekt* interpretieren.

In neuerer Zeit ist für *ebene* Schirme eine Modifikation der Kirchhoffschen Theorie entwickelt worden, die das hier vorliegende *gemischte Randwertproblem* (für die volle Ebene) durch zwei andere Randwertprobleme (ein Dirichletsches bzw. ein Neumannsches) ersetzt (Ziff. 35). Der dabei begangene Fehler läßt sich durch ein Verfahren von W. Franz schrittweise verkleinern (Abschn. IIb, Ziff. 37), wobei die Konvergenz des Verfahrens allerdings durch die auftretenden Kantensingularitäten (Ziff. 38) in Frage gestellt wird (das Verfahren von Franz läßt sich auch bei beliebigen Körperformen zur schrittweisen Verbesserung der Kirchhoffschen Näherung heranziehen).

Um die Kantenbedingung von vorne herein zu berücksichtigen, hat W. Braunbek vorgeschlagen, die Kirchhoffschen Randwerte so abzuändern, daß sie in *Kantennähe*, mit den Werten übereinstimmen, die die strenge Sommerfeldsche Theorie der Beugung an der *Halbebene* liefert (Abschn. B Ia). Dies erscheint solange gerechtfertigt, als der Krümmungsradius der Schirmkante überall groß gegen die Wellenlänge ist (für Körper beliebiger Gestalt übernimmt die geometrische Schattengrenze auf deren Oberfläche gewissermaßen die Rolle der beugenden Schirmkante). Das Braunbeksche Verfahren dürfte das *erste Glied* einer *asymptotischen Entwicklung* der *strengen Lösung* für *kleine Wellenlängen* liefern.

In jüngster Zeit ist von J. B. Keller eine *„geometrische Beugungstheorie“* entwickelt worden, die die *geometrische Optik* mit ihren Systemen einfallender, gebrochener und reflektierter Strahlen durch die Konzeption der sog. *„gebeugten Strahlen“* erweitert (Abschn. IIc). Die Geometrie dieser Strahlen wird durch eine Erweiterung des *Fermatschen Prinzips* festgelegt, das einen *extremalen Wert des optischen Weges zwischen Quell- und Aufpunkt längs der gebeugten Strahlen fordert.* Diese unterscheiden sich von den reflektierten Strahlen durch die Nebenbedingung, daß sie — per definitionem — mit der Oberfläche des beugenden Körpers nicht nur einen Punkt sondern eine *Linie* gemeinsam haben und so auch in das geometrisch optische Schattengebiet gelangen können. Für stetig gekrümmte Oberflächen stellt ein die Fläche tangierend treffender Strahl, der längs einer *geodätischen Linie* auf ihr weiterläuft und sie tangierend in Richtung Aufpunkt wieder verläßt, eine solche extremale (kürzeste) Verbindung dar. Dadurch erscheint also die geometrisch optische Schattengrenze auf der Oberfläche als Ausgangsort für die gebeugten Strahlen. Bei ebenen Schirmen gehen gebeugte Strahlen lediglich von der Schirmkante aus und zwar ist jeder Kantenpunkt Ausgangsort eines *Strahlenkegels*, dessen halber Öffnungswinkel durch den Winkel zwischen Kantentangente und einfallendem Strahl gegeben ist. Die geometrische Beugungstheorie ist also gewissermaßen eine heuristische Verfeinerung und quantitative Vervollständigung der Youngschen Konzeption (Streuung an der Kante).

Die Intensitätsverhältnisse (bzw. Amplitudenverhältnisse) längs der Strahlen werden mit Hilfe des *Energiesatzes* festgelegt, der eine einfache Beziehung zwischen zwei beliebigen Querschnitten einer aus Strahlen gebildeten Röhre liefert; diese wiederum lassen sich mit Hilfe der Kaustikeigenschaften der Strahlensysteme berechnen. Mit Hilfe einer weiteren einfachen Annahme über die Phasenveränderung längs des Strahles, läßt sich so jedem Punkt des Strahles ein Wellenfeld zuordnen, wenn das Feld an irgendeinem (charakteristischen) Punkt des

Strahles festgelegt wird. Dies geschieht, indem man das Feld etwa am Auftreffpunkt des Strahles auf das Objekt mit Hilfe der strengen Lösung eines möglichst einfachen Randwertproblems berechnet, dessen Geometrie nur in der engsten Umgebung des Auftreffpunktes mit dem gegebenen Objekt übereinzustimmen braucht (bei Kantenpunkten wird hier — wie bei Braunbek — die Beugung an der Halbebene herangezogen). Es können aber, wo dies zweckmäßig ist, auch andere Punkte die Rolle von charakteristischen Punkten übernehmen (z. B. Brennpunkte). Das Gesamtfeld in jedem Aufpunkt ergibt sich durch Addition der Felder sämtlicher durch diesen Punkt gehenden Strahlen.

Das Verfahren ist besonders dadurch sehr anpassungsfähig, daß auch Strahlen, die etwa zwei oder mehr Punkte mit der Kante gemeinsam haben (also unter *dieser* Nebenbedingung die kürzeste Verbindung zwischen Quell- und Aufpunkt darstellen) ohne weiteres erfaßt werden können *(mehrfach gebeugte Strahlen)*. Keller hat nun gezeigt, daß die einfach gebeugten Strahlen genau dasselbe Feld liefern, wie die (asymptotisch ausgewertete) Methode von Braunbek (abgesehen von der Umgebung der Kante, der geometrischen Schattengrenze sowie von Brennpunkten und Kaustiken, wo das geometrische Verfahren in unzulässiger Weise singulär wird). Mit Hilfe der mehrfach gebeugten Strahlen lassen sich dann dazu höhere Näherungen berechnen. Diese sind insbesondere zur Berechnung des *Streu- bzw. Durchlaßkoeffizienten* (mit Hilfe des Imaginärteils der komplexen Fernfeldamplitude in Richtung der einfallenden Welle, vgl. Ziff. 100 und 102) von Bedeutung, da hier der Beitrag der einfach gebeugten Strahlen *verschwindet*.

Offenbar sind alle geschilderten heuristischen Approximationsverfahren auf den Fall zugeschnitten, daß sämtliche Abmessungen des Objekts groß gegen die Wellenlänge der einfallenden Welle sind. Dieser Fall liegt nun einerseits bei den klassischen Beugungsexperimenten tatsächlich vor, rückt aber andererseits infolge der fortschreitenden Entwicklung der Ultrakurzwellentechnik auch ins Blickfeld des Praktikers. Ein Vergleich der Ergebnisse des Braunbekschen bzw. Kellerschen Verfahrens (für einfach gebeugte Strahlen) mit strengen Lösungen spezieller Beugungsprobleme zeigt nun, daß durch diese Verfahren, das *erste Glied* einer *asymptotischen* Entwicklung der strengen Lösung des Randwertproblems nach fallenden Potenzen der Wellenzahl geliefert wird [abgesehen von gewissen Flächen, Linien und Punkten mit Kaustikeigenschaft, wo der Charakter dieser Entwicklungen umschlägt (Abschn. IIc, Ziff. 44)].

a) Die Kirchhoffsche Beugungstheorie.

Die traditionelle Darstellung der Beugungstheorie schließt gewöhnlich an das Vorgehen Kirchhoffs[1] an. Dieser ging von der strengen Fassung des Huygensschen Prinzips (in der skalaren Form) aus (Ziff. 8), setzte jedoch bei der Anwendung der Integralformel einfach plausible Werte für die beiden dort auftretenden Randwerte ein, so daß das Verfahren die Lösung einer bestimmten *Sprungwertaufgabe* darstellt (vgl. Ziff. 10) — worauf zuerst Rubinowicz[2] und Kottler[3] hingewiesen haben — die mit der durch die physikalischen Bedingungen ge-

[1] Vgl. G. Kirchhoff: Sitzgsber. Berl. Akad. Wiss. 641 (1882). — Ann. Phys. **18**, 663 (1883). — Vorlesung über mathematische Physik, Bd. 2. Leipzig 1891. (5. Vorlesg.)

[2] A. Rubinowicz: Ann. Phys. **53**, 257 (1917); **73**, 339 (1924); **81**, 170 (1926). Man vergleiche auch die umfassende Darstellung in der Monographie von A. Rubinowicz: Die Beugungswelle in der Kirchhoffschen Theorie der Beugung. Warschau 1957.

[3] F. Kottler: Ann. Phys. **70**, 405 (1923). Siehe auch W. Franz: Z. Naturforsch. **3**a, 500 (1948). — S. A. Schelkunoff: Comm. Pure Appl. Math. **4**, 43 (1951).

forderten Lösung einer *Randwertaufgabe* nichts zu tun hat. Trotzdem liefert das Kirchhoffsche Verfahren im Grenzfall: „*Lineardimensionen der beugenden Körper groß gegen die Wellenlänge*" in der *Fernzone* vorzügliche Übereinstimmung mit der Erfahrung; dagegen versagt es in der Nähe von Kanten vollständig, da es dort in einer die Kantenbedingungen verletzenden Weise singulär wird.

In der Tat findet die instrumentelle Optik mit der (über die *Fresnelsche* Theorie von 1818 praktisch nicht hinausgehenden) Kirchhoffschen Beugungstheorie ihr Auskommen[1]. Andererseits wird die Kirchhoffsche Theorie den Bedürfnissen der Mikrowellentechnik nicht mehr gerecht. Gerade hier bietet sich aber die günstigste Möglichkeit, die Ergebnisse der strengen (als Randwertproblem formulierten) Beugungstheorie mit dem Experiment zu vergleichen. Im Mikrowellengebiet läßt sich nämlich die Idealisierung der ideal leitenden Körper und Schirme viel weitgehender realisieren als in der Lichtoptik. Außerdem kann das Verhältnis von Wellenlänge zu Objektabmessungen in weiten Grenzen variiert werden.

Die analytische Beziehung zwischen dem (Kirchhoffschen) Sprungwertproblem und dem Randwertproblem dürfte darin bestehen, daß das *Fernfeld* der Lösung des Randwertproblems für *kleine* Wellenlängen (d.h. klein gegen jede vorkommende Objektabmessung) *asymptotisch* in das *Fernfeld* der Lösung des Kirchhoffschen Sprungwertproblems übergeht. Allerdings nur in einem *kleinen Winkelbereich*, der als Umgebung der geometrischen Schattengrenze bzw. als *Umgebung der Einfallsrichtung* (bei ebener Primärwelle) gekennzeichnet werden kann. Ferner muß diese Übereinstimmung *unabhängig* von der auf der Körperoberfläche geforderten Randbedingung bestehen. Diesen Sachverhalt — dessen allgemeiner Beweis noch aussteht (vgl. dazu Ziff. 44) — werden wir bei der Beugung an der Halbebene (Ziff. 116), am Spalt (Ziff. 124) und an der Kreisscheibe (Ziff. 134) bestätigt finden. Eine weitere Bestätigung ergibt sich aus der in Ziff. 39 zu besprechenden Braunbekschen Näherung, die in der Umgebung der Einfallsrichtung mit der Kirchhoffschen Lösung übereinstimmt. Wir wollen dagegen schon hier betonen, daß die Braunbeksche Näherung im *gesamten* Feldgebiet mit der asymptotischen Lösung des Randwertproblems übereinstimmt.

30. Kirchhoffsche Lösung. Wir betrachten einen streuenden oder beugenden Körper (Fig. 19a und b) im Felde einer Punktquelle Q. Die im Sinne der *geometrischen Optik* scharfe *Schattengrenze* (S_g) tangiert die Körper je in einer *Schattenlinie* (C). Man denke sich in diese Linie eine beliebige Fläche (L) eingespannt [im Streufall ist (C) *innerer* Rand der Fläche (L), die sich irgendwie im Endlichen oder Unendlichen *hinter* der Quelle Q schließen möge]. Die Fläche (L) bildet zusammen mit dem „unbeleuchteten" Teil (S'') der Oberfläche der Körper eine geschlossene Fläche $(S'')+(L)$, die den Raum in den quellenfreien Raumteil T^+ und den Raumteil mit Quellen T^- teilt. Nach der *geometrischen Optik* herrscht in T^+ folgender Feldzustand: in dem von (L) und (S_g) begrenzten „Kegelstumpf" T_g herrscht die der Quelle entsprechende ungestörte Feldverteilung v_0, außerhalb verschwindet das Feld. Diese geometrisch optische Feldverteilung v_g läßt sich nach dem Huygensschen Prinzip (8.5) durch ein Integral über die Begrenzung des Kegelstumpfes darstellen $(\mathfrak{r} \in T^+)$:

$$v_g(\mathfrak{r}) = \begin{Bmatrix} v_0(\mathfrak{r}) \\ 0 \end{Bmatrix} = \int\limits_{S_g+L} \Omega_0(\mathfrak{r}, \hat{\mathfrak{r}}')\, d\,\hat{\mathfrak{r}}' \tag{30.1}$$

---

[1] Über die zahlreichen Anwendungen der *Fresnel-Kirchhoffschen* Beugungstheorie in der instrumentellen Optik vergleiche man M. Born u. E. Wolf: Principles of Optics, S. 369—552. London-New York-Paris-Los Angeles: Pergamon Press 1959, sowie dieses Handbuch, Bd. XXIV (M. Françon).

mit

$$\Omega_0(\mathfrak{r}, \hat{\mathfrak{r}}') = \left\{ v_0(\hat{\mathfrak{r}}') \frac{\partial}{\partial n'} - \frac{\partial v_0(\hat{\mathfrak{r}}')}{\partial n'} \right\} G(\mathfrak{r} - \hat{\mathfrak{r}}'); \tag{30.1a}$$

dabei gibt also das Oberflächenintegral den Wert v_0 für $\mathfrak{r}$ innerhalb T_g bzw. 0 für $\mathfrak{r}$ außerhalb T_g. Für eine später folgende Anwendung geben wir dem Integranden Ω_0 noch die Form

$$\left.\begin{aligned} &\Omega_0(\mathfrak{r}, \mathfrak{r}') = (\mathfrak{n}' \mathfrak{V}_0(\mathfrak{r}, \mathfrak{r}')) \\ \text{mit} \qquad &\mathfrak{V}_0(\mathfrak{r}, \mathfrak{r}') = \{v_0(\mathfrak{r}') \nabla' - \nabla' v_0(\mathfrak{r}')\} G(\mathfrak{r} - \mathfrak{r}'). \end{aligned}\right\} \tag{30.1b}$$

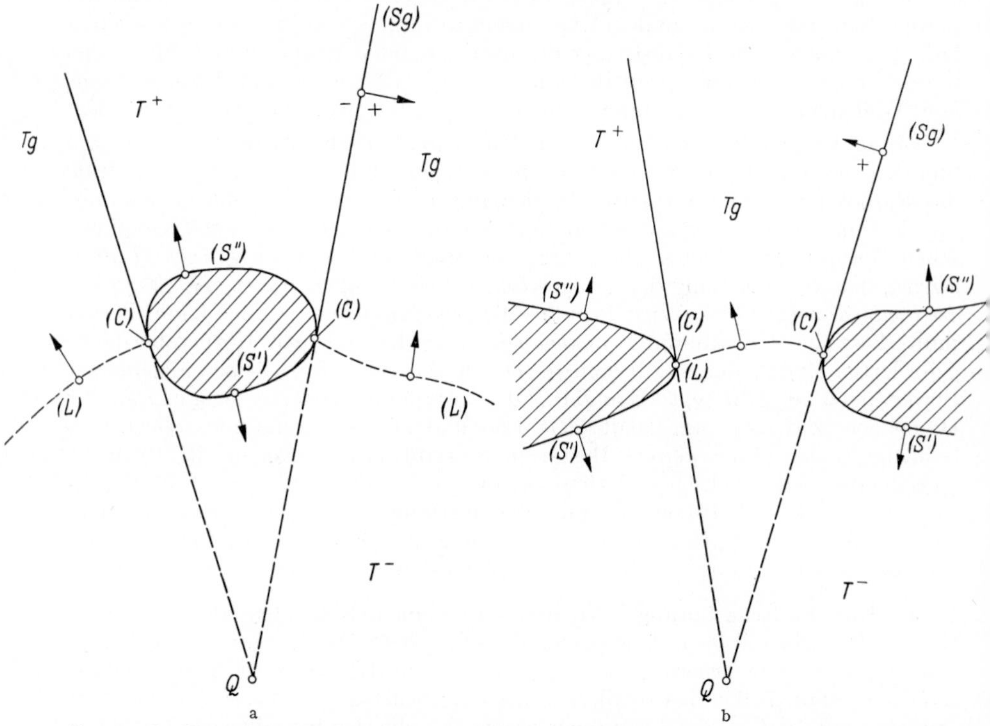

Fig. 19. a Zur Kirchhoffschen Theorie der Streuung an einem ausgedehnten Körper. b Zur Kirchhoffschen Theorie der Beugung an einem Schirm von endlicher Dicke.

Hier ist $\mathfrak{V}_0$ analog (8.4) quellenfrei bis auf zwei Punktquellen:

$$\operatorname{div}' \mathfrak{V}_0(\mathfrak{r}, \mathfrak{r}') = v_0(\mathfrak{r}) \{\delta(\mathfrak{r} - \mathfrak{r}') - \delta(\mathfrak{r}_0 - \mathfrak{r}')\}, \tag{30.1c}$$

wobei $\mathfrak{r}_0$ den Ortsektor des Quellpunktes Q bedeutet und $v_0(\mathfrak{r})$ die von Q auslaufende *Kugelwelle*:

$$v_0(\mathfrak{r}) = G(\mathfrak{r} - \mathfrak{r}_0) = \frac{1}{4\pi} \frac{e^{i|\mathfrak{r} - \mathfrak{r}_0|}}{|\mathfrak{r} - \mathfrak{r}_0|}.$$

Legen wir den Bezugspunkt des Ortsvektors in die Quelle Q ($\mathfrak{r}_0 = 0$) und setzen die expliziten Ausdrücke für G und v_0 in (30.1b) ein, so ergibt sich

$$\left.\begin{aligned} 16\pi^2 \mathfrak{V}_0 &= \frac{e^{ir'}}{r'} \nabla' \frac{e^{iR}}{R} - \frac{e^{iR}}{R} \nabla' \frac{e^{ir'}}{r'} \\ &= -\frac{e^{i(r'+R)}}{r' R} \left\{ \left(\frac{i}{r'} - \frac{1}{r'^2} \right) \mathfrak{r}' - \left(\frac{i}{R} - \frac{1}{R^2} \right) \mathfrak{R} \right\} \end{aligned}\right\} \tag{30.1d}$$

mit

$$\mathfrak{R} = \mathfrak{r}' - \mathfrak{r}.$$

Das Feld (30.1) erleidet beim Hindurchtreten durch die Schattengrenze (S_g) (von der positiven nach der negativen Seite, vgl. Fig. 19a und b) die Sprünge

$$\{v_g\}_+ - \{v_g\}_- = v_0, \quad \left\{\frac{\partial v_g}{\partial n}\right\}_+ - \left\{\frac{\partial v_g}{\partial n}\right\}_- = \frac{\partial v_0}{\partial n}.$$

Diese widersprechen jedoch der in T^+ ausnahmslos gültigen homogenen Wellengleichung $(\Delta + 1) \cdots = 0$ (sie entsprechen fiktiven flächenhaften Quellverteilungen). Wir konstruieren nun eine *überall* in T^+ der Wellengleichung und der Ausstrahlungsbedingung genügende Lösung v_K, indem wir zu v_g eine Lösung hinzufügen, die beim Hindurchtreten durch (S_g) die *entgegengesetzt gleichen* Sprünge besitzt wie v_g, sonst aber überall in T^+ regulär ist. Dieser Zusatzterm bestimmt sich also aus einer *Sprungwertaufgabe*, die nach (10.1) die Lösung $-\int\limits_{S_g} \Omega_0\, d\sigma$ besitzt. Damit erhalten wir aus (30.1) die „*regularisierte*" Lösung

$$v_K(\mathfrak{r}) = v_g(\mathfrak{r}) - \int\limits_{S_g} \Omega_0(\mathfrak{r}, \hat{\mathfrak{r}}')\, d\hat{\mathfrak{r}}' = \int\limits_{L} \Omega_0(\mathfrak{r}, \hat{\mathfrak{r}}')\, d\hat{\mathfrak{r}}' \qquad (\mathfrak{r} \in T^+). \tag{30.2}$$

Dies ist die *Kirchhoffsche Lösung*[1], die sich dahingehend interpretieren läßt, daß das Wellenfeld in T^+ durch die Superposition von „*Elementarwellen*" zustande kommt, die von den Punkten der Öffnung (L) ausgehen, in Übereinstimmung mit den Huygens-Fresnelschen Vorstellungen. Insbesondere können wir die Fläche (L) auch so deformieren, daß sie sich der „beleuchteten Seite" (S') der Körper anschmiegt. Dabei bleibt die Fläche jedoch an der Singularität in Q „hängen", d.h. wir müssen eine kleine Q umgebende Kugel mit zur Fläche hinzurechnen. Der Beitrag $\oint \Omega_0\, d\sigma$ dieser Kugel ergibt aber gerade $v_0(\mathfrak{r})$. Damit können wir (30.2) auch in der Form

$$v_K(\mathfrak{r}) = v_0(\mathfrak{r}) + \int\limits_{S'} \Omega_0(\mathfrak{r}, \hat{\mathfrak{r}}')\, d\hat{\mathfrak{r}}' \qquad (\mathfrak{r} \in T^+) \tag{30.2'}$$

schreiben. Das Gebiet T^+ ist jedoch jetzt der ganze Raum mit Ausnahme der Körper und der Quelle.

In die Kirchhoffsche Lösung geht lediglich die Schattenlinie (C) ein, nicht dagegen die sonstige Gestalt der „schattenwerfenden" Körper, ebensowenig wie die Gestalt der Fläche (L) bei gegebener Berandung. Dies ist eine unmittelbare Folge der Quellenfreiheit von $\mathfrak{B}_0$. Wir wollen im folgenden den streuenden bzw. beugenden Körper auf einen (unendlich dünnen) Schirm (S) zusammendrücken (Fig. 20a und b). Die Schattenlinie (C) wird dann im allgemeinen mit dem Rand des Schirmes zusammenfallen.

[1] KIRCHHOFF gelangte bekanntlich zu dieser Formel, indem er in der Darstellung des Huygensschen Prinzips (8.5) die Fläche $(S'') + (L)$ wählte und für die dort eingehenden Randwerte die mehr oder weniger plausiblen *Annahmen* machte:

$$v = v_0, \ \frac{\partial v}{\partial n} = \frac{\partial v_0}{\partial n} \quad auf\ (L); \qquad v = \frac{\partial v}{\partial n} = 0 \quad auf\ (S''),$$

mit denen ebenfalls (30.2) resultiert. Die auf diesen Annahmen beruhende „Ableitung" der Lösung (30.2) — die in fast alle Lehrbücher der Optik eingegangen ist — ist aber in sich widerspruchig, da die Randwerte von v und $\partial v/\partial n$ einer jeden Lösung der Wellengleichung in dem funktionellen Zusammenhang (9.6) stehen müssen, also *nicht beide* willkürlich vorgegeben werden können. Darauf — sowie auf die daraus folgende Tatsache, daß die Lösung (30.2) die von KIRCHHOFF angenommenen Randwerte *nicht* reproduziert — hat wohl erstmals H. POINCARÉ hingewiesen (Théorie mathématique de la lumière 2, 187, Paris 1892). Die im Text gegebene Ableitung, die dieser Kritik nicht ausgesetzt ist, zeigt deutlich, daß die Kirchhoffsche Lösung mit einem Randwertproblem nichts zu tun hat.

Wir wollen nun die Lösung (30.2) gemäß der Wellengleichung *stetig durch die Öffnung hindurch* nach T^- fortsetzen und zwar so, daß sie in T^- dieselbe Singularität wie v_0 besitzt. Zu diesem Zweck bemerken wir, daß nach (8.5) folgende Beziehung gilt

$$\int_{S+L} \Omega_0(\mathfrak{r}, \hat{\mathfrak{r}}')\, d\hat{\mathfrak{r}}' = \begin{cases} v_0(\mathfrak{r}) & (\mathfrak{r} \in T^+) \\ 0 & (\mathfrak{r} \in T^-). \end{cases} \tag{30.3}$$

Mit ihrer Hilfe können wir (30.2) auch so schreiben:

$$v_K(\mathfrak{r}) = v_0(\mathfrak{r}) - \int_S \Omega_0(\mathfrak{r}, \hat{\mathfrak{r}}')\, d\hat{\mathfrak{r}}. \tag{30.2''}$$

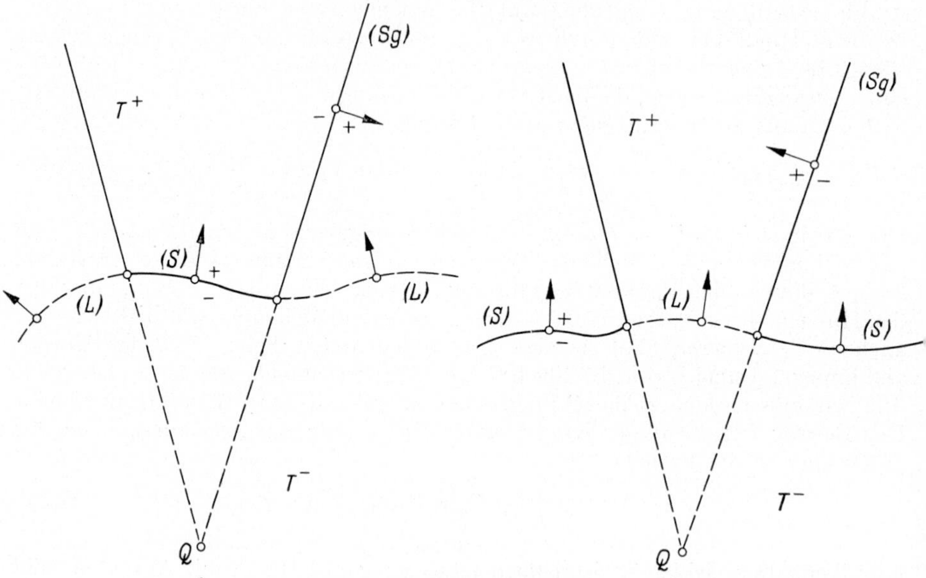

Fig. 20. a Zur Streuung an einem unendlich dünnen Schirm nach Kichhoff. b Zur Beugung an der Öffnung in einem unendlich dünnen Schirm nach Kirchhoff.

Dies ergibt sich auch, wenn wir in (30.2) (L) so deformieren, daß sich die Fläche der negativen Seite von (S) anschmiegt, vgl. (30.2′). Das Integral über den Schirm (S) verhält sich aber beim Hindurchtreten durch die Öffnung (L) *regulär* — im Gegensatz zur Lösung (30.2), mit der (30.2″) nur in T^+ übereinstimmt,— ferner besitzt (30.2″) in T^- dieselbe Singularität wie v_0. Gl. (30.2″) ist also in T^- die gesuchte Fortsetzung von (30.2) von T^+ nach T^-. Schließlich können wir (30.2″) mit Hilfe von (30.3) auch in der Form

$$v_K(\mathfrak{r}) = \begin{cases} \int_L \Omega_0(\mathfrak{r}, \hat{\mathfrak{r}}')\, d\hat{\mathfrak{r}}' & (\mathfrak{r} \in T^+) \\ v_0(\mathfrak{r}) + \int_L \Omega_0(\mathfrak{r}, \hat{\mathfrak{r}}')\, d\hat{\mathfrak{r}}' & (\mathfrak{r} \in T^-) \end{cases} \tag{30.2'''}$$

schreiben. An Gl. (30.2″) bzw. (30.2‴) erkennt man also, daß die Kirchhoffsche Lösung v_K eine Lösung der Wellengleichung darstellt, die in T^- dieselbe Singularität wie v_0 besitzt und beim Hindurchtreten durch den *Schirm* (S) die *Sprünge*

$$\{v_K\}_+ - \{v_K\}_- = v_0, \quad \left\{\frac{\partial v_K}{\partial n}\right\}_+ - \left\{\frac{\partial v_K}{\partial n}\right\}_- = \frac{\partial v_0}{\partial n} \tag{30.4}$$

aufweist. In Gl. (30.2‴) kommt dies dadurch zum Ausdruck, daß die einfallende Welle v_0 beim Übergang nach T^+ längs des Schirmes (S) „abgeschnitten" ist.

Wir haben gesehen, daß in der Kirchhoffschen Beugungstheorie der „Beugungseffekt" darin besteht, daß die Unstetigkeiten der geometrisch-optischen Feldverteilung im Sinne der Wellengleichung „ausgeglättet" werden. Die ausgeglättete Lösung v_K kann nach Belieben als Superpolition von Elementarwellen aufgefaßt werden, die von der „Öffnung" (L) oder dem „Schirm" (S) ausgehen, vgl. (30.2‴) oder (30.2″). Insbesondere die zweite Auffassung erlaubt es, den Zusammenhang der Kirchhoffschen Lösung mit der durch die physikalische Problemstellung geforderten Lösung einer Randwertaufgabe wenigstens qualitativ zu überblicken. Die von den Flächenelementen des Schirmes (S) ausgehenden Elementarwellen in (30.2″) sind voneinander vollständig *unabhängig* [die „Belegungsdichte" ist durch die Sprungwerte (30.4) gegeben]. Das heißt, die von der Quelle einem Flächenelement zugestrahlte Welle wird nach Maßgabe eines „*Richtungsfaktors*" [der durch das skalare Produkt der Flächennormale mit der geschweiften Klammer in (30.1 d) gegeben ist] zum Aufpunkt weitergestrahlt und zwar *ohne Wechselwirkung* mit den übrigen Flächenelementen. Anders bei den als Randwertaufgabe formulierten Beugungsproblemen. Hier wird die Verteilung der Belegungsdichte (Flächenstrom) einerseits durch die einfallende Welle, andererseits durch die von *sämtlichen* übrigen Flächenelementen *einander zugestrahlten* Sekundärwellen so reguliert, daß sich auf dem Schirm der entsprechende Randwert einstellt. Die Durchführung dieser Konzeption führt auf eine Integralgleichung [vgl. (11.2)], worauf wir in Abschn. III ausführlich eingehen werden.

Die Kirchhoffsche Lösung v_K ist die Lösung des *Sprungwertproblems* (30.4), die dieselbe Singularität wie v_0 besitzt. Sie kann gemäß der Wellengleichung in einen unendlich vielblättrigen Riemannschen Raum fortgesetzt werden. Der *Verzweigungsschnitt* ist hier der Schirm (S), sein Rand (C) ist *Verzweigungslinie*. In diesem Verzweigungsschnitt ist der „*physikalische*" Raum mit den „*mathematischen Räumen*" zusammenzuheften. Die durch den Verzweigungsschnitt aus dem physikalischen Raum in die mathematischen gelangende *einfallende* Welle v_0 läuft sich in diesem tot. Dieser analytische Sachverhalt soll nach KOTTLER zur Definition des „*schwarzen Schirmes*" dienen. Da aber die Konstruktion unendlich verzweigter Lösungen der Wellengleichung keineswegs eindeutig ist — beispielsweise könnte das Verhalten der Wellenfunktion in den mathematischen Räumen noch weitgehend variiert werden — so ist diese Definition *nicht* eindeutig. (Vgl. auch Ziff. 29; die dort eingeführten verzweigten Lösungen mit $p \to \infty$ unterscheiden sich von der hier betrachteten unendlich verzweigten Lösung dadurch, daß v_K der Kantenbedingung *nicht* genügt, die Kante also zusätzlich strahlt.)

Da die Kirchhoffsche Lösung das Verhalten physikalisch realer Schirme (die durch Randwerte zu beschreiben sind) bezüglich des Fernfeldes in der Umgebung der Schattengrenze nach Ausweis des Experiments richtig wiedergibt, liegt die Annahme nahe, daß sie der erste Schritt eines für *kleine* Wellenlängen λ schnell konvergierenden Approximationsverfahrens zur Lösung der Randwertaufgabe sei. Dieses sollte die exakte Lösung etwa in Form einer Potenzreihe nach steigenden Potenzen in λ approximieren. Es ist vorgeschlagen worden, die von (30.2″) tatsächlich auf der gesamten Fläche $(S)+(L)$ angenommenen Werte von v_K und $\partial v_K/\partial n$ in die Helmholtzsche Formel (8.5) einzusetzen, um eine zweite Näherung zu berechnen[1]. Dieses Verfahren kann jedoch nicht zum Ziele führen, da es nach den Ausführungen von Ziff. 8 wieder genau zu der Kirchhoffschen Lösung $v_K(\mathfrak{r})$ zurückführt. Konsequente Verfahren zur Verbesserung der Kirchhoffschen Lösung

[1] Siehe etwa M. BORN: Optik, S. 152. Berlin 1933.

werden wir in Abschn. IIb, c besprechen. Wir heben hervor, daß sich die Kirchhoffsche Lösung im allgemeinen *nicht* als erstes Glied der oben erwähnten Reihe auffassen läßt.

31. Übertragung auf den vektoriellen Fall. Die entsprechenden Überlegungen gelten auch für die *elektromagnetischen Analoga* der Kirchhoffschen Lösung: Man fordert hier den Sprung $[\mathfrak{n}\,\mathfrak{E}_0(\hat{\mathfrak{r}})]$ und $[\mathfrak{n}\,\mathfrak{H}_0(\hat{\mathfrak{r}})]$ der Tangentialkomponenten der Feldvektoren beim Hindurchtreten durch den Schirm (S). Mit Hilfe von (14.1) ergibt sich so

$$\left.\begin{aligned}\mathfrak{E}_K(\mathfrak{r}) &= \operatorname{rot}\int\limits_L [\mathfrak{n}'\,\mathfrak{E}_0(\hat{\mathfrak{r}}')]\,G(\mathfrak{r}-\hat{\mathfrak{r}}')\,d\hat{\mathfrak{r}}' \\ &\quad + i\operatorname{rot}\operatorname{rot}\int\limits_L [\mathfrak{n}'\,\mathfrak{H}_0(\hat{\mathfrak{r}}')]\,G(\mathfrak{r}-\hat{\mathfrak{r}}')\,d\hat{\mathfrak{r}}' + \begin{cases}\mathfrak{E}_0(\mathfrak{r}) & \mathfrak{r}\ \mathit{in}\ T^-\\ 0 & \mathfrak{r}\ \mathit{in}\ T^+.\end{cases}\end{aligned}\right\} \qquad (31.1\,\mathrm{a})$$

$$\left.\begin{aligned}\mathfrak{H}_K(\mathfrak{r}) &= \operatorname{rot}\int\limits_L [\mathfrak{n}'\,\mathfrak{H}_0(\hat{\mathfrak{r}}')]\,G(\mathfrak{r}-\hat{\mathfrak{r}}')\,d\hat{\mathfrak{r}}' \\ &\quad - i\operatorname{rot}\operatorname{rot}\int\limits_L [\mathfrak{n}'\,\mathfrak{E}_0(\hat{\mathfrak{r}}')]\,G(\mathfrak{r}-\hat{\mathfrak{r}}')\,d\hat{\mathfrak{r}}' + \begin{cases}\mathfrak{H}_0(\mathfrak{r}) & \mathfrak{r}\ \mathit{in}\ T^-\\ 0 & \mathfrak{r}\ \mathit{in}\ T^+.\end{cases}\end{aligned}\right\} \qquad (31.1\,\mathrm{b})$$

$\mathfrak{E}_0$, $\mathfrak{H}_0$ bedeute hier die auf den Schirm auffallende Welle. Die Gln. (31.1a, b) stellen also eine Lösung der Maxwellschen Gleichungen dar, deren elektrischer bzw. magnetischer Vektor beim Durchtritt durch den Schirm (S) sich bezüglich seiner Tangentialkomponente unstetig um den Wert $[\mathfrak{n}\,\mathfrak{E}_0]$ bzw. $[\mathfrak{n}\,\mathfrak{H}_0]$ ändert.

32. Das Youngsche Prinzip im Rahmen der Kirchhoffschen Theorie. Die Kirchhoffsche Lösung besitzt nun eine weitere interessante analytische Eigenschaft, die einerseits eine schöne physikalische Deutung zuläßt, andererseits aber gerade ihre prinzipielle Unzulänglichkeit vor Augen führt. Wir meinen die Möglichkeit der Umformung in ein *Linienintegral* über den *Rand* (C) der Öffnung (L). Hierin kommt, wie sich zeigt, ein schon von Th. Young 1802 hervorgehobener Aspekt der Beugungstheorie zum Ausdruck, nämlich die Auffassung, daß die Beugung durch Interferenz einer *vom Rande der Öffnung ausgehenden Welle* mit dem im Sinne der geometrischen Optik sich ausbreitenden Wellenfeld zustandekommt. Die strenge mathematische Formulierung dieses Gedankens im Rahmen der Kirchhoffschen Theorie hat erst Maggi[1] 1888 und besonders durchsichtig A. Rubinowicz[2] 1917 gegeben. Die folgende Darstellung folgt einem neueren Beweisgang von Rubinowicz[3]. Die Möglichkeit der Überführung des Flächenintegrals in ein Linienintegral ergibt sich aus der Tatsache, daß das Flächenintegral der Fluß eines quellenfreien Vektors ist (Stokesscher Satz).

Analytisch liegen hier analoge Verhältnisse vor wie in der Theorie der linearen stationären Ströme. Der in der Kirchhoffschen Theorie als Sprungfläche aufgefaßte Schirm (S) entspricht dem in die Strombahn eingespannten magnetischen Blatt Ampères. Faßt man dagegen den Strom als linienförmige Feldsingularität auf, so gelangt man zur Darstellung von Biot-Savart. Dem entspricht in der Kirchhoffschen Theorie die Felddarstellung mittels eines Linienintegrals über den Rand des Schirmes nach Maggi-Rubinowicz. In physikalischer Hinsicht ist zu bemerken, daß der lineare stationäre Strom in der Tat als Quelle des Magnetfeldes zu betrachten ist. Andererseits ist in der Beugungstheorie die Punktquelle Q

[1] G.A. Maggi: Ann. di Math. **16**, 21 (1888).

[2] A. Rubinowicz: Ann. Phys. **53**, 257 (1917); **73**, 339 (1924); **81**, 170 (1926). Siehe auch F. Kottler: Ann. Phys. **70**, 405 (1923). — C.N. Ramachandran: Proc. Ind. Acad. Sci. A **21**, 165 (1945). — Y.V. Kathavate: Proc. Ind. Acad. Sci. A **21**, 177 (1945). — R.S. Ingarden: Acta phy. polon. **14**, 77 (1955). — L.C. Martin: Proc. Phys. Soc. Lond. **55**, 104 (1943); B **62**, 713 (1949).

[3] A. Rubinowicz: Acta phys. polon. **12**, 225 (1954). — Die Beugungswelle in der Kirchhoffschen Theorie der Beugung. Warschau 1957.

die einzige (energieliefernde) Feldsingularität; der als zusätzliche Feldquelle wirkende *„leuchtende Rand“* ist im Rahmen des Randwertproblems nicht legitim (er wird durch die Kantenbedingung ausgeschlossen).

Wir gehen davon aus, daß der Vektor $\mathfrak{V}_0$ in Gl. (30.1 b) im wesentlichen quellenfrei ist, vgl. (30.1 c). Es gilt also

$$\mathfrak{V}_0(\mathfrak{r}, \mathfrak{r}') = \operatorname{rot}' \mathfrak{U}_0(\mathfrak{r}, \mathfrak{r}'), \tag{32.1}$$

falls $\mathfrak{r}'$ nicht mit $\mathfrak{r}$ oder dem Quellpunkt Q zusammenfällt (Q sei Koordinatenursprung). Setzt man hier links die Darstellung (30.1 d) ein, so erhält man eine Differentialgleichung für das bis auf einen Gradienten bestimmte *„Vektorpotential“* $\mathfrak{U}_0$. Um sie zu lösen bemerken wir, daß $\mathfrak{V}_0$ stets in der von $\mathfrak{r}'$ und $\mathfrak{R}$ aufgespannten Ebene liegt (Fig. 21). Dies ist gewährleistet, wenn $\mathfrak{U}_0$ stets auf dieser Ebene senkrecht steht. Wir machen daher den Ansatz

$$\mathfrak{U}_0 = [\mathfrak{r}' \mathfrak{R}]\, \Phi(\mathfrak{r}', \mathfrak{R}) \tag{32.2}$$

aus dem

$$\left.\begin{aligned} \operatorname{rot}' \mathfrak{U}_0 = {} & \mathfrak{r}' \{2 + (\mathfrak{R}\, \nabla')\}\, \Phi \\ & - \mathfrak{R} \{2 + (\mathfrak{r}'\, \nabla')\}\, \Phi \end{aligned}\right\} \tag{32.3}$$

folgt. Mit Hilfe der Identität

$$\begin{aligned} \{2 + (\mathfrak{r}'\, \nabla')\}\, \Phi &= \frac{1}{r'^2} (\mathfrak{r}'\, \nabla'\, r'^2\, \Phi) \\ &= \frac{1}{r'} \frac{\partial}{\partial r'} (r'^2\, \Phi) \end{aligned}$$

und einer entsprechenden, in der $\mathfrak{r}'$ mit $\mathfrak{R}$ vertauscht ist, können wir dafür auch schreiben

$$\left.\begin{aligned} \operatorname{rot}' \mathfrak{U}_0 = {} & \frac{\mathfrak{r}'}{R} \frac{\partial}{\partial R} (R^2\, \Phi) \\ & - \frac{\mathfrak{R}}{r'} \frac{\partial}{\partial r'} (r'^2\, \Phi). \end{aligned}\right\} \tag{32.3'}$$

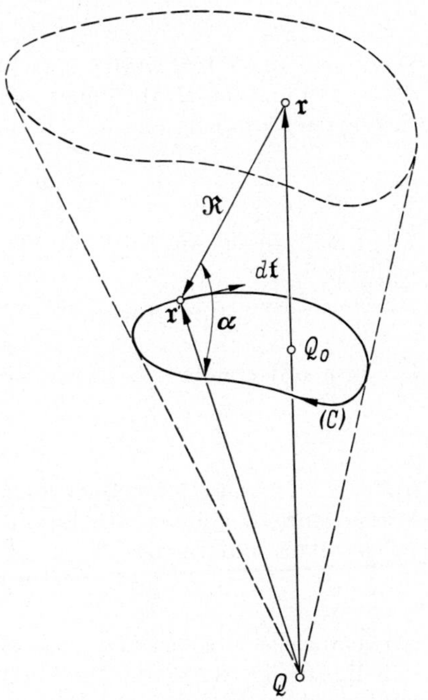

Fig. 21. Zur Umformung des Kirchhoffschen Integrals nach A. Rubinowicz.

Vergleichen wir dies mit (30.1 d), so ergibt sich durch Gleichsetzen des Koeffizienten von $\mathfrak{R}$ und $\mathfrak{r}'$

$$\left.\begin{aligned} \frac{\partial}{\partial r'} (r'^2\, \Phi) &= -\frac{e^{i(r'+R)}}{16\pi^2} \left(\frac{i}{R^2} - \frac{1}{R^3}\right) \\ \frac{\partial}{\partial R} (R^2\, \Phi) &= -\frac{e^{i(r'+R)}}{16\pi^2} \left(\frac{i}{r'^2} - \frac{1}{r'^3}\right). \end{aligned}\right\} \tag{32.4}$$

Hier geht die zweite Gleichung aus der ersten hervor, wenn man $\mathfrak{r}'$ mit $\mathfrak{R}$ vertauscht. Es muß daher Φ in den beiden Argumenten $\mathfrak{r}'$ und $\mathfrak{R}$ symmetrisch sein und wir brauchen uns nur mit einer dieser Differentialgleichungen zu beschäftigen. Die erste Gl. (32.4) wird gelöst, indem wir die rechte Seite nach r' integrieren. Das Integral wollen wir durch partielle Integration auswerten. Zu diesem Zweck schreiben wir

$$i \frac{e^{i(r'+R)}}{R^2} = \frac{\partial}{\partial r'} \left\{\frac{e^{i(r'+R)}}{u}\right\} - e^{i(r'+R)} \frac{\partial}{\partial r'} \left(\frac{1}{u}\right) \tag{32.5}$$

mit

$$u = R^2 \frac{\partial (r' + R)}{\partial r'} = \frac{R}{r'} \{r' R + (\mathfrak{r}' \mathfrak{R})\}. \tag{32.6}$$

Aus (32.6) ergibt sich nun

$$\frac{\partial u}{\partial r'} = \frac{u^2}{R^3}$$

und damit

$$\frac{\partial}{\partial r'} \left(\frac{1}{u}\right) = - \frac{1}{R^3}.$$

Trägt man dies in (32.5) ein, so folgt

$$e^{i(r'+R)} \left(\frac{i}{R^2} - \frac{1}{R^3}\right) = \frac{\partial}{\partial r'} \left\{\frac{e^{i(r'+R)}}{u}\right\}. \tag{32.5'}$$

Setzt man diese Identität rechts in die erste Gl. (32.4) ein, so ergibt sich (bis auf eine nur von R abhängige willkürliche Funktion, die jedoch zufolge der Symmetriebedingung gleich Null zu setzen ist)

$$\Phi = - \frac{e^{i(r'+R)}}{16 \pi^2 r'^2 u}.$$

Trägt man diesen Ausdruck mit dem Wert für u aus (32.6) in (32.2) ein, so folgt schließlich

$$16 \pi^2 \mathfrak{U}_0 = - \frac{e^{i(r'+R)}}{r' R} \frac{[\mathfrak{r}' \mathfrak{R}]}{r' R + (\mathfrak{r}' \mathfrak{R})}. \tag{32.7}$$

Der hier auftretende „*Richtungsfaktor*" hat den Betrag

$$\frac{|[\mathfrak{r}' \mathfrak{R}]|}{r' R + (\mathfrak{r}' \mathfrak{R})} = \frac{\sin \alpha}{1 + \cos \alpha} = \tan \frac{\alpha}{2}, \tag{32.8}$$

wobei α der von $\mathfrak{r}'$ und $\mathfrak{R}$ eingeschlossene Winkel ist (s. Fig. 21). Nach diesen Vorbereitungen können wir das Flächenintegral in (30.2‴) mittels des Stokesschen Satzes umformen:

$$\int_L (\mathfrak{n}' \mathfrak{V}_0)\, d\hat{\mathfrak{r}}' = \oint_C (\mathfrak{U}_0\, d\mathfrak{t}) \tag{32.9}$$

[$d\mathfrak{t}$ vektorielles Bogenelement des Randes (C)]. Dabei ist jedoch darauf zu achten, daß $\mathfrak{U}_0$ zufolge (32.8) auf der Verbindungslinie Quellpunkt—Aufpunkt singulär wird, da dort $\alpha = \pi$ ist. Der Durchstoßpunkt Q_0 dieser Linie mit der in (C) eingespannten Fläche (L) ist bei Anwendung des Stokesschen Satzes durch eine kleine geschlossene Kurve aus der Fläche (L) auszuschneiden. Einfacher ist es jedoch, die Fläche (L) (bei festgehaltenem Rande) über den Aufpunkt hinwegzuziehen, dann ist $\mathfrak{U}_0$ auf (L) überall regulär und es gilt (32.9). Beim Hinwegziehen von (L) über den Aufpunkt tritt jedoch zufolge (30.1 c) der Term $v_0(\mathfrak{r})$ hinzu. Damit geht (30.2‴) endgültig in die folgende Form über

$$\left.\begin{aligned} v_K(\mathfrak{r}) &= v_g(\mathfrak{r}) + \oint_C v_0(\mathfrak{r}')\, G(\mathfrak{r} - \mathfrak{r}') \frac{([\mathfrak{r}' \mathfrak{r}]\, d\mathfrak{t})}{r' |\mathfrak{r}' - \mathfrak{r}| + (\mathfrak{r}', \mathfrak{r}' - \mathfrak{r})} \\ &= v_g(\mathfrak{r}) + \frac{1}{16\pi^2} \oint_C \frac{e^{i(r' + |\mathfrak{r}' - \mathfrak{r}|)}}{r' |\mathfrak{r}' - \mathfrak{r}|} \frac{([\mathfrak{r}' \mathfrak{r}]\, d\mathfrak{t})}{r' |\mathfrak{r}' - \mathfrak{r}| + (\mathfrak{r}', \mathfrak{r}' - \mathfrak{r})}, \end{aligned}\right\} \tag{32.10}$$

dabei ist $v_g(\mathfrak{r})$ die *geometrisch-optische Feldverteilung*, d.h.

$$v_g(\mathfrak{r}) = \begin{Bmatrix} v_0(\mathfrak{r}) \\ 0 \end{Bmatrix} = \begin{Bmatrix} \frac{1}{4\pi} \frac{e^{ir}}{r} \\ 0 \end{Bmatrix}, \tag{32.11}$$

je nachdem ob $\mathfrak{r}$ *innerhalb oder außerhalb des im Sinne der geometrischen Optik beleuchteten Gebiets liegt. Beleuchtet* ist dabei der Raum *vor* dem Schirm — von der Lichtquelle aus gesehen — und der Stumpf des Kegels hinter dem Schirm, dessen Spitze die Lichtquelle ist und dessen Erzeugende durch den Rand (C) der Öffnung (L) gehen. *Beschattet* ist das übrige Gebiet *hinter* dem Schirm.

In Gl. (32.10) tritt uns nun das Eigentümliche der neuen Auffassung des Beugungsvorganges entgegen: Das gesamte Feld ist eine Überlagerung des Feldes v_g im Sinne der geometrischen Optik und eines zusätzlichen Feldes *infolge von Kugelwellen, welche von den Randpunkten der Öffnung ausgehen* (Linienintegral), die wir als *Youngsche Welle* bezeichnen wollen. Diese Auffassung entspricht nämlich genau der Vorstellung von Th. Young[1]. Wir können hier von Elementarwellen sprechen, die von den einzelnen Elementen des Randes abgestrahlt werden. Dabei tritt ein Richtungsfaktor auf [letzter Term des Integranden in (32.10)], der von der Lage des Elements bezüglich Quell- und Aufpunkt abhängt. Charakteristisch ist, daß wiederum keine Wechselwirkung zwischen den Elementen auftritt. Die Form der Elementarwellen ist übrigens nicht eindeutig, da $\mathfrak{U}_0$ nur bis auf einen Gradienten eindeutig ist. Die Auswertung des Linienintegrals wird durch die Anwendung der *Methode der stationären Phase* sehr erleichtert. Nur diejenigen Punkte des Randes liefern einen wesentlichen Beitrag zum Integral, in denen die Phase $r'+R$ beim Fortschreiten längs des Randes konstant bleibt; die Beiträge aller übrigen Punkte löschen sich infolge der sehr schnell veränderlichen Phase durch Interferenz benachbarter Punkte aus. Die Phase ist in denjenigen Punkten stationär, die der „*Reflexionsbedingung*"

$$\cos(\mathfrak{r}', \mathfrak{t}) = -\cos(\mathfrak{R}, \mathfrak{t}) \tag{32.12}$$

genügen.

Da die der Wellengleichung genügende Feldfunktion $v_K(\mathfrak{r})$ an der geometrischen Schattengrenze *stetig* ist und stetige Ableitungen besitzt, so muß die *Unstetigkeit der geometrischen Lichtverteilung an der Schattengrenze* gerade durch eine entsprechende Unstetigkeit des Linienintegrals ausgeglichen werden. Dies ist in der Tat der Fall und beruht darauf, daß bei Annäherung des Aufpunktes $\mathfrak{r}$ an die Schattengrenze (sowohl von der einen wie von der anderen Seite her) $r'R + (\mathfrak{r}'\mathfrak{R})$ im *Nenner* für einen bestimmten Randpunkt $\to 0$ abnimmt.

Abschließend betonen wir noch einmal, daß Ausgangspunkt der Kirchhoffschen Theorie nicht der physikalisch reale Schirm ist, der die Randbedingungen festlegt, sondern die fiktive Sprungfläche der geometrischen Schattengrenze, die sich in einer konsequenten Theorie der Randwertaufgabe erst im Grenzfall $\lambda \to 0$ ergeben müßte (und zwar unabhängig von der auf dem Schirm geforderten Randbedingung), statt von vorne herein zum Ausgangspunkt der Theorie gemacht zu werden.

Die durchgeführte Umformung läßt außerdem einen weiteren prinzipiellen Mangel der Kirchhoffschen Theorie ohne weiteres erkennen: Das die *Youngsche Welle* darstellende *Linienintegral* wird auf dem Rande selbst so stark singulär (nämlich logarithmisch), daß die *Kantenbedingung verletzt wird*. Eine „*vom Rande ausgehende*" Youngsche Welle kann demnach bestenfalls *asymptotisch in der Fernzone auftreten* (wie sich z.B. an Hand der strengen Theorie der Beugung an der Halbebene nachweisen läßt; s. Ziff. 114)[2]. In ähnlicher Weise muß auch schon die Unstetigkeit der Wellenfunktion v_K in unmittelbarer Nähe der Kante beim

[1] Th. Young: Phil. Trans. Roy. Soc. Lond. **20**, 26 (1802).

[2] Über die experimentelle Beobachtung s. den zusammenfassenden Bericht bei A. Rubinowicz: Die Beugungswelle in der Kirchhoffschen Theorie der Beugung. V. 9. Warschau 1957.

Umlauf um diese Kante als eine unzulässige Singularität angesehen werden (Ziff. 38).

Schließlich sei noch erwähnt, daß das Youngsche Prinzip sich auch auf die vektoriellen Gleichungen (31.1 a, b) ausdehnen läßt. Man wird dabei davon ausgehen, daß die Flächenintegrale als „*Fluß*" eines *quellenfreien Tensors* $\boldsymbol{\Phi}_K(\mathfrak{r},\mathfrak{r}')$ dargestellt werden können, der somit der Rotor eines anderen Tensors ist, wodurch wiederum die Anwendung des Stokesschen Satzes ermöglicht wird[1].

33. Babinetsches Theorem. In der Kirchhoffschen Theorie heißen zwei *Schirme* (S_1) und (S_2) „*komplementär*", wenn der eine dort „*undurchlässig*" ist, wo der andere ein Loch hat und umgekehrt; beide zusammen also eine *geschlossene* Fläche (S) bilden. Das nach (30.2) berechnete Feld hinter (S_1) (von der Quelle aus gesehen) sei $v_K^{(S_1)}$, das hinter (S_2) $v_K^{(S_2)}$. Dann ist $v_K^{(S_1)}+v_K^{(S_2)}=v_0$, da sich die Integration in (30.2) nun auf die *geschlossene* Oberfläche $(S_1)+(S_2)=(S)$ bezieht, deren Wert nach dem Huygensschen Prinzip (8.5) gleich der einfallenden Welle v_0 ist. Dies ist das *Babinetsche Theorem* der *Kirchhoffschen Theorie*[2]. Man kann es unter Beachtung von (32.10) und (32.11) auch in der Form aussprechen, daß *die Youngschen Beugungswellen komplementärer Schirme bis aufs Vorzeichen gleich sind.*

34. Die Greensche Funktion für den eben begrenzten Halbraum. Wählt man in (10.1) eine *ebene* Integrationsfläche $z=0$, so *verteilt sich der Sprung* (10.2) aus *Symmetriegründen zu gleichen Teilen auf beide Seiten der Fläche* $z=0$. Dies bedeutet aber die Gültigkeit der Formeln

$$\left.\begin{aligned} -\lim_{z\to\pm 0}\frac{\partial}{\partial z}\int\limits_S \chi(\hat{\mathfrak{r}}')\,G(\mathfrak{r}-\hat{\mathfrak{r}}')\,d\hat{\mathfrak{r}}' &= \lim_{z\to\pm 0}\int\limits_S \chi(\hat{\mathfrak{r}}')\frac{\partial}{\partial z'}G(\mathfrak{r}-\hat{\mathfrak{r}}')\,d\hat{\mathfrak{r}}'\\ &= \begin{cases}\pm\frac{1}{2}\chi(\hat{\mathfrak{r}}) & \textit{für } \hat{\mathfrak{r}} \textit{ auf } (S)\\ 0 & \textit{für } \hat{\mathfrak{r}} \textit{ auf } (L).\end{cases}\end{aligned}\right\}\tag{34.1}$$

Hier sind (S) und (L) beliebige sich zur vollen Ebene $z=0$ ergänzende ebene *(„komplementäre")* Bereiche; ferner ist $\chi(\hat{\mathfrak{r}})$ eine beliebige auf (S) definierte Funktion, die man sich auf (L) durch $\chi\equiv 0$ ergänzt denken kann (man beachte, daß hier die positive z-Achse als Normale $\mathfrak{n}$ gewählt wurde).

Zufolge (34.1) *reproduzieren* nun die Funktionen

$$v(\mathfrak{r}) = \pm 2\int v(\hat{\mathfrak{r}}')\frac{\partial}{\partial z'}G(\mathfrak{r}-\hat{\mathfrak{r}}')\,d\hat{\mathfrak{r}}',\quad z\gtrless 0 \tag{34.2}$$

bzw.

$$v(\mathfrak{r}) = \mp 2\int \frac{\partial v(\hat{\mathfrak{r}}')}{\partial z'}G(\mathfrak{r}-\hat{\mathfrak{r}}')\,d\hat{\mathfrak{r}}',\quad z\gtrless 0 \tag{34.3}$$

(die Integration hat über die *ganze* Ebene $z=0$ zu erfolgen) die rechterhand willkürlich eingesetzten Werte von $v(\hat{\mathfrak{r}})$ bzw. $\frac{\partial v(\hat{\mathfrak{r}})}{\partial z}$, wenn man sich der Ebene $z=0$ von der positiven oder negativen Seite her nähert. Dies hat seinen Grund darin, daß die Funktion

$$2\frac{\partial}{\partial z}G(\mathfrak{r}-\hat{\mathfrak{r}}') = \frac{\partial}{\partial z'}G^{(1)}(\mathfrak{r}\,|\,\hat{\mathfrak{r}}')$$

[1] Die Durchführung der Rechnung findet sich bei O. Laporte u. J. Meixner: Z. Physik **153**, 129 (1958).

[2] Man hat hier historisch zwischen einer älteren und einer neueren Fassung des Babinetschen Prinzips zu unterscheiden: die ältere und engere bezieht sich nur auf die *Intensitätsverteilung* des *Fraunhoferschen Fernfeldes*, die neuere auf die Amplituden an einer beliebigen Stelle des Beugungsfeldes (diese letztere Fassung ist oben kurz angedeutet). Man vgl. hierzu etwa A. Sommerfeld: Vorlesungen über theoretische Physik, Bd. IV, S. 207ff. Wiesbaden 1950.

bzw.

$$2\,G(\mathfrak{r}-\hat{\mathfrak{r}}') = G^{(2)}(\mathfrak{r}\,|\,\hat{\mathfrak{r}}')$$

mit der Greenschen Funktion erster bzw. zweiter Art

$$G^{(1,2)}(\mathfrak{r}\,|\,\mathfrak{r}') = G(\mathfrak{r}\,|\,\hat{\mathfrak{r}}', z') \mp G(\mathfrak{r}\,|\,\hat{\mathfrak{r}}', -z')$$

für den durch die Ebene $z=0$ begrenzten Halbraum zusammenhängt, wie man sie mit Hilfe des Spiegelungsprinzips aus der Greenschen Funktion des freien Raumes leicht konstruieren kann[1].

35. Modifizierte Kirchhoffsche Theorie für ebene Schirme. Wir betrachten nun zunächst den skalaren Fall für die Randbedingung $\partial v/\partial z=0$ (*s-Fall*) auf dem ebenen Schirm (S) in der Ebene $z=0$ (s. Fig. 22; die entsprechenden Verhältnisse für den *p-Fall* veranschaulicht Fig. 23). Aus Ziff. 26 wissen wir [vgl. Gl. (26.3′ *s*)], daß dann in *Strenge* $v=v_0$ auf (L) sein muß. Bei der Beugung an *ebenen* Schirmen liegt also sozusagen ein *gemischtes Randwertproblem* vor: auf (S) ist $\partial v/\partial z=0$, auf (L) $v=v_0$ vorgegeben. Für die Anwendung von (34.2) oder (34.3) braucht man jedoch den Wert von v *oder* $\partial v/\partial z$ auf der *ganzen* Ebene $z=0$.

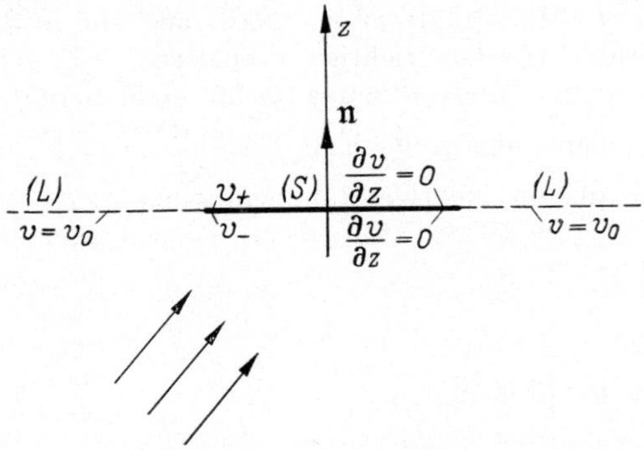

Fig. 22. Gemischte Randwerte beim ebenen Schirm (*s*-Fall).

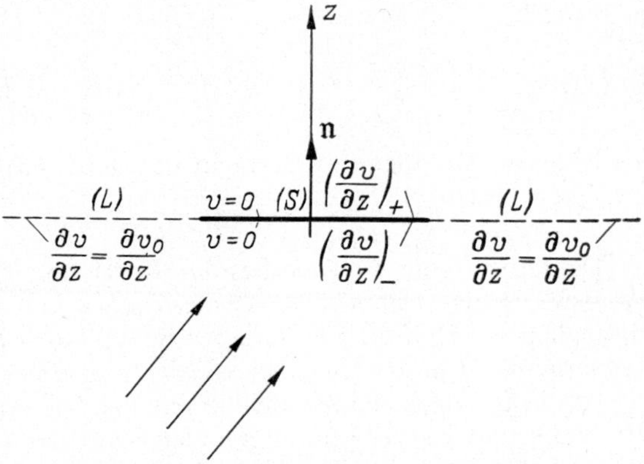

Fig. 23. Gemischte Randwerte beim ebenen Schirm (*p*-Fall).

Liegt nun die Quelle der einfallenden Welle v_0 im Halbraum $z<0$, so ergibt sich mit Hilfe des Huygensschen Prinzips (8.5) für $z>0$

$$v(\mathfrak{r}) = \int\limits_L \left\{v_0(\hat{\mathfrak{r}}')\,\frac{\partial}{\partial z'} - \frac{\partial v(\hat{\mathfrak{r}}')}{\partial z'}\right\} G(\mathfrak{r}-\hat{\mathfrak{r}}')\,d\hat{\mathfrak{r}}' + \int\limits_S v_+(\hat{\mathfrak{r}}')\,\frac{\partial}{\partial z'}\,G(\mathfrak{r}-\hat{\mathfrak{r}}')\,d\hat{\mathfrak{r}}'. \tag{35.1 s}$$

Andererseits liefert Gl. (34.2) bzw. (34.3) in unserm Fall hinter dem Schirm ($z>0$)

$$v(\mathfrak{r}) = 2\int\limits_L v_0(\hat{\mathfrak{r}}')\,\frac{\partial}{\partial z'}\,G(\mathfrak{r}-\hat{\mathfrak{r}}')\,d\hat{\mathfrak{r}}' + 2\int\limits_S v_+(\hat{\mathfrak{r}}')\,\frac{\partial}{\partial z'}\,G(\mathfrak{r}-\hat{\mathfrak{r}}')\,d\hat{\mathfrak{r}}' \tag{35.2 s}$$

bzw.

$$v(\mathfrak{r}) = -2\int\limits_L \frac{\partial v(\hat{\mathfrak{r}}')}{\partial z'}\,G(\mathfrak{r}-\hat{\mathfrak{r}}')\,d\hat{\mathfrak{r}}'. \tag{35.3 s}$$

Gl. (35.2 *s*) bzw. (35.3 *s*) ist dabei so konstruiert, daß sie wegen (34.1) die Bedingung $v=v_0$ auf (L) bzw. $\partial v/\partial z=0$ auf (S) automatisch erfüllt. Unbekannt

[1] Siehe etwa A. Sommerfeld: Vorlesungen über theoretische Physik, Bd. IV, S. 204. Wiesbaden 1950.

sind jetzt nur noch v_+ auf (S) *oder* $\partial v/\partial z$ auf (L), während man bei Anwendung der Formel (35.1 s) beide Größen kennen muß; sie ist einfach das *arithmetische Mittel* von (35.2 s) und (35.3 s). Für die jeweils unbekannten Größen ergeben sich lineare Integralgleichungen, indem man an (35.2 s) die Forderung $\partial v/\partial z=0$ auf (S) bzw. an (35.3 s) die Forderung $v=v_0$ auf (L) stellt, während an (35.1 s) beide Forderungen *gleichzeitig* gestellt werden müssen; vgl. dazu Abschn. IIIa.

Unter Umgehung der Auflösung dieser Integralgleichungen machen wir nun „plausible" Annahmen, setzen also in Gl. (35.2 s) im *Sinne Kirchhoffs* $v_+=0$ auf (S). Man erhält so eine Näherung, die *in der Öffnung* gut sein wird, da sie innerhalb (L) das richtige Verhalten $v=v_0$ zeigt; auf dem Schirm erfüllt sie jedoch die Randbedingung *nicht*, sondern die *„falsche" Randbedingung* $v_+=0$. Setzt man andererseits in (35.3 s) $\frac{\partial v(\hat{\mathfrak{r}})}{\partial z}=\frac{\partial v_0(\hat{\mathfrak{r}})}{\partial z}$ auf (L), so erhält man eine Näherung, die die richtige Randbedingung $\partial v/\partial z=0$ auf (S) erfüllt, jedoch *in der Öffnung die falsche*. Für ebene Schirme können also neben der Kirchhoffschen Lösung $(z>0)$:

$$v_K(\mathfrak{r})=\int\limits_L\left\{v_0(\hat{\mathfrak{r}}')\frac{\partial}{\partial z'}-\frac{\partial v_0(\hat{\mathfrak{r}}')}{\partial z'}\right\}G(\mathfrak{r}-\hat{\mathfrak{r}}')\,d\hat{\mathfrak{r}}' \qquad (35.1\,\mathrm{a})$$

auch die Funktionen

$$v_K^{(1)}(\mathfrak{r})=2\int\limits_L v_0(\hat{\mathfrak{r}}')\frac{\partial}{\partial z'}G(\mathfrak{r}-\hat{\mathfrak{r}}')\,d\hat{\mathfrak{r}}'=v_0(\mathfrak{r})-2\int\limits_S v_0(\hat{\mathfrak{r}}')\frac{\partial}{\partial z'}G(\mathfrak{r}-\hat{\mathfrak{r}}')\,d\hat{\mathfrak{r}}' \qquad (35.2\,\mathrm{a})^1$$

bzw.

$$v_K^{(2)}(\mathfrak{r})=-2\int\limits_L\frac{\partial v_0(\hat{\mathfrak{r}}')}{\partial z'}G(\mathfrak{r}-\hat{\mathfrak{r}}')\,d\hat{\mathfrak{r}}'=v_0(\mathfrak{r})+2\int\limits_S\frac{\partial v_0(\hat{\mathfrak{r}}')}{\partial z'}G(\mathfrak{r}-\hat{\mathfrak{r}}')\,d\hat{\mathfrak{r}}' \qquad (35.3\,\mathrm{a})^1$$

als Näherungslösungen in Betracht gezogen werden; dabei gilt

$$2v_K=v_K^{(1)}+v_K^{(2)}. \qquad (35.4)$$

Da ferner G in *z symmetrisch*, $\partial G/\partial z'$ hingegen *antisymmetrisch* ist, so ist $v_K^{(2)}$ bzw. $v_K^{(1)}$ das *Doppelte des symmetrischen bzw. antisymmetrischen Teils von* v_K (bezüglich z). Daher läßt sich $v_K^{(2)}$ bzw. $v_K^{(1)}$ auch als der *symmetrische* bzw. *antisymmetrische Teil des Rubinowiczschen Linienintegrals* (32.10) berechnen.

Die Frage nach der Brauchbarkeit der Näherung (35.2a) und (35.3a) haben Meixner und Fritze[2] durch Vergleich mit der exakten Lösung der Randwertaufgabe für ein kreisrundes Loch (bzw. der durch das Babinetsche Prinzip damit zusammenhängenden Lösung für den kreisförmigen Schirm) diskutiert. Severin und Starke[3] haben diese Frage durch Schallexperimente geprüft[4].

36. Das vektorielle Problem. Wir wollen hier nur noch die *elektromagnetischen Analoga* der Formeln (34.2) und (34.3) angeben:

$$\left.\begin{aligned}\mathfrak{E}(\mathfrak{r})&=\pm 2\,\mathrm{rot}\int[\mathfrak{n}\,\mathfrak{E}(\hat{\mathfrak{r}}')]\,G(\mathfrak{r}-\hat{\mathfrak{r}}')\,d\hat{\mathfrak{r}}'\\ \mathfrak{H}(\mathfrak{r})&=\mp 2i\,\mathrm{rot}\,\mathrm{rot}\int[\mathfrak{n}\,\mathfrak{E}(\hat{\mathfrak{r}}')]\,G(\mathfrak{r}-\hat{\mathfrak{r}}')\,d\hat{\mathfrak{r}}'\end{aligned}\right\}\quad z\gtrless 0, \qquad (36.1)$$

bzw.

$$\left.\begin{aligned}\mathfrak{E}(\mathfrak{r})&=\pm 2i\,\mathrm{rot}\,\mathrm{rot}\int[\mathfrak{n}\,\mathfrak{H}(\hat{\mathfrak{r}}')]\,G(\mathfrak{r}-\hat{\mathfrak{r}}')\,d\hat{\mathfrak{r}}'\\ \mathfrak{H}(\mathfrak{r})&=\mp 2\,\mathrm{rot}\int[\mathfrak{n}\,\mathfrak{H}(\hat{\mathfrak{r}}')]\,G(\mathfrak{r}-\hat{\mathfrak{r}}')\,d\hat{\mathfrak{r}}'\end{aligned}\right\}\quad z\gtrless 0. \qquad (36.2)$$

---

[1] Die zweite Form von (35.2a) bzw. (35.3a) ergibt sich jeweils, indem man die einfallende Welle $v_0(\mathfrak{r})$ für $z>0$ durch (34.2) bzw. (34.3) darstellt.

[2] J. Meixner u. U. Fritze: Z. angew. Phys. **1**, 535 (1949).

[3] H. Severin u. C. Starke: Acustica, Akust. Beih. **2**, 59 (1952).

[4] Man vgl. zu diesem Fragenkomplex das Referat von J.C. Bouwkamp: Progr. Phys. **17**, 35 (1954).

Die Integration hat hier wieder über die *ganze* Ebene $z=0$ zu erfolgen, $\mathfrak{n}$ weist in die Richtung der positiven z-Achse. Gl. (36.1) *reproduziert* die beliebig in sie eingesetzten Werte von $[\mathfrak{n}\mathfrak{E}]$, (36.2) diejenigen von $[\mathfrak{n}\mathfrak{H}]$ auf der Ebene $z=0$. Man erkennt dies leicht mit Hilfe von Gl. (13.3): Aus (36.1) folgt damit z.B.

$$[\mathfrak{n}\mathfrak{E}] = \pm 2\nabla(\mathfrak{n}\int[\mathfrak{n}\mathfrak{E}]\,G\,d\hat{\mathfrak{r}}') \mp 2(\mathfrak{n}\nabla)\int[\mathfrak{n}\mathfrak{E}]\,G\,d\hat{\mathfrak{r}}', \qquad z \gtrless 0;$$

der erste Term rechts verschwindet hier, da $\mathfrak{n}$ konstant ist, der zweite liefert mit Hilfe von Gl. (34.1) den Wert $[\mathfrak{n}\mathfrak{E}]$, wenn man sich der Ebene $z=0$ von oben oder von unten her nähert.

Liegt in der Ebene $z=0$ ein ideal leitender Schirm (S) mit Löchern (L), so gilt *streng* $[\mathfrak{n}\mathfrak{E}]=0$ auf (S), $[\mathfrak{n}\mathfrak{H}]=[\mathfrak{n}\mathfrak{H}_0]$ auf (L); vgl. (26.4') (s. Fig. 24). Leider brauchen wir für die Anwendung von (36.1) oder (36.2) die Kenntnis von $[\mathfrak{n}\mathfrak{E}]$

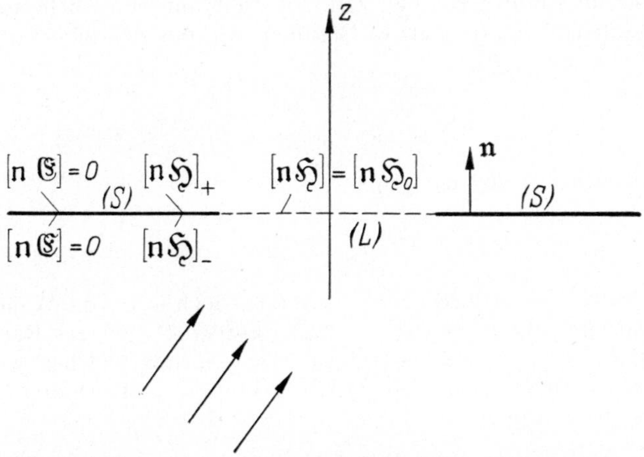

Fig. 24. Gemischte Randwerte beim ebenen Schirm (elektromagnetischer Fall).

oder $[\mathfrak{n}\mathfrak{H}]$ auf der *ganzen* Ebene $z=0$, d.h. auf $(S)+(L)$. Die „*Kirchhoffschen Annahmen*“ $[\mathfrak{n}\mathfrak{E}]=[\mathfrak{n}\mathfrak{E}_0]$ auf (L) oder $[\mathfrak{n}\mathfrak{H}]_+=0$ auf (S) führen zu Näherungen der Art (35.2a) oder (35.3a), nämlich $(z>0)$:

$$\left.\begin{aligned} \mathfrak{E}_K^{(1)}(\mathfrak{r}) &= 2i\,\mathrm{rot}\,\mathrm{rot}\int_L[\mathfrak{n}\mathfrak{H}_0]\,G(\mathfrak{r}-\hat{\mathfrak{r}}')\,d\hat{\mathfrak{r}}',\\ \mathfrak{H}_K^{(1)}(\mathfrak{r}) &= 2\,\mathrm{rot}\int_L[\mathfrak{n}\mathfrak{H}_0]\,G(\mathfrak{r}-\hat{\mathfrak{r}}')\,d\hat{\mathfrak{r}}', \end{aligned}\right\} \tag{36.1a}$$

$$\left.\begin{aligned} \mathfrak{E}_K^{(2)}(\mathfrak{r}) &= 2\,\mathrm{rot}\int_L[\mathfrak{n}\mathfrak{E}_0]\,G(\mathfrak{r}-\hat{\mathfrak{r}}')\,d\hat{\mathfrak{r}}',\\ \mathfrak{H}_K^{(2)}(\mathfrak{r}) &= -2i\,\mathrm{rot}\,\mathrm{rot}\int_L[\mathfrak{n}\mathfrak{E}_0]\,G(\mathfrak{r}-\hat{\mathfrak{r}}')\,d\hat{\mathfrak{r}}'. \end{aligned}\right\} \tag{36.2a}$$

Diese Formeln, deren halbe Summe $\frac{1}{2}\{\mathfrak{E}_K^{(1)}+\mathfrak{E}_K^{(2)}\}$, $\frac{1}{2}\{\mathfrak{H}_K^{(1)}+\mathfrak{H}_K^{(2)}\}$ wieder mit der ursprünglichen Kirchhoffschen Lösung (31.1a, b) übereinstimmt, wird dann von Nutzen sein, wenn man sich neben der Feldverteilung auch über die *Polarisationsverhältnisse* des Beugungsfeldes einen ersten Überblick verschaffen will. Eine Rechtfertigung des heuristischen Verfahrens ergibt sich auch hier erst nachträglich durch Vergleich mit der in einfachen Fällen *streng* durchführbaren Lösung (Kreisscheibe) bzw. mit dem Experiment[1].

[1] Vgl. dazu etwa H. SEVERIN: Z. Naturforsch. **1**a, 487 (1946). — Z. angew. Phys. **2**, 499 (1950). — Z. Physik **129**, 426 (1950). — M. J. EHRLICH: Diss. Univ. California 1951. — J.P. VASSEUR: Ann. de Phys. **7**, 506 (1952). — W. ANDREJEWSKI: Diss. Aachen 1952. — J.C. BOUWKAMP: Progr. Phys. **17**, 35 (1954).

b) Das Iterationsverfahren von W. Franz und die Methode von W. Braunbek.

Die Kirchhoffsche Methode ersetzt das Randwertproblem durch ein anderes einfacher zu lösendes Problem (Sprungwertproblem bzw. „falsches" Randwertproblem). Der dabei begangene Fehler ist analytisch schwer zu übersehen. Wir wollen zwei Verfahren besprechen, die diesen Fehler zu verkleinern suchen.

37. Iterationsverfahren von W. Franz[1]. Wir beschränken uns auf *ebene* Schirme (S) mit Löchern (L) in der Ebene $z=0$ (Franz hat jedoch sein Verfahren auch auf beliebig gekrümmte Oberflächen erweitert[1]). Ferner legen wir die Randbedingungen $\partial v/\partial n=0$ auf (S) zugrunde (behandeln also nur den *s-Fall*, vgl. Ziff. 4; die Randbedingung $v=0$ läßt sich entsprechend behandeln) und unterscheiden zwischen *Streufall* [(S) liegt ganz im Endlichen] und *Beugungsfall* [(L) liegt ganz im Endlichen]; vgl. Ziff. 26. Fällt nun eine Welle $v_0(\mathfrak{r})$ aus dem Raum $z<0$ auf den Schirm auf, so beginnen wir mit der *„nullten Näherung"*:

Beugung:

$$v_0^{(1)}=\begin{cases}0, & z>0,\\ v_0+v^0, & z<0\end{cases} \tag{37.1a}$$

[v^0 ist die *reflektierte Welle*; vgl. (26.8)].

Streuung:

$$v_0^{(2)}=v_0, \qquad z\gtrless 0. \tag{37.1b}$$

Gl. (37.1a) erfüllt die Randbedingung, verletzt jedoch in (L) die Wellengleichung, da sie dort springt: $(v_0^{(1)})_+-(v_0^{(1)})_-=-2v_0$, während (37.1b) die Randbedingung verletzt: $\partial v_0^{(2)}/\partial z=\partial v_0/\partial z$, aber stetig ist. Den Sprung gleichen wir durch ein *Kirchhoffsches Integral* aus — vgl. (10.1), (10.2) — und erhalten so die erste Näherung für die *Beugung*

$$v_1^{(1)}=v_0^{(1)}+2\int\limits_L v_0\frac{\partial G}{\partial z'}\,d\sigma'=v_0^{(1)}+w_0^{(1)}, \qquad z\gtrless 0. \tag{37.2a}$$

Für die *Streuung* erhalten wir die erste Näherung, indem wir zu (37.1b) eine Lösung hinzufügen, die die Randwerte $-\frac{\partial v_0}{\partial z}$ besitzt; vgl. (34.3)

$$v_1^{(2)}=v_0^{(2)}\pm 2\int\limits_S \frac{\partial v_0}{\partial z'}G\,d\sigma'=v_0^{(2)}\mp w_0^{(2)}, \qquad z\gtrless 0. \tag{37.2b}$$

Nun verletzt (37.2a) die Randbedingung: $\partial v_1^{(1)}/\partial z=\partial w_0^{(1)}/\partial z$, während (37.2b) in der Öffnung unstetig ist: $(v_1^{(2)})_+-(v_1^{(2)})_-=-2w_0^{(2)}$. Dies macht die zweite Näherung für die Beugung bzw. Streuung nötig:

$$v_2^{(1)}=v_1^{(1)}\pm 2\int\limits_S \frac{\partial w_0^{(1)}}{\partial z'}G\,d\sigma'=v_1^{(1)}\mp w_1^{(1)}, \qquad z\gtrless 0, \tag{37.3a}$$

bzw.

$$v_2^{(2)}=v_1^{(2)}+2\int\limits_L w_0^{(2)}\frac{\partial G}{\partial z'}\,d\sigma'=v_1^{(2)}+w_1^{(2)}, \qquad z\gtrless 0. \tag{37.3b}$$

Das Verfahren läßt sich auf diese Weise beliebig fortsetzen, indem man in den einzelnen Schritten abwechselnd die Randbedingung und die Wellengleichung (d.h. die Forderung der Stetigkeit in der Öffnung) befriedigt. Man erhält so ein Iterationsverfahren mit den allgemeinen geraden bzw. ungeraden Schritten für

[1] W. Franz: Z. Physik **125**, 563 (1949); Proc. Phys. Soc. Lond. A **63**, 925 (1950).

die *Beugung*

$$\left.\begin{aligned} v_{2\nu}^{(1)} &= v_{2\nu-1}^{(1)} \pm 2\int\limits_S \frac{\partial w_{2\nu-2}^{(1)}}{\partial z'} G\,d\sigma' = v_{2\nu-1}^{(1)} \mp w_{2\nu-1}^{(1)}, \quad z \gtrless 0,\\ v_{2\nu+1}^{(1)} &= v_{2\nu}^{(1)} + 2\int\limits_L w_{2\nu-1}^{(1)} \frac{\partial G}{\partial z'}\,d\sigma' = v_{2\nu}^{(1)} + w_{2\nu}^{(1)}, \quad z \gtrless 0 \end{aligned}\right\} \tag{37.4a}$$

mit den Werten der Normalableitung auf der Ebene $z=0$

$$\frac{\partial v_{2\nu}^{(1)}}{\partial z} = \left\{\begin{matrix} \frac{\partial w_0^{1)}}{\partial z} + \frac{\partial w_2^{(1)}}{\partial z} + \cdots \frac{\partial w_{2\nu-2}^{(1)}}{\partial z} & auf\ (L),\\ 0 & auf\ (S) \end{matrix}\right\} \tag{37.5a}$$

und den Sprungwerten beim Hindurchtreten durch die Fläche $z=0$

$$(v_{2\nu}^{(1)})_+ - (v_{2\nu}^{(1)})_- = -\left\{\begin{matrix} 2w_{2\nu-1}^{(1)} & auf\ (L),\\ 2v_0 + 2w_1^{(1)} + 2w_3^{(1)} + \cdots 2w_{2\nu-1}^{(1)} & auf\ (S) \end{matrix}\right\} \tag{37.6a}$$

bzw.

$$\frac{\partial v_{2\nu+1}^{(1)}}{\partial z'} = \left\{\begin{matrix} \frac{\partial w_0^{(1)}}{\partial z} + \frac{\partial w_2^{(1)}}{\partial z} + \cdots \frac{\partial w_{2\nu}^{(1)}}{\partial z} & auf\ (L),\\ \frac{\partial w_{2\nu}^{(1)}}{\partial z} & auf\ (S) \end{matrix}\right\} \tag{37.7a}$$

und

$$(v_{2\nu+1}^{(1)})_+ - (v_{2\nu+1}^{(1)})_- = -\left\{\begin{matrix} 0 & auf\ (L),\\ 2v_0 + 2w_1^{(1)} + 2w_3^{(1)} + \cdots 2w_{2\nu-1}^{(1)} & auf\ (S). \end{matrix}\right\} \tag{37.8a}$$

Entsprechend gilt für die *Streuung*

$$\left.\begin{aligned} v_{2\nu}^{(2)} &= v_{2\nu-1}^{(2)} + 2\int\limits_L w_{2\nu-2}^{(2)} \frac{\partial G}{\partial z'}\,d\sigma' = v_{2\nu-1}^{(2)} + w_{2\nu-1}^{(2)}, \quad z \gtrless 0,\\ v_{2\nu+1}^{(2)} &= v_{2\nu}^{(2)} \pm 2\int\limits_S \frac{\partial w_{2\nu-1}^{(2)}}{\partial z'} G\,d\sigma' = v_{2\nu}^{(2)} \mp w_{2\nu}^{(2)}, \quad z \gtrless 0 \end{aligned}\right\} \tag{37.4b}$$

mit den Werten der Normalableitung auf der Ebene $z=0$

$$\frac{\partial v_{2\nu}^{(2)}}{\partial z} = \left\{\begin{matrix} \frac{\partial w_{2\nu-1}^{(2)}}{\partial z} & auf\ (S),\\ \frac{\partial v_0}{\partial z} + \frac{\partial w_1^{(2)}}{\partial z} + \frac{\partial w_3^{(2)}}{\partial z} + \cdots \frac{\partial w_{2\nu-1}^{(2)}}{\partial z} & auf\ (L) \end{matrix}\right\} \tag{37.5b}$$

und den Sprungwerten beim Hindurchtreten durch die Ebene $z=0$

$$(v_{2\nu}^{(2)})_+ - (v_{2\nu}^{(2)})_- = -\left\{\begin{matrix} 2w_0^{(2)} + 2w_2^{(2)} + \cdots 2w_{2\nu-0}^{(2)} & auf\ (S),\\ 0 & auf\ (L) \end{matrix}\right\} \tag{37.6b}$$

bzw.

$$\frac{\partial v_{2\nu+1}^{(2)}}{\partial z} = \left\{\begin{matrix} 0 & auf\ (S),\\ \frac{\partial v_0}{\partial z} + \frac{\partial w_1^{(2)}}{\partial z} + \frac{\partial w_3^{(2)}}{\partial z} + \cdots \frac{\partial w_{2\nu-1}^{(2)}}{\partial z} & auf\ (L) \end{matrix}\right\} \tag{37.7b}$$

und

$$(v_{2\nu+1}^{(2)})_+ - (v_{2\nu+1}^{(2)})_- = -\left\{\begin{matrix} 2w_0^{(2)} + 2w_2^{(2)} + \cdots 2w_{2\nu}^{(2)} & auf\ (S),\\ 2w_{2\nu}^{(2)} & auf\ (L). \end{matrix}\right\} \tag{37.8b}$$

Wie man sieht, kann man dieses Iterationsverfahren auch als eine Methode auffassen, die *Normalableitung* $\partial v/\partial z$ in der *Öffnung* bzw. den *Sprung* des Funktionswertes $v_+ - v_-$ beim Hindurchtreten durch den *Schirm* (*Flächenstrom*, vgl. Ziff. 46) schrittweise zu approximieren.

38. Kantenbedingung und Konvergenzschwierigkeiten. Hinsichtlich der Konvergenz der Methode ergeben sich allerdings Schwierigkeiten. Infolge der Symmetrie bzw. Antisymmetrie von Integralen der Form

$$\int_S \frac{\partial w}{\partial z'} G \, d\sigma' \quad \text{bzw.} \quad \int_L w \frac{\partial G}{\partial z'} d\sigma'$$

bezüglich z lassen sich diese Integrale nämlich wieder als symmetrische bzw. antisymmetrische Bestandteile von Integralen der Form

$$\int_{S,L} \left(\frac{\partial w}{\partial z'} G - w \frac{\partial G}{\partial z'} \right) d\sigma'$$

berechnen. Letztere Integrale können aber (als Fluß eines quellenfreien Vektors aufgefaßt) nach dem Stokesschen Satz in *Linienintegrale über den Rand der Öffnung* verwandelt werden (s. Ziff. 32). Somit ist für jeden einzelnen Näherungsschritt des Franzschen Verfahrens das *Youngsche Prinzip streng durchführbar*, was nach Ziff. 32 eine *Verletzung der Kantenbedingung bedeutet.* Dies hat außerdem zur Folge, daß die höheren Näherungen des Verfahrens zu *divergenten* Integralen führen.

Die Kantensingularitäten rühren nämlich von Integralen der Form

$$\Phi = \int_L \varphi \frac{\partial G}{\partial z'} d\sigma'$$

her, da sich der Wert dieses Integrals um den Betrag φ sprunghaft ändert, wenn man durch (L) hindurchtritt. Dieser Sprung wird beim Umlaufen des Randes von (L) durch Φ *stetig wieder ausgeglichen.* Je kleiner jedoch der Radius ϱ des Kreises wird, auf dem man den Rand umläuft, desto schneller muß diese stetige Änderung (als Funktion des Drehwinkels betrachtet) erfolgen und zwar umgekehrt proportional zum Umfang des Kreises. Daher verhält sich der Gradient von Φ in Richtung der Kreistangente wie ϱ^{-1}. Je nachdem aus welcher Richtung man sich der Kante nähert, erhält man verschiedene Werte für Φ (schlimmstenfalls *logarithmisch divergente*); die Kantenbedingung (23.5 b), (23.5 c) ist also verletzt. Man erkennt dies auch daran, daß die Feldenergie (16.6) in der Umgebung der Kante nicht integrierbar ist, da sie einen Term $\int \varrho^{-2} \cdot \varrho \, d\varrho$ enthält, der von dem Glied mit $|\operatorname{grad} v|^2$ herrührt und logarithmisch divergiert.

Integrale der Form

$$\int_S \psi G \, d\sigma'$$

verhalten sich hingegen an der Kante *stetig*, erfüllen also die Kantenbedingung. Ferner divergieren Integrale der Gestalt

$$\int_S \frac{\partial \Phi}{\partial z'} G \, d\sigma'$$

— infolge des Beitrages des Randstreifens — ebenfalls logarithmisch.

Diese Singularitäten lassen sich nur vermeiden, wenn φ gegen den Rand hin *stetig zu Null geht.* Deshalb schlägt Franz[1] vor, die in den ungeraden bzw. geraden Näherungsschritten berechneten Werte von $w_{2\nu-2}^{(2)}$ bzw. $w_{2\nu-1}^{(1)}$ *jenseits* der Öffnung (L), also auf dem Schirm (S) irgendwie stetig zu Null gehen zu lassen und das Integral Φ auch über den Schirm zu erstrecken. Würde man Φ bereits

[1] W. Franz: Z. Physik **128**, 432 (1950).

innerhalb der Öffnung gegen den Rand hin willkürlich nach Null abnehmen lassen, so würde die durch Φ auf (L) bewirkte Korrektur in der Nähe der Kante hinfällig werden; die Konvergenz des Verfahrens wäre dort also von vorne herein in Frage gestellt. Erstreckt man das Integral jedoch auch über den Schirm (S) — mit vom Rande her willkürlich auf Null abnehmendem φ — so wird nichts wesentliches verdorben, da Φ sowieso die Randbedingung auf (S) verletzt, wodurch der nächste Näherungsschritt notwendig wird. Das Verfahren enthält so allerdings ein Moment der Willkür, das es verhindert, anzugeben, in welchem analytischen Sinne die Methode gegen die strenge Lösung der Randwertaufgabe konvergiert (wenn überhaupt).

39. W. BRAUNBEKs Methode. Wie man die Wahl von φ *auf dem Schirm* beim ersten Näherungsschritt zweckmäßig treffen kann, hat BRAUNBEK[1] gezeigt. Er geht von Formel (35.2 *s*) aus und ersetzt den (zu Kantensingularitäten führenden) Kirchhoffschen Wert $v_+ = 0$ auf (S) durch einen Wert von v_+, der *innerhalb eines Saumes von der Breite einiger Wellenlängen* um die Öffnung herum stetig vom strengen Wert $v = v_0$ auf *dem Rande* des Schirmes gegen Null abfällt (wenn man sich längs des Schirmes senkrecht zum Schirmrande von diesem entfernt). Die Werte $v_+(\hat{\mathfrak{r}})$ auf dem Schirm wählt nun BRAUNBEK — unter der Voraussetzung, daß der *Krümmungsradius des Schirmrandes überall sehr groß gegen die Wellenlänge λ ist — so*, wie das von der *strengen Sommerfeldschen Lösung für die Beugung an der Halbebene* (s. Ziff. 117) her bekannt ist. Das Verfahren ersetzt also jedes Kantenelement (Streifen von der Breite einiger Wellenlängen und

Tabelle 1 *s*.

	Randwerte in *s*-Fall $\partial v/\partial n = 0$ auf (S)			
	$v_+(\hat{\mathfrak{r}})$		$\partial v(\hat{\mathfrak{r}})/\partial z$	
	Schirm (S)	Öffnung (L)	Schirm (S)	Öffnung (L)
streng	$(\hat{\Delta}+1)\int\limits_S [v_+(\hat{\mathfrak{r}}') - v_0]\, G(\hat{\mathfrak{r}}-\hat{\mathfrak{r}}')\, d\hat{\mathfrak{r}}' = -\frac{1}{2}\frac{\partial v_0}{\partial z}$	v_0	0	$\int\limits_L \frac{\partial v(\hat{\mathfrak{r}}')}{\partial z'}\, G(\hat{\mathfrak{r}}-\hat{\mathfrak{r}}')\, d\hat{\mathfrak{r}}' = -\frac{1}{2} v_0$
KIRCHHOFF	0	v_0	0	$\frac{\partial v_0}{\partial z}$
BRAUNBEK	$v_0 \int\limits_\varrho^\infty \frac{e^{i\left(\tau-\frac{\pi}{4}\right)}}{\sqrt{\pi\tau}}\, d\tau$	v_0	0	$\frac{\partial v_0}{\partial z}\left\{1 + \frac{e^{i\left(\varrho+\frac{\pi}{4}\right)}}{\sqrt{\pi\varrho}} - \int\limits_\varrho^\infty \frac{e^{i\left(\tau-\frac{\pi}{4}\right)}}{\sqrt{\pi\tau}}\, d\tau\right\}$

infinitesimaler Länge entlang der Kante) durch die tangierende Halbebene, für die das Beugungsproblem streng lösbar ist und summiert dann über sämtliche Kantenelemente.

Entsprechend kann man auch von der Formel (35.3 *s*) ausgehen und dort unter dem Integral statt des Kirchhoffschen Ersatzwertes $\partial v_0/\partial z$ denjenigen Wert einsetzen, der sich für die das Kantenelement tangierende Halbebene nach der Sommerfeldschen Theorie in der Öffnung ergibt.

Tabelle 1 *s* stellt die Randwerte von v und $\partial v/\partial z$ auf der Schirmebene $z = 0$ zusammen. In der ersten Zeile sind die strengen Randwerte angegeben, soweit

[1] W. BRAUNBEK: Z. Physik **127**, 381 (1950).

sie unmittelbar bekannt sind (vgl. Fig. 22), bzw. ihre Definition durch eine Integralgleichung, wo dies nicht der Fall ist [die Integralgleichungen werden in Ziff. 50 abgeleitet; für den dort eingeführten *Flächenstrom* gilt $v_+ - v_- = 2(v_+ - v_0)$]. Die nächste Zeile enthält die Kirchhoffschen Ersatzwerte. Ganz unten sind die Ersatzwerte nach der Methode von Braunbek angegeben, wie sie aus der strengen Theorie der Beugung an der Halbebene folgen (vgl. Ziff. 117); sie gelten nur für den Fall *senkrechten Einfalls einer ebenen Welle* $v_0(\mathfrak{r}) = A\,\mathrm{e}^{iz}$. Die Größe ϱ bedeutet den senkrechten Abstand von der Schirmkante.

Wir fügen noch die ganz entsprechend aufgebaute Tabelle 1*p* für den *p-Fall* an (vgl. Fig. 23; bezüglich der Braunbekschen Ersatzwerte gelten dieselben Einschränkungen wie im *s*-Fall). Die Integralgleichungen, die die strengen Werte

Tabelle 1*p*.

	Randwerte im *p*-Fall $v = 0$ auf (S)			
	$v(\hat{\mathfrak{r}})$		$\left(\frac{\partial v(\hat{\mathfrak{r}})}{\partial z}\right)_+$	
	Schirm (S)	Öffnung (L)	Schirm (S)	Öffnung (L)
streng	0	$(\hat{\Delta}+1)\int\limits_L v(\hat{\mathfrak{r}}')\,G(\hat{\mathfrak{r}}-\hat{\mathfrak{r}}')\,d\hat{\mathfrak{r}}' = \frac{1}{2}\frac{\partial v_0}{\partial z}$	$\int\limits_S\left[\left(\frac{\partial v(\hat{\mathfrak{r}}')}{\partial z'}\right)_+ - \frac{\partial v_0}{\partial z'}\right]G(\hat{\mathfrak{r}}-\hat{\mathfrak{r}}')\,d\hat{\mathfrak{r}}' = \frac{1}{2}v_0$	$\frac{\partial v_0}{\partial z}$
Kirchhoff	0	v_0	0	$\frac{\partial v_0}{\partial z}$
Braunbek	0	$v_0\left\{1 - \int\limits_\varrho^\infty \frac{\mathrm{e}^{i\left(\tau-\frac{\pi}{4}\right)}}{\sqrt{\pi\tau}}\,d\tau\right\}$	$\frac{\partial v_0}{\partial z}\left\{\int\limits_\varrho^\infty \frac{\mathrm{e}^{i\left(\tau-\frac{\pi}{4}\right)}}{\sqrt{\tau\pi}}\,d\tau - \frac{\mathrm{e}^{i\left(\varrho+\frac{\pi}{4}\right)}}{\sqrt{\pi\varrho}}\right\}$	$\frac{\partial v_0}{\partial z}$

von v und $(\partial v/\partial z)_+$ definieren, werden in Ziff. 46 und 47 abgeleitet. Dabei ist die Beziehung $(\partial v/\partial z)_+ - (\partial v/\partial z)_- = 2[(\partial v/\partial z)_+ - \partial v_0/\partial z]$ zu beachten. Das entsprechende Beugungsfeld ist dann mit Hilfe der Formeln (34.2) oder (34.3) zu berechnen, je nachdem ob man die linke oder die rechte Hälfte der Tabellen benutzen will.

Im allgemeinen elektromagnetischen Fall gelten die entsprechenden Formeln (36.1) oder (36.2), für die man die Ersatzrandwerte aus der linken bzw. rechten Hälfte der Tabelle 2 entnehmen kann ($\hat{\mathfrak{E}}$, $\hat{\mathfrak{H}}$ bzw. $\hat{\mathfrak{E}}_0$, $\hat{\mathfrak{H}}_0$ bedeutet die zur Schirmebene *parallelen* Komponenten der entsprechenden Feldvektoren).

Die Definition der strengen Randwerte — soweit sie nicht unmittelbar aus der Randbedingung bzw. aus dem Babinetschen Theorem [vgl. (26.4′) sowie Fig. 24] folgen — durch eine Integrodifferentialgleichung wird in Ziff. 53 und 56 ausführlich erläutert. Von den Kirchhoffschen Ersatzwerten in der zweiten Reihe der Tabelle haben wir bereits in Gl. (36.1a) (36.2a) Gebrauch gemacht, während die Braunbekschen Ersatzwerte[1] der dritten Zeile wieder nur für die *senkrechte Inzidenz* einer *ebenen elektromagnetischen Welle* $\mathfrak{E}_0$, $\mathfrak{H}_0$ beliebiger Polarisation) gelten (das ^ über $\mathfrak{E}_0$ und $\mathfrak{H}_0$ kann also hier auch wegbleiben). Schließlich bedeutet $\hat{\mathfrak{E}}_{0\perp}$ bzw. $\hat{\mathfrak{H}}_{0\perp}$ die Komponente der Feldvektoren des einfallenden Feldes in der Schirmebene *senkrecht zur Schirmkante* (ϱ ist wieder der senkrechte Abstand von der Kante).

[1] Vgl. dazu W. Frahn: Diplomarbeit Aachen 1951. — W. Franz: Theorie der Beugung elektromagnetischer Wellen, S. 103. Berlin 1957.

Wie man an den in den Tabellen 1 *s*, *p* bzw. 2 angegebenen Braunbekschen Korrekturen der Kirchhoffschen Ersatzwerte erkennt, fallen sie für große ϱ wie $1/\sqrt{\varrho}$ ab und besitzen im übrigen eine schnell veränderliche Phase, so daß merkliche Beiträge zu den entsprechenden Flächenintegralen (34.2), (34.3) bzw. (36.1), (36.2) nur von den Punkten zu erwarten sind, wo die Phase *stationär* ist, d.h. für $\varrho = 0$ (vgl. dazu auch Ziff. 44). Die Braunbekschen Ersatzwerte brauchen also im allgemeinen nur für einen schmalen Randstreifen längs der Schirmkante in Anspruch genommen zu werden, wo annähernd die Verhältnisse der Sommerfeldschen Halbebene herrschen dürften. Wir werden in Ziff. 134 die Beugung an der Kreisscheibe nach diesem Verfahren behandeln.

Tabelle 2.

	Randwerte im elektromagnetischen Fall $[\mathfrak{n}\,\mathfrak{E}] = 0$ auf (S)			
	$\hat{\mathfrak{E}}(\hat{\mathfrak{r}})$		$\hat{\mathfrak{H}}_{+}(\hat{\mathfrak{r}})$	
	Schirm (S)	Öffnung (L)	Schirm (S)	Öffnung (L)
streng	0	$(\widehat{\mathrm{grad}}\,\widehat{\mathrm{div}} + 1) \int\limits_L [\mathfrak{n}\,\hat{\mathfrak{E}}(\hat{\mathfrak{r}}')] \cdot G(\hat{\mathfrak{r}} - \hat{\mathfrak{r}}')\, d\hat{\mathfrak{r}}' = \frac{i}{2}\hat{\mathfrak{H}}_0$	$(\widehat{\mathrm{grad}}\,\widehat{\mathrm{div}} + 1) \int\limits_S [\mathfrak{n}, \hat{\mathfrak{H}}_{+}(\hat{\mathfrak{r}}') - \hat{\mathfrak{H}}_0] \cdot G(\hat{\mathfrak{r}} - \hat{\mathfrak{r}}')\, d\hat{\mathfrak{r}}' = \frac{i}{2}\hat{\mathfrak{E}}_0$	$\hat{\mathfrak{H}}_0$
KIRCHHOFF	0	$\hat{\mathfrak{E}}_0$	0	$\hat{\mathfrak{H}}_0$
BRAUNBEK	0	$\hat{\mathfrak{E}}_0 \left\{1 - \int\limits_{\varrho}^{\infty} \frac{e^{i\left(\tau - \frac{\pi}{4}\right)}}{\sqrt{\pi\tau}}\, d\tau\right\} + \hat{\mathfrak{E}}_{0\perp} \frac{e^{i\left(\varrho + \frac{\pi}{4}\right)}}{\sqrt{\pi\varrho}}$	$\hat{\mathfrak{H}}_0 \int\limits_{\varrho}^{\infty} \frac{e^{i\left(\tau - \frac{\pi}{4}\right)}}{\sqrt{\pi\tau}}\, d\tau - \hat{\mathfrak{H}}_{0\perp} \frac{e^{i\left(\varrho - \frac{\pi}{4}\right)}}{\sqrt{\pi\varrho}}$	$\hat{\mathfrak{H}}_0$

40. Eine strengere Rechtfertigung der Braunbekschen Ersatzwerte muß auf dem Wege über die Integralgleichungen gesucht werden, indem man sie *asymptotisch* für den Fall zu lösen sucht, daß der Krümmungsradius der Randkurve überall sehr groß gegen die Wellenlänge der einfallenden Welle ist[1]. Das ist bisher nur in Spezialfällen[2] gelungen. Diese liefern Gründe, die zu der Annahme berechtigen, daß die Braunbekschen Ersatzwerte tatsächlich das *Hauptglied* einer solchen asymptotischen Entwicklung darstellen.

Denkt man sich das Braunbeksche Verfahren etwa auf die Beugung am (unendlich langen) Spalt angewandt, so entspricht es der Superposition der

[1] Da wir im allgemeinen Teil alle Längen in Vielfachen der Wellenlänge messen, besteht das Problem darin, eine Entwicklung nach *fallenden* (eventuell gebrochenen) *Potenzen* eines charakteristischen Krümmungsradius bzw. einer Objektabmessung (oder mehrerer solcher Größen) zu finden. Eine solche Reihe bedeutet gleichzeitig eine Entwicklung nach *wachsenden Potenzen* der *Wellenlänge*. Solche Entwicklungen sind erfahrungsgemäß (wie etwa bei den Zylinderfunktionen) nicht konvergent, sondern *asymptotisch* (semikonvergent). Wir wollen deshalb kurz von einer asymptotischen Entwicklung in λ bzw. $k = 2\pi/\lambda$ sprechen. Asymptotische Reihen für große k-Werte sind in der Praxis besonders brauchbar, da schon das Hauptglied in einem großen Frequenzbereich bis herunter zu mäßig kleinen k-Werten eine gute Näherung liefert. Andererseits sind die im allgemeinen *konvergenten* Entwicklungen für *kleine* k-Werte auch bei Berücksichtigung mehrerer Glieder nur für einen kleinen Frequenzbereich brauchbar. Das bekannteste Beispiel für diesen Sachverhalt sind die Zylinderfunktionen.

[2] Vgl. H. LEVINE: N.Y. Univ. Res. Rep. No. EM-84 (1955); Techn. Rep. 51 u. 61, Appl. Math. a. Stat. Lab., Stanford Univ. 1956/57. — K. WESTPFAHL: Ann. Phys. **4**, 283 (1959).

Felder zweier Sommerfeldscher Halbebenen, die jede von der einfallenden Welle getroffen wird (also ohne Wechselwirkung der beiden Halbebenen aufeinander). Das ist aber genau die Näherung, die der *erste Schritt des Schwarzschildschen Iterationsverfahrens*[1] liefert. Dieses Verfahren berücksichtigt in höheren Näherungen die *Zustrahlung* der beiden Spaltbacken (infolge der auf ihnen fließenden Flächenströme in erster, zweiter usw. Näherung) (vgl. Ziff. 122). Nun hat SCHWARZSCHILD zwar in Strenge gezeigt, daß sein Verfahren keine asymptotische Entwicklung für große Spaltbreiten liefert, sondern für beliebige Spaltbreiten *konvergiert.* Wir werden aber in Ziff. 122 zeigen, daß das *erste Glied* des Schwarzschildschen Verfahrens mit dem *Hauptglied* der asymptotischen Entwicklung für große Spaltbreiten übereinstimmt.

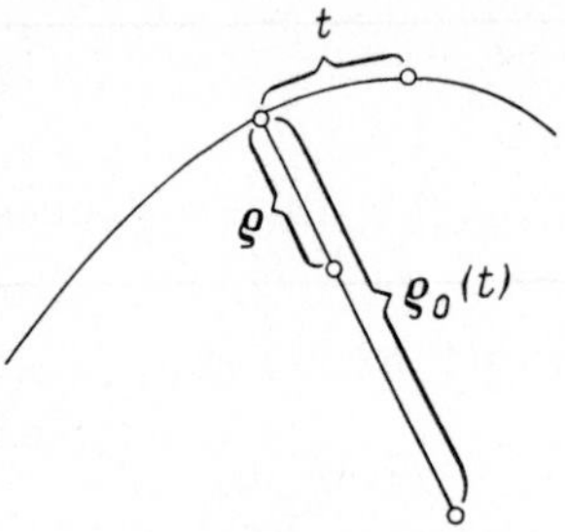

Fig. 25. Orthogonale Koordinaten in Kantennähe.

Ein weiterer Hinweis darauf, daß das Braunbeksche Verfahren das Hauptglied der asymptotischen Entwicklung der strengen Lösung des Randwertproblems ist, ergibt sich daraus, daß die *beiden* Braunbekschen Näherungen — die man erhält, je nachdem man die rechte oder die linke Seite der vorstehenden Tabellen benutzt — *dasselbe Hauptglied* der asymptotischen Entwicklung liefern. Dies wurde zunächst von BRAUNBEK[2] für das an einer Kreisscheibe gebeugte Feld auf der Symmetrieachse der Scheibe gezeigt (abgesehen von der unmittelbaren Umgebung des Scheibenmittelpunkts). Es läßt sich jedoch auch allgemein zeigen.

Wir betrachten etwa den *s-Fall*, dann liefert die rechte bzw. linke Seite der Tabelle 1*s*, wenn man die Braunbekschen Ersatzwerte in (35.2*s*) bzw. (35.3*s*) einsetzt (für $z>0,\ v_0=\mathrm{e}^{iz}$)

$$v_B^{(1)}(\mathfrak{r}) = v_K^{(1)} + \frac{2\,\mathrm{e}^{-\frac{i\pi}{4}}}{\sqrt{\pi}} \oint dt' \int\limits_0 d\varrho' \int\limits_{\varrho'}^{\infty} \frac{\mathrm{e}^{i\tau}}{\sqrt{\tau}}\, d\tau\, \frac{\partial}{\partial z'}\, G(\mathfrak{r}-\hat{\mathfrak{r}}')\left(1 \mp \frac{\varrho'}{\varrho_0(t')}\right) \tag{40.1s}$$

bzw.

$$v_B^{(2)}(\mathfrak{r}) = v_K^{(2)} + \frac{2\,\mathrm{e}^{-\frac{i\pi}{4}}}{\sqrt{\pi}} \oint dt' \int\limits_0 d\varrho' \left\{\int\limits_{\varrho'}^{\infty} \frac{\mathrm{e}^{i\tau}}{\sqrt{\tau}}\, d\tau - i\,\frac{\mathrm{e}^{i\varrho'}}{\sqrt{\varrho'}}\right\} G(\mathfrak{r}-\hat{\mathfrak{r}}')\left(1 \pm \frac{\varrho'}{\varrho_0(t')}\right). \tag{40.2s}$$

Hier treten zunächst die Kirchhoffschen Näherungen (35.2a) bzw. (35.3a) auf; ferner haben wir in den Braunbekschen Korrekturtermen die Integration über den Schirm (S) bzw. die Öffnung (L) auf einen Streifen längs des Randes beschränkt. Führt man nämlich die Bogenlänge t längs der Kante sowie den senkrechten Abstand ϱ von der Kante als Koordinaten ein (vgl. Fig. 25), so läßt sich jedem Flächenpunkte $\hat{\mathfrak{r}}$ eines Randstreifens, dessen Breite überall klein gegen den *Krümmungsradius* $\varrho_0(t)$ der Kante ist, eindeutig ein Koordinatenpaar (t,ϱ) zuordnen und es gilt für das Flächenelement $d\hat{\mathfrak{f}} = \left(1 \pm \frac{\varrho}{\varrho_0(t)}\right) dt\, d\varrho$, wobei das obere bzw. untere Vorzeichen auf der Seite der Randkurve gilt, auf der die in der Schirmebene liegenden Kurvennormalen divergieren bzw. konvergieren. In den Gln. (40.2*s*) gilt — unter der Voraussetzung einer geschlossenen konvexen Randkurve — das obere bzw. untere Vorzeichen für den „Streufall“ bzw. „Beugungsfall“ (vgl. Ziff. 20). Die t-Integration hat sich über die gesamte Länge der Kante

[1] K. SCHWARZSCHILD: Math. Ann. **55**, 177 (1902).
[2] W. BRAUNBEK: Z. Physik **127**, 405 (1950); **138**, 80 (1954).

zu erstrecken, während für die ϱ-Integration keine obere Grenze angegeben worden ist, da der Integrand nur merkliche Beiträge in Nähe der unteren Grenze $\varrho = 0$ liefert

Die Integrale in (40.1s) und (40.2s) können nun mit Hilfe des *Prinzips der stationären Phase* asymptotisch entwickelt werden (insbesondere für Aufpunkte, die weit von der Kante entfernt sind) und zwar liegen — wie J.B. KELLER[1] u. Mitarb. gezeigt haben — die Punkte, in denen die Phase stationär ist, jeweils so auf dem Rande, daß ihr Abstand vom Aufpunkt ein Maximum bzw. Minimum ist *(Glanzpunkte)*.

Ferner lassen sich — worauf wir in Ziff. 35 schon hingewiesen hatten — die Kirchhoffschen Terme $v_K^{(1)}$ bzw. $v_K^{(2)}$ auch als (bezüglich z) antisymmetrischer bzw. symmetrischer Teil des Rubinowiczschen Linienintegrals (32.10) berechnen. Dieses kann nun (wie erwähnt) ebenfalls mit Hilfe des Prinzips der stationären Phase asymptotisch ausgewertet werden[2]; man kann aber die Flächenintegrale (35.2a) und (35.3a) auch direkt mit Hilfe des (auf zweidimensionale Bereiche erweiterten) Prinzips der stationären Phase asymptotisch berechnen[3]. Dabei erhält man stationäre Punkte im Innern der Öffnung und auf derem Rande. Die inneren Punkte liefern aber gerade die geometrisch optische Lichtverteilung v_g, die auch bei der Rubinoviczschen Umformung auftrat — vgl. (32.10) —, während die Punkte auf dem Rande wieder einen Randeffekt im Sinne des Th. Youngschen Prinzips liefern. Dieses ist also auch in der Braunbekschen Näherung durchführbar, jedoch (im Gegensatz zur Kirchhoffschen Theorie) nur im Fernfeld, wie zu erwarten. Wir werden die so erhaltenen Formeln in der geometrischen Beugungstheorie (Ziff. 44) wiederfinden und dort diskutieren. Die asymptotische Entwicklung von (40.1s) und (40.2s) führt zum gleichen Hauptglied.

Während also die Kirchhoffsche Lösung in keinen so einfachen analytischen Zusammenhang mit der strengen Lösung des Randwertproblems gebracht werden kann, dürfte das Braunbeksche Verfahren das Hauptglied der asymptotischen Entwicklung der strengen Lösung liefern (auch in Kantennähe: die Kantenbedingung ist erfüllt). Es ist somit der Kirchhoffschen Lösung in denjenigen Fällen vorzuziehen, in denen man sich nicht auf die nächste Umgebung der Einfallsrichtung (bzw. der Schattengrenze) beschränken will (dort liefern beide Verfahren im Fernfeld übereinstimmende Ergebnisse), zumal es sich asymptotisch ebenso leicht auswerten läßt, wie diese. Zu diesem Schluß kommt auch ANDREJEWSKI[4], der die Ergebnisse der Braunbekschen Methode mit der strengen Lösung für die Kreisscheibe vergleicht.

c) Die geometrische Beugungstheorie von J. B. KELLER.

Von einem scheinbar ganz anderen heuristischen Ausgangspunkt her hat J.B. KELLER[5] die asymptotische Lösung des Randwertproblems zu gewinnen

[1] J.B. KELLER, R.M. LEWIS u. B.D. SECKLER: N. Y. Univ. Res. Rep. No. EM-96 (1956). — J. Appl. Phys. **28**, 570 (1957).

[2] A. RUBINOWICZ: Ann. d. Phys. **73**, 339 (1924). — Die Beugungswelle in der Kirchhoffschen Theorie der Beugung, Kap. V. Warschau 1957.

[3] J.B. KELLER, R.M. LEWIS u. B.D. SECKLER: l. c. — Man vergleiche zum Prinzip der stationären Phase für Flächenintegrale auch N. G. VAN KAMPEN: Physica, Haag **14**, 575 (1949); **16**, 817 (1950). — R. K. LUNEBERG: N. Y. Univ. Res. Rep. No. EM-15 (1949). — J. FOCKE: Verh. sächs. Akad. Wiss. **101**, 1 (1954). — M.I. KONTOROVITCH u. U.K. MURAVÉV: J. techn. Phys. USSR. **12**, 394 (1952). — H. BREMMER: Physica, Haag **18**, 469 (1952). — G. BRAUN: Acta phys. Austr. **10**, 8 (1956). — D.S. JONES u. M. KLINE: N. Y. Univ. Res. Rep. No. EM-100 (1956); J. Math. Phys. **37**, 1 (1958).

[4] W. ANDREJEWSKY: Diss. Aachen 1952; Z. angew. Phys. **5**, 179 (1958).

[5] J.B. KELLER: Symposium on Microwave Optics, Eaton Electronic Research Laboratory, McGill University, Montreal 1953. Siehe auch J. B. KELLER: N. Y. Univ. Res. Rep. No. EM-115 (1958). — Calculus of Variations and its Applications (ed. L. M. GRAVES), S. 27ff. New York—Toronto—London: McGraw-Hill 1958.

gesucht. Gewöhnlich wird der Beugungseffekt als Abweichung von den Gesetzen der geometrischen Optik aufgefaßt; er läßt sich jedoch durch eine einfache Verallgemeinerung dieser Gesetze asymptotisch erfassen. Die geometrische Optik operiert mit der Konzeption der *Phasen- oder Wellenflächen* (die durch die *Eikonalgleichung* beschrieben werden) und deren Orthogonaltrajektorien — den *Strahlen* (die durch das *Fermatsche Prinzip des kürzesten Lichtweges* festgelegt sind). Diese Konzeption ergibt sich auch näherungsweise aus der Wellengleichung, solange die Krümmungsradien der Wellenflächen überall sehr groß gegen die Wellenlänge sind. (Dies ist in der Nähe von Brennpunkten bzw. Kaustiken und stark gekrümmten Oberflächen der Objekte im Feld nicht mehr der Fall.) Beschränkt man sich auf ein stückweise homogenes Medium, so sind die von der Lichtquelle zum Aufpunkt gehenden Strahlen *Geradenstücke*, die mit den Trennflächen der Medien ein oder mehrere diskrete Punkte (die nicht auf eventuellen Kanten der Grenzflächen liegen sollen) gemeinsam haben, wo sie Knicke aufweisen. So ergeben sich die ein- oder mehrfach gebrochenen und reflektierten Strahlensysteme, die eine scharfe Schattengrenze erzeugen (durch die hindurch kein Strahl gelangt).

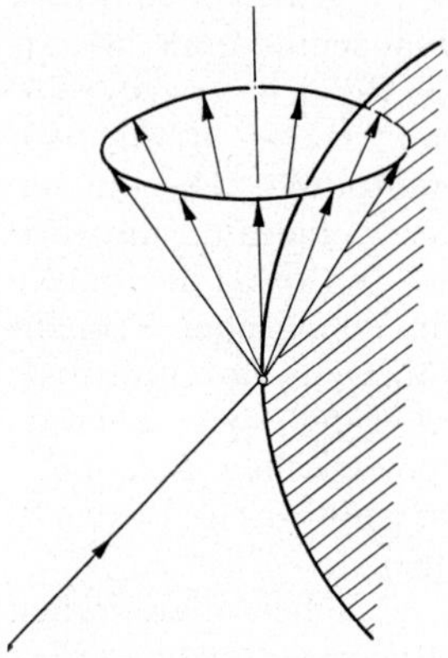

Fig. 26. Kegel gebeugter Strahlen bei dem Verfahren von J. B. Keller.

41. Gebeugte Strahlen. Läßt man jedoch unter den konkurrierenden Strahlen, die den Lichtweg stationär machen sollen, auch solche zu, die mit den Grenzflächen glatte *Kurvenstücke* oder eine beliebige Anzahl von *Punkten auf* etwa vorhandenen *Kanten* gemeinsam haben, so können *diese* Strahlen in das geometrische Schattengebiet gelangen. Wir wollen sie deshalb mit J.B. Keller als „*gebeugte Strahlen*" bezeichnen. Bei der genaueren Durchführung dieses Gedankens wollen wir uns hier auf *ebene Schirme* mit beliebig geformten Öffnungen beschränken, dann gehen gebeugte Strahlen nur von den Kanten aus[1]. Die kürzeste Verbindung zwischen Quellpunkt Q und Aufpunkt P, die *einen* Punkt mit der Kante gemeinsam hat, besteht aus zwei Halbstrahlen durch Q und P (dem einfallenden und gebeugten Strahl), die sich an einem Punkt der Kante so treffen, daß sie *gleiche Winkel mit der Kantentangente* in diesem Punkt einschließen. Dabei liegen diese Geradenstücke auf verschiedenen Seiten der Ebene durch den Kantenpunkt, die die Kantentangente zur Normalen hat *(Kantenbeugungsgesetz)*. Es erzeugt also jeder auf einen Kantenpunkt auftreffende einfallende Strahl einen von diesem Kantenpunkt ausgehenden *Kegel gebeugter Strahlen*, dessen Achse die Kantentangente und dessen halber Öffnungswinkel der Winkel zwischen einfallendem Strahl und Kantentangente ist (s. Fig. 26). Bei senkrechter Inzidenz entartet dieser Kegel zu einer Ebene. Die Anzahl der gebeugten Strahlen, die durch irgendeinen Aufpunkt P geht, läßt sich nun auf Grund des Gesetzes der Kantenbeugung leicht ermitteln.

Beispielsweise erhält man für eine glatte geschlossene konvexe Kantenkurve und senkrechte Inzidenz der einfallenden ebenen Welle genau *zwei gebeugte Strahlen* durch jeden (nicht auf der Kante liegenden) Aufpunkt P, die von Kantenpunkten ausgehen, die den größten bzw. kleinsten Abstand von P haben. Ferner

[1] Wir folgen der Arbeit von J.B. Keller: N. Y. Univ. Res. Rep. No. EM-92 (1956); J. Appl. Phys. **28**, 426 (1957). Siehe auch J.B. Keller, R.M. Levis und B.D. Seckler: N. Y. Univ. Res. Rep. No. EM-81 (1955); Comm. Pure Appl. Math. **9**, 207 (1956). — R.N. Buchal u. J.B. Keller: N. Y. Univ. Res. Rep. No. EM-131 (1959). — S.N. Karp u. J.B. Keller: N. Y. Univ. Res. Rep. No. EM-143 (1959).

geht durch jeden Punkt P vor dem Schirm noch ein einfallender und (gegebenenfalls) ein reflektierter Strahl, während die Punkte P hinter dem Schirm nur dann von einem einfallenden Strahl getroffen werden können, wenn sie nicht im geometrischen Schattengebiet liegen. (Hat die Kantenkurve ein Symmetriezentrum, so bedürfen die Aufpunkte auf der Symmetrieachse einer gesonderten Betrachtung, insbesondere ist die Symmetrieachse beim Kreis Brennlinie.)

Trifft ein *(einfach)* gebeugter Strahl die Kante noch einmal, so wird der entsprechende Kantenpunkt Ausgangspunkt *zweifach* gebeugter Strahlen, indem der einfach gebeugte Strahl wie ein einfallender Strahl (streifender Inzidenz) behandelt wird. Entsprechend lassen sich auch *mehrfach gebeugte* Strahlen betrachten. Trifft schließlich ein einfallender Strahl einen Punkt der Kante, wo diese einen *Knick* hat, so muß das Beugungsgesetz etwas modifiziert werden *(„Eckenbeugung“)*, worauf wir aber nicht eingehen wollen.

42. Das den Strahlen zugeordnete Feld. Das Beugungsbild kommt nun dadurch zustande, daß die oben konstruierten durch einen Aufpunkt P gehenden Strahlen miteinander *interferieren*. Um diesen Effekt zu beschreiben, müssen wir jedem Strahl ein Feld zuordnen. Dies kann nach einem Gedanken von R. K. LUNEBERG[1] geschehen, den wir jetzt im Anschluß an J. B. KELLER[2] entwickeln wollen.

Bezeichnet man den Abstand eines beliebigen Punktes P auf dem Strahl von einem geeignet gewählten Punkt P' (auf demselben Strahl) mit s (das wir in Richtung der Lichtfortpflanzung positiv zählen wollen), so werde jedem Strahl ein Feld von der Gestalt $v(P', P) = A(s)\, e^{ik\Phi(s)}$ zugeordnet[3]. Die reelle *Amplitude* A kann als Vektor aufgefaßt werden, wenn es sich darum handelt Polarisationseffekte zu beschreiben; wir wollen uns jedoch hier auf das skalare Problem beschränken. Für die *Phase* Φ machen wir den Ansatz

$$\Phi(s) = \Phi' + s \tag{42.1}$$

(der mit Hilfe der Eikonalgleichung näher begründet werden kann); dabei ist Φ' die Phase im Punkte P'.

Zur Ermittlung der Amplitude konstruieren wir um den betrachteten Strahl herum eine Röhre aus infinitesimal benachbarten Strahlen (Elementarbüschel) mit den Querschnitten $d\sigma'$ im Punkte P' und $d\sigma$ im Punkte P. Die durch einen solchen Querschnitt sekundlich hindurchtretende *Energie* wollen wir proportional zu $A^2\, d\sigma$ annehmen. Infolge des *Energieerhaltungssatzes* (für ein nicht absorbierendes Medium) ist diese Größe längs der ganzen Röhre eine Konstante. Somit gilt $A^2\, d\sigma = A'^2\, d\sigma'$, wobei A' die Amplitude im Punkte P' ist. Die Querschnitte sind nun infinitesimale Bereiche der zu den Strahlensystemen gehörigen Wellenflächen. Diese werden sich (im allgemeinen nicht-homozentrischen Fall) irgendwo längs des betrachteten Strahles auf zwei zueinander senkrechte *Brennlinien* zusammenziehen[4]. Bezeichnet nun ϱ_1 bzw. ϱ_2 den Abstand des Punktes P' von diesen beiden Brennlinien, so gilt nach dem Strahlensatz (s. Fig. 27)

$$\frac{d\sigma'}{d\sigma} = \frac{\varrho_1 \varrho_2}{(\varrho_1 + s)(\varrho_2 + s)}, \tag{42.2}$$

wenn wir die Flächenelemente des Elementarbüschels als Rechtecke betrachten. (Man kann dies natürlich auch aus den differentialgeometrischen Eigenschaften

[1] R. K. LUNEBERG: Mathematical Theory of Optics. Providence, R. J.: Brown Univ. 1944. — Propagation of electromagnetic waves. New York Univ. 1948.

[2] Siehe Fußnote 1, S. 290.

[3] Wir wollen in dieser Ziffer von unserer dimensionslosen Schreibweise abgehen, da das explizite Auftreten der Wellenlänge $\lambda = 2\pi/k$ hier Vorteile mit sich bringt.

[4] Vgl. M. BORN: Optik, S. 53. Berlin: Springer 1933.

der Wellenflächen ableiten; ϱ_1 und ϱ_2 sind dann die *Hauptkrümmungsradien* der Wellenfläche im Punkt P', die wir dann *positiv* zählen wollen, wenn die Krümmungsmittelpunkte *vor* der Wellenfläche liegen.) Für die Amplitude im Punkt P erhält man so aus dem Energiesatz

$$A(s) = A' \sqrt{\frac{\varrho_1 \varrho_2}{(\varrho_1 + s)(\varrho_2 + s)}}. \tag{42.3}$$

Für das Feld im Punkte P auf einem Strahl erhalten wir also aus (42.1) und (42.3)

$$v(P', P) = A' \sqrt{\frac{\varrho_1 \varrho_2}{(\varrho_1 + s)(\varrho_2 + s)}}\, e^{ik(\Phi' + s)}. \tag{42.4}$$

Das Feld verhält sich demnach für $s \to \infty$ wie eine Kugelwelle e^{iks}/s, wenn beide Brennlinien des Elementarbüschels im Endlichen liegen (andernfalls ergeben sich Zylinderwellen oder ebene Wellen, je nachdem ob eine oder beide Brennlinien ins Unendliche rücken). Andererseits wird es am Ort der Brennlinien selbst ($s \to -\varrho_1$ oder $s \to -\varrho_2$) singulär, wie in einer geometrischen Theorie nicht anders zu erwarten ist.

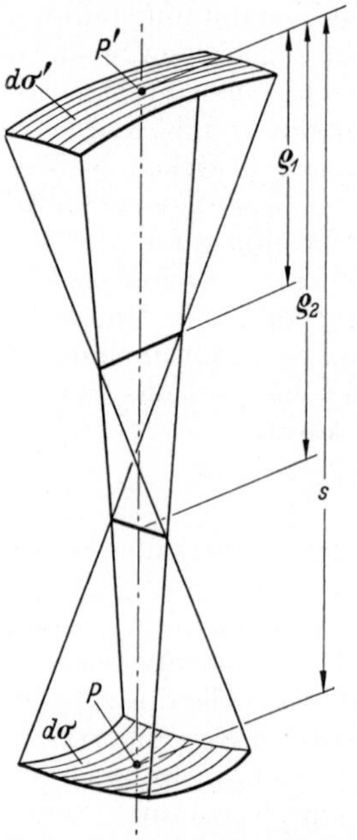

Fig. 27. Nicht-homozentrisches Strahlenbündel mit seinen beiden Brennlinien.

Nun hatten wir oben gesehen, daß das System der *gebeugten Strahlen* aus Strahlenkegeln besteht, deren Spitzen auf dem Schirmrande liegen. Der *Schirmrand ist also eine Brennlinie (Youngsches Prinzip)*. Es ist nun zweckmäßig, den „*Anfangspunkt*" P' für das System der gebeugten Strahlen jeweils auf den Rand zu verlegen. Dann wird zwar, wie wir oben gesehen haben, A' unendlich groß, jedoch die Größe $A'' = A' \sqrt{\varrho_2}$ bleibt für $\varrho_2 \to 0$ endlich (dabei sei ϱ_2 der Abstand des Punktes P' von derjenigen Brennlinie, die von der Kante gebildet wird), wie man aus (42.3) erkennt. Für das Feld auf einem von der Kante *einfach gebeugten Strahl* erhalten wir also mit $\varrho_2 \to 0$ aus (42.4)

$$v^{(1)}(P', P) = A'' \sqrt{\frac{\varrho_1}{s(\varrho_1 + s)}}\, e^{ik(\Phi' + s)}; \tag{42.4'}$$

dabei ist s der Abstand des Aufpunktes P von dem Kantenpunkt P', von dem der Strahl ausgeht und ϱ_1 ist der von P' aus gemessene Abstand der anderen Kaustik, die zu dem Strahlensystem gehört.

Um ϱ_1 zu berechnen, müssen wir das von der Kante ausgehende Strahlensystem etwas genauer betrachten. Dazu führen wir auf der Randkurve die *Bogenlänge* t ein (von irgendeinem zweckmäßig gewählten Anfangspunkt aus gemessen). Es möge nun der Vektor $\mathfrak{x}(t)$ die Randkurve beschreiben, während $\mathfrak{y}$ der Ortsvektor eines beliebigen Punktes des von den gebeugten Strahlen gebildeten Kegels in $\mathfrak{x}(t)$ sei. Schließt ferner ein auf die Kante auftreffender einfallender Strahl mit der Kantentangente $\dot{\mathfrak{x}}(t)$ den Winkel $\alpha(t)$ ein, so ist dies zugleich der halbe Öffnungswinkel des gebeugten Strahlenkegels, für dessen Gleichung also gilt (wegen $\dot{\mathfrak{x}}^2 = 1$)

$$\big(\mathfrak{y} - \mathfrak{x}(t), \dot{\mathfrak{x}}(t)\big) = |\mathfrak{y} - \mathfrak{x}(t)| \cos\alpha(t). \tag{42.5}$$

Die *Einhüllende* dieser einparametrigen Schar von Kegeln ist nun gleichzeitig die *Brennfläche* des gebeugten Strahlensystems. Um die Gleichung dieser Einhüllenden zu finden, differenzieren wir (42.5) nach der Bogenlänge t. Man erhält so

$$(\mathfrak{y}-\mathfrak{x},\ddot{\mathfrak{x}})-\dot{\mathfrak{x}}^2=-\dot{\alpha}|\mathfrak{y}-\mathfrak{x}|\sin\alpha-\frac{\cos\alpha}{|\mathfrak{y}-\mathfrak{x}|}(\mathfrak{y}-\mathfrak{x},\dot{\mathfrak{x}}) \tag{42.6}$$

oder wegen (42.5)

$$(\mathfrak{y}-\mathfrak{x},\ddot{\mathfrak{x}}+\dot{\alpha}\operatorname{tg}\alpha\,\dot{\mathfrak{x}})=1-\cos^2\alpha. \tag{42.6'}$$

Da nun t die Bogenlänge der Randkurve ist, so folgt nach elementaren differentialgeometrischen Sätzen $\dot{\mathfrak{x}}=\mathfrak{t}$, $\ddot{\mathfrak{x}}=\mathfrak{s}/\varrho_0$, wobei $\mathfrak{t}$ der Tangenteneinheitsvektor der Kante sei, während $\mathfrak{s}$ die *Kurvennormale* bedeute und ϱ_0 den Krümmungsradius der Kantenkurve (s. Fig. 28). Wir können daher mit (42.6') und (42.5) die Gleichung der

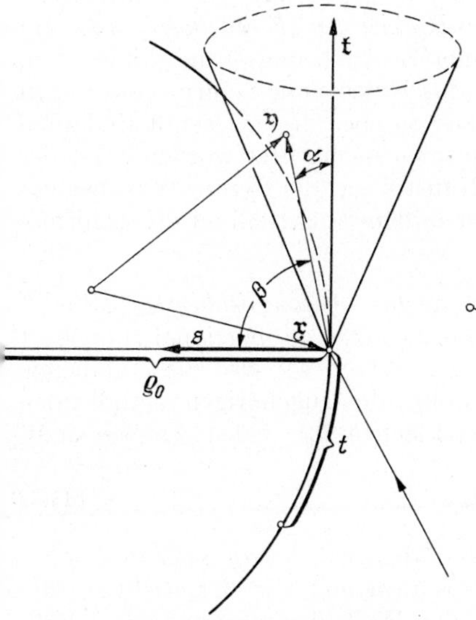

Fig. 28. Zur Gleichung für den Strahlenkegel.

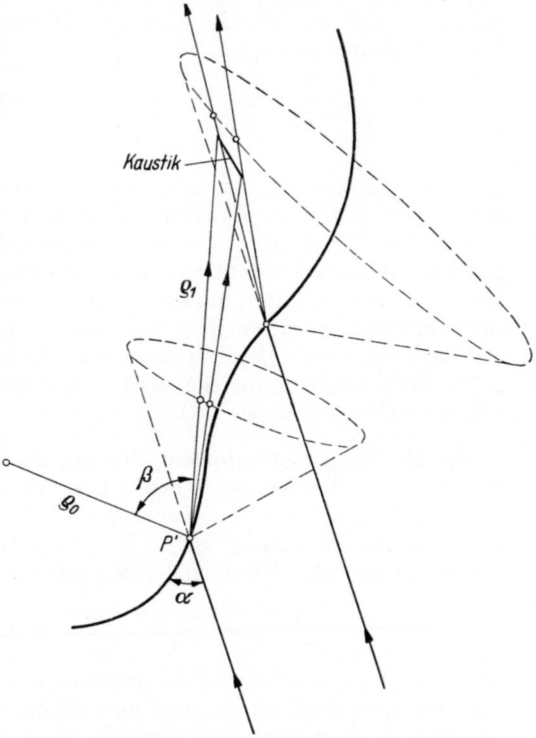

Fig. 29. Zur Gleichung für die Einhüllende der Strahlenkegel.

Brennfläche der gebeugten Strahlen in der Form schreiben

$$\left.\begin{aligned}(\mathfrak{y}-\mathfrak{x},\mathfrak{s}+\varrho_0\dot{\alpha}\operatorname{tg}\alpha\cdot\mathfrak{t})&=\varrho_0\sin^2\alpha,\\(\mathfrak{y}-\mathfrak{x},\mathfrak{t})&=|\mathfrak{y}-\mathfrak{x}|\cos\alpha.\end{aligned}\right\} \tag{42.7}$$

Führt man schließlich noch den Winkel β zwischen den gebeugten Strahlen und der Kurvennormale $\mathfrak{s}$ ein, so gilt

$$\cos\beta=\frac{(\mathfrak{y}-\mathfrak{x},\mathfrak{s})}{|\mathfrak{y}-\mathfrak{x}|} \tag{42.8}$$

und damit können wir Gl. (42.6) auch in der Gestalt schreiben

$$|\mathfrak{y}-\mathfrak{x}|(\cos\beta+\varrho_0\dot{\alpha}\sin\alpha)=\varrho_0\sin^2\alpha. \tag{42.6''}$$

Der Abstand ϱ_1 der Kaustik (42.7) vom Schirmrande längs eines unter dem Winkel β gegen die Normale $\mathfrak{s}$ der Kante gebeugten Strahles ist nun gerade $\varrho_1=-|\mathfrak{y}-\mathfrak{x}|$ (vgl. Fig. 29; die Kaustik liegt hier hinter P', daher ist ϱ_1 negativ zu rechnen). Somit folgt aus (42.6'')

$$\varrho_1=-\frac{\varrho_0\sin^2\alpha}{\cos\beta+\varrho_0\dot{\alpha}\sin\alpha}. \tag{42.9}$$

Setzt man diesen Wert in (42.4′) ein, so erhält man

$$v^{1)}(P', P) = \frac{A''\, e^{ik(\Phi'+s)}}{\sqrt{s\left(1 - s\,\dfrac{\cos\beta + \varrho_0\,\dot\alpha\sin\alpha}{\varrho_0\sin^2\alpha}\right)}}\,. \tag{42.10}$$

Bevor wir nun dazu übergehen, auch noch die letzte unbestimmt gebliebene Größe $A''\, e^{ik\Phi'}$ in (42.10) zu ermitteln, wollen wir Gl. (42.7) für ein einfaches Beispiel diskutieren. Wir wählen dazu die *senkrechte Inzidenz* einer ebenen Welle, dann ist $\alpha(t) \equiv \pi/2$ also $\dot\alpha(t) \equiv 0$. Damit folgt aus (42.7) für die Gleichung der Brennfläche der gebeugten Strahlen

$$\left.\begin{aligned}(\mathfrak{y} - \mathfrak{x}, \mathfrak{s}) &= \varrho_0\,,\\ (\mathfrak{y} - \mathfrak{x}, \mathfrak{t}) &= 0\,.\end{aligned}\right\} \tag{42.7′}$$

Die Kaustik besteht also aus einem *geraden* (senkrecht auf der Schirmfläche stehenden) *Zylinder, dessen Querschnitt die Evolute der Kantenkurve ist.* Im Streufall muß sich also diese Kaustik auf einer Beobachtungsebene (hinter dem Schirm) als *helle Linie* abzeichnen, die sich durch den vom Schirm geworfenen geometrischen Schatten hindurchzieht. Linien von eben dieser Gestalt sind auch tatsächlich im Schattenriß von Beugungsschirmen beobachtet worden[1]. Ist der Schirm eine *Kreisscheibe,* so schrumpft die Kaustik auf die Symmetrieachse des Schirmes zusammen, die sich als heller Punkt in dem Schattenbild des Schirmes abzeichnet *(Poissonscher Fleck).*

43. Der Beugungskoeffizient. Zur Bestimmung des „*Anfangsfeldwertes*“ $A''e^{ik\Phi'}$ in (42.10) machen wir die naheliegende Annahme, daß er proportional zum Wert des *einfallenden Feldes* im Kantenpunkt P' ist. Setzen wir also die einfallende Welle in der Gestalt $v_0 = A_0\, e^{i\Phi_0}$ voraus (wobei die zugehörigen einfallenden Strahlen durch die Orthogonaltrajektorien der Flächen $\Phi_0 = \text{const}$ gegeben sind), so gilt

$$A''\, e^{ik\Phi'} = B\, A_0\, e^{ik\Phi_0}. \tag{43.1}$$

Der hier eingeführte Proportionalitätsfaktor B — der sog. „*Beugungskoeffizient*“ — wird noch von der Randbedingung auf dem Schirm und von der Richtung der einfallenden und gebeugten Strahlen sowie der Wellenlänge abhängen. (Falls man Polarisationseffekte mit erfassen will ist A_0 als Vektor und B demgemäß als *Tensor* anzusetzen[2].) Zur Bestimmung von B betrachten wir die engste (in ihren Dimensionen gegen die Wellenlänge kleine) Umgebung des Kantenpunktes P' wo wir (wenn die Kante dort keine Ecke hat, was wir ausschließen wollen) die Verhältnisse der Sommerfeldschen Halbebene antreffen werden. Die Randwertaufgabe für die Halbebene werden wir in Abschn. B Ia streng behandeln, allerdings nur für den Fall der senkrechten Inzidenz einer ebenen Welle. Die Verallgemeinerung für beliebige (auch schräg zur Kante gelegene) Einfallsrichtung bereitet jedoch keinerlei Schwierigkeiten[3]. Entwickelt man diese strenge Lösung für die Beugung an der Halbebene asymptotisch für das Fernfeld, so ergibt sich ein Ausdruck, der mit (42.4′) und (43.1) genau übereinstimmt, wenn man diese Gleichungen für die Beugung an der geraden Kante spezialisiert (hier gibt es durch jeden Punkt nur einen einfach gebeugten Strahl und keine mehrfach gebeugten

[1] J. Coulson u. G. G. Becknell: Phys. Rev. **20**, 594, 607 (1922).

[2] Vgl. J. B. Keller: l. c.

[3] Vgl. z. B. H. S. Carslaw: Proc. Lond. Math. Soc. **30**, 121 (1899). — P. C. Clemmow: Proc. Roy. Soc. Lond., Ser. A **205**, 286 (1951). — M. Born u. E. Wolf: Principles of Optics, S. 575ff. London-New York-Paris-Los Angeles: Pergamon Press 1959.

Strahlen) und überdies B den folgenden Wert gibt

$$B = -\frac{e^{\frac{i\pi}{4}}}{2\sqrt{2\pi k}}\,\frac{1}{\sin\alpha}\left\{\frac{1}{\cos\frac{\vartheta-\vartheta_0}{2}} \pm \frac{1}{\sin\frac{\vartheta+\vartheta_0}{2}}\right\}. \tag{43.2}$$

Dabei sind ϑ bzw. ϑ_0 die Winkel, die die *Projektion* des gebeugten bzw. einfallenden Strahles in die zur Kante normale Ebene mit der Normale $\mathfrak{n}$ des *Schirmes* einschließen (s. Fig. 30). Ferner gilt das obere Vorzeichen in (43.2) für die Randbedingung $v=0$ auf (S), das untere für $\partial v/\partial n = 0$ auf (S).

Indem wir den Beugungskoeffizienten auch für beliebig gekrümmte Schirmkanten übernehmen — falls nur der Krümmungsradius ϱ_0 der Kante überall *groß* gegen die Wellenlänge λ ist — so folgt aus (42.10) und (43.1) mit (43.2)

$$\left.\begin{aligned} &v^{(1)}(P',P)\\ &= -\frac{A_0\, e^{ik(\Phi_0+s)+\frac{i\pi}{4}}}{2\sqrt{2\pi k s\left(1 - s\,\frac{\cos\beta+\varrho_0\,\dot\alpha\sin\alpha}{\varrho_0\sin^2\alpha}\right)}}\,\cdot\\ &\cdot\frac{1}{\sin\alpha}\left\{\frac{1}{\cos\frac{\vartheta-\vartheta_0}{2}} \pm \frac{1}{\sin\frac{\vartheta+\vartheta_0}{2}}\right\}.\end{aligned}\right\} \tag{43.3}$$

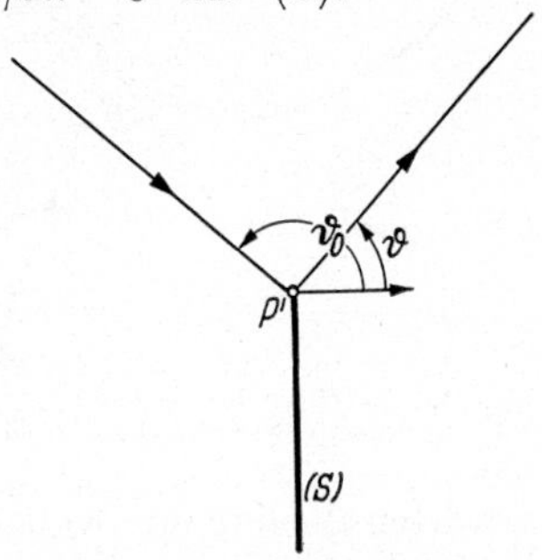

Fig. 30. Zur Definition der Winkel ϑ und ϑ_0 in einer zur Kante senkrechten Ebene.

Dies ist also das Feld, das ein *einfach gebeugter* durch P gehender *Strahl* zum Gesamtfeld beiträgt. Dabei beziehen sich sämtliche Größen auf den Kantenpunkt P', von dem der gebeugte Strahl ausgeht.

44. Gesamtfeld. Um das Gesamtfeld zu erhalten, müssen sämtliche durch P gehenden gebeugten Strahlen ermittelt werden. (Sie lassen sich auf Grund des Gesetzes der Kantenbeugung leicht bestimmen, für glatte geschlossene konvexe Kanten gibt es, wie erwähnt, nur zwei einfach gebeugte Strahlen durch jeden Aufpunkt.) Ferner ist noch der Beitrag der einfallenden und reflektierten Strahlen zu berücksichtigen. Für Aufpunkte P hinter dem Schirm liefern die durch die Öffnung gehenden einfallenden Strahlen den Beitrag v_g; vgl. Gl. (32.11). Somit erhält man hinter dem Schirm für das Feld der *einfallenden* und *einfach gebeugten Strahlen*

$$\left.\begin{aligned} v^{(1)}(P) = v_g(P) - \frac{e^{\frac{i\pi}{4}}}{2\sqrt{2\pi k}}\sum_{P'}\frac{A_0\, e^{ik(\Phi_0+s)}}{\sqrt{s\left(1 - s\,\frac{\cos\beta+\varrho_0\,\dot\alpha\sin\alpha}{\varrho_0\sin^2\alpha}\right)}}\,\cdot\\ \cdot\frac{1}{\sin\alpha}\left\{\frac{1}{\cos\frac{\vartheta-\vartheta_0}{2}} \pm \frac{1}{\sin\frac{\vartheta+\vartheta_0}{2}}\right\},\end{aligned}\right\} \tag{44.1}$$

wobei über sämtliche Kantenpunkte P' zu summieren ist, von denen aus einfach gebeugte Strahlen durch P gehen (s. Fig. 31).

Für Punkte vor dem Schirm ist v_g durch $v_0 + v_g^0$ zu ersetzen, wobei v_g^0 das Feld ist, das den nach der geometrischen Optik am Schirm (S) reflektierten Strahlen zuzuordnen ist. Der Raum wird also durch die einfallenden bzw. reflektierten Strahlensysteme in drei Gebiete I, II, III eingeteilt (s. Fig. 32), deren scharfe Grenzen (S') und (S'') durch die Wirkung der gebeugten Strahlen aufgelöst werden. Dies kommt allerdings durch Gl. (44.1) nicht ohne weiteres zum

Ausdruck, vielmehr wird (44.1) auf den geometrischen Schattengrenzen (S') ($\vartheta = \pi + \vartheta_0$) und den Grenzen der reflektierten Strahlen (S'') ($\vartheta = -\vartheta_0$) singulär. Dies ist eine Folge davon, daß der Beugungskoeffizient (43.2) dort singulär wird, der durch eine asymptotische Auswertung der strengen Lösung für die Beugung an der Halbebene gewonnen wurde. Diese Auswertung ist jedoch in der Umgebung der Schattengrenzen unzulässig und muß dort durch ein andere Auswertung der strengen Lösung ersetzt werden (vgl. Ziff. 114). Damit ergibt sich dann auch ein Beugungskoeffizient, der auf den Schattengrenzen regulär ist.

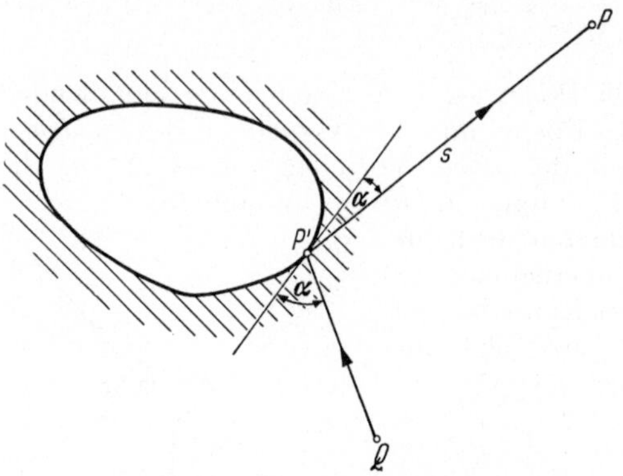

Fig. 31. An einem Kantenpunkt P' einfach gebeugter Strahl durch den Aufpunkt P (nach J.B. KELLER).

Ferner ist (44.1) in den Kantenpunkten P' ($s = 0$) so singulär, daß dort die Kantenbedingung verletzt wird. Das ist nicht anderszu erwarten, da die ganze Konzeption auf die Verhältnisse des Fernfeldes zugeschnitten ist, für das die Kante wie eine leuchtende Linie wirkt (Brennlinie der gebeugten Strahlen). Schließlich wird (44.1) auch noch an den Punkten der durch (42.7) gegebenen Kaustik der gebeugten Strahlen singulär.

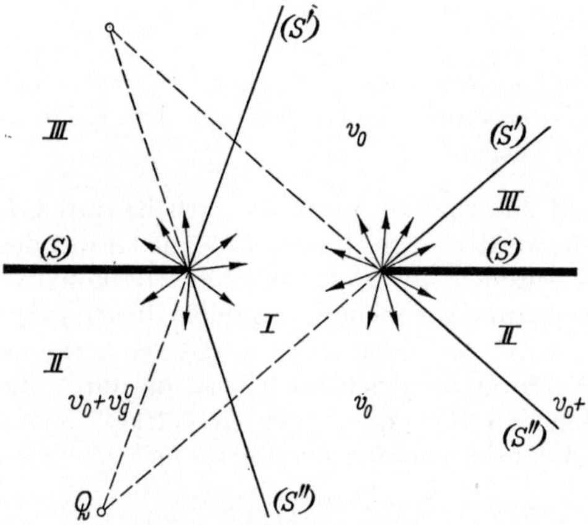

Fig. 32. Gebietseinteilungen nach der geometrischen Optik und einfach gebeugte Strahlen.

Um die Singularitäten auf den Kaustiken zu vermeiden, hat man so vorzugehen, daß man eine strenge Lösung der Wellengleichung in der engeren Umgebung der Kaustik aufsucht, die die unzulässige Singularität in ein Lichtgebirge endlicher Amplitude und Ausdehnung auflöst. Für Brennpunkte und Brennlinien sind solche Lösungen schon von P. DEBYE[1] gefunden worden (*Brennpunktsbeugung*). Diese Lösung kann asymptotisch im Abstand vieler Wellenlängen von der Kaustik in ein Strahlensystem der oben betrachteten Art aufgelöst werden. Andererseits liefert sie eine Modifikation der geometrischen Theorie, die an der Kaustik endlich bleibt[2].

Wie nicht anders zu erwarten, ergibt auch die asymptotische Auswertung der durch das Braunbeksche Verfahren gewonnenen Gl. (40.1 s) bzw. (40.2 s) genau die Gl. (44.1) (für den s-Fall, unteres Vorzeichen)[3]. Andererseits kann im

[1] P. DEBYE: Ann. d. Phys. **30**, 755 (1909); vgl. auch M. BORN: Optik, S. 195ff. Berlin 1933. A. SOMMERFELD: Vorlesungen Bd. IV, S. 325ff. Wiesbaden 1950. — Über die neuere Entwicklung der Brennpunktsbeugung vgl. M. BORN u. E. WOLF: Principles of Optics, S. 434ff. 1959.

[2] Vgl. dazu J. KAY u. J.B. KELLER: N.Y. Univ. Res. Rep. No. EM-55 (1953). — J. Appl. Phys. **25**, 876 (1954). — J.B. KELLER: N.Y. Univ. Res. Rep. No. EM-92 (1956), Appendix 4. — J. KAY: N.Y., Univ. Res. Rep. No. EM-138 (1958).

[3] J.B. KELLER, R.M. LEWIS u. B.D. SECKLER: N.Y. Univ. Res. Rep. No. EM-96 (1956). — J. Appl. Phys. **28**, 570 (1957).

Bereich der oben erwähnten Singularitäten die geometrische Theorie durch eine entsprechend modifizierte Auswertung der Braunbekschen Integrale ergänzt werden. Aus den im Anschluß an die Braunbeksche Theorie dargelegten Gründen kann also die Formel (44.1) als das *Hauptglied der asymptotischen Entwicklung der strengen Lösung der Randwertaufgabe* betrachtet werden (abgesehen von der Umgebung der Kaustiken und der Schattengrenze, wo die asymptotische Entwicklung einen anderen Charakter annimmt). Die geometrische Theorie liefert also das Hauptglied in expliziter Form durch einfache geometrische Überlegungen, ohne daß — wie beim Braunbek-Verfahren — eine Integration nötig ist. Sie ist also — sofern sie für die Umgebung der Kaustiken durch die angedeutete Modifikation ergänzt wird — eine äußerst leistungsfähige und dabei elementare Theorie, die der physikalischen Anschauung entgegen kommt[1].

Darüber hinaus ist die Theorie ohne weiteres in der Lage durch Berücksichtigung *mehrfach gebeugter Strahlen* höhere Näherungen zu berechnen. Für zweifach gebeugte Strahlen (deren Geometrie sich mit Hilfe des zweimal angewandten Gesetzes der Kantenbeugung ergibt) erhält man das zugehörige Feld, indem man (43.3) als streifend vom ersten Kantenpunkt her einfallendes Feld betrachtet und die gleichen Überlegungen für den zweiten Kantenpunkt noch einmal durchführt (s. Fig. 33). Dadurch wird es also möglich, auch die *Wechselwirkung* der einzelnen Kantenelemente zu berücksichtigen, was im Rahmen der Braubekschen und erst recht der Kirchhoffschen Theorie nicht der Fall ist. Auch hierzu finden sich in den Arbeiten von J. B. KELLER ins Einzelne gehende Ausführungen (besonders für den Spalt und die Kreisscheibe).

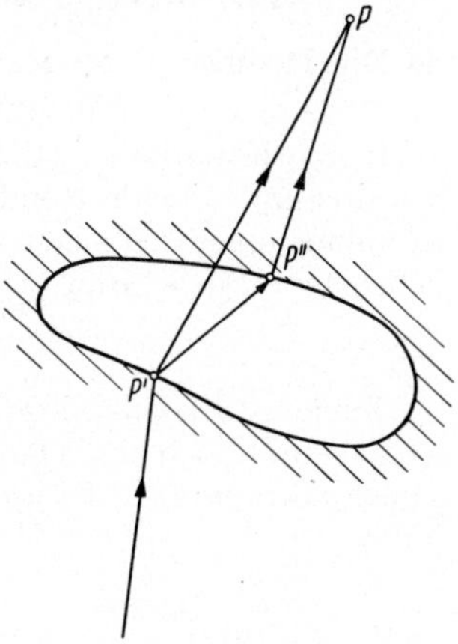

Fig. 33. Ein an P' und P'' zweifach gebeugter Strahl durch den Aufpunkt P (nach J. B. KELLER).

Da das Feld der einfach gebeugten Strahlen gemäß (43.3) eine Frequenzabhängigkeit wie $k^{-\frac{1}{2}}$ zeigt, so ergibt sich für die zweifach gebeugten Strahlen die Ordnung k^{-1} und es ist zu vermuten, daß dies unter Umständen bereits das vollständige Glied höherer Ordnung der asymptotischen Entwicklung der strengen Lösung ist. Eine Entscheidung darüber kann erst eine asymptotische Entwicklung mit Hilfe der Integralgleichungstheorie bringen. In dieser Richtung liegen Arbeiten von H. LEVINE[2] über die Beugung an der kreisförmigen Öffnung, in der sich alle wesentlichen Elemente der elementaren geometrischen Theorie wiederfinden (vgl. Ziff. 134).

45. Für konvexe Körper ohne Kanten läßt sich die geometrische Theorie — wie schon in der Einleitung erwähnt — ebenfalls durchführen. Hier laufen die gebeugten Strahlen längs geodätischen Linien auf der Oberfläche des Körpers in den geometrischen Schatten hinein[3]. Sie entsprechen dadurch genau der „*Kriechwelle*", die W. FRANZ und K. DEPPERMANN aus der Integralgleichungstheorie stetig

---

[1] Es ist bemerkenswert, daß die geometrische Beugungstheorie ohne weiteres eine *korpuskulare* Interpretation zuläßt; im Gegensatz zur traditionellen Auffassung, nach der der Beugungseffekt nur aus der Wellenvorstellung heraus zu verstehen ist.

[2] H. LEVINE: N. Y. Univ. Res. Rep. No. EM-84 (1955). — Techn. Rep. 51, Appl. Math. a. Stat. Lab., Stanford Univ. 1956.

[3] J. B. KELLER: Trans. Inst. Radio Engrs. **AP-4**, 312 (1956). — N. Y. Univ. Res. Rep. No. EM-94 (1956); No. EM-115 (1958). — B. R. LEVY u. J. B. KELLER: N. Y. Univ. Res. Rep. No. EM-109 (1957). — Siehe auch F. G. FRIEDLANDER: Proc. Cambridge Phil. Soc. **38**, 383 (1942).

gekrümmter Körperoberflächen (Abschn. IIId) für den Kreiszylinder[1] und die Kugel[2] asymptotisch abgeleitet haben. Die quantitative Durchführung der geometrischen Konzeption[3] liefert hier wieder Übereinstimmung mit dem Hauptglied der asymptotischen Entwicklung der strengen Lösung des Randwertproblems, soweit sie sich für Körper ohne Kanten durch eine an die geometrische Optik anschließende Störungsrechnung (erweiterte *Luneberg-Kline-Methode*) durchführen läßt[4]. Für die Beugung am Kreiszylinder und an der Kugel sowie am elliptischen Zylinder lassen sich die Ergebnisse der geometrischen Theorie überdies mit Hilfe der „*Watson-Transformation*" der expliziten Lösung[5–7] verifizieren. Wir werden darauf in Abschn. B II a und b genauer eingehen.

III. Strenge Verfahren (Integralgleichungstheorie).

a) Die Reduktion der Randwertaufgabe auf eine Integrodifferentialgleichung für den Flächenstrom (ebene Schirme).

In mathematischer Hinsicht reduziert das Huygenssche Prinzip das ursprünglich dreidimensionale Randwertproblem auf ein *zweidimensionales* Problem. Dies ist nunmehr genauer zu charakterisieren. Wir beschränken uns zunächst im wesentlichen auf *ebene* Schirme (S) mit Löchern (L) (in der Ebene $z=0$).

a 1) Skalares Problem.

Zunächst zur Charakterisierung des dreidimensionalen Problems: Im Halbraum $z<0$ befinde sich eine Quelle, die das (ungestörte) Feld v_0 hervorruft. Gesucht ist eine Funktion v, für die im p- bzw. s-*Fall* gilt (vgl. Ziff. 4 und 26 sowie Fig. 22 u. 23 auf S. 279);

$$\Delta v + v = 0, \qquad z \gtrless 0, \tag{I}$$

$$v_+ - v_- = 0 \text{ auf } (L) \text{ (gleichbedeutend mit } v = v_0 \text{ auf } (L) \text{ im } s\text{-Fall)}, \tag{Ia}$$

$$\left(\frac{\partial v}{\partial z}\right)_+ - \left(\frac{\partial v}{\partial z}\right)_- = 0 \text{ auf } (L) \text{ (gleichbedeutend mit } \frac{\partial v}{\partial z} = \frac{\partial v_0}{\partial z} \text{ auf } (L) \text{ im } p\text{-Fall)}, \tag{Ib}$$

$$v = 0 \text{ bzw. } \frac{\partial v}{\partial z} = 0 \text{ auf } (S) \text{ (Randbedingung)}, \tag{IIp, s}$$

v *befriedigt die Ausstrahlungsbedingung* (17.2) *bzw.* (17.3)[8] (III)

v *erfüllt die Kantenbedingung* (23.5 a—c). (IV)

---

[1] W. Franz u. K. Deppermann: Ann. d. Phys. **10**, 361 (1952). — W. Franz: Theorie der Beugung elektromagnetischer Wellen. S. 70ff. Berlin 1957.

[2] K. Deppermann u. W. Franz: Ann. d. Phys. **14**, 253 (1954). — Für beliebige konvexe Körper s. hierzu auch V. Fock: J. Phys. USSR. **10**, 130, 399 (1946).

[3] Siehe Fußnote 3, S. 297.

[4] F. G. Friedlander u. J. B. Keller: Comm. Pure Appl. Math. **8**, 387 (1955). Vgl. auch F. G. Friedlander: Proc. Cambridge Phil. Soc. **43**, 284 (1946). — R. K. Luneberg: l. c. Fußnote 1, S. 291 sowie N. Y. Univ. Res. Rep. No. EM-14 (1950). — M. Kline: Comm. Pure Appl. Math. **4**, 225 (1951); **8**, 595 (1955). — H. Bremmer: Comm. Pure Appl. Math. **4**, 419 (1951). — E. T. Copson: Comm. Pure Appl. Math. **4**, 427 (1951). — J. B. Keller, R. M. Lewis u. B. D. Seckler: Comm. Pure Appl. Math. **9**, 207 (1956). — W. L. Miranker: N. Y. Univ. Res. Rep. No. BR-21 (1956). — R. M. Lewis: N. Y. Univ. Res. Rep. No. MME-8 (1957).

[5] W. Franz: Z. Naturforsch. **9**a, 705 (1954). — Theorie der Beugung elektromagnetischer Wellen. S. 33ff. Berlin 1957. — Imai: Z. Physik **137**, 31 (1954).

[6] H. Bremmer: Terrestrial radio waves. New York-Amsterdam-London-Brussels: Elsevier Press 1949. — B. Friedman: Comm. Pure Appl. Math. **4**, 317 (1951).

[7] B. Levy: N. Y. Univ. Res. Rep. No. EM-121 (1958). — J. B. Keller u. B. R. Levy: N. Y. Univ. Res. Rep. No. EM-147 (1959).

[8] Wenn v_0 eine ebene Welle ist, ist die Ausstrahlungsbedingung so abzuändern, daß Einstrahlung ausschließlich aus der Einfallsrichtung erfolgt; vgl. D. S. Jones: Proc. Cambridge Phil. Soc. **48**, 733 (1952).

Durch diese Daten ist v nach Ziff. 20 *eindeutig* bestimmt; (I a) und (I b) ergänzt (I) für $z=0$ *auf* (L) und bedeutet die *stetige* Fortsetzbarkeit der Lösung der Wellengleichung durch die Öffnung hindurch.

Wir behandeln zunächst den *p-Fall* und wollen ferner die beiden in Ziff. 26 genannten Fälle unterscheiden:

46. Streufall. Hier machen wir den Ansatz [vgl. (26.1 p) und Fig. 34 u. 35]

$$v(\mathfrak{r}) = v_0(\mathfrak{r}) - \int_S \psi(\hat{\mathfrak{r}}')\, G(\mathfrak{r}-\hat{\mathfrak{r}}')\, d\hat{\mathfrak{r}}', \qquad z \gtrless 0, \tag{46.1 p}$$

der alle obigen Forderungen *bis auf die Randbedingung* (II p) (für eine große Klasse von Funktionen ψ) befriedigt. Gl. (46.1 p) ist nämlich nichts anderes als das Kirchhoffsche Integral (10.1) mit $\varphi=0$, erfüllt also die Wellengleichung (I) und die Stetigkeitsforderungen (I a, b). Darauf, daß dieses Integral die Kantenbedingung

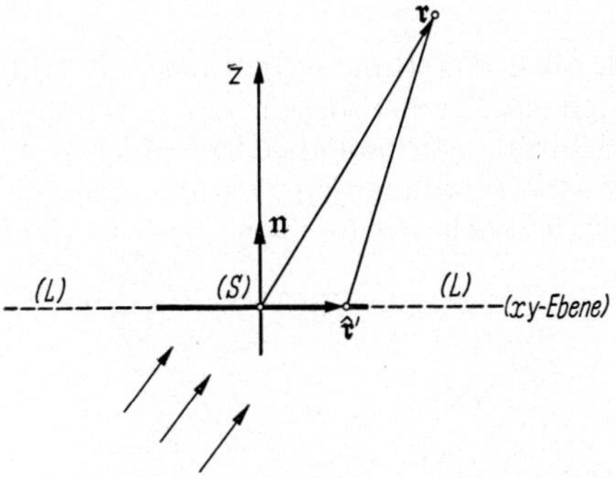

Fig. 34.

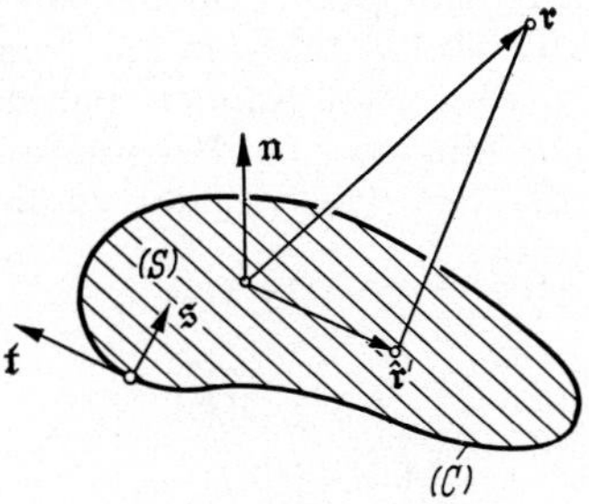

Fig. 35.

Fig. 34 u. 35. Im Text gebrauchte Bezeichnungen für die Streuung am ebenen Schirm.

(IV) erfüllt, hatten wir bereits in Ziff. 38 hingewiesen. Die Erfüllung der Ausstrahlungsbedingungen (III) folgt aus der Tatsache, daß G diese Bedingung erfüllt. Der längs (S) verbleibende *Sprung* der *Normalableitung* [vgl. (10.2)]

$$\left(\frac{\partial v}{\partial z}\right)_+ - \left(\frac{\partial v}{\partial z}\right)_- = \psi(\hat{\mathfrak{r}}), \quad \hat{\mathfrak{r}} \;\; \textit{auf} \;\; (S) \tag{46.1' p}$$

hat — elektromagnetisch gesprochen — im wesentlichen die physikalische Bedeutung eines *elektrischen Flächenstroms*. Betrachtet man nämlich den *zweidimensionalen* p-Fall, so ist nach Ziff. 4 $v=\mathfrak{E}_y$, daher folgt nach (4.1 p)

$$\psi = \left(\frac{\partial v}{\partial z}\right)_+ - \left(\frac{\partial v}{\partial z}\right)_- = -\,i\,(\mathfrak{H}_+ - \mathfrak{H}_-)_x = -\,i\,\mathfrak{J}_y \quad (\mathfrak{J} = [\mathfrak{n}, \mathfrak{H}_+ - \mathfrak{H}_-]); \tag{46.1'' p}$$

wir haben also einen *parallel* zur Schirmkante (y-Richtung) fließenden elektrischen Flächenstrom im Schirmmaterial, den die einfallende Welle dort erzeugt und der zur Ausstrahlung der Streuwelle führt. Diese anschauliche Deutung der Beugungserscheinungen geht auf H. POINCARÉ[1] zurück. Die mathematische Formulierung verdankt man für den skalaren Fall Lord RAYLEIGH[2]; er hatte allerdings mehr den akustischen dreidimensionalen Fall im Auge, wo ψ eine entsprechend modifizierte akustische Bedeutung hat.

Die Reduktion des dreidimensionalen Problems auf ein zweidimensionales ist damit bewerkstelligt; letzteres besteht nunmehr in der Bestimmung der Größe ψ.

---

[1] H. POINCARÉ: C. R. Acad. Sci., Paris **113**, 519 (1891).
[2] Lord RAYLEIGH: Phil. Mag. **43**, 259 (1897).

Dazu benützen wir die noch unerfüllte Forderung (IIp) (Randbedingung) und erhalten

$$\int_S \psi(\hat{\mathfrak{r}}')\, G(\hat{\mathfrak{r}} - \hat{\mathfrak{r}}')\, d\hat{\mathfrak{r}}' = v_0(\hat{\mathfrak{r}}) \quad \textit{für } \hat{\mathfrak{r}} \textit{ auf } (S). \tag{46.2p}$$

Dies ist eine inhomogene *Integralgleichung erster Art* für ψ. Nach der Kantenbedingung (23.4) muß sich ψ ($\sim \mathfrak{J}_y$ im ebenen Fall) am Rande des Schirmes wie $\varrho^{-\frac{1}{2}}$ verhalten (ϱ = Abstand von der Schirmkante), dies braucht jedoch nicht eigens gefordert zu werden, sondern muß sich bei der Auflösung von (46.2p) von selbst ergeben.

Übrigens gilt (46.1p), (46.2p) auch für beliebig *gekrümmte* Schirme (S), da dann ebenfalls längs (S) der Sprung ψ auftritt. Das Rayleighsche Verfahren eröffnet eine neue Phase der Beugungstheorie, indem es statt mehr oder weniger plausiblen Annahmen über den Flächenstrom ψ (Kirchhoff) dessen exakte Berechnung in Angriff nimmt.

47. Beugungsfall. Im Prinzip läßt sich auch das *Beugungsproblem* mit Hilfe der Gln. (46.1p) und (46.2p) behandeln, jedoch hat bei diesem der Schirm gewissermaßen zwei Ränder, nämlich die Schirmkante und das Unendliche. Es ist daher einfacher bei Beugungsproblemen eine Formulierung zu wählen, bei der statt des Schirmes (S) das endlich begrenzte Loch (L) ins Spiel kommt (vgl.

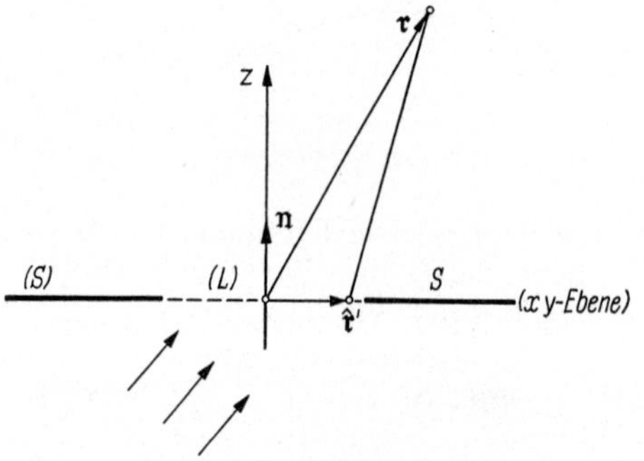

Fig. 36.

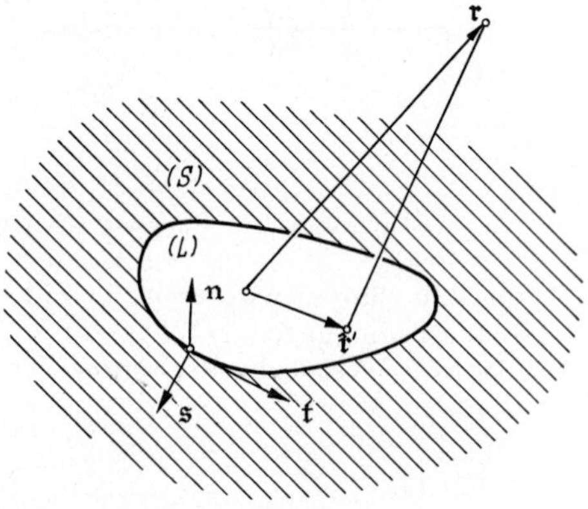

Fig. 37.

Fig. 36 u. 37. Im Text gebrauchte Bezeichnungen für die Beugung an einer Öffnung im ebenen Schirm.

Fig. 36 u. 37). Für *ebene* Schirme erreichen wir dies mit Hilfe der die Randwerte reproduzierenden Formel (34.2) bei Berücksichtigung des Ansatzes (26.6p):

$$v(\mathfrak{r}) = \pm 2 \int_L \varphi(\hat{\mathfrak{r}}')\, \frac{\partial}{\partial z'} G(\mathfrak{r} - \hat{\mathfrak{r}}')\, d\hat{\mathfrak{r}}' + \begin{cases} 0, & z > 0 \\ v_0(\mathfrak{r}) - v^0(\mathfrak{r}), & z < 0 \end{cases} \tag{47.1p}$$

(das obere Vorzeichen bezieht sich auf $z > 0$, das untere auf $z < 0$). Der Ausdruck (47.1p) reproduziert nämlich auf (S) nach Gl. (34.1) den Wert $v = 0$, erfüllt also die Randbedingung (IIp); auf (L) reproduziert er den Wert φ und ist somit dort stetig. Die Größe φ hat also die Bedeutung des Feldes in der Öffnung; im zweidimensionalen Fall ist daher φ die elektrische Feldstärke in der Öffnung [$\varphi = \mathfrak{E}_y$ auf (L)]. Zu befriedigen sind jetzt noch die Stetigkeit von $\partial v/\partial z$ auf (L), Gl. (Ib) und die Kantenbedingung (IV); letztere wird ja durch Ausdrücke der Form (47.1p) im allgemeinen verletzt (vgl. Ziff. 38). Das Erfülltsein der Ausstrahlungsbedingung (III) ist evident.

Für die Berechnung des Feldes φ in der Öffnung haben wir also (Ib) und (IV) zur Verfügung und erhalten zunächst aus (Ib):

$$\lim_{z\to\pm 0}\frac{\partial}{\partial z}\int\limits_L \varphi(\hat{\mathfrak{r}}')\frac{\partial}{\partial z'}G(\mathfrak{r}-\hat{\mathfrak{r}}')\,d\hat{\mathfrak{r}}' = \frac{1}{2}\frac{\partial v_0(\hat{\mathfrak{r}})}{\partial z} \quad \textit{für } \hat{\mathfrak{r}} \textit{ auf } (L). \qquad (47.2p)$$

Diese Beziehung garantiert die Stetigkeit von $\partial v/\partial z$ in der Öffnung. Ihr mathematischer Charakter ist etwas komplizierter als derjenige von (46.2p): Die Differentiation nach z kann jetzt nicht ohne weiteres unter dem Integral ausgeführt werden, da dann der „*Kern*“ $\frac{\partial^2}{\partial z\,\partial z'}G(\hat{\mathfrak{r}}-\hat{\mathfrak{r}}')$ für $\hat{\mathfrak{r}}\to\hat{\mathfrak{r}}'$ so stark singulär wird, daß das Flächenintegral divergiert; wir wollen daher (47.2p) als „*Pseudointegralgleichung*“ bezeichnen.

Dieser Schwierigkeit kann man auf verschiedene Weise Herr werden. Zunächst ziehen wir auch die Differentiation $\frac{\partial}{\partial z'}$ als $-\frac{\partial}{\partial z}$ vor das Integral und erhalten so an Stelle von (47.2p)

$$\left.\begin{aligned} &(\hat{\Delta}+1)\int\limits_L \varphi(\hat{\mathfrak{r}}')\,G(\hat{\mathfrak{r}}-\hat{\mathfrak{r}}')\,d\hat{\mathfrak{r}}' = \frac{1}{2}\frac{\partial v_0(\hat{\mathfrak{r}})}{\partial z} \qquad \textit{für } \hat{\mathfrak{r}} \textit{ auf } (L) \\ &\left(\hat{\Delta} = \widehat{\operatorname{div}}\,\widehat{\operatorname{grad}} = \frac{\partial^2}{\partial x^2}+\frac{\partial^2}{\partial y^2}\right). \end{aligned}\right\} \qquad (47.3p)$$

Man beachte, daß $\int \varphi\, G\, d\hat{\mathfrak{r}}'$ für $\mathfrak{r}\neq\hat{\mathfrak{r}}'$ der Wellengleichung $(\Delta+1)\ldots$ genügt und daß sich die Operation $\hat{\Delta}$ nur auf die Koordinaten $\hat{\mathfrak{r}}$ bezieht, so daß man den Grenzübergang $z\to\pm 0$ an $G(\mathfrak{r}-\hat{\mathfrak{r}}')$ nach der Umformung ausführen kann. Gl. (47.3p) können wir nun in die *Differentialgleichung*

$$(\hat{\Delta}+1)\,Y(\hat{\mathfrak{r}}) = \frac{1}{2}\frac{\partial v_0(\hat{\mathfrak{r}})}{\partial z} \qquad \textit{für } \hat{\mathfrak{r}} \textit{ auf } (L) \qquad (47.4p)$$

und die *Integralgleichung erster Art*

$$\int\limits_L \varphi(\hat{\mathfrak{r}}')\,G(\hat{\mathfrak{r}}-\hat{\mathfrak{r}}')\,d\hat{\mathfrak{r}}' = Y(\hat{\mathfrak{r}}) \qquad \textit{für } \hat{\mathfrak{r}} \textit{ auf } (L), \qquad (47.5p)$$

zerlegen, deren Inhomogenität Y also erst nach Lösung der Differentialgleichung (47.4p) bekannt ist. Um die Lösung von (47.4p) eindeutig definieren zu können, benötigen wir für $Y(\hat{\mathfrak{r}})$ noch eine *Randbedingung*. Diese hat ersichtlich aus der Kantenbedingung (IV) hervorzugehen, die somit hier automatisch ins Spiel kommt.

48. Umformungen unter Heranziehung der Kantenbedingung. In Ziff. 38 haben wir schon darauf hingewiesen (und werden es weiter unten noch genauer begründen), daß das Integral in (47.1p) zu unzulässigen Kantensingularitäten führt, es sei denn, φ nimmt gegen den Rand (C) hin stetig nach Null ab. Wir müssen also auf jeden Fall fordern

$$\varphi = 0 \qquad \textit{auf } (C). \qquad (47.6p)$$

Nach der Kantenbedingung (23.3p) muß φ wie $\varrho^{\frac{1}{2}}$ verschwinden, wenn ϱ der Abstand von der Kante ist. Da v gemäß der Randbedingung (IIp) auf (S) verschwindet, so können wir $\varphi\equiv 0$ auf (S) definieren und dann (47.6p) alsForderung der Stetigkeit von φ beim Überschreiten von (C) interpretieren. Ohne auf die Übertragung der Kantenbedingung auf die Größe Y einzugehen, kann man so vorgehen, daß man die Differentialgleichung (47.4p) bis auf eine beliebige Lösung der *homogenen* Gl. (47.4p) löst, mit dieser Lösung $\varphi(\hat{\mathfrak{r}})$ aus (47.5p) berechnet und dann nachträglich die unbestimmt gebliebene homogene Lösung von (47.4p)

mit Hilfe von (47.6p) ermittelt. Diesen Weg schlagen Levine und Schwinger[1] bei der kreisförmigen Öffnung sowie Sommerfeld[2] beim unendlich langen Spalt ein (vgl. Teil B, Abschn. Ib und c).

Wir bemerken noch, daß sich $Y(\mathfrak{r})$ im zylindrischen Fall elektromagnetisch als *Fitzgeraldscher Vektor* deuten läßt; er ist parallel zur Schirmebene und steht hier *senkrecht* auf den Schirmkanten (s. Ziff. 53).

Ein anderer Weg, um den Ausdruck (47.3p) zu behandeln, besteht in einer Umformung mittels einmaliger partieller Integration[3]: Wir berechnen zunächst den $\widehat{\text{grad}}$ von $Y(\mathfrak{r})$ für $z \neq 0$ und formen ihn mit Hilfe des Stokesschen Satzes für ebene Flächenstücke (L) (in symbolischer Form):

$$\int_L \hat{\nabla} \ldots d\sigma = \oint_C \mathfrak{s} \ldots dt \tag{48.1}$$

[$\mathfrak{s}$ = Einheitsvektor in Richtung der nach innen gerichteten *Normale des Randes* (C), vgl. Fig. 35, dt = Linienelement des Randes] um:

$$\left.\begin{aligned} \widehat{\text{grad}} \int_L \varphi(\hat{\mathfrak{r}}')\, G(\mathfrak{r} - \hat{\mathfrak{r}}')\, d\hat{\mathfrak{r}}' &= - \int_L \hat{\nabla}'(\varphi\, G)\, d\hat{\mathfrak{r}}' + \int_L G\, \hat{\nabla}' \varphi\, d\hat{\mathfrak{r}}' \\ &= - \oint_C \mathfrak{s}' \varphi\, G\, dt' + \int_L G\, \widehat{\text{grad}}' \varphi\, d\hat{\mathfrak{r}}'. \end{aligned}\right\} \tag{48.2}$$

Das Linienintegral *divergiert* aber, wenn der Aufpunkt $\mathfrak{r}$ auf den Rand rückt. Um diese Divergenz zu beseitigen, müssen wir verlangen, daß φ auf (C) verschwindet, wir stoßen hier also nochmals auf die Notwendigkeit der Forderung (47.6p). Somit folgt

$$\hat{\Delta} \int_L \varphi(\hat{\mathfrak{r}}')\, G(\mathfrak{r} - \hat{\mathfrak{r}}')\, d\hat{\mathfrak{r}}' = \int_L \left(\widehat{\text{grad}}\, G(\mathfrak{r} - \hat{\mathfrak{r}}')\, \widehat{\text{grad}}'\, \varphi(\hat{\mathfrak{r}}')\right) d\hat{\mathfrak{r}}'. \tag{48.3}$$

Jetzt können wir den Grenzübergang $z \to \pm 0$ ausführen (falls das zweite uneigentliche Integral als *Hauptwert* definiert wird) und erhalten aus (47.3p)

$$\left.\begin{aligned} \int_L \left\{\varphi(\hat{\mathfrak{r}}')\, G(\hat{\mathfrak{r}} - \hat{\mathfrak{r}}') + \left(\widehat{\text{grad}}'\, \varphi(\hat{\mathfrak{r}}')\, \widehat{\text{grad}}\, G(\hat{\mathfrak{r}} - \hat{\mathfrak{r}}')\right)\right\} d\hat{\mathfrak{r}}' = \frac{1}{2}\, \frac{\partial v_0(\hat{\mathfrak{r}})}{\partial z} \\ \textit{für } \hat{\mathfrak{r}} \textit{ auf } (L). \end{aligned}\right\} \tag{48.4p}$$

Gl. (48.3p) ist eine *Integrodifferentialgleichung* für φ, zu der noch die Randbedingung $\varphi = 0$ (47.6p), hinzutritt. Wählt man also (48.4p) als Ausgangspunkt für die Behandlung des Beugungsproblems, so hat man (47.6p) als Kantenbedingung zu betrachten.

Schließlich könnte man daran denken, das bedingt konvergente Integral durch nochmalige partielle Integration — d.h. Anwendung des Stokesschen Satzes (48.1) — fortzuschaffen (zunächst sei wieder $z \neq 0$):

$$\left.\begin{aligned} \int_L \left(\widehat{\text{grad}}'\, \varphi(\hat{\mathfrak{r}}')\, \widehat{\text{grad}}\, G(\mathfrak{r} - \hat{\mathfrak{r}}')\right) d\hat{\mathfrak{r}}' &= - \int_L (\hat{\nabla}', G\, \hat{\nabla}' \varphi)\, d'\hat{\mathfrak{r}} \\ + \int_L G\, \hat{\Delta}' \varphi\, d\hat{\mathfrak{r}}' &= - \oint_C \frac{\partial \varphi}{\partial s'}\, G\, dt' + \int_L G\, \hat{\Delta}' \varphi\, d\hat{\mathfrak{r}}'. \end{aligned}\right\} \tag{48.5}$$

Hier ist zunächst wieder das Linienintegral divergent, falls der Aufpunkt auf den Rand rückt. Versucht man jedoch, diese Singularität durch die Forderung

[1] H. Levine u. J. Schwinger: Phys. Rev. **74**, 958 (1948) Append. 1.

[2] A. Sommerfeld: Vorlesung über theoretische Physik, Bd. 4, S. 283, 1950; auf den Zusammenhang mit der Kantenbedingung gehen Levine u. Schwinger sowie Sommerfeld nicht ein.

[3] A.-W. Maue: Z. Physik **126**, 601 (1949).

$\partial\varphi/\partial s = 0$ zu beseitigen, so gerät man mit der Kantenbedingung (23.3*p*) in Konflikt: nach dieser ist nämlich $\varphi \sim \varrho^{\frac{1}{2}}$, also $\frac{\partial\varphi}{\partial s} \sim \varrho^{-\frac{1}{2}}$. Ferner ist am Rande $\varDelta\varphi \sim \varrho^{-\frac{3}{2}}$; daher divergiert auch das Flächenintegral rechterhand in (48.5).

Um hier weiter zu kommen, erinnern wir uns daran, daß der Rand des Schirmes die Rolle einer *Verzweigungslinie* für die Funktion φ spielt (vgl. Ziff. 22, 23 und 28). Wir denken uns nun die linkerhand in (48.5) geforderte Flächenintegration in der Umgebung des Randes in eine Integrationsrichtung senkrecht zum Rande (Integration nach ϱ) und eine zu ihm parallele aufgespalten. Die ϱ-Integration ist nun bis zum Verzweigungspunkt $\varrho = 0$ zu erstrecken; wir wollen jedoch dem Punkt $\varrho = 0$ in der *komplexen* ϱ-Ebene ausweichen und die ϱ-Integration durch den halben Wert des um $\varrho = 0$ herum geführten *komplexen Schleifenintegrals* ersetzen. Führen wir nun die rechterhand in Gl. (48.5) angedeutete partielle Integration durch, so tritt jetzt *kein Randintegral* mehr auf (wir haben ja nur geschlossene Integrationswege) und wir erhalten an Stelle von (48.4*p*)

$$\int\limits_L (\hat{\varDelta}' + 1)\,\varphi(\hat{\mathfrak{r}}') \cdot G(\hat{\mathfrak{r}} - \hat{\mathfrak{r}}')\,d'\hat{\mathfrak{r}} = \frac{1}{2}\,\frac{\partial v_0(\hat{\mathfrak{r}})}{\partial z} \quad \textit{für } \hat{\mathfrak{r}} \textit{ auf } (L). \tag{48.6p}$$

Dieses Integral ist im oben dargelegten Sinn aufzufassen (Schleifenintegral um die Verzweigungslinien). Gl. (48.6*p*) ist ebenfalls eine *Integrodifferentialgleichung* für φ, in der jedoch die zweiten Differentialquotienten von φ auftreten [im Gegensatz zu (48.4*p*), wo nur erste Differentialquotienten vorkommen]. Zu (48.6*p*) tritt noch die Randbedingung (47.6*p*) hinzu.

Um die analytischen Verhältnisse besser überblicken zu können, spalten wir nun (48.6*p*) in eine Integralgleichung und eine Differentialgleichung auf, indem wir $\hat{\varDelta}\varphi + \varphi = V$ setzen; dann folgt nämlich für V die *Integralgleichung*

$$\int\limits_L V(\hat{\mathfrak{r}}')\,G(\hat{\mathfrak{r}} - \hat{\mathfrak{r}}')\,d\hat{\mathfrak{r}}' = \frac{1}{2}\,\frac{\partial v_0(\hat{\mathfrak{r}})}{\partial z} \quad \textit{für } \hat{\mathfrak{r}} \textit{ auf } (L). \tag{48.7p}$$

Ist diese gelöst, so erhält man φ aus der *Differentialgleichung*

mit der Randbedingung (47.6*p*)
$$\left.\begin{aligned} (\hat{\varDelta} + 1)\,\varphi(\hat{\mathfrak{r}}) &= V(\hat{\mathfrak{r}}), & \hat{\mathfrak{r}} \textit{ auf } (L),\\ \varphi &= 0 & \textit{auf } (C). \end{aligned}\right\} \tag{48.8p}$$

Das zweidimensionale Problem der Berechnung des Feldes φ in der Öffnung ist also jetzt in den Gln. (48.7*p*) und (48.8*p*) enthalten. Sie sind formal den Gln. (47.4*p*), (47.5*p*) sehr ähnlich [nur ist dort *zuerst* die erste Randwertaufgabe für die inhomogene Wellengleichung und *danach* eine inhomogene Integralgleichung erster Art mit dem symmetrischen Kern $G(\hat{\mathfrak{r}} - \hat{\mathfrak{r}}')$ zu lösen, während es hier umgekehrt ist]. Ferner bemerken wir, daß sich ja die Lösung φ von (47.5*p*) am Rande wie $\varrho^{\frac{1}{2}}$ verhalten muß, woraus für V ein Verhalten $\sim \varrho^{-\frac{3}{2}}$ folgt [vgl. (48.8*p*)].

Die Randwertaufgabe für die inhomogene Wellengleichung ist eindeutig [Eigenwerte des Bereiches (L) ausgeschlossen]. Andererseits konnte MAGNUS[1] nachweisen, daß auch die Lösung der Integralgleichung (48.7*p*) eindeutig ist (die homogene Gleichung hat nämlich nur die triviale Lösung $V = 0$).

Die Behandlung des Beugungsproblems mit Hilfe des Ansatzes (47.1*p*) ist insbesondere dann vorteilhaft, wenn die Dimensionen der Öffnung (L) klein gegen die Wellenlänge sind. Dann läßt sich nämlich die Greensche Funktion

[1] W. MAGNUS: Jber. dtsch. Math.-Ver. **52**, 177 (1942).

nach $\hat{\mathfrak{r}} - \hat{\mathfrak{r}}'$ entwickeln, was einen bequemen Zugang zur Entwicklung der Lösung nach fallenden Potenzen der Wellenlänge eröffnet (s. Abschn. IIIf; man erinnere sich daran, daß die Koordinaten in Vielfachen der Wellenlänge gemessen werden). Der Ansatz (47.1*p*) ist allerdings auf ebene Schirme beschränkt; für gekrümmte Schirme müßte man mit der Greenschen Funktion der Fläche $(S)+(L)$ arbeiten.

Die analytische Schwierigkeit der Gl. (46.2*p*) bzw. (47.3*p*) besteht offensichtlich darin, daß sie nur auf (S) bzw. (L) gilt und sich nicht auf die ganze Ebene $z=0$ bezieht. In der Tat lauten diese Gleichungen vervollständigt:

für *Streuung*

$$\int\limits_S \psi(\hat{\mathfrak{r}}')\, G(\hat{\mathfrak{r}}-\hat{\mathfrak{r}}')\, d\hat{\mathfrak{r}}' = \left\{\begin{matrix} v_0(\hat{\mathfrak{r}}) & \hat{\mathfrak{r}} \textit{ auf } (S) \\ v_0(\hat{\mathfrak{r}}) - \varphi(\hat{\mathfrak{r}}) & \hat{\mathfrak{r}} \textit{ auf } (L), \end{matrix}\right\} \tag{48.9p}$$

für *Beugung*

$$(\hat{\Delta}+1)\int\limits_L \varphi(\hat{\mathfrak{r}}')\, G(\hat{\mathfrak{r}}-\hat{\mathfrak{r}}')\, d\hat{\mathfrak{r}}' = \left\{\begin{matrix} \frac{1}{2}\frac{\partial v_0}{\partial z} + \frac{1}{4}\psi(\hat{\mathfrak{r}}) & \hat{\mathfrak{r}} \textit{ auf } (S) \\ \frac{1}{2}\frac{\partial v_0}{\partial z} & \hat{\mathfrak{r}} \textit{ auf } (L). \end{matrix}\right\} \tag{48.10p}$$

Die Gln. (48.9*p*) und (48.10*p*) gelten für ein und dasselbe Problem, wenn wir es einmal als Streuung, das andere Mal als Beugung behandeln und stellen außerdem den analytischen Zusammenhang zwischen $\varphi(\hat{\mathfrak{r}})$ und $\psi(\hat{\mathfrak{r}})$ her, wobei die Kenntnis *einer* der beiden Größen bereits genügt, um das Problem vollständig zu lösen.

49. Das zylindrische Problem. Wir wollen nun noch die wichtigsten Formeln zwecks späterer Verwendung (Teil B, Abschn. Ia und b) für den Fall explizit angeben, daß $\partial/\partial y = 0$ ist [zylindrisches Problem, $\mathfrak{r}=(x,z)$]. Nur dann ist ja

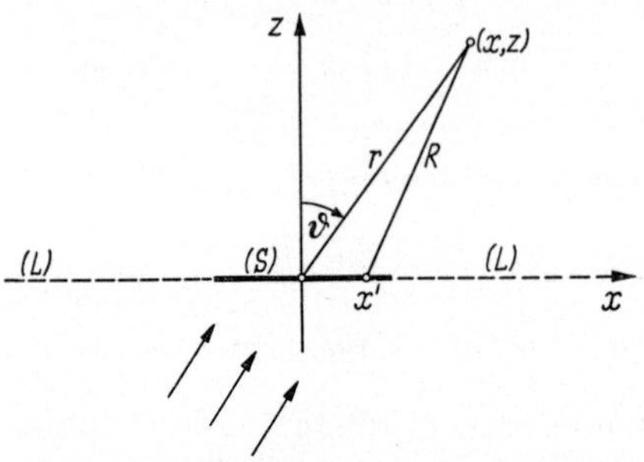

Fig. 38. Zur Streuung an einem ebenen Streifen.

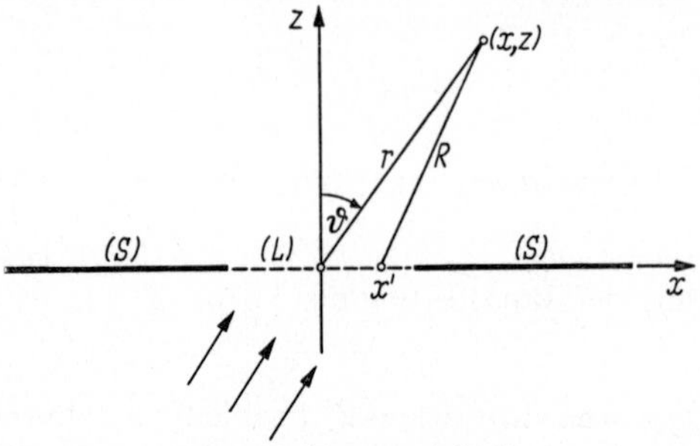

Fig. 39. Zur Beugung am Spalt.

die skalare Theorie auf elektromagnetische Beugungsprobleme unmittelbar anwendbar. Es handle sich also um ebene Schirme, die durch Geraden parallel zur y-Achse begrenzt seien (Halbebene, Spalt, Gitter usw.), (S) sei die Spur dieser Schirme auf der x-Achse. (L) seien die übrigen Teile dieser Achse. Mit Hilfe von (8.3a) folgt dann aus (46.1*p*) für den *Streufall* (Fig. 38):

$$\left.\begin{aligned} v(\mathfrak{r}) &= v_0(\mathfrak{r}) - \frac{i}{4}\int\limits_S \psi(x')\, H_0^{(1)}(R)\, dx', \qquad z \gtrless 0, \\ (R &= \sqrt{(x-x')^2+z^2}). \end{aligned}\right\} \tag{49.1p}$$

ψ berechnet sich hier aus der Integralgleichung [vgl. (46.2*p*)]:

$$\int\limits_S \psi(x')\, H_0^{(1)}(|x-x'|)\, dx' = -4i\, v_0, \qquad x \textit{ auf } (S). \tag{49.2p}$$

Der Ansatz (47.1*p*) für den *Beugungsfall* lautet (Fig. 39):

$$v(\mathfrak{r}) = \pm \frac{i}{2} \int\limits_L \varphi(x') \frac{\partial}{\partial z'} H_0^{(1)}(R)dx' + \begin{cases} 0, & z > 0 \\ v_0(\mathfrak{r}) - v^0(\mathfrak{r}), & z < 0 \end{cases} \qquad (49.3p)$$

und (47.3*p*) liefert jetzt

$$\left(\frac{d^2}{dx^2} + 1\right) \int\limits_L \varphi(x') H_0^{(1)}(|x - x'|)\, dx' = -2i \frac{\partial v_0}{\partial z}, \qquad x \text{ auf } (L). \qquad (49.4p)$$

Diese *Pseudointegralgleichung* für φ läßt sich hier in die *Differentialgleichung*

$$\left(\frac{d^2}{dx^2} + 1\right) Y(x) = -2i \frac{\partial v_0}{\partial z}, \qquad x \text{ auf } (L) \qquad (49.5p)$$

und die *Integralgleichung*

$$\int\limits_L \varphi(x') H_0^{(1)}(|x - x'|)\, dx' = Y(x), \qquad x \text{ auf } (L) \qquad (49.5'p)$$

zerlegen, wobei noch die Bedingung $\varphi = 0$ für die Randpunkte von (L) zu beachten ist. Oder es kann (49.4*p*) in die *Integrodifferentialgleichung*

$$\int\limits_L \left\{\varphi(x') H_0^{(1)}(|x - x'|) - \frac{d\varphi}{dx'} \cdot \frac{d}{dx'} H_0^{(1)}(|x - x'|)\right\} dx' = -2i \frac{\partial v_0}{\partial z}, \qquad x \text{ auf } (L) \qquad (49.6p)$$

übergeführt werden. Dabei ist der zweite Teil des Integrals als *Cauchyscher Hauptwert* aufzufassen und die Kantenbedingung $\varphi = 0$ hinzuzunehmen. Will man bedingt konvergente Integrale vermeiden, so wird man auf die *Integrodifferentialgleichung*

$$\int\limits_L \left(\frac{d^2}{dx'^2} + 1\right) \varphi(x') \cdot H_0^{(1)}(|x - x'|)\, dx' = -2i \frac{\partial v_0}{\partial z}, \qquad x \text{ auf } (L) \qquad (49.7p)$$

geführt. Die Randpunkte von (L) sind hier wieder Verzweigungspunkte der zweiwertigen Funktion $\varphi(x)$; das Integral ist als halber Wert des Schleifenintegrals (in der komplexen x'-Ebene) um die Verzweigungspunkte zu berechnen. Gl. (49.7*p*) kann auch in die *Integralgleichung*

$$\int\limits_L V(x') H_0^{(1)}(|x - x'|)\, dx' = -2i \frac{\partial v_0}{\partial z}, \qquad x \text{ auf } (L) \qquad (49.8p)$$

und die *Differentialgleichung*

$$\left(\frac{d^2}{dx^2} + 1\right) \varphi(x) = V(x), \qquad \text{mit } \varphi = 0 \textit{ in den Randpunkten von } (L), \qquad (49.9p)$$

aufgespalten werden.

Die Beziehungen (48.9*p*) und (48.10*p*) lauten jetzt explizit

$$\left.\begin{aligned}
&\textit{(Streuung)} \\
&\int\limits_S \psi(x') H_0^{(1)}(|x - x'|)\, dx' = \begin{cases} -4i\, v_0, & x \text{ auf } (S) \\ -4i\,[v_0 - \varphi(x)], & x \text{ auf } (L), \end{cases} \\
&\textit{(Beugung)} \\
&\left(\frac{d^2}{dx^2} + 1\right) \int\limits_L \varphi(x') H_0^{(1)}(|x - x'|)\, dx' = \begin{cases} -i\left[2 \frac{\partial v_0}{\partial z} + \psi(x)\right], & x \text{ auf } (S) \\ -2i \frac{\partial v_0}{\partial z}, & x \text{ auf } (L). \end{cases}
\end{aligned}\right\} \qquad (49.10p)$$

50. Der s-Fall. Für diesen machen wir die Ansätze [vgl. (26.1 *s*) bzw. (26.6 *s*)]

Streufall:

$$v(\mathfrak{r}) = v_0(\mathfrak{r}) + \int\limits_S \varphi(\hat{\mathfrak{r}}') \frac{\partial}{\partial z'} G(\mathfrak{r}-\hat{\mathfrak{r}}')\, d\hat{\mathfrak{r}}', \qquad z \gtrless 0, \tag{50.1 s}$$

Beugungsfall:

$$v(\mathfrak{r}) = \mp 2 \int\limits_L \psi(\hat{\mathfrak{r}}')\, G(\mathfrak{r}-\hat{\mathfrak{r}}')\, d\hat{\mathfrak{r}}' + \begin{Bmatrix} 0, & z>0 \\ v_0(\mathfrak{r}) + v^0(\mathfrak{r}), & z<0. \end{Bmatrix} \tag{50.2 s}$$

(Ersterer mit n' statt z' auch für gekrümmte Schirme brauchbar, letzterer nur für ebene.) Gl. (50.1 *s*) erfüllt die Forderungen (I) bis (Ib) und (III), Gl. (50.2 *s*) hingegen (I) und (Ib) bis (IV). Dabei gilt

$$v_+ - v_- = \varphi(\hat{\mathfrak{r}}), \qquad \hat{\mathfrak{r}} \textit{ auf } (S) \tag{50.2' s}$$

bzw.

$$\frac{\partial v}{\partial z} = \psi(\hat{\mathfrak{r}}), \qquad \hat{\mathfrak{r}} \textit{ auf } (L). \tag{50.2'' s}$$

Im zylindrischen Fall ($\partial/\partial y = 0$) hat also φ wegen $v = \mathfrak{H}_y$ die Bedeutung eines senkrecht zur y-Achse, d.h. senkrecht zu den Schirmkanten fließenden *elektrischen Flächenstromes* $\mathfrak{J}_x = -(\mathfrak{H}_+ - \mathfrak{H}_-)_y$. Andererseits gilt dann nach Gl. (4.1 *s*) $\psi = \partial v/\partial z = i\,\mathfrak{E}_x$, ψ ist also im wesentlichen die in der Öffnung liegende Komponente der elektrischen Feldstärke; diese steht ja senkrecht auf der Kante ($\mathfrak{E}_y = 0$). ψ muß sich bei Annäherung an den Schirmrand wie $\varrho^{-\frac{1}{2}}$ (ϱ = Abstand von der Kante) verhalten; vgl. (23.3 b). Dies ist jedoch *keine* Nebenbedingung, sondern muß sich wieder aus dem Formalismus von selbst ergeben.

Die Randbedingung (II*s*) liefert in Anwendung auf (50.1 *s*)

$$(\hat{\Delta}+1) \int\limits_S \varphi(\hat{\mathfrak{r}}')\, G(\hat{\mathfrak{r}}-\hat{\mathfrak{r}}')\, d\hat{\mathfrak{r}}' = -\frac{\partial v_0(\hat{\mathfrak{r}})}{\partial z}, \qquad \hat{\mathfrak{r}} \textit{ auf } (S), \tag{50.3 s}$$

wozu noch die Bedingung $\varphi = 0$ auf dem Rand von (S) als Ausdruck der Forderung (IV) kommt [*Kantenbedingung*; nach dieser muß φ wie $\varrho^{\frac{1}{2}}$ an der Kante, d.h. für $\varrho \to 0$ verschwinden, vgl. (23.4)]. Die Pseudointegralgleichung (50.3 *s*) läßt sich genau wie (47.3 *p*) weiterbehandeln. Andererseits liefert die Forderung der Stetigkeit von v auf (L), Gl. (Ia), auf (50.2 *s*) angewandt

$$\int\limits_L \psi(\hat{\mathfrak{r}}')\, G(\hat{\mathfrak{r}}-\hat{\mathfrak{r}}')\, d\hat{\mathfrak{r}}' = -\tfrac{1}{2} v_0(\hat{\mathfrak{r}}), \qquad \hat{\mathfrak{r}} \textit{ auf } (L). \tag{50.4 s}$$

Die Integralgleichungen (50.3 *s*) bzw. (50.4 *s*) sind wieder der geeignete Ausgangspunkt für eine Entwicklung nach fallenden Potenzen in λ.

Vervollständigt lautet die Gl. (50.3 *s*) bzw. (50.4 *s*) (wieder für ein und dasselbe Problem, jedoch einmal als Streuung, das andere Mal als Beugung behandelt):

(Streuung)

$$(\hat{\Delta}+1) \int\limits_S \varphi(\hat{\mathfrak{r}}')\, G(\hat{\mathfrak{r}}-\hat{\mathfrak{r}}')\, d\hat{\mathfrak{r}}' = \begin{Bmatrix} -\dfrac{\partial v_0}{\partial z} + \psi(\hat{\mathfrak{r}}), & \hat{\mathfrak{r}} \textit{ auf } (L) \\ -\dfrac{\partial v_0}{\partial z}, & \hat{\mathfrak{r}} \textit{ auf } (S) \end{Bmatrix} \tag{50.5 s}$$

bzw. *(Beugung)*

$$\int\limits_L \psi(\hat{\mathfrak{r}}')\, G(\hat{\mathfrak{r}}-\hat{\mathfrak{r}}')\, d\hat{\mathfrak{r}}' = \begin{Bmatrix} -\tfrac{1}{2} v_0(\hat{\mathfrak{r}}), & \hat{\mathfrak{r}} \textit{ auf } (L) \\ -\tfrac{1}{2} v_0(\hat{\mathfrak{r}}) - \tfrac{1}{4}\varphi(\hat{\mathfrak{r}}), & \hat{\mathfrak{r}} \textit{ auf } (S). \end{Bmatrix} \tag{50.6 s}$$

Im *zylindrischen Fall* nimmt (50.1 *s*) bzw. (50.2*s*) die Gestalt an

Streufall:

$$v(\mathfrak{r}) = v_0(\mathfrak{r}) - \frac{i}{4}\frac{\partial}{\partial z}\int\limits_S \varphi(x')\, H_0^{(1)}(R)\, dx', \quad z \gtrless 0 \quad \left(R = \sqrt{(x-x')^2+z^2}\right); \tag{50.7s}$$

Beugungsfall:

$$v(\mathfrak{r}) = \mp \frac{i}{2}\int\limits_L \psi(x')\, H_0^{(1)}(R)\, dx' + \begin{Bmatrix} 0, & z>0 \\ v_0(\mathfrak{r}) + v^0(\mathfrak{r}), & z<0. \end{Bmatrix} \tag{50.8s}$$

Gl. (50.5*s*) bzw. (50.6*s*) lautet hier:

(Streuung)

$$\left(\frac{d^2}{dx^2}+1\right)\int\limits_S \varphi(x')\, H_0^{(1)}(|x-x'|)\, dx' = \begin{Bmatrix} 4i\left[\frac{\partial v_0}{\partial z} - \psi(x)\right], & x \text{ auf } (L) \\ 4i\,\frac{\partial v_0}{\partial z}, & x \text{ auf } (S), \end{Bmatrix} \tag{50.9s}$$

bzw. *(Beugung)*

$$\int\limits_L \psi(x')\, H_0^{(1)}(|x-x'|)\, dx' = \begin{Bmatrix} 2i\,v_0, & x \text{ auf } (L) \\ i\left[2v_0 + \varphi(x)\right], & x \text{ auf } (S). \end{Bmatrix} \tag{50.10s}$$

a 2) Vektorielles Problem.

Aufstellung der Integralgleichungen.

Die für das skalare Problem durchgeführte Zurückführung der dreidimensionalen Randwertaufgabe auf eine zweidimensionale Integralgleichung (Pseudointegralgleichung) soll jetzt auf vektorielle Probleme erweitert werden. Wir betrachten wieder ideal leitende unendlich dünne *ebene* Schirme (S) mit Löchern (L) in der Ebene $z=0$. Die Anregung erfolge aus dem Raum $z<0$ durch das primäre Wellenfeld $\mathfrak{E}_0$, $\mathfrak{H}_0$. Wir stellen für die Feldvektoren $\mathfrak{E}$, $\mathfrak{H}$ die Bedingungen zusammen (Ziff. 20 und 26) ($\mathfrak{n}$ Einheitsvektor in Richtung der positiven z-Achse; vgl. dazu Fig. 24 auf S. 281):

$$\operatorname{rot}\mathfrak{E} = i\,\mathfrak{H}, \quad \operatorname{rot}\mathfrak{H} = -i\,\mathfrak{E}, \quad z \gtrless 0, \tag{I'}$$

$$[\mathfrak{n}, \mathfrak{E}_+ - \mathfrak{E}_-] = 0 \quad \textit{auf } (L), \tag{I'a}$$

$$[\mathfrak{n}, \mathfrak{H}_+ - \mathfrak{H}_-] = 0 \quad (\textit{gleichbedeutend mit } [\mathfrak{n}\,\mathfrak{H}] = [\mathfrak{n}\,\mathfrak{H}_0]) \textit{ auf } (L), \tag{I'b}$$

$$[\mathfrak{n}\,\mathfrak{E}] = 0 \quad \textit{auf } (S) \quad (\textit{Randbedingung}), \tag{II'}$$

$\mathfrak{E}$, $\mathfrak{H}$ *befriedigen die Ausstrahlungsbedingung* (18.3, 3 a), (III')

$\mathfrak{E}$, $\mathfrak{H}$ *erfüllen die Kantenbedingungen* (23.3 a, b). (IV')

Dabei stellen (I'a) und (I'b) wieder die Ergänzung von (I') für $z=0$ auf (L) dar (Stetigkeit des Feldes in der Öffnung). Diese Forderungen (I') bis (IV') lassen sich, genau wie im skalaren Fall, durch zwei verschiedene Ansätze, die auf den Streu- bzw. Beugungsfall zugeschnitten sind, teilweise erfüllen, die über das Babinetsche Prinzip (Abschn. I e) innerlich zusammenhängen.

51. Streufall. Der ideal leitende (nicht notwendig ebene) Schirm wirkt als Sprungfläche für die Tangentialkomponente der magnetischen Feldstärke. Dies läßt sich (wie schon gesagt) nach POINCARÉ so interpretieren, daß die Primärwelle auf dem Schirm einen Flächenstrom $\mathfrak{J} = [\mathfrak{n}, \mathfrak{H}_+ - \mathfrak{H}_-]$ induziert, der sich durch Strahlung der einzelnen Stromelemente so einstellt, daß er zur Ausstrahlung eines Streufeldes führt, das zusammen mit der Primärwelle auf dem Schirm die Randbedingung erfüllt. Zur analytischen Durchführung dieses Gedankens stützen wir uns auf die Formulierung (14.1) des Sprungwertproblems, wobei wir zu bedenken haben, daß die Tangentialkomponente von $\mathfrak{E}$ infolge der Randbedingung (II′) längs (*S*) stetig ist. Der Ansatz

$$\left.\begin{aligned}\mathfrak{E}(\mathfrak{r}) &= \mathfrak{E}_0(\mathfrak{r}) + i \operatorname{rot}\operatorname{rot}\int\limits_S \mathfrak{J}(\hat{\mathfrak{r}}')\, G(\mathfrak{r}-\hat{\mathfrak{r}}')\, d\hat{\mathfrak{f}}' \\ \mathfrak{H}(\mathfrak{r}) &= \mathfrak{H}_0(\mathfrak{r}) + \operatorname{rot}\int\limits_S \mathfrak{J}(\hat{\mathfrak{r}}')\, G(\mathfrak{r}-\hat{\mathfrak{r}}')\, d\hat{\mathfrak{f}}'\end{aligned}\right\}\; z \gtrless 0 \tag{51.1}$$

erfüllt somit ersichtlich die Forderungen (I′) bis (I′b) (Feldgleichungen sowie Stetigkeit in der Öffnung) und (III′) (Ausstrahlungsbedingung). Die Anwendung der Randbedingung (II′) führt nun auf die Beziehung

$$\lim_{z\to\pm 0}\left[\mathfrak{n}, \operatorname{rot}\operatorname{rot}\int\limits_S \mathfrak{J}(\hat{\mathfrak{r}}')\, G(\mathfrak{r}-\hat{\mathfrak{r}}')\, d\hat{\mathfrak{f}}'\right] = i\,[\mathfrak{n}\,\mathfrak{E}_0] \quad \textit{für } \hat{\mathfrak{r}} \textit{ auf } (S), \tag{51.2}$$

durch die jedoch $\mathfrak{J}(\hat{\mathfrak{r}})$ noch nicht vollständig definiert ist, da der Grenzwert bei Ausführung der Operation rot rot *unter* dem Integral *divergiert (Pseudointegralgleichung)*. Bevor wir auf die Überwindung dieser Schwierigkeit durch das Eingreifen der Kantenbedingung (IV′) eingehen, behandeln wir das Beugungsproblem.

52. Beugungsfall. Hier ist es wieder zweckmäßig, die Aufmerksamkeit auf die Vorgänge in der Öffnung (*L*) zu richten, da sie jetzt gegenüber (*S*) die einfachere geometrische Gestalt besitzt. Für *ebene* Schirme gelingt dies wiederum einfach, da der Greensche Tensor der vollen Ebene bekannt ist. Wir erhalten nämlich bei Anwendung von Gl. (36.1) bei Beachtung der Randbedingung (II′) und des Ansatzes (26.7)

$$\left.\begin{aligned}\mathfrak{E}(\mathfrak{r}) &= \begin{Bmatrix} 0 \\ \mathfrak{E}_0(\mathfrak{r}) + \mathfrak{E}^0(\mathfrak{r})\end{Bmatrix} \pm 2\operatorname{rot}\int\limits_L \mathfrak{L}(\hat{\mathfrak{r}}')\, G(\mathfrak{r}-\hat{\mathfrak{r}}')\, d\hat{\mathfrak{f}}', \quad z \gtrless 0, \\ \mathfrak{H}(\mathfrak{r}) &= \begin{Bmatrix} 0 \\ \mathfrak{H}_0(\mathfrak{r}) + \mathfrak{H}^0(\mathfrak{r})\end{Bmatrix} \mp 2i \operatorname{rot}\operatorname{rot}\int\limits_L \mathfrak{L}(\hat{\mathfrak{r}}')\, G(\mathfrak{r}-\hat{\mathfrak{r}}')\, d\hat{\mathfrak{f}}', \quad z \gtrless 0,\end{aligned}\right\} \tag{52.1}$$

wobei $\mathfrak{L} = [\mathfrak{n}\,\mathfrak{E}]$ gesetzt wurde. Gl. (52.1) reproduziert die Randwerte $[\mathfrak{n}\,\mathfrak{E}] = 0$ auf (*S*) und $[\mathfrak{n}\,\mathfrak{E}] = \mathfrak{L}$ auf (*L*), erfüllt also die Randbedingung (II′) und die Stetigkeitsbedingung (I′a) [Feldgleichungen (I′) und Ausstrahlungsbedingung (III′) sind selbstverständlich ebenfalls erfüllt]. Die Forderung der Stetigkeit der Tangentialkomponente von $\mathfrak{H}$, (I′b), führt jetzt auf die *Pseudointegralgleichung*

$$\lim_{z\to\pm 0}\left[\mathfrak{n}, \operatorname{rot}\operatorname{rot}\int\limits_L \mathfrak{L}(\hat{\mathfrak{r}}')\, G(\mathfrak{r}-\hat{\mathfrak{r}}')\, d\hat{\mathfrak{f}}'\right] = \frac{i}{2}\,[\mathfrak{n}\,\mathfrak{H}_0] \quad \textit{für } \hat{\mathfrak{r}} \textit{ auf } (L). \tag{52.2}$$

Die Gln. (51.2) bzw. (52.2) unterscheiden sich in analytischer Hinsicht nur dadurch, daß sie sich auf die komplementären Bereiche (*S*) bzw. (*L*) beziehen. Je nachdem, ob die Dimensionen von (*S*) oder (*L*) klein gegen die Wellenlänge sind, wird man (51.2) oder (52.2) zum Ausgangspunkt einer Entwicklung der Lösung nach fallenden Potenzen in λ machen (s. Abschn. IIIf).

Die in Ziff. 26 aus Symmetriebetrachtungen abgeleitete Beziehung $[\mathfrak{n}\,\mathfrak{H}] = [\mathfrak{n}\,\mathfrak{H}_0]$ auf (*L*) läßt sich auch an (51.1) und (52.1) leicht verifizieren: Aus (51.1) folgt

$$\begin{aligned}[\mathfrak{n}\,\mathfrak{H}] &= [\mathfrak{n}\,\mathfrak{H}_0] + \left[\mathfrak{n}\left[\nabla\int\limits_S \mathfrak{J}\, G\, d\hat{\mathfrak{f}}'\right]\right] \\ &= [\mathfrak{n}\,\mathfrak{H}_0] + \nabla\int\limits_S (\mathfrak{n}\,\mathfrak{J})\, G\, d\hat{\mathfrak{f}}' - (\mathfrak{n}\,\nabla)\int\limits_S \mathfrak{J}\, G\, d\hat{\mathfrak{f}}';\end{aligned}$$

das erste Integral verschwindet wegen $(\mathfrak{n}\,\mathfrak{J}) = 0$, das zweite wegen (34.1) auf (*L*). Aus (52.1) folgt die genannte Beziehung unmittelbar mit Hilfe von (52.2). Auch die Normalkomponente der elektrischen Feldstärke in der Öffnung (L) läßt sich mit Hilfe von (3.2a) sofort angeben:

$$(\mathfrak{n}\,\mathfrak{E}) = -i\left(\hat{\nabla}[\mathfrak{n}\,\mathfrak{H}_0]\right) = i\left(\mathfrak{n}\,[\nabla\,\mathfrak{H}_0]\right) = (\mathfrak{n}\,\mathfrak{E}_0) \quad \textit{auf } (L), \tag{52.3}$$

da $\mathfrak{E}_0$, $\mathfrak{H}_0$ den Maxwellschen Gleichungen (2.1b) genügen.

53. Hertzscher und Fitzgeraldscher Vektor. Übrigens ist Gl. (51.1) nichts anderes als die Darstellung des Streufeldes mit Hilfe des *Hertzschen* Vektors (parallel zur Ebene $z=0$):

$$\mathfrak{Z}_S(\mathfrak{r}) = i\int_S \mathfrak{J}(\hat{\mathfrak{r}}')\,G(\mathfrak{r}-\hat{\mathfrak{r}}')\,d\hat{\mathfrak{r}}', \quad z \gtrless 0 \tag{53.1}$$

in der üblichen Form

$$\left.\begin{aligned} \mathfrak{E} &= \mathfrak{E}_0 + \operatorname{rot}\operatorname{rot}\mathfrak{Z}_S \\ \mathfrak{H} &= \mathfrak{H}_0 - i\operatorname{rot}\mathfrak{Z}_S \end{aligned}\right\} \quad z \gtrless 0. \tag{53.2}$$

Andererseits ist (52.1) eine Darstellung des Beugungsfeldes mit Hilfe des *Fitzgeraldschen* Vektors (ebenfalls parallel zur Ebene $z=0$):

$$\mathfrak{Y}_B(\mathfrak{r}) = 2i\int_L \mathfrak{L}(\hat{\mathfrak{r}}')\,G(\mathfrak{r}-\hat{\mathfrak{r}}')\,d\hat{\mathfrak{r}}', \quad z \gtrless 0 \tag{53.1a}$$

in der Gestalt

$$\left.\begin{aligned} \mathfrak{E} &= \mp\, i\operatorname{rot}\mathfrak{Y}_B + \begin{cases} 0 & z>0 \\ \mathfrak{E}_0 + \mathfrak{E}^0 & z<0 \end{cases} \\ \mathfrak{H} &= \mp\operatorname{rot}\operatorname{rot}\mathfrak{Y}_B + \begin{cases} 0 & z>0 \\ \mathfrak{H}_0 + \mathfrak{H}^0 & z<0. \end{cases} \end{aligned}\right\} \tag{53.2a}$$

Man könnte selbstverständlich zur Behandlung des vektoriellen Beugungsproblems auch direkt den Ansatz (53.1), (53.2) oder (53.1a), (53.2a) machen und gelangt dann ebenfalls zu den Pseudointegralgleichungen (51.2) oder (52.2), mit deren Hilfe die Größen $\mathfrak{J}$ bzw. $\mathfrak{L}$ zu bestimmen sind.

Eingreifen der Kantenbedingung.

Wir wenden uns nun zur Diskussion der Gln. (51.2) bzw. (52.2), wobei die Behandlung der entsprechenden skalaren Gl. (47.2*p*) als Vorbild dient. Zunächst benutzen wir die Identität rot rot = grad div $-\Delta$ und beachten die mit Hilfe der Wellengleichung (8.2) folgende Beziehung

$$\Delta\int_S \mathfrak{J}\,G\,d\hat{\mathfrak{r}}' = -\int_S \mathfrak{J}\,G\,d\hat{\mathfrak{r}}', \quad \text{d.h.} \quad \Delta\mathfrak{Z}_S + \mathfrak{Z}_S = 0,$$

sowie die Tatsache, daß $\mathfrak{Z}_S$ keine z-Komponente hat. Damit folgt aus (51.2)

$$[\mathfrak{n}\,\hat{\nabla}]\,\widehat{\operatorname{div}}\int_S \mathfrak{J}(\hat{\mathfrak{r}}')\,G(\hat{\mathfrak{r}}-\hat{\mathfrak{r}}')\,d\hat{\mathfrak{r}}' + \int_S [\mathfrak{n}\,\mathfrak{J}(\hat{\mathfrak{r}}')]\,G(\hat{\mathfrak{r}}-\hat{\mathfrak{r}}')\,d\hat{\mathfrak{r}}' = i\,[\mathfrak{n}\,\mathfrak{E}_0]$$
$$\textit{für } \hat{\mathfrak{r}} \textit{ auf } (S).$$

Diese Gleichung hat gegenüber (51.2) den Vorzug, daß sich die Differentiationen vor dem ersten Integral nur auf $\hat{\mathfrak{r}}$ beziehen (also nicht auf z), so daß der Grenzübergang $z \to \pm 0$ an $G(\mathfrak{r}-\hat{\mathfrak{r}}')$ vollzogen werden konnte. Gl. (53.3) läßt sich noch etwas vereinfachen, indem wir sie vektoriell mit $\mathfrak{n}$ multiplizieren, die entstehenden doppelten Vektorprodukte entwickeln und beachten, daß der Vektor $\int_S \mathfrak{J}(\hat{\mathfrak{r}}')\,G(\hat{\mathfrak{r}}-\hat{\mathfrak{r}}')\,d\hat{\mathfrak{r}}'$ von z unabhängig ist und keine z-Komponente besitzt:

$$(\widehat{\operatorname{grad}}\,\widehat{\operatorname{div}} + 1)\int_S \mathfrak{J}(\hat{\mathfrak{r}}')\,G(\hat{\mathfrak{r}}-\hat{\mathfrak{r}}')\,d\hat{\mathfrak{r}}' = i\,\hat{\mathfrak{E}}_0(\hat{\mathfrak{r}}) \quad \textit{für } \hat{\mathfrak{r}} \textit{ auf } (S). \tag{A}$$

Dabei bedeutet $\hat{\mathfrak{E}}_0$ die Komponente der einfallenden elektrischen Feldstärke, die *parallel* zum Schirm ist (vgl. Ziff. 3). Ferner bedeutet das Zeichen $\hat{}$ über den Operatoren div und grad, daß die Differentiation nach z unterbleiben soll (gemäß unserer allgemeinen Verabredung in Ziff. 3 können wir also auch schreiben $\widehat{\text{grad}}\,\widehat{\text{div}} = \hat{\nabla}\hat{\nabla}$). Dieser Hinweis erübrigt sich zwar, da $\int\limits_S \mathfrak{J}(\hat{\mathfrak{r}}')\,G(\hat{\mathfrak{r}}-\hat{\mathfrak{r}}')\,d\hat{\mathfrak{r}}'$ ohnedies nicht von z abhängt, er macht aber deutlich, daß wir es in (53.4) nur noch mit einem *zweidimensionalen* Problem zu tun haben und setzt (53.3) in Analogie zu der skalaren Gl. (47.3 *p*).

54. Methode des Hertzschen Vektors. Wir zerlegen nun (A) zunächst wieder in die *Differentialgleichung*

$$(\widehat{\text{grad}}\,\widehat{\text{div}} + 1)\,\mathfrak{Z}_S(\hat{\mathfrak{r}}) = \hat{\mathfrak{E}}_0(\hat{\mathfrak{r}}) \qquad \textit{für } \hat{\mathfrak{r}} \textit{ auf } (S) \tag{54.1}$$

für den (in der Schirmebene liegenden) Vektor $\mathfrak{Z}_S(\hat{\mathfrak{r}})$ [d.h. den Hertzschen Vektor auf (S)] und die *Integralgleichung*

$$\int\limits_S \mathfrak{J}(\hat{\mathfrak{r}}')\,G(\hat{\mathfrak{r}}-\hat{\mathfrak{r}}')\,d\hat{\mathfrak{r}}' = i\,\mathfrak{Z}_S(\hat{\mathfrak{r}}) \qquad \textit{für } \hat{\mathfrak{r}} \textit{ auf } (S) \tag{54.2}$$

für den Flächenstrom $\mathfrak{J}$, deren Inhomogenität $\mathfrak{Z}_S(\hat{\mathfrak{r}})$ zuvor aus der Differentialgleichung (54.1) berechnet werden muß. Zu dieser muß noch eine Randbedingung treten, die wieder aus der Kantenbedingung (IV′) hervorzugehen hat. Führen wir statt der zum Schirm parallelen Komponente $\hat{\mathfrak{E}}_0$ der elektrischen Feldstärke der Primärwelle den Hertzschen Vektor $\mathfrak{Z}_0$ der Primärwelle ein, so folgt wie oben — unter der Annahme, daß $\mathfrak{Z}_0$ keine zum Schirm senkrechte Komponente hat — die Darstellung

$$\hat{\mathfrak{E}}_0(\hat{\mathfrak{r}}) = -(\widehat{\text{grad}}\,\widehat{\text{div}} + 1)\,\mathfrak{Z}_0(\hat{\mathfrak{r}})\,. \tag{54.3}$$

Wir können also (54.1) auch in der Form

$$(\widehat{\text{grad}}\,\widehat{\text{div}} + 1)\,\{\mathfrak{Z}_0(\hat{\mathfrak{r}}) + \mathfrak{Z}_S(\hat{\mathfrak{r}})\} = 0 \qquad \textit{für } \hat{\mathfrak{r}} \textit{ auf } (S) \tag{54.4}$$

schreiben, aus der durch Anwendung der Operation $\widehat{\text{rot}}$ folgt, daß der Vektor $\mathfrak{Z}_0(\hat{\mathfrak{r}}) + \mathfrak{Z}_S(\hat{\mathfrak{r}})$ wirbelfrei ist (vgl. Ziff. 7):

$$\mathfrak{Z}_0(\hat{\mathfrak{r}}) + \mathfrak{Z}_S(\hat{\mathfrak{r}}) = \widehat{\text{grad}}\,\Phi(\hat{\mathfrak{r}}), \qquad \textit{für } \hat{\mathfrak{r}} \textit{ auf } (S)\,. \tag{54.5}$$

Unter Beachtung von (54.5) könne wir also (54.4) in der Gestalt

$$(\hat{\Delta} + 1)\,\Phi(\hat{\mathfrak{r}}) = 0, \qquad \hat{\mathfrak{r}} \textit{ auf } (S), \tag{54.1′}$$

schreiben, die dasselbe wie

$$\widehat{\text{div}}\,(\mathfrak{Z}_0 + \mathfrak{Z}_S) + \Phi = 0, \qquad \hat{\mathfrak{r}} \textit{ auf } (S)$$

bedeutet (Lorentz-Konvention). Wir haben also das skalare Potential Φ aus der homogenen Wellengleichung (54.1′) zu berechnen, zu der noch eine (inhomogene) Randbedingung treten muß, die wieder mit der Kantenbedingung zusammenhängt. Danach ist die Flächenstromdichte $\mathfrak{J}$ mit Hilfe der Integralgleichung (54.2) zu bestimmen, die bei Beachtung von (54.5) übergeht in

$$\int\limits_S \mathfrak{J}(\hat{\mathfrak{r}}')\,G(\hat{\mathfrak{r}}-\hat{\mathfrak{r}}')\,d\hat{\mathfrak{r}}' = i\,\widehat{\text{grad}}\,\Phi(\hat{\mathfrak{r}}) - i\,\mathfrak{Z}_0(\hat{\mathfrak{r}}) \qquad \textit{für } \hat{\mathfrak{r}} \textit{ auf } (S)\,. \tag{54.2′}$$

Bezüglich der in Gl. (25.1) angegebenen Form der Kantenbedingung für den Hertzschen Vektor bemerken wir, daß wir uns jetzt auf dem Schirm ($\varphi = 0$) befinden (d.h. wir interessieren uns nur für das Verhalten von $\mathfrak{Z}$, wenn wir uns *längs des Schirmes* der Kante nähern). Dort wird also das Verhalten von $\mathfrak{Z}$ durch *reguläre* Glieder dargestellt.

Ohne Rücksicht auf die Kantenbedingung für den Hertzschen Vektor kann man so vorgehen, daß man die Lösung von (54.1) bzw. (54.1′) zunächst mit unbestimmten Koeffizienten ansetzt, die dann nachträglich mit Hilfe der Kantenbedingung (23.4) für die Flächenstromdichte $\mathfrak{J}$ zu bestimmen sind. Den Gln. (54.1) und (54.2) äquivalente Formulierungen sind erstmals von BETHE[1] und COPSON[2] angegeben worden.

55. Überführung in eine Integrodifferentialgleichung. Andererseits läßt sich zur Berechnung von $\mathfrak{J}$ auch hier wieder der Weg über eine *Integrodifferentialgleichung* einschlagen, indem die Differentiationen nach $\hat{\mathfrak{r}}$ vor dem Integral (A) unter dieses genommen und in solche nach $\hat{\mathfrak{r}}'$ umgewandelt werden, so daß partiell integriert werden kann. Wir berechnen zunächst ($z \neq 0$)

$$\left.\begin{aligned} \widehat{\operatorname{div}} \int_S \mathfrak{J}(\hat{\mathfrak{r}}')\, G(\mathfrak{r}-\hat{\mathfrak{r}}')\, d\hat{\mathfrak{r}}' &= -\int_S (\hat{V}', \mathfrak{J}\, G)\, d\hat{\mathfrak{r}}' + \int_S G(\hat{V}'\, \mathfrak{J})\, d'\hat{\mathfrak{r}} \\ &= -\oint_C (\mathfrak{s}'\, \mathfrak{J})\, G\, dt' + \int_S G\, \widehat{\operatorname{div}}'\, \mathfrak{J}\, d\hat{\mathfrak{r}}', \end{aligned}\right\} \tag{55.1}$$

dabei haben wir auf das erste Integral rechts den Stokesschen Satz (48.1) angewandt. Das Linienintegral führt wieder zu einem unzulässig divergenten Ausdruck falls der Aufpunkt $\mathfrak{r}$ auf den Rand rückt. Dies läßt sich nur vermeiden, falls

$$(\mathfrak{s}\, \mathfrak{J}) = 0 \qquad \textit{auf } (C) \tag{55.2}$$

[nach (23.4) muß $(\mathfrak{s}\,\mathfrak{J})$ wie $\varrho^{\frac{1}{2}}$ an der Kante, d.h. für $\varrho \to 0$ verschwinden]. Die Gl. (55.2) besagt, daß der Flächenstrom $\mathfrak{J}$ längs (C) *keine Normalkomponente* haben darf, was anschaulich ohne weiteres einleuchtet. Beachtet man also (55.2) und führt (55.1) in (53.4) ein, so folgt im Limes $z \to \pm 0$

$$\int_S \{\widehat{\operatorname{div}}'\, \mathfrak{J}(\hat{\mathfrak{r}}') \cdot \widehat{\operatorname{grad}} + \mathfrak{J}(\hat{\mathfrak{r}}')\}\, G(\hat{\mathfrak{r}}-\hat{\mathfrak{r}}')\, d\hat{\mathfrak{r}}' = i\, \hat{\mathfrak{E}}_0(\hat{\mathfrak{r}}) \quad \textit{für } \hat{\mathfrak{r}} \textit{ auf } (S). \tag{55.3}$$

Dies ist die Integrodifferentialgleichung für $\mathfrak{J}$ von MAUE[3], der sie auch für gekrümmte Schirme (S) ableitete [für die Ansatz (51.1) ebenfalls zum Ziel führt, vgl. Ziff. 77]. Das erste Integral in (55.3) ist nur bedingt konvergent; man hat es als *Hauptwert* zu definieren (der Punkt $\hat{\mathfrak{r}}$ ist durch einen kleinen Kreis mit verschwindendem Radius aus dem Integrationsgebiet auszuschließen). Bei der Formulierung des zweidimensionalen Problems für den Flächenstrom $\mathfrak{J}$ in Form der Integrodifferentialgleichung (55.3) begegnet uns also die Kantenbedingung (als notwendige Bedingung) in der physikalisch durchsichtigen Gestalt (55.2).

56. Die Methode von MAGNUS. Zur Vermeidung des bedingt konvergenten Integrals kann man eine *zweite* partielle Integration ausführen. Der nächstliegende Weg wäre eine nochmalige Anwendung des Stokesschen Satzes (48.1) in der Form

$$\left.\begin{aligned} \int_S \widehat{\operatorname{div}}'\, \mathfrak{J}(\hat{\mathfrak{r}}')\, \widehat{\operatorname{grad}}\, G(\mathfrak{r}-\hat{\mathfrak{r}}')\, d\hat{\mathfrak{r}}' &= -\int_S \hat{V}'(G\, \widehat{\operatorname{div}}'\, \mathfrak{J})\, d\hat{\mathfrak{r}}' \\ + \int_S G\, \hat{V}'\, \widehat{\operatorname{div}}'\, \mathfrak{J}\, d\hat{\mathfrak{r}}' &= -\oint_C \mathfrak{s}'\, G\, \widehat{\operatorname{div}}'\, \mathfrak{J}\, dt' + \int_S G\, \widehat{\operatorname{grad}}'\, \widehat{\operatorname{div}}'\, \mathfrak{J}\, d\hat{\mathfrak{r}}'. \end{aligned}\right\} \tag{56.1}$$

---

[1] H.A. BETHE: Phys. Rev. **66**, 163 (1944). — Siehe auch R.K. LUNEBERG: Mathematical Theory of Optics. Providence: Brown Univ. 1944.

[2] E. T. COPSON: Proc. Roy. Soc. Lond. **186**, 100 (1946); **202**, 760 (1950). Vgl. auch G. TORALDO DI FRANCIA: Nuovo Cim. **7**, 967 (1950). C. J. BOUWKAMP: N. Y. Univ. Res. Rep. EM-50 (1953); Progr. Phys. **17**, 35 (1954). — H. LEVINE u. J. SCHWINGER: Comm. Pure Appl. Math. **3**, 355 (1950).

[3] A.-W. MAUE: Z. Physik **126**, 601 (1949).

Dieser Weg ist jedoch aus denselben Gründen *nicht* gangbar, wie sie im Anschluß an Gl. (48.5) dargelegt wurden: Zur Beseitigung des (für auf dem Rand des Schirmes gelegene Aufpunkte) divergenten Linienintegrals wäre die zusätzliche Forderung $\widehat{\mathrm{div}}\,\mathfrak{J}=0$ notwendig, die der Kantenbedingung (23.4) widerspricht. Nach dieser ist $\widehat{\mathrm{div}}\,\mathfrak{J}\sim\varrho^{-\frac{1}{2}}$ und ferner $\widehat{\mathrm{grad}}\,\widehat{\mathrm{div}}\,\mathfrak{J}\sim\varrho^{-\frac{3}{2}}$, daher ist auch das Flächenintegral rechterhand in (56.1) — bei reellem Integrationsweg — divergent. Hier bietet sich wieder der Ausweg, die Komponente der Flächenintegration *senkrecht* zum Rande als *komplexes* Integral längs einer den Punkt $\varrho=0$ umschlingenden Schleife aufzufassen (der Rand ist ja *Verzweigungslinie* für den Flächenstrom, der als *Differenz* der tangentialen magnetischen Feldstärke zu beiden Seiten des Schirmes definiert ist, so daß sich eventuelle reguläre Terme von $\mathfrak{H}$ wegheben). Bei der partiellen Integration tritt dann kein Linienintegral auf und wir gelangen zu der *Integrodifferentialgleichung* von Magnus[1]

$$\int\limits_S (\widehat{\mathrm{grad}}'\,\widehat{\mathrm{div}}' + 1)\,\mathfrak{J}(\hat{\mathfrak{r}}')\cdot G(\hat{\mathfrak{r}}-\hat{\mathfrak{r}}')\,d\hat{\mathfrak{r}}' = i\,\widehat{\mathfrak{E}}_0 \quad \textit{für } \hat{\mathfrak{r}} \textit{ auf } (S). \tag{56.2}$$

Wir zerlegen nun (56.2) nach Magnus in eine reine *Integralgleichung* und eine *Differentialgleichung*, indem wir den in der Ebene $z=0$ liegenden Vektor

$$\mathfrak{B}(\hat{\mathfrak{r}}) = \mathfrak{J} + \widehat{\mathrm{grad}}\,\widehat{\mathrm{div}}\,\mathfrak{J} \tag{56.3}$$

einführen und ihn so bestimmen, daß

$$\int\limits_S \mathfrak{B}(\hat{\mathfrak{r}}')\,G(\hat{\mathfrak{r}}-\hat{\mathfrak{r}}')\,d\hat{\mathfrak{r}}' = i\,\widehat{\mathfrak{E}}_0(\hat{\mathfrak{r}}) \quad \textit{für } \hat{\mathfrak{r}} \textit{ auf } (S). \tag{56.4}$$

Ist diese Integralgleichung für $\mathfrak{B}$ gelöst, so ist gemäß (56.3) der Flächenstrom $\mathfrak{J}$ bis auf den Gradienten ($\widehat{\mathrm{grad}}$) der Flächenladung $\eta=-i\,\widehat{\mathrm{div}}\,\mathfrak{J}$ (vgl. Ziff. 3) bekannt. Letztere bestimmt sich aus der Differentialgleichung

und der Randbedingung

$$\left.\begin{aligned} (\hat{\Delta}+1)\,\eta(\hat{\mathfrak{r}}) &= -i\,\widehat{\mathrm{div}}\,\mathfrak{B} \quad \textit{für } \hat{\mathfrak{r}} \textit{ auf } (S)\\ \frac{\partial\eta}{\partial s} &= -i\,(\mathfrak{s}\,\mathfrak{B}) \quad \textit{längs } (C). \end{aligned}\right\} \tag{56.5}$$

Man erhält (56.5), indem man die Divergenz ($\widehat{\mathrm{div}}$) von $\widehat{\mathfrak{B}}$ bildet:

$$(\hat{\nabla}\,\mathfrak{B}) = \hat{\nabla}^2(\hat{\nabla}\,\mathfrak{J}) + (\hat{\nabla}\,\mathfrak{J})$$

bzw. die Normalkomponente von $\mathfrak{B}$ [man beachte (55.2)]:

$$(\mathfrak{s}\,\mathfrak{B}) = (\mathfrak{s}\,\hat{\nabla})\,(\hat{\nabla}\,\mathfrak{J}) + (\mathfrak{s}\,\mathfrak{J}). \tag{56.6}$$

Obwohl die Reduktion des dreidimensionalen Problems (I′) bis (IV′) auf das zweidimensionale Problem (56.4), (56.5) formal besonders einfach ist, müssen wir doch auf folgende Schwierigkeit hinweisen: Wie bereits oben bemerkt, muß sich $(\mathfrak{s}\,\mathfrak{B})$ nach der Kantenbedingung (23.4) wie $\varrho^{-\frac{3}{2}}$ bei Annäherung an die Kante verhalten [die ϱ-Integration ist in (56.4) als komplexes Schleifenintegral aufzufassen], daher hat die Randbedingung für η, zweite Gl. (56.5), unmittelbar keinen Sinn. Man muß deshalb zunächst die Randbedingung $\partial\eta/\partial s = i\,(\mathfrak{s}\,\mathfrak{B})$ für eine noch innerhalb (S) gelegene Kurve (C_0) befriedigen und dann den Limes $(C_0)\to(C)$ ausführen.

[1] W. Magnus: Jber. dtsch. Math.-Ver. **52**, 177 (1943). Magnus betrachtet allerdings nur reelle Integrationswege und fordert daher neben (55.2) auch noch die Randbedingung $\widehat{\mathrm{div}}\,\mathfrak{J}=0$. Dadurch ist aber das Verhalten der Flächenladung $\eta=-i\,\widehat{\mathrm{div}}\,\mathfrak{J}$ auf dem Rande (in der Kantenbedingung widersprechender Weise) festgelegt. Magnus sieht sich daher gezwungen, für η innerhalb des Schirmes eine Singularität zuzulassen, was phyikalisch sinnlos ist.

Wir betrachten noch kurz die Pseudointegralgleichung (52.2) für die „*magnetische Flächenstromdichte*“ $\mathfrak{L} = [\mathfrak{n}\,\mathfrak{E}]$ [der Name rechtfertigt sich durch die Bemerkung, daß die Tangentialkomponente der *elektrischen* Feldstärke des *Beugungsterms* von Gl. (52.1) beim Hindurchtreten durch die Öffnung den Sprung $\mathfrak{L}$ aufweist] und schreiben sie zunächst analog zu (A) in der Gestalt

$$(\widehat{\operatorname{grad}}\,\widehat{\operatorname{div}} + 1) \int\limits_L \mathfrak{L}(\hat{\mathfrak{r}}')\, G(\hat{\mathfrak{r}} - \hat{\mathfrak{r}}')\, d\hat{\mathfrak{r}}' = \frac{i}{2}\, \widehat{\mathfrak{H}}_0(\hat{\mathfrak{r}}) \quad \textit{für } \hat{\mathfrak{r}} \textit{ auf } (L). \tag{B}$$

Sie zerfällt in die *Differentialgleichung*

$$(\widehat{\operatorname{grad}}\,\widehat{\operatorname{div}} + 1)\, \mathfrak{Y}_B(\hat{\mathfrak{r}}) = \widehat{\mathfrak{H}}_0(\hat{\mathfrak{r}}) \quad \textit{für } \hat{\mathfrak{r}} \textit{ auf } (L) \tag{56.7}$$

und die *Integralgleichung*

$$\int\limits_L \mathfrak{L}(\hat{\mathfrak{r}}')\, G(\hat{\mathfrak{r}} - \hat{\mathfrak{r}}')\, d\hat{\mathfrak{r}}' = \frac{i}{2}\, \mathfrak{Y}_B(\hat{\mathfrak{r}}) \quad \textit{für } \hat{\mathfrak{r}} \textit{ auf } (L). \tag{56.8}$$

Andererseits läßt sich (B) umformen in die *Integrodifferentialgleichung*

$$\left.\begin{aligned} \int\limits_L \{\widehat{\operatorname{div}}'\,\mathfrak{L}(\hat{\mathfrak{r}}') \cdot \widehat{\operatorname{grad}} + \mathfrak{L}(\hat{\mathfrak{r}}')\}\, G(\hat{\mathfrak{r}} - \hat{\mathfrak{r}}')\, d\hat{\mathfrak{r}}' = \frac{i}{2}\, \widehat{\mathfrak{H}}_0(\hat{\mathfrak{r}}) \\ \textit{für } \hat{\mathfrak{r}} \textit{ auf } (L) \end{aligned}\right\} \tag{56.9}$$

mit der Nebenbedingung

$$(\mathfrak{s}\,\mathfrak{L}) = 0 \quad \text{längs } (C) \tag{56.10}$$

sowie der Definition des uneigentlichen Integrals durch seinen Hauptwert. Nach (23.3a) muß $(\mathfrak{s}\,\mathfrak{L}) = -(\mathfrak{t}\,\mathfrak{E})$ ($\mathfrak{t}$ = Tangenteneinheitsvektor der Randkurve, vgl. Ziff. 21 und Fig. 12) wieder wie $\varrho^{\frac{1}{2}}$ für $\varrho \to 0$ verschwinden.

Schließlich kann man die Integration senkrecht zum Rande wieder als komplexes Schleifenintegral definieren und gelangt dann durch nochmalige partielle Integration zur Umformung des bedingt konvergenten Integrals:

$$\int\limits_L (\widehat{\operatorname{grad}}'\,\widehat{\operatorname{div}}' + 1)\, \mathfrak{L}(\hat{\mathfrak{r}}') \cdot G(\hat{\mathfrak{r}} - \hat{\mathfrak{r}}')\, d\hat{\mathfrak{r}}' = \frac{i}{2}\, \widehat{\mathfrak{H}}_0(\hat{\mathfrak{r}}) \quad \textit{für } \hat{\mathfrak{r}} \textit{ auf } (L). \tag{56.2a}$$

Diese Integrodifferentialgleichung für $\mathfrak{L}$ läßt sich wieder in die Integralgleichung

$$\int\limits_L \widehat{\mathfrak{V}}(\hat{\mathfrak{r}}')\, G(\hat{\mathfrak{r}} - \hat{\mathfrak{r}}')\, d\hat{\mathfrak{r}}' = \frac{i}{2}\, \widehat{\mathfrak{H}}_0(\hat{\mathfrak{r}}) \quad \textit{für } \hat{\mathfrak{r}} \textit{ auf } (L) \tag{56.4a}$$

für den Vektor

$$\widehat{\mathfrak{V}}(\hat{\mathfrak{r}}) = \mathfrak{L} - i\, \widehat{\operatorname{grad}}\, \hat{\eta} \quad \text{mit} \quad \hat{\eta} = i\, \widehat{\operatorname{div}}\, \mathfrak{L} \tag{56.3a}$$

und die Differentialgleichung

$$(\hat{\Delta} + 1)\, \hat{\eta}(\hat{\mathfrak{r}}) = i\, \widehat{\operatorname{div}}\, \widehat{\mathfrak{V}} \quad \textit{für } \hat{\mathfrak{r}} \textit{ auf } (L)$$

bei der Randbedingung

$$\frac{\partial \hat{\eta}}{\partial s} = i\, (\mathfrak{s}\, \widehat{\mathfrak{V}}) \quad \textit{längs } (C) \tag{56.5a}$$

für die „magnetische Ladungsdichte“ $\hat{\eta}$ zerlegen. Damit ist auch im Beugungsfall die Reduktion auf ein zweidimensionales Problem gelungen [man beachte jedoch das im Anschluß an Gl. (56.5) Gesagte].

57. Die Verhältnisse an der Kante. Der ursprüngliche Sinn der in Ziff. 21 zunächst auf das *dreidimensionale* Randwertproblem zugeschnittenen Kantenbedingung war, die energieliefernde Ausstrahlung der Kanten zu verhindern (und damit die Eindeutigkeit des dreidimensionalen Problems zu garantieren). Dieser Sachverhalt ist bei der Zurückführung auf ein zweidimensionales Problem in den Hintergrund getreten. Hier begegnen wir nur der Kantenbedingung

$$(\mathfrak{s}\,\mathfrak{J}) = (\mathfrak{s}\,[\mathfrak{n},\, \mathfrak{H}_+ - \mathfrak{H}_-]) = -\,(\mathfrak{t},\, \mathfrak{H}_+ - \mathfrak{H}_-) = 0 \quad \textit{auf } (C).$$

Diese Gleichung gilt, wenn man sich der Kante in der Ebene $z=0$ *vom Schirm her* nähert. Außerdem gilt dann zufolge der Randbedingung (II′) $[\mathfrak{n}\,\mathfrak{E}] = (\mathfrak{n}\,\mathfrak{H}) = 0$. Andererseits verhalten sich bei dieser Annäherung nach Gl. (23.3b) die Komponenten $(\mathfrak{s},\, \mathfrak{H}_+ - \mathfrak{H}_-) = (\mathfrak{t}\,\mathfrak{J})$ und $(\mathfrak{n},\, \mathfrak{E}_+ - \mathfrak{E}_-) = \eta = -i\,\widehat{\operatorname{div}}\,\mathfrak{J}$ wie $\varrho^{-\frac{1}{2}}$ (das Randverhalten von η ist bereits aus der *Elektrostatik* geläufig). Diese Singularität braucht jedoch in der oben dargelegten Fassung der Beugungstheorie *nicht* noch durch eine zusätzliche Bedingung eingeschränkt zu werden, sondern ergibt sich von selbst in der richtigen Größenordnung, da das Problem in dieser Fassung bereits eindeutig ist.

Nähert man sich nun der Kante *von der Öffnung her* (in der Ebene $z=0$), so brauchen wir jetzt *nur* die Kantenbedingung

$$(\mathfrak{s}\,\mathfrak{L}) = -\,(\mathfrak{t}\,\mathfrak{E}) = 0 \quad \textit{auf } (C).$$

Die übrigen Feldkomponenten müssen von selbst das richtige Randverhalten zeigen.

Wir erwähnen noch die Beziehung $\hat{\eta} = i\,\widehat{\operatorname{div}}\,\mathfrak{L} = (\mathfrak{n}\,\mathfrak{H})$ [vgl. (3.2b)], die eine unmittelbare Folge der Maxwellschen Gleichungen ist. Wir wollen sie hier aber einschaltweise auch noch explizit mit Hilfe der zweiten Gleichung (52.1) verifizieren, um die Geschlossenheit des ganzen Formalismus zu demonstrieren. Zunächst folgt aus $[\mathfrak{n},\, \mathfrak{E}_0 + \mathfrak{E}^0] = 0$ mit Hilfe von (3.2b) $(\mathfrak{n},\, \mathfrak{H}_0 + \mathfrak{H}^0) = 0$. Daher folgt aus (52.1)

$$\begin{aligned}(\mathfrak{n}\,\mathfrak{H}) &= \pm\, 2i\Big(\mathfrak{n}\Big[\nabla\Big[\nabla\int_L \mathfrak{L}\,G\,d\hat{\mathfrak{r}}'\Big]\Big]\Big)\\ &= \mp\, 2i\Big(\nabla\Big[\mathfrak{n}\Big[\nabla\int_L \mathfrak{L}\,G\,d\hat{\mathfrak{r}}'\Big]\Big]\Big) = \pm\, 2i\Big\{(\mathfrak{n}\,\nabla)\Big(\nabla\int_L \mathfrak{L}\,G\,d\hat{\mathfrak{r}}'\Big) - \nabla^2\Big(\mathfrak{n}\int_L \mathfrak{L}\,G\,d\hat{\mathfrak{r}}'\Big)\Big\}.\end{aligned}$$

Das letzte Integral verschwindet hier wegen $(\mathfrak{n}\,\mathfrak{L}) = 0$, während $\Big(\nabla\int_L \mathfrak{L}\,G\,d\hat{\mathfrak{r}}'\Big)$ mit Hilfe des Stokesschen Satzes (48.1) und der Forderung $(\mathfrak{s}\,\mathfrak{L}) = 0$ in $\int_L G\,\widehat{\operatorname{div}}'\,\mathfrak{L}\,d\hat{\mathfrak{r}}'$ verwandelt werden kann. Mit Hilfe von (34.1) folgt somit die zu beweisende Gleichung

$$\begin{aligned}\lim_{z\to\pm 0}(\mathfrak{n}\,\mathfrak{H}) &= \pm\, 2i\lim_{z\to\pm 0}(\mathfrak{n}\,\nabla)\int_L \widehat{\operatorname{div}}'\,\mathfrak{L}(\hat{\mathfrak{r}}')\,G(\mathfrak{r}-\hat{\mathfrak{r}}')\,d\hat{\mathfrak{r}}'\\ &= \begin{cases} i\,\widehat{\operatorname{div}}\,\mathfrak{L}(\hat{\mathfrak{r}}) & \text{für } \hat{\mathfrak{r}} \text{ auf } (L)\\ 0 & \text{für } \hat{\mathfrak{r}} \text{ auf } (S).\end{cases}\end{aligned}$$

Wenn man sich der Kante von der Öffnung her nähert, sind außer $(\mathfrak{t}\,\mathfrak{E}) \to 0$ auch noch die Komponenten $[\mathfrak{n}\,\mathfrak{H}]$ und $(\mathfrak{n}\,\mathfrak{E})$ bekannt, die nach Ziff. 26 die Werte $[\mathfrak{n}\,\mathfrak{H}_0]$ und $(\mathfrak{n}\,\mathfrak{E}_0)$ annehmen. Die Komponenten $(\mathfrak{s}\,\mathfrak{E}) = (\mathfrak{t}\,\mathfrak{L})$ und $\hat{\eta} = (\mathfrak{n}\,\mathfrak{H}) = i\,\widehat{\operatorname{div}}\,\mathfrak{L}$ verhalten sich wieder $\sim \varrho^{-\frac{1}{2}}$ [vgl. Gl. (23.3b), ersteres entspricht der „*Spitzenwirkung der Elektrostatik*"], jedoch braucht diese Singularität *nicht* eigens eingeschränkt zu werden (s. oben).

Da die Komponente $(\mathfrak{s}\,\mathfrak{E})$ bei Annäherung an die Kante vom Schirm her *verschwindet* (sie verschwindet ja wegen der Randbedingung überall auf dem Schirm), so ist sie also (wie schon in Ziff. 23 erwähnt) beim Überschreiten der

Kante (in der Ebene $z=0$) *unstetig* (mit unendlich großen Sprungwerten). Entsprechendes gilt für die Komponenten $(\mathfrak{s}\mathfrak{H})$, $(\mathfrak{n}\mathfrak{E})$ und $(\mathfrak{n}\mathfrak{H})$. Andererseits sind die Komponenten $(\mathfrak{t}\mathfrak{E})$ und $(\mathfrak{t}\mathfrak{H})$ beim Überqueren der Kante *stetig*.

Ergänzungen.

58. Elektrodynamische Potentiale. In systematischer Hinsicht ist noch erwähnenswert, daß sich die Gln. (53.2) bzw. (53.2a) wegen $(\Delta+1)\,\mathfrak{Z}_S=0$ bzw. $(\Delta+1)\,\mathfrak{Y}_B=0$ auch in der Form

$$\left.\begin{aligned}\mathfrak{E}&=\mathfrak{E}_0+i\,\mathfrak{A}_S-\operatorname{grad}\Phi_S\\ \mathfrak{H}&=\mathfrak{H}_0+\operatorname{rot}\mathfrak{A}_S\end{aligned}\right\}\quad z\gtrless 0 \tag{58.1}$$

mit

$$\left.\begin{aligned}\mathfrak{A}_S(\mathfrak{r})&=-i\,\mathfrak{Z}_S(\mathfrak{r})=-\int\limits_S \mathfrak{J}(\hat{\mathfrak{r}}')\,G(\mathfrak{r}-\hat{\mathfrak{r}}')\,d\hat{\mathfrak{r}}',\\ \Phi_S(\mathfrak{r})&=-\operatorname{div}\mathfrak{Z}_S=i\int\limits_S \widehat{\operatorname{div}}'\,\mathfrak{J}(\hat{\mathfrak{r}}')\,G(\mathfrak{r}-\hat{\mathfrak{r}}')\,d\hat{\mathfrak{r}}'\\ &=-\int\limits_S \eta(\hat{\mathfrak{r}}')\,G(\mathfrak{r}-\hat{\mathfrak{r}}')\,d\hat{\mathfrak{r}}',\qquad \operatorname{div}\mathfrak{A}_S-i\,\Phi_S=0\end{aligned}\right\} \tag{58.2}$$

bzw.

$$\left.\begin{aligned}\mathfrak{E}&=\pm\operatorname{rot}\widehat{\mathfrak{A}}_B+\begin{cases}0, & z>0\\ \mathfrak{E}_0+\mathfrak{E}^0, & z<0,\end{cases}\\ \mathfrak{H}&=\mp i\,\widehat{\mathfrak{A}}_B\pm\operatorname{grad}\widehat{\Phi}_B+\begin{cases}0, & z>0\\ \mathfrak{H}_0+\mathfrak{H}^0, & z<0\end{cases}\end{aligned}\right\} \tag{58.1a}$$

mit

$$\left.\begin{aligned}\widehat{\mathfrak{A}}_B(\mathfrak{r})&=-i\,\mathfrak{Y}_B(\mathfrak{r})=2\int\limits_L \mathfrak{L}(\hat{\mathfrak{r}}')\,G(\mathfrak{r}-\hat{\mathfrak{r}}')\,d\hat{\mathfrak{r}}',\qquad z\gtrless 0,\\ \widehat{\Phi}_B(\mathfrak{r})&=-\operatorname{div}\mathfrak{Y}_B=-2i\int\limits_L \widehat{\operatorname{div}}'\,\mathfrak{L}(\hat{\mathfrak{r}}')\,G(\mathfrak{r}-\hat{\mathfrak{r}}')\,d\hat{\mathfrak{r}}'\\ &=-2\int\limits_L \hat{\eta}(\hat{\mathfrak{r}}')\,G(\mathfrak{r}-\hat{\mathfrak{r}}')\,d\hat{\mathfrak{r}}',\qquad \operatorname{div}\widehat{\mathfrak{A}}_B-i\,\widehat{\Phi}_B=0\end{aligned}\right\} \tag{58.2a}$$

schreiben lassen, also in der üblichen Form mit Hilfe eines *Vektor-* und eines *skalaren Potentials*. Bemerkenswert ist dabei, daß Linienintegrale, die als linienhafte Verteilung von elektrischer bzw. magnetischer Ladung längs des Randes (C) von (S) bzw. (L) zu deuten wären, *nicht* auftreten. Es ist dies eine Folge der Gl. (55.2) bzw. (56.10), mit anderen Worten der Kantenbedingung.

Es sei auch noch auf folgenden Zusammenhang hingewiesen: wendet man die Formel (12.6a) auf eine geschlossene Fläche an, die aus einer unendlich großen Kugel besteht, sowie aus einer Fläche, die sich einem beliebig gekrümmten ideal leitenden Schirme (S) beiderseitig eng anschmiegt, so entsteht [falls man wieder den Sprung der Tangentialkomponente der magnetischen bzw. der Normalkomponente der elektrischen Feldstärke mit $[\mathfrak{n},\mathfrak{H}_+-\mathfrak{H}_-]=\mathfrak{J}$ bzw. $(\mathfrak{n},\mathfrak{E}_+-\mathfrak{E}_-)=\eta$ bezeichnet]:

$$\mathfrak{E}(\mathfrak{r})=\mathfrak{E}_0(\mathfrak{r})+i\int\limits_S \mathfrak{J}(\hat{\mathfrak{r}}')\,G(\mathfrak{r}-\hat{\mathfrak{r}}')\,d\hat{\mathfrak{r}}'-\operatorname{grad}\int\limits_S \eta(\hat{\mathfrak{r}}')\,G(\mathfrak{r}-\hat{\mathfrak{r}}')\,d\hat{\mathfrak{r}}'$$

in Übereinstimmung mit (58.1) und (58.2). Das Integral über die Kugel liefert nämlich zufolge der Ausstrahlungsbedingung (Ziff. 18) die einfallende Welle $\mathfrak{E}_0$, falls Einstrahlung aus dem Unendlichen erfolgt (ebene Welle). Erfolgt die Anregung hingegen durch Kugelwellen, so ist deren Ursprung aus dem Integrationsgebiet durch eine kleine Kugel auszuschließen, die dann gerade wieder den Beitrag $\mathfrak{E}_0$ zum Integral liefert. Beachten wir nun noch die allgemeine Beziehung

(3.3 a): $(\mathfrak{n}, \mathfrak{E}_+ - \mathfrak{E}_-) = \eta = -i\,\widehat{\mathrm{div}}\,\mathfrak{J}$, so folgt

$$\mathfrak{E}(\mathfrak{r}) = \mathfrak{E}_0 + i \int_S \{\mathfrak{J}(\hat{\mathfrak{r}}')\, G(\mathfrak{r} - \hat{\mathfrak{r}}') + \widehat{\mathrm{div}}'\,\mathfrak{J}(\hat{\mathfrak{r}}')\, \widehat{\mathrm{grad}}\, G(\mathfrak{r} - \hat{\mathfrak{r}}')\}\, d\hat{\mathfrak{r}}'.$$

Die Randbedingung $[\mathfrak{n}\,\mathfrak{E}] = 0$ führt dann unmittelbar auf die Integrodifferentialgleichung

$$\int_S [\mathfrak{n}, \mathfrak{J}(\hat{\mathfrak{r}}')\, G(\hat{\mathfrak{r}} - \hat{\mathfrak{r}}') + \widehat{\mathrm{div}}'\,\mathfrak{J}(\hat{\mathfrak{r}}')\, \widehat{\mathrm{grad}}\, G(\hat{\mathfrak{r}} - \hat{\mathfrak{r}}')]\, d\hat{\mathfrak{r}}' = i\,[\mathfrak{n}\,\mathfrak{E}_0] \quad \textit{für } \hat{\mathfrak{r}} \textit{ auf } (S), \tag{58.3}$$

die für *ebene* Schirme mit Gl. (A) auf S. 309 übereinstimmt. Das obige $\mathfrak{E}$ erfüllt jedoch zusammen mit

$$\mathfrak{H}(\mathfrak{r}) = \mathfrak{H}_0 + \mathrm{rot} \int_S \mathfrak{J}(\hat{\mathfrak{r}}')\, G(\mathfrak{r} - \hat{\mathfrak{r}}')\, d\hat{\mathfrak{r}}',$$

dann und nur dann die Maxwellschen Gleichungen, wenn $(\mathfrak{s}\,\mathfrak{J}) = 0$ längs des Randes (C) von (S).

59. Babinetsches Theorem. Abschließend betrachten wir die *Streuung* der Welle $\mathfrak{E}_0$, $\mathfrak{H}_0$ an einem ebenen Schirm (S) mit Löchern (L), für die wir die Formulierung (51.1), (51.2) verwenden; daneben behandeln wir das *Beugungsproblem* für die einfallende Welle $\widehat{\mathfrak{E}}_0 = -\mathfrak{H}_0$, $\widehat{\mathfrak{H}}_0 = \mathfrak{E}_0$ und den komplementären Schirm (L) mit Löchern (S) mit Hilfe des Formalismus (52.1), (52.2). Bezeichnet man mit $\mathfrak{E}^{(S)}$, $\mathfrak{H}^{(S)}$ die Lösung des ersten Problems, mit $\widehat{\mathfrak{E}}^{(L)}$, $\widehat{\mathfrak{H}}^{(L)}$ hingegen diejenige des zweiten, so liefert der Vergleich beider Darstellungen (infolge ihrer Eindeutigkeit) unmittelbar die Beziehung $\mathfrak{J} = 2\mathfrak{L}$ und damit

$$\left.\begin{aligned} \widehat{\mathfrak{E}}^{(L)} &= \pm\,\mathfrak{H}^{(S)} - \begin{cases} \mathfrak{H}_0, & z > 0 \\ -\,\mathfrak{H}^0, & z < 0 \end{cases} \\ \widehat{\mathfrak{H}}^{(L)} &= \mp\,\mathfrak{E}^{(S)} + \begin{cases} \mathfrak{E}_0, & z > 0 \\ -\,\mathfrak{E}^0, & z < 0. \end{cases} \end{aligned}\right\} \tag{59.1}$$

Dies ist das *Babinetsche Theorem*, das wir in Ziff. 27 bereits aus allgemeinen Symmetrieüberlegungen gewonnen hatten; vgl. Gl. (27.8).

b) Die Reduktion der Randwertaufgabe auf duale Integralgleichungen für das Fernfeld (ebene Schirme, Methode der Fourier-Transformation).

Das in Abschn. a) dargestellte Verfahren läßt sich charakterisieren als Entwicklung der Lösung unserer Randwertaufgabe nach *Kugelwellen* (im dreidimensionalen Fall) bzw. *Zylinderwellen* (im zweidimensionalen Fall), die von den Punkten der Öffnung (Beugungsfall) oder des Schirms (Streufall) ausgehen. Die „Entwicklungskoeffizienten" haben die Bedeutung des Feldes in der Öffnung oder des Flächenstroms auf dem Schirm. Andererseits kann man eine Entwicklung nach *ebenen Wellen* vornehmen. Die dabei auftretenden Fourier-Koeffizienten haben ebenfalls eine anschauliche physikalische Bedeutung; sie beschreiben nämlich im wesentlichen die Abhängigkeit des *Fraunhoferschen Fernfeldes* vom Beugungswinkel *(Strahlungsdiagramm)*.

Wir wollen uns bei der Darstellung dieser zweiten Methode im skalaren Fall auf das zweidimensionale Problem beschränken, und die Erweiterung auf drei Dimensionen erst im Rahmen der vektoriellen Theorie vornehmen.

b 1) Skalare Theorie.

60. Aufstellung der Integralgleichungen für die Fourier-Amplituden. Den Ausgangspunkt bilde die Fourier-Darstellung der Zylinderwelle[1]:

$$H_0^{(1)}(R) = \frac{1}{\pi} \int_{-\infty}^{\infty} e^{i[(x-x')\alpha + |z-z'|\sqrt{1-\alpha^2}]} \frac{d\alpha}{\sqrt{1-\alpha^2}} \tag{60.1}$$

(den Verzweigungspunkten $+1$ bzw. -1 ist dabei durch einen kleinen Halbkreis in der unteren bzw. oberen α-Halbebene auszuweichen, s. Fig. 40, ferner ist die Wurzel $\sqrt{1-\alpha^2}$ für $|\alpha| < 1$ positiv zu wählen). Wenden wir uns zunächst dem *p-Fall* zu, so nimmt die Felddarstellung Gl. (49.1p) bzw. (49.3p) mit (60.1) die folgende Gestalt an

Streufall:

$$v(\mathfrak{r}) = v_0(\mathfrak{r}) - \frac{i}{4\pi} \int_{-\infty}^{\infty} \frac{\overline{\psi}(\alpha)}{\sqrt{1-\alpha^2}} e^{i(\alpha x + \sqrt{1-\alpha^2}|z|)} d\alpha, \quad z \gtrless 0, \tag{60.2p}$$

bzw.

Beugungsfall:

$$v(\mathfrak{r}) = \frac{1}{2\pi} \int_{-\infty}^{\infty} \overline{\varphi}(\alpha) e^{i(\alpha x + \sqrt{1-\alpha^2}|z|)} d\alpha + \begin{cases} 0, & z > 0 \\ v_0(\mathfrak{r}) - v^0(\mathfrak{r}), & z < 0 \end{cases} \tag{60.3p}$$

mit den *Fourier-Amplituden*

$$^{-}(\alpha) = \int_S \psi(x) e^{-i\alpha x} dx \tag{60.4p}$$

bzw.

$$\overline{\varphi}(\alpha) = \int_L \varphi(x) e^{-i\alpha x} dx, \tag{60.5p}$$

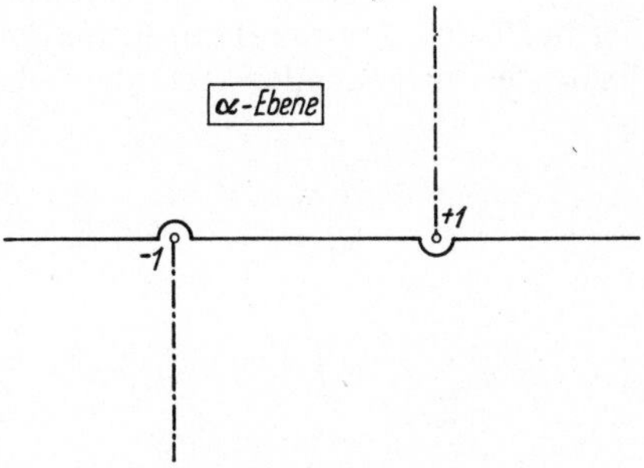

Fig. 40. Integrationsweg bei der Fourier-Darstellung der Hankel-Funktion.

auf deren Bestimmung das Problem nunmehr reduziert ist. Die Größe $\overline{\psi}(\alpha)$ ist in unserer elektromagnetischen Terminologie (vgl. Ziff. 46 und 47) als *Fourier-Transformierte* des *Flächenstromes* auf dem Schirm zu unterpretieren, während $\overline{\varphi}(\alpha)$ die *Transformierte* des *Feldes* v *in der Öffnung* bedeutet. Zur Berechnung dieser Größen stehen die Gln. (49.10p) zur Verfügung, die mit (60.1) umgeschrieben werden können:

(Streuung)

$$\int_{-\infty}^{\infty} \frac{\overline{\psi}(\alpha)}{\sqrt{1-\alpha^2}} e^{i\alpha x} d\alpha = \begin{cases} -4\pi i v_0 & \textit{für } x \textit{ auf } (S) \\ -4\pi i [v_0 - \varphi(x)] & \textit{für } x \textit{ auf } (L), \end{cases} \tag{60.6p}$$

(Beugung)

$$\int_{-\infty}^{\infty} \sqrt{1-\alpha^2}\, \overline{\varphi}(\alpha) e^{i\alpha x} d\alpha = \begin{cases} -\pi i \left[2 \frac{\partial v_0}{\partial z} + \psi(x)\right] & \textit{für } x \textit{ auf } (S) \\ -2\pi i \frac{\partial v_0}{\partial z} & \textit{für } x \textit{ auf } (L). \end{cases} \tag{60.7p}$$

Aus (60.4p) und (60.6p) folgt somit für $\overline{\psi}$ das System *simultaner Integralgleichungen* für die *Streuung*

$$\left.\begin{aligned} &\int_{-\infty}^{\infty} \overline{\psi}(\alpha) e^{i\alpha x} d\alpha = 0 && \textit{für } x \textit{ auf } (L), \\ &\int_{-\infty}^{\infty} \frac{\overline{\psi}(\alpha)}{\sqrt{1-\alpha^2}} e^{i\alpha x} d\alpha = -4\pi i v_0 && \textit{für } x \textit{ auf } (S), \end{aligned}\right\} \tag{60.8p}$$

[1] G. N. WATSON: Theory of Besselfunctions, S. 416. Cambridge 1944.

während für $\overline{\varphi}$ aus (60.5*p*) und (60.7*p*) für die *Beugung* folgt

$$\left.\begin{aligned} &\int_{-\infty}^{\infty} \overline{\varphi}(\alpha)\, e^{i\alpha x}\, d\alpha = 0 && \textit{für } x \textit{ auf } (S), \\ &\int_{-\infty}^{\infty} \sqrt{1-\alpha^2}\, \overline{\varphi}(\alpha)\, e^{i\alpha x}\, d\alpha = -2\pi i \frac{\partial v_0}{\partial z} && \textit{für } x \textit{ auf } (L). \end{aligned}\right\} \qquad (60.9p)$$

Die beiden Integralgleichungen der Systeme (60.8*p*) und (60.9*p*) beziehen sich je auf einen der zueinander komplementären Teile (S) bzw. (L) der x-Achse, sie werden als „*duale*" *Integralgleichungen* bezeichnet[1]. Man erhält sie auch unmittelbar, wenn man für die Lösung des Beugungsproblems den *Fourier-Ansatz* (60.2*p*) bzw. (60.3*p*) macht und die Stetigkeit von $\partial v/\partial z$ in (L) sowie das Verschwinden von v auf (S) fordert. Dieser Weg ist von BOOKER und CLEMMOW[2] sowie HÖNL[3] eingeschlagen worden.

61. Zusammenhang zwischen Streu- und Beugungsproblem. Kantenbedingung. Die beiden Fourier-Ansätze (60.2*p*) und (60.3*p*) und die daraus folgenden Integralgleichungen sind hier im Gegensatz zu den Ansätzen (49.1*p*) und (49.3*p*) (die sich auf komplementäre Integrationsbereiche beziehen) nahezu identisch, daher muß zwischen $\overline{\psi}$ und $\overline{\varphi}$ ein *einfacher Zusammenhang* bestehen. Man erhält ihn leicht durch Fourier-Transformation von (60.6*p*) bzw. (60.7*p*) (ein Querstrich bedeutet im folgenden stets den Übergang zur Fourier-Transformierten)

$$-\frac{\overline{\psi}}{\sqrt{1-\alpha^2}} = 2i \int_{-\infty}^{\infty} v_0\, e^{-i\alpha x}\, dx - 2i \int_L \varphi(x)\, e^{-i\alpha x}\, dx = 2i\,(\overline{v}_0 - \overline{\varphi}) \qquad (61.1p)$$

bzw.

$$\sqrt{1-\alpha^2}\, \overline{\varphi} = -i \int_{-\infty}^{\infty} \frac{\partial v_0}{\partial z}\, e^{-i\alpha x}\, dx - \frac{i}{2} \int_S \psi(x)\, e^{-i\alpha x}\, dx = -i\, \overline{\frac{\partial v_0}{\partial z}} - \frac{i}{2}\, \overline{\psi}. \qquad (61.2p)$$

Diese beiden Gleichungen sind *identisch:* da v_0 eine Lösung der Wellengleichung ist, gilt nämlich

$$\overline{\frac{\partial v_0}{\partial z}} = i\sqrt{1-\alpha^2}\, \overline{v}_0. \qquad (61.3)$$

Der gesuchte Zusammenhang lautet also

$$\overline{\psi}(\alpha) = -2i\sqrt{1-\alpha^2}\, [\overline{v}_0(\alpha) - \overline{\varphi}(\alpha)]. \qquad (61.4p)$$

Die Gl. (61.4*p*), die die Fourier-Transformierten des Flächenstroms und des Feldes in der Öffnung miteinander verknüpft, führt auch die analytische Vereinfachung vor Augen, die die Unterscheidung zwischen Streu- und Beugungsproblem im allgemeinen mit sich bringt. $\overline{v}_0$ hat nämlich — falls wir für v_0 eine *ebene* Welle annehmen — δ-funktionsartigen Charakter, daher muß also nach (61.4*p*) *entweder* $\overline{\psi}$ *oder* $\overline{\varphi}$ ebenfalls eine δ-artige Singularität besitzen. Im Streufall ist nun gerade $\overline{\psi}$, im Beugungsfall hingegen $\overline{\varphi}$ *singularitätenfrei* (während umgekehrt $\overline{\varphi}$ im Streu- und $\overline{\psi}$ im Beugungsfall δ-Singularitäten besitzen).

[1] Vgl. E. C. TICHMARCH: Theory of Fourier-Integrals, S. 334. Oxford 1937. — C. J. TRANTER: Integral Transforms in Mathematical Physics, 2. Aufl., Kap. 8. London u. New York 1956.

[2] H. G. BOOKER u. P. C. CLEMMOW: Proc. Inst. Elect. Engrs. **97**, 11 (1950). — P. C. CLEMMOW: Proc. Roy. Soc. Lond. **205**, 286 (1951).

[3] H. HÖNL: Z. Physik **131**, 290 (1952).

Übrigens ist (61.1*p*) mit *willkürlichem* $\varphi(x)$ die allgemeine Lösung der zweiten *(inhomogenen)* Integralgleichung (60.8*p*), (61.2*p*) mit *willkürlichem* $\psi(x)$ diejenige der zweiten Integralgleichung (60.9*p*). Setzt man diese Lösungen jeweils in die *(homogenen)* Integralgleichungen ein, so kommt man zu den Rayleighschen Integralgleichungen (49.4*p*) bzw. (49.2*p*) zurück. Ebenso kommt man zu ihnen zurück, wenn man (60.4*p*) bzw. (60.5*p*) als allgemeine Lösung der jeweils ersten (homogenen) Integralgleichung von (60.8*p*) bzw. (60.9*p*) betrachtet und sie in die (inhomogene) Gleichung einsetzt. Die Integration über α läßt sich nämlich dann ausführen (wenn man die Integrationsreihenfolge vertauscht) und ergibt gerade den „Hankel-Kern" $H_0^{(1)}(|x-x'|)$ bzw. $(d^2/dx^2+1)\,H_0^{(1)}(|x-x'|)$[1].

Die Schwierigkeit bei der Auflösung des Systems (60.8*p*) bzw. (60.9*p*) besteht aber gerade in der *simultanen* Erfüllung jeweils *beider* Integralgleichungen für $\bar{\psi}$ bzw. für $\bar{\varphi}$. Eine *Kantenbedingung* ist bei der Aufstellung der Gl. (60.8*p*) bzw. (60.9*p*) explizit nicht in Erscheinung getreten, es erhebt sich daher zunächst die Frage, ob diese Integralgleichungssysteme *eindeutige* Lösungen besitzen. Implizit haben wir allerdings gewisse einschränkende Voraussetzungen hinsichtlich des Verhaltens von $\bar{\psi}$ bzw. $\bar{\varphi}$ für $\alpha\to\infty$ gemacht, um die Konvergenz entsprechender Integrale zu erreichen und die stillschweigend vorausgesetzte Vertauschbarkeit entsprechender Integrationsreihenfolgen zu gewährleisten. Das Verhalten der Fourier-Amplituden $\bar{\psi}$ und $\bar{\varphi}$ für $|\alpha|\to\infty$ ist nun bestimmend für die Art einer eventuellen Singularität der Größen ψ und φ. In Ziff. 46 und 48 sahen wir aber, daß ψ sich bei Annäherung an den Rand ($\varrho\to 0$) wie $\varrho^{-\frac{1}{2}}$ verhalten muß, während φ dann wie $\varrho^{\frac{1}{2}}$ verschwindet. Einer Singularität vom Charakter $\varrho^{-\frac{1}{2}}$ für $\varrho\to 0$ entspricht bei der Fourier-Analyse ein Verhalten wie $\alpha^{-\frac{1}{2}}$ für $|\alpha|\to\infty$, während sich dann $\bar{\varphi}$ in Übereinstimmung mit Gl. (61.4*p*) wie $\alpha^{-\frac{3}{2}}$ verhalten muß. Daß *keine* einschneidenderen Forderungen an $\bar{\psi}$ bzw. $\bar{\varphi}$ zu stellen sind, konnten Hönl und Maue[2] beweisen, indem sie zeigten, daß das zu (60.8*p*) bzw. (60.9*p*) gehörige *homogene* Integralgleichungssystem *keine* Lösung zuläßt, die die Kantenbedingung verletzt, womit die *Eindeutigkeit* des inhomogenen Systems indirekt bewiesen ist, da unser Integrationsproblem bei Hinzunahme der Kantenbedingung eindeutig definiert ist.

62. Zusammenhang zwischen Fourier-Amplitude und Strahlungscharakteristik. Um zu einer physikalisch anschaulichen Deutung der Größen $\bar{\psi}$ und $\bar{\varphi}$ zu gelangen, betrachten wir Aufpunkte, die sehr weit vom Schirm bzw. der Öffnung entfernt sind und wählen den Koordinatenursprung auf (*S*) bzw. auf (*L*). Es gibt dann stets Aufpunkte, deren Koordinaten *groß* gegen die Dimensionen von Schirm oder Öffnung sowie auch groß gegen die Wellenlänge sind *(Fernfeld)*. Wir betrachten nun zunächst noch einmal die Darstellung des Streu- bzw. Beugungsfeldes mit Hilfe der vom Schirm bzw. der Öffnung ausstrahlenden *Zylinderwellen* und können nun die Größe $R=[(x-x')^2+z^2]^{\frac{1}{2}}$ für das Fernfeld entwickeln:

$$R = r - x'\sin\vartheta + \cdots, \qquad \frac{x'}{r} \ll 1, \tag{62.1}$$

falls r, ϑ die Polarkoordinaten des Aufpunktes sind (ϑ ist dabei der gegen die positive z-Achse zu messende *Beugungswinkel*, s. Fig. 38 und 39 auf S. 304). Wegen der Voraussetzung $r \gg 1$ kann man für die Zylinderwelle (Hankelsche Funktion) $H_0^{(1)}(R)$ die *Hankelsche Näherung*

$$\left.\begin{aligned} &H_0^{(1)}(R) \to \sqrt{\frac{2}{\pi i}}\cdot\frac{e^{ir}}{\sqrt{r}}\,e^{-ix'\sin\vartheta} \\ \text{bzw.}\quad &\frac{\partial}{\partial z}H_0^{(1)}(R) \to i\sqrt{\frac{2}{\pi i}}\,\frac{e^{ir}}{\sqrt{r}}\cos\vartheta\,e^{-ix'\sin\vartheta} \end{aligned}\right\} \tag{62.2}$$

[1] E. Groschwitz u. H. Hönl: Z. Physik **131**, 305 (1952).

[2] H. Hönl u. A.-W. Maue: Z. Physik **132**, 569 (1952).

verwenden. Führen wir diese Näherung in die Felddarstellung (49.1 p) bzw. (49.3 p) ein, so folgt

(Streuung)

$$v(\mathfrak{r}) \to v_0(\mathfrak{r}) - \frac{i}{2\sqrt{2\pi i}} \frac{e^{ir}}{\sqrt{r}} \int\limits_S \psi(x')\, e^{-ix'\sin\vartheta} dx', \quad z \gtrless 0, \quad r \to \infty \tag{62.3p}$$

bzw.

(Beugung)

$$v(\mathfrak{r}) \to \pm \frac{1}{\sqrt{2\pi i}} \frac{e^{ir}}{\sqrt{r}} \cos\vartheta \int\limits_L \varphi(x')\, e^{-ix'\sin\vartheta} dx' + \begin{Bmatrix} 0, & z>0 \\ v_0(\mathfrak{r}) - v^0(\mathfrak{r}), & z<0 \end{Bmatrix} r \to \infty. \tag{62.4p}$$

Diese Formeln haben die Gestalt der Ausstrahlungsbedingung (17.3 a). Setzen wir sie in die Form

(Streuung)

$$v(\mathfrak{r}) \to v_0(\mathfrak{r}) + A_p(\vartheta) \frac{e^{ir}}{\sqrt{r}}, \quad z \gtrless 0, \quad r \to \infty, \tag{63.3'p}$$

(Beugung)

$$v(\mathfrak{r}) \to \pm B_p(\vartheta) \frac{e^{ir}}{\sqrt{r}} + \begin{Bmatrix} 0, & z>0 \\ v_0(\mathfrak{r}) - v^0(\mathfrak{r}), & z<0 \end{Bmatrix} \quad r \to \infty \tag{63.4'p}$$

mit

(Streuung)

$$A_p(\vartheta) = -\frac{i}{2\sqrt{2\pi i}} \int\limits_S \psi(x')\, e^{-ix'\sin\vartheta} dx' \tag{62.5p}$$

bzw.

(Beugung)

$$B_p(\vartheta) = \frac{1}{\sqrt{2\pi i}} \cos\vartheta \int\limits_L \varphi(x')\, e^{-ix'\sin\vartheta} dx', \tag{62.6p}$$

so beschreibt $A_p(\vartheta)$ bzw. $B_p(\vartheta)$ die *Winkelabhängigkeit* des *Fernfeldes* (Fraunhofersches Beugungsfeld).

Vergleichen wir das Strahlungsdiagramm (62.5 p), (62.6 p) mit den Definitionsgleichungen (60.4 p) und (60.5 p) so erhalten wir

(Streuung)

$$A_p(\vartheta) = -\frac{i}{2\sqrt{2\pi i}} \overline{\psi}(\sin\vartheta) \tag{62.7p}$$

(Beugung)

$$B_p(\vartheta) = \frac{1}{\sqrt{2\pi i}} \cos\vartheta\, \overline{\varphi}(\sin\vartheta). \tag{62.8p}$$

Die Größen $\overline{\psi}(\sin\vartheta)$ bzw. $\overline{\varphi}(\sin\vartheta)$ stimmen also (für $|\alpha| \leqq 1$) im wesentlichen mit dem Fraunhoferschen Beugungsfeld überein. Die *Strahlungscharakteristik des Fernfeldes* ist also durch die *Fourier-Transformierte* des *Oberflächenstromes* auf dem Schirm bzw. des *Feldes in der Öffnung* gegeben. Diesen bemerkenswerten Zusammenhang erhält man auch unmittelbar aus der Fourier-Darstellung des Feldes (60.2 p) bzw. (60.3 p), wenn man für die Aufpunkte des Fernfeldes die *Sattelpunktmethode* anwendet. Hierzu führt man am besten Polarkoordinaten $x = r\sin\vartheta$, $z = r\cos\vartheta$, $\alpha = \sin\chi$, $\sqrt{1-\alpha^2} = \cos\chi$ ein, dann nimmt der Exponent der

Gln. (60.2*p*), (60.3*p*) für $z \gtrless 0$, $\vartheta \lessgtr \frac{\pi}{2}$ die Gestalt $\pm i r \cos(\vartheta \mp \chi)$ an. Der Sattelpunkt liegt also bei $\chi = \pm\, \vartheta$ $\left(\text{mod.}\ \pi,\ |\chi| < \frac{\pi}{2}\right)$ und die *langsam veränderlichen* Faktoren $\overline{\psi}$ und $\overline{\varphi}$ können mit $\alpha = \sin\vartheta$, $\sqrt{1-\alpha^2} = \pm\cos\vartheta$ vor das Integral genommen werden. Dieses Verfahren ist selbstverständlich nur so lange anwendbar, als kein *Pol* von $\overline{\psi}$ oder $\overline{\varphi}$ in der *Nähe des Sattelpunktes liegt*[1]. Solche Pole repräsentieren im allgemeinen die im Sinne der geometrischen Optik *reflektierte Welle*. Wenn man diese von vorne herein in Ansatz bringt (vgl. den Unterschied im Ansatz für das Streu- bzw. Beugungsproblem), treten also keine Pole auf (bei der Beugung an der Halbebene läßt sich ein Pol weder bei $\overline{\psi}$ noch bei $\overline{\varphi}$ vermeiden, da sie auf der Grenze zwischen Beugung und Streuung liegt, vgl. Ziff. 115).

Gl. (62.3*p*) bzw. (62.4*p*) ist in Übereinstimmung mit der geläufigen Vorstellung, daß das Fraunhofersche Beugungsfeld durch Superposition von ebenen Wellen zustande kommt, die von den einzelnen Punkten des Schirmes bzw. der Öffnung in die Richtung ϑ abgestrahlt werden[2]. Andererseits ist darauf hinzuweisen, daß $\overline{\psi}$ bzw. $\overline{\varphi}$ für $|\alpha| > 1$ die Bedeutung einer Amplitude hat, die zu *inhomogenen* ebenen Wellen gehört (nämlich solchen, die mit wachsendem $|z|$ eine Dämpfung erleiden). Dies folgt unmittelbar aus der Gl. (60.2*p*) bzw. (60.3*p*), da für $|\alpha| > 1$ der Faktor von $|z|$ in der Klammer des Exponenten positiv imaginär wird. Übrigens treten solche inhomogenen Wellen bereits bei der Fourier-Analyse der Zylinderwelle (60.1) auf; man wird daher *nicht* vermuten dürfen, daß sie die Rolle von Oberflächenwellen etwa längs des Schirmes (S) spielen.

63. Zurückführung der Integralgleichungen auf ein algebraisches Problem. Die beiden dualen Integralgleichungen (60.8*p*) bzw. (60.9*p*) konnten bis jetzt nur für den Fall der Halbebene in geschlossener Form gelöst werden (s. Ziff. 115). Man wird daher in allgemeineren Fällen nach Näherungsmethoden suchen müssen. Hier ist folgendes Verfahren naheliegend[3]. Wir behandeln beispielsweise den Streufall (60.8*p*) und konstruieren ein orthonormales Funktionensystem $\overline{\psi}_\nu(\alpha)$ in der Form

$$\overline{\psi}_\nu(\alpha) = \int_S \psi_\nu(x)\, e^{-i\alpha x}\, dx. \tag{63.1}$$

Wesentlich ist hier die Darstellung der $\overline{\psi}_\nu(\alpha)$ durch ein Fourier-Integral über den *begrenzten Bereich* (S) (Schirm). Für die $\psi_\nu(x)$ kann ein beliebiges bezüglich (S) orthogonales Funktionensystem gewählt werden (wie es sich mit Hilfe des Schmidtschen Orthogonalisierungsverfahrens[4] stets konstruieren läßt); es folgt dann (bei entsprechender Normierung)

$$\int_{-\infty}^{\infty} \overline{\psi}_\nu(\alpha)\, \overline{\psi}_\mu^*(\alpha)\, d\alpha = 2\pi \int_S \psi_\nu(x)\, \psi_\mu(x)\, dx = \delta_{\nu\mu} \tag{63.2}$$

[$\overline{\psi}_\mu^*$ ist das konjugiert komplexe von $\overline{\psi}_\mu$; die $\psi_\nu(x)$ wollen wir *reell* wählen]. Wir entwickeln nun die Funktionen $e^{ix\alpha}$ und $v_0(x, 0)$ im Bereich (S)

$$\left.\begin{aligned} e^{ix\alpha} &= 2\pi \sum_{\nu=0}^{\infty} \overline{\psi}_\nu^*(\alpha)\, \psi_\nu(x), \\ -4\pi i\, v_0(x, 0) &= \sum_{\nu=0}^{\infty} c_\nu \psi_\nu(x) \end{aligned}\right\} \text{ auf } (S) \tag{63.3}$$

---

[1] Vgl. P.C. CLEMMOW: Proc. Roy. Soc. Lond. **205**, 286 (1951).

[2] Auch die Kirchhoffsche Beugungstheorie läßt sich durch Überlagerung von *ebenen* Wellen aufbauen; vgl. H. SCHEFFERS: Ann. Phys. **42**, 211 (1942).

[3] K. WESTPFAHL: Z. Physik **141**, 354 (1955). — C. J. TRANTER: Integraltransforms in Mathematical Physics, 2. Aufl., Kap. 8. 1956.

[4] Vgl. G. HAMEL: Integralgleichungen, 2. Aufl., S. 60. Berlin 1949.

und machen für $\overline{\psi}(\alpha)$ den Ansatz

$$\overline{\psi}(\alpha) = \sum_{\nu=0}^{\infty} a_\nu \overline{\psi}_\nu(\alpha). \tag{63.4}$$

Gl. (63.4) erfüllt nun die erste Integralgleichung (60.8*p*) zufolge der nur über (*S*) geführten Integration in Gl. (63.1) *gliedweise*. Setzt man (63.4) in die zweite Gl. (60.8*p*) ein, so erhält man bei Beachtung von (63.3)

$$\sum_{\nu=0}^{\infty} \sum_{\mu=0}^{\infty} a_\nu C_{\nu\mu} \psi_\mu(x) = \sum_{\mu=0}^{\infty} c_\mu \psi_\mu(x) \tag{63.5}$$

mit

$$C_{\nu\mu} = 2\pi \int_{-\infty}^{\infty} \frac{\overline{\psi}_\nu(\alpha)\,\overline{\psi}_\mu^*(\alpha)}{\sqrt{1-\alpha^2}}\, d\alpha. \tag{63.6}$$

Wir erhalten also durch Vergleich der Koeffizienten von $\psi_\nu(x)$ auf beiden Seiten von (63.5) das System

$$\sum_{\nu=0}^{\infty} a_\nu C_{\nu\mu} = c_\mu, \qquad \mu = 0, 1, 2, \ldots \tag{63.7}$$

unendlich vieler linearer Gleichungen für die Entwicklungskoeffizienten a_ν. Mit ihrer Hilfe erhalten wir die Lösung der dualen Integralgleichungen (60.8*p*) in der Gestalt (63.4) und damit gleichzeitig die Lösung der Rayleighschen Integralgleichung (49.2*p*) über (60.4*p*) in der Form

$$\psi(x) = \sum_{\nu=0}^{\infty} a_\nu \psi_\nu(x). \tag{63.8}$$

Die Auflösung des Systems (63.7) läßt sich im allgemeinen nur näherungsweise durchführen, indem man es bei $\nu = \mu = N$ *abbricht* und aus dem so gewonnenen endlichen System die ersten N a_ν berechnet. Wir kommen darauf und auf damit zusammenhängende Eindeutigkeits- und Konvergenzfragen in Ziff. 107 noch zurück. Bezüglich der Wahl des Funktionensystems $\overline{\psi}_\nu(\alpha)$ bzw. $\psi_\nu(x)$ in (63.1) vergleiche man auch Ziff. 95. Die Auflösung von (60.9*p*) erfolgt nach dem gleichen Schema, nur hat man hier für die [bezüglich (*L*) orthogonalen] $\varphi_\nu(x)$ noch die Erfüllung der Randbedingung „$\varphi_\nu = 0$ auf dem Rand von (*L*)“ zu verlangen (vgl. Ziff. 49 und 120).

64. Umformung der Integralgleichungen für die Fernfeldamplitude. Die oben entwickelte Lösungsmethode kann auch als *Ritzsches* Verfahren zur Lösung eines Variationsproblems aufgefaßt werden (s. Ziff. 107). Wir wollen nun noch eine anders geartete *Iterationsmethode* zur Berechnung der Fourier-Amplituden $\overline{\psi}$ bzw. $\overline{\varphi}$ entwickeln[1]. Zu diesem Zweck soll die Fourier-Transformation in einem etwas anderen Zusammenhang auf die Rayleighschen Integralgleichungen von Ziff. 49 angewandt werden. Zunächst bemerken wir, daß die Größen ψ (Flächenstrom) bzw. φ (Feld in der Öffnung) nur auf (*S*) bzw. in (*L*) definiert sind. Wir setzen fest, daß sie außerhalb dieser Bereiche verschwinden sollen, wie dies auch in den Gln. (60.4*p*) bzw. (60.5*p*) zum Ausdruck kommt. Diesem Sachverhalt kann man dadurch Rechnung tragen, daß man die „*Sieboperatoren*“

$$\Theta_L(x) = \begin{Bmatrix} 1 & \textit{für } x \textit{ auf } (L) \\ 0 & \textit{für } x \textit{ auf } (S) \end{Bmatrix} \tag{64.1}$$

[1] K. Westpfahl: l. c. und Ann. Phys. (7) 4, 283 (1959).

und

$$\Theta_S(x) = 1 - \Theta_L(x) = \begin{Bmatrix} 0 & \textit{für } x \textit{ auf } (L) \\ 1 & \textit{für } x \textit{ auf } (S) \end{Bmatrix} \tag{64.1a}$$

einführt.

Es folgt dann auseinander:

$$\left.\begin{aligned} \Theta_L \psi = 0 \rightarrow \Theta_S \psi = \psi \\ \Theta_S \varphi = 0 \rightarrow \Theta_L \varphi = \varphi \end{aligned}\right\} \tag{64.2}$$

Andererseits lassen sich die auf die Ebene $z=0$ bezüglichen Gln. (49.10p) jetzt einfacher in der Form schreiben:

$$\left.\begin{aligned} &(\textit{Streuung}) \quad \int_{-\infty}^{\infty} \psi(x') H_0^{(1)}(|x-x'|)\, dx' = -4i\,[v_0 - \varphi(x)] \\ &(\textit{Beugung}) \quad \left(\frac{d^2}{dx^2}+1\right)\int_{-\infty}^{\infty} \varphi(x') H_0^{(1)}(|x-x'|)\, dx' = -i\left[2\frac{\partial v_0}{\partial z} + \psi(x)\right], \end{aligned}\right\} \tag{64.3p}$$

wobei beide Seiten dieser Gleichungen infolge der „*Nebenbedingung*" (64.2) für den *gesamten* Bereich $-\infty < x < \infty$ Gültigkeit haben. Der Vorteil dieser Schreibweise besteht darin, daß nun die Integrale linkerhand vom Faltungstypus (im Sinne der Fourier-Transformation) sind. Unter Verwendung der üblichen *Faltungssymbolik*

$$\int_{-\infty}^{\infty} f(x')\, g(x-x')\, dx' = f * g = g * f \tag{64.4}$$

können wir daher (64.3p) auch schreiben

$$\left.\begin{aligned} \psi * H &= -4i\,(v_0 - \varphi)\,, \\ \left(\frac{d^2}{dx^2}+1\right)\varphi * H &= -i\left(2\frac{\partial v_0}{\partial z} + \psi\right) \end{aligned}\right\} \tag{64.5p}$$

mit

$$H(x) = H_0^{(1)}(|x|)\,. \tag{64.6}$$

Wir legen hier wie bisher die Fourier-Transformation in der Form

$$\left.\begin{aligned} \bar{f}(\alpha) &= \int_{-\infty}^{\infty} f(x)\, e^{-i\alpha x}\, dx \\ f(x) &= \frac{1}{2\pi}\int_{-\infty}^{\infty} \bar{f}(\alpha)\, e^{i\alpha x}\, d\alpha \end{aligned}\right\} \tag{64.7}$$

zugrunde und benutzen die aus den der Definition (64.4) unmittelbar folgenden Regeln

$$\left.\begin{aligned} &\overline{f*g} = \bar{f}\,\bar{g}\,, \qquad \overline{fg} = \bar{f} * \bar{g} \\ &\bar{f} * \bar{g} = \frac{1}{2\pi}\int_{-\infty}^{\infty} \bar{f}(\alpha')\, \bar{g}(\alpha-\alpha')\, d\alpha'. \end{aligned}\right\} \tag{64.7a}$$

mit

Beachtet man nun die aus (60.1) folgende Formel

$$\bar{H}(\alpha) = \frac{2}{\sqrt{1-\alpha^2}} \tag{64.8}$$

und die allgemeine Regel

$$\overline{\frac{d^2 f}{dx^2}} = -\alpha^2 \bar{f} \qquad \left(\text{falls } f \text{ und } \frac{df}{dx} \text{ für } x \rightarrow \pm\infty \text{ verschwindet}\right), \tag{64.9}$$

so kommt man durch Fourier-Transformation von (64.5 *p*) unmittelbar auf (61.1 *p*) bzw. (61.2 *p*) zurück und damit auf die Integralgleichungen für die Fourier-Transformierten $\overline{\psi}(\alpha)$ und $\overline{\varphi}(\alpha)$, Gl. (60.6 *p*) und (60.7 *p*).

Wir wollen jedoch jetzt, um einen neuen Gesichtspunkt zu gewinnen, die Gln. (64.5 *p*) mit Θ_S bzw. Θ_L multiplizieren und erhalten so bei Beachtung von (64.2)

$$\left.\begin{aligned} &\Theta_S\,(\psi * H) = \psi^0, \\ &\Theta_L\Big(\frac{d^2}{d x^2}+1\Big)\,(\varphi * H) = 4\varphi^0 \end{aligned}\right\} \qquad (64.10\,p)$$

mit

$$\psi^0 = -\,4 i\,\Theta_S\, v_0, \quad \varphi^0 = -\frac{i}{2}\,\Theta_L\,\frac{\partial v_0}{\partial z}. \qquad (64.10'\,p)$$

Die Anwendung der Fourier-Transformation *(Faltungssatz)* liefert jetzt bei Berücksichtigung von Gl. (64.7 *a*) sowie der Nebenbedingung (64.2) für die *Streuung*

$$\left.\begin{aligned} &\overline{\Theta}_S * (\overline{H}\,\overline{\psi}) = \overline{\psi}^0 \\ &\overline{\Theta}_S * \overline{\psi} = \overline{\psi} \end{aligned}\right\} \qquad (64.11\,p)$$

bzw. für die *Beugung* [bei Berücksichtigung der Gln. (64.9) und (64.8)]

$$\left.\begin{aligned} &\overline{\Theta}_L * (\overline{H}^{-1}\,\overline{\varphi}) = \overline{\varphi}^0 \\ &\overline{\Theta}_L * \overline{\varphi} = \overline{\varphi}\,. \end{aligned}\right\} \qquad (64.12\,p)$$

Wir haben also für $\overline{\psi}$ bzw. $\overline{\varphi}$ zwei simultane Integralgleichungen vom *Faltungstypus* gewonnen, die mit den dualen Integralgleichungen (60.8 *p*) bzw. (60.9 *p*) äquivalent sind. Ausführlich geschrieben lauten die Gln. (64.11 *p*) bzw. (64.12 *p*) bei Beachtung von (64.7 a) und (64.8)

(Streuung)

$$\left.\begin{aligned} &\frac{1}{\pi}\int\limits_{-\infty}^{\infty}\frac{\overline{\psi}(\alpha')}{\sqrt{1-\alpha'^2}}\,\overline{\Theta}_S(\alpha-\alpha')\,d\alpha' = \overline{\psi}^0(\alpha) \\ &\overline{\psi}(\alpha) = \frac{1}{2\pi}\int\limits_{-\infty}^{\infty}\overline{\psi}(\alpha')\,\overline{\Theta}_S(\alpha-\alpha')\,d\alpha' \end{aligned}\right\} \qquad (64.11'\,p)$$

(Beugung)

$$\left.\begin{aligned} &\frac{1}{4\pi}\int\limits_{-\infty}^{\infty}\overline{\varphi}(\alpha')\sqrt{1-\alpha'^2}\,\overline{\Theta}_L(\alpha-\alpha')\,d\alpha' = \overline{\varphi}^0(\alpha) \\ &\overline{\varphi}(\alpha) = \frac{1}{2\pi}\int\limits_{-\infty}^{\infty}\overline{\varphi}(\alpha')\,\overline{\Theta}_L(\alpha-\alpha')\,d\alpha'. \end{aligned}\right\} \qquad (64.12'\,p)$$

Man erhält die Gln. (64.11′ *p*) bzw. (64.12′ *p*) übrigens auch unmittelbar aus (60.8 *p*) bzw. (60.9 *p*), indem man letztere mit $\exp(-i x \alpha')$ multipliziert und jeweils über den Gültigkeitsbereich (L) bzw. (S) der entsprechenden Integralgleichung (bezüglich x) integriert [1].

Für die in den Gln. (64.11 *p*) und (64.12 *p*) auftretenden Funktionen $\overline{\Theta}_S(\alpha)$ und $\overline{\Theta}_L(\alpha)$ bestehen [falls (S) und (L) komplementäre Bereiche sind] die Beziehungen

$$\left.\begin{aligned} &\overline{\Theta}_S * \overline{\Theta}_L = 0, \quad \overline{\Theta}_S + \overline{\Theta}_L = \overline{1} = 2\pi\,\delta(\alpha), \\ &\overline{\Theta}_S * \overline{\Theta}_S = \overline{\Theta}_S, \quad \overline{\Theta}_L * \overline{\Theta}_L = \overline{\Theta}_L, \end{aligned}\right\} \qquad (64.13)$$

[1] Die *homogene* Integralgleichung (64.12′) tritt auch in der Theorie der optischen Abbildung auf; vgl. L. Mandelstam: Festschrift H. Weber, S. 228. Leipzig u. Berlin 1912.

die unmittelbar durch Fourier-Transformation aus den evidenten Gleichungen $\Theta_S \Theta_L = 0$, $\Theta_S + \Theta_L = 1$, $\Theta_S \Theta_S = \Theta_S$ und $\Theta_L \Theta_L = \Theta_L$ folgen. Im Streufall hat also $\overline{\Theta}_L$ δ-funktionsartigen Charakter, während dies im Beugungsfall für $\overline{\Theta}_S$ der Fall ist. Setzt man nun jeweils die zweite Gleichung der Gln. (64.11p) und (64.12p) in die erste ein, so erhält man für $\overline{\psi}$ bzw. $\overline{\varphi}$ je eine einzige Integralgleichung

$$\left.\begin{aligned} &\overline{\Theta}_S * \overline{H}(\overline{\Theta}_S * \overline{\psi}) = \overline{\psi}^0 \quad (\textit{Streuung}) \\ \text{bzw.}\quad &\overline{\Theta}_L * \overline{H}^{-1}(\overline{\Theta}_L * \overline{\varphi}) = \overline{\varphi}^0 \quad (\textit{Beugung}). \end{aligned}\right\} \tag{64.14p}$$

Dies sind Integralgleichungen, die mit Hilfe der „*iterierten Kerne*“

$$\left.\begin{aligned} &K_S(\alpha, \alpha') = \frac{1}{2\pi^2} \int_{-\infty}^{\infty} \overline{\Theta}_S(\alpha - \alpha'')\, \overline{\Theta}_S(\alpha'' - \alpha') \frac{d\alpha''}{\sqrt{1 - \alpha''^2}} \\ \text{bzw.}\quad &K_L(\alpha, \alpha') = \frac{1}{8\pi^2} \int_{-\infty}^{\infty} \overline{\Theta}_L(\alpha - \alpha'') \sqrt{1 - \alpha''^2}\, \overline{\Theta}_L(\alpha'' - \alpha')\, d\alpha'' \end{aligned}\right\} \tag{64.15p}$$

die Gestalt annehmen

$$\int_{-\infty}^{\infty} \overline{\psi}(\alpha')\, K_S(\alpha, \alpha')\, d\alpha' = \overline{\psi}^0(\alpha), \qquad \int_{-\infty}^{\infty} \overline{\varphi}(\alpha')\, K_L(\alpha, \alpha')\, d\alpha' = \overline{\varphi}^0(\alpha); \tag{64.14'p}$$

sie sind jedoch nicht mehr vom einfachen Faltungstypus. Ferner sind die Kerne (64.15p) im allgemeinen recht komplizierte Funktionen. Die $\overline{\Theta}_S$ bzw. $\overline{\Theta}_L$ haben zwar eine einfache Gestalt (beispielsweise ist für den Spalt der Breite $2b$ $\overline{\Theta}_L = 2\frac{\sin b\alpha}{\alpha}$), die in (64.15$p$) geforderte Integration führt jedoch im allgemeinen wegen der Zweiwertigkeit der Wurzel $\sqrt{1-\alpha^2}$ nicht auf elementare Funktionen (eine Ausnahme bildet die Halbebene).

65. Iterationsverfahren im Anschluß an die Kirchhoffsche Lösung. Auf die Integralgleichungen (64.11'p), (64.12'p) kommen wir in Abschn. III c zurück. Zur näherungsweisen Lösung bietet sich folgendes Verfahren an, das wir für Gl. (64.11p) darstellen wollen: In nullter Näherung $\overline{\psi}_0$ setzen wir

$$\overline{H}\, \overline{\psi}_0 = \overline{\psi}^0. \tag{65.1p}$$

Diese Lösung erfüllt übrigens die erste Gl. (64.11p) streng, da nach Gln. (64.10'p) und (64.13) $\overline{\Theta}_S * \overline{\psi}^0 = \overline{\psi}^0$ ist, falls man beachtet, daß für die Faltung das assoziative Gesetz gilt. Die höheren Näherungen lassen sich dann abwechselnd aus den beiden Integralgleichungen (64.11p) berechnen, nämlich nach dem Schema:

$$\left.\begin{aligned} &\overline{H}\, \overline{\psi}_{2n} = \overline{\psi}^0 + \overline{H}\, \overline{\psi}_{2n-1} - \overline{\Theta}_S * \overline{H}\, \overline{\psi}_{2n-1}, \qquad n \geqq 1, \\ &\overline{\psi}_{2n+1} = \overline{\Theta}_S * \overline{\psi}_{2n}, \qquad n \geqq 0. \end{aligned}\right\} \tag{65.2p}$$

Der ersten Zeile von (65.2p) liegt die erste Gleichung (64.11p) zugrunde, die man sich mit Hilfe von (64.13) formal in der Gestalt

$$\overline{H}\, \overline{\psi} = \overline{\psi}^0 + \overline{\Theta}_L * \overline{H}\, \overline{\psi} \tag{65.3p}$$

geschrieben denke [Gl. (65.3p) ist eine Umwandlung der Integralgleichung $\overline{\Theta}_S * \overline{H}\, \overline{\psi} = \overline{\psi}^0$, die von erster Art ist, in eine solche von der zweiten Art; diese Operation hat jedoch zunächst nur formalen Charakter, da $\overline{\Theta}_L$ im Streufall einen δ-funktionsartigen Anteil besitzt]. Die zweite Zeile von (65.2p) folgt unmittelbar aus der zweiten Gleichung (64.11p). Durch unser Iterationsverfahren (65.2p) wird also wechselweise die erste bzw. zweite Integralgleichung (65.3p) erfüllt. Diese Integralgleichungen garantieren in ihrer ursprünglichen Form, Gl. (60.8p), die Stetigkeit des Feldes in der Öffnung bzw. die Erfüllung der Randbedingung auf dem Schirm. Gl. (65.2p) entspricht also genau dem Iterationsverfahren von Franz (Ziff. 37), jedoch ist es hier unmittelbar auf die *Fernfeldamplitude* $\overline{\psi}$ zugeschnitten, bei der das Dilema der *Kantensingularitäten* (Ziff. 38) nicht zu befürchten ist[1].

Das Iterationsverfahren (65.2p) läßt sich noch in eine andere Gestalt bringen, wenn man die ungeraden Schritte eliminiert [indem man die zweite Gleichung (65.2p) in die erste einsetzt]:

$$\overline{\psi}_{2n} = \overline{\psi}_0 + \Omega_S\, \overline{\psi}_{2n-2}, \qquad n \geqq 1, \tag{65.2'p}$$

wobei wir unter Ω_S den Operator

$$\Omega_S = \frac{1}{2\pi}\int\limits_{-\infty}^{\infty}\left\{\overline{\Theta}_S(\alpha-\alpha') - \frac{1}{2\pi}\sqrt{1-\alpha^2}\int\limits_{-\infty}^{\infty}\overline{\Theta}_S(\alpha-\alpha'')\,\frac{\overline{\Theta}_S(\alpha''-\alpha')}{\sqrt{1-\alpha''^2}}\,d\alpha''\right\}\ldots d\alpha' \tag{65.3}$$

verstehen. Gl. (65.2'p) ist aber nichts anderes als eine Iterationsvorschrift zur Lösung der Integralgleichung

$$\overline{\psi} = \overline{\psi}_0 + \Omega_S\,\overline{\psi}, \tag{65.3'p}$$

die man erhält, indem man die zweite Gleichung (64.11p) in Gl. (65.3p) einsetzt. Die Integralgleichung (65.3'p) ist also ebenfalls mit (64.11p) äquivalent; sie ist jedoch im Gegensatz zu (64.14'p) eine Integralgleichung *zweiter Art*, für die man daher die einfache Iterationsmethode (65.2'p) angeben kann. Durch ν-fache Iteration ergibt sich die Lösung für $\nu\to\infty$ in der Form

$$\overline{\psi} = \lim_{\nu\to\infty}\sum_{n=0}^{\nu}\Omega_S^n\,\overline{\psi}_0 = (1-\Omega_S)^{-1}\,\overline{\psi}_0. \tag{65.4p}$$

Gl. (65.4p) ist nichts anderes als die „*Neumannsche Reihe*" für die Integralgleichung (65.3'p). Sie stellt — falls sie konvergiert — tatsächlich eine Lösung dar, wie man erkennt, wenn man (65.3'p) in der Form $(1-\Omega_S)\,\overline{\psi} = \overline{\psi}^0$ schreibt.

Auf ganz entsprechendem Wege läßt sich das Gleichungssystem (64.12p) für die Beugung durch die Neumannsche Reihe

$$\overline{\varphi} = \sum_{n=0}^{\infty}\Omega_L^n\,\overline{\varphi}_0 = (1-\Omega_L)^{-1}\,\overline{\varphi}_0 \tag{65.5p}$$

mit

$$\overline{\varphi}_0 = \overline{H}\,\overline{\varphi}^0 \tag{65.6p}$$

und

$$\Omega_L = \frac{1}{2\pi}\int\limits_{-\infty}^{\infty}\left\{\overline{\Theta}_L(\alpha-\alpha') - \frac{1}{2\pi\sqrt{1-\alpha^2}}\int\limits_{-\infty}^{\infty}\overline{\Theta}_L(\alpha-\alpha'')\sqrt{1-\alpha''^2}\,\overline{\Theta}_L(\alpha''-\alpha')\,d\alpha''\right\}\ldots d\alpha' \quad (65$$

lösen.

Wie sich schon durch den Hinweis auf die Analogie zum Franzschen Verfahren (Ziff. 37) ergibt, liefert unser Iterationsverfahren (65.4p) und (65.5p) eine *schrittweise Verbesserung der Kirchhoffschen Näherung des Fraunhoferschen Fernfeldes*[2]. In der Tat stellen die Größen $\overline{\psi}_0$ bzw. $\overline{\varphi}_0$ im wesentlichen die Kirchhoffsche

[1] Über die Konvergenz des Verfahrens ist allerdings nichts bekannt. Insbesondere liefert es *keine* Entwicklung nach steigenden Potenzen der Wellenlänge λ.

[2] Der Wert des Verfahrens ist jedoch dadurch sehr begrenzt, daß über die Konvergenzeigenschaften nichts bekannt ist.

Form des Fernfeldes im Streu- bzw. Beugungsfall dar. Berechnen wir nämlich die in (62.7*p*), (62.8*p*) definierten Amplituden in der durch die Gln. (64.10′*p*) und (65.1*p*) bzw. (65.6*p*) gegebenen nullten Näherung, so folgt ($\alpha=\sin\vartheta$, ϑ = Beugungswinkel)

Streuung

Beugung

$$\left.\begin{aligned} A_0(\vartheta) &= \pm\frac{1}{2}\sqrt{\frac{2}{\pi i}}\cos\vartheta\cdot\overline{\Theta}_S * \overline{v}_0 \\ B_0(\vartheta) &= \pm\frac{i}{2}\sqrt{\frac{2}{\pi i}}\cdot\overline{\Theta}_L * \overline{\frac{\partial v_0}{\partial z}} \end{aligned}\right\} z \gtrless 0. \qquad (65.8p)$$

Diese Ausdrücke sind aber mit den von der Kirchhoffschen Theorie gelieferten *identisch.* So gilt beispielsweise bei senkrechter Inzidenz einer ebenen Welle $v_0=e^{iz}$ auf einen Spalt (in der xy-Ebene) der Breite $2b$:

$$\overline{\frac{\partial v_0}{\partial z}} = 2\pi i\,\delta(\alpha), \qquad \overline{\Theta}_L(\alpha) = 2\,\frac{\sin\alpha b}{\alpha}$$

damit folgt aus (65.8*p*) für $z>0$

$$B_0(\vartheta) = \sqrt{\frac{2}{\pi i}}\,\frac{\sin(b\sin\vartheta)}{\sin\vartheta},$$

d.h. der bekannte Kirchhoffsche Ausdruck für das Fraunhofersche Beugungsfeld (man beachte, daß wir alle Längen in Vielfachen der Wellenlänge messen).

66. Ergänzung bezüglich des s-Falles. Mit dem *p*-Fall ist nach dem Babinetschen Theorem (27.7) auch der dazu komplementäre *s*-Fall gelöst. Wir geben jedoch zur späteren Verwendung (in Abschn. B Ib) noch die wichtigsten Formeln für den *s*-Fall an. Hier sind die beiden Ansätze (50.7*s*) bzw. (50.8*s*) zuständig, die mit Hilfe von (60.1) umgeschrieben werden können:

(Streuung)

$$v(\mathfrak{r}) = v_0(\mathfrak{r}) \pm \frac{1}{4\pi}\int_{-\infty}^{\infty}\overline{\varphi}(\alpha)\,e^{i(x\alpha+|z|\sqrt{1-\alpha^2})}\,d\alpha, \qquad z \gtrless 0$$

bzw. *(Beugung)*

$$v(\mathfrak{r}) = \mp\frac{i}{2\pi}\int_{-\infty}^{\infty}\frac{\overline{\psi}(\alpha)}{\sqrt{1-\alpha^2}}\,e^{i(x\alpha+|z|\sqrt{1-\alpha^2})}\,d\alpha + \begin{cases} 0, & z>0 \\ v_0(\mathfrak{r})+v^0(\mathfrak{r}), & z<0 \end{cases} \qquad (66.1s)$$

mit den Fourier-Amplituden (Fraunhofersches Fernfeld)

bzw.

$$\left.\begin{aligned} \overline{\varphi}(\alpha) &= \int_S \varphi(x)\,e^{-i\alpha x}\,dx \\ \overline{\psi}(\alpha) &= \int_L \psi(x)\,e^{-i\alpha x}\,dx. \end{aligned}\right\} \qquad (66.2s)$$

Für diese gelten die Beziehungen (50.9*s*) bzw. (50.10*s*), die jetzt lauten

$$\int_{-\infty}^{\infty}\sqrt{1-\alpha^2}\,\overline{\varphi}(\alpha)\,e^{i\alpha x}\,d\alpha = \begin{cases} 4\pi i\left[\dfrac{\partial v_0}{\partial z}-\psi(x)\right], & x \text{ auf } (L) \\ 4\pi i\,\dfrac{\partial v_0}{\partial z}, & x \text{ auf } (S) \end{cases} \qquad (66.3s)$$

bzw.

$$\int_{-\infty}^{\infty}\frac{\overline{\psi}(\alpha)}{\sqrt{1-\alpha^2}}\,e^{i\alpha x}\,d\alpha = \begin{cases} 2\pi i\,v_0, & x \text{ auf } (L) \\ \pi i\,[2v_0+\varphi(x)], & x \text{ auf } (S). \end{cases} \qquad (66.4s)$$

$\overline{\varphi}$ bzw. $\overline{\psi}$ sind hier also aus den dualen Integralgleichungen

$$\left.\begin{aligned}&\int_{-\infty}^{\infty}\overline{\varphi}(\alpha)\, e^{i\alpha x}\, d\alpha = 0, && x \text{ auf } (L)\\ &\int_{-\infty}^{\infty}\sqrt{1-\alpha^2}\,\overline{\varphi}(\alpha)\, e^{i\alpha x} d\alpha = 4\pi i \frac{\partial v_0}{\partial z}, && x \text{ auf } (S)\end{aligned}\right\} \qquad (66.5\,s)$$

bzw.

$$\left.\begin{aligned}&\int_{-\infty}^{\infty}\overline{\psi}(\alpha)\, e^{i\alpha x}\, d\alpha = 0, && x \text{ auf } (S)\\ &\int_{-\infty}^{\infty}\frac{\overline{\psi}(\alpha)}{\sqrt{1-\alpha^2}}\, e^{i\alpha x}\, d\alpha = 2\pi i v_0, && x \text{ auf } (L)\end{aligned}\right\} \qquad (66.6\,s)$$

zu bestimmen. Als Ausdruck des *Babinetschen Theorems* zeigen diese Gleichungen weitgehende Analogie zu denjenigen des p-Falls.

b 2) Vektorielle Theorie[1].

67. Die Integralgleichungen für die Fourier-Transformierten der Flächenstromdichten. Auch im vektoriellen Fall ist es möglich, die in Abschnitt III a 2 gegebene Formulierung des Streu- bzw. Beugungsproblems so umzuschreiben, daß nur noch die Fourier-Transformierte der elektrischen Flächenstromdichte auf dem Schirm bzw. der „magnetischen Flächenstromdichte“ in der Öffnung auftritt. Physikalisch bedeutet dies im wesentlichen wieder den Übergang von den nur auf (S) bzw. (L) definierten Flächenströmen zur *Winkelabhängigkeit des Fraunhoferschen Fernfeldes*. Dieser Übergang bringt es mit sich, daß die für Flächengrößen zu fordernde Kantenbedingung nicht mehr explizit in Erscheinung tritt. Das mathematische Hilfsmittel ist hier die *Fourier-Darstellung des Greenschen Tensors* des freien Raumes (bzw. eben begrenzten Halbraumes), die die Zerlegung in ein Aggregat von ebenen Wellen bedeutet.

Zunächst lautet die Fourier-Zerlegung der Greenschen Funktion des freien Raumes für die dreidimensionale Wellengleichung[2]

$$G(\mathfrak{r}-\mathfrak{r}') = \frac{1}{4\pi}\frac{e^{i|\mathfrak{r}-\mathfrak{r}'|}}{|\mathfrak{r}-\mathfrak{r}'|} = \frac{i}{8\pi^2}\int e^{i(\mathfrak{k}_\pm,\mathfrak{r}-\mathfrak{r}')}\frac{d\mathfrak{k}}{\gamma(\mathfrak{k})} \quad \text{für } z \gtrless 0, \qquad (67.1)$$

dabei bedeute $\mathfrak{k}_\pm$ den *Einheitsvektor*

$$\mathfrak{k}_\pm = (\alpha, \beta, \pm\gamma) = (\mathfrak{k}, \pm\gamma) \qquad (67.2)$$

(das obere Vorzeichen gelte für $z>0$, das untere für $z<0$), während $\mathfrak{k}$ den ebenen Vektor $(\alpha, \beta, 0)$ bezeichne und γ die folgende Bedeutung habe:

$$\gamma(\mathfrak{k}) = \left\{\begin{matrix}\sqrt{1-\mathfrak{k}^2} & \text{für } \mathfrak{k}^2<1\\ i\sqrt{\mathfrak{k}^2-1} & \text{für } \mathfrak{k}^2>1\end{matrix}\right\} \qquad (67.3)$$

(wobei die Wurzeln positiv zu nehmen sind). Ferner soll $d\mathfrak{k}$ für $d\alpha\, d\beta$ stehen. Die Integration in Gl. (67.1) ist über den Bereich $-\infty \cdots \alpha, \beta \cdots +\infty$ zu erstrecken. Mit Hilfe der Beziehung

$$\nabla e^{i(\mathfrak{k}_\pm,\mathfrak{r})} = i\,\mathfrak{k}_\pm\, e^{i(\mathfrak{k}_\pm,\mathfrak{r})} \quad \text{für } z \gtrless 0 \qquad (67.4)$$

[1] K. Westpfahl: Z. Physik **141**, 354 (1955).
[2] H. Weyl: Ann. Physik **60**, 481 (1919).

erhalten wir nun für den *Greenschen Tensor* (12.9) die Fourier-Darstellung

$$\boldsymbol{\Gamma}(\mathfrak{r}-\mathfrak{r}') = \frac{i}{8\pi^2}\int (\mathfrak{k}_\pm \mathfrak{k}_\pm - \mathbf{1})\, e^{i(\mathfrak{k}_\pm, \mathfrak{r}-\mathfrak{r}')} \frac{d\mathfrak{k}}{\gamma(\mathfrak{k})} \quad \text{für } z \gtrless 0. \tag{67.5}$$

Im folgenden ist es einfacher, mit dem in Ziff. 53 eingeführten Hertzschen bzw. Fitzgeraldschen Vektor zu operieren, anstatt mit dem Greenschen Tensor (67.5). Setzen wir also (67.1) in (53.1) bzw. (53.1a) ein, so folgt:

$$\mathfrak{Z}_S(\mathfrak{r}) = -\frac{1}{8\pi^2}\int \overline{\mathfrak{J}}(\mathfrak{k})\, e^{i(\mathfrak{k}_\pm, \mathfrak{r})} \frac{d\mathfrak{k}}{\gamma(\mathfrak{k})} \quad \text{für } z \gtrless 0 \tag{67.6}$$

bzw.

$$\mathfrak{Y}_B(\mathfrak{r}) = -\frac{1}{4\pi^2}\int \overline{\mathfrak{L}}(\mathfrak{k})\, e^{i(\mathfrak{k}_\pm, \mathfrak{r})} \frac{d\mathfrak{k}}{\gamma(\mathfrak{k})} \quad \text{für } z \gtrless 0 \tag{67.6a}$$

mit der *Fourier-Transformierten der elektrischen Flächenstromdichte auf dem Schirm* bzw. der *„magnetischen Flächenstromdichte" in der Öffnung*

$$\overline{\mathfrak{J}}(\mathfrak{k}) = \int_S \mathfrak{J}(\hat{\mathfrak{r}})\, e^{-i(\mathfrak{k}\hat{\mathfrak{r}})}\, d\hat{\mathfrak{r}} \tag{67.7}$$

bzw.

$$\overline{\mathfrak{L}}(\mathfrak{k}) = \int_L \mathfrak{L}(\hat{\mathfrak{r}})\, e^{-i(\mathfrak{k}\hat{\mathfrak{r}})}\, d\hat{\mathfrak{r}}. \tag{67.7a}$$

Gehen wir nun mit der Darstellung (67.6) in die Formeln (53.2) ein, so folgt mit Hilfe von (67.4)

$$\left.\begin{aligned} \mathfrak{E}(\mathfrak{r}) &= \mathfrak{E}_0(\mathfrak{r}) + \frac{1}{8\pi^2}\int [\mathfrak{k}_\pm[\mathfrak{k}_\pm, \overline{\mathfrak{J}}]]\, e^{i(\mathfrak{k}_\pm, \mathfrak{r})} \frac{d\mathfrak{k}}{\gamma(\mathfrak{k})} \\ \mathfrak{H}(\mathfrak{r}) &= \mathfrak{H}_0(\mathfrak{r}) - \frac{1}{8\pi^2}\int [\mathfrak{k}_\pm, \overline{\mathfrak{J}}] \frac{d\mathfrak{k}}{\gamma(\mathfrak{k})}. \end{aligned}\right\} \quad \text{für } z \gtrless 0, \tag{67.8}$$

Durch Zerlegung des Streufeldes in eine zum Schirm (Normale $\mathfrak{n}$) *senkrechte* und eine zu ihm *parallele* Komponente erhält man daraus [$\overline{\mathfrak{J}}$ hat nach Gl. (67.7) keine z-Komponente]:

(Streuung)

$$\left.\begin{aligned} \mathfrak{E}(\mathfrak{r}) &= \mathfrak{E}_0(\mathfrak{r}) \pm \frac{1}{8\pi^2}\,\mathfrak{n}\int (\mathfrak{k}\overline{\mathfrak{J}})\, e^{i(\mathfrak{k}_\pm, \mathfrak{r})}\, d\mathfrak{k} - \frac{1}{8\pi^2}\int \{\mathfrak{k}(\mathfrak{k}\overline{\mathfrak{J}}) - \overline{\mathfrak{J}}\}\, e^{i(\mathfrak{k}_\pm, \mathfrak{r})} \frac{d\mathfrak{k}}{\gamma(\mathfrak{k})} \\ \mathfrak{H}(\mathfrak{r}) &= \mathfrak{H}_0(\mathfrak{r}) + \frac{1}{8\pi^2}\,\mathfrak{n}\int (\mathfrak{n}[\mathfrak{k}\overline{\mathfrak{J}}])\, e^{i(\mathfrak{k}_\pm, \mathfrak{r})} \frac{d\mathfrak{k}}{\gamma(\mathfrak{k})} \mp \frac{1}{8\pi^2}\int [\mathfrak{n}\overline{\mathfrak{J}}]\, e^{i(\mathfrak{k}_\pm, \mathfrak{r})}\, d\mathfrak{k} \\ &\qquad \textit{für } z \gtrless 0. \end{aligned}\right\} \tag{67.9}$$

Ebenso ergibt sich durch Einsetzen von (67.6a) in Gl. (53.2a) die Darstellung

(Beugung)

$$\left.\begin{aligned} \mathfrak{E}(\mathfrak{r}) &= \mp \frac{1}{4\pi^2}\,\mathfrak{n}\int (\mathfrak{n}[\mathfrak{k}\overline{\mathfrak{L}}])\, e^{i(\mathfrak{k}_\pm, \mathfrak{r})} \frac{d\mathfrak{k}}{\gamma(\mathfrak{k})} \\ &\quad - \frac{1}{4\pi^2}\int [\mathfrak{n}\overline{\mathfrak{L}}]\, e^{i(\mathfrak{k}_\pm, \mathfrak{r})}\, d\mathfrak{k} + \begin{cases} 0 & \textit{für } z > 0 \\ \mathfrak{E}_0(\mathfrak{r}) + \mathfrak{E}^0(\mathfrak{r}) & \textit{für } z < 0 \end{cases} \\ \mathfrak{H}(\mathfrak{r}) &= -\frac{1}{4\pi^2}\,\mathfrak{n}\int (\mathfrak{k}\overline{\mathfrak{L}})\, e^{i(\mathfrak{k}_\pm, \mathfrak{r})}\, d\mathfrak{k} \\ &\quad \mp \frac{1}{4\pi^2}\int \{\mathfrak{k}(\mathfrak{k}\overline{\mathfrak{L}}) - \overline{\mathfrak{L}}\}\, e^{i(\mathfrak{k}_\pm, \mathfrak{r})} \frac{d\mathfrak{k}}{\gamma(\mathfrak{k})} + \begin{cases} 0 & \textit{für } z > 0 \\ \mathfrak{H}_0(\mathfrak{r}) + \mathfrak{H}^0(\mathfrak{r}) & \textit{für } z < 0. \end{cases} \end{aligned}\right\} \tag{67.9a}$$

Durch die Gln. (67.9) bzw. (67.9a) haben wir eine Fourier-Darstellung der Feldvektoren gefunden, die für beliebige vektorielle Fourier-Amplituden $\overline{\mathfrak{J}}(\mathfrak{k})$ bzw.

$\overline{\mathfrak{L}}(\mathfrak{k})$ den Maxwellschen Gleichungen genügt (mit Ausnahme der Ebene $z=0$). Die Fourier-Amplituden werden durch die Rand- und Stetigkeitsbedingung auf dieser Ebene festgelegt. Zunächst ergibt sich aus (67.9) ein Sprung der Tangentialkomponente der magnetischen und der Normalkomponente der elektrischen Feldstärke gemäß

$$\left.\begin{aligned}[\mathfrak{n}, \mathfrak{H}_+ - \mathfrak{H}_-] &= \frac{1}{4\pi^2}\int \overline{\mathfrak{J}}\, e^{i(\mathfrak{k}\hat{\mathfrak{r}})}\, d\mathfrak{k}\\ (\mathfrak{n}, \mathfrak{E}_+ - \mathfrak{E}_-) &= \frac{1}{4\pi^2}\int (\mathfrak{k}\overline{\mathfrak{J}})\, e^{i(\mathfrak{k}\hat{\mathfrak{r}})}\, d\mathfrak{k} = -i\,\widehat{\operatorname{div}}[\mathfrak{n}, \mathfrak{H}_+ - \mathfrak{H}_-].\end{aligned}\right\} \tag{67.10}$$

Entsprechend folgt für diese Sprünge aus Gl. (67.9a)

$$\left.\begin{aligned}[\mathfrak{n}, \mathfrak{H}_+ - \mathfrak{H}_-] &= -2[\mathfrak{n}\,\mathfrak{H}_0] - \frac{1}{2\pi^2}\int \{[\mathfrak{n}\mathfrak{k}](\mathfrak{k}\overline{\mathfrak{L}}) - [\mathfrak{n}\overline{\mathfrak{L}}]\}\, e^{i(\mathfrak{k}\hat{\mathfrak{r}})}\frac{d\mathfrak{k}}{\gamma(\mathfrak{k})}\\ (\mathfrak{n}, \mathfrak{E}_+ - \mathfrak{E}_-) &= -2(\mathfrak{n}\,\mathfrak{E}_0) - \frac{1}{2\pi^2}\int (\mathfrak{n}[\mathfrak{k}\overline{\mathfrak{L}}])\, e^{i(\mathfrak{k}\hat{\mathfrak{r}})}\frac{d\mathfrak{k}}{\gamma(\mathfrak{k})}\\ &= -i\,\widehat{\operatorname{div}}[\mathfrak{n}, \mathfrak{H}_+ - \mathfrak{H}_-].\end{aligned}\right\} \tag{67.10a}$$

[Die zweite Gl. (67.10) bzw. (67.10a) ist jeweils eine Folge der ersten und der zu beiden Seiten von $z=0$ gültigen Maxwellschen Gleichungen; vgl. (3.3a).]

Die Anwendung der *Randbedingung* — Verschwinden der zum Schirm tangentialen elektrischen Feldstärke auf (S) — und der *Stetigkeitsbedingung* — Unterdrückung des Sprungs der magnetischen Feldstärke (d.h. des Flächenstroms) auf (L) — liefert jetzt unmittelbar die *simultan* zu erfüllenden *dualen Integralgleichungen*

(Streuung)

$$\left.\begin{aligned}&\int \overline{\boldsymbol{\Gamma}}(\mathfrak{k})\cdot\overline{\mathfrak{J}}(\mathfrak{k})\, e^{i(\mathfrak{k}\hat{\mathfrak{r}})}\, d\mathfrak{k} = -8\pi^2\hat{\mathfrak{E}}_0(\hat{\mathfrak{r}}) && \textit{für } \hat{\mathfrak{r}} \textit{ auf } (S),\\ &\int \overline{\mathfrak{J}}(\mathfrak{k})\, e^{i(\mathfrak{k}\hat{\mathfrak{r}})}\, d\mathfrak{k} = 0 && \textit{für } \hat{\mathfrak{r}} \textit{ auf } (L),\end{aligned}\right\} \tag{67.11}$$

(Beugung)

$$\left.\begin{aligned}&\int \overline{\mathfrak{L}}(\mathfrak{k})\, e^{i(\mathfrak{k}\hat{\mathfrak{r}})}\, d\mathfrak{k} = 0 && \textit{für } \hat{\mathfrak{r}} \textit{ auf } (S),\\ &\int \overline{\boldsymbol{\Gamma}}(\mathfrak{k})\cdot\overline{\mathfrak{L}}(\mathfrak{k})\, e^{i(\mathfrak{k}\hat{\mathfrak{r}})}\, d\mathfrak{k} = -4\pi^2\hat{\mathfrak{H}}_0(\hat{\mathfrak{r}}) && \textit{für } \hat{\mathfrak{r}} \textit{ auf } (L).\end{aligned}\right\} \tag{67.11a}$$

Hier haben wir zur Vereinfachung der Schreibweise den *Tensor*

$$\overline{\boldsymbol{\Gamma}}(\mathfrak{k}) = \frac{\mathfrak{k}\mathfrak{k} - \mathbf{1}}{\gamma(\mathfrak{k})} \tag{67.12}$$

eingeführt, der im wesentlichen (bis auf die zum Schirm normalen Komponenten) die *Fourier-Transformierte des Greenschen Tensors* (67.5) ist. Die *inhomogene* Integralgleichung (67.11) bzw. (67.11a) ist nichts anderes als die Übertragung der Pseudointegralgleichung (51.2) bzw. (52.2) auf die Transformierte $\overline{\mathfrak{J}}$ bzw. $\overline{\mathfrak{L}}$ mit Hilfe der Darstellung (67.1) [die simultan zu erfüllende *homogene* Integralgleichung von (67.11) bzw. (67.11a) ergibt sich dann einfach durch Fourier-Transformation der Gl. (67.7) bzw. (67.7a)]. Durch den Übergang zu den Fourier-Transformierten fallen also die Schwierigkeiten, die durch die Singularität der Greenschen Funktion auftraten und die erst durch Berücksichtigung der Kantenbedingung überwunden werden konnten (Ziff. 55, 56) fort.

Die Kantenbedingung tritt in unserer jetzigen Formulierung wieder nicht explizit in Erscheinung. Die *Randsingularitäten* von $\mathfrak{J}$ bzw. $\mathfrak{L}$ spiegeln sich im Verhalten der Fourier-Transformierten $\overline{\mathfrak{J}}$ bzw. $\overline{\mathfrak{L}}$ im *Unendlichen* der $\mathfrak{k}$-Ebene wieder. Dieses wird durch die Integralgleichungen (67.11) bzw. (67.11a) dadurch eingeschränkt, daß diese Integrale ja existieren sollen.

68. Zusammenhang zwischen Streu- und Beugungsproblem. Behandelt man wieder ein und dasselbe Problem sowohl mit Hilfe des Streu- wie des Beugungsformalismus, so können wir die inhomogene Integralgleichung (67.11) bzw. (67.11a) für den komplementären Bereich wie folgt ergänzen:

$$\frac{1}{4\pi^2}\int \overline{\boldsymbol{\Gamma}}(\mathfrak{k})\cdot\overline{\mathfrak{J}}(\mathfrak{k})\, e^{i(\mathfrak{k}\hat{\mathfrak{r}})}\, d\mathfrak{k} = \left\{\begin{array}{ll} -2\hat{\mathfrak{E}}_0, & \hat{\mathfrak{r}}\ auf\ (S) \\ -2[\mathfrak{n}\mathfrak{L}] - 2\hat{\mathfrak{E}}_0, & \hat{\mathfrak{r}}\ auf\ (L) \end{array}\right\} \tag{68.1}$$

$$\frac{1}{4\pi^2}\int \overline{\boldsymbol{\Gamma}}(\mathfrak{k})\,\overline{\mathfrak{L}}\cdot(\mathfrak{k})\, e^{i(\mathfrak{k}\hat{\mathfrak{r}})}\, d\mathfrak{k} = \left\{\begin{array}{ll} \frac{1}{2}[\mathfrak{n}\mathfrak{J}] - \hat{\mathfrak{H}}_0, & \hat{\mathfrak{r}}\ auf\ (S) \\ -\hat{\mathfrak{H}}_0, & \hat{\mathfrak{r}}\ auf\ (L)\,. \end{array}\right\} \tag{68.1a}$$

Durch *Fourier-Umkehr* folgt daraus

$$\left.\begin{array}{l} \overline{\boldsymbol{\Gamma}}(\mathfrak{k})\cdot\overline{\mathfrak{J}}(\mathfrak{k}) = -2\{[\mathfrak{n}\overline{\mathfrak{L}}(\mathfrak{k})] + \overline{\hat{\mathfrak{E}}}_0\} \\ \overline{\boldsymbol{\Gamma}}(\mathfrak{k})\cdot\overline{\mathfrak{L}}(\mathfrak{k}) = \{\frac{1}{2}[\mathfrak{n}\overline{\mathfrak{J}}(\mathfrak{k})] - \overline{\hat{\mathfrak{H}}}_0\}. \end{array}\right\} \tag{68.2}$$

Dies sind zwei verschiedene Schreibweisen *ein und derselben* Beziehung, die zwischen den Fourier-Transformierten $\overline{\mathfrak{J}}$ und $\overline{\mathfrak{L}}$ besteht.

Die Fourier-Transformierten $\overline{\mathfrak{E}}_0$ bzw. $\overline{\mathfrak{H}}_0$ haben nun — falls wir eine ebene einfallende Welle annehmen — δ-funktionsartigen Charakter, während im *Streufall* $\overline{\mathfrak{J}}$, im *Beugungsfall* $\overline{\mathfrak{L}}$ singularitäten*frei* ist (die Singularität der Größe $\overline{\mathfrak{L}}$ im Streu- und $\overline{\mathfrak{J}}$ im *Beugungs*fall hängt wieder mit den geometrisch-optischen Verhältnissen des jeweiligen Problems zusammen).

69. Das Fernfeld. Die Fourier-Transformierte der elektrischen bzw. „magnetischen" Flächenstromdichte hängt auch im vektoriellen Fall eng mit der *Strahlungscharakteristik des Fraunhoferschen Fernfeldes* des entsprechenden Ausstrahlungsproblems zusammen. Während sich in der Nähe des Schirmes die ebenen Wellen, in die wir das Beugungsphänomen aufgelöst haben, zu einem meist recht komplizierten Nahfeld superponieren, treten sie im Fernfeld als in die einzelnen Richtungen auslaufende Komponenten auseinander. Dieser physikalische Sachverhalt wird wieder durch die Anwendung der Sattelpunktmethode auf die Integrale (67.5) bzw. (67.6), (67.6a) mathematisch nachgezeichnet. Noch einfacher ist es aber, von der Darstellung (53.1) bzw. (53.1a) des Hertzschen bzw. Fitzgeraldschen Vektors aus zum Fernfeld überzugehen. Mit

$$\left.\begin{array}{l} |\mathfrak{r}-\hat{\mathfrak{r}}'| \to r - (\mathfrak{e}\,\hat{\mathfrak{r}}') \\ G(\mathfrak{r}-\hat{\mathfrak{r}}') \to \frac{1}{4\pi}\frac{e^{ir}}{r}\, e^{-i(\mathfrak{e}\hat{\mathfrak{r}}')} \end{array}\right\} r\to\infty \tag{69.1}$$

($\mathfrak{e}$ = Einheitsvektor in Richtung des Aufpunktes $\mathfrak{r}=\mathfrak{e}r$) folgt nämlich aus den genannten Formeln

$$\left.\begin{array}{ll} \mathfrak{Z}_S(\mathfrak{r}) \to \frac{i}{4\pi}\frac{e^{ir}}{r}\int\limits_S \mathfrak{J}(\hat{\mathfrak{r}})\, e^{-i(\mathfrak{e}\hat{\mathfrak{r}})}\, d\hat{\mathfrak{r}} & \textit{für } z \gtrless 0 \\ \mathfrak{Y}_B(\mathfrak{r}) \to \frac{i}{2\pi}\frac{e^{ir}}{r}\int\limits_L \mathfrak{L}(\hat{\mathfrak{r}})\, e^{-i(\mathfrak{e}\hat{\mathfrak{r}})}\, d\hat{\mathfrak{r}} & \textit{für } z \gtrless 0 \end{array}\right\} r\to\infty. \tag{69.2}$$

Setzt man hier (67.7) bzw. (67.7a) ein, so folgt

$$\left.\begin{array}{l} \mathfrak{Z}_S(\mathfrak{r}) \to \frac{i}{4\pi}\frac{e^{ir}}{r}\overline{\mathfrak{J}}(\mathfrak{e}) \\ \mathfrak{Y}_B(\mathfrak{r}) \to \frac{i}{2\pi}\frac{e^{ir}}{r}\overline{\mathfrak{L}}(\mathfrak{e}) \end{array}\right\} \textit{für } z \gtrless 0,\ r\to\infty. \tag{69.2a}$$

Für das Fernfeld der Feldvektoren selber findet man also mit Hilfe von (53.2) bzw. (53.2a)

(Streuung)

$$\left.\begin{aligned} \mathfrak{E}(\mathfrak{r}) &\to \mathfrak{E}_0 - \frac{i}{4\pi}[\mathfrak{e}[\mathfrak{e}\overline{\mathfrak{J}}(\mathfrak{e})]]\frac{e^{ir}}{r} \\ \mathfrak{H}(\mathfrak{r}) &\to \mathfrak{H}_0 + \frac{i}{4\pi}[\mathfrak{e}\overline{\mathfrak{J}}(\mathfrak{e})]\frac{e^{ir}}{r} \end{aligned}\right\} \text{ für } z \gtrless 0, \quad r \to \infty; \tag{69.3}$$

(Beugung)

$$\left.\begin{aligned} \mathfrak{E}(\mathfrak{r}) &\to \pm \frac{i}{2\pi}[\mathfrak{e}\overline{\mathfrak{L}}(\mathfrak{e})]\frac{e^{ir}}{r} + \begin{cases} 0 & \text{für } z > 0 \\ \mathfrak{E}_0 + \mathfrak{E}^0 & \text{für } z < 0 \end{cases} \\ \mathfrak{H}(\mathfrak{r}) &\to \pm \frac{i}{2\pi}[\mathfrak{e}[\mathfrak{e}\overline{\mathfrak{L}}(\mathfrak{e})]]\frac{e^{ir}}{r} + \begin{cases} 0 & \text{für } z > 0 \\ \mathfrak{H}_0 + \mathfrak{H}^0 & \text{für } z < 0 \end{cases} \end{aligned}\right\} r \to \infty. \tag{69.3a}$$

Diese Darstellung ist in Übereinstimmung mit der elektromagnetischen *Ausstrahlungsbedingung* (18.4). Im Streufall können wir uns nun $\overline{\mathfrak{J}}$, Gl. (67.7), in eine Reihe nach fallenden Potenzen der Wellenlänge λ entwickelt denken (indem wir den Retardierungsfaktor $e^{-i(\mathfrak{e}\hat{\mathfrak{r}})}$ entwickeln) und erhalten so für das Fernfeld (69.3) eine Reihe, deren einzelne Glieder als die Strahlung entsprechender elektrischer und magnetischer *Multipole* der Stromverteilung $\mathfrak{J}$ gedeutet werden können. Das erste Glied ist das Fernfeld des *elektrischen Dipols* vom Moment $\int\limits_S \mathfrak{J}(\hat{\mathfrak{r}})\,d\hat{\mathfrak{r}}$. Die entsprechende Entwicklung für das Beugungsfeld (69.3a) beginnt mit dem Fernfeld eines *magnetischen Dipols* vom Moment $\int\limits_L \mathfrak{L}(\hat{\mathfrak{r}})\,d\hat{\mathfrak{r}}$.

70. Reduktion auf ein algebraisches Problem. Die simultan zu erfüllenden dualen Integralgleichungen (67.11) bzw. (67.11a) lassen sich mit Hilfe eines geeigneten Funktionensystems wieder auf ein lineares Gleichungssystem mit unendlich vielen Unbekannten zurückführen. Wir erläutern das Verfahren für den Streufall und führen hier ein orthonormales Funktionensystem $\overline{\mathfrak{V}}_\nu(\mathfrak{k})$ ein, das gemäß

$$\overline{\mathfrak{V}}_\nu(\mathfrak{k}) = \int\limits_S \mathfrak{V}_\nu(\hat{\mathfrak{r}})\, e^{-i(\mathfrak{k}\hat{\mathfrak{r}})}\, d\hat{\mathfrak{r}} \tag{70.1}$$

darstellbar sei. Es besitzt also die Fourier-Umkehrung

$$\mathfrak{V}_\nu(\hat{\mathfrak{r}}) = \frac{1}{4\pi^2}\int \overline{\mathfrak{V}}_\nu(\mathfrak{k})\, e^{i(\mathfrak{k}\hat{\mathfrak{r}})}\, d\mathfrak{k}, \tag{70.1a}$$

so daß

$$\int (\overline{\mathfrak{V}}_\nu \overline{\mathfrak{V}}_\mu^*)\, d\mathfrak{k} = 4\pi^2 \int\limits_S (\mathfrak{V}_\nu \mathfrak{V}_\mu^*)\, d\hat{\mathfrak{r}} = \delta_{\nu\mu}. \tag{70.2}$$

Für $\hat{\mathfrak{r}}$ auf (S) können wir nun den Tensor $\overline{\boldsymbol{\Gamma}}(\mathfrak{k})\, e^{i(\mathfrak{k}\hat{\mathfrak{r}})}$ nach unserem Orthonormalsystem entwickeln

$$\overline{\boldsymbol{\Gamma}}(\mathfrak{k})\, e^{i(\mathfrak{k}\hat{\mathfrak{r}})} = 4\pi^2\, \overline{\boldsymbol{\Gamma}}(\mathfrak{k}) \cdot \sum_{\nu=0}^{\infty} \overline{\mathfrak{V}}_\nu^*(\mathfrak{k})\, \mathfrak{V}_\nu(\hat{\mathfrak{r}}) \qquad \text{für } \hat{\mathfrak{r}} \text{ auf } (S), \tag{70.3}$$

dabei bedeute $\overline{\mathfrak{V}}_\nu^* \mathfrak{V}_\nu$ das *dyadische* Produkt der beiden Vektoren. Man bestätigt (70.3) leicht durch skalare Multiplikation mit $\mathfrak{V}_\mu^*(\hat{\mathfrak{r}})$ und nachfolgender Integration bezüglich $\hat{\mathfrak{r}}$ über den Bereich (S) unter Beachtung der Orthogonalitätsrelation (70.2). Ebenso entwickeln wir

$$-2\hat{\mathfrak{E}}_0(\hat{\mathfrak{r}}) = \sum_{\nu=0}^{\infty} c_\nu \mathfrak{V}_\nu(\hat{\mathfrak{r}}) \qquad \text{für } \hat{\mathfrak{r}} \text{ auf } (S). \tag{70.3a}$$

Der Ansatz

$$\overline{\mathfrak{J}}(\mathfrak{k}) = \sum_{\nu=0}^{\infty} a_\nu \overline{\mathfrak{V}}_\nu(\mathfrak{k}) \tag{70.4}$$

erfüllt nun die *homogene* Integralgleichung (67.11) zufolge Gl. (70.1) *gliedweise*; setzen wir andererseits (70.3) bis (70.4) in die *inhomogene* Integralgleichung (67.11) ein (nachdem wir dort die Reihenfolge von $\overline{\boldsymbol{\Gamma}}$ und $\overline{\mathfrak{J}}$ vertauscht haben), so erhalten wir durch Vergleich der Koeffizienten von $\mathfrak{V}_\nu(\hat{\mathfrak{r}})$ auf beiden Seiten der so entstehenden Gleichungen das System

$$\sum_{\nu=0}^{\infty} a_\nu C_{\nu\mu} = c_\mu \qquad \text{für } \mu = 0, 1, 2, \ldots \tag{70.5}$$

mit

$$\left.\begin{aligned} C_{\nu\mu} &= \int (\overline{\mathfrak{V}}_\nu \overline{\boldsymbol{\Gamma}} \overline{\mathfrak{V}}_\mu^*)\, d\mathfrak{k} = \int \{(\mathfrak{k}\overline{\mathfrak{V}}_\nu)(\mathfrak{k}\overline{\mathfrak{V}}_\mu^*) - (\overline{\mathfrak{V}}_\nu \overline{\mathfrak{V}}_\mu^*)\} \frac{d\mathfrak{k}}{\gamma(\mathfrak{k})} \\ c_\nu &= -8\pi^2 \int_S (\hat{\mathfrak{E}}_0 \mathfrak{V}_\nu^*)\, d\hat{\mathfrak{r}}. \end{aligned}\right\} \tag{70.6}$$

Damit ist auch im vektoriellen Fall die Zurückführung auf ein algebraisches Problem durchgeführt. Bei praktischen Rechnungen wird man sich, wie üblich, damit begnügen müssen, die ersten N Koeffizienten dadurch zu berechnen, daß man für $\nu, \mu > N$ die $C_{\nu\mu} = 0$ setzt. Die Brauchbarkeit dieser Näherung wird wesentlich von der geschickten Wahl der $\mathfrak{V}_\nu$ abhängen. Diese ist insbesondere so zu treffen, daß

$$(\mathfrak{s}\mathfrak{V}_\nu) = 0 \qquad \text{auf } (C), \tag{70.7}$$

damit die Flächenstromdichte

$$\mathfrak{J}(\hat{\mathfrak{r}}) = \sum_{\nu=0}^{\infty} a_\nu \mathfrak{V}_\nu(\hat{\mathfrak{r}}) \tag{70.4a}$$

die Kantenbedingung $(\mathfrak{s}\mathfrak{J}) = 0$ erfüllt (s. Ziff. 55). Ferner wird man die weitere Kenntnis des Verhaltens der Stromdichte gemäß $\mathfrak{J}_{\|} \sim \varrho^{-\frac{1}{2}}$, vgl. (23.4), ausnutzen. Dadurch erweist sich das Verfahren als für den *statischen Grenzfall* besonders geeignet, wo gewissermaßen der ganze Schirm (bzw. die gesamte Öffnung) als Randzone betrachtet werden kann (vgl. auch Ziff. 95).

71. Übergang zu den Integralgleichungen vom Faltungstypus, Iteration im Anschluß an die Kirchhoffsche Lösung. Unser Ziel ist wieder, die beiden dualen Integralgleichungen (67.11) bzw. (67.11a) durch eine einzige äquivalente inhomogene Fredholmsche Integralgleichung zu ersetzen, um die Lösung in Gestalt einer Neumannschen Reihe entwickeln zu können. Um dies zu erreichen, multiplizieren wir jeweils die auf (L) bezügliche Integralgleichung mit dem in Gl. (64.1) eingeführten (zweidimensional erweiterten) „Sieboperator"

$$\Theta_L(\hat{\mathfrak{r}}) = \left\{\begin{matrix} 1 & \textit{für } \hat{\mathfrak{r}} \textit{ auf } (L) \\ 0 & \textit{für } \hat{\mathfrak{r}} \textit{ auf } (S), \end{matrix}\right\} \tag{71.1}$$

bzw. die auf (S) bezügliche mit

$$\Theta_S(\hat{\mathfrak{r}}) = 1 - \Theta_L(\hat{\mathfrak{r}}) = \left\{\begin{matrix} 0 & \textit{für } \hat{\mathfrak{r}} \textit{ auf } (L) \\ 1 & \textit{für } \hat{\mathfrak{r}} \textit{ auf } (S). \end{matrix}\right\} \tag{71.1a}$$

Dadurch entsteht

(Streuung)

$$\left.\begin{aligned} &\int \overline{\boldsymbol{\Gamma}}(\mathfrak{k}) \cdot \overline{\mathfrak{J}}(\mathfrak{k})\, \Theta_S(\hat{\mathfrak{r}})\, e^{i(\mathfrak{k}\hat{\mathfrak{r}})}\, d\mathfrak{k} = 4\pi^2 \mathfrak{J}^0(\hat{\mathfrak{r}}), \\ &\int \overline{\mathfrak{J}}(\mathfrak{k})\, \{1 - \Theta_S(\hat{\mathfrak{r}})\}\, e^{i(\mathfrak{k}\hat{\mathfrak{r}})}\, d\mathfrak{k} = 0 \end{aligned}\right\} \tag{71.2}$$

bzw.

(Beugung)

$$\left.\begin{aligned} &\int \overline{\mathfrak{L}}(\mathfrak{k})\,\{1-\Theta_L(\hat{\mathfrak{r}})\}\,e^{i(\mathfrak{k}\hat{\mathfrak{r}})}\,d\mathfrak{k}=0\,,\\ &\int \overline{\boldsymbol{\Gamma}}(\mathfrak{k})\cdot\overline{\mathfrak{L}}(\mathfrak{k})\,\Theta_L(\hat{\mathfrak{r}})\,e^{i(\mathfrak{k}\hat{\mathfrak{r}})}\,d\mathfrak{k}=4\pi^2\,\mathfrak{L}^0(\hat{\mathfrak{r}}),\end{aligned}\right\}\tag{71.2a}$$

mit

$$\left.\begin{aligned} \mathfrak{J}^0(\hat{\mathfrak{r}}) &= -\,2\Theta_S(\hat{\mathfrak{r}})\,\hat{\mathfrak{E}}_0(\hat{\mathfrak{r}})\,,\\ \mathfrak{L}^0(\hat{\mathfrak{r}}) &= -\,\Theta_L(\hat{\mathfrak{r}})\,\hat{\mathfrak{H}}_0(\hat{\mathfrak{r}})\,.\end{aligned}\right\}\tag{71.3}$$

Der Vorzug dieser Schreibweise besteht darin, daß jetzt die Integralgleichungen (71.2), (71.2a) auf der *ganzen* Ebene $z=0$, d.h. für *alle* $\hat{\mathfrak{r}}$, gelten. Wir können daher auf diese Integralgleichungen die zweidimensionale Fourier-Transformation anwenden und erhalten in verständlicher Schreibweise

(Streuung)

$$\left.\begin{aligned} \frac{1}{4\pi^2}\int \overline{\boldsymbol{\Gamma}}(\mathfrak{k}')\cdot\overline{\mathfrak{J}}(\mathfrak{k}')\,\overline{\Theta}_S(\mathfrak{k}-\mathfrak{k}')\,d\mathfrak{k}' &= \overline{\mathfrak{J}}^0(\mathfrak{k})\\ \overline{\mathfrak{J}}(\mathfrak{k}) = \frac{1}{4\pi^2}\int \overline{\mathfrak{J}}(\mathfrak{k}')\,\overline{\Theta}_S(\mathfrak{k}-\mathfrak{k}')\,d\mathfrak{k}' &\end{aligned}\right\}\tag{71.4}$$

bzw.

(Beugung)

$$\left.\begin{aligned} \overline{\mathfrak{L}}(\mathfrak{k}) = \frac{1}{4\pi^2}\int \overline{\mathfrak{L}}(\mathfrak{k}')\,\overline{\Theta}_L(\mathfrak{k}-\mathfrak{k}')\,d\mathfrak{k}' &\\ \frac{1}{4\pi^2}\int \overline{\boldsymbol{\Gamma}}(\mathfrak{k}')\cdot\overline{\mathfrak{L}}(\mathfrak{k}')\,\overline{\Theta}_L(\mathfrak{k}-\mathfrak{k}')\,d\mathfrak{k} &= \overline{\mathfrak{L}}^0(\mathfrak{k})\,.\end{aligned}\right\}\tag{71.4a}$$

Dies sind wieder je zwei simultan zu erfüllende Integralgleichungen vom *Faltungstypus*, die den dualen Integralgleichungen (67.11), (67.11a) äquivalent sind. Die in (71.4), (71.4a) auftretenden Integrale [*einschließlich* des Faktors $(2\pi)^{-2}$] kürzen wir durch die übliche Faltungssymbolik ab:

(Streuung)

$$\begin{aligned} \overline{\Theta}_S * \overline{\boldsymbol{\Gamma}}\cdot\overline{\mathfrak{J}} &= \overline{\mathfrak{J}}^0\\ \overline{\mathfrak{J}} &= \overline{\Theta}_S * \overline{\mathfrak{J}}\,;\end{aligned}\tag{71.4'}$$

(Beugung)

$$\begin{aligned} \overline{\Theta}_L * \overline{\boldsymbol{\Gamma}}\cdot\overline{\mathfrak{L}} &= \overline{\mathfrak{L}}^0\\ \overline{\mathfrak{L}} &= \overline{\Theta}_L * \overline{\mathfrak{L}}.\end{aligned}\tag{71.4a'}$$

Diese simultanen Integralgleichungen lassen sich wieder leicht in je eine einzige inhomogene Fredholmsche Integralgleichung *erster Art* zusammenfassen, indem man jeweils die homogene Integralgleichung von (71.4′) bzw. (71.4a′) in die inhomogene einsetzt. Es entsteht so

$$\overline{\Theta}_S * \overline{\boldsymbol{\Gamma}}\cdot(\overline{\Theta}_S\,\overline{\mathfrak{J}}) = \overline{\mathfrak{J}}^0 \quad \textit{(Streuung)}\tag{71.5}$$

bzw.

$$\overline{\Theta}_L * \overline{\boldsymbol{\Gamma}}\cdot(\overline{\Theta}_L\,\overline{\mathfrak{L}}) = \overline{\mathfrak{L}}^0 \quad \textit{(Beugung)}.\tag{71.5a}$$

Ausführlich geschrieben lauten diese Integralgleichungen

$$\int \boldsymbol{K}_S(\mathfrak{k},\mathfrak{k}')\cdot\overline{\mathfrak{J}}(\mathfrak{k}')\,d\mathfrak{k}' = \overline{\mathfrak{J}}^0(\mathfrak{k})\tag{71.5'}$$

bzw.

$$\int \boldsymbol{K}_L(\mathfrak{k},\mathfrak{k}')\cdot\overline{\mathfrak{L}}(\mathfrak{k}')\,d\mathfrak{k}' = \overline{\mathfrak{L}}^0(\mathfrak{k})\tag{71.5a'}$$

mit den „*iterierten*" tensoriellen Kernen

$$\left.\begin{aligned} \boldsymbol{K}_S(\mathfrak{k},\mathfrak{k}') &= \frac{1}{16\pi^4}\int \overline{\Theta}_S(\mathfrak{k}-\mathfrak{k}'')\,\overline{\boldsymbol{\Gamma}}(\mathfrak{k}'')\,\overline{\Theta}_S(\mathfrak{k}''-\mathfrak{k}')\,d\mathfrak{k}'' \\ \boldsymbol{K}_L(\mathfrak{k},\mathfrak{k}') &= \frac{1}{16\pi^4}\int \overline{\Theta}_L(\mathfrak{k}-\mathfrak{k}'')\,\overline{\boldsymbol{\Gamma}}(\mathfrak{k}'')\,\overline{\Theta}_L(\mathfrak{k}''-\mathfrak{k}')\,d\mathfrak{k}''. \end{aligned}\right\} \tag{71.6}$$

Für die angenäherte Lösung der Integralgleichungen (71.4) bzw. (71.4a) ist es von Vorteil, daß es mit Hilfe eines kleinen Kunstgriffes auch hier wieder gelingt, eine mit (71.5′) bzw. (71.5a′) äquivalente Integralgleichung *zweiter Art* anzugeben. Zu diesem Zweck schreiben wir jeweils die *inhomogene* Integralgleichung (71.4′) bzw. (71.4a′) formal in der Gestalt

$$\overline{\boldsymbol{\Gamma}}\cdot\overline{\mathfrak{J}} = \overline{\mathfrak{J}}^0 + \overline{\Theta}_L * \overline{\boldsymbol{\Gamma}}\cdot\overline{\mathfrak{J}} \tag{71.7}$$

bzw.

$$\overline{\boldsymbol{\Gamma}}\cdot\overline{\mathfrak{L}} = \overline{\mathfrak{L}}^0 + \overline{\Theta}_S * \overline{\boldsymbol{\Gamma}}\cdot\overline{\mathfrak{L}}. \tag{71.7a}$$

Setzen wir nun hier jeweils die *homogene* Integralgleichung von Gl. (71.4′) bzw. (71.4a′) ein, so folgt

$$\overline{\mathfrak{J}} = \overline{\boldsymbol{\Gamma}}^{-1}\cdot\overline{\mathfrak{J}}^0 + \overline{\boldsymbol{\Gamma}}^{-1}\cdot\left[\overline{\Theta}_L * \overline{\boldsymbol{\Gamma}}\cdot(\overline{\Theta}_S * \overline{\mathfrak{J}})\right] \tag{71.7′}$$

bzw.

$$\overline{\mathfrak{L}} = \overline{\boldsymbol{\Gamma}}^{-1}\cdot\overline{\mathfrak{L}}^0 + \overline{\boldsymbol{\Gamma}}^{-1}\cdot\left[\overline{\Theta}_S * \overline{\boldsymbol{\Gamma}}\cdot(\overline{\Theta}_L * \overline{\mathfrak{L}})\right]. \tag{71.7a′}$$

Dies ist in der Tat je eine Integralgleichung *zweiter Art* für $\overline{\mathfrak{J}}$ bzw. $\overline{\mathfrak{L}}$, die wir mit Hilfe der Operatoren

$$\boldsymbol{\Omega}_S = \frac{1}{4\pi^2}\int\left\{\boldsymbol{1}\,\overline{\Theta}_S(\mathfrak{k}-\mathfrak{k}') - \frac{1}{4\pi^2}\overline{\boldsymbol{\Gamma}}^{-1}(\mathfrak{k})\cdot\int\overline{\Theta}_S(\mathfrak{k}-\mathfrak{k}'')\,\overline{\boldsymbol{\Gamma}}(\mathfrak{k}'')\,\overline{\Theta}_S(\mathfrak{k}''-\mathfrak{k}')\,d\mathfrak{k}''\right\}\ldots d\mathfrak{k}' \tag{71.8}$$

bzw.

$$\boldsymbol{\Omega}_L = \frac{1}{4\pi^2}\int\left\{\boldsymbol{1}\,\overline{\Theta}_L(\mathfrak{k}-\mathfrak{k}') - \frac{1}{4\pi^2}\overline{\boldsymbol{\Gamma}}^{-1}(\mathfrak{k})\cdot\int\overline{\Theta}_L(\mathfrak{k}-\mathfrak{k}'')\,\overline{\boldsymbol{\Gamma}}(\mathfrak{k}'')\,\overline{\Theta}_L(\mathfrak{k}''-\mathfrak{k}')\,d\mathfrak{k}''\right\}\ldots d\mathfrak{k}' \tag{71.8a}$$

in der Gestalt

$$\overline{\mathfrak{J}} = \overline{\boldsymbol{\Gamma}}^{-1}\cdot\overline{\mathfrak{J}}^0 + \boldsymbol{\Omega}_S\,\overline{\mathfrak{J}} \qquad \textit{(Streuung)} \tag{71.9}$$

bzw.

$$\overline{\mathfrak{L}} = \overline{\boldsymbol{\Gamma}}^{-1}\cdot\overline{\mathfrak{L}}^0 + \boldsymbol{\Omega}_L\,\overline{\mathfrak{L}} \qquad \textit{(Beugung)} \tag{71.9a}$$

schreiben wollen. Dabei haben wir von der Beziehung $\overline{\Theta}_L = \overline{1} - \overline{\Theta}_S$, $\overline{1} = 4\pi\,\delta(\mathfrak{k})$ bzw. $\overline{\Theta}_S = \overline{1} - \overline{\Theta}_L$ Gebrauch gemacht, da im Streufall $\overline{\Theta}_S$, im Beugungsfall $\overline{\Theta}_L$ *keine* δ-Singularität besitzt.

Für die Integralgleichung (71.9) bzw. (71.9a) führt nun die Iterationsvorschrift

$$\left.\begin{aligned} \overline{\mathfrak{J}}_0 &= \overline{\boldsymbol{\Gamma}}^{-1}\cdot\overline{\mathfrak{J}}^0 \\ \overline{\mathfrak{J}}_\nu &= \overline{\mathfrak{J}}_0 + \boldsymbol{\Omega}_S\,\overline{\mathfrak{J}}_{\nu-1}, \quad \nu \geqq 1 \end{aligned}\right\} \tag{71.10}$$

bzw.

$$\left.\begin{aligned} \overline{\mathfrak{L}}_0 &= \overline{\boldsymbol{\Gamma}}^{-1}\cdot\overline{\mathfrak{L}}^0 \\ \overline{\mathfrak{L}}_\nu &= \overline{\mathfrak{L}}_0 + \boldsymbol{\Omega}_L\,\overline{\mathfrak{L}}_{\nu-1}, \quad \nu \geqq 1 \end{aligned}\right\} \tag{71.10a}$$

durch sukzessive Anwendung wieder auf die *Neumannsche Reihe:*

(Streuung)

$$\overline{\mathfrak{J}} = \sum_{\nu=0}^{\infty}\boldsymbol{\Omega}_S^\nu\,\overline{\mathfrak{J}}_0 = (\boldsymbol{1}-\boldsymbol{\Omega}_S)^{-1}\,\overline{\mathfrak{J}}_0 \tag{71.11}$$

bzw.

(Beugung)

$$\overline{\mathfrak{L}} = \sum_{\nu=0}^{\infty} \boldsymbol{\Omega}_L^{\nu}\, \overline{\mathfrak{L}}_0 = (\mathbf{1}-\boldsymbol{\Omega}_L)^{-1}\, \overline{\mathfrak{L}}_0. \tag{71.11a}$$

Für das erste Glied dieser Reihen erhalten wir aus (71.3) und jeweils der ersten Gleichung (71.10) bzw. (71.10a)

$$\overline{\mathfrak{J}}_0 = -2\,\overline{\boldsymbol{\Gamma}}^{-1}\cdot\big(\overline{\Theta}_S * \hat{\overline{\mathfrak{E}}}_0\big), \qquad \overline{\mathfrak{L}}_0 = -\,\overline{\boldsymbol{\Gamma}}^{-1}\cdot\big(\overline{\Theta}_L * \hat{\overline{\mathfrak{H}}}_0\big). \tag{71.12}$$

Gl. (71.12) ist im wesentlichen wieder die *Kirchhoffsche Form des Fraunhoferschen Fernfeldes.* Das durch (69.3) bzw. (69.3a) gegebene Fernfeld läßt sich nämlich mit Hilfe des Tensors $\boldsymbol{e}(\mathfrak{e}) = \mathfrak{e}\,\mathfrak{e} - \mathbf{1}$ ($\mathfrak{e}$ = Einheitsvektor in der Beobachtungsrichtung, $\mathfrak{r} = \mathfrak{e}\,r$) auch in die Form bringen

(Streuung)

$$\left.\begin{aligned} \mathfrak{E}(\mathfrak{r}) &\to \mathfrak{E}_0 - \frac{i}{4\pi}\,\frac{e^{ir}}{r}\,\boldsymbol{e}\cdot\overline{\mathfrak{J}}(\mathfrak{e}) \\ \mathfrak{H}(\mathfrak{r}) &\to \mathfrak{H}_0 - \frac{i}{4\pi}\,\frac{e^{ir}}{r}\,[\mathfrak{e}\,\boldsymbol{e}]\cdot\overline{\mathfrak{J}}(\mathfrak{e}) \end{aligned}\right\}\ \textit{für}\ \ z \gtrless 0,\quad r\to\infty \tag{71.13}$$

bzw.

(Beugung)

$$\left.\begin{aligned} \mathfrak{E}(\mathfrak{r}) &\to \mp\frac{i}{2\pi}\,\frac{e^{ir}}{r}\,[\mathfrak{e}\,\boldsymbol{e}]\cdot\overline{\mathfrak{L}}(\mathfrak{e}) + \begin{cases} 0 & \textit{für } z>0 \\ \mathfrak{E}_0 + \mathfrak{E}^0 & \textit{für } z<0 \end{cases} \\ \mathfrak{H}(\mathfrak{r}) &\to \pm\frac{i}{2\pi}\,\frac{e^{ir}}{r}\,\boldsymbol{e}\cdot\overline{\mathfrak{L}}(\mathfrak{e}) + \begin{cases} 0 & \textit{für } z>0 \\ \mathfrak{H}_0 + \mathfrak{H}^0 & \textit{für } z<0 \end{cases} \end{aligned}\right\}\ r\to\infty. \tag{71.13a}$$

Setzen wir hier die Reihe (71.11) bzw. (71.11a) ein, so folgt bei Beachtung von Gl. (71.12)

(Streuung)

$$\left.\begin{aligned} \mathfrak{E}_S(\mathfrak{r}) \to -\frac{i}{4\pi}\,\frac{e^{ir}}{r}\big\{-2\,\overline{\Theta}_S * \hat{\overline{\mathfrak{E}}}_0 + \boldsymbol{e}\cdot\boldsymbol{\Omega}_S\,\overline{\mathfrak{J}}_0 + \boldsymbol{e}\cdot\boldsymbol{\Omega}_S^2\,\overline{\mathfrak{J}}_0 + \cdots\big\}_{\mathfrak{k}=\mathfrak{e}} \\ \text{für}\quad z\gtrless 0,\quad r\to\infty, \end{aligned}\right\} \tag{71.13'}$$

(Beugung)

$$\left.\begin{aligned} \mathfrak{H}_B(\mathfrak{r}) \to \pm\frac{i}{2\pi}\,\frac{e^{ir}}{r}\big\{-\,\overline{\Theta}_L * \hat{\overline{\mathfrak{H}}}_0 + \boldsymbol{e}\cdot\boldsymbol{\Omega}_L\,\overline{\mathfrak{L}}_0 + \boldsymbol{e}\cdot\boldsymbol{\Omega}_L^2\,\overline{\mathfrak{L}}_0 + \cdots\big\}_{\mathfrak{k}=\mathfrak{e}} \\ \text{für}\quad z\gtrless 0,\quad r\to\infty. \end{aligned}\right\} \tag{71.13a'}$$

Denkt man sich hier für $\mathfrak{E}_0$, $\mathfrak{H}_0$ eine *ebene* Welle eingesetzt, so ist $\overline{\mathfrak{E}}_0$ bzw. $\overline{\mathfrak{H}}_0$ im wesentlichen eine δ-Funktion, so daß man in dem ersten Glied von (71.13) bzw. (71.13a') die Kirchhoffsche Gestalt des Fernfeldes wiedererkennt.

c) Das Wiener-Hopf-Verfahren und die Methode der singulären Integralgleichungen.

Auf die Integralgleichungen für ebene Schirme (Abschn. IIIa) bzw. auf die äquivalenten dualen Integralgleichungen (Abschn. IIIb) lassen sich *funktionentheoretische* Methoden anwenden, die im einfachsten Fall (Halbebene) zu einer Lösung in geschlossener Form führen. In allgemeineren Fällen haben sie sich als Ausgangspunkt geeigneter Näherungsverfahren bewährt. Der Anwendungsbereich dieser Methoden ist nicht auf ebene Schirme beschränkt, sondern umfaßt eine wesentlich weitere Klasse von Beugungsproblemen, in die vor allem die *Ausstrahlung* offener und transversal geschlitzter *Wellenleiter* gehören. In der Tat läßt sich die Methode der dualen Integralgleichungen — die den geeigneten Ausgangspunkt für den Einsatz der funktionentheoretischen Verfahren bildet — auf diese Probleme erweitern. Wir wollen diese Erweiterung hier kurz besprechen, da erst sie einen Einblick in die Tragweite dieser Verfahren vermittelt. Dabei müssen wir uns auf das wesentlichste beschränken, behandeln insbesondere nur das skalare Problem für die Randbedingung $v=0$. Bezüglich aller Einzelheiten sei auf die weiter unten angegebene Literatur verwiesen. Die Anwendung der in Rede stehenden funktionentheoretischen Methoden („Faktorisierung", analytische Fortsetzung, Liouvillescher Satz) auf Integralgleichungen einer bestimmten Klasse geht auf WIENER und HOPF[1] zurück. Die Überführung der Integralgleichungen mittels Fourier-Transformation (im *komplexen* Bereich) in die Funktionalgleichungen, auf die das Wiener-Hopf-Verfahren anwendbar ist, kann dadurch vereinfacht werden, daß man die Wellengleichung *vor* Anwendung der Randbedingung transformiert. Die Rand- bzw. Stetigkeitsbedingung führt dann direkt auf die Funktionalgleichungen[2]. Andererseits lassen sich die dualen Integralgleichungen auch auf *singuläre Integralgleichungen vom Cauchyschen Typ* zurückführen. Die Theorie der letzteren ist in neuerer Zeit namentlich von MUSKHELISHVILI und seiner Schule systematisch ausgebaut worden[3]. Die dabei im Vordergrund stehende Methode der *Cauchyschen Integrale* enthält das Wiener-Hopf-Verfahren als Spezialfall[4]. Wir wollen die Anwendung dieser Methoden auf Beugungsprobleme im folgenden kurz darstellen[5].

72. Zur Theorie der Beugung an offenen Wellenleitern. Zunächst formulieren wir das Beugungsproblem für einen *offenen* transversal *geschlitzten* geraden *Wellenleiter*, dessen (unendlich dünne) Wandung aus beliebig vielen Teilen eines Zylinders (vorerst beliebigen Querschnitts, der einfach oder mehrfach zusammenhängend sein kann) bestehen möge (s. Fig. 41). Die *Kanten* sollen in *parallelen* Ebenen liegen, die senkrecht auf den Erzeugenden des Zylinders stehen *(Kantenebenen)*. Je nach der Anzahl der Kantenebenen wollen wir von einem Einkanten- bzw. Mehrkantenproblem sprechen. So bildet ein offener, sich einseitig ins Unendliche erstreckende Wellenleiter ein *Einkantenproblem* (einfachster Spezialfall: Halbebene). Ein transversaler Schlitz beliebiger Breite (senkrecht zu den Erzeugenden) in einem beiderseitig ins Unendliche reichenden

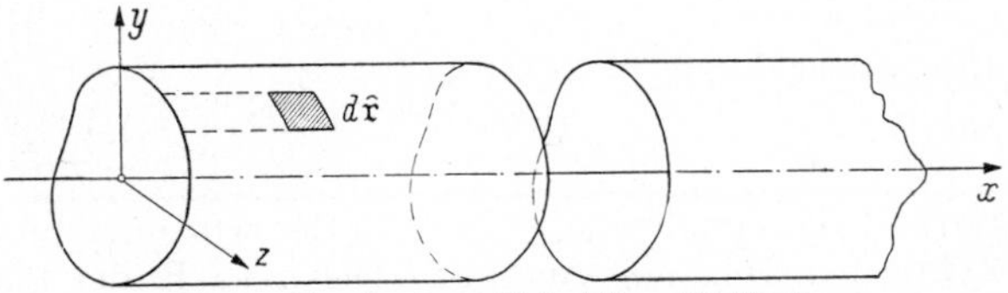

Fig. 41. Unterbrochener Wellenleiter mit 3 Kanten.

[1] N. WIENER u. E. HOPF: Sitzgsber. Berl. Akad. Wiss. 696 (1931). Vgl. auch R. PALEY u. N. WIENER: Fourier-Transforms in the Complex Domain. New York 1934. — E.C. TICHMARCH: Theory of Fourier-Integrals, S. 339—342. Oxford 1937. — V.A. FOCK: Matem Sbornik **1**, 14 (1944). Eine eingehende Darstellung der zahlreichen Anwendungen (vorwiegend aus der Beugungstheorie) bei B. NOBLE: Methods based on the Wiener-Hopf Technique for the Solution of Partial Differential Equations. London: Pergamon Press 1958.

[2] D.S. JONES: Quart. J. Math. Oxford **3**, 189 (1952). Die Monographie von B. NOBLE l. c.[1] verwendet im wesentlichen diese Methode.

[3] Man vgl. die Monographie von N.J. MUSKHELISHVILI: Singular Integral Equations, Groningen 1953 (Übersetzung aus dem Russischen 1946), sowie S.A. MICHLIN: Singuläre Integralgleichungen [Russ.], Uspechi Math. Nauk III **3** (25), 29—112 (1948) und W.D. KUPRADSE: Randwertaufgaben der Schwingungstheorie und Integralgleichungen, Kap. 5, Berlin 1956 (Übersetzung aus dem Russischen).

[4] Vgl. dazu A. SPARENBERG: Kon. Nat. Akad. Wet. A **59**, 29 (1956).

[5] L. LEWIN: Advanced Theory of Waveguides. London 1951. — P.M. MORSE u. H. FESHBACH: Methods of Theoretical Physics. Bd. II, Kap. 11.4. New York-Toronto-London 1953. — B. NOBLE l. c.[1]. — K. WESTPFAHL: Zur Theorie einer Klasse von Beugungsproblemen mittels singulärer Integralgleichungen I. Ann. Phys. **4**, 283 (1959). (Teil II im Erscheinen.)

Zylinder stellt ein *Zweikantenproblem* dar (dazu gehört auch ein Spalt in einem ebenen Schirm). Desgleichen ein beidseitig offener Zylinder (Wellenleiter endlicher Länge). Fig. 41 zeigt ein Dreikantenproblem. Zwei (offene geschlitzte) Wellenleiter, die sich zum vollständigen (beiderseits ins Unendliche reichenden) Zylinder ergänzen, wollen wir als komplementär bezeichnen. Die Erzeugenden des Zylinders seien parallel zur x-Achse; die Zahl der Kantenebenen vorerst noch beliebig. Die einzelnen Zylinderteile sollen mit (S_ν) bezeichnet werden; der gesamte Wellenleiter mit $(S) = \sum\limits_\nu (S_\nu)$. In der Querschnittsebene (yz-Ebene) führen wir orthogonale krummlinige Koordinaten (η, ζ) ein, so daß $\zeta = \text{const} = \zeta_0$ mit der Spur des Zylinders in der yz-Ebene zusammenfällt (s. Fig. 42). In den Zylinderkoordinaten x, η, ζ können wir dann schreiben

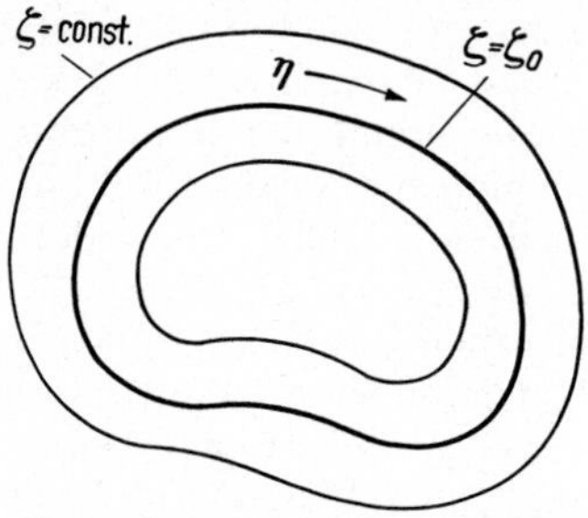

Fig. 42. Separationskoordinaten in einer Querschnittsebene des Wellenleiters.

$$|\mathfrak{r} - \mathfrak{r}'| = \sqrt{(x - x')^2 + \chi(\eta, \zeta; \eta', \zeta')}. \tag{72.1}$$

Hat ferner das Linienelement in den Koordinaten η, ζ die Gestalt $ds^2 = g_\eta \, d\eta^2 + g_\zeta \, d\zeta^2$, so gilt für ein Flächenelement des Wellenleiters (Fig. 41) $d\hat{\mathfrak{r}} = \sqrt{g_\eta} \, d\eta \, dx$. Die Lösung der Randwertaufgabe

$$\left.\begin{aligned} (\Delta + 1)\, v(\mathfrak{r}) &= 0, \quad \mathfrak{r} \notin (S) \\ v(\mathfrak{r}) &= 0, \quad \mathfrak{r} \in (S) \end{aligned}\right\} \tag{72.2}$$

die noch durch die *Ausstrahlungsbedingung* (vgl. Ziff. 17) und *Kantenbedingung* (vgl. Ziff. 23) zu ergänzen ist, können wir wie in Ziff. 46 in der Form

$$v(\mathfrak{r}) = v_0(\mathfrak{r}) - \int\limits_S \psi(\hat{\mathfrak{r}}') \, G(\mathfrak{r} - \hat{\mathfrak{r}}') \, d\hat{\mathfrak{r}}' \tag{72.3}$$

darstellen. Für den *Flächenstrom* $\psi(\hat{\mathfrak{r}})$ folgt mit Hilfe der Randbedingung die Integralgleichung

$$\int\limits_S \psi(\hat{\mathfrak{r}}') \, G(\hat{\mathfrak{r}} - \hat{\mathfrak{r}}') \, d\hat{\mathfrak{r}}' = v_0(\hat{\mathfrak{r}}), \quad \hat{\mathfrak{r}} \in (S). \tag{72.4}$$

$v_0(\mathfrak{r})$ ist die einfallende Welle, von der wir annehmen wollen, daß $v_0(\hat{\mathfrak{r}})$ auf dem Zylinder unabhängig von η ist. Dies ist z.B. der Fall, wenn v_0 eine ebene Welle ist, die sich in Richtung der x-Achse ausbreitet: $v_0 = e^{ix}$. Außerdem kann v_0 auch eine der geeignet gewählten *Rohrwellen* sein, die sich in dem ungeschlitzten beidseitig ins Unendliche reichenden Wellenleiter fortpflanzen können[1]. Ohne hierauf näher einzugehen, setzen wir für das folgende $v_0(\hat{\mathfrak{r}}) = v_0(x, \eta, \zeta_0) = f(x)$. Ferner soll vorausgesetzt werden, daß auch $\psi(\hat{\mathfrak{r}})$ nicht von η abhängt: $\psi(\hat{\mathfrak{r}}) = \psi(x)$. Dies ist dann der Fall, wenn

$$\oint G(\hat{\mathfrak{r}} - \hat{\mathfrak{r}}') \sqrt{g_\eta} \, d\eta' = K(x - x') \tag{72.5}$$

nicht von η abhängt. Dabei hat die Integration über den gesamten η'-Bereich zu erfolgen und es gilt mit (72.1)

$$G(\mathfrak{r} - \hat{\mathfrak{r}}') = \frac{1}{4\pi} \frac{\exp\left\{i\sqrt{(x - x')^2 + \chi(\eta, \zeta; \eta', \zeta_0)}\right\}}{\sqrt{(x - x')^2 + \chi(\eta, \zeta; \eta', \zeta_0)}} \tag{72.6}$$

(s. die Beispiele weiter unten). Mit (72.5) geht die Integralgleichung (72.4) in die Form

$$\int\limits_S \psi(x') \, K(x - x') \, dx' = f(x), \quad x \in (S) \tag{72.4'}$$

[1] Vgl. etwa G. GOUBAU: Elektromagnetische Wellenleiter und Hohlräume, Kap. I. Stuttgart 1955. — N. MARCUWITZ: Wavequide Handbook. New York-Toronto-London: McGraw-Hill 1951.

über. Dabei seien diejenigen Stücke der x-Achse, die den Zylinderstücken (S_ν) entsprechen, ebenfalls mit (S_ν) bezeichnet. Die übrigen Teile der x-Achse wollen wir wieder mit (L) bezeichnen. Läßt sich nun $K(x)$ als Fourier-Integral

$$K(x) = \frac{1}{2\pi} \int_{-\infty}^{\infty} L(\alpha)\, e^{i\alpha x}\, d\alpha \tag{72.7}$$

darstellen und führen wir die Fourier-Transformierte des Flächenstroms

$$\overline{\psi}(\alpha) = \int_S \psi(x)\, e^{-i\alpha x}\, dx \tag{72.8}$$

ein, so geht (72.4) in die *dualen Integralgleichungen*

$$\left.\begin{aligned} \frac{1}{2\pi} \int_{-\infty}^{\infty} L(\alpha)\, \overline{\psi}(\alpha)\, e^{i\alpha x}\, d\alpha &= f(x), \quad x \in (S), \\ \int_{-\infty}^{\infty} \overline{\psi}(\alpha)\, e^{i\alpha x}\, d\alpha &= 0, \qquad x \in (L) \end{aligned}\right\} \tag{72.9}$$

über, die formal mit (60.8p) übereinstimmen. Wir können daher nach dem Vorgang von Ziff. 64 auch hier zu den mit (72.9) äquivalenten Integralgleichungen vom Faltungstypus übergehen, indem wir (72.9) mit $e^{-i\alpha' x}$ multiplizieren und über den entsprechenden x-Bereich integrieren [vgl. (64.11'p)]:

$$\left.\begin{aligned} \frac{1}{2\pi} \int_{-\infty}^{\infty} L(\alpha')\, \overline{\psi}(\alpha')\, \overline{\Theta}_S(\alpha - \alpha')\, d\alpha' &= \overline{f}(\alpha), \\ \int_{-\infty}^{\infty} \overline{\psi}(\alpha')\, \overline{\Theta}_L(\alpha - \alpha')\, d\alpha' &= 0 \end{aligned}\right\} \tag{72.9'}$$

mit

$$\left.\begin{aligned} \overline{\Theta}_S(\alpha) &= \int_S e^{-i\alpha x}\, dx, \\ \overline{\Theta}_L(\alpha) &= \int_L e^{-i\alpha x}\, dx = 2\pi\, \delta(\alpha) - \overline{\Theta}_S(\alpha), \\ \overline{f}(\alpha) &= \int_S f(x)\, e^{-i\alpha x}\, dx. \end{aligned}\right\} \tag{72.9''}$$

Diese Gleichungen haben gegenüber (72.9) den Vorzug, daß die beiden Variablen α und α' die gleiche physikalische Bedeutung haben (Wellenzahlen).

73. Beispiele[1]. *α) Plattenwellenleiter.* Der Wellenleiter bestehe aus Teilen zweier paralleler Ebenen, deren Spur in der yz-Ebene parallel der y-Achse sei und die Gleichung $z = \pm\varepsilon$ habe (Plattenabstand 2ε; s. Fig. 43[2]). Gl. (72.5) nimmt hier mit Hilfe von (8.3a) und (60.1) die Form an

$$\left.\begin{aligned} K(x - x') &= \oint G(\mathfrak{r} - \mathfrak{r}')\, dy' = \frac{i}{4} \left\{ H_0^1(|x - x'|) + H_0^1\left(\sqrt{(2\varepsilon)^2 + (x - x')^2}\right) \right\} \\ &= \frac{i}{4\pi} \int_{-\infty}^{\infty} \frac{1 + e^{i2\varepsilon\sqrt{1-\alpha^2}}}{\sqrt{1 - \alpha^2}}\, e^{i\alpha(x - x')}\, d\alpha \end{aligned}\right\} \tag{73.1}$$

[1] Eine Zusammenstellung der in der Literatur behandelten Wellenleiterprobleme mittels der Wiener-Hopf-Methode bei C. J. Bouwkamp: Progr. Phys., Lond. **17**, § 7 (1954). — B. Noble: Methods based on Wiener-Hopf Technique. 1958.

[2] Alle Längen sind in Vielfachen der Wellenlänge zu messen; vgl. Ziff. 2.

also

$$L(\alpha) = \frac{i}{2}\,\frac{1 + e^{i2\varepsilon\sqrt{1-\alpha^2}}}{\sqrt{1-\alpha^2}}. \tag{73.2}$$

Dabei ist über $-\infty < y' < \infty$ zu integrieren, wobei jedoch zwei Terme mit $|\mathfrak{r} - \hat{\mathfrak{r}}'| = \sqrt{(x-x')^2 + (y-y')^2 + (z\pm\varepsilon)^2}$ zu berücksichtigen sind; auf diese Weise entsteht zunächst

$$\left.\begin{aligned}\oint G(\mathfrak{r}-\hat{\mathfrak{r}})\,dy' &= \frac{i}{4}\left\{H_0^1\left(\sqrt{(x-x')^2+(z-\varepsilon)^2}\right) + H_0^1\left(\sqrt{(x-x')^2+(z+\varepsilon)^2}\right)\right\}\\ &= \frac{i}{4\pi}\int\limits_{-\infty}^{\infty}\left\{e^{i\sqrt{1-\alpha^2}|z-\varepsilon|} + e^{i\sqrt{1-\alpha^2}|z+\varepsilon|}\right\}\frac{e^{i\alpha(x-x')}}{\sqrt{1-\alpha^2}}\,d\alpha\end{aligned}\right\} \tag{73.1'}$$

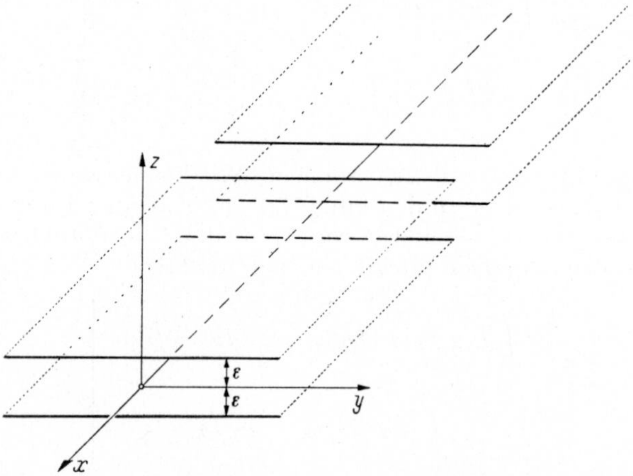

Fig. 43. Plattenwellenleiter mit 6 Kanten in 3 Kantenebenen (Dreikantenproblem).

und dies geht für $z = \pm\varepsilon$ in (73.1) über. Multipliziert man (73.1′) mit $\psi(x')$ und integriert über $x' \in S$, so erhält man eine Darstellung des Gesamtfeldes (72.3) mit Hilfe der Transformierten $\overline{\psi}(\alpha)$ in Gestalt eines Fourier-Integrals:

$$v(x,z) = v_0(x,z) - \frac{i}{4\pi}\int\limits_{-\infty}^{\infty}\frac{\overline{\psi}(\alpha)}{\sqrt{1-\alpha^2}}\left\{e^{i\sqrt{1-\alpha^2}|z-\varepsilon|} + e^{i\sqrt{1-\alpha^2}|z+\varepsilon|}\right\}e^{i\alpha x}\,d\alpha. \tag{73.1''}$$

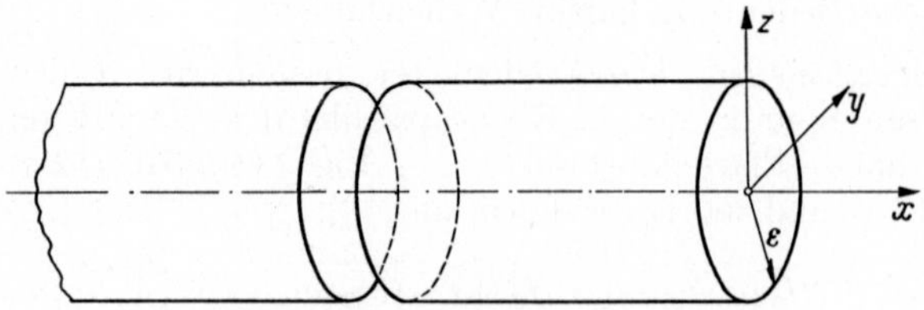

Fig. 44. Kreisrohrwellenleiter (Dreikantenproblem).

Man kann hier zur Lösung des Randwertproblems (72.2) auch direkt einen die Wellengleichung lösenden *Fourier-Ansatz* der Form (73.1″) machen. Man gelangt so durch die Forderung der Randbedingung $v = 0$ für $z = \pm\varepsilon$, $x \in (S)$ sowie der Stetigkeitsforderung für $\partial v/\partial z$ für $z = \pm\varepsilon$, $x \in (L)$ unmittelbar auf die dualen Integralgleichungen (72.9). Entsprechende Formeln gelten für einen Wellenleiter, der aus mehr als zwei parallelen Ebenen gebildet wird.

β) Kreisrohrwellenleiter. Wir führen Zylinderkoordinaten x, ϱ, φ ein mit $\varrho = \varepsilon$ für die Spur des Zylinders in der $\varrho\varphi$-Ebene; vgl. Fig. 44. Gl. (72.5) nimmt dann die folgende Gestalt an[1]

$$\left.\begin{aligned} K(x-x') &= \oint G(\hat{\mathfrak{r}}-\hat{\mathfrak{r}}')\,\varepsilon\,d\varphi' \\ &= \frac{\varepsilon}{4\pi}\int\limits_0^{2\pi} \frac{\exp\{i\sqrt{(x-x')^2+2\varepsilon^2[1-\cos(\varphi-\varphi')]}\}}{\sqrt{(x-x')^2+2\varepsilon^2[1-\cos(\varphi-\varphi')]}}\,d\varphi' \\ &= \frac{i\varepsilon}{4}\int\limits_{-\infty}^{\infty} J_0(\varepsilon\sqrt{1-\alpha^2})\,H_0^1(\varepsilon\sqrt{1-\alpha^2})\,e^{i\alpha(x-x')}\,d\alpha \end{aligned}\right\} \tag{73.3}$$

[J_0 Besselsche Funktion zum Index 0; für die Wurzel $\sqrt{1-\alpha^2}$ gilt das im Anschluß an Gl. (60.1) gesagte] und damit

$$L(\alpha) = \frac{i\pi\varepsilon}{2} J_0(\varepsilon\sqrt{1-\alpha^2})\,H_0^1(\varepsilon\sqrt{1-\alpha^2})\,. \tag{73.4}$$

Auch hier können wir das Feld (72.3) direkt mit Hilfe der Transformierten $\overline{\psi}(\alpha)$ aus Gl. (72.8) darstellen, wenn wir zunächst die φ'-Integration ausführen:

$$\left.\begin{aligned} &\oint G(\mathfrak{r}-\hat{\mathfrak{r}}')\,\varepsilon\,d\varphi' \\ &= \frac{\varepsilon}{4\pi}\int\limits_0^{2\pi} \frac{\exp\{i\sqrt{(x-x')^2+\varrho^2+\varepsilon^2-2\varrho\,\varepsilon\cos(\varphi-\varphi')}\}}{\sqrt{(x-x')^2+\varrho^2+\varepsilon^2-2\varrho\,\varepsilon\cos(\varphi-\varphi')}}\,d\varphi' \\ &= \frac{i\varepsilon}{4}\int\limits_{-\infty}^{\infty} \left\{\begin{matrix} J_0\left(\varrho\sqrt{1-\alpha^2}\right) H_0^1\left(\varepsilon\sqrt{1-\alpha^2}\right) \\ J_0\left(\varepsilon\sqrt{1-\alpha^2}\right) H_0^1\left(\varrho\sqrt{1-\alpha^2}\right) \end{matrix}\right\} e^{i\alpha(x-x')}\,d\alpha,\ \varrho \lessgtr \varepsilon, \end{aligned}\right\} \tag{73.3'}$$

wobei in der letzten Formel die obere Zeile in der geschweiften Klammer für $\varrho < \varepsilon$ gilt, die untere für $\varrho > \varepsilon$. Multipliziert man diese Gleichung wieder mit $\psi(x')$ und integriert über $x' \in (S)$, so erhält man an Stelle von (72.3) die Felddarstellung

$$\left.\begin{aligned} v(x,\varrho) &= v_0(x,\varrho) \\ &- \frac{i\varepsilon}{4}\int\limits_{-\infty}^{\infty} \overline{\psi}(\alpha) \left\{\begin{matrix} J_0\left(\varrho\sqrt{1-\alpha^2}\right) H_0^1\left(\varepsilon\sqrt{1-\alpha^2}\right) \\ J_0\left(\varepsilon\sqrt{1-\alpha^2}\right) H_0^1\left(\varrho\sqrt{1-\alpha^2}\right) \end{matrix}\right\} e^{i\alpha x}\,d\alpha, \qquad \varrho \lessgtr \varepsilon. \end{aligned}\right\} \tag{73.3''}$$

Hier ist der Integrand eine partikuläre Lösung der Wellengleichung, die für $\varrho = 0$ regulär ist und für $\varrho \to \infty$ der Ausstrahlungsbedingung genügt. Durch Überlagerung solcher partikulärer Lösungen läßt sich die Lösung des Randwertproblems auch direkt aufbauen. Es führt dann die Randbedingung $v = 0$ für $\varrho = \varepsilon$, $x \in (S)$ und die Stetigkeitsforderung für $\partial v/\partial\varrho$ für $\varrho = \varepsilon$, $x \in (L)$ wieder unmittelbar auf die dualen Integralgleichungen (72.9)[2]. Entsprechende Überlegungen lassen sich für Wellenleiterquerschnitte durchführen, die aus zwei (oder mehreren) konzentrischen Kreisen bestehen[3].

Allgemeinere Querschnitte lassen sich nach analogen Verfahren behandeln, wenn die Wellengleichung in den Zylinderkoordinaten x, η, ζ separierbar ist[4].

[1] Vgl. W. Magnus u. F. Oberhettinger: Formeln und Sätze für die speziellen Funktionen der mathematischen Physik, 2. Aufl., S. 204. Berlin 1948.

[2] Man vgl. dazu L. A. Vainstein: Bull. Acad. Sci. URSS. Sér. Phys. **19**, 911 (1949). — S. N. Karp: N.Y. Univ. Res. Rep. No. EM-25 (1950); Comm. Pure Appl. Math. **3**, 411 (1950).

[3] L. L. Bailin: J. Res. Nat. Bur. Stand. **47**, 315 (1951).

[4] Man vgl. S. N. Karp: l. c. — Elliptische Querschnitte behandelt J. Blass: Diss. Polyt. Inst. Brooklyn 1951.

Die obigen Beispiele bezogen sich auf verschiedene *Querschnitte*. Wir wollen jetzt Beispiele betrachten, die sich hinsichtlich der Anzahl der *Kantenebenen* unterscheiden.

γ) Einkantenproblem. Der Wellenleiter erstrecke sich von $x=0$ nach $x\to\infty$ (Kantenebene $x=0$). Die Integralgleichung (72.4′) für den Flächenstrom

$$\int_0^\infty \psi(x')\,K(x-x')\,dx' = f(x) \qquad (x>0) \tag{73.5}$$

ist vom Wiener-Hopfschen Typus[1]. Die mit ihr äquivalente duale Integralgleichung (72.9) lautet hier

$$\left.\begin{aligned} \frac{1}{2\pi}\int_{-\infty}^{\infty} L(\alpha)\,\overline{\psi}(\alpha)\,e^{i\alpha x}\,d\alpha &= f(x) \qquad (x>0),\\ \int_{-\infty}^{\infty} \overline{\psi}(\alpha)\,e^{i\alpha x}\,d\alpha &= 0 \qquad (x<0).\end{aligned}\right\} \tag{73.6}$$

Zu den Integralgleichungen (72.9′) übergehend, multiplizieren wir (73.6) mit $e^{-i\alpha' x}$ und integrieren über $0<x<\infty$ bzw. $-\infty<x<0$. Vertauscht man die Integrationsreihenfolgen, so konvergiert das Integral über x, wenn wir dafür sorgen, daß α einen positiven bzw. negativen Imaginärteil besitzt. Dies erreichen wir, indem wir bei der ersten Integralgleichung (73.6) den α-Integrationsweg etwas in die obere komplexe α-Halbebene verschieben, bei der zweiten hingegen in die untere. Nach Ausführung der x-Integration können wir den α-Integrationsweg wieder mit der reellen Achse zusammenfallen lassen; müssen dann aber im Auge behalten, daß dem (bei der x-Integration entstandenen) Pol $\alpha=\alpha'$ in der oberen bzw. unteren α-Halbebene (durch einen unendlich kleinen Halbkreis) auszuweichen ist. Dies wollen wir durch einen entsprechenden Haken am Integralzeichen andeuten. Gl. (73.6) geht also damit in die Gestalt über

$$\left.\begin{aligned} \frac{1}{2\pi i}\int_{-\infty}^{\infty} L(\alpha')\,\overline{\psi}(\alpha')\,\frac{d\alpha'}{\alpha'-\alpha} &= -\overline{f}(\alpha)\\ \int_{-\infty}^{\infty} \overline{\psi}(\alpha')\,\frac{d\alpha'}{\alpha'-\alpha} &= 0\end{aligned}\right\} \tag{73.7}$$

mit

$$\overline{f}(\alpha) = \int_0^\infty f(x)\,e^{-i\alpha x}\,dx. \tag{73.7′}$$

Wir können uns auch der geläufigen Bezeichnungsweise

$$\left.\begin{aligned} \overline{\Theta}_S(\alpha) &= \int_0^\infty e^{-i\alpha x}\,dx = 2\pi\,\delta_-(\alpha) = \pi\,\delta(\alpha) + P\frac{1}{i\alpha}\\ \overline{\Theta}_L(\alpha) &= \int_{-\infty}^0 e^{-i\alpha x}\,dx = 2\pi\,\delta_+(\alpha) = \pi\,\delta(\alpha) - P\frac{1}{i\alpha}\end{aligned}\right\} \tag{73.8}$$

bedienen. Die beim Einsetzen von (73.8) in (72.9′) auftretenden singulären Integrale sind dann als *Cauchysche Hauptwerte* aufzufassen (worauf das Zeichen P hinweisen soll). Die Verwendungen von *Hakenintegralen* in (73.7), die wir auch

[1] Vgl. Fußnote 1 auf S. 337.

durch die Symbole

$$\overline{\Theta}_S(\alpha'-\alpha)=\frac{-i}{\alpha'-\underset{\smile}{\alpha}},\qquad \overline{\Theta}_L(\alpha'-\alpha)=\frac{i}{\alpha'-\underset{\frown}{\alpha}}=\overline{\Theta}_S(\alpha-\alpha') \tag{73.8'}$$

zum Ausdruck bringen können, ist jedoch für das Folgende bequemer (die Haken unter α sollen andeuten, in welchem Sinne dem Pol $\alpha'=\alpha$ bei einer α'-Integration durch einen unendlich kleinen Halbkreis in der komplexen α'-Ebene auszuweichen ist). Die singulären Integralgleichungen (73.7) des Einkantenproblems werden wir in der nächsten Ziffer eingehender betrachten.

δ) Zweikantenprobleme. Die beiden Kantenebenen seien durch $x=\pm\varepsilon$ gegeben. Es sind hier die beiden komplementären Fälle zu unterscheiden, daß entweder (S) oder (L) das Intervall $-\varepsilon\leqq x\leqq\varepsilon$ einnehmen. Der erste Fall entspricht einem beiderseitig offenen Wellenleiter der Länge 2ε, der zweite einem auf beiden Seiten ins Unendliche reichenden Wellenleiter, der einen transversalen Schlitz der Breite 2ε besitzt. Die dualen Integralgleichungen (72.9) nehmen für den Wellenleiter der Länge 2ε die Form an

$$\left.\begin{aligned}\frac{1}{2\pi}\int_{-\infty}^{\infty} L(\alpha)\,\overline{\psi}(\alpha)\,e^{i\alpha x}\,d\alpha &= f(x) \qquad (|x|<\varepsilon),\\ \int_{-\infty}^{\infty}\overline{\psi}(\alpha)\,e^{i\alpha x}\,d\alpha &= 0 \qquad (|x|>\varepsilon).\end{aligned}\right\} \tag{73.9}$$

Dies geht wegen

$$\overline{\Theta}_S(\alpha)=2\,\frac{\sin\varepsilon\alpha}{\alpha},\qquad \overline{\Theta}_L(\alpha)=2\pi\,\delta(\alpha)-2\,\frac{\sin\varepsilon\alpha}{\alpha} \tag{73.10}$$

zufolge (72.9′) in die Form über

$$\left.\begin{aligned}\frac{1}{\pi}\int_{-\infty}^{\infty} L(\alpha')\,\overline{\psi}(\alpha')\,\frac{\sin\varepsilon(\alpha'-\alpha)}{\alpha'-\alpha}\,d\alpha' &= \overline{f}(\alpha),\\ \overline{\psi}(\alpha)-\frac{1}{\pi}\int_{-\infty}^{\infty}\overline{\psi}(\alpha')\,\frac{\sin\varepsilon(\alpha'-\alpha)}{\alpha'-\alpha}\,d\alpha' &= 0\end{aligned}\right\} \tag{73.9a}$$

mit

$$\overline{\psi}(\alpha)=\int_{-\varepsilon}^{\varepsilon}\psi(x)\,e^{-i\alpha x}\,dx,\qquad \overline{f}(\alpha)=\int_{-\varepsilon}^{\varepsilon}f(x)\,e^{-i\alpha x}\,dx. \tag{73.11}$$

Entsprechend ergibt sich für das *komplementäre* Problem des Wellenleiters mit einem Querschlitz der Breite 2ε

$$\left.\begin{aligned}\frac{1}{2\pi}\int_{-\infty}^{\infty} L(\alpha)\,\overline{\psi}(\alpha)\,e^{i\alpha x}\,d\alpha &= f(x) \qquad (|x|>\varepsilon),\\ \int_{-\infty}^{\infty}\overline{\psi}(\alpha)\,e^{i\alpha x}\,d\alpha &= 0 \qquad (|x|<\varepsilon)\end{aligned}\right\} \tag{73.9'}$$

bzw.

$$\left.\begin{aligned}L(\alpha)\,\overline{\psi}(\alpha)-\frac{1}{\pi}\int_{-\infty}^{\infty} L(\alpha')\,\overline{\psi}(\alpha')\,\frac{\sin\varepsilon(\alpha'-\alpha)}{\alpha'-\alpha}\,d\alpha' &= \overline{f}(\alpha)\\ \int_{-\infty}^{\infty}\overline{\psi}(\alpha')\,\frac{\sin\varepsilon(\alpha'-\alpha)}{\alpha'-\alpha}\,d\alpha' &= 0\end{aligned}\right\} \tag{73.9'a}$$

mit

$$\left.\begin{array}{c}\overline{\psi}(\alpha)\\ \overline{f}(\alpha)\end{array}\right\} = \left\{ \int\limits_{-\infty}^{-\varepsilon} + \int\limits_{\varepsilon}^{\infty} \right\} \begin{array}{c}\psi(x)\\ f(x)\end{array} \, e^{-i\alpha x}\,dx. \tag{73.11'}$$

Hier führt die Substitution

$$\varphi(\alpha) = L(\alpha)\,\overline{\psi}(\alpha)$$

auf

$$\left.\begin{array}{c} \displaystyle\int\limits_{-\infty}^{\infty} \frac{\varphi(\alpha')}{L(\alpha')}\,\frac{\sin\varepsilon(\alpha'-\alpha)}{\alpha'-\alpha}\,d\alpha' = 0,\\[3mm] \displaystyle\varphi(\alpha) - \frac{1}{\pi}\int\limits_{-\infty}^{\infty}\varphi(\alpha')\,\frac{\sin\varepsilon(\alpha'-\alpha)}{\alpha'-\alpha}\,d\alpha' = \overline{f}(\alpha). \end{array}\right\} \tag{73.9''a}$$

Diese Integralgleichung geht — abgesehen von der Inhomogenität — aus (73.9a) hervor, indem man $L(\alpha)$ durch $L^{-1}(\alpha)$ ersetzt. Ein entsprechender Sachverhalt findet sich auch bei der allgemeinen Gleichung (72.9'), wenn man sie für zwei komplementäre Probleme anschreibt.

Man kann auch die *Wechselwirkung* der durch die beiden Kantenebenen getrennten Teile des Wellenleiters (bzw. seines Komplements) explizit hervortreten lassen. Zu diesem Zweck betrachten wir etwa Gl. (73.9') und zerlegen die Fernfeldamplitude $\overline{\psi}(\alpha)$ sowie $\overline{f}(\alpha)$ in die von den beiden Wellenleiterelementen herrührenden Anteile

$$\left.\begin{array}{l} \left.\begin{array}{c}\overline{\psi}_1(\alpha)\\ \overline{f}_1(\alpha)\end{array}\right\} = \displaystyle\int\limits_{\varepsilon}^{\infty}\begin{array}{c}\psi(x)\\ f(x)\end{array}e^{-i\alpha x}\,dx,\qquad \left.\begin{array}{c}\overline{\psi}_2(\alpha)\\ \overline{f}_2(\alpha)\end{array}\right\} = \displaystyle\int\limits_{-\infty}^{-\varepsilon}\begin{array}{c}\psi(x)\\ f(x)\end{array}e^{-i\alpha x}\,dx,\\[4mm] \overline{\psi}(\alpha) = \overline{\psi}_1(\alpha)+\overline{\psi}_2(\alpha),\qquad \overline{f}(\alpha) = \overline{f}_1(\alpha)+\overline{f}_2(\alpha). \end{array}\right\} \tag{73.11''}$$

Mit diesen Größen können wir Gl. (73.9') in folgender Form aufspalten

$$\left.\begin{array}{c} \displaystyle\frac{1}{2\pi}\int\limits_{-\infty}^{\infty}L(\alpha)\,\overline{\psi}(\alpha)\,e^{i\alpha x}\,d\alpha = f(x)\quad (x>\varepsilon),\\[4mm] \displaystyle\int\limits_{-\infty}^{\infty}\overline{\psi}_1(\alpha)\,e^{i\alpha x}\,d\alpha = 0\qquad (x<\varepsilon) \end{array}\right\} \tag{73.12a}$$

und

$$\left.\begin{array}{c} \displaystyle\int\limits_{-\infty}^{\infty}\overline{\psi}_2(\alpha)\,e^{i\alpha x}\,d\alpha = 0\qquad (x>-\varepsilon),\\[4mm] \displaystyle\frac{1}{2\pi}\int\limits_{-\infty}^{\infty}L(\alpha)\,\overline{\psi}(\alpha)\,e^{i\alpha x}\,d\alpha = f(x)\quad (x<-\varepsilon). \end{array}\right\} \tag{73.12b}$$

Diese Gleichungen haben eine analoge Gestalt wie die Gln. (73.6) für das Einkantenproblem. Sie lassen sich daher entsprechend (73.7) umformen:

$$\left.\begin{array}{c} \displaystyle\frac{1}{2\pi i}\oint\limits_{-\infty}^{\infty}L(\alpha')\,\{\overline{\psi}_1(\alpha')+\overline{\psi}_2(\alpha')\}\,\frac{e^{i\varepsilon(\alpha'-\alpha)}}{\alpha'-\alpha}\,d\alpha' = -\overline{f}_1(\alpha),\\[4mm] \displaystyle\oint\limits_{-\infty}^{\infty}\overline{\psi}_1(\alpha')\,\frac{e^{i\varepsilon\alpha'}}{\alpha'-\alpha}\,d\alpha' = 0 \end{array}\right\} \tag{73.12'a}$$

und

$$\left.\begin{aligned} \oint_{-\infty}^{\infty} \overline{\psi}_2(\alpha') \frac{e^{-i\varepsilon\alpha'}}{\alpha'-\alpha}\, d\alpha' = 0\,, \\ \frac{1}{2\pi i}\oint_{-\infty}^{\infty} L(\alpha')\,\{\overline{\psi}_2(\alpha') + \overline{\psi}_1(\alpha')\}\,\frac{e^{-i\varepsilon(\alpha'-\alpha)}}{\alpha'-\alpha}\, d\alpha = \overline{f}_2(\alpha)\,. \end{aligned}\right\} \qquad (73.12'\text{b})$$

Es ergeben sich also für $\overline{\psi}_1(\alpha)$ und $\overline{\psi}_2(\alpha)$ zwei durch die Wechselwirkung der Wellenleiterelemente *gekoppelte* Einkantenprobleme.

74. Zur Theorie der singulären Integralgleichungen. Die singulären Integralgleichungen (73.7) des Einkantenproblems lassen sich mit Hilfe der funktionentheoretischen Methoden lösen, wie sie zur Behandlung singulärer Integralgleichungen vom *Cauchyschen Typus*:

$$A(\alpha)\,\varphi(\alpha) + \frac{1}{2\pi i}\oint_{-\infty}^{\infty} \frac{B(\alpha')\,\varphi(\alpha')}{\alpha'-\alpha}\, d\alpha' = f(\alpha) \qquad (74.1)$$

[wobei $A(\alpha)$, $B(\alpha)$ und $f(\alpha)$ gegeben und $\varphi(\alpha)$ gesucht ist] entwickelt worden sind[1]. Um diese hier kurz darzulegen, betrachten wir *Cauchysche Integrale* der Form

$$\Phi(\alpha) = \frac{1}{2\pi i}\int_{-\infty}^{\infty} \frac{\varphi(\alpha')}{\alpha'-\alpha}\, d\alpha' \quad (\alpha \text{ komplex})\,. \qquad (74.2)$$

$\Phi(\alpha)$ ist eine sowohl in der oberen α-Halbebene S^+ als auch der unteren S^- *holomorphe* Funktion der komplexen Variablen α [einschließlich des unendlich fernen Punktes bei entsprechenden Voraussetzungen über die Funktion $\varphi(\alpha)$]. Nähert sich jedoch α aus S^+ bzw. aus S^- der reellen Achse, so ergeben sich *verschiedene* Randwerte:

$$\Phi^+(\alpha) = \frac{1}{2\pi i}\oint_{-\infty}^{\infty} \frac{\varphi(\alpha')}{\alpha'-\alpha}\, d\alpha' = \frac{1}{2}\,\varphi(\alpha) + \frac{1}{2\pi i}\fint_{-\infty}^{\infty} \frac{\varphi(\alpha')}{\alpha'-\alpha}\, d\alpha' \qquad (74.3^+)$$

bzw.

$$\Phi^-(\alpha) = \frac{1}{2\pi i}\oint_{-\infty}^{\infty} \frac{\varphi(\alpha')}{\alpha'-\alpha}\, d\alpha = -\frac{1}{2}\,\varphi(\alpha) + \frac{1}{2\pi i}\fint_{-\infty}^{\infty} \frac{\varphi(\alpha')}{\alpha'-\alpha}\, d\alpha'\,. \qquad (74.3^-)$$

Dabei bedeutet das Integral mit dem Balken rechts den *Cauchyschen Hauptwert.* $\Phi(\alpha)$ ist also eine *stückweise holomorphe* Funktion, die beim Überschreiten der reellen Achse den Sprung

$$\Phi^+(\alpha) - \Phi^-(\alpha) = \varphi(\alpha) \qquad (\alpha \text{ reell}) \qquad (74.4)$$

aufweist. Umgekehrt unterscheidet sich jede analytische Funktion mit denselben Eigenschaften wie $\Phi(\alpha)$ von (74.2) nur durch eine Konstante [da die Differenz zweier stückweise holomorpher Funktionen mit der Eigenschaft (74.4) in der ganzen α-Ebene holomorph ist]. Gl. (74.2) löst also das Sprungwertproblem (74.4) für stückweise holomorphe Funktionen.

Für zwei Cauchysche Integrale der Form (74.3) gilt die *Vertauschungsformel*

$$\left.\begin{aligned} \oint_{-\infty}^{\infty} d\alpha' \frac{\varphi(\alpha')}{\alpha'-\alpha} \oint_{-\infty}^{\infty} \frac{\psi(\alpha'')}{\alpha''-\alpha'}\, d\alpha'' = \int_{-\infty}^{\infty} d\alpha''\,\psi(\alpha'') \oint_{-\infty}^{\infty} \frac{\varphi(\alpha')\, d\alpha'}{(\alpha'-\alpha)\,(\alpha''-\alpha')}\,, \\ \oint_{-\infty}^{\infty} d\alpha' \frac{\varphi(\alpha')}{\alpha'-\alpha} \oint_{-\infty}^{\infty} \frac{\psi(\alpha'')}{\alpha''-\alpha'}\, d\alpha'' = \int_{-\infty}^{\infty} d\alpha''\,\psi(\alpha'') \oint_{-\infty}^{\infty} \frac{\varphi(\alpha')\, d\alpha'}{(\alpha'-\alpha)\,(\alpha''-\alpha')} \end{aligned}\right\} \qquad (74.5)$$

[1] Man vgl. die S. 337, Fußnote 3, zitierte Literatur.

(das Doppelkantenintegral rechts ist so zu führen, daß den beiden Polen $\alpha'=\alpha$ und $\alpha'=\alpha''$ auf der reellen Achse in der durch die Haken angedeuteten Weise auszuweichen ist). Man hat also bei der Vertauschung der Integrationsreihenfolge jeweils die Haken *„umzuklappen“*. Sind Cauchysche Integrale mit gleichen Haken zu vertauschen, so ist zunächst einer der Haken mit Hilfe von (74.4) umzuklappen.

Schreiben wir nun die Integralgleichung der Einkantenprobleme (73.7) in der etwas allgemeineren Gestalt

$$\left.\begin{aligned} \frac{1}{2\pi i}\int_{-\infty}^{\infty} L(\alpha')\,\varphi(\alpha')\,\frac{d\alpha'}{\alpha'-\alpha} &= f(\alpha),\\ \frac{1}{2\pi i}\int_{-\infty}^{\infty} \varphi(\alpha')\,\frac{d\alpha'}{\alpha'-\alpha} &= g(\alpha), \end{aligned}\right\} \tag{74.6}$$

so ist sie offenbar nur lösbar, falls $f(\alpha)$ bzw. $g(\alpha)$ in S^- bzw. S^+ holomorphe Funktionen sind (da dies für die entsprechenden linken Seiten der Fall ist). Wir können daher nach dem Cauchyschen Satz Gl. (74.6) auch in der Form

$$\left.\begin{aligned} \int_{-\infty}^{\infty} \{L(\alpha')\,\varphi(\alpha')+f(\alpha')\}\,\frac{d\alpha'}{\alpha'-\alpha} &= 0\\ \int_{-\infty}^{\infty} \{\varphi(\alpha')-g(\alpha')\}\,\frac{d\alpha'}{\alpha'-\alpha} &= 0 \end{aligned}\right\} \tag{74.6'}$$

schreiben [auf die sich übrigens auch (74.1) leicht zurückführen läßt]. Diese Gleichungen besagen nun nach dem *Cauchyschen Satz*, daß die geschweifte Klammer in der oberen bzw. unteren Gleichung (74.6′) in S^+ bzw. S^- holomorph sein muß:

$$\left.\begin{aligned} L(\alpha)\,\varphi(\alpha)+f(\alpha) &= \Phi^+(\alpha),\\ \varphi(\alpha)-g(\alpha) &= \Phi^-(\alpha). \end{aligned}\right\} \tag{74.7}$$

Dabei bedeuten $\Phi^+(\alpha)$ bzw. $\Phi^-(\alpha)$ zwei zunächst beliebige in S^+ bzw. S^- holomorphe Funktionen. Da nun die beiden Gleichungen (74.7) auf der reellen Achse *simultan* gelten müssen, so folgt durch Elimination von $\varphi(\alpha)$

$$\Phi^+(\alpha)-L(\alpha)\,\Phi^-(x)=f(\alpha)+L(\alpha)\,g(\alpha) \qquad (\alpha \text{ reell}). \tag{74.7'}$$

Dies können wir als eine Funktionalgleichung für die *stückweise holomorphe* Funktion

$$\Phi(\alpha)=\left\{\begin{matrix} \Phi^+(\alpha), & \alpha\in S^+\\ \Phi^-(\alpha), & \alpha\in S^- \end{matrix}\right\} \tag{74.8}$$

auffassen; ihre Randwerte müssen der Relation (74.7′) genügen (*Hilbert-Problem* der Funktionentheorie[1]). Bei der Lösung dieses Problems kommt es darauf an, $L(\alpha)$ in der Form

$$L(\alpha)=\frac{L^+(\alpha)}{L^-(\alpha)} \tag{74.9}$$

aufzuspalten (zu *„faktorisieren“*), wobei $L^+(\alpha)$ bzw. $L^-(\alpha)$ in S^+ bzw. S^- holomorph ist und dort *keine Nullstellen* hat. Zu diesem Zweck bilden wir

$$\ln L(\alpha)=\ln L^+(\alpha)-\ln L^-(\alpha) \tag{74.9'}$$

[1] Gl. (74.7′) bildet auch den Ausgangspunkt der Wiener-Hopf-Methode, die mit dem im Text darzustellenden Verfahren im wesentlichen übereinstimmt; vgl. etwa B. NOBLE l. c. S. 37.

(α reell; unter ln irgendeinen Zweig des Logarithmus verstanden), wobei wir im folgenden annehmen wollen, daß $L(\alpha)$ für *reelle* α *weder Nullstellen noch Pole* und $\ln L(\alpha)$ *eindeutig* ist. Genauer gesagt soll $L(\alpha)$ in einem beliebig schmalen, die reelle Achse enthaltenden Streifen holomorph sein und dort keine Nullstellen besitzen, sowie der Bedingung $\arg \ln L(\alpha) \Big|_{-\infty}^{\infty} = 0$ genügen. Nehmen wir an, die durch analytische Fortsetzung gebildete Funktion

$$\Gamma(\alpha) = \begin{cases} \ln L^+(\alpha), & \alpha \in S^+ \\ \ln L^-(\alpha), & \alpha \in S^- \end{cases} \tag{74.10}$$

sei stückweise holomorph, so gilt nach (74.9′) (α reell)

$$\Gamma^+(\alpha) - \Gamma^-(\alpha) = \ln L(\alpha) \tag{74.9''}$$

und dieses Sprungwertproblem hat nach (74.2), (74.4) die Lösung (bis auf eine für das folgende irrelevante Konstante, α komplex):

$$\Gamma(\alpha) = \frac{1}{2\pi i} \int_{-\infty}^{\infty} \ln L(\alpha') \frac{d\alpha'}{\alpha' - \alpha}. \tag{74.10'}$$

Damit ist die gesuchte Aufspaltung gefunden:

$$\left.\begin{aligned} L^+(\alpha) &= e^{\Gamma^+(\alpha)} = \exp\left\{\frac{1}{2i\pi} \oint_{-\infty}^{\infty} \ln L(\alpha') \frac{d\alpha'}{\alpha' - \alpha}\right\}, \\ L^-(\alpha) &= e^{\Gamma^-(\alpha)} = \exp\left\{\frac{1}{2\pi i} \oint_{-\infty}^{\infty} \ln L(\alpha') \frac{d\alpha'}{\alpha' - \alpha}\right\}. \end{aligned}\right\} \tag{74.11}$$

Über das Verhalten von $L^+(\alpha)$ bzw. $L^-(\alpha)$ im *Unendlichen* von S^+ bzw. S^- wollen wir voraussetzen, daß es von der folgenden Form sei

$$\left.\begin{aligned} L^+(\alpha) = O(\alpha^{\gamma_1}), \quad L^-(\alpha) = O(\alpha^{\gamma_2}) \quad (|\alpha| \to \infty) \\ \text{mit} \qquad -1 < \gamma_{1,2} < 1 \end{aligned}\right\} \tag{74.12}$$

(ohne auf die Bedingungen einzugehen, die dadurch zusätzlich an $L(\alpha)$ gestellt werden müssen[1]). Nach Durchführung der Faktorisierung macht die Lösung des Hilbert-Problems (74.7′) keine Schwierigkeiten mehr. Schreibt man nämlich (74.7′) mit Hilfe von (74.9) in der Form (α reell)

$$\frac{\Phi^+(\alpha)}{L^+(\alpha)} - \frac{\Phi^-(\alpha)}{L^-(\alpha)} = \frac{f(\alpha)}{L^+(\alpha)} + \frac{g(\alpha)}{L^-(\alpha)}, \tag{74.13}$$

so ist dadurch für die stückweise holomorphe Funktion

$$\Omega(\alpha) = \begin{cases} \dfrac{\Phi^+(\alpha)}{L^+(\alpha)}, & \alpha \in S^+ \\ \dfrac{\Phi^-(\alpha)}{L^-(\alpha)}, & \alpha \in S^- \end{cases} \tag{74.14}$$

[1] Für die Durchführung der in (74.11) angegebenen Faktorisierung findet man bei B. Noble l. c. rechnerische Details für eine größere Zahl praktisch wichtiger Beispiele.

ein Sprungwertproblem der Form (74.4) gegeben, das nach (74.2) die Lösung hat (α komplex):

$$\Omega(\alpha) = \frac{1}{2\pi i} \int_{-\infty}^{\infty} \left\{ \frac{f(\alpha')}{L^+(\alpha')} + \frac{g(\alpha')}{L^-(\alpha')} \right\} \frac{d\alpha'}{\alpha' - \alpha} + C. \tag{74.14'}$$

Damit ist auch die Lösung der Ausgangsgleichung (74.6) gefunden, wenn man (74.14′) mit (74.14) in (74.7) einsetzt. Wir können diese Lösung in der Form schreiben

$$\varphi(\alpha) = \frac{L^-(\alpha)}{2\pi i} \left\{ \oint_{-\infty}^{\infty} \frac{f(\alpha')}{L^+(\alpha')} \frac{d\alpha'}{\alpha' - \alpha} + \oint_{-\infty}^{\infty} \frac{g(\alpha')}{L^-(\alpha')} \frac{d\alpha'}{\alpha' - \alpha} \right\} + C L^-(\alpha). \tag{74.15}$$

Der zweite Term mit der willkürlichen Konstanten C ist offensichtlich die Lösung der *homogenen* Integralgleichung (74.6). In der Tat wird beim Einsetzen dieses Terms in (74.6) der Integrand des oberen bzw. unteren Integrals in (74.6) in S^+ bzw. S^- holomorph. Schließt man den Integrationsweg über das Unendliche der oberen bzw. unteren Halbebene, so verschwinden also die Integrale längs der geschlossenen Wege. Der Beitrag des Rückweges liefert keinen Beitrag, wenn $L^+(\alpha)$ bzw. $L^-(\alpha)$ im Unendlichen beliebig schwach verschwindet [d.h. für $\gamma_1 < 0$ *und* $\gamma_2 < 0$ in (74.12)]. Wie sich leicht zeigen läßt, ist jedoch der erste Term von (74.15) auch dann noch eine Lösung von (74.6), wenn $L^+(\alpha)$ und (oder) $L^-(\alpha)$ allenfalls schwächer als die erste Potenz von α im Unendlichen singulär wird (d.h. für $0 \leqq \gamma_{1,2} < 1$). In diesem Fall ist $C = 0$ zu setzen; die Lösung von (74.6) ist dann *eindeutig*.

Gl. (74.15) stellt die *allgemeine Lösung des Einkantenproblems* dar. Als einfachstes Beispiel betrachten wir die Beugung an der einfachen *Halbebene* [für diese ist in (73.2) $\varepsilon = 0$ zu setzen]. Für die Funktion

$$L(\alpha) = \frac{i}{\sqrt{1-\alpha^2}} \tag{74.16}$$

läßt sich die Faktorisierung (74.9) sofort angeben:

$$L^+(\alpha) = \frac{i}{\sqrt{1+\alpha}}, \qquad L^-(\alpha) = \sqrt{1-\alpha}. \tag{74.16'}$$

Hier ist $\gamma_1 = -\frac{1}{2}$, $\gamma_2 = \frac{1}{2}$, die Lösung der Integralgleichung (73.7) ist also *eindeutig*. Bei der Formulierung unserer Beugungsprobleme mittels singulärer Integralgleichungen erübrigt sich somit die Vorgabe einer Kantenbedingung (Abschn. I d 2). Implizit ist jedoch die Kantenbedingung in der Forderung der Existenz (und entsprechenden Vertauschbarkeit) der Integrale unseres Formalismus enthalten. Die Lösung von (73.7) ergibt sich nach (74.15):

$$\bar{\psi}(\alpha) = \frac{\sqrt{1-\alpha}}{2\pi} \oint_{-\infty}^{\infty} \sqrt{1+\alpha'}\, \bar{f}(\alpha') \frac{d\alpha'}{\alpha' - \alpha}. \tag{74.17}$$

Handelt es sich insbesondere um eine einfallende *ebene* Welle, deren Ausbreitungsrichtung senkrecht auf der Schirmkante steht und mit der x-Achse den Winkel ϑ_0 einschließt, so gilt [$\cos\vartheta_0 = \alpha_0$, vgl. (73.8′)]

$$f(x) = e^{i\alpha_0 x} \to \bar{f}(\alpha) = \frac{-i}{\alpha - \alpha_0}; \tag{74.18}$$

damit folgt aus (74.17)

$$\overline{\psi}(\alpha) = \frac{\sqrt{1-\alpha}}{2\pi i} \int_{-\infty}^{\infty} \frac{\sqrt{1+\alpha'}\, d\alpha'}{(\alpha'-\mathfrak{z}_0)(\alpha'-\alpha)} = -\frac{\sqrt{1+\alpha}\sqrt{1-\alpha}}{\alpha-\mathfrak{z}_0}. \tag{74.19}$$

Diese Lösung werden wir in Abschn. B Ia wiederfinden und diskutieren. Kompliziertere durchgerechnete Beispiele finden sich in der eingangs zitierten Literatur.

Zur Behandlung des *Zweikantenproblems* gehen wir von den singulären Integralgleichungen (73.12′a, b) aus. Bringen wir in Gl. (73.12′a) das Wechselwirkungsglied mit $\overline{\psi}_2(\alpha)$ auf die rechte Seite, so ergeben sich für $\overline{\psi}_1(\alpha)$ Gleichungen der Form (74.6). Ihre Lösung lautet nach (74.15) (eindeutig für $0 \leqq \gamma_{1,2} < 1$)

$$\left.\begin{aligned} \overline{\psi}_1(\alpha) = -\frac{e^{-i\varepsilon\alpha}L^-(\alpha)}{2\pi i} \oint_{-\infty}^{\infty} \frac{d\alpha'}{(\alpha'-\alpha)\,L^+(\alpha')}\,\cdot \\ \cdot\left\{e^{i\varepsilon\alpha'}\overline{f}_1(\alpha') + \frac{1}{2\pi i}\oint_{-\infty}^{\infty} L(\alpha'')\, e^{i\varepsilon\alpha''}\,\overline{\psi}_2(\alpha'')\,\frac{d\alpha''}{\alpha''-\alpha'}\right\}. \end{aligned}\right\} \tag{74.20}$$

Hier können wir die Vertauschungsformel (74.5) anwenden und das innere Integral mittels Residienkalkül — unter Beachtung von Gl. (74.12) — auswerten. Zusammen mit der sich entsprechend aus (73.12′b) ergebenden Gleichung folgt so

$$\left.\begin{aligned} \frac{e^{i\varepsilon\alpha}}{L^-(\alpha)}\,\overline{\psi}_1(\alpha) &= \frac{1}{2\pi i}\oint_{-\infty}^{\infty}\left\{\frac{\overline{\psi}_2(\alpha')}{L^-(\alpha')} - \frac{\overline{f}_1(\alpha')}{L^+(\alpha')}\right\}\frac{e^{i\varepsilon\alpha'}}{\alpha'-\alpha}\,d\alpha' \\ e^{-i\varepsilon\alpha}L^+(\alpha)\,\overline{\psi}_2(\alpha) &= -\frac{1}{2\pi i}\oint_{-\infty}^{\infty}\{L^+(\alpha')\,\overline{\psi}_1(\alpha') - L^-(\alpha')\,\overline{f}_2(\alpha')\}\,\frac{e^{-i\varepsilon\alpha'}}{\alpha'-\alpha}\,d\alpha''. \end{aligned}\right\} \tag{74.20′}$$

Die ist ein *System singulärer Integralgleichungen* des Typs (74.1). Der hier auftretende Faktor $e^{\pm i\varepsilon\alpha}$ ist für Zweikantenprobleme typisch. Er erschwert die Anwendung funktionentheoretischer Methoden, da er im unendlich fernen Punkt *wesentlich singulär* wird und dieser Punkt *auf* dem Integrationsweg liegt. Um diese Singularität fortzuschaffen, schlagen wir folgenden Weg ein. Mit Hilfe der Größen

$$\hat{\psi}_1(\alpha) = \frac{e^{i\varepsilon\alpha}}{L^-(\alpha)}\,\overline{\psi}_1(\alpha), \qquad \hat{\psi}_2(\alpha) = e^{-i\varepsilon\alpha}L^+(\alpha)\,\overline{\psi}_2(\alpha) \tag{74.21}$$

und

$$\left.\begin{aligned} g_1(\alpha) &= -\frac{1}{2\pi i}\oint_{-\infty}^{\infty}\frac{\overline{f}_1(\alpha')}{L^+(\alpha')}\,\frac{e^{i\varepsilon\alpha'}}{\alpha'-\alpha}\,d\alpha', \\ g_2(\alpha) &= \frac{1}{2\pi i}\oint_{-\infty}^{\infty}L^-(\alpha')\,\overline{f}_2(\alpha')\,\frac{e^{-i\varepsilon\alpha'}}{\alpha'-\alpha}\,d\alpha' \end{aligned}\right\} \tag{74.22}$$

können wir Gl. (74.20′) in der Form schreiben

$$\left.\begin{aligned} \hat{\psi}_1(\alpha) - \frac{1}{2\pi i}\oint_{-\infty}^{\infty}\frac{e^{2i\varepsilon\alpha'}}{L^+(\alpha')\,L^-(\alpha')}\,\hat{\psi}_2(\alpha')\,\frac{d\alpha'}{\alpha'-\alpha} &= g_1(\alpha), \\ \hat{\psi}_2(\alpha) + \frac{1}{2\pi i}\oint_{-\infty}^{\infty}e^{-2i\varepsilon\alpha'}L^+(\alpha')\,L^-(\alpha')\,\hat{\psi}_1(\alpha')\,\frac{d\alpha'}{\alpha'-\alpha} &= g_2(\alpha). \end{aligned}\right\} \tag{74.20″}$$

Die Faktoren von $\hat{\psi}_1$ und $\hat{\psi}_2$ *unter* den Integralen lassen sich nun mit Hilfe von (74.4) *additiv* in zwei Terme zerlegen, von denen der eine in S^+ der andere S^- holomorph ist:

$$\left.\begin{aligned}\frac{e^{2i\varepsilon\alpha}}{L^+(\alpha)\,L^-(\alpha)} &= \frac{1}{2\pi i}\left\{\oint\limits_{-\infty}^{\infty} - \oint\limits_{-\infty}^{\infty}\right\}\frac{e^{2i\varepsilon\alpha'}}{L^+(\alpha')\,L^-(\alpha')}\,\frac{d\alpha'}{\alpha'-\alpha},\\ e^{-2i\varepsilon\alpha}L^+(\alpha)\,L^-(\alpha) &= \frac{1}{2\pi i}\left\{\oint\limits_{-\infty}^{\infty} - \oint\limits_{-\infty}^{\infty}\right\}e^{-2i\varepsilon\alpha'}L^+(\alpha')\,L^-(\alpha')\,\frac{d\alpha'}{\alpha'-\alpha}.\end{aligned}\right\}\quad(74.21\,\text{a})$$

Ferner ergibt sich aus (74.20′), daß $\hat{\psi}_1(\alpha)$ bzw. $\hat{\psi}_2(\alpha)$ in S^- bzw. S^+ holomorph sind (da die rechts stehenden Integrale dort holomorph sind). Wir können also beim Einsetzen von (74.21 a) in (74.20″) den in S^+ bzw. S^- holomorphen Term des Integranden des oberen bzw. unteren Integrals in (74.20″) fortlassen. Gl. (74.20″) geht also in die Gestalt über:

$$\left.\begin{aligned}\hat{\psi}_1(\alpha) + \frac{1}{2\pi i}\oint\limits_{-\infty}^{\infty} A_1(\alpha')\,\hat{\psi}_2(\alpha')\,\frac{d\alpha'}{\alpha'-\alpha} &= g_1(\alpha),\\ \hat{\psi}_2(\alpha) + \frac{1}{2\pi i}\oint\limits_{-\infty}^{\infty} A_2(\alpha')\,\hat{\psi}_1(\alpha')\,\frac{d\alpha'}{\alpha'-\alpha} &= g_2(\alpha)\end{aligned}\right\}\quad(74.20''')$$

mit

$$\left.\begin{aligned}A_1(\alpha) &= \frac{1}{2\pi i}\oint\limits_{-\infty}^{\infty}\frac{e^{2i\varepsilon\alpha'}}{L^+(\alpha')\,L^-(\alpha')}\,\frac{d\alpha'}{\alpha'-\alpha},\\ A_2(\alpha) &= \frac{1}{2\pi i}\oint\limits_{-\infty}^{\infty} e^{-2i\varepsilon\alpha'}L^+(\alpha')\,L^-(\alpha')\,\frac{d\alpha'}{\alpha'-\alpha}.\end{aligned}\right\}\quad(74.21')$$

Das Gleichungssystem (74.20‴) ist ebenso wie (74.20″) von der Form (74.1). Die Koeffizienten (74.21′) sind jedoch [im Gegensatz zu (74.21 a)] im unendlich fernen Punkt *regulär* (oder zeigen dort wenigstens ein *algebraisches* Verhalten; man vgl. dazu das in Ziff. 122 durchgerechnete Beispiel). Ein allgemeines Verfahren um Gleichungen des Typs (74.20‴) geschlossen aufzulösen, ist bisher noch nicht gefunden worden. Nur im Grenzfall $\varepsilon \gg 1$ läßt sich die asymptotische Lösung von Gl. (74.20‴) relativ leicht gewinnen. Dies soll in Abschn. B I b 2 für die Beugung am Spalt gezeigt werden[1].

Da $\hat{\psi}_1(\alpha)$ und $g_1(\alpha)$ in S^-, $\hat{\psi}_2(\alpha)$ und $g_2(\alpha)$ in S^+ holomorph sind, können wir (74.20‴) auch in der zu (74.6′) analogen Form

$$\left.\begin{aligned}\oint\limits_{-\infty}^{\infty}\{\hat{\psi}_1(\alpha') - A_1(\alpha')\,\hat{\psi}_2(\alpha') - g_1(\alpha')\}\,\frac{d\alpha'}{\alpha'-\alpha} &= 0,\\ \oint\limits_{-\infty}^{\infty}\{A_2(\alpha')\,\hat{\psi}_1(\alpha') + \hat{\psi}_2(\alpha') - g_2(\alpha')\}\,\frac{d\alpha'}{\alpha'-\alpha} &= 0\end{aligned}\right\}\quad(74.22)$$

schreiben. Entsprechend läßt sich ein *n-Kantenproblem* auf n Gleichungen der Form

$$\sum_{\mu=1}^{n} A_{\nu\mu}(\alpha)\,\varphi_\mu(\alpha) + \frac{1}{2\pi i}\oint\limits_{-\infty}^{\infty} B_\nu(\alpha')\,\varphi_\nu(\alpha')\,\frac{d\alpha'}{\alpha'-\alpha} = f_\nu(\alpha) \qquad (\nu = 1, 2, \ldots, n) \quad (74.23)$$

[1] Für kompliziertere Wellenleiterprobleme sei auf die Literatur verwiesen. Man vgl. B. Noble: l. c. Chap. V.

zurückführen bzw. auf das damit äquivalente System

$$\left.\begin{aligned} \oint_{-\infty}^{\infty}\left\{\sum_{\mu=1}^{n} A_{\nu\mu}(\alpha')\,\varphi_\mu(\alpha') - f_\nu(\alpha')\right\}\frac{d\alpha'}{\alpha'-\alpha} &= 0,\\ \oint_{-\infty}^{\infty}\left\{\sum_{\mu=1}^{n}[A_{\nu\mu}(\alpha') + \delta_{\nu\mu}B_\mu(\alpha')]\,\varphi_\mu(\alpha') - f_\nu(\alpha')\right\}\frac{d\alpha'}{\alpha'-\alpha} &= 0\\ (\nu = 1, 2, \ldots, n). \end{aligned}\right\} \tag{74.23'}$$

d) Die Integralgleichungstheorie für ideal leitende Körper endlichen Volumens ohne Kanten.

75. Einleitung. Bisher wurden hauptsächlich Probleme betrachtet, bei denen es sich um die Beugung an unendlich dünnen, insbesondere ebenen Schirmen handelte. Wir wollen nun Körper endlichen Volumens betrachten, die wir ebenfalls als *ideale Leiter* behandeln. Die in Ziff. 5 dargestellte Separationsmethode führt hier nur dann zum Ziel, wenn die Lösung der separierten Wellengleichung bereits tabulierte höhere transzendente Funktionen liefert.

Anschaulicher und allgemeiner ist die aus der Potentialtheorie bekannte Methode, das Randwertproblem auf eine Integralgleichung zurückzuführen, die sich nur noch auf die *Oberfläche* des Körpers bezieht. Wir wollen dieses Verfahren hier für die Beugungstheorie darstellen; ein Störungsverfahren zur angenäherten Lösung der Integralgleichungen wird in Abschn. IIIe entwickelt werden (Rayleighsches Verfahren). Zunächst läßt sich für den elektrischen Flächenstrom eine Integralgleichung *erster Art* aufstellen, die der in Abschn. IIIa für Schirme abgeleiteten vollkommen analog ist. Andererseits ist es aber bei *geschlossenen* ideal leitenden Flächen auch möglich, den elektrischen Flächenstrom durch eine Integralgleichung *zweiter Art* zu bestimmen. Das Auftreten dieses Integralgleichungstyps läßt nach der Fredholm-Hilbertschen Theorie die Existenz von nicht trivialen Lösungen der zugehörigen *homogenen* Integralgleichung erwarten. In unserem Falle sind es die Flächenströme, die zu den *Eigenschwingungen* des von der stromführenden Fläche umschlossenen *Innenraums* gehören. Hierdurch wird jedoch auch das Außenraumproblem modifiziert, indem bei Existenz von „*Eigenströmen*“ das Außenfeld nicht mehr *allein* durch *elektrische* Flächenströme beschrieben werden kann. Vielmehr muß noch die Strahlung von *magnetischen* Flächenströmen überlagert werden, um die Existenz einer Lösung der Integralgleichung für eine beliebige Inhomogenität zu garantieren; dabei sind jetzt die elektrischen Ströme in geeigneter Weise aus Eigenlösungen aufzubauen.

d1) Aufstellung der Integralgleichung für den Flächenstrom.

76. Beim skalaren Problem unterscheiden wir wieder einen p- und einen s-Fall wie in Ziff. 4. Von *Kanten* der beugenden Objekte wollen wir hier *absehen*. Gesucht ist also die Funktion v, die durch die Daten

$$\Delta v + v = 0 \quad \textit{außerhalb und innerhalb von } (S), \tag{I}$$

$$v = 0 \quad \textit{bzw.} \quad \frac{\partial v}{\partial n} = 0 \quad \textit{auf } (S), \tag{II$p, s$}$$

$$v \textit{ befriedigt die Ausstrahlungsbedingung } (17.2) \textit{ bzw. } (17.3) \tag{III}$$

eindeutig festgelegt ist. Durch (IIp, s) wird garantiert, daß das Innere von (S) feldfrei ist [$v \equiv 0$ *innerhalb* (S)] — auch wenn es nicht mit ideal leitendem

Material ausgefüllt ist — falls nur der Parameter k aus Gl. (2.4) *kein Eigenwert* des Hohlraums mit der Oberfläche (S) ist; dann und nur dann ist ja bekanntlich das *Innenraum*problem (I), (IIp, s) eindeutig lösbar[1]. *Eigenschwingungen* bzw. *Resonanzeffekte* des Innenraums sollen zunächst *außer Betracht* bleiben. Somit ist also v im p-Fall beim Durchtritt durch (S) *stetig*, während $\partial v/\partial n$ dort *springt*. Wir bezeichnen diesen Sprung mit ψ, haben also $\psi = (\partial v/\partial n)_+$, da $(\partial v/\partial n)_-$ verschwindet (s. Fig. 45). Mit Hilfe des *Huygensschen Prinzips* (8.5) erhalten wir also im *p-Fall* (falls wir den Beitrag der durch das Primärfeld v_0 vorgegebenen Singularität berücksichtigen, die durch eine kleine Kugel aus dem Integrationsgebiet auszuschließen ist; vgl. Ziff. 11)

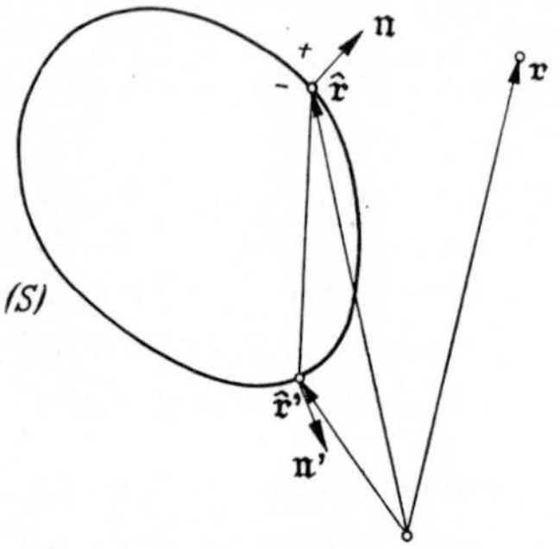

Fig. 45. Zum Randwertproblem bei räumlich ausgedehnten Körpern.

$$v(\mathfrak{r}) = v_0(\mathfrak{r}) - \oint\limits_S \psi(\hat{\mathfrak{r}}')\, G(\mathfrak{r} - \hat{\mathfrak{r}}')\, d\hat{\mathfrak{r}}'. \qquad (76.1\,p)$$

Andererseits erhält man auf Grund ganz entsprechender Überlegungen im *s-Fall*

$$v(\mathfrak{r}) = v_0(\mathfrak{r}) + \oint\limits_S \varphi(\hat{\mathfrak{r}}')\, \frac{\partial}{\partial n'}\, G(\mathfrak{r} - \hat{\mathfrak{r}}')\, d\hat{\mathfrak{r}}'. \qquad (76.1\,s)$$

Hier ist $\varphi = v_+$ der Sprung den v beim Hindurchtreten durch (S) aufweist. ψ bzw. φ sind also elektromagnetisch als elektrische *Flächenströme* zu interpretieren. In der Tat bedeuten diese Größen im *zweidimensionalen Fall* den Sprung der Tangentialkomponente der *magnetischen Feldstärke*, wie man mit Hilfe der Ausführungen zu Beginn von Ziff. 4 leicht bestätigt. Der Kürze halber wollen wir ψ bzw. φ auch im dreidimensionalen Fall als „Flächenstrom" bezeichnen, obwohl diese Größen dann strenggenommen nur noch akustisch interpretiert werden können. Man könnte in Anlehnung an die Potentialtheorie auch sagen, (76.1p) ist eine Felddarstellung mit Hilfe von „*Einfachstrahlern*" der Belegungsdichte ψ, (76.1s) eine solche durch „*Dipolstrahler*" der Dichte φ.

α) Die Integralgleichung erster Art für den Flächenstrom. Die Gln. (76.1p, s) erfüllen die Forderungen (I) und (III), während die Randbedingung (IIp, s), angewandt auf (76.1p) bzw. (76.1s), zu der Gleichung

$$\oint\limits_S \psi(\hat{\mathfrak{r}}')\, G(\mathfrak{r} - \hat{\mathfrak{r}}')\, d\hat{\mathfrak{r}}' = v_0(\hat{\mathfrak{r}}) \qquad (76.2\,p)$$

bzw.

$$\lim_{\mathfrak{r}\to\hat{\mathfrak{r}}+0} \frac{\partial}{\partial n} \oint\limits_S \varphi(\hat{\mathfrak{r}}')\, \frac{\partial}{\partial n'}\, G(\mathfrak{r} - \hat{\mathfrak{r}}')\, d\hat{\mathfrak{r}}' = -\frac{\partial v_0(\hat{\mathfrak{r}})}{\partial n} \qquad (76.2\,s)$$

führt.

Der Grenzübergang $\mathfrak{r}\to\hat{\mathfrak{r}}+0$ bedeute wie bisher die Annäherung des Aufpunktes $\mathfrak{r}$ an einen Punkt $\hat{\mathfrak{r}}$ der Fläche (S) mit der (äußeren) Normale $\mathfrak{n}$ von der positiven Seite. Dieser Grenzprozeß führt zu einem *divergenten* Ausdruck, wenn man mit der Ableitung $\partial/\partial n$ *unter* das Integral gehen will[2]. Man kann dann jedoch wie in Ziff. 48 mit Hilfe der Umformung

$$\frac{\partial^2}{\partial n\, \partial n'} = (\mathfrak{n}\,\nabla)\,(\mathfrak{n}'\,\nabla') = -(\mathfrak{n}\,\mathfrak{n}')\,\Delta - \left([\mathfrak{n}'\,\hat{\nabla}']\,[\mathfrak{n}\,\hat{\nabla}]\right) \qquad (76.3)$$

---

[1] Da die Strahlungsquelle (Feldsingularität) hier selbstverständlich im Außenraum liegt, lautet die eindeutige Innenraumlösung $v \equiv 0$.

[2] Das heißt, falls man die Differentiation vor der Integration ausführt.

die normal zur Fläche gerichtete Differentiation in eine *tangential gerichtete* verwandeln:

$$\left.\begin{aligned}\frac{\partial}{\partial n}\oint_S \varphi(\hat{\mathfrak{r}}')\,\frac{\partial}{\partial n'}\,G(\mathfrak{r}-\hat{\mathfrak{r}}')\,d\hat{\mathfrak{r}}' &= \oint_S (\mathfrak{n}\,\mathfrak{n}')\,\varphi(\hat{\mathfrak{r}}')\,G(\mathfrak{r}-\hat{\mathfrak{r}}')\,d\hat{\mathfrak{r}}'\\ &\quad-\oint_S \varphi(\hat{\mathfrak{r}}')\left([\mathfrak{n}'\,\hat{\nabla}']\,[\mathfrak{n}\,\hat{\nabla}]\right)G(\mathfrak{r}-\hat{\mathfrak{r}}')\,d\hat{\mathfrak{r}}'\end{aligned}\right\}\tag{76.4}$$

[dabei haben wir von der Wellengleichung $(\Delta+1)\,G=0$ Gebrauch gemacht]. Mit Hilfe des Stokesschen Satzes können wir jetzt in dem zweiten Integral eine Differentiation auf φ abwälzen [ein Linienintegral tritt hier nicht auf, da ja die Fläche (S) geschlossen ist] und erhalten

$$\left.\begin{aligned}\frac{\partial}{\partial n}\oint_S \varphi(\hat{\mathfrak{r}}')\,\frac{\partial}{\partial n'}\,G(\mathfrak{r}-\hat{\mathfrak{r}}')\,d\hat{\mathfrak{r}}' &= \oint_S (\mathfrak{n}\,\mathfrak{n}')\,\varphi(\hat{\mathfrak{r}}')\,G(\mathfrak{r}-\hat{\mathfrak{r}}')\,d\hat{\mathfrak{r}}'\\ &\quad+\oint_S \left([\mathfrak{n}'\,\hat{\nabla}'\,\varphi(\hat{\mathfrak{r}}')]\,[\mathfrak{n}\,\hat{\nabla}\,G(\mathfrak{r}-\hat{\mathfrak{r}}')]\right)d\hat{\mathfrak{r}}'.\end{aligned}\right\}\tag{76.5}$$

Jetzt können wir den in (76.2 *s*) geforderten Grenzübergang ausführen:

$$\oint_S\left\{(\mathfrak{n}\,\mathfrak{n}')\,\varphi(\hat{\mathfrak{r}}')\,G(\hat{\mathfrak{r}}-\hat{\mathfrak{r}}')+\left([\mathfrak{n}'\,\widehat{\operatorname{grad}}'\varphi(\hat{\mathfrak{r}}')]\,[\mathfrak{n}\,\widehat{\operatorname{grad}}\,G(\hat{\mathfrak{r}}-\hat{\mathfrak{r}}')]\right)\right\}d\hat{\mathfrak{r}}'=-\frac{\partial v_0(\hat{\mathfrak{r}})}{\partial n}.\tag{76.2′s}$$

Wir haben also zur Berechnung von ψ die *inhomogene Integralgleichung (erster Art)* (76.2 *p*) erhalten, während φ aus der *Integrodifferentialgleichung* (76.2′ *s*) zu berechnen ist. Somit verlaufen die Betrachtungen ganz analog wie diejenigen, die in Ziff. 48 für unendlich dünne Schirme angestellt wurden.

β) Die Fredholmsche Integralgleichung zweiter Art. Im Gegensatz zu den *berandeten* Schirmen ist es aber möglich, für den vorliegenden Fall des Körpers mit *geschlossener* Oberfläche sowohl für ψ wie für φ eine inhomogene *Fredholmsche Integralgleichung zweiter Art* abzuleiten, wie wir es in Ziff. 11 schon angedeutet haben.

Stellt man nämlich an Gl. (76.1 *p*) die Forderung $(\partial v/\partial n)_- = 0$, $(\partial v/\partial n)_+ = \psi$, so erhält man mit Hilfe der beiden Gleichungen (9.4) übereinstimmend

$$\frac{1}{2}\,\psi(\hat{\mathfrak{r}})+\oint_S \psi(\hat{\mathfrak{r}}')\,\frac{\partial}{\partial n}\,G(\hat{\mathfrak{r}}-\hat{\mathfrak{r}}')\,d\hat{\mathfrak{r}}'=\frac{\partial v_0(\hat{\mathfrak{r}})}{\partial n}.\tag{76.6p}$$

Dies ist eine *Fredholmsche Integralgleichung zweiter Art für den Flächenstrom* ψ (das Integral ist hier als *Hauptwert* aufzufassen). Zu ihrer Aufstellung haben wir die Randbedingung (II *p*) gar nicht explizit heranzuziehen brauchen; sie ist nämlich von selbst erfüllt, wenn ψ Gl. (76.6 *p*) befriedigt. In der Tat folgt durch Einsetzen von (76.6 *p*) in die zweite Gleichung (9.4) (unteres Vorzeichen), daß $(\partial v/\partial n)_- = 0$ ist und daher $v\equiv 0$ innerhalb (S) (falls *k kein Eigenwert* ist). Somit gilt auch $v_- = 0$ auf (S), wodurch man schließlich wegen der *Stetigkeit* von (76.1 *p*) beim Durchtritt durch (S) auch zu $v_+ = 0$ gelangt.

Ganz entsprechende Überlegungen, wie sie für (76.1 *p*) durchgeführt wurden, liefern bei Übertragung auf (76.1 *s*) mit Hilfe der Grenzwerte (9.2″) und der Forderungen $v_- = 0$, $v_+ = \varphi$ übereinstimmend

$$\frac{1}{2}\,\varphi(\hat{\mathfrak{r}})-\oint_S \varphi(\hat{\mathfrak{r}}')\,\frac{\partial}{\partial n'}\,G(\hat{\mathfrak{r}}-\hat{\mathfrak{r}}')\,d\hat{\mathfrak{r}}'=v_0(\hat{\mathfrak{r}}).\tag{76.7s}$$

Zufolge (76.7 *s*) nimmt nun (76.1 *s*) den inneren Randwert $v_- = 0$ an, was wiederum auf $v\equiv 0$ innerhalb (S) führt [abgesehen von den Eigenschwingungen, deren der

Hohlraum (S) für diskrete k-Werte fähig ist und die wir zunächst ausschließen], also auch $(\partial v/\partial n)_- = 0$ zur Folge hat. Durch (76.1 s) wird dieser Wert stetig auf die Außenseite von (S) fortgesetzt, wodurch die Erfüllung der Randbedingung (II s) garantiert wird.

Gl. (76.6s) ist eine Integralgleichung für φ von der gleichen Art wie (76.6p); abgesehen von der veränderten rechten Seite (Inhomogenität) sind jedoch auch die „*Kerne*“ verschieden:

$$K_p(\hat{\mathfrak{r}}, \hat{\mathfrak{r}}') = \frac{\partial}{\partial n} G(\hat{\mathfrak{r}} - \hat{\mathfrak{r}}') = \frac{(\mathfrak{n}, \hat{\mathfrak{r}} - \hat{\mathfrak{r}}')}{4\pi |\hat{\mathfrak{r}} - \hat{\mathfrak{r}}'|^3} (i|\hat{\mathfrak{r}} - \hat{\mathfrak{r}}'| - 1)\, e^{i|\hat{\mathfrak{r}} - \hat{\mathfrak{r}}'|} \qquad (76.6'p)$$

bzw.

$$K_s(\hat{\mathfrak{r}}, \hat{\mathfrak{r}}') = -\frac{\partial}{\partial n'} G(\hat{\mathfrak{r}} - \hat{\mathfrak{r}}') = \frac{(\mathfrak{n}', \hat{\mathfrak{r}} - \hat{\mathfrak{r}}')}{4\pi |\hat{\mathfrak{r}} - \hat{\mathfrak{r}}'|^3} (i|\hat{\mathfrak{r}} - \hat{\mathfrak{r}}'| - 1)\, e^{i|\hat{\mathfrak{r}} - \hat{\mathfrak{r}}'|}, \qquad (76.7's)$$

da die Flächennormale $\mathfrak{n} = \mathfrak{n}(\hat{\mathfrak{r}})$ bzw. $\mathfrak{n}' = \mathfrak{n}(\hat{\mathfrak{r}}')$ eingeht. Diese Kerne sind *nicht* symmetrisch, vielmehr gilt für die „*transponierten*“ Kerne

$$K_p(\hat{\mathfrak{r}}', \hat{\mathfrak{r}}) = -K_s(\hat{\mathfrak{r}}, \hat{\mathfrak{r}}'). \qquad (76.8p\,s)$$

77. Elektromagnetisches Problem. Dieses besteht darin, ein Vektorfeld $\mathfrak{E}$, $\mathfrak{H}$ so zu bestimmen, das

$$\operatorname{rot} \mathfrak{E} = i\,\mathfrak{H}; \quad \operatorname{rot} \mathfrak{H} = -i\,\mathfrak{E} \quad \text{außerhalb und innerhalb } (S), \qquad (\mathrm{I}')$$

$$[\mathfrak{n}\,\mathfrak{E}] = 0 \quad \textit{auf } (S), \qquad (\mathrm{II}')$$

$\mathfrak{E}$, $\mathfrak{H}$ *die Ausstrahlungsbedingung* (18.3), (18.3a) (III′)

erfüllt.

Bei Ausschluß von Eigenschwingungen sorgt die Lösung dafür, daß das Innere von (S) wieder feldfrei ist; die Tangentialkomponente von $\mathfrak{E}$ ist beim Hindurchtreten durch (S) stetig, während die Tangentialkomponente von $\mathfrak{H}$ dann von $[\mathfrak{n}\,\mathfrak{H}]_- = 0$ auf $[\mathfrak{n}\,\mathfrak{H}]_+ = \mathfrak{J}$ springt. Daher läßt sich das gesuchte Feld durch die Formel (14.1) darstellen, die in unserem Falle lautet

$$\left.\begin{aligned} \mathfrak{E}(\mathfrak{r}) &= \mathfrak{E}_0(\mathfrak{r}) + i \operatorname{rot}\operatorname{rot} \oint_S \mathfrak{J}(\hat{\mathfrak{r}}')\, G(\mathfrak{r} - \hat{\mathfrak{r}}')\, d\hat{\mathfrak{r}}', \\ \mathfrak{H}(\mathfrak{r}) &= \mathfrak{H}_0(\mathfrak{r}) + \operatorname{rot} \oint_S \mathfrak{J}(\hat{\mathfrak{r}}')\, G(\mathfrak{r} - \hat{\mathfrak{r}}')\, d\hat{\mathfrak{r}}'. \end{aligned}\right\} \qquad (77.1)$$

Diese Gleichungen stimmen in der Form mit (51.1) überein, die dort für berandete Schirme aufgestellt wurden. Genau wie in Ziff. 51 führt auch hier die Randbedingung (II′) auf die *Pseudointegralgleichung*

$$\lim_{\mathfrak{r} \to + \hat{\mathfrak{r}}} [\mathfrak{n}, \operatorname{rot}\operatorname{rot} \oint_S \mathfrak{J}(\hat{\mathfrak{r}}')\, G(\mathfrak{r} - \hat{\mathfrak{r}}')\, d\hat{\mathfrak{r}}'] = i\,[\mathfrak{n}\,\mathfrak{E}_0], \qquad (77.2)$$

die mit Hilfe der Identität rot rot = grad div $-\Delta$ und Heranziehung der Wellengleichung $(\Delta + 1)\,G = 0$ sowie $\nabla G = -\nabla' G$ mittels einer *partiellen Integration* in die *Integrodifferentialgleichung*

$$\oint_S [\mathfrak{n}, \mathfrak{J}(\hat{\mathfrak{r}}')\, G(\hat{\mathfrak{r}} - \hat{\mathfrak{r}}') + \widehat{\operatorname{div}}'\, \mathfrak{J}(\hat{\mathfrak{r}}')\, \widehat{\operatorname{grad}}\, G(\hat{\mathfrak{r}} - \hat{\mathfrak{r}}')]\, d\hat{\mathfrak{r}}' = i\,[\mathfrak{n}\,\mathfrak{E}_0(\hat{\mathfrak{r}})] \qquad (77.3)$$

umgeformt werden kann. Sie stimmt mit Gl. (58.3), die für unendlich dünne berandete Schirme (S) abgeleitet wurde, überein. In dem jetzt von uns betrach teten Fall läßt sich jedoch für $\mathfrak{J}$ auch wieder eine reine Integralgleichung *zweiter* Art ableiten. Berechnen wir nämlich mit Hilfe der zweiten Gleichung (77.1) die Tangentialkomponente der magnetischen Feldstärke, so folgt unter Heranziehung der Grenzwerte (13.4) und der Forderung $[\mathfrak{n}\,\mathfrak{H}]_+ = \mathfrak{J}$ die inhomogene Fredholmsche Integralgleichung zweiter Art:

$$\tfrac{1}{2}\mathfrak{J}(\hat{\mathfrak{r}}) + \oint\limits_S [\mathfrak{n}\,[\mathfrak{J}(\hat{\mathfrak{r}}')\ \mathrm{grad}\,G(\hat{\mathfrak{r}}-\hat{\mathfrak{r}}')]]\,d\hat{\mathfrak{r}}' = [\mathfrak{n}\,\mathfrak{H}_0(\hat{\mathfrak{r}})] \tag{77.4}$$

für den Flächenstrom $\mathfrak{J}$. Diese Integralgleichung läßt sich auch übersichtlicher in der Form schreiben

$$\tfrac{1}{2}\mathfrak{J}(\hat{\mathfrak{r}}) + \oint\limits_S \mathfrak{J}(\hat{\mathfrak{r}}')\cdot \boldsymbol{K}(\hat{\mathfrak{r}},\hat{\mathfrak{r}}')\,d\hat{\mathfrak{r}}' = [\mathfrak{n}\,\mathfrak{H}_0(\hat{\mathfrak{r}})], \tag{77.4'}$$

wobei der „*tensorielle Kern*" durch

$$\boldsymbol{K}(\hat{\mathfrak{r}},\hat{\mathfrak{r}}') = \mathbf{1}\left(\mathfrak{n}\,\mathrm{grad}\,G(\hat{\mathfrak{r}}-\hat{\mathfrak{r}}')\right) - \mathfrak{n}\,\mathrm{grad}\,G(\hat{\mathfrak{r}}-\hat{\mathfrak{r}}') \tag{77.5}$$

zu definieren ist (der zweite Term ist als *dyadisches* Produkt von $\mathfrak{n}$ und grad G zu lesen). Ferner ist

$$\mathrm{grad}\,G(\hat{\mathfrak{r}}-\hat{\mathfrak{r}}') = \frac{\hat{\mathfrak{r}}-\hat{\mathfrak{r}}'}{4\pi|\hat{\mathfrak{r}}-\hat{\mathfrak{r}}'|^3}\,(i\,|\hat{\mathfrak{r}}-\hat{\mathfrak{r}}'|-1)\,e^{i|\hat{\mathfrak{r}}-\hat{\mathfrak{r}}'|}. \tag{77.5'}$$

Die Gl. (77.4) garantiert die Erfüllung der Randbedingung (II') für $\mathfrak{E}$, da man durch Einsetzen von (77.4) in die zweite Gleichung (13.4) (unteres Vorzeichen) auf $[\mathfrak{n}\,\mathfrak{H}]_- = 0$ geführt wird, was mit $\mathfrak{H}\equiv 0$ innerhalb (S) gleichbedeutend ist (Eigenschwingungen ausgeschlossen). Damit folgt aber auch $\mathfrak{E} = i\,\mathrm{rot}\,\mathfrak{H} \equiv 0$ innerhalb (S), also $[\mathfrak{n}\,\mathfrak{E}]_- = 0$. Dieser Randwert wird durch die Gl. (77.1) stetig auf die positive Seite der Fläche (S) übertragen.

Die Integralgleichungen (76.6*p*), (76.7*s*) und (77.4) für den *elektrischen* Flächenstrom sowie solche, die bei einer äquivalenten Darstellung mit Hilfe *magnetischer* Flächenströme — auf die wir noch zu sprechen kommen — auftreten, sind von mehreren Autoren behandelt worden[1]. CL. MÜLLER[2], der auch den allgemeineren Fall des Körpers beliebiger Dielektrizitätskonstante und Permeabilität untersucht, bei dem sowohl elektrische als auch magnetische Flächenströme gleichzeitig in Ansatz gebracht werden müssen, diskutiert darüber hinaus die *Existenz- und Eindeutigkeitsfragen* vom Standpunkt der Fredholm-Hilbertschen Integralgleichungstheorie eingehend, worauf wir hier nicht eingehen können. V.A. FOCK[3] entwickelt Näherungslösungen für den Fall, daß die Hauptkrümmungsradien der Oberfläche überall sehr groß gegen die Wellenlänge sind. Wir werden eine analoge Methode bei der Behandlung der Beugung an Zylinder und Kugel (Ziff. 145 und 150) behandeln, die auf FRANZ und DEPPERMANN[4] zurückgeht. Der Einfluß von *Kanten* wird von A.-W. MAUE[1] diskutiert.

---

[1] A.-W. MAUE: Z. Physik **126**, 601 (1949). — CL. MÜLLER: Abh. dtsch. Akad. Westberlin Nr. 3 (1945/46). — Arch. Math. **1**, 296 (1948/49). — Math. Ann. **123**, 345 (1951). — Comm. Pure Appl. Math. **8**, 635 (1955). — V.A. FOCK: J. of Phys. USSR. **10**, 130, 399 (1946). — Bull. Acad. Sci. URSS. Sér. Phys. **10**, 171 (1946). — Phil. Mag. **39**, 149 (1948). — Uspechi fiz. Nauk **43**, 587 (1950). — R.B. BARRAR u. C.L. DOLPH: J. Rational Mech. Anal. **3**, 726 (1954). — P.P. LAX: Comm. Pure Appl. Math. **7**, 633 (1954). Siehe auch W. STERNBERG: Comp. math. **3**, 254 (1936). — H. FREUDENTHAL: Comp. math. **6**, 221 (1938). — V. KUPRADSE: Math. Sbor. **41**, Heft 4 (1934). — C. R. Acad. Sci. URSS. **10**, 7 (1936); **16**, 165 (1937). — Comp. math. **6**, 228 (1938).

[2] CL. MÜLLER: l. c. [1] sowie die umfassende Monographie: Grundprobleme der mathematischen Theorie elektromagnetischer Schwingungen. Berlin: Springer 1957. Siehe auch W.K. SAUNDERS: Proc. Nat. Acad. Sci. U.S.A. **38**, 342 (1952).

[3] V. A. FOCK: l. c. [1].

[4] W. FRANZ u. K. DEPPERMANN: Ann. Phys. **10**, 361 (1952); **14**, 253 (1954).

d2) Die Bedeutung der Eigenschwingungen des Innenraums für das Außenraumproblem.

Obwohl das Problem der Eigenschwingungen abgeschlossener Hohlräume nicht zu unserem Thema gehört, so müssen wir hier doch kurz auf die Rolle eingehen, die diese Eigenschwingungen für das *Außenraumproblem* spielen. Wir sahen ja bereits, daß die Zurückführung des Randwertproblems für den *Außenraum* auf eine Integralgleichung *zweiter* Art für den Flächenstrom nur dann eindeutig möglich ist, wenn wir annehmen, daß der *Innenraum keine Eigenschwingungen* zu der betrachteten Frequenz besitzt. Das Auftreten von Integralgleichungen zweiter Art weist nun gerade auf die Möglichkeit von „*Eigenströmen*" (d.h. Lösungen der transponierten *homogenen* Integralgleichungen) hin, und wir werden gleich sehen, daß sie zu den Eigenschwingungen des *Innenraumproblems* gehören. Ferner werden wir zeigen, daß diese Eigenströme stets nur ein Feld in den Innenraum „abstrahlen", im Außenraum löscht es sich durch Interferenz aus. Damit hängt zusammen, daß das Außenraumproblem stets eindeutig lösbar ist (wie es ja auf Grund des Eindeutigkeitsbeweises in Ziff. 20 sein muß), obwohl es nach dem *Fredholmschen Alternativsatz* zunächst so aussieht, als ob es bei Existenz von „Eigenströmen" nur dann Lösungen gäbe, wenn die Inhomogenität der entsprechenden Integralgleichungen (76.6*p*) bzw. (76.7*s*) „*orthogonal*" zu den entsprechenden Eigenströmen ist. In der Tat gilt diese Einschränkung nur für das Innenraumproblem und bedeutet dort anschaulich, daß erzwungene Schwingungen im Rhythmus einer Eigenschwingung — ohne Resonanzkatastrophe — nur dann möglich sind, wenn das Feld der Strahlungsquelle *wattlos* wirkt. Wir beschränken uns im wesentlichen auf das skalare Problem, behalten aber die (dann nur im zweidimensionalen Fall mögliche) elektromagnetische Interpretation bei.

78. Die Wechselbeziehung zwischen Innen- und Außenraumproblem. Elektrische Eigenströme. Zunächst notieren wir noch einmal unser Ergebnis, zu dem wir im vorigen Abschnitt unter *Ausschluß des Resonanzfalles* (in dem das *Innenraumproblem* mehrdeutig wird) gelangten [vgl. (76.1*p*) und (76.6*p*) bzw. (76.1*s*) und (76.7*s*)].

Außenraumproblem

p-Fall

$$\left.\begin{aligned} &v(\mathfrak{r}) = v_0(\mathfrak{r}) - \oint_S \psi_a(\hat{\mathfrak{r}}')\, G(\mathfrak{r}-\hat{\mathfrak{r}}')\, d\hat{\mathfrak{r}}' && \textit{(elektrisches Feld)}\\ &\tfrac{1}{2}\psi_a(\hat{\mathfrak{r}}) + \oint_S \psi_a(\hat{\mathfrak{r}}')\, K_p(\hat{\mathfrak{r}},\hat{\mathfrak{r}}')\, d\hat{\mathfrak{r}}' = \frac{\partial v_0}{\partial n} && \textit{(elektrischer Flächenstrom),}\end{aligned}\right\}\quad (78.1\,p)$$

s-Fall

$$\left.\begin{aligned} &v(\mathfrak{r}) = v_0(\mathfrak{r}) + \oint_S \varphi_a(\hat{\mathfrak{r}}')\, \frac{\partial}{\partial n'} G(\mathfrak{r}-\hat{\mathfrak{r}}')\, d\hat{\mathfrak{r}}' && \textit{(magnetisches Feld)}\\ &\tfrac{1}{2}\varphi_a(\hat{\mathfrak{r}}) + \oint_S \varphi_a(\hat{\mathfrak{r}}')\, K_s(\hat{\mathfrak{r}},\hat{\mathfrak{r}}')\, d\hat{\mathfrak{r}}' = v_0 && \textit{(elektrischer Flächenstrom).}\end{aligned}\right\}\quad (78.1\,s)$$

Auf Grund von ganz entsprechenden Überlegungen für den von (S) umschlossenen *Innenraum* gelangen wir *eindeutig* (auf Grund der ausnahmslosen *Eindeutigkeit* des *Außenraumproblems*) zu der Formulierung:

Innenraumproblem

p-Fall

$$\left.\begin{aligned} v(\mathfrak{r}) &= v_0(\mathfrak{r}) - \oint_S \psi_i(\hat{\mathfrak{r}}')\, G(\mathfrak{r}-\hat{\mathfrak{r}}')\, d\hat{\mathfrak{r}}' && \textit{(elektrisches Feld)} \\ -\frac{1}{2}\psi_i(\hat{\mathfrak{r}}) &+ \oint_S \psi_i(\hat{\mathfrak{r}}')\, K_p(\hat{\mathfrak{r}},\hat{\mathfrak{r}}')\, d\hat{\mathfrak{r}}' = \frac{\partial v_0}{\partial n} && \textit{(elektrischer Flächenstrom)}, \end{aligned}\right\} \quad (78.1'p)$$

s-Fall

$$\left.\begin{aligned} v(\mathfrak{r}) &= v_0(\mathfrak{r}) + \oint_S \varphi_i(\hat{\mathfrak{r}}')\, \frac{\partial}{\partial n'} G(\mathfrak{r}-\hat{\mathfrak{r}}')\, d\hat{\mathfrak{r}}' && \textit{(magnetisches Feld)} \\ -\tfrac{1}{2}\varphi_i(\hat{\mathfrak{r}}) &+ \oint_S \varphi_i(\hat{\mathfrak{r}}')\, K_s(\hat{\mathfrak{r}},\hat{\mathfrak{r}}')\, d\hat{\mathfrak{r}}' = v_0 && \textit{(elektrischer Flächenstrom)}. \end{aligned}\right\} \quad (78.1's)$$

(Die in Klammern angegebene elektromagnetische Interpretation bezieht sich auf den zweidimensionalen Fall, vgl. Ziff. 4.)

Unsere Darstellungen gelten bei beiden Problemen im *ganzen* Raum; die entsprechenden Flächenströme ψ_a, φ_a bzw. ψ_i, φ_i sorgen nämlich (auf Grund der Integralgleichungen, durch die sie definiert sind) dafür, daß das Feld im Innenraum bzw. Außenraum (durch Interferenz) *verschwindet.*

Multiplizieren wir nun im p-Fall die Integralgleichung (78.1p) mit einer zunächst beliebigen Funktion $\Phi(\hat{\mathfrak{r}})$ und integrieren über (S), so folgt durch Vertauschung der Integrationsvariablen im Doppelintegral und Ersetzung des transponierten Kernes durch seinen Wert (76.8p s)

$$\oint_S \psi_a(\hat{\mathfrak{r}})\left\{-\frac{1}{2}\Phi(\hat{\mathfrak{r}}) + \oint_S \Phi(\hat{\mathfrak{r}}')\, K_s(\hat{\mathfrak{r}},\hat{\mathfrak{r}}')\, d\hat{\mathfrak{r}}'\right\} d\hat{\mathfrak{r}} = -\oint_S \Phi(\hat{\mathfrak{r}})\,\frac{\partial v_0}{\partial n}\, d\hat{\mathfrak{r}}.$$

Hat also die *homogene* Integralgleichung

$$-\tfrac{1}{2}\Phi(\hat{\mathfrak{r}}) + \oint_S \Phi(\hat{\mathfrak{r}}')\, K_s(\hat{\mathfrak{r}},\hat{\mathfrak{r}}')\, d\hat{\mathfrak{r}}' = 0 \quad \textit{(elektrischer s-Eigenstrom)} \qquad (78.2s)$$

Lösungen, so ist die inhomogene Integralgleichung (78.1p) offensichtlich nur dann lösbar, wenn die Inhomogenität $\partial v_0/\partial n$ *orthogonal* zu den *Eigenlösungen* Φ ist *(Fredholmscher Alternativsatz).* Gl. (78.2s) ist nun nichts anderes, als die im *s-Fall* zum *homogenen Innenraum*problem gehörige Integralgleichung. Die Eigenlösungen von (78.2s) sind also diejenigen Flächenströme, die zu den Eigenschwingungen des Innenraums im s-Fall gehören *(„s-Eigenströme“).* Es gibt im Falle der j-fachen *Entartung* einer Eigenfrequenz ω_ν j Eigenlösungen $\Phi_\nu^{(1)}, \Phi_\nu^{(2)} \ldots \Phi_\nu^{(j)}$, die wir als zueinander orthogonal und normiert annehmen können. Die Lösbarkeitsbedingung für die Integralgleichung (78.1p) lautet also für den *Fall der s-Resonanz* bei der Eigenfrequenz ω_ν

$$\oint_S \Phi_\nu^{(l)}(\hat{\mathfrak{r}})\,\frac{\partial v_0}{\partial n}\, d\hat{\mathfrak{r}} = 0 \qquad \text{für } l = 1, 2, \ldots, j. \qquad (78.3p)$$

Existieren s-Eigenströme, so kann also das Außenfeld im allgemeinen nicht durch *elektrische* Flächenströme ψ_a erzeugt werden, die durch (78.1p) definiert sind [gerade den Fall von s-Eigenschwingungen mußten wir ja bereits bei der Ableitung der Gl. (76.6p) ausschließen], sondern nur falls $\partial v_0/\partial n$ orthogonal zu den $\Phi_\nu^{(l)}$ ist.

Ebenso kann das Außenraumproblem im s-Fall im allgemeinen nicht eindeutig mit Hilfe von durch (78.1 s) definierten *elektrischen* Flächenströmen φ_a dargestellt werden, wenn „*p-Eigenströme*" $\Psi_\nu^{(l)}$ existieren; die als Lösungen der zu (78.1 s) gehörigen *homogenen transponierten* Integralgleichung

$$-\tfrac{1}{2}\Psi(\hat{\mathfrak{r}}) + \oint_S \Psi(\hat{\mathfrak{r}}')\, K_p(\hat{\mathfrak{r}}, \hat{\mathfrak{r}}')\, d\hat{\mathfrak{r}}' = 0 \quad \textit{(elektrischer p-Eigenstrom)} \tag{78.2p}$$

definiert sind. Es sei denn v_0 ist orthogonal zu den Eigenlösungen $\Psi_\nu^{(l)}$

$$\oint_S \Psi_\nu^{(l)}(\hat{\mathfrak{r}})\, v_0\, d\hat{\mathfrak{r}} = 0 \qquad \text{für } l = 1, 2, \ldots j. \tag{78.3s}$$

79. Die abschirmende Wirkung des idealen Leiters. Es ist nun leicht zu sehen, daß auf (S) fließende Eigenströme nach *außen* kein Feld abstrahlen; mit anderen Worten, daß die als unendlich dünn idealisierte Fläche (S) bei den Randwerten $v = 0$ bzw. $\partial v/\partial n = 0$ die im Inneren von (S) möglichen Eigenschwingungen *nach außen hin vollständig abschirmt*. Für das von den s-Eigenströmen abgestrahlte Feld gilt nämlich

$$V_s(\mathfrak{r}) = -\oint_S \Phi(\hat{\mathfrak{r}}')\, \frac{\partial}{\partial n'} G(\mathfrak{r} - \hat{\mathfrak{r}}')\, d\hat{\mathfrak{r}}' \tag{79.1s}$$

und wir erhalten mit Hilfe von Gl. (9.2'')

$$\lim_{\mathfrak{r}\to\hat{\mathfrak{r}}\pm 0} V_s(\mathfrak{r}) = \mp \tfrac{1}{2}\Phi(\hat{\mathfrak{r}}) + \oint_S \Phi(\hat{\mathfrak{r}}')\, K_s(\hat{\mathfrak{r}}, \hat{\mathfrak{r}}')\, d\hat{\mathfrak{r}}'. \tag{79.1's}$$

Da nun die s-Eigenströme Φ der homogenen Integralgleichung (78.2s) genügen, so gilt auf der Außenseite von (S) $(V_s)_+ = 0$, woraus man nach dem Eindeutigkeitsbeweis für das Außenraumproblem von Ziff. 20 auf $V_s \equiv 0$ im Außenraum schließen kann. Somit folgt aus der Stetigkeit des Normalgradienten von (79.1 s) $\left(\frac{\partial V_s}{\partial n}\right)_\pm = 0$, während (79.1's) auf $(V_s)_- = \Phi(\hat{\mathfrak{r}})$ führt. Gl. (79.1 s) stellt also in der Tat die *s-Eigenschwingungen des Inneren* von (S) dar, die nach außen hin *vollständig abgeschirmt* werden, und es gilt zusammengefaßt

$$(V_s)_- = \Phi, \qquad (V_s)_+ = 0, \qquad \left(\frac{\partial V_s}{\partial n}\right)_\pm = 0. \tag{79.1''s}$$

Ganz entsprechendes gilt für die *p-Eigenschwingungen*

$$V_p(\mathfrak{r}) = \oint_S \Psi(\hat{\mathfrak{r}}')\, G(\mathfrak{r} - \hat{\mathfrak{r}}')\, d\hat{\mathfrak{r}}'; \tag{79.1p}$$

denn hier folgt auf Grund der Grenzwerte (9.4), der homogenen Integralgleichung (78.2p) für die p-Eigenströme Ψ, der Eindeutigkeit des Außenraumproblems sowie der Stetigkeit von V_p beim Hindurchtreten durch (S):

$$(V_p)_\pm = 0, \qquad \left(\frac{\partial V_p}{\partial n}\right)_- = \Psi, \qquad \left(\frac{\partial V_p}{\partial n}\right)_+ = 0. \tag{79.1'p}$$

Es ist nun noch die Frage zu untersuchen, was die oben gefundene Einschränkung (78.3p) bzw. (78.3s) der Lösbarkeit des Außenraumproblems zu bedeuten hat, da ja in Ziff. 20 der Eindeutigkeitsbeweis ohne solche Einschränkungen geführt werden konnte. Um es vorweg zu nehmen, die Notwendigkeit dieser Einschränkung wird — genau wie beim äußeren Dirichletschen Problem der Potentialtheorie[1] — nur vorgetäuscht durch unsere Darstellung des Feldes als

[1] Siehe z.B. PH. FRANK u. R. v. MISES: Die Differential- und Integralgleichungen der Mechanik und Physik, 1. Aufl., Bd. I, S. 499ff. Braunschweig 1925.

Strahlung von *elektrischen Flächenströmen* und deren Bestimmung durch Integralgleichungen *zweiter Art.* Hält man an den Integralgleichungen zweiter Art fest, so muß in den Fällen, in denen die Bedingung (78.3 *p*) bzw. (78.3 *s*) nicht erfüllt ist, noch ein Feld überlagert werden, das als Strahlung *magnetischer* Flächenströme auf (*S*) zu interpretieren ist.

80. Magnetische Eigenströme. Für das Folgende ist es wichtig, daß bei *Abwesenheit von Eigenschwingungen* auch eine Darstellung des Außen- bzw. Innenfeldes durch *magnetische* Flächenströme *allein* möglich ist. Dies geht aus folgenden Überlegungen hervor: Aus dem Ansatz

p-Fall

$$v(\mathfrak{r}) = v_0(\mathfrak{r}) + \oint_S \widehat{\psi}(\hat{\mathfrak{r}}') \frac{\partial}{\partial n'} G(\mathfrak{r}-\hat{\mathfrak{r}}')\, d\hat{\mathfrak{r}}' \quad \textit{(elektrisches Feld)} \qquad (80.1\,p)$$

bzw.

s-Fall

$$v(\mathfrak{r}) = v_0(\mathfrak{r}) - \oint_S \widehat{\varphi}(\hat{\mathfrak{r}}')\, G(\mathfrak{r}-\hat{\mathfrak{r}}')\, d\hat{\mathfrak{r}}' \quad \textit{(magnetisches Feld)} \qquad (80.1\,s)$$

folgt nämlich mit Hilfe der Grenzwerte (9.2″) bzw. (9.4) aus der Randbedingung $v=0$ bzw. $\partial v/\partial n=0$ für die magnetischen Flächenströme $\widehat{\psi}$ bzw. $\widehat{\varphi}$:

p-Fall

$$\mp \tfrac{1}{2}\widehat{\psi}(\hat{\mathfrak{r}}) + \oint_S \widehat{\psi}(\hat{\mathfrak{r}}')\, K_s(\hat{\mathfrak{r}},\hat{\mathfrak{r}}')\, d\hat{\mathfrak{r}}' = v_0 \quad \textit{(magnetischer Flächenstrom)} \qquad (80.2\,p)$$

s-Fall

$$\mp \tfrac{1}{2}\widehat{\varphi}(\hat{\mathfrak{r}}) + \oint_S \widehat{\varphi}(\hat{\mathfrak{r}}')\, K_p(\hat{\mathfrak{r}},\hat{\mathfrak{r}}')\, d\hat{\mathfrak{r}}' = \frac{\partial v_0}{\partial n} \quad \textit{(magnetischer Flächenstrom)}, \qquad (80.2\,s)$$

wobei das obere Vorzeichen für das *Außenraum-*, das untere für das *Innenraumproblem* gilt (die in Klammern angegebene elektromagnetische Deutung bezieht sich wieder auf den zweidimensionalen Fall).

Das Außenraumproblem ist hier bei Existenz von Eigenschwingungen scheinbar wieder nur unter der Einschränkung lösbar, daß

$$\oint_S \widehat{\Phi}_\nu^{(l)}(\hat{\mathfrak{r}})\, v_0\, d\hat{\mathfrak{r}} = 0 \qquad (80.3\,p)$$

bzw.

$$\oint_S \widehat{\Psi}_\nu^{(l)}(\hat{\mathfrak{r}})\, \frac{\partial v_0}{\partial n}\, d\hat{\mathfrak{r}} = 0, \qquad (80.3\,s)$$

wobei die „*magnetischen s-* bzw. *p-Eigenströme*“ als Eigenlösungen der *homogenen* Integralgleichungen

$$\tfrac{1}{2}\widehat{\Phi}(\hat{\mathfrak{r}}) + \oint_S \widehat{\Phi}(\hat{\mathfrak{r}}')\, K_p(\hat{\mathfrak{r}},\hat{\mathfrak{r}}')\, d\hat{\mathfrak{r}}' = 0 \quad \textit{(magnetischer s-Eigenstrom)}, \qquad (80.4\,s)$$

$$\tfrac{1}{2}\widehat{\Psi}(\hat{\mathfrak{r}}) + \oint_S \widehat{\Psi}(\hat{\mathfrak{r}}')\, K_s(\hat{\mathfrak{r}},\hat{\mathfrak{r}}')\, d\hat{\mathfrak{r}}' = 0 \quad \textit{(magnetischer p-Eigenstrom)} \qquad (80.4\,p)$$

definiert sind. Diese Eigenströme gehören wieder zu den Eigenschwingungen des Innenraumes. Mit Hilfe der Beziehung (76.8*p s*) erkennt man leicht, daß es sich bei den Gln. (80.4*s*), (80.4*p*) einfach um die *transponierten* Gln. (78.2*s*), (78.2*p*) handelt. Somit haben (78.2*s*) und (80.4*s*) sowie (78.2*p*) und (80.4*p*) *dieselben* Eigenwerte, nämlich gerade die Eigenfrequenzen des Hohlraumes im *s*-

bzw. p-Fall. Der Übergang zur Darstellung mit Hilfe magnetischer Flächenströme bedeutet also mathematisch nichts anderes als den Übergang zur transponierten Integralgleichung. Wir heben jedoch hervor, daß die Felddarstellung (80.1 p, s) durch *magnetische* Flächenströme im Gegensatze zur Darstellung (76.1 p), (76.2 s) durch elektrische Ströme *nicht* im ganzen Raum gilt, sondern jeweils nur im Außenraum bzw. Innenraum, da das Feld im komplementären Raumgebiet nicht mehr verschwindet.

81. Das Zusammenwirken von elektrischen und magnetischen Flächenströmen im Resonanzfall. Ist nun bei *Existenz von Eigenschwingungen* des Innenraums die Bedingung (80.3 p) bzw. (80.3 s) *erfüllt,* so sind die Lösungen der Integralgleichung (80.2 p) bzw. (80.2 s) (oberes Vorzeichen) nur bis auf beliebige Linearkombinationen der Lösungen der homogenen Gleichungen bestimmt, d. h. also bis auf die durch Gl. (78.2 s) bzw. (78.2 p) definierten Eigenströme $\Phi^{(l)}$ bzw. $\Psi^{(l)}$ (den Index ν lassen wir jetzt weg, da sich alles folgende auf ein und dieselbe Resonanzfrequenz ω_ν beziehen soll). Wie wir gesehen haben, strahlen diese Ströme aber kein Feld in den *Außenraum* ab, so daß die *Felddarstellung* trotzdem eindeutig ist.

Allein dies ist auch dann der Fall, wenn man die Einschränkungen (80.3 p), (80.3 s) fallen läßt. Um dies zu zeigen, beschränken wir uns auf den p-Fall und schreiben jetzt statt (80.3 p)

$$\oint_S \widehat{\Phi}^{(l)} v_0 \, d\hat{\mathfrak{r}} = A_l \tag{81.1 p}$$

mit beliebigem $A_l \neq 0$. Wir machen nun statt (80.1 p) den Ansatz

$$v(\mathfrak{r}) = v_0(\mathfrak{r}) + \oint_S \widehat{\psi}(\hat{\mathfrak{r}}') \frac{\partial}{\partial n'} G(\mathfrak{r}-\hat{\mathfrak{r}}') \, d\hat{\mathfrak{r}}' - \sum_{l=1}^{j} a_l \oint_S \widehat{\Phi}^{(l)}(\hat{\mathfrak{r}}') \, G(\mathfrak{r}-\hat{\mathfrak{r}}') \, d\hat{\mathfrak{r}}', \tag{81.2 p}$$

superponieren also der Strahlung des *magnetischen Flächenstroms*

$$\widehat{\psi} = v_+ - v_- \; [=(\mathfrak{E}_y)_+ - (\mathfrak{E}_y)_- \text{ im zylindrischen Fall, vgl. Ziff. 4}]$$

noch diejenige eines *elektrischen Flächenstroms*

$$\sum_{l=1}^{j} a_l \widehat{\Phi}^{(l)} = \left(\frac{\partial v}{\partial n}\right)_+ - \left(\frac{\partial v}{\partial n}\right)_-$$

$$[= (\mathfrak{H}_n)_+ - (\mathfrak{H}_n)_- \text{ im zylindrischen Fall}],$$

den wir in geeigneter Weise aus Eigenströmen $\widehat{\Phi}^{(l)}$ aufbauen wollen. Die Wahl dieser Linearkombination ergibt sich, indem wir die Randbedingung $v = 0$ auf (81.2 p) anwenden ($\mathfrak{r} \to \hat{\mathfrak{r}} + 0$):

$$-\tfrac{1}{2}\widehat{\psi}(\hat{\mathfrak{r}}) + \oint_S \widehat{\psi}(\hat{\mathfrak{r}}') K_s(\hat{\mathfrak{r}}, \hat{\mathfrak{r}}') \, d\hat{\mathfrak{r}}' = v_0 - \sum_{l=1}^{j} a_l \oint_S \widehat{\Phi}^{(l)}(\hat{\mathfrak{r}}') \, G(\hat{\mathfrak{r}} - \hat{\mathfrak{r}}') \, d\hat{\mathfrak{r}}' \tag{81.3 p}$$

und nun die a_l so bestimmen, daß die Inhomogenität

$$v_0 - \sum_{l=1}^{j} a_l \oint_S \widehat{\Phi}^{(l)}(\hat{\mathfrak{r}}') \, G(\mathfrak{r}-\hat{\mathfrak{r}}') \, d\hat{\mathfrak{r}}'$$

dieser Integralgleichung für $\widehat{\psi}$ zu *sämtlichen* $\widehat{\Phi}^{(l)}$, $l = 1, 2, \ldots, j$ *orthogonal* wird. Dies führt mit Hilfe der Gl. (81.1 p) auf das Gleichungssystem:

$$\sum_{l'=1}^{j} a_{l'} C_{l l'} = A_l \qquad \text{für } l = 1, 2, \ldots, j \tag{81.4}$$

mit

$$C_{ll'} = \oint_S \oint_S d\hat{\mathfrak{r}}\, \widehat{\Phi}^{(l)}(\hat{\mathfrak{r}})\, G(\hat{\mathfrak{r}} - \hat{\mathfrak{r}}')\, \widehat{\Phi}^{(l')}(\hat{\mathfrak{r}}')\, d\hat{\mathfrak{r}}'. \tag{81.5p}$$

Nun läßt sich zeigen, daß die Determinante der $|C_{ll'}|$ des Gleichungssystems (81.4) stets von null verschieden ist[1]. Somit sind also die a_l eindeutig aus (81.4) bestimmbar; der Flächenstrom $\widehat{\psi}$ ist damit durch Gl. (81.3p) festgelegt bis auf beliebige Linearkombinationen der Lösungen der homogenen Gleichung (78.2s). Diese liefern aber zu (81.2p) im Außenraum keinen Beitrag. Es läßt sich übrigens zeigen[1], daß auch $\widehat{\psi}$ selbst *eindeutig* festgelegt werden kann, indem man die Linearkombination so wählt, daß $\widehat{\psi}$ zu sämtlichen $\Phi^{(l)}$ orthogonal wird.

Damit ist gezeigt, daß auch im Falle der Existenz von Eigenschwingungen des Innenraums die Methode der Integralgleichungen zweiter Art für das Randwertproblem des Außenraums zur eindeutigen Lösung führt[2]. Die Felddarstellung muß dann allerdings durch die Überlagerung der Felder elektrischer *und* magnetischer Flächenströme erweitert werden. (Dies war jedoch, wie wir in Ziff. 76α sahen, bei Verwendung von Integralgleichungen erster Art nicht der Fall.) Ferner ist die Methode zunächst an die Voraussetzung gebunden, daß die Oberfläche der beugenden Körper überall eine eindeutige Tangentialebene besitzt (Ausschluß von Kanten)[3]. Andererseits konnten wir bei dieser

[1] H. WEYL: Math. Z. **55**, 187 (1952). Ein methodisch vereinfachter Beweis findet sich bei CL. MÜLLER: Math. Z. **56**, 80 (1952). Siehe auch die analogen Entwicklungen bei W.D. KUPRADSE: Randwertaufgaben der Schwingungstheorie und Integralgleichungen, § 10, Berlin 1956, die auf eine Arbeit KUPRADSEs aus dem Jahre 1943 zurückgehen. — Die Größen $C_{ll'}$ bezeichnet WEYL als *Kapazitätskoeffizienten des Strahlungsfeldes* in Analogie zur *Elektrostatik*, wo die Energie W eines Feldes von j Leitern mit den vorgegebenen Ladungen Q_l, $l = 1, 2, \ldots, j$ in der Form $W = \frac{1}{2} \sum_{l,l'} C^0_{ll'} Q_l Q_{l'}$ geschrieben werden kann. Hier sind die $C^0_{ll'}$ die *statischen* Kapazitätskoeffizienten

$$C^0_{ll'} = \oint_{S_l} \oint_{S_{l'}} \frac{\eta_l(\hat{\mathfrak{r}})\, \eta_{l'}(\hat{\mathfrak{r}}')}{4\pi |\hat{\mathfrak{r}}_l - \hat{\mathfrak{r}}_{l'}|}\, d\hat{\mathfrak{r}}\, d\hat{\mathfrak{r}}' \tag{81.5}$$

und $\eta_l(\hat{\mathfrak{r}})$ — die *Gleichgewichtsverteilung* der Einheitsladung auf der Oberfläche des Leiters l (bei Anwesenheit der übrigen Leiter) — ist durch eine ganz entsprechende homogene Integralgleichung zweiter Art definiert wie unsere Eigenströme (vgl. FRANK-MISES l. c.). Es sei jedoch darauf hingewiesen, daß bei unserem dynamischen Problem der Index l die Eigenfunktionen numeriert, die zum (j-fach) entarteten Eigenwert ω_ν des Innenraums gehören, während im statischen Fall durch l die einzelnen getrennten Leiter abgezählt werden. Die Existenz j linear unabhängiger Eigenlösungen beruht also einmal auf der j-fachen Entartung des Eigenwertes, das andere Mal auf dem aus j unzusammenhängenden Teilen bestehenden Integrationsbereich. — Der Beweis von CL. MÜLLER wird im wesentlichen durch Anwendung der Greenschen Formel (für den Außenraum) auf die Funktion

$$\widehat{v}_s(\mathfrak{r}) = \oint_S \widehat{\Phi}(\hat{\mathfrak{r}}')\, G(\mathfrak{r} - \hat{\mathfrak{r}}')\, d\hat{\mathfrak{r}}'$$

und die dazu konjugiert komplexe Größe geführt, wobei die Randwerte

$$(\widehat{v}_s)_\pm = \oint_S \widehat{\Phi}(\hat{\mathfrak{r}}')\, G(\hat{\mathfrak{r}} - \hat{\mathfrak{r}}')\, d\hat{\mathfrak{r}}', \qquad \left(\frac{\partial \widehat{v}_s}{\partial n}\right)_- = 0, \qquad \left(\frac{\partial \widehat{v}_s}{\partial n}\right)_+ = \widehat{\Phi}$$

und die Ausstrahlungsbedingung

$$\lim_{r\to\infty} r \left(\frac{\partial \widehat{v}_s}{\partial r} - i\, \widehat{v}_s\right) = 0$$

ins Spiel kommen.

[2] Dies ist in mathematischer Hinsicht wichtig, da die *Existenzfragen* unserer Randwertprobleme nur über die Integralgleichungen zweiter Art geklärt werden konnten; vgl. H. WEYL l. c. — CL. MÜLLER l. c. — W.D. KUPRADSE l. c.

[3] Für den Fall von Kanten vgl. A.-W. MAUE, l. c.

Methode die Frage klären, welche Stromverteilungen auf (S) es gibt, die nicht zur Ausstrahlung eines Feldes in den Außenraum führen (Eigenströme) — eine Frage, die wohl erstmals Magnus[1] angeschnitten hat, die er jedoch nur für ebene Flächenstücke klären konnte (dort gibt es natürlich keine Eigenströme), da er nur Integralgleichungen erster Art betrachtet.

82. Vektorielle Felder. Auf den dreidimensionalen elektromagnetischen Fall lassen sich die Methoden und Ergebnisse des skalaren Problems fast wörtlich übertragen[2]. Wir begnügen uns mit der Zusammenstellung der wichtigsten Formeln. Zunächst können wir unser Randwertproblem (I′) bis (III′) auch hier mit Hilfe magnetischer Flächenströme $\mathfrak{L}$ lösen. Statt (77.1) gilt dann

$$\left.\begin{aligned} \mathfrak{E}(\mathfrak{r}) &= \mathfrak{E}_0(\mathfrak{r}) + \operatorname{rot} \oint_S \mathfrak{L}(\hat{\mathfrak{r}}')\, G(\mathfrak{r}-\hat{\mathfrak{r}}')\, d\hat{\mathfrak{r}}', \\ \mathfrak{H}(\mathfrak{r}) &= \mathfrak{H}_0(\mathfrak{r}) - i \operatorname{rot}\operatorname{rot} \oint_S \mathfrak{L}(\hat{\mathfrak{r}}')\, G(\mathfrak{r}-\hat{\mathfrak{r}}')\, d\hat{\mathfrak{r}}, \end{aligned}\right\} \tag{82.1}$$

und die Randbedingung $[\mathfrak{n}\,\mathfrak{E}]_\pm = 0$ in Verbindung mit den Grenzwerten (13.4) liefert

$$\mp \tfrac{1}{2}\mathfrak{L}(\hat{\mathfrak{r}}) + \oint_S \mathfrak{L}(\hat{\mathfrak{r}}') \cdot \boldsymbol{K}(\hat{\mathfrak{r}}, \hat{\mathfrak{r}}')\, d\hat{\mathfrak{r}}' = [\mathfrak{n}\,\mathfrak{E}_0], \tag{82.2}$$

wobei das obere Vorzeichen für das Außenraum-, das untere für das Innenraumproblem gilt und die Darstellung (82.1) jeweils nur für den Außenraum bzw. Innenraum Gültigkeit hat. Bei Existenz von nicht trivialen Lösungen der zu (82.2) gehörigen homogenen Integralgleichung hat (82.2) auch für das Außenraumproblem im allgemeinen keine Lösung mehr, und wir müssen (82.1) erweitern:

$$\mathfrak{E}(\mathfrak{r}) = \mathfrak{E}_0(\mathfrak{r}) + \operatorname{rot} \oint_S \mathfrak{L}(\hat{\mathfrak{r}}')\, G(\mathfrak{r}+\hat{\mathfrak{r}}')\, d\hat{\mathfrak{r}}' + i \operatorname{rot}\operatorname{rot} \sum_{l=1}^{j} a_l \oint_S \mathfrak{J}^{(l)}(\hat{\mathfrak{r}}')\, G(\mathfrak{r}-\hat{\mathfrak{r}}')\, d\hat{\mathfrak{r}}', \tag{82.1′}$$

wo $\mathfrak{J}^{(l)}$ die zur Eigenfrequenz ω_ν gehörigen j Eigenlösungen der homogenen Integralgleichung

$$-\tfrac{1}{2}\mathfrak{J}(\hat{\mathfrak{r}}) + \oint_S \boldsymbol{K}^*(\hat{\mathfrak{r}}', \hat{\mathfrak{r}}) \cdot \mathfrak{J}(\hat{\mathfrak{r}}')\, d\hat{\mathfrak{r}}' = 0 \tag{82.3}$$

sind (der Stern bedeutet den Übergang zur konjugiert komplexen Größe). Die a_l sind hier wiederum eindeutig aus der Forderung bestimmbar, daß die Inhomogenität der mit Hilfe der Randbedingung $[\mathfrak{n}\,\mathfrak{E}] = 0$ aus (82.1′) folgenden Integralgleichung

$$\left.\begin{aligned} &-\tfrac{1}{2}\mathfrak{L}(\hat{\mathfrak{r}}) + \oint_S \mathfrak{L}(\hat{\mathfrak{r}}') \cdot \boldsymbol{K}(\hat{\mathfrak{r}}, \hat{\mathfrak{r}}')\, d\hat{\mathfrak{r}}' \\ &= \Big[\mathfrak{n}, \mathfrak{E}_0 + i \sum_{l=1}^{j} a_l \oint_S \{\mathfrak{J}^{(l)}(\hat{\mathfrak{r}}')\, G(\hat{\mathfrak{r}}-\hat{\mathfrak{r}}') + \widehat{\operatorname{div}}'\, \mathfrak{J}(\hat{\mathfrak{r}}')\, \widehat{\operatorname{grad}}\, G(\hat{\mathfrak{r}}-\hat{\mathfrak{r}}')\}\, d\hat{\mathfrak{r}}'\Big] \end{aligned}\right\} \tag{82.2′}$$

zu sämtlichen $\mathfrak{J}^{(l)*}$ *orthogonal* ist. $\mathfrak{L}(\hat{\mathfrak{r}})$ ist dann aus (82.2′) eindeutig bestimmbar unter der Nebenbedingung, daß $\mathfrak{L}$ zu allen j konjugiert komplexen Lösungen der *homogenen* Integralgleichung (82.2) orthogonal ist:

$$\oint_S \mathfrak{L}\,\mathfrak{L}^{(l)*}\, d\hat{\mathfrak{r}} = 0. \tag{82.4}$$

---

[1] W. Magnus: Jber. dtsch. Math.-Ver. **52**, 177 (1943).

[2] Cl. Müller: Math. Z. **56**, 261 (1952). — Grundprobleme der mathematischen Theorie elektromagnetischer Schwingungen, § 24. Berlin: Springer 1957. — H. Weyl: Math. Z. **56**, 105 (1952).

e) Iterationsverfahren für mehrere beugende Objekte.

83. Einleitung. Bei unseren bisherigen Betrachtungen haben wir zwar die Anzahl der räumlich getrennten „streuenden" oder „beugenden" Objekte offengelassen, hatten dabei aber im wesentlichen den einfachsten Fall eines einzigen Körpers vor Augen. Wir setzen nunmehr ausdrücklich voraus, daß gleichzeitig mehrere (gleich- oder verschiedenartige) Körper (oder Öffnungen) vorhanden sind. Das Beugungsfeld jedes einzelnen isoliert gedachten Körpers soll als bekannt betrachtet werden. Es ist dann die Frage von Interesse, wie das Beugungsfeld des einzelnen Körpers in das Gesamtbeugungsbild aller Körper eingeht. (Das einfache Superpositionsprinzip gilt hier offensichtlich nicht, da das Einzelfeld jeweils nur die *Randbedingung* für *einen Körper* erfüllt.) Diese Frage läßt sich im Rahmen der Kirchhoffschen Theorie (insbesondere für das Fraunhofersche Fernfeld) leicht beantworten[1]: bei der Beugung an mehreren etwa gleichartigen Objekten tritt das Einzelfeld als „*Formfaktor*" im Gesamtfeld in Erscheinung. Das entsprechende Problem läßt sich auch im Rahmen einer strengen Theorie behandeln, wofür in der Literatur einige Ansätze vorliegen.

Die Wechselwirkung *zweier* streuender Körper wurde erstmals von SCHWARZSCHILD[2] bei Gelegenheit der Untersuchung der Beugung am Spalt behandelt. Dabei wird die Zustrahlung der beiden Spaltbacken berücksichtigt, deren jede als eine Sommerfeldsche Halbebene idealisiert werden kann und wobei die Lösung für das *Sommerfeldsche* Problem der Beugung an einer Halbebene bereits bekannt ist (vgl. Abschn. B Ia und Ziff. 122). Beim Vorhandensein *mehrerer* streuender bzw. beugender Körper erweist sich jedoch das Schwarzschildsche Verfahren, das an die Greensche Funktion *der Einzelkörper* anknüpft, als nicht sehr geeignet und kann durch ein einfacheres ersetzt werden, das nur noch die Greensche Funktion des *freien Raumes* benutzt und auf einer direkten Anwendung des Huygensschen Prinzips beruht. Letzteres Verfahren gestattet auch, in übersichtlicher Weise den Anschluß an die herkömmliche Beugungstheorie der Gitter oder auch nichtperiodischer Anordnungen von Körpersystemen zu gewinnen. Endlich soll das Problem der Zustrahlung *zweier* streuender Zylinder bei senkrechtem Einfall einer ebenen Primärwelle etwas ausführlicher erörtert werden.

e 1) Schwarzschildsches Verfahren für zwei Objekte.

84. Aufstellung der Integralgleichungen. Wir erläutern zunächst die allgemeine Formulierung des skalaren Wechselwirkungsproblems durch BAKER und COPSON[3]. Gegeben seien zwei Körper mit den Oberflächen (S_1) (Ortsvektor $\hat{\mathfrak{r}}_1$) und (S_2) (Ortsvektor $\hat{\mathfrak{r}}_2$, s. Fig. 46); gesucht ist die Lösung der Wellengleichung $(\varDelta+1)\,v=0$ bei der Randbedingung $\partial v/\partial n=0$ (s-Fall) auf (S_1) *und* (S_2) sowie der Ausstrahlungs- und Kantenbedingung (sofern Kanten vorhanden sind). Es werde angenommen, daß die entsprechenden Lösungen für jeden *einzelnen* Körper bekannt seien. Als „Strahlungsquelle" soll dabei eine von $\mathfrak{r}_0$ ausgehende Kugelwelle $v_0(\mathfrak{r})=\dfrac{e^{i|\mathfrak{r}-\mathfrak{r}_0|}}{4\pi|\mathfrak{r}-\mathfrak{r}_0|}$ vorausgesetzt werden, und wir wollen diese Lösungen mit $G_i(\mathfrak{r},\mathfrak{r}_0)$ $(i=1, 2)$ bezeichnen. G_i ist dann nichts anderes als die *Greensche Funktion* (zweiter Art) für die Fläche (S_i), denn sie erfüllt die Differentialgleichung $(\varDelta+1)\,G_i(\mathfrak{r},\mathfrak{r}_0)=-\delta(\mathfrak{r}-\mathfrak{r}_0)$ und die Randbedingung $\dfrac{\partial}{\partial n_i}\,G_i=0$ auf (S_i) (sowie die Ausstrahlungs- und Kanten-

[1] Vgl. z.B. M. BORN: Optik, S. 161ff. Berlin: Springer 1933.
[2] K. SCHWARZSCHILD: Math. Ann. **55**, 177 (1902).
[3] B. B. BAKER u. E. T. COPSON: HUYGENS' Principle, S. 177ff. Oxford 1950.

bedingung). Nach der Theorie der Greenschen Funktion vgl. Ziff. 9 und 34 stellt nun

$$u_i(\mathfrak{r}) = \int_{S_i} \varphi_i(\hat{\mathfrak{r}}_i)\, G_i(\mathfrak{r} - \hat{\mathfrak{r}}_i)\, d\hat{\mathfrak{r}}_i$$

eine außerhalb (S_i) singularitätenfreie Lösung der Wellengleichung dar, deren *Normalgradient* $\partial u_i/\partial n_i$ auf (S_i) den *vorgegebenen* Wert φ_i annimmt.

Wir wollen den Normalgradienten von v_0 auf (S_i) mit $\varphi_0(\hat{\mathfrak{r}}_i)$ bezeichnen und betrachten die beiden Funktionen

$$\left.\begin{aligned} v_1(\mathfrak{r}) &= -\int_{S_1} [\varphi_2(\hat{\mathfrak{r}}_1) + \varphi_0(\hat{\mathfrak{r}}_1)]\, G_1(\mathfrak{r}, \hat{\mathfrak{r}}_1)\, d\hat{\mathfrak{r}}_1, \\ v_2(\mathfrak{r}) &= -\int_{S_2} [\varphi_1(\hat{\mathfrak{r}}_2) + \varphi_0(\hat{\mathfrak{r}}_2)]\, G_2(\mathfrak{r}, \hat{\mathfrak{r}}_2)\, d\hat{\mathfrak{r}}_2, \end{aligned}\right\} \tag{84.1s}$$

wobei $\varphi_2(\hat{\mathfrak{r}}_1)$ den Normalgradienten bedeuten soll, den v_2 auf (S_1) annimmt, $\varphi_1(\hat{\mathfrak{r}}_2)$ entsprechend denjenigen von v_1 auf (S_2). Es gilt also

$$\left.\begin{aligned} \varphi_1(\hat{\mathfrak{r}}_2) &= -\int_{S_1} [\varphi_2(\hat{\mathfrak{r}}_1) + \varphi_0(\hat{\mathfrak{r}}_1)]\, \frac{\partial}{\partial n_2} G_1(\hat{\mathfrak{r}}_2, \hat{\mathfrak{r}}_1)\, d\hat{\mathfrak{r}}_1, \\ \varphi_2(\hat{\mathfrak{r}}_1) &= -\int_{S_2} [\varphi_1(\hat{\mathfrak{r}}_2) + \varphi_0(\hat{\mathfrak{r}}_2)]\, \frac{\partial}{\partial n_1} G_2(\hat{\mathfrak{r}}_1, \hat{\mathfrak{r}}_2)\, d\hat{\mathfrak{r}}_2, \end{aligned}\right\} \tag{84.2s}$$

ferner erfüllt $v_S = v_1 + v_2$ auf (S_1) die Randbedingung $\partial v_S/\partial n_1 = -\varphi_0(\hat{\mathfrak{r}}_1)$ und ebenso auf (S_2) $\partial v_S/\partial n_2 = -\varphi_0(\hat{\mathfrak{r}}_2)$. Somit erfüllt also die folgende Lösung der Wellengleichung

$$v(\mathfrak{r}) = v_0(\mathfrak{r}) + v_S(\mathfrak{r}) = v_0(\mathfrak{r}) + v_1(\mathfrak{r}) + v_2(\mathfrak{r}) \tag{84.3}$$

sowohl auf (S_1) *wie* auf (S_2) die Randbedingung $\partial v/\partial n = 0$, sowie die Ausstrahlungs- und Kantenbedingung: Gl. (84.3) ist die gesuchte Lösung unseres Beugungsproblems bei Anwesenheit *beider* Körper. Diese setzt nunmehr die simultane Auflösung des Integralgleichungssystems (84.2s) voraus; es besteht aus zwei *inhomogenen* Fredholmschen Integralgleichungen *zweiter Art*. Um dies zu verdeutlichen, schreiben wir es in der Form

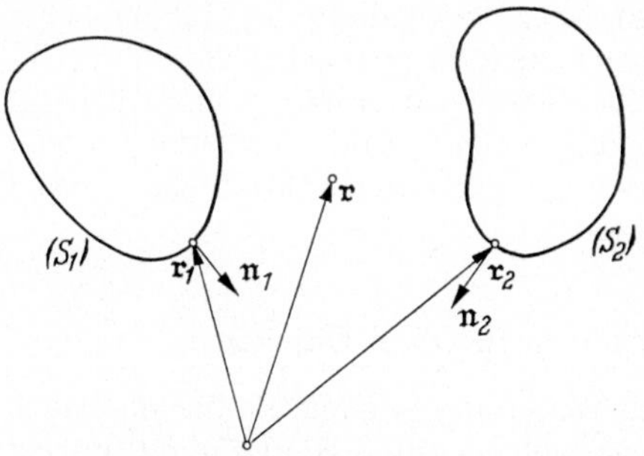

Fig. 46. Zum Schwarzschildschen Iterationsverfahren für die Wechselwirkung zweier Körper.

$$\left.\begin{aligned} \varphi_1(\hat{\mathfrak{r}}_2) &= \Phi_1(\hat{\mathfrak{r}}_2) - \int_{S_1} \varphi_2(\hat{\mathfrak{r}}_1)\cdot \\ &\quad \cdot K_{12}(\hat{\mathfrak{r}}_2, \hat{\mathfrak{r}}_1)\, d\hat{\mathfrak{r}}_1, \\ \varphi_2(\hat{\mathfrak{r}}_1) &= \Phi_2(\hat{\mathfrak{r}}_1) - \int_{S_2} \varphi_1(\hat{\mathfrak{r}}_2)\cdot \\ &\quad \cdot K_{21}(\hat{\mathfrak{r}}_1, \hat{\mathfrak{r}}_2)\, d\hat{\mathfrak{r}}_2 \end{aligned}\right\} \tag{84.2's}$$

mit den Inhomogenitäten

$$\left.\begin{aligned} \Phi_1(\hat{\mathfrak{r}}_2) &= -\int_{S_1} \varphi_0(\hat{\mathfrak{r}}_1)\, K_{12}(\hat{\mathfrak{r}}_2, \hat{\mathfrak{r}}_1)\, d\hat{\mathfrak{r}}_1, \\ \Phi_2(\hat{\mathfrak{r}}_1) &= -\int_{S_2} \varphi_0(\hat{\mathfrak{r}}_2)\, K_{21}(\hat{\mathfrak{r}}_1, \hat{\mathfrak{r}}_2)\, d\hat{\mathfrak{r}}_2 \end{aligned}\right\} \tag{84.4s}$$

und den Kernen

$$\left.\begin{aligned} K_{12}(\hat{\mathfrak{r}}_2, \hat{\mathfrak{r}}_1) &= \frac{\partial}{\partial n_2} G_1(\hat{\mathfrak{r}}_2, \hat{\mathfrak{r}}_1), \\ K_{21}(\hat{\mathfrak{r}}_1, \hat{\mathfrak{r}}_2) &= \frac{\partial}{\partial n_1} G_2(\hat{\mathfrak{r}}_1, \hat{\mathfrak{r}}_2). \end{aligned}\right\} \tag{84.5s}$$

Hier können wir die zweite Gleichung (84.2′s) in die erste einsetzen und erhalten so eine inhomogene Fredholmsche Integralgleichung zweiter Art, in der nur noch

φ_1 vorkommt und die den „*iterierten*“ *Kern*

$$\int_{S_1} K_{12}(\hat{\mathfrak{r}}_2, \hat{\mathfrak{r}}_1)\, K_{21}(\hat{\mathfrak{r}}_1, \hat{\mathfrak{r}}_1)\, d\hat{\mathfrak{r}}_1 \tag{84.6}$$

besitzt. φ_2 ergibt sich dann aus φ_1 durch „*einfache Quadratur*“ aus der zweiten Gleichung (84.2′s).

Auch zwei unendlich dünne Schirme können nach diesem Verfahren behandelt werden, wenn nur die Greensche Funktion jedes einzelnen Schirmes bekannt ist. Der Vorteil der Methode besteht darin, daß sich die Integralgleichungen jeweils nur auf *einen* Körper (S_1) oder (S_2) beziehen, wodurch die geometrischen Verhältnisse vereinfacht werden. Erkauft wird diese Vereinfachung allerdings durch den wesentlich komplizierteren iterierten Kern (84.6).

85. Iteration. Bei der Lösung des Systems (84.2′s) liegt es nahe, von der nullten Näherung

$$\varphi_1^{(0)} = \Phi_1, \qquad \varphi_2^{(0)} = \Phi_2 \tag{85.1}$$

auszugehen und diese dann jeweils in die rechte Seite von (84.2′s) einzusetzen. Dadurch wird man zu einer *ersten* Näherung $\varphi_1^{(1)}$ und $\varphi_2^{(1)}$ geführt und kann durch Wiederholung des Verfahrens beliebig hohe Näherungen berechnen nach dem Schema

$$\left.\begin{aligned} \varphi_1^{(\nu)}(\hat{\mathfrak{r}}_2) &= \Phi_1(\hat{\mathfrak{r}}_2) - \int_{S_1} \varphi_2^{(\nu-1)}(\hat{\mathfrak{r}}_1)\, K_{12}(\hat{\mathfrak{r}}_2, \hat{\mathfrak{r}}_1)\, d\hat{\mathfrak{r}}_1, \\ \varphi_2^{(\nu)}(\hat{\mathfrak{r}}_1) &= \Phi_2(\hat{\mathfrak{r}}_1) - \int_{S_2} \varphi_1^{(\nu-1)}(\hat{\mathfrak{r}}_2)\, K_{21}(\hat{\mathfrak{r}}_1, \hat{\mathfrak{r}}_2)\, d\hat{\mathfrak{r}}_2. \end{aligned}\right\} \tag{85.2}$$

Dies ist im Prinzip das *Iterationsverfahren*, das SCHWARZSCHILD[1] entwickelt hat, um die Beugung am Spalt zu berechnen, wobei die Greensche Funktion der *Halbebene* — gewissermaßen als erste Integrationsstufe — im oben dargelegten Sinn eingeht.

SCHWARZSCHILDs mehr physikalische Überlegungen gingen dabei davon aus, daß in der nullten Näherung (85.1) $\varphi_1^{(0)}$ einfach der Welle entspricht, die durch Streuung der Primärwelle v_0 an (S_1) entsteht, ohne Rücksicht auf die Anwesenheit von (S_2), ebenso beschreibt $\varphi_2^{(0)}$ lediglich die Streuung an (S_2) ohne Rücksicht auf (S_1). In der Tat wird ja das Beugungsproblem für (S_1) allein durch

$$v_1^{(0)}(\mathfrak{r}) = v_0(\mathfrak{r}) - \int_{S_1} \varphi_0(\hat{\mathfrak{r}}_1)\, G_1(\mathfrak{r}, \hat{\mathfrak{r}}_1)\, d\hat{\mathfrak{r}}_1 \tag{85.3 s}$$

gelöst, dasjenige für (S_2) hingegen durch

$$v_2^{(0)}(\mathfrak{r}) = v_0(\mathfrak{r}) - \int_{S_2} \varphi_0(\hat{\mathfrak{r}}_2)\, G_2(\mathfrak{r}, \hat{\mathfrak{r}}_2)\, d\hat{\mathfrak{r}}_2. \tag{85.3′s}$$

Daher stellt also $\Phi_1(\hat{\mathfrak{r}}_2)$, Gl. (84.4s), den Normalgradienten der *Streuwelle nullter Näherung* $-\int_{S_1} \varphi_0(\hat{\mathfrak{r}}_1)\, G_1(\mathfrak{r}, \hat{\mathfrak{r}}_1)\, d\hat{\mathfrak{r}}_1$ auf (S_2) dar (entsprechendes gilt für Φ_2). Die *nullte* Näherung stellt also in der Tat die Überlagerung der beiden Einzelfelder dar, die die Körper (S_1) und (S_2) für sich allein erzeugen. Die *erste* Näherung beschreibt dann die Streuung an (S_2), wenn als „einfallende Welle“ die an (S_1) gestreute Welle nullter Näherung betrachtet wird (und umgekehrt) und so fort. Aus diesen Betrachtungen ergibt sich auch ein Anhaltspunkt, um zu übersehen, unter welchen Bedingungen schon wenige Schritte des Iterationsverfahrens zu einer brauchbaren Näherung führen werden. Nämlich dann, wenn die beiden streuenden Objekte soweit voneinander entfernt sind, daß die Amplitude der von dem einen Körper ausgehenden Streuwelle am Ort des anderen gegenüber

[1] K. SCHWARZSCHILD: l. c.

der einfallenden Welle klein ist. Schwarzschild konnte nun nachweisen, daß sein Iterationsverfahren *konvergiert*; allerdings ist die Konvergenz so schlecht, daß die Methode für praktische Rechnungen bisher keine Bedeutung gewonnen hat. Anders liegen dagegen die Verhältnisse, wenn das Medium, in das die Körper eingebettet sind, absorbiert (d.h. wenn die Wellenzahl k einen *positiven Imaginärteil* hat), da dann die von den Körpern ausgehenden Streuwellen mit dem zurückgelegten Weg exponentiell geschwächt werden[1].

e2) Direkte Anwendung des Huygensschen Prinzips auf die Streuung mehrerer Körper.

Wir wollen das Problem zweier Körper noch untereinem anderen analytischen Gesichtspunkt betrachten, der uns weiterführt und dem daher eine größere praktische Bedeutung zukommen dürfte[2]. Um möglichst einfache Verhältnisse zu haben, legen wir jedoch jetzt den p-Fall für die Streuung zugrunde.

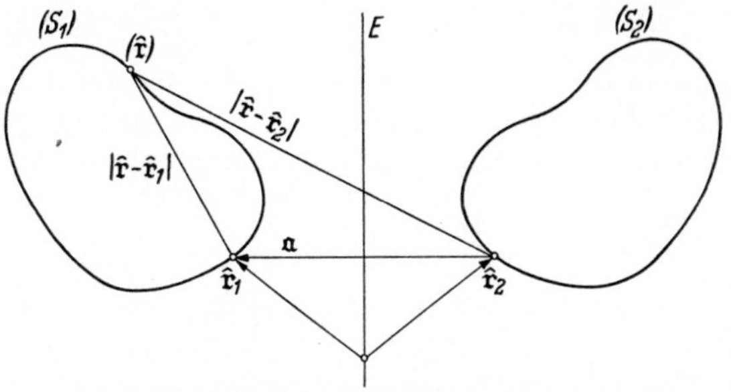

Fig. 47. Zum Iterationsverfahren für die Wechselwirkung zweier Zylinder in spiegel-symmetrischer Lage.

86. Iterationsverfahren für die Wechselwirkung zweier Objekte. Zunächst setzen wir eine beliebige Zahl von streuenden Objekten voraus. Sowohl für den Fall unendlich dünner berandeter Schirme (Abschn. IIIa) als auch für Körper endlichen Volumens (Abschn. IIId) läßt sich die sich ergebende Feldverteilung in die Form

$$v(\mathfrak{r}) = v_0(\mathfrak{r}) - \sum_i \int_{S_i} \psi_i(\hat{\mathfrak{r}}_i)\, G(\mathfrak{r} - \hat{\mathfrak{r}}_i)\, d\hat{\mathfrak{r}}_i \qquad (86.1\,p)$$

bringen [vgl. (46.1 p) bzw. (76.1 p)]; dabei sind die $\psi_i(\hat{\mathfrak{r}}_i)$ die auf den Oberflächen (S_i) der Körper induzierten *Flächenströme*.

Zur Berechnung der Flächenströme ψ_i beschränken wir uns jetzt (um möglichst einfache Verhältnisse zu haben) auf *zwei parallele Zylinder* (oder spaltförmige Öffnungen), die durch *Spiegelung an einer Ebene E* auseinander hervorgehen (s. Fig. 47). Ferner wollen wir als einfallende Welle v_0 entweder eine *ebene* Welle voraussetzen, deren Phasenebenen senkrecht zur Ebene E und parallel zu den Erzeugenden der Zylinder sind oder auch eine Zylinderwelle, deren singuläre Linie auf E liegt und parallel zu den Erzeugenden ist. In durch Spiegelung auseinander hervorgehenden Punkten $\hat{\mathfrak{r}}_1$ und $\hat{\mathfrak{r}}_2$ der beiden Zylinder sind dann die Flächenströme aus Symmetriegründen einander *gleich*. Sie sind aber natürlich *nicht* gleich demjenigen Flächenstrom, der auf einem einzelnen Zylinder fließt, der *allein* der einfallenden Welle ausgesetzt ist; vielmehr wird er sich gerade nach Maßgabe der Strahlung einstellen, die die beiden Zylinder einander zustrahlen. Diese Veränderung des Flächenstromes (gegenüber dem Fall unendlich weit voneinander entfernter Zylinder), die der Kirchhoffschen Theorie naturgemäß entgehen muß, wollen wir durch *Störungsrechnung* ermitteln. [Der elektrische Vektor $\mathfrak{E}_y = v$ schwingt in Richtung der

[1] Vgl. hierzu E. N. Fox: Phil. Trans. Roy. Soc. Lond. A **241**, 71 (1948); **242**, 1 (1949).
[2] S. N. Karp: Symposium on Microwave Optics. McGill University Montreal, Canada 1953.

Erzeugenden: p-Fall. $G(\mathfrak{r}-\hat{\mathfrak{r}}_i)$ bedeutet in Gl. (86.1 p) die Greensche Funktion des *freien* Raumes; im ebenen Fall also $G(\mathfrak{r}-\hat{\mathfrak{r}}_i) = \frac{i}{4} H_0^{(1)}(|\mathfrak{r}-\hat{\mathfrak{r}}_i|)$, vgl. (8.3a).]

Die Flächenströme ψ_i sind als Lösungen der Integralgleichungen

$$\int\limits_{S_1} \psi_1(\hat{\mathfrak{r}}_1)\, G(\hat{\mathfrak{r}}-\hat{\mathfrak{r}}_1)\, d\hat{\mathfrak{r}}_1 + \int\limits_{S_2} \psi_2(\hat{\mathfrak{r}}_2)\, G(\hat{\mathfrak{r}}-\hat{\mathfrak{r}}_2)\, d\hat{\mathfrak{r}}_2 = v_0(\hat{\mathfrak{r}}) \quad \textit{für } \hat{\mathfrak{r}} \textit{ auf } (S_1) \textit{ und } (S_2) \tag{86.1$'p$}$$

zu bestimmen, die sich unmittelbar aus der Randbedingung $v=0$ ergeben, vgl. (46.2 p) und (76.2 p). Verbindet der Vektor $\mathfrak{a}$ zwei durch Spiegelung auseinander hervorgehende Punkte $\hat{\mathfrak{r}}_1$ und $\hat{\mathfrak{r}}_2$ der Zylinderquerschnitte (S_1) und (S_2), so gilt für $\hat{\mathfrak{r}}$ auf (S_1) $|\hat{\mathfrak{r}}-\hat{\mathfrak{r}}_2| = |\hat{\mathfrak{r}}-\hat{\mathfrak{r}}_1+\mathfrak{a}| \geqq b$, wobei b der kleinste Abstand zweier Punkte sei, von denen der eine auf (S_1) und der andere auf (S_2) liegt (vgl. Fig. 47). Wir können also statt (86.1′p) auch schreiben

$$\int\limits_{S_1} \psi(\hat{\mathfrak{r}}_1)\,\{G(\hat{\mathfrak{r}}-\hat{\mathfrak{r}}_1) + G(\hat{\mathfrak{r}}-\hat{\mathfrak{r}}_1+\mathfrak{a})\}\, d\hat{\mathfrak{r}}_1 = v_0(\hat{\mathfrak{r}}), \quad \hat{\mathfrak{r}} \textit{ auf } (S_1), \tag{86.1$''p$}$$

denn es ist $\psi_1(\hat{\mathfrak{r}}_1) = \psi_2(\hat{\mathfrak{r}}_2) = \psi(\hat{\mathfrak{r}}_1)$ und wir brauchen $\hat{\mathfrak{r}}$ jetzt nurmehr auf (S_1) wandern zu lassen. Liegt nämlich $\hat{\mathfrak{r}}$ auf (S_2), so folgt aus (86.1″p)

$$\int\limits_{S_2} \psi(\hat{\mathfrak{r}}_2)\,\{G(\hat{\mathfrak{r}}-\hat{\mathfrak{r}}_2) + G(\hat{\mathfrak{r}}-\hat{\mathfrak{r}}_2+\mathfrak{a})\}\, d\hat{\mathfrak{r}}_2 = v_0(\hat{\mathfrak{r}}), \quad \hat{\mathfrak{r}} \textit{ auf } (S_2),$$

was aus Symmetriegründen mit (86.1″p) identisch ist. Wenn wir jetzt annehmen, daß die beiden Zylinder so weit voneinander entfernt sind, daß die Strahlungswechselwirkung, die sie *aufeinander* ausüben, als *kleine Störung* betrachtet werden kann, so läßt sich (86.1″p) wiederum durch ein Iterationsverfahren lösen. Ist nämlich der Abstand b der Zylinder groß gegen die Wellenlänge (die wir als Längeneinheit benutzen): $b \gg 1$, so ist das Argument des zweiten Gliedes in der geschweiften Klammer stets groß gegen 1; dieses Glied ist also $\sim 1/\sqrt{b} \ll 1$ (Hankelsche Näherung) und somit sehr klein gegen das erste Glied, dessen Argument Null werden kann (die Hankel-Funktion wird dann logarithmisch unendlich).

Führen wir nun der übersichtlichen Schreibweise zuliebe die beiden Integraloperatoren

$$\left.\begin{aligned} \Omega_0 &= \int\limits_{S_1} G(\hat{\mathfrak{r}}-\hat{\mathfrak{r}}') \ldots d\hat{\mathfrak{r}}', \\ \Omega_1 &= \int\limits_{S_1} G(\hat{\mathfrak{r}}-\hat{\mathfrak{r}}'+\mathfrak{a}) \ldots d\hat{\mathfrak{r}}' \end{aligned}\right\} \tag{86.2}$$

ein, so können wir (86.1″p) in der Form schreiben:

$$(\Omega_0+\Omega_1)\,\psi = v_0, \tag{86.1$'''p$}$$

dabei gilt symbolisch $\Omega_0 \gg \Omega_1$. Wir treiben nun Störungsrechnung, indem wir ψ in eine Reihe

$$\psi = \sum_{\nu=0}^{\infty} \psi_\nu \tag{86.3}$$

entwickeln, von deren Gliedern wir wie üblich annehmen, daß ψ_ν in demselben Maße klein gegen $\psi_{\nu-1}$ ist wie Ω_1 gegen Ω_0. Setzen wir also den Ansatz (86.3) in die Integralgleichung (86.1‴p) ein, so folgt durch Vergleich gleicher Größenordnungen auf beiden Seiten von dieser Gleichung:

$$\left.\begin{aligned} \Omega_0\,\psi_0 &= v_0 \\ \Omega_0\,\psi_1 &= -\,\Omega_1\,\psi_0 \\ &\ldots\ldots\ldots\ldots \\ \Omega_0\,\psi_\nu &= -\,\Omega_1\,\psi_{\nu-1}. \end{aligned}\right\} \tag{86.4}$$

Die ψ_ν lassen sich also sukzessive berechnen und zwar dient dazu jeweils eine Integralgleichung mit stets *gleichem Kern* $G(\hat{\mathfrak{r}}-\hat{\mathfrak{r}}_1)$ [vgl. (86.2)], nur die rechts stehende Inhomogenität ist jeweils eine andere (die mit wachsendem ν im allgemeinen fortschreitend komplizierter wird). Der Operator Ω_0 ist nun derjenige, der bei der Streuung an einem *einzelnen* Zylinder auftritt. In der Tat ist die erste Gleichung (86.4) nichts anderes als die Integralgleichung für den Flächenstrom ψ_0, der auf einem *einzelnen* (allein anwesenden Körper) fließt und deren Lösung als bekannt vorausgesetzt werden soll. Auch die übrigen in (86.4) auftretenden Größen lassen sich anschaulich deuten. So stellt $-\Omega_1\psi_0$ offensichtlich diejenige Streuwelle dar, die (S_1) trifft, wenn auf (S_2) der Flächenstrom ψ_0 fließt [man vgl. die zweite Gleichung (86.2) und beachte, daß die Streuwelle von der Form $-\int_{S_2}\psi(\hat{\mathfrak{r}}_2)\,G(\mathfrak{r}-\hat{\mathfrak{r}}_2)\,d\hat{\mathfrak{r}}_2$ ist]. Dadurch wird auf (S_1) der Flächenstrom ψ_1 hervorgerufen. Fließt dieser auf (S_2), so strahlt er die Streuwelle $-\Omega_1\psi_1$ nach (S_1) herüber, die dort den Flächenstrom ψ_2 auslöst und so fort. Durch die einzelnen Glieder der Reihe (86.3) wird also der Beugungsvorgang in eine Aufeinanderfolge von Streuwirkungen aufgelöst, die die beiden Körper wechselseitig aufeinander ausüben *(Mehrfachstreuung)*. Wir finden hier dieselben Verhältnisse wie unter Ziff. 85 wieder, jedoch sind sie hier einer Berechnung leichter zugänglich (s. weiter unten).

87. Zur Konvergenz. Ein spezielles Konvergenzproblem von der Art, wie es durch die Reihe (86.3) — deren Glieder aus (86.4) zu bestimmen sind — gestellt wird, wurde von SCHWARZSCHILD behandelt (wie bereits erwähnt). Im allgemeinen Fall ist es nützlich, sich klarzumachen, daß die Reihe (86.3) auch als Lösung der Integralgleichung zweiter Art

$$\psi(\hat{\mathfrak{r}}) = \psi_0(\hat{\mathfrak{r}}) - \int_{S_1}\psi(\hat{\mathfrak{r}}')\,F(\hat{\mathfrak{r}},\hat{\mathfrak{r}}')\,d\hat{\mathfrak{r}}',\ \mathfrak{r}\ auf\ (S_1) \tag{87.1}$$

in Gestalt einer Neumannschen Reihe aufgefaßt werden kann. Dabei ist $F(\hat{\mathfrak{r}},\hat{\mathfrak{r}}_1)$ die Lösung der Integralgleichung

$$\int_{S_1}F(\hat{\mathfrak{r}}_2,\hat{\mathfrak{r}}_1')\,G(\hat{\mathfrak{r}}_1-\hat{\mathfrak{r}}_1')\,d\hat{\mathfrak{r}}_1' = G(\hat{\mathfrak{r}}_1-\hat{\mathfrak{r}}_2),\quad \hat{\mathfrak{r}}_1\ auf\ (S_1),\quad \hat{\mathfrak{r}}_2\ auf\ (S_2). \tag{87.2}$$

$F(\hat{\mathfrak{r}}_2,\hat{\mathfrak{r}}_1)$ ist also derjenige Flächenstrom, der in $\hat{\mathfrak{r}}_1$ auf (S_1) hervorgerufen wird, wenn (S_1) von einer Zylinderwelle $G(\hat{\mathfrak{r}}-\hat{\mathfrak{r}}_2)$ mit $\hat{\mathfrak{r}}_2$ auf (S_2) bestrahlt wird. Um unsere Behauptung einzusehen, führen wir den Operator

$$\Theta = \int_{S_1}F(\hat{\mathfrak{r}},\hat{\mathfrak{r}}')\ldots d\hat{\mathfrak{r}}' \tag{87.3}$$

ein und schreiben (87.1) in der Form $(1+\Theta)\,\psi=\psi_0$. Die Lösung dieser Integralgleichung in Gestalt der Neumannschen Reihe lautet dann symbolisch

$$\psi = (1+\Theta)^{-1}\psi_0 = \sum_{\nu=0}^{\infty}(-1)^\nu\,\Theta^\nu\psi_0. \tag{87.4}$$

Andererseits können wir aber auch die Lösung von (86.1‴p) symbolisch wie folgt schreiben

$$\psi = (1+\Omega_0^{-1}\Omega_1)^{-1}\Omega_0^{-1}v_0 = \sum_{\nu=1}^{\infty}(-1)^\nu(\Omega_0^{-1}\Omega_1)^\nu\,\Omega_0^{-1}v_0. \tag{87.5}$$

Nun ist aber zufolge der ersten Gleichung (86.4) $\Omega_0^{-1}v_0=\psi_0$; ferner ist $\Theta=\Omega_0^{-1}\Omega_1$ — man erkennt dies, wenn man die Gln. (86.2), (87.2) und (87.3) miteinander vergleicht — daher stimmen (87.4) und (87.5) miteinander überein [die Reihe (87.5) ist aber nichts anderes als die Reihe (86.3) in Verbindung mit (86.4)]. Da nun die Flächenstromdichte $F(\hat{\mathfrak{r}}_2,\hat{\mathfrak{r}}_1)$ aus physikalischen Gründen als beschränkt vorausgesetzt werden kann, läßt sich die Konvergenz der Neumannschen Reihe (87.4) auf die übliche Weise[1] zeigen.

88. Zustrahlung zweier Zylinder. Wir gehen dazu über, die unter Ziff. 86 dargestellte Methode der praktischen Auswertung einen Schritt näher zu bringen[2]. Die beiden Zylinder mögen durch Spiegelung an der yz-Ebene auseinander hervorgehen [die y-Achse legen wir in die Richtung der Mantellinien der Zylinder; die Anregung erfolge durch eine ebene Welle, die in Richtung der positiven z-Achse einfalle, s. Fig. 48]. Ferner wollen wir annehmen, daß der kleinste Abstand groß gegen die Wellenlänge sei und daß der Querschnitt je unter kleinem Blickwinkel erscheine, wenn er von einem Punkte des anderen Zylinders aus betrachtet wird. Messen wir nun die x-Koordinate von $\mathfrak{r}_1$ von einem Ursprung O_1 innerhalb (S_1) aus, ebenso die von $\mathfrak{r}_2$ von dem entsprechenden Ursprung O_2 innerhalb des Spiegelbildes (S_2) in spiegelbildlicher Richtung, so gilt für $\mathfrak{r}$ auf (S_1) näherungsweise

$$\left.\begin{aligned}|\mathfrak{r}-\mathfrak{r}_2| = a - x(s) - \\ - x(s_2) + \cdots.\end{aligned}\right\} \quad (88.1)$$

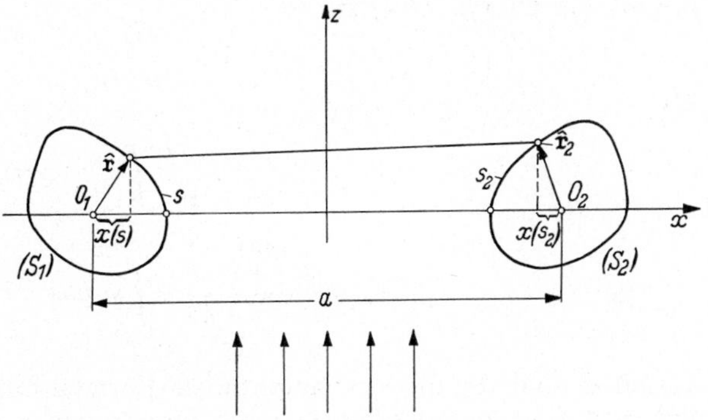

Fig. 48. Zur Zustrahlung zweier Zylinder in spiegelsymmetrischer Lage.

Dabei sei s bzw. s_2 die Bogenlänge des Punktes $\mathfrak{r}$ bzw. $\mathfrak{r}_2$ (oder ein anderer geeigneter Parameter) (vgl. Fig. 48). Schreiben wir nun zur Abkürzung $G(\mathfrak{r}(s) - \mathfrak{r}_1(s_1)) = G(s, s_1)$ und entsprechend für s_2, so können wir für die Greensche Funktion $G(s, s_2)$ die Hankelsche Näherung heranziehen:

$$G(s, s_2) = \frac{e^{\frac{i\pi}{4}}}{2\sqrt{2\pi}} \cdot \frac{e^{ia}}{\sqrt{a}} e^{-i[x(s)+x(s_2)]}. \quad (88.2)$$

Dabei wurde von Gl. (88.1) Gebrauch gemacht und der langsam veränderliche Faktor $|\mathfrak{r} - \mathfrak{r}_2|^{-\frac{1}{2}}$ direkt durch $a^{-\frac{1}{2}}$ ersetzt, was stets dann gerechtfertigt ist, wenn die Lineardimension des Querschnitts in x-Richtung klein gegen a ist. Unter dieser weiteren Voraussetzung reduziert sich — wie wir gleich sehen werden — die Reihe (86.3) auf nur zwei Glieder [in der durch (88.2) charakterisierten Näherung]. Die Integralgleichung (86.1''p) nimmt jetzt mit Hilfe von (88.2) die Form an

$$\int_{S_1} \psi(s') G(s, s') \, ds' = v_0(s) + A\, e^{-ix(s)} \quad \textit{für } s \textit{ auf } (S_1) \quad (88.3p)$$

mit

$$A = \frac{e^{-\frac{3\pi i}{4}}}{2\sqrt{2\pi}} \cdot \frac{e^{ia}}{\sqrt{a}} \int_{S_1} \psi(s)\, e^{-ix(s)} \, ds. \quad (88.4)$$

Die Anwesenheit des zweiten Zylinders macht sich also auf (S_1) nur dadurch bemerkbar, daß zu der einfallenden Welle $v_0 = e^{iz(s)}$ eine ebene Welle $A\, e^{-ix(s)}$

[1] Vgl. etwa G. Hamel: Integralgleichungen, 2. Aufl., S. 26. Berlin 1949.

[2] Höhere Näherungen berechnen N. Zitron u. S. N. Karp: N.Y. Univ. Res. Rep. No. EM-126 (1959).

aus der Richtung, in der der andere Zylinder liegt, hinzutritt. Die Amplitude (und Phase) A dieser Welle ist die Amplitude der Streustrahlung des Körpers (S_2), wenn auf ihm der Gesamtflächenstrom ψ fließt. Wegen ihrer Linearität können wir Gl. (89.3p) durch den Ansatz $\psi=\psi_0+A\psi_1$ lösen mit

$$\left.\begin{aligned}\int_{S_1}\psi_0(s')\,G(s,s')\,ds' &= e^{iz(s)},\\ \int_{S_1}\psi_1(s')\,G(s,s')\,ds' &= e^{-ix(s)}.\end{aligned}\right\}\qquad(88.3'p)$$

Der Flächenstrom setzt sich also additiv aus zwei Anteilen zusammen: 1. dem durch die einfallende Welle e^{iz} induzierten, 2. dem durch die ebene Welle $A\,e^{-ix}$ hervorgerufenen. Dabei ergibt sich die Amplitude A durch Einsetzen von $\psi=\psi_0+A\psi_1$ in die Gl. (88.4) zu

$$A=\frac{A_0}{1-A_1}$$

mit

$$\left.\begin{aligned}A_0 &= \frac{e^{-\frac{3\pi i}{4}}}{2\sqrt{2\pi}}\cdot\frac{e^{ia}}{\sqrt{a}}\int_{S_1}\psi_0(s)\,e^{-ix(s)}\,ds,\\ A_1 &= \frac{e^{-\frac{3\pi i}{4}}}{2\sqrt{2\pi}}\,\frac{e^{ia}}{\sqrt{a}}\cdot\int_{S_1}\psi_1(s)\,e^{-ix(s)}\,ds.\end{aligned}\right\}\qquad(88.4')$$

A_0 und A_1 sind also die Streuamplituden (Formfaktoren), die von den Strömen ψ_0 und ψ_1 auf einem isolierten Zylinder hervorgerufen werden. Nach Lösung der (sich nur auf *einen* Zylinder beziehenden) Integralgleichungen (88.3'p) ergibt sich also der Flächenstrom auf den *wechselwirkenden* Zylindern zu

$$\psi(s)=\psi_0(s)+\frac{A_0}{1-A_1}\psi_1(s).\qquad(88.5)$$

Entsprechende Methoden lassen sich auch für mehrere beugende Zylinder entwickeln sowie für allgemeinere räumliche Anordnungen (z. B. mehrere komplanare Schirme). Ebenso für die andere Randbedingung (s-Fall) und das räumliche elektromagnetische Problem.

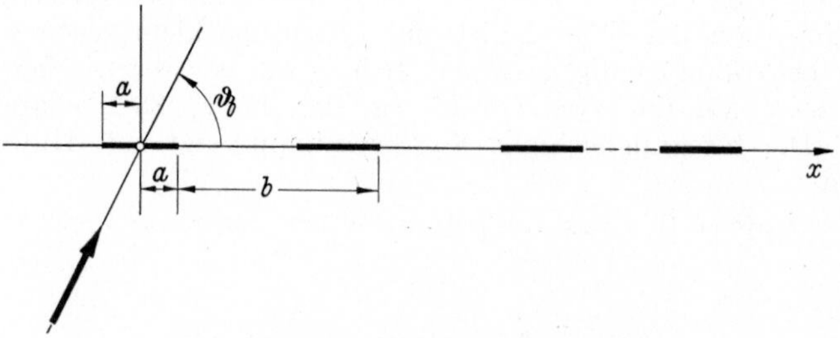

Fig. 49. Zur Theorie der Beugung am Streifengitter.

89. Ansatz einer strengen Gittertheorie. Von besonderem Interesse ist das aus gleichen parallelen Zylindern (beliebigen Querschnitts) gebildete ebene Gitter. Wir wollen als einfaches Beispiel kurz ein *Streifengitter* von N (unendlich dünnen) Streifen der Breite $2a$ mit der Gitterkonstante b betrachten (vgl. Fig. 49). Die Flächenstromdichten auf den einzelnen Streifen sind mittels Integralgleichungen der Form (49.2p) zu ermitteln. Diese nehmen hier für eine unter dem Winkel ϑ_0

einfallende ebene Welle die folgende Form an

$$\sum_{\nu=0}^{N-1} \int_{-a+\nu b}^{a+\nu b} \psi_\nu(x')\, H_0^1(|x-x'|)\, dx' = -4i\, e^{i\alpha_0 x} \quad (x \in S), \qquad (\alpha_0 = \cos\vartheta_0); \tag{89.1}$$

dabei besteht der Schirm $S = \sum_{\nu=0}^{N-1} S_\nu$ aus den N Streifen $S_\nu\,(-a+\nu\, b < x < a+\nu\, b)$.

Wir gehen sogleich zur Fourier-Transformierten

$$\overline{\psi}_\nu(x) = \int_{-a+\nu b}^{a+\nu b} \psi_\nu(\alpha)\, e^{-i\alpha x}\, dx \tag{89.2}$$

über, aus der sich das Fraunhofersche Fernfeld durch Superposition der einzelnen Streifenbeiträge in der Form

$$\overline{\psi}(\alpha) = \sum_{\nu=0}^{N-1} \overline{\psi}_\nu(\alpha) \tag{89.2'}$$

ergibt (vgl. Ziff. 62). Für die $\overline{\psi}_\nu(\alpha)$ erhält man nach dem Verfahren von Ziff. 60 mittels (60.1) die dualen Integralgleichungen

$$\left.\begin{aligned} &\sum_{\nu=0}^{N-1} \int_{-\infty}^{\infty} \frac{\overline{\psi}_\nu(\alpha)}{\sqrt{1-\alpha^2}}\, e^{i\alpha x}\, d\alpha = -4\pi i\, e^{i\alpha_0 x} \qquad (x \in S) \\ &\int_{-\infty}^{\infty} \overline{\psi}_\nu(\alpha)\, e^{i\alpha x}\, d\alpha = 0 \qquad (x \notin S_\nu,\ \nu = 0, 1, \ldots, N-1). \end{aligned}\right\} \tag{89.3}$$

Multipliziert man diese Gleichungen mit $e^{-i\alpha' x}$ und integriert die erste über $x \in S_\nu$, die zweite über $x \notin S_\nu$ (vgl. Ziff. 64), so erhalten wir ein Gleichungssystem, das sich in folgender Form schreiben läßt

$$\left.\begin{aligned} &\int_{-\infty}^{\infty} \frac{\overline{\psi}_\nu(\alpha')}{\sqrt{1-\alpha'^2}}\, e^{i\nu b\alpha'}\, \frac{\sin a(\alpha'-\alpha)}{\alpha'-\alpha}\, d\alpha' = -4\pi i\, e^{i\nu b\alpha}\, \frac{\sin a(\alpha-\alpha_0)}{\alpha-\alpha_0} \\ &\qquad\qquad - \int_{-\infty}^{\infty} \sum_{\substack{\mu=0\\ \mu\neq\nu}}^{N-1} \frac{\overline{\psi}_\mu(\alpha')}{\sqrt{1-\alpha'^2}}\, e^{i\nu b\alpha'}\, \frac{\sin a(\alpha'-\alpha)}{\alpha'-\alpha}\, d\alpha', \\ &\overline{\psi}_\nu(\alpha)\, e^{i\nu b\alpha} - \frac{1}{\pi} \int_{-\infty}^{\infty} \overline{\psi}_\nu(\alpha')\, e^{i\nu b\alpha'}\, \frac{\sin a(\alpha'-\alpha)}{\alpha'-\alpha}\, d\alpha' = 0 \quad (\nu = 0, 1, \ldots N-1). \end{aligned}\right\} \tag{89.4}$$

Ohne das Summenglied auf der rechten Seite der ersten dieser Gleichungen stimmt (89.4) mit den Integralgleichungen überein, die sich für die Streuamplitude des *einzelnen* (isolierten) Streifens ergeben (vgl. Ziff. 64 und 118). (Der Faktor $e^{i\nu b\alpha}$ deutet an, daß der ν-te Streifen um $\nu\, b$ nach rechts verschoben ist.) Durch das Summenglied kommt also die *Wechselwirkung* der einzelnen Gitterelemente untereinander zum Ausdruck[1].

Entsprechende Überlegungen lassen sich auch für ein Gitter aus Zylindern beliebigen Querschnitts anstellen. Unter der Voraussetzung, daß die Gitterkonstante groß gegen die Wellenlänge ist, läßt sich zeigen, daß das Fernfeld als Superposition der Streufelder der einzelnen (nicht wechselwirkenden) Gitter-

[1] G.L. Baldwin u. A.E. Heins: Math. Scand. **2**, 103 (1954), haben ein solches Gitterproblem auf ein äquivalentes Wellenleiterproblem zurückgeführt, das sich mittels des Wiener-Hopf-Verfahrens lösen läßt. Vgl. auch S.N. Karp u. W.E. Williams: Proc. Cambridge Phil. Soc. **53**, 683 (1957).

elemente aufgefaßt werden kann, wobei jedoch bei der einfallenden Welle neben der Primärwelle noch eine *streifend* einfallende ebene Welle zu berücksichtigen ist, die der *Wechselwirkung* der Zylinder Rechnung trägt[1]. Wir können hier nicht mehr tun, als die einschlägige Literatur zusammenzustellen[2], die den fortschreitenden Erfolg in den Bemühungen wiederspiegelt, den Einfluß der Gestalt des einzelnen Gitterelements sowie die Wechselwirkung dieser Elemente untereinander exakt zu erfassen.

f) Die Rayleighsche Näherung und die daran anschließende Störungsrechnung.

90. Einleitung. Ist die Wellenlänge *groß* gegenüber den Abmessungen des feldverändernden Objekts (Körper oder Öffnung), so wird die geometrisch-optische Schattengrenze vollständig verwischt und die Kirchhoffsche Theorie (Abschn. IIa) wird auch für das Fernfeld unbrauchbar. Diese dem Kirchhoffschen Grenzfall ($\lambda \to 0$) gerade entgegengesetzten Verhältnisse liegen im *Rayleighschen Grenzfall* ($\lambda \to \infty$) vor. Hier sind die Objekte in ein (in ihrem Bereich) *nahezu statisches* (zeitlich nur sehr langsam veränderliches) Feld eingebettet. Rayleigh[3] berechnet daher ihre Wirkung, indem er die *statische* Feldverteilung in ihrer Umgebung bestimmt und daraus mit Hilfe des Huygensschen Prinzips das Fernfeld ermittelt. Auf diese Weise wird sichergestellt, daß in einer in ihren Abmessungen gegen die Wellenlänge kleinen Umgebung des Objekts die (durch die Randbedingungen erzwungene) nahezu *korrekte* Feldverteilung herauskommt (insbesondere wird also so die *Kantenbedingung* erfüllt, die ja in Ziff. 23 aus dem statischen Grenzfall abgeleitet wurde).

Im *Streufall* ist also für den streuenden Körper das statische Problem zu lösen, während im *Beugungsfall* (endlich begrenzte Öffnung in einem ebenen Schirm) die Öffnungsfläche als unendlich dünner idealer *magnetischer Leiter* (mit $\mu \to \infty$, $\varepsilon \to 0$; vgl. Ziff. 2) behandelt werden kann (vgl. auch Ziff. 26), dessen Einfluß auf ein vorgegebenes statisches Feld zu untersuchen ist.

---

[1] Vgl. die weiter unten angeführten Arbeiten von S.N. Karp.

[2] H. Lamb: Proc. Lond. Math. Soc. **29**, 523 (1898). — Lord Rayleigh: Proc. Roy. Soc. Lond. A **79**, 399 (1907). — Theory of Sound, 2. Aufl., Bd. II, § 272a. London 1926. — C. Schäfer u. F. Reiche: Ann. Phys. **32**, 577 (1910); **35**, 817 (1911). — W. Voigt: Göttinger Nachr. **1911**, 41; **1912**, 385. — W. v. Ignatowsky: Ann. Phys. **44**, 369 (1914). — R. Gans: Ann. Phys. **61**, 447 (1920). — Eine Übersicht über die ältere Literatur bei G. Wolfsohn: Handbuch der Physik, Bd. 20, Kap. 7, Ziff. 9. Berlin 1928. — U. Fano: Ann. Phys. **32**, 393 (1938). W. Wessel: Hochfrequenztechn. **54**, 62 (1939). — K. Artmann: Z. Physik **119**, 529 (1942). — C.G. MacFarlane: J. Instn. Electr. Engrs. **93**, 1523 (1946). — J.F. Carlson u. A.E. Heins: Quart. Appl. Math. **4**, 313 (1947); **5**, 82 (1947). — R. Honerjäger: Ann. Phys. **4**, 25 (1948). — J.W. Miles: Quart. Appl. Math. **7**, 45 (1949). — W. Franz: Z. angew. Phys. **1**, 416 (1949). — A.E. Heins: Quart. Appl. Math. **8**, 281 (1950). — T. Sakurai: J. Phys. Soc. Japan **5**, 203 (1950). — E. Hulthen: Ark. Fys. **2**, 439 (1950). — J. Shmoys: J. Opt. Soc. Amer. **41**, 324 (1951). — V. Twersky: J. Appl. Phys. **22**, 825 (1951). — J. Acoust. Soc. Amer. **24**, 42 (1952). — J. Appl. Phys. **23**, 407, 1099 (1952). — J. Opt. Soc. **42**, 855 (1952). — J. Appl. Phys. **24**, 659 (1953); **25**, 859 (1954). — Univ. Res. Rep. No. EM-59 (1953). — Elec. Def. Labor. Mountain View, Calif. Eng. Rep. EDL-E 5 (1955). — S.N. Karp: Bull. Amer. Phys. Soc. Phys. Rev. **86**, 586 (1952). — W. Sollfrey u. J. Shmoys: N.Y. Univ. Res. Rep. No. EM-41 (1952). — E.A. Lewis u. J.P. Casey: J. Appl. Phys. **23**, 605 (1952). — F. Reiche: N.Y. Univ. Res. Rep. No. EM-61 (1953). — W.E. Groves: J. Appl. Phys. **24**, 845 (1953). — G. v. Trentini: Z. angew. Phys. **5**, 221 (1953). — J. Opt. Soc. Amer. **45**, 883 (1955). — R. Müller: Z. Naturforsch. **8**a, 56 (1953). — J.R. Wait: Canad. J. Phys. **32**, 571 (1954). — J.E. Storrer u. J. Sevick: J. Appl. Phys. **32**, 571 (1954). — S. N. Karp: N.Y. Univ. Res. Rep. No. EM-85 (1955). — W. Messerschmidt: Optik **12**, 298 (1955). — L.A. Vainstein: Zh. Tekn. Fiz. **25**, 847 (1955). — S.N. Karp u. J. Radlow: N.Y. Univ. Res. Rep. No. EM-90 (1956).

[3] Lord Rayleigh: Phil. Mag. **43**, 259 (1897). — Proc. Roy. Soc. Lond. **89**, 194 (1913). Abgedruckt in Sci. Papers **4**, 283 (1903); **6**, 161 (1920).

RAYLEIGH behandelte das statische Problem mit den üblichen potentialtheoretischen Methoden. Wir wollen darüberhinaus zeigen, daß die *quasistatische Lösung* der *erste Schritt einer Störungsrechnung* ist, die sich in der gewohnten Form für die Lösung der in Abschn. IIIa und IIId abgeleiteten Integralgleichungen entwickeln läßt. Diese Störungsrechnung, die unseres Wissens erstmals BOUWKAMP[1] bei der Behandlung der akustischen Beugung an der kreisförmigen Öffnung angewandt hat (vgl. Abschn. BIc2), konvergiert naturgemäß nur dann gut, wenn die Lineardimensionen des beugenden Objekts *klein* gegen die Wellenlänge sind. Als Entwicklungsparameter treten demgemäß die Verhältnisse der Lineardimensionen des Objekts zur Wellenlänge auf, die als klein gegen 1 vorausgesetzt werden sollen (wir wollen uns hier auf einen einzigen solchen Parameter beschränken).

Es sei also ε das Verhältnis einer charakteristischen Abmessung des Beugungsobjekts zur Wellenlänge und wir denken uns die Transformation $\hat{\mathfrak{r}} \to \varepsilon\,\hat{\mathfrak{r}}$, $d\hat{\mathfrak{r}} \to \varepsilon^2 d\hat{\mathfrak{r}}$ in den Integralgleichungen von Abschn. IIIa und IIId durchgeführt, wobei $\varepsilon \ll 1$ und $|\hat{\mathfrak{r}}|$ im ganzen Integrationsbereich höchstens von der Größenordnung 1 sein soll.

f1) Das skalare Problem für ebene Schirme.

91. Das Rechenschema der Störungstheorie. Wir behandeln den *p-Fall* (der *s*-Fall ist dann nach dem Babinetschen Theorem mit eingeschlossen[2]), wollen jedoch den Streu- und Beugungs-Fall (vgl. Ziff. 26) getrennt betrachten. Wir haben also von der Integralgleichung (46.2p) bzw. der Pseudointegralgleichung (47.2p) auszugehen, die wir jetzt in den *neuen* Variablen in der Form schreiben wollen

Streuung

$$\int\limits_S \psi(\varepsilon\,\hat{\mathfrak{r}}')\, G(\varepsilon\,|\hat{\mathfrak{r}}-\hat{\mathfrak{r}}'|)\, d\hat{\mathfrak{r}}' = D(\varepsilon\,\hat{\mathfrak{r}}) \quad \textit{für } \hat{\mathfrak{r}} \textit{ auf } (S), \tag{91.1}$$

Beugung

$$\lim_{z\to 0} \frac{\partial^2}{\partial z^2} \int\limits_L \varphi(\varepsilon\,\hat{\mathfrak{r}}')\, G(\varepsilon\,|\hat{\mathfrak{r}}-\hat{\mathfrak{r}}'|)\, d\hat{\mathfrak{r}}' = F(\varepsilon\,\hat{\mathfrak{r}}) \quad \textit{für } \hat{\mathfrak{r}} \textit{ auf } (L) \tag{91.1a}$$

mit

$$\left.\begin{aligned} D(\varepsilon\,\hat{\mathfrak{r}}) &= \frac{1}{\varepsilon^2}\, v_0(\varepsilon\,\hat{\mathfrak{r}}), \qquad F(\varepsilon\,\hat{\mathfrak{r}}) = -\frac{1}{2\varepsilon}\,\frac{\partial v_0(\varepsilon\,\hat{\mathfrak{r}})}{\partial z},\\ G(\varepsilon\,|\hat{\mathfrak{r}}-\hat{\mathfrak{r}}'|) &= \frac{1}{4\pi}\,\frac{e^{i\varepsilon|\hat{\mathfrak{r}}-\hat{\mathfrak{r}}'|}}{\varepsilon\,|\hat{\mathfrak{r}}-\hat{\mathfrak{r}}'|}. \end{aligned}\right\} \tag{91.2}$$

Unser Ziel ist, die Lösung dieser Gleichungen in eine *Potenzreihe nach* ε zu entwickeln:

$$\left.\begin{aligned} \psi(\varepsilon\,\hat{\mathfrak{r}}) &= \frac{1}{\varepsilon} \sum_{\nu=0}^{\infty} \varepsilon^\nu\, \psi^{(\nu)}(\hat{\mathfrak{r}}),\\ \varphi(\varepsilon\,\hat{\mathfrak{r}}) &= \varepsilon \sum_{\nu=0}^{\infty} \varepsilon^\nu\, \varphi^{(\nu)}(\hat{\mathfrak{r}}). \end{aligned}\right\} \tag{91.3}$$

---

[1] C. J. BOUWKAMP: Physica, Haag **16**, 1 (1950). — J. W. MILES: Acoustica **2**, 287 (1952). — J. Acoust. Soc. Amer. **24**, 324 (1952). Nach derselben Methode behandeln BOUWKAMP: N. Y. Univ. Res. Rep. No. EM-50 (1953) sowie R. MÜLLER u. K. WESTPFAHL: Z. Physik **134**, 245 (1953) die Beugung am Spalt (vgl. Abschn. BIb2).

[2] Der p-Fall entspricht der Randbedingung $v=0$ auf (S), der s-Fall der Randbedingung $\partial v/\partial z = 0$ auf (S); man vgl. Ziff. 4.

Zu diesem Zweck entwickeln wir zunächst den „*Kern*“ G und die „*Inhomogenitäten*“ rechts in (91.1) und (91.1a) in solche Potenzreihen[1]

$$\left.\begin{aligned} G(\varepsilon|\hat{\mathfrak{r}}-\hat{\mathfrak{r}}'|) &= \frac{1}{\varepsilon}\sum_{\nu=0}^{\infty}\varepsilon^{\nu}\, G^{(\nu)}(\hat{\mathfrak{r}}-\hat{\mathfrak{r}}') \\ &= \frac{1}{4\pi\varepsilon}\left\{\frac{1}{|\hat{\mathfrak{r}}-\hat{\mathfrak{r}}'|}+i\varepsilon-\frac{\varepsilon^2}{2}|\hat{\mathfrak{r}}-\hat{\mathfrak{r}}'|+\cdots\frac{(i\varepsilon)^{\nu}}{\nu!}|\hat{\mathfrak{r}}-\hat{\mathfrak{r}}'|^{\nu-1}+\cdots\right\}, \\ D(\varepsilon\,\hat{\mathfrak{r}}) &= \frac{1}{\varepsilon^2}\{D^{(0)}(\hat{\mathfrak{r}})+\varepsilon\, D^{(1)}(\hat{\mathfrak{r}})+\varepsilon^2 D^{(2)}(\hat{\mathfrak{r}})+\cdots\}, \\ F(\varepsilon\,\hat{\mathfrak{r}}) &= F^{(0)}(\hat{\mathfrak{r}})+\varepsilon\, F^{(1)}(\hat{\mathfrak{r}})+\varepsilon^2 F^{(2)}(\hat{\mathfrak{r}})+\cdots. \end{aligned}\right\} \qquad (91.4)$$

Setzen wir nun (91.3) und (91.4) in Gl. (91.1) bzw. (91.1a) ein, so folgt durch Vergleich der Koeffizienten gleicher Potenzen von ε auf beiden Seiten der so entstehenden Gleichungen das Gleichungssystem

$$\left.\begin{aligned} \int_S \psi^{(\nu)}(\hat{\mathfrak{r}}')\, G^{(0)}(\hat{\mathfrak{r}}-\hat{\mathfrak{r}}')\, d\hat{\mathfrak{r}}' &= D^{(\nu)}(\hat{\mathfrak{r}}) - \sum_{\mu=1}^{\nu}\int_S \psi^{(\nu-\mu)}(\hat{\mathfrak{r}}')\, G^{(\mu)}(\hat{\mathfrak{r}}-\hat{\mathfrak{r}}')\, d\hat{\mathfrak{r}}' \\ &\textit{für } \nu = 0, 1, 2, \ldots \textit{ und für } \hat{\mathfrak{r}} \textit{ auf } (S) \end{aligned}\right\} \qquad (91.5)$$

bzw.

$$\left.\begin{aligned} &\lim_{z\to 0}\frac{\partial^2}{\partial z^2}\int_L \varphi^{(\nu)}(\hat{\mathfrak{r}}')\, G^{(0)}(\mathfrak{r}-\hat{\mathfrak{r}}')\, d\hat{\mathfrak{r}}' \\ &\quad = F^{(\nu)}(\hat{\mathfrak{r}}) - \lim_{z\to 0}\frac{\partial^2}{\partial z^2}\sum_{\mu=1}^{\nu}\int_L \varphi^{(\nu-\mu)}(\hat{\mathfrak{r}}')\, G^{(\mu)}(\mathfrak{r}-\hat{\mathfrak{r}}')\, d\hat{\mathfrak{r}}' \\ &\qquad \textit{für } \nu = 0, 1, 2, \ldots \textit{ und für } \hat{\mathfrak{r}} \textit{ auf } (L)\,. \end{aligned}\right\} \qquad (91.5\text{a})$$

Setzen wir hier in Gl. (91.5) den Ausdruck für $G^{(\nu)}(\hat{\mathfrak{r}}-\hat{\mathfrak{r}}')$ aus (91.4) ein, so folgt

$$\left.\begin{aligned} \int_S \frac{\psi^{(\nu)}(\hat{\mathfrak{r}}')}{|\hat{\mathfrak{r}}-\hat{\mathfrak{r}}'|}\, d\hat{\mathfrak{r}}' &= 4\pi\, D^{(\nu)}(\hat{\mathfrak{r}}) - \sum_{\mu=1}^{\nu}\frac{i^{\mu}}{\mu!}\int_S \psi^{(\nu-\mu)}(\hat{\mathfrak{r}}')\, |\hat{\mathfrak{r}}-\hat{\mathfrak{r}}'|^{\mu-1}\, d\hat{\mathfrak{r}}' \\ &\equiv f^{(\nu)}(\hat{\mathfrak{r}}) \qquad \textit{für } \nu = 0, 1, 2, \ldots \text{ und } \textit{für } \hat{\mathfrak{r}} \textit{ auf } (S) \end{aligned}\right\} \qquad (91.5')$$

oder ausführlich geschrieben

Streuung (p-Fall)

$$\left.\begin{aligned} &\int_S \frac{\psi^{(0)}(\hat{\mathfrak{r}}')}{|\hat{\mathfrak{r}}-\hat{\mathfrak{r}}'|}\, d\hat{\mathfrak{r}}' = 4\pi\, D^{(0)}(\hat{\mathfrak{r}})\,, \\ &\int_S \frac{\psi^{(1)}(\hat{\mathfrak{r}}')}{|\hat{\mathfrak{r}}-\hat{\mathfrak{r}}'|}\, d\hat{\mathfrak{r}}' = 4\pi\, D^{(1)}(\hat{\mathfrak{r}}) + S^{(1)}\,, \\ &\cdots\cdots\cdots\cdots\cdots\cdots\cdots\cdots \\ &\int_S \frac{\psi^{(\nu)}(\hat{\mathfrak{r}}')}{|\hat{\mathfrak{r}}-\hat{\mathfrak{r}}'|}\, d\hat{\mathfrak{r}}' = 4\pi\, D^{(\nu)}(\hat{\mathfrak{r}}) + S^{(\nu)} + \frac{1}{2}\int_S \psi^{(\nu-2)}(\hat{\mathfrak{r}}')\, |\hat{\mathfrak{r}}-\hat{\mathfrak{r}}'|\, d\hat{\mathfrak{r}}' \\ &\qquad + \frac{i}{3!}\int_S \psi^{(\nu-3)}(\hat{\mathfrak{r}})\, |\hat{\mathfrak{r}}-\hat{\mathfrak{r}}'|^2 d\hat{\mathfrak{r}}' + \cdots - \frac{i^{\nu}}{\nu!}\int_S \psi^{(0)}(\hat{\mathfrak{r}}')\, |\hat{\mathfrak{r}}-\hat{\mathfrak{r}}'|^{\nu-1} d\hat{\mathfrak{r}}', \\ &\hspace{20em} \nu \geqq 2, \quad \hat{\mathfrak{r}} \textit{ auf } (S)\,. \end{aligned}\right\} \qquad (91.5'')$$

[1] Bei der Entwicklung von D und F denken wir insbesondere an *ebene* Wellen $v_0(\varepsilon\mathfrak{r}) = \exp[i\varepsilon(\mathfrak{e}_0\mathfrak{r})]$, so daß die Entwicklung für D mit ε^{-2}, diejenige für F mit ε^0 beginnt: $D^{(0)} = 1$, $F^{(0)} = -i(\mathfrak{n}\,\mathfrak{e}_0)/2$ ($\mathfrak{e}_0$ Einheitsvektor in der Einfallsrichtung, $\mathfrak{n}$ Schirmnormale). Dem entsprechen die in (91.3) vor dem Summenzeichen auftretenden Potenzen in ε.

Hier haben wir zur Abkürzung die Konstanten

$$S^{(\nu)} = -i \int_S \psi^{(\nu-1)}(\hat{\mathfrak{r}}')\, d\hat{\mathfrak{r}}', \qquad \nu > 0 \tag{91.6}$$

eingeführt.

Setzen wir nun auch in (91.5a) die Ausdrücke (91.4) für $G^{(\mu)}(\mathfrak{r}-\hat{\mathfrak{r}}')$ ein, so ergibt sich zunächst wegen $4\pi G^{(1)} = i$ das Glied mit $\mu = 1$ rechterhand in (91.5a) als konstant, verschwindet also bei der Differentiation nach z. Die übrigen Glieder können wir mit Hilfe der Beziehung

$$\frac{\partial^2}{\partial z^2} |\mathfrak{r}-\mathfrak{r}'|^{\mu-1} = (\mu-1)\,|\mathfrak{r}-\mathfrak{r}'|^{\mu-3} + (\mu-1)(\mu-3)\, z^2\, |\mathfrak{r}-\mathfrak{r}'|^{\mu-5} \tag{91.7}$$

vereinfachen:

$$\lim_{z\to 0} \frac{\partial^2}{\partial z^2} G^{(\mu)}(\mathfrak{r}-\hat{\mathfrak{r}}') = \frac{i^\mu}{4\pi}\, \frac{\mu-1}{\mu!}\, |\hat{\mathfrak{r}}-\hat{\mathfrak{r}}'|^{\mu-3}. \tag{91.8}$$

Dabei haben wir den Differentialoperator $\lim\limits_{z\to 0} \frac{\partial^2}{\partial z^2}$ mit dem Integral rechter Hand in (91.5a) vertauschen können, da die so entstehenden Integrale für $\mu \geqq 2$ konvergieren. Dies ist jedoch linker Hand in (91.5a) nicht der Fall. Hier treten also dieselben Schwierigkeiten auf, die uns bei Behandlung der Gl. (47.2p) begegneten, die also auch dem statischen Grenzfall eigentümlich sind. In der Tat genügt das Integral linker Hand der *Potentialgleichung* $\Delta \cdots = 0$, daher können wir $\partial^2/\partial z^2$ durch $-\hat{\Delta}$ ersetzen und erhalten so mit (91.8) aus (91.5a)

$$\left.\begin{aligned} \hat{\Delta} \int_L \frac{\varphi^{(\nu)}(\hat{\mathfrak{r}}')}{|\hat{\mathfrak{r}}-\hat{\mathfrak{r}}'|}\, d\hat{\mathfrak{r}}' &= -4\pi F^{(\nu)}(\hat{\mathfrak{r}}) + \sum_{\mu=2}^{\nu} i^\mu \frac{\mu-1}{\mu!} \int_L \varphi^{(\nu-\mu)}(\hat{\mathfrak{r}}')\, |\hat{\mathfrak{r}}-\hat{\mathfrak{r}}'|^{\mu-3}\, d\hat{\mathfrak{r}}' \\ &\equiv g^{(\nu)}(\hat{\mathfrak{r}}) \qquad \textit{für } \nu = 0, 1, 2, \ldots \qquad \text{und } \textit{für } \hat{\mathfrak{r}} \textit{ auf } (L)\,. \end{aligned}\right\} \tag{91.5'a}$$

Ausführlich geschrieben erhalten wir hier

Beugung (p-Fall)

$$\left.\begin{aligned} \hat{\Delta} \int_L \frac{\varphi^{(0)}(\hat{\mathfrak{r}}')}{|\hat{\mathfrak{r}}-\hat{\mathfrak{r}}'|}\, d\hat{\mathfrak{r}}' &= -4\pi F^{(0)}(\hat{\mathfrak{r}}), \\ \hat{\Delta} \int_L \frac{\varphi^{(1)}(\hat{\mathfrak{r}}')}{|\hat{\mathfrak{r}}-\hat{\mathfrak{r}}'|}\, d\hat{\mathfrak{r}}' &= -4\pi F^{(1)}(\hat{\mathfrak{r}}), \\ & \cdots\cdots\cdots\cdots \\ \hat{\Delta} \int_L \frac{\varphi^{(\nu)}(\hat{\mathfrak{r}}')}{|\hat{\mathfrak{r}}-\hat{\mathfrak{r}}'|}\, d\hat{\mathfrak{r}}' &= -4\pi F^{(\nu)}(\hat{\mathfrak{r}}) - \frac{1}{2} \int_L \frac{\varphi^{(\nu-2)}(\hat{\mathfrak{r}}')}{|\hat{\mathfrak{r}}-\hat{\mathfrak{r}}'|}\, d\hat{\mathfrak{r}}' \\ &\quad - \frac{i}{3} \int_L \varphi^{(\nu-3)}(\hat{\mathfrak{r}}')\, d\hat{\mathfrak{r}}' + \frac{1}{8} \int_L \varphi^{(\nu-4)}(\hat{\mathfrak{r}}')\, |\hat{\mathfrak{r}}-\hat{\mathfrak{r}}'|\, d\hat{\mathfrak{r}}' + \cdots \\ &\quad + i^\nu \frac{\nu-1}{\nu!} \int_L \varphi^{(0)}(\hat{\mathfrak{r}}')\, |\hat{\mathfrak{r}}-\hat{\mathfrak{r}}'|^{\nu-3}\, d\hat{\mathfrak{r}}', \quad \nu \geqq 2, \quad \hat{\mathfrak{r}} \textit{ auf } (L). \end{aligned}\right\} \tag{91.5''a}$$

Die linken Seiten der Gln. (91.5'a), (91.5''a) lassen sich hier ebenso behandeln, wie wir das für die Gl. (47.3p) erläutert haben. Da nämlich der „Kern“ $\hat{\Delta}\frac{1}{|\hat{\mathfrak{r}}-\hat{\mathfrak{r}}'|}$ *nicht integrabel* ist, so haben wir es bei (91.5'a) bzw. (91.5''a) nicht mit reinen Integralgleichungen zu tun, sondern mit *Integrodifferentialgleichungen*. Daher sind die $\varphi^{(\nu)}$ durch (91.5'a), (91.5''a) *nicht eindeutig* bestimmt, sondern müssen noch der *Randbedingung*

$$\varphi^{(\nu)} = 0 \quad \textit{auf dem Rande } (C) \textit{ von } (L) \tag{91.9}$$

unterworfen werden; vgl. (47.6p). Dies kommt unmittelbar zum Ausdruck, wenn man die mit (47.2p) äquivalenten Gln. (47.4p) und (47.5p) zum Ausgangspunkt nimmt. Sie lauten in den neuen Variablen

$$(\hat{\varDelta} + \varepsilon^2)\, Y(\varepsilon\,\hat{\mathfrak{r}}) = -\,\varepsilon^2 F(\varepsilon\,\hat{\mathfrak{r}})\,, \tag{91.1b}$$

$$\int_L \varphi(\varepsilon\,\hat{\mathfrak{r}}')\, G(\varepsilon\,|\hat{\mathfrak{r}} - \hat{\mathfrak{r}}'|)\, d\hat{\mathfrak{r}}' = \varepsilon^{-2}\, Y(\varepsilon\,\hat{\mathfrak{r}})\,. \tag{91.1c}$$

Führt man hier die Entwicklung

$$Y(\varepsilon\,\hat{\mathfrak{r}}) = \varepsilon^2 \sum_{\nu=0}^{\infty} \varepsilon^\nu\, Y^{(\nu)}(\hat{\mathfrak{r}}) \tag{91.3a}$$

sowie die einschlägigen Reihen (91.3) und (91.4) ein, so folgt durch Koeffizientenvergleich

$$\left.\begin{aligned} \hat{\varDelta} Y^{(0)}(\hat{\mathfrak{r}}) &= -\,F^{(0)}(\hat{\mathfrak{r}})\,,\\ \hat{\varDelta} Y^{(1)}(\hat{\mathfrak{r}}) &= -\,F^{(1)}(\hat{\mathfrak{r}})\,,\\ &\ldots\ldots\ldots\ldots\\ \hat{\varDelta} Y^{(\nu)}(\hat{\mathfrak{r}}) &= -\,F^{(\nu)}(\hat{\mathfrak{r}}) - Y^{(\nu-2)}(\hat{\mathfrak{r}})\,,\quad \nu \geqq 2 \end{aligned}\right\} \tag{91.5b}$$

und

$$\left.\begin{aligned} \int_L \frac{\varphi^{(\nu)}(\hat{\mathfrak{r}}')}{|\hat{\mathfrak{r}} - \hat{\mathfrak{r}}'|}\, d\hat{\mathfrak{r}} &= 4\pi\, Y^{(\nu)}(\hat{\mathfrak{r}}) - \sum_{\mu=1}^{\nu} \frac{i^\mu}{\mu!} \int_L \varphi^{(\nu-\mu)}(\hat{\mathfrak{r}}')\, |\hat{\mathfrak{r}} - \hat{\mathfrak{r}}'|^{\mu-1}\, d\hat{\mathfrak{r}}'\\ &\equiv y^{(\nu)}(\hat{\mathfrak{r}}) \quad \textit{für } \nu = 0, 1, 2, \ldots \text{ und } \textit{für } \hat{\mathfrak{r}} \textit{ auf } (L)\,. \end{aligned}\right\} \tag{91.5c}$$

oder ausführlich

$$\left.\begin{aligned} &\int_L \frac{\varphi^{(0)}(\hat{\mathfrak{r}}')}{|\hat{\mathfrak{r}} - \hat{\mathfrak{r}}'|}\, d\hat{\mathfrak{r}}' = 4\pi\, Y^{(0)}(\hat{\mathfrak{r}})\,,\\ &\int_L \frac{\varphi^{(1)}(\hat{\mathfrak{r}})}{|\hat{\mathfrak{r}} - \hat{\mathfrak{r}}'|}\, d\hat{\mathfrak{r}}' = 4\pi\, Y^{(1)}(\hat{\mathfrak{r}}) - i \int_L \varphi^{(0)}(\hat{\mathfrak{r}}')\, d\hat{\mathfrak{r}}'\,,\\ &\ldots\ldots\ldots\ldots\ldots\ldots\ldots\ldots\\ &\int_L \frac{\varphi^{(\nu)}(\hat{\mathfrak{r}}')}{|\hat{\mathfrak{r}} - \hat{\mathfrak{r}}'|}\, d\hat{\mathfrak{r}}' = 4\pi\, Y^{(\nu)}(\hat{\mathfrak{r}}) - i \int_L \varphi^{(\nu-1)}(\hat{\mathfrak{r}}')\, d\hat{\mathfrak{r}}'\\ &\qquad + \frac{1}{2} \int_L \varphi^{(\nu-2)}(\hat{\mathfrak{r}}')\, |\hat{\mathfrak{r}} - \hat{\mathfrak{r}}'|\, d\hat{\mathfrak{r}}' + \frac{i}{3!} \int_L \varphi^{(\nu-3)}(\hat{\mathfrak{r}}')\, |\hat{\mathfrak{r}} - \hat{\mathfrak{r}}'|^2\, d\hat{\mathfrak{r}}'\\ &\qquad + \cdots - \frac{i^\nu}{\nu!} \int_L \varphi^{(0)}(\hat{\mathfrak{r}}')\, |\hat{\mathfrak{r}} - \hat{\mathfrak{r}}'|^{\nu-1}\, d\hat{\mathfrak{r}}'\,, \quad \nu \geqq 1\,,\ \hat{\mathfrak{r}} \textit{ aus } (L)\,. \end{aligned}\right\} \tag{91.5'c}$$

Hier sind zuerst die Hilfsgrößen $Y^{(\nu)}$ aus den *Poissonschen Differentialgleichungen* (91.5b) zu berechnen — da Randbedingungen für die $Y^{(\nu)}$ zunächst nicht bekannt sind, kann dies nur bis auf eine willkürliche Lösung der Potentialgleichung $\hat{\varDelta} \cdots = 0$ geschehen — sodann müssen die $\varphi^{(\nu)}$ nacheinander aus den Fredholmschen Integralgleichungen erster Art (91.5′c) bestimmt werden. Die unbestimmt gebliebene Potentialfunktion ist dann nachträglich mit Hilfe der Randbedingung für die $\varphi^{(\nu)}$, Gl. (91.9), zu spezialisieren.

92. Die Rolle der statischen Lösung. In den Gleichungssystemen (91.5′) bzw. (91.5′a) oder (91.5b) und (91.5c) haben wir das gesuchte Rechenschema für die Störungsrechnung vor uns. Beginnend mit $\psi^{(0)}$ bzw. $\varphi^{(0)}$ lassen sich die $\psi^{(\nu)}$ bzw. $\varphi^{(\nu)}$ sukzessiv auseinander berechnen, und zwar dient dazu jedesmal *dieselbe* einfache Integralgleichung (91.5′) bzw. (91.5c) mit dem *statischen* Kern $\frac{1}{|\mathfrak{r}-\mathfrak{r}'|}$. Nur die rechts stehenden Störungsglieder werden mit wachsendem ν komplizierter. Wir haben es also beim „*ungestörten*" Problem mit einer Randwertaufgabe der *Potentialtheorie* zu tun. In der Tat kann die erste Gl. (91.5″) als Integralgleichung für die Bestimmung derjenigen *elektrischen Ladungsdichte* $\psi^{(0)}(\hat{\mathfrak{r}})$ auf der Scheibe (S) gedeutet werden, die zu einem *elektrostatischen Potential* führt, das auf (S) den vorgegebenen Wert $D^{(0)}(\hat{\mathfrak{r}})$ annimmt. Bei den meisten Anwendungen handelt es sich um eine *ebene, einfallende Welle* v_0, dann ist $D^{(0)}$ *konstant* $= 1$, so daß $\psi^{(0)}$ einfach die Ladungsdichte der ideal leitenden Scheibe (S) mit Potential $D^{(0)}$ gegen das Unendliche ist. Entsprechend ist $\varphi^{(0)}$ als *Dipolbelegungsdichte* einer *Doppelschicht* (L) zu interpretieren, die zu einem elektrostatischen Potential führt, dessen Normalgradient auf (L) den vorgegebenen Wert $F^{(0)}(\hat{\mathfrak{r}})$ annimmt [vgl. Gl. (91.5a) für $\nu=0$].

93. Weitere Ausführungen. Das statische Problem soll hier als gelöst vorausgesetzt werden, d.h. die *Eigenfunktionen* $\Phi_\mu(\hat{\mathfrak{r}})$ bzw. $\Psi_\mu(\hat{\mathfrak{r}})$ des *Kerns* $\frac{1}{|\hat{\mathfrak{r}}-\hat{\mathfrak{r}}'|}$ bezüglich des *ebenen Bereichs* (S) *bzw.* (L) als *bekannt* betrachtet werden. Diese sind Lösungen der Fredholmschen Integralgleichung *zweiter Art:*

$$\Phi_\mu(\hat{\mathfrak{r}}) = \lambda_\mu^{(S)} \int\limits_S \frac{\Phi_\mu(\hat{\mathfrak{r}}')}{|\hat{\mathfrak{r}}-\hat{\mathfrak{r}}'|}\, d\hat{\mathfrak{r}}' \tag{93.1}$$

bzw.

$$\Psi_\mu(\hat{\mathfrak{r}}) = \lambda_\mu^{(L)} \int\limits_L \frac{\Psi_\mu(\hat{\mathfrak{r}}')}{|\hat{\mathfrak{r}}-\hat{\mathfrak{r}}'|}\, d\hat{\mathfrak{r}}', \tag{93.1a}$$

so daß sich also der Kern $\frac{1}{|\hat{\mathfrak{r}}-\hat{\mathfrak{r}}'|}$ nach dem Entwicklungssatz in der Gestalt

$$\frac{1}{|\hat{\mathfrak{r}}-\hat{\mathfrak{r}}'|} = \sum_{\mu=0}^{\infty} \frac{\Phi_\mu(\hat{\mathfrak{r}})\,\Phi_\mu(\hat{\mathfrak{r}}')}{\lambda_\mu^{(S)}} \quad \textit{für } \hat{\mathfrak{r}} \textit{ und } \hat{\mathfrak{r}}' \textit{ auf } (S) \tag{93.2}$$

bzw.

$$\frac{1}{|\hat{\mathfrak{r}}-\hat{\mathfrak{r}}'|} = \sum_{\mu=0}^{\infty} \frac{\Psi_\mu(\hat{\mathfrak{r}})\,\Psi_\mu(\hat{\mathfrak{r}}')}{\lambda_\mu^{(L)}} \quad \textit{für } \hat{\mathfrak{r}} \textit{ und } \hat{\mathfrak{r}}' \textit{ auf } (L) \tag{93.2a}$$

darstellen läßt. Die Φ_μ bzw. Ψ_μ sind dabei als *normiert* vorausgesetzt:

$$\int\limits_S \Phi_\nu(\hat{\mathfrak{r}})\,\Phi_\mu(\hat{\mathfrak{r}})\,d\hat{\mathfrak{r}} = \delta_{\nu\mu}, \tag{93.3}$$

$$\int\limits_L \Psi_\nu(\hat{\mathfrak{r}})\,\Psi_\mu(\hat{\mathfrak{r}})\,d\hat{\mathfrak{r}} = \delta_{\nu\mu}. \tag{93.3a}$$

Führen wir nun in unsere Integralgleichungen (91.5′) bzw. (91.5′a) oder (91.5c) die Kerndarstellung (93.2) bzw. (93.2a) sowie die Ansätze

$$\psi^{(\nu)}(\hat{\mathfrak{r}}) = \sum_{\mu=0}^{\infty} a_\mu^{(\nu)}\,\Phi_\mu(\hat{\mathfrak{r}}), \tag{93.4}$$

$$\varphi^{(\nu)}(\hat{\mathfrak{r}}) = \sum_{\mu=0}^{\infty} b_\mu^{(\nu)}\,\Psi_\mu(\hat{\mathfrak{r}}) \tag{93.4a}$$

ein, so ergeben sich infolge der Orthonormalität (93.3) bzw. (93.3a) die Gleichungen

$$\sum_{\mu=0}^{\infty} \frac{a_\mu^{(\nu)}}{\lambda_\mu^{(S)}}\,\Phi_\mu(\hat{\mathfrak{r}}) = f^{(\nu)}(\hat{\mathfrak{r}}) \tag{93.5}$$

bzw.

$$\hat{\Delta}\sum_{\mu=0}^{\infty}\frac{b_\mu^{(\nu)}}{\lambda_\mu^{(L)}}\Psi_\mu(\hat{\mathfrak{r}}) = g^{(\nu)}(\hat{\mathfrak{r}}) \tag{93.5a}$$

oder

$$\sum_{\mu=0}^{\infty}\frac{b_\mu^{(\nu)}}{\lambda_\mu^{(L)}}\Psi_\mu(\hat{\mathfrak{r}}) = y^{(\nu)}(\hat{\mathfrak{r}}). \tag{93.5b}$$

Aus (93.7) erhält man den gesuchten *Entwicklungskoeffizienten* $a_\mu^{(\nu)}$ unmittelbar in *Fourierscher Weise:*

$$a_\mu^{(\nu)} = \lambda_\mu^{(S)}\int_S f^{(\nu)}(\hat{\mathfrak{r}})\,\Phi_\mu(\hat{\mathfrak{r}})\,d\hat{\mathfrak{r}}, \qquad \left.\begin{matrix}\nu\\ \mu\end{matrix}\right\} = 0, 1, 2, \ldots \tag{93.6}$$

Hingegen ist die Berechnung von $b_\mu^{(\nu)}$ aus (93.5a) formal nicht ganz so einfach, macht aber in der Praxis im allgemeinen keine Schwierigkeiten (vgl. Abschn. B I b 2 und c 2).

94. Die Funktion der Kantenbedingung. Bei der Berechnung der $b_\mu^{(\nu)}$ bleibt eine dieser Größen (bei festgehaltenem ν) *unbestimmt* und muß nachträglich aus der Kantenbedingung (91.9) bestimmt werden. Dies folgt aus der Tatsache, daß die Lösungen der Pseudointegralgleichungen (91.5′a) *nicht eindeutig* sind. Es hat vielmehr auch die *homogene* Gleichung [d.h. Gl. (91.5′a) für $g^{(\nu)}=0$] nichttriviale Lösungen, und zwar ist unter diesen Lösungen gerade die „*Ladungsdichte*“ φ_0 einer ideal leitenden Scheibe (L) mit konstantem Potential. In der Tat wird diese Ladungsdichte definiert durch die Integralgleichung $\int_L \frac{\varphi_0(\hat{\mathfrak{r}}')}{|\hat{\mathfrak{r}}-\hat{\mathfrak{r}}'|}\,d\hat{\mathfrak{r}}' = V_0 =$ const; wenden wir nun auf diese Gleichung den Operator $\hat{\Delta}$ an, so entsteht gerade die homogene Gl. (91.5′a)[1]. Die Lösung der inhomogenen Gl. (91.5′a) ist also nur bis auf Lösungen vom Typus der Ladungsdichte φ_0 eindeutig; diese werden aber *gerade durch die Kantenbedingung* (91.9) *ausgeschlossen*. Bekanntlich wird ja die auf einer ideal leitenden Scheibe sitzende Ladungsdichte an den Rändern der Scheibe unendlich groß (wie $\varrho^{-\frac{1}{2}}$, wenn ϱ der Abstand von der Kante ist), während die $\varphi^{(\nu)}$ nach (91.9) *am Rande verschwinden* sollen.

Andererseits folgt aus (93.7b)

$$b_\mu^{(\nu)} = \lambda_\mu^{(L)}\int_L y^{(\nu)}(\hat{\mathfrak{r}})\,\Psi_\mu(\hat{\mathfrak{r}})\,d\hat{\mathfrak{r}}. \tag{94.1}$$

Dabei ist jedoch zu bedenken, daß in den durch (91.5c) definierten $y^{(\nu)}$ die $Y^{(\nu)}$ nur bis auf eine Potentialfunktion ermittelt werden konnten. Diese ist gerade wieder so zu bestimmen, daß Lösungen vom Typus φ_0, die die Kantenbedingung verletzen, ausgeschieden werden.

95. Ergänzungen. Mit Hilfe des durch (93.6) bzw. (94.1) definierten Koeffizientenschemas haben wir im Prinzip eine strenge Lösung unserer Integralgleichungen (91.1) bzw. (91.1a) gewonnen — die Konvergenz des Verfahrens

[1] Die übrigen Lösungen der homogenen Gl. (91.5′a) genügen der Integralgleichung $\int_L \frac{\varphi_0(\hat{\mathfrak{r}}')}{|\hat{\mathfrak{r}}-\hat{\mathfrak{r}}'|}\,d\hat{\mathfrak{r}}' =$ *beliebige Potentialfunktion* $V_0(\hat{\mathfrak{r}})$ d.h. $\hat{\Delta}V_0(\hat{\mathfrak{r}}) = 0$; jedoch ist aus physikalischen Gründen anzunehmen, daß auch diese Lösungen sämtlich die Kantenbedingung (91.9) verletzen.

vorausgesetzt[1] — wenn nur die Eigenfunktionen Φ_μ bzw. Ψ_μ des *statischen* Kerns bekannt sind. Da nun in die in (93.6) bzw. (94.1) auftretenden $f^{(\nu)}$ bzw. $y^{(\nu)}$ gemäß (91.5′) bzw. (91.5c) auch Koeffizienten $a_\mu^{(\varrho)}$ bzw. $b_\mu^{(\varrho)}$ mit $\varrho<\nu$ eingehen, so lassen sich für die $a_\mu^{(\nu)}$ bzw. $b_\mu^{(\nu)}$ *Rekursionsformeln* gewinnen, auf die wir hier jedoch nicht näher eingehen wollen. Als Folge dieser Rekursionsformeln fällt das Schema der $a_\mu^{(\nu)}$ bzw. $b_\mu^{(\nu)}$ im allgemeinen „*dreieckig*" aus, indem die $a_\mu^{(\nu)}$ bzw. $b_\mu^{(\nu)}$ für *$\mu<\nu$ verschwinden*; man vergleiche die Beispiele in Abschn. BIb2 und c2.

Schließlich bemerken wir noch, daß die „*Eigenfunktionen*" Φ_μ bzw. Ψ_μ auch ein geeignetes Orthogonalsystem bilden, um die in Ziff. 63 behandelte Zurückführung des Streu- bzw. Beugungsproblems auf die Auflösung eines (unendlichen) linearen Gleichungssystems durchzuführen. Von unserem jetzigen Standpunkt aus sind dann die a_μ aus Gl. (63.8) gegeben durch $a_\mu=\sum_{\nu=0}^{\infty}\varepsilon^\nu a_\mu^{(\nu)}$. Das in Ziff. 63 dargestellte Verfahren liefert also im Prinzip eine Methode, um die a_μ *direkt* (ohne den Umweg über die Entwicklung nach ε) zu berechnen. Aber abgesehen davon, daß die a_μ aus dem *unendlichen* linearen Gleichungssystem (63.7) zu bestimmen sind (was im allgemeinen sowieso nur näherungsweise geschehen kann) ist in der Praxis die Auswertung der Integrale $C_{\nu\mu}$ in Gl. (63.6) im allgemeinen auch nur als Potenzreihe in ε möglich (vgl. Ziff. 120), so daß auch hier die a_μ in der (nur für kleine ε brauchbaren) Form $\sum_\nu \varepsilon^\nu a_\mu^{(\nu)}$ berechnet werden können.

96. Entwicklung der Fernfeldamplitude nach dem Störungsparameter. Die in den Anwendungen hauptsächlich interessierende Größe ist die Winkelverteilung des Fernfeldes, das wir in der Gestalt schreiben:

Streuung

$$v(\mathfrak{r})\to v_0(\mathfrak{r})+A(\mathfrak{e})\frac{e^{ir}}{r},\quad z\gtrless 0, \tag{96.1}$$

Beugung

$$v(\mathfrak{r})\to\pm B(\mathfrak{e})\frac{e^{ir}}{r}+\begin{Bmatrix}0, & z>0\\ v_0(\mathfrak{r})-v^0(\mathfrak{r}), & z<0\end{Bmatrix} \tag{96.1a}$$

($\mathfrak{e}$ = Einheitsvektor in Richtung des Aufpunktes $\mathfrak{r}=\mathfrak{e}r$).

Die *Fernfeldamplituden* sind dabei durch die Darstellung

$$A(\mathfrak{e})=-\frac{1}{4\pi}\int_S \psi(\hat{\mathfrak{r}})\,e^{-i(\mathfrak{e}\hat{\mathfrak{r}})}\,d\hat{\mathfrak{r}} \tag{96.2}$$

bzw.

$$B(\mathfrak{e})=\frac{i}{2\pi}(\mathfrak{n}\,\mathfrak{e})\int_L \varphi(\hat{\mathfrak{r}})\,e^{-i(\mathfrak{e}\hat{\mathfrak{r}})}\,d\hat{\mathfrak{r}} \tag{96.2a}$$

($\mathfrak{n}$ = Schirmnormale)

zu definieren, die man erhält, wenn man in der Felddarstellung (46.1p) bzw. (47.1p) für die Greensche Funktion $G(\mathfrak{r}-\hat{\mathfrak{r}}')$ ihren asymptotischen Wert $\frac{e^{ir}}{4\pi r}\,e^{-i(\mathfrak{e}\hat{\mathfrak{r}}')}$ einsetzt (für das zweidimensionale Problem vgl. man Ziff. 62). Geht man nun zu den neuen Koordinaten $\hat{\mathfrak{r}}\to\varepsilon\hat{\mathfrak{r}}$ über und trägt die Entwicklung (91.3) sowie

[1] Über die Konvergenz ist nichts bekannt. In den Fällen, in denen ein numerischer Vergleich mit der exakten Lösung möglich ist (z.B. Spalt, Ziff. 124 und Kreisscheibe, Ziff. 128) zeigt sich, daß die Reihenentwicklung nach steigenden Potenzen von ε nur für $\varepsilon\lesssim 1$ brauchbar ist (auch wenn *mehrere* Glieder der Reihe mitgenommen werden). Der Konvergenzradius der Reihenentwicklung dürfte demnach gegebenenfalls die Größenordnung 1 haben. Vgl. dazu W. MAGNUS: N.Y. Univ. Res. Rep. No. EM-80 (1955). — D.S. JONES: Comm. Pure Appl. Math. **9**, 713 (1956).

diejenige für den „*Retardierungsfaktor*“ $e^{-i(\mathfrak{e}\hat{\mathfrak{r}})}$ in (96.2) bzw. (96.2a) ein, so folgt

$$\left.\begin{aligned} &\textit{Streuung}\qquad A(\mathfrak{e}) = \varepsilon\sum_{\nu=0}^{\infty}\varepsilon^{\nu} A^{(\nu)}(\mathfrak{e}),\\ &A^{(\nu)}(\mathfrak{e}) = -\frac{1}{4\pi}\sum_{\mu=0}^{\nu}\frac{(-i)^{\mu}}{\mu!}\int\limits_{S}(\mathfrak{e}\,\hat{\mathfrak{r}})^{\mu}\,\psi^{(\nu-\mu)}(\hat{\mathfrak{r}})\,d\hat{\mathfrak{r}}\end{aligned}\right\}\tag{96.3}$$

bzw.

$$\left.\begin{aligned} &\textit{Beugung}\qquad B(\mathfrak{e}) = (\mathfrak{n}\,\mathfrak{e})\,\varepsilon^{3}\sum_{\nu=0}^{\infty}\varepsilon^{\nu} B^{(\nu)}(\mathfrak{e}),\\ &B^{(\nu)}(\mathfrak{e}) = \frac{i}{2\pi}\sum_{\mu=0}^{\nu}\frac{(-i)^{\mu}}{\mu!}\int\limits_{L}(\mathfrak{e}\,\hat{\mathfrak{r}})^{\mu}\,\varphi^{(\nu-\mu)}(\hat{\mathfrak{r}})\,d\hat{\mathfrak{r}}.\end{aligned}\right\}\tag{96.3a}$$

Die Entwicklungskoeffizienten haben also die Form „*höherer Momente*“ der „*höheren Ladungsverteilungen*“ $\psi^{(\mu)}$ bzw. $\varphi^{(\mu)}$. Es ist bemerkenswert, daß bei der Randbedingung $v=0$ für $\varepsilon \ll 1$ die Streustrahlung einer Scheibe wesentlich intensiver ist als die durch ein Loch von derselben Gestalt hindurchgehende Strahlung (nämlich um den Faktor ε^2; man vgl. die ε-Abhängigkeit der Amplituden A und B). Für die Randbedingung $\frac{\partial v}{\partial z}=0$ ist es nach dem Babinetschen Theorem genau umgekehrt. Die Fernfeldamplitude $A^{(0)}$ ist *richtungsunabhängig*. Für eine *ebene* einfallende Welle ist $4\pi A^{(0)}$ die *statische Kapazität C* der Scheibe (S) (gegen das Unendliche). Dies Ergebnis Rayleighs ergibt sich aus der Bemerkung von Ziff. 92, wonach $\psi^{(0)}$ die Ladungsdichte der Scheibe ist, wenn sie auf das Potential $D^{(0)}=1$ gebracht wird.

f 2) Skalares Problem für Körper endlichen Volumens.

Die im vorangehenden entwickelte Störungsrechnung für ebene Schirme läßt sich ohne weiteres auch auf Körper endlichen Volumens übertragen. Die Verhältnisse liegen hier sogar insofern einfacher, als die Oberfläche (S) nun eine *geschlossene* und — wie wir annehmen wollen — überall *glatte Fläche* ist (so daß die Kantenbedingung wegfällt). Wie wir in Ziff. 76 gesehen haben, können wir in diesem Falle unser Problem jedoch auch mit Hilfe von *Integralgleichungen zweiter Art* behandeln, für die wir die Rayleighsche Störungstheorie nun noch kurz entwickeln wollen. Als „*ungestörtes*“ Problem begegnet uns hier das Dirichletsche *(p-Fall)* bzw. Neumannsche Problem *(s-Fall)* der Potentialtheorie in dem gewohnten Gewand der Integralgleichungen zweiter Art (F. Neumann, Poincaré)[1].

97. Rechenschema. Wir behandeln den p- bzw. s-Fall mit Hilfe eines auf (S) fließenden *magnetischen* Flächenstroms $\widehat{\psi}$ bzw. $\widehat{\varphi}$, der aus der Integralgleichung (80.2p) bzw. (80.2s) (für das Außenraumproblem) zu bestimmen ist. Sie hat in unseren neuen Koordinaten die Form

$$-\frac{1}{2\varepsilon^2}\widehat{\psi}(\varepsilon\,\hat{\mathfrak{r}}) + \oint\limits_{S}\widehat{\psi}(\varepsilon\,\hat{\mathfrak{r}}')\,K_s(\varepsilon\,\hat{\mathfrak{r}},\varepsilon\,\hat{\mathfrak{r}}')\,d\hat{\mathfrak{r}}' = D(\varepsilon\,\hat{\mathfrak{r}})\tag{97.1}$$

bzw.

$$-\frac{1}{2\varepsilon^2}\widehat{\varphi}(\varepsilon\,\hat{\mathfrak{r}}) - \oint\limits_{S}\widehat{\varphi}(\varepsilon\,\hat{\mathfrak{r}}')\,K_s(\varepsilon\,\hat{\mathfrak{r}}',\varepsilon\,\hat{\mathfrak{r}})\,d\hat{\mathfrak{r}}' = F(\varepsilon\,\hat{\mathfrak{r}}).\tag{97.1a}$$

Dabei haben wir davon Gebrauch gemacht, daß die Kerne K_s und K_p nach Gl. (76.8ps) bis auf das Vorzeichen zueinander transponiert sind. Nun folgt

[1] Siehe z. B. Ph. Frank u. R. v. Mises: Die Differential- und Integralgleichungen der Mechanik und Physik, 1. Aufl., Bd. I, S. 489ff. Braunschweig 1925.

nach Gl. (76.7′s) die Darstellung

$$\left.\begin{aligned} K_s(\varepsilon\hat{\mathfrak{r}}, \varepsilon\hat{\mathfrak{r}}') &= \frac{(\mathfrak{n}', \hat{\mathfrak{r}} - \hat{\mathfrak{r}}')}{4\pi\varepsilon^2|\hat{\mathfrak{r}} - \hat{\mathfrak{r}}'|^3}(i\varepsilon|\hat{\mathfrak{r}} - \hat{\mathfrak{r}}'| - 1)\, e^{i\varepsilon|\hat{\mathfrak{r}} - \hat{\mathfrak{r}}'|} \\ &= \frac{(\mathfrak{n}', \hat{\mathfrak{r}} - \hat{\mathfrak{r}}')}{4\pi\varepsilon^2}\left\{\frac{-1}{|\hat{\mathfrak{r}} - \hat{\mathfrak{r}}'|^3} - \frac{\varepsilon^2}{2}\frac{1}{|\hat{\mathfrak{r}} - \hat{\mathfrak{r}}'|} - \frac{i\varepsilon^3}{3} + \cdots \right. \\ &\qquad \left. + (i\varepsilon)^\nu \cdot \frac{\nu - 1}{\nu!}|\hat{\mathfrak{r}} - \hat{\mathfrak{r}}'|^{\nu-3} + \cdots\right\}. \end{aligned}\right\} \tag{97.2}$$

Ferner gilt für die in (97.1), (97.1a) rechterhand eingeführten Abkürzungen

$$D(\varepsilon\hat{\mathfrak{r}}) = \frac{1}{\varepsilon^2}v_0(\varepsilon\hat{\mathfrak{r}}) = \frac{1}{\varepsilon^2}\{D^{(0)}(\hat{\mathfrak{r}}) + \varepsilon D^{(1)}(\hat{\mathfrak{r}}) + \varepsilon^2 D^{(2)}(\hat{\mathfrak{r}}) + \cdots\}, \tag{97.3}$$

$$F(\varepsilon\hat{\mathfrak{r}}) = \frac{1}{\varepsilon^2}\frac{\partial v_0(\varepsilon\hat{\mathfrak{r}})}{\partial(\varepsilon n)} = \frac{1}{\varepsilon^2}\{F^{(0)}(\hat{\mathfrak{r}}) + \varepsilon F^{(1)}(\hat{\mathfrak{r}}) + \varepsilon^2 F^{(2)}(\hat{\mathfrak{r}}) + \cdots\}. \tag{97.3a}$$

Für die Glieder der Entwicklungen

$$\widehat{\psi}(\varepsilon\hat{\mathfrak{r}}) = \widehat{\psi}^{(0)}(\hat{\mathfrak{r}}) + \varepsilon\widehat{\psi}^{(1)}(\hat{\mathfrak{r}}) + \varepsilon^2\widehat{\psi}^{(2)}(\hat{\mathfrak{r}}) + \cdots, \tag{97.4}$$

$$\widehat{\varphi}(\varepsilon\hat{\mathfrak{r}}) = \widehat{\varphi}^{(0)}(\hat{\mathfrak{r}}) + \varepsilon\widehat{\varphi}^{(1)}(\hat{\mathfrak{r}}) + \varepsilon^2\widehat{\varphi}^{(2)}(\hat{\mathfrak{r}}) + \cdots \tag{97.4a}$$

erhalten wir nun folgendes *System von Integralgleichungen*, indem wir diese Entwicklungen in (97.1) bzw. (97.1a) einsetzen und die Koeffizienten gleicher Potenzen von ε auf beiden Seiten der so entstehenden Gleichungen miteinander vergleichen:

$$\left.\begin{aligned} 2\pi\widehat{\psi}^{(\nu)}(\hat{\mathfrak{r}}) + \oint_S \frac{(\mathfrak{n}', \hat{\mathfrak{r}} - \hat{\mathfrak{r}}')}{|\hat{\mathfrak{r}} - \hat{\mathfrak{r}}'|^3}\widehat{\psi}^{(\nu)}(\hat{\mathfrak{r}}')\, d\hat{\mathfrak{r}}' &= -4\pi D^{(\nu)}(\hat{\mathfrak{r}}) \\ + \sum_{\mu=2}^{\nu} i^\mu \frac{\mu - 1}{\mu!} \oint_S \widehat{\psi}^{(\nu-\mu)}(\hat{\mathfrak{r}}')\,(\mathfrak{n}', \hat{\mathfrak{r}} - \hat{\mathfrak{r}}')\,|\hat{\mathfrak{r}} - \hat{\mathfrak{r}}'|^{\mu-3}\, d\hat{\mathfrak{r}}' \\ \equiv f^{(\nu)}(\hat{\mathfrak{r}}), \qquad \nu = 0, 1, 2, \ldots, \end{aligned}\right\} \tag{97.5}$$

bzw.

$$\left.\begin{aligned} 2\pi\widehat{\varphi}^{(\nu)}(\hat{\mathfrak{r}}) + \oint_S \widehat{\varphi}(\hat{\mathfrak{r}}') \frac{(\mathfrak{n}, \hat{\mathfrak{r}} - \hat{\mathfrak{r}}')}{|\hat{\mathfrak{r}} - \hat{\mathfrak{r}}'|^3}\, d\hat{\mathfrak{r}}' &= -4\pi F^{(\nu)}(\hat{\mathfrak{r}}) \\ + \sum_{\mu=2}^{\nu} i^\mu \frac{\mu - 1}{\mu!} \oint_S \widehat{\varphi}^{(\nu-\mu)}(\hat{\mathfrak{r}}')\,(\mathfrak{n}, \hat{\mathfrak{r}} - \hat{\mathfrak{r}}')\,|\hat{\mathfrak{r}} - \hat{\mathfrak{r}}'|^{\mu-3}\, d\hat{\mathfrak{r}}' \\ \equiv g^{(\nu)}(\hat{\mathfrak{r}}), \qquad \nu = 0, 1, 2, \ldots. \end{aligned}\right\} \tag{97.5a}$$

Die $\psi^{(\nu)}$ sind also *sukzessive* mit Hilfe der folgenden Integralgleichungen zweiter Art zu berechnen:

$$\left.\begin{aligned} 2\pi\widehat{\psi}^{(0)}(\hat{\mathfrak{r}}) + \oint_S \widehat{\psi}^{(0)}(\hat{\mathfrak{r}}') \frac{(\mathfrak{n}', \hat{\mathfrak{r}} - \hat{\mathfrak{r}}')}{|\hat{\mathfrak{r}} - \hat{\mathfrak{r}}'|^3}\, d\hat{\mathfrak{r}}' &= -4\pi D^{(0)}(\hat{\mathfrak{r}}), \\ 2\pi\widehat{\psi}^{(1)}(\hat{\mathfrak{r}}) + \oint_S \widehat{\psi}^{(1)}(\hat{\mathfrak{r}}') \frac{(\mathfrak{n}', \hat{\mathfrak{r}} - \hat{\mathfrak{r}}')}{|\hat{\mathfrak{r}} - \hat{\mathfrak{r}}'|^3}\, d\hat{\mathfrak{r}}' &= -4\pi D^{(1)}(\hat{\mathfrak{r}}), \\ \cdots\cdots\cdots\cdots\cdots\cdots\cdots \\ 2\pi\widehat{\psi}^{(\nu)}(\hat{\mathfrak{r}}) + \oint_S \widehat{\psi}^{(\nu)}(\hat{\mathfrak{r}}') \frac{(\mathfrak{n}', \hat{\mathfrak{r}} - \hat{\mathfrak{r}}')}{|\hat{\mathfrak{r}} - \hat{\mathfrak{r}}'|^3}\, d\hat{\mathfrak{r}}' &= -4\pi D^{(\nu)}(\hat{\mathfrak{r}}) \\ - \frac{1}{2}\oint_S \widehat{\psi}^{(\nu-2)}(\hat{\mathfrak{r}}') \frac{(\mathfrak{n}', \hat{\mathfrak{r}} - \hat{\mathfrak{r}}')}{|\hat{\mathfrak{r}} - \hat{\mathfrak{r}}'|}\, d\hat{\mathfrak{r}}' - \frac{i}{3}\oint_S \widehat{\psi}^{(\nu-3)}(\hat{\mathfrak{r}}')\,(\mathfrak{n}', \hat{\mathfrak{r}} - \hat{\mathfrak{r}}')\, d\hat{\mathfrak{r}}' + \cdots \\ + i^\nu \frac{\nu - 1}{\nu!}\oint_S \widehat{\psi}^{(0)}(\hat{\mathfrak{r}}')\,(\mathfrak{n}', \hat{\mathfrak{r}} - \hat{\mathfrak{r}}')\,|\hat{\mathfrak{r}} - \hat{\mathfrak{r}}'|^{\nu-3}\, d\hat{\mathfrak{r}}', \quad \nu \geqq 2. \end{aligned}\right\} \tag{97.5'}$$

Das entsprechende Gleichungssystem für die $\varphi^{(\nu)}$ erhält man aus (97.5′) indem man $\mathfrak{n}'$ durch $\mathfrak{n}$ und $D^{(\nu)}$ durch $F^{(\nu)}$ ersetzt.

98. Zusammenhang mit der Potentialtheorie. Die hier für $\widehat{\psi}^{(0)}$ bzw. $\widehat{\varphi}^{(0)}$ sich ergebende Integralgleichung tritt in der *Potentialtheorie* bei der Lösung des *äußeren Dirichletschen* bzw. *Neumannschen Problems* auf (erste bzw. zweite Randwertaufgabe der Potentialtheorie)[1]. $\widehat{\psi}^{(0)}$ bedeutet dort die Dichte derjenigen *Doppelbelegung* der Fläche (S), die im Außenraum zu dem Potential

$$-\frac{1}{4\pi}\oint \widehat{\psi}^{(0)}(\hat{\mathfrak{r}}')\,\frac{\partial}{\partial n'}\,\frac{1}{|\hat{\mathfrak{r}}-\hat{\mathfrak{r}}'|}\,d\hat{\mathfrak{r}}'$$

führt, das auf (S) den vorgegebenen Wert $-D^{(0)}(\hat{\mathfrak{r}})$ annimmt. Die höheren Näherungen $\widehat{\psi}^{(\nu)}$ lassen sich als Dichten von Doppelbelegungen deuten, die zu Potentialen führen, die auf (S) die (komplexen) Werte $f^{(\nu)}(\hat{\mathfrak{r}})$ annehmen. Andererseits ist $\widehat{\varphi}^{(0)}$ diejenige Dichte einer *Einfachbelegung* der Fläche (S), deren Potential

$$\frac{1}{4\pi}\oint \widehat{\varphi}^{(0)}(\hat{\mathfrak{r}}')\,\frac{d\hat{\mathfrak{r}}'}{|\hat{\mathfrak{r}}-\hat{\mathfrak{r}}'|}$$

im Außenraum auf (S) den vorgegebenen Normalgradienten $-F^{(0)}(\hat{\mathfrak{r}})$ annimmt.

Für die beiden von uns gewonnenen Integralgleichungen (95.5) und (95.5a) für die $\widehat{\psi}^{(\nu)}$ bzw. $\widehat{\varphi}^{(\nu)}$ gelten nun die aus der Potentialtheorie bekannten Sätze:

a) Die *homogene Gleichung* (97.5) *hat* eine Eigenlösung $\Big(\frac{1}{2\pi}$ ist also ein Eigenwert des Kerns $\frac{(\mathfrak{n}',\,\hat{\mathfrak{r}}-\hat{\mathfrak{r}}')}{|\hat{\mathfrak{r}}-\hat{\mathfrak{r}}'|^3}\Big)$. Das Produkt dieses Kerns mit dem Flächenelement $d\hat{\mathfrak{r}}'$ hat nämlich nach Ziff. 9 die Bedeutung des *räumlichen Winkels* $d\omega$, unter dem $d\hat{\mathfrak{r}}'$ (mit der Normalen $\mathfrak{n}'$) von dem Flächenpunkt $\hat{\mathfrak{r}}$ aus erscheint

$$\frac{(\mathfrak{n}',\,\hat{\mathfrak{r}}-\hat{\mathfrak{r}}')}{|\hat{\mathfrak{r}}'-\hat{\mathfrak{r}}|^3}\,d\hat{\mathfrak{r}}' = d\,\omega\,(\hat{\mathfrak{r}},\hat{\mathfrak{r}}')\,.$$

Daher ist $\widehat{\psi}^{(\nu)}=\text{const}$ eine (und wie sich zeigen läßt die einzige) Lösung der homogenen Gleichung (97.5). Die *inhomogene* Integralgleichung (97.5) hat somit nur bedingungsweise (vieldeutige) Lösungen.

b) Die *homogene Gleichung* (97.5a) hat *keine* nichttriviale Lösung; die *inhomogene* Integralgleichung (97.5a) hat daher stets eine eindeutige Lösung.

Das Neumannsche Problem ist also stets eindeutig lösbar; allein dies gilt im wesentlichen auch für das Dirichletsche Problem (trotz Satz a), worauf wir hier jedoch nicht näher eingehen können[2].

Die an die Rayleighsche Näherung anschließende Störungsrechnung läßt sich nach einem, dem oben dargestellten ganz analogen Verfahren auch auf vektorielle elektromagnetische Probleme übertragen[3]. Wir werden darauf bei der Behandlung der Streuung elektromagnetischer Wellen an der Kreisscheibe zurückkommen (Ziff. 132).

g) Streu- und Transmissionsfaktor.

99. Definitionen. Bei der Durchführung des Eindeutigkeitsbeweises in Ziff. 20 wurden die energetischen Verhältnisse bei Ausstrahlungsproblemen betrachtet. — Im Gegensatz zur Gesamtenergie statischer Felder ist die gesamte Feldenergie bei Ausstrahlungsproblemen notwendig unendlich (wegen des im Zeitmittel konstanten Energieflusses der monochromatischen Strahlungsquellen). Beim *statio-*

[1] Frank-Mises: l. c. S. 493.

[2] Frank-Mises: l. c. S. 497ff. — Die dabei zu verwendende Methode ist derjenigen von Ziff. 81 analog, für die sie als Vorbild gedient hat.

[3] H. A. Bethe: Phys. Rev. **66**, 163 (1944). — E. T. Copson: Proc. Roy. Soc. Lond. **186**, 100 (1946); **202**, 277 (1950). — C. J. Bouwkamp: Philips Res. Rep. **5**, 401 (1950). — N.Y. Univ. Res. Rep. EM-50 (1953). — A. F. Stevenson: J. Appl. Phys. **24**, 1134 (1953).

nären Problem richtet sich das praktische und theoretische Interesse auf den zeitlichen Mittelwert des von dem beugenden Objekt *gestreuten integralen Energiestromes*; sein Verhältnis zur Energiestrom*dichte* der *einfallenden* Welle wird als „*Streuquerschnitt*" Q des Objektes bezeichnet. Diese Definition haben wir den Verhältnissen beim *Streuproblem* angepaßt (ganz im endlichen gelegenes Objekt, vgl. Ziff. 20 und 26). Beim *Beugungsfall* (ganz im endlichen gelegene Öffnung, vgl. wie oben) hingegen ist die entsprechende Größe der sog. „*Durchlaßquerschnitt*" T, das ist der gesamte im Zeitmittel durch die *Öffnung hindurchgehende Energiestrom* im Verhältnis zur Energiestrom*dichte* der einfallenden Welle. In den Anwendungen handelt es sich meistens um die Streuung bzw. Beugung von *ebenen* Wellen; ist nun S' bzw.

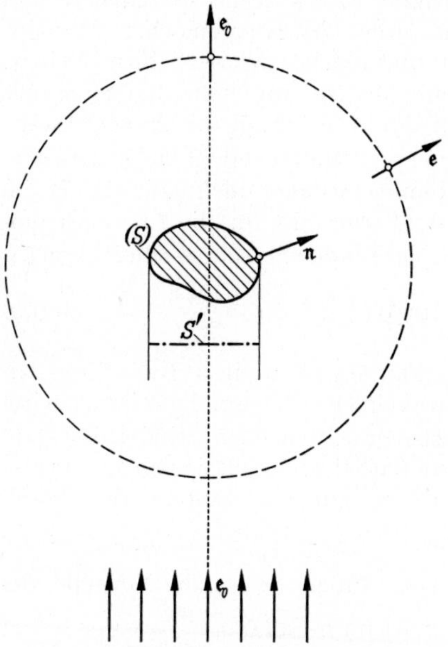

Fig. 50. Zur Definition des Streuquerschnitts und Streukoeffizienten.

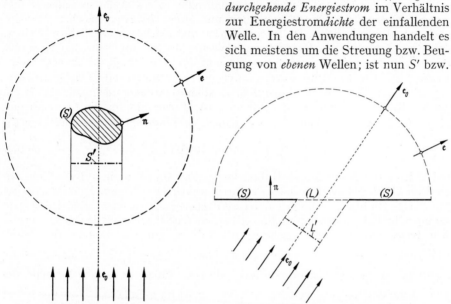

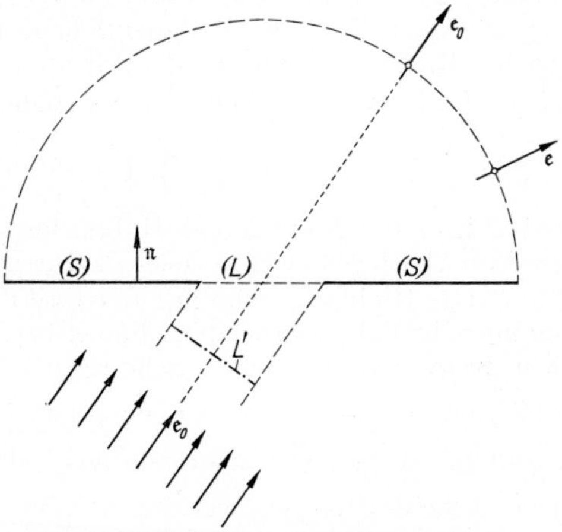

Fig. 51. Zur Definition des Durchlaßquerschnitts und Transmissionskoeffizienten.

L' der *geometrische* Querschnitt, den der streuende Körper (S) bzw. die beugende Öffnung (L) der aus gegebener Richtung einfallenden ebenen Welle darbietet (Projektion, s. Fig. 50 und 51), so bezeichnet man $\sigma = Q/S'$ bzw. $\tau = T/L'$ als „*Streu-*" bzw. „*Transmissionskoeffizient*". Er ist also gegeben durch den tatsächlich im Zeitmittel gestreuten bzw. durchtretenden gesamten Energiestrom im Verhältnis zu demjenigen Energiestrom, der nach der *geometrischen Optik* auf Körper bzw. Öffnung auftrifft.

In die obigen Definitionen gehen sinngemäß nur die *Streu-* bzw. *Beugungswelle* ein; der integrale Energiestrom, den das *Gesamtwellenfeld* liefert, ist aus Gründen der Energieerhaltung einzig von der vorgegebenen Ergiebigkeit der *vorgegebenen* Strahlungsquelle abhängig (für eine *ebene* einfallende Welle verschwindet er). Hingegen sind Streu- bzw. Durchlaßquerschnitt für die jeweilige Beugungsanordnung charakteristische Größen, die auch der Messung leicht zugänglich sind. Der Streu- bzw. Transmissionskoeffizient besitzt ähnliche Minimaleigenschaften wie die elektrische (bzw. magnetische) Gesamtenergie bei statischen Problemen (s. Abschn. IIIh).

g 1) Das skalare Problem.

100. Im Streufall gilt sowohl für unendlich dünne berandete (ebene oder gekrümmte) Schirme als auch für Körper endlichen Volumens die Felddarstellung

$$v(\mathfrak{r}) = e^{i(\mathfrak{e}_0\mathfrak{r})} + v_S(\mathfrak{r}), \qquad (100.1)$$

wobei im p-Fall $[v=0$ auf $(S)]$:

$$v_S(\mathfrak{r}) = -\oint_S \psi(\hat{\mathfrak{r}}')\, G(\mathfrak{r}-\hat{\mathfrak{r}}')\, d\hat{\mathfrak{r}}', \qquad (100.1'p)$$

im s-Fall $[\partial v/\partial n = 0$ auf $(S)]$:

$$v_S(\mathfrak{r}) = \oint_S \varphi(\hat{\mathfrak{r}}')\, \frac{\partial}{\partial n'} G(\mathfrak{r}-\hat{\mathfrak{r}}')\, d\hat{\mathfrak{r}}'; \qquad (100.1's)$$

vgl. (46.1 p), (76.1 p) bzw. (50.1 s), (76.1 s). Hier haben wir die einfallende Welle v_0 zu einer in der Richtung $\mathfrak{e}_0\,(\mathfrak{e}_0^2=1)$ einfallenden *ebenen* Welle spezialisiert und für die *Streuwelle* v_S ihre Darstellung mit Hilfe des Huygensschen Prinzips noch einmal angeschrieben. Die Integration hat über den berandeten Schirm (S) bzw. die Oberfläche (S) des Körpers zu erfolgen. Der gesamte von der *Streuwelle* hervorgerufene *mittlere Energiestrom* ist nun durch den Fluß des *Poyntingschen Vektors* $\overline{\mathfrak{S}}_S$, Gl. (16.5) mit $v=v_S$, durch eine (S) umhüllende Fläche gegeben. Auf die Gestalt und Lage dieser Fläche kommt es dabei nicht an, da $\overline{\mathfrak{S}}_S$ im ganzen Raume außerhalb (S) quellenfrei ist. Ferner gilt für die Energiestromdichte der einfallenden Welle $|\overline{\mathfrak{S}}_0| = \frac{1}{2}$, daher folgt für den Streuquerschnitt von (S)

$$Q = \frac{1}{|\overline{\mathfrak{S}}_0|} \oint (\mathfrak{e}\,\overline{\mathfrak{S}}_S)\, d\sigma = \operatorname{Im} \oint v_S^* \frac{\partial v_S}{\partial n}\, d\sigma, \qquad (100.2)$$

dabei ist $\mathfrak{e}$ die Normale der Hüllfläche (s. Fig. 50). Für diese betrachten wir zwei verschiedene Lagen, in denen die Integration in (100.2) besonders einfach wird.

a) Die Hüllfläche falle mit der Oberfläche des streuenden Hindernisses zusammen; im Falle des unendlich dünnen berandeten Schirmes soll sie sich diesem also von *beiden* Seiten dicht anschmiegen. Auf (S) gilt nun zufolge der *Randbedingung* $v_S = -v_0 = -e^{i(\mathfrak{e}_0\hat{\mathfrak{r}})}$ im p-Fall bzw. $\frac{\partial v_S}{\partial n} = -\frac{\partial v_0}{\partial n} = -i(\mathfrak{n}\,\mathfrak{e}_0)\, e^{i(\mathfrak{e}_0\hat{\mathfrak{r}})}$ im s-Fall ($\mathfrak{n}$ ist die Schirmnormale bzw. die ins Äußere weisende Normale der Oberfläche des Körpers, vgl. Fig. 50). Ferner ist im p-Fall $\psi = \left(\frac{\partial v_S}{\partial n}\right)_+ - \left(\frac{\partial v_S}{\partial n}\right)_-$ der Sprung von $\frac{\partial v_S}{\partial n}$ zu beiden Seiten des berandeten Schirmes (vgl. Ziff. 46) und $\psi = \left(\frac{\partial v_S}{\partial n}\right)_+ + \frac{\partial v_0}{\partial n}$ für die Oberfläche eines Körpers endlichen Volumens (vgl. Ziff. 76). Hingegen ist im *s-Fall* $\varphi = (v_S)_+ - (v_S)_-$ der Sprung des Wertes von v_S zu beiden Seiten des Schirmes (vgl. Ziff. 50) und $\varphi = (v_S)_+ + v_0$ für die Oberfläche eines Körpers, vgl. Ziff. 76. Damit folgt jetzt aus (100.2)

$$Q_p = -\operatorname{Im} \oint_S \mathrm{e}^{-i(\mathfrak{e}_0\hat{\mathfrak{r}})}\, \psi(\hat{\mathfrak{r}})\, d\hat{\mathfrak{r}} \qquad (p\text{-Fall}) \qquad (100.3\,p)$$

bzw.

$$Q_s = -\operatorname{Re} \oint_S (\mathfrak{e}\,\mathfrak{n})\, \mathrm{e}^{-i(\mathfrak{e}_0\hat{\mathfrak{r}})}\, \varphi(\hat{\mathfrak{r}})\, d\hat{\mathfrak{r}} \qquad (s\text{-Fall}), \qquad (100.3\,s)$$

hier ist (S) der Schirm bzw. die Oberfläche des Körpers. Dabei haben wir berücksichtigt, daß für Körper endlichen Volumens der zunächst auftretende Term $\operatorname{Im} \oint v_0^* \frac{\partial v_0}{\partial n}\, d\sigma$ verschwindet, da $\overline{\mathfrak{S}}_0 = \frac{1}{2} \operatorname{Im}\,(v_0 \operatorname{grad} v_0^*)$ quellenfrei ist (bis auf die vorgegebene Punktsingularität, die hier im Unendlichen liegt).

b) Die Hüllfläche sei eine Kugel mit nach unendlich strebendem Radius. Nun können wir in (100.2) für v_S die *asymptotischen* Ausdrücke einsetzen, die sich aus (100.1′p) bzw. (100.1′s) in der Gestalt

$$v_S(\mathfrak{r}) \to -\frac{1}{4\pi} \frac{\mathrm{e}^{ir}}{r} \oint_S \psi(\hat{\mathfrak{r}}')\, \mathrm{e}^{-i(\mathfrak{e}\hat{\mathfrak{r}}')}\, d\hat{\mathfrak{r}}', \qquad r\to\infty \qquad (100.4\,p)$$

bzw.

$$v_S(\mathfrak{r}) \to -\frac{i}{4\pi}\frac{e^{ir}}{r}\oint_S (\mathfrak{n}'\,\mathfrak{e})\,\varphi(\hat{\mathfrak{r}}')\,e^{-i(\mathfrak{e}\hat{\mathfrak{r}}')}\,d\hat{\mathfrak{r}}', \qquad r\to\infty \tag{100.4s}$$

ergeben. Hier haben wir von den asymptotisch gültigen Werten

$$\left.\begin{aligned} &|\mathfrak{r}-\hat{\mathfrak{r}}'| \to r - (\mathfrak{e}\,\hat{\mathfrak{r}}'),\\ &G(\mathfrak{r}-\hat{\mathfrak{r}}') \to \frac{1}{4\pi}\frac{e^{ir}}{r}\,e^{-i(\mathfrak{e}\hat{\mathfrak{r}}')},\\ &\frac{\partial}{\partial n'}G(\mathfrak{r}-\hat{\mathfrak{r}}') \to -\frac{i}{4\pi}\frac{e^{ir}}{r}\,(\mathfrak{n}'\,\mathfrak{e})\,e^{-i(\mathfrak{e}\hat{\mathfrak{r}}')} \end{aligned}\right\} \qquad r\to\infty \tag{100.5}$$

Gebrauch gemacht ($\mathfrak{e}$ ist der Einheitsvektor in der Richtung von $\mathfrak{r}=\mathfrak{e}r$). Wir bringen nun (100.4) noch ausdrücklich in die Gestalt einer auslaufenden Kugelwelle, deren Amplitude $A(\mathfrak{e})$ nun aber winkelabhängig ist (Fraunhofersches Fernfeld):

$$v_S(\mathfrak{r}) \to A(\mathfrak{e})\,\frac{e^{ir}}{r}, \qquad r\to\infty, \tag{100.6}$$

wobei

$$A_p(\mathfrak{e}) = -\frac{1}{4\pi}\oint_S \psi(\hat{\mathfrak{r}}')\,e^{-i(\mathfrak{e}\hat{\mathfrak{r}}')}\,d\hat{\mathfrak{r}}' \tag{100.7p}$$

bzw.

$$A_s(\mathfrak{e}) = -\frac{i}{4\pi}\oint_S (\mathfrak{n}'\,\mathfrak{e})\,\varphi(\hat{\mathfrak{r}}')\,e^{-i(\mathfrak{e}\hat{\mathfrak{r}}')}\,d\hat{\mathfrak{r}}'. \tag{100.7s}$$

Trägt man nun (100.6) in (100.2) ein, so ergibt sich zunächst, vgl. (19.1)[1]:

$$Q = \oint A(\mathfrak{e})\,A^*(\mathfrak{e})\,d\omega, \tag{100.8p s}$$

wobei $d\omega$ das *Flächenelement der Einheitskugel* bedeutet und über alle Richtungen $\mathfrak{e}$ zu integrieren ist.

Bemerkenswerterweise läßt sich nun die in (100.8) vorgesehene Integration ganz allgemein umgehen. Vergleichen wir nämlich (100.3 *p*, *s*) mit (100.7*p*, *s*), so läßt sich Q ersichtlich auch in die Form setzen:

$$Q = 4\pi\,\mathrm{Im}\,A(\mathfrak{e}_0). \tag{100.8'ps}$$

Anstatt also zur Bestimmung des Streuquerschnitts Q das Absolutquadrat der Fernfeldamplitude $A(\mathfrak{e})$ über alle Richtungen zu integrieren, *erhält man Q auch als das 4π-fache des Imaginärteils derjenigen Fernfeldamplitude, die hinter dem Streuer in Richtung der einfallenden Welle beobachtet wird* (vgl. Fig. 50). Dieser Zusammenhang, der auch für die experimentelle Bestimmung von Q von Bedeutung ist, wurde erstmals von LEVINE und SCHWINGER gefunden[2] und wird meist als „*optisches Theorem*" bezeichnet. Man kann sich das Zustandekommen dieses zunächst verblüffenden Satzes durch folgende Überlegung verständlich machen: Der *gesamte* durch die unendlich ferne Feldbegrenzung tretende (zeitlich gemittelte) Energiefluß muß durch die vorgegebene Feldquelle (Feldsingularität) gedeckt werden (für eine einfallende ebene Welle verschwindet er also, da sie im Endlichen

[1] Überall, wo Q ohne den Index *p* bzw. *s* auftritt, gelten die Formeln sowohl im *p*- wie im *s*-Fall, entsprechendes gilt für A und später für T.

[2] H. LEVINE u. J. SCHWINGER: Phys. Rev. **74**, 958 (1948). — J. E. STORER u. J. SEVICK: J. Appl. Phys. **25**, 369 (1954). Vgl. auch E. FEENBERG: Phys. Rev. **40**, 40 (1932); M. LAX: Phys. Rev. **78**, 306 (1950), wo ein entsprechendes Theorem für den wellenmechanischen Wirkungsquerschnitt aufgestellt wird.

keine Quelle besitzt):

$$\oint (\mathfrak{e}\,\overline{\mathfrak{S}})\,d\sigma = \oint (\mathfrak{e}\,\overline{\mathfrak{S}}_0)\,d\sigma = 0. \tag{100.9a}$$

Schreibt man nun $\overline{\mathfrak{S}}$ in der Gestalt

$$\overline{\mathfrak{S}} = \overline{\mathfrak{S}}_0 + \overline{\mathfrak{S}}_{0S} + \overline{\mathfrak{S}}_S, \tag{100.9b}$$

so folgt aus (100.9a), daß das *Wechselwirkungsglied* $\oint (\mathfrak{e}\,\mathfrak{S}_{0S})\,d\sigma$ dem *Streuglied* $\oint (\mathfrak{e}\,\mathfrak{S}_S)\,d\sigma$ *entgegengesetzt gleich* sein muß, d.h. [vgl. (16.5) und (100.2)]:

$$\mathrm{Im}\oint\left(v_0^*\frac{\partial v_S}{\partial n} + v_S^*\frac{\partial v_0}{\partial n}\right)d\sigma = -\,\mathrm{Im}\oint v_S^*\frac{\partial v_S}{\partial n}\,d\sigma = -\,Q. \tag{100.9c}$$

Setzen wir nun links $v_0 = \mathrm{e}^{i(\mathfrak{e}_0\mathfrak{r})}$ und für v_S den asymptotischen Ausdruck (100.6) ein, während wir für Q (100.8′ps) eintragen, so folgt mit $d\sigma = r^2\,d\omega$

$$\lim_{r\to\infty}\mathrm{Re}\oint \mathrm{e}^{i[1-(\mathfrak{e}_0\mathfrak{e})]r}\,[(\mathfrak{e}_0\,\mathfrak{e})+1]\,r\,A(\mathfrak{e})\,d\omega = -\,4\pi\,\mathrm{Im}\,A(\mathfrak{e}_0). \tag{100.9d}$$

Man kann dies auch direkt bestätigen, indem man auf das Integral links das *Prinzip der stationären Phase* anwendet, das für $r\to\infty$ den exakten Wert liefert. Das Ergebnis, daß sich die Beiträge der einzelnen Richtungen im Wechselwirkungsglied *gegen*seitig *weginterferieren* — bis auf die Richtung der *einfallenden* Welle — besagt: einfallende und gestreute Wellen interferieren im Unendlichen nicht miteinander, außer in der Einfallsrichtung.

101. Für ebene Schirme kann man an Stelle von (100.7p, s) auch schreiben

$$A_p(\mathfrak{e}) = -\frac{1}{4\pi}\,\overline{\psi}(\mathfrak{e}) \tag{101.1p}$$

bzw.

$$A_s(\mathfrak{e}) = -\frac{i}{4\pi}\,(\mathfrak{n}\,\mathfrak{e})\,\overline{\varphi}(\mathfrak{e}), \tag{101.1s}$$

wobei

$$\left.\begin{aligned}\overline{\psi}(\mathfrak{e}) &= \int_S \psi(\hat{\mathfrak{r}})\,\mathrm{e}^{-i(\mathfrak{e}\hat{\mathfrak{r}})}\,d\hat{\mathfrak{r}},\\ \overline{\varphi}(\mathfrak{e}) &= \int_S \varphi(\hat{\mathfrak{r}})\,\mathrm{e}^{-i(\mathfrak{e}\hat{\mathfrak{r}})}\,d\hat{\mathfrak{r}}\end{aligned}\right\} \tag{101.2}$$

die *Fourier-Transformierte* des Flächenstroms $\psi(\hat{\mathfrak{r}})$ bzw. $\varphi(\hat{\mathfrak{r}})$ auf dem Schirm bedeutet; vgl. (60.4p, 5p). Der Streuquerschnitt läßt sich mit Hilfe dieser Größen bei Beachtung von (100.8′ps) in der Gestalt schreiben

$$Q_p = -\,\mathrm{Im}\,\overline{\psi}(\mathfrak{e}_0) \tag{101.3p}$$

bzw.

$$Q_s = -\,(\mathfrak{n}\,\mathfrak{e}_0)\,\mathrm{Re}\,\overline{\varphi}(\mathfrak{e}_0). \tag{101.3s}$$

Ist das Problem zudem noch *zweidimensional* ($\partial/\partial y = 0$; ebene Schirme mit Rändern parallel zur y-Achse), so tritt an die Stelle von (100.3p, s)

$$Q_p = -\,\mathrm{Im}\int_S \psi(x)\,\mathrm{e}^{-ix\sin\vartheta_0}\,dx \tag{101.4p}$$

bzw.

$$Q_s = -\,\cos\vartheta_0\,\mathrm{Re}\int_S \varphi(x)\,\mathrm{e}^{-ix\sin\vartheta_0}\,dx, \tag{101.4s}$$

ϑ_0 ist der gegen die z-Achse (Schirmnormale) gemessene *Einfallswinkel*. Andererseits gilt jetzt für das Fernfeld

$$v_S(\mathfrak{r}) \to A(\vartheta)\,\frac{\mathrm{e}^{ir}}{\sqrt{r}}, \qquad r\to\infty \tag{101.5}$$

mit

$$A_p(\vartheta) = \frac{-i}{2\sqrt{2\pi i}} \int_S \psi(x)\, e^{-ix\sin\vartheta}\, dx = \frac{-i}{2\sqrt{2\pi i}}\, \overline{\psi}(\sin\vartheta) \qquad (101.6p)$$

bzw.

$$A_s(\vartheta) = \frac{\cos\vartheta}{2\sqrt{2\pi i}} \int_S \varphi(x)\, e^{-ix\sin\vartheta}\, dx = \frac{\cos\vartheta}{2\sqrt{2\pi i}}\, \overline{\varphi}(\sin\vartheta); \qquad (101.6s)$$

vgl. (62.3*p*) und (62.7*p*). Damit folgt aus (101.4*p*, *s*) und (101.6*p*, *s*)

$$Q = \int_0^{2\pi} A(\vartheta)\, A^*(\vartheta)\, d\vartheta = -2\sqrt{2\pi}\, \mathrm{Re}\left\{e^{\frac{i\pi}{4}} A(\vartheta_0)\right\} \qquad (101.7)$$

oder

$$Q_p = -\,\mathrm{Im}\, \overline{\psi}(\sin\vartheta_0) \qquad (101.8p)$$

bzw.

$$Q_s = -\,\cos\vartheta_0\, \mathrm{Re}\, \overline{\varphi}(\sin\vartheta_0)\,. \qquad (101.8s)$$

102. Beim Beugungsfall können wir bei der Berechnung des Durchlaßquerschnitts T vom Babinetschen Theorem Gebrauch machen (Ziff. 27). Nach diesem liefert die Lösung des *Streuproblems* für den *ebenen Schirm* (S) im p- bzw. s-Fall zugleich die Lösung des *Beugungsproblems* für die *Öffnung* (L) von derselben Gestalt wie (S) in einem ebenen unendlich ausgedehnten Schirm im s- bzw. p-Fall. Der durch das Loch (L) im Zeitmittel hindurchgehende Energiestrom ist demnach die Hälfte des von dem Schirm $(S) = (L)$ (in beide Halbräume) gestreuten gesamten Energiestromes (die Streuwelle v_S ist ja bezüglich der Schirmebene symmetrisch bzw. antisymmetrisch) unter Vertauschung von p- und s-Fall. Es gilt also für *komplementäre* Probleme

$$2\, T_{p,s} = Q_{s,p} \qquad (102.1)$$

dabei ist T mit Hilfe der Beugungswelle v_B, vgl. Ziff. 27, zu berechnen:

$$T = \frac{1}{|\mathfrak{S}_0|} \int (\mathfrak{e}\, \overline{\mathfrak{S}}_B)\, d\sigma = \mathrm{Im} \int v_B^*\, \frac{\partial v_B}{\partial n}\, d\sigma. \qquad (102.2)$$

Hier hat die Integration entweder über die *Öffnung* (L) oder über die *Halbkugel* (mit nach Unendlich strebendem Radius) in dem der Strahlungsquelle abgewandten Halbraum zu erfolgen (s. Fig. 51). Wir erhalten so die Darstellung, vgl. (100.3*p*, *s*)

$$T_p = -\,(\mathfrak{n}\,\mathfrak{e}_0)\, \mathrm{Re} \int_L \varphi(\hat{\mathfrak{r}})\, e^{-i(\mathfrak{e}_0 \hat{\mathfrak{r}})}\, d\hat{\mathfrak{r}} = -\,(\mathfrak{n}\,\mathfrak{e}_0)\, \mathrm{Re}\, \overline{\varphi}(\mathfrak{e}_0) \qquad (102.3p)$$

bzw.

$$T_s = -\,\mathrm{Im} \int_L \psi(\hat{\mathfrak{r}})\, e^{-i(\mathfrak{e}_0 \hat{\mathfrak{r}})}\, d\hat{\mathfrak{r}} = -\,\mathrm{Im}\, \overline{\psi}(\mathfrak{e}_0)\,. \qquad (102.3s)$$

Hier ist φ das Feld v in der Öffnung (L) bzw. $\psi = \partial v/\partial z$ in (L) (vgl. Ziff. 47 und 50). Diese Größen sind gerade *halb* so groß, wie die entsprechenden „*Flächenströme*", die auf dem komplementären Schirm fließen. Schreibt man das Beugungsfeld *asymptotisch* in der Form

$$v_B(\mathfrak{r}) \to B(\mathfrak{e})\, \frac{e^{ir}}{r}; \qquad z > 0,\ r \to \infty, \qquad (102.4)$$

so gilt auch

$$T = \oint_L B(\mathfrak{e})\, B^*(\mathfrak{e})\, d\omega = 2\pi\, \mathrm{Im}\, B(\mathfrak{e}_0)\,, \qquad (102.5)$$

wobei die Integration über die *halbe* Einheitskugel zu erfolgen hat.

Die entsprechenden Formeln im zweidimensionalen Fall sind

$$T_p = -\cos\vartheta_0 \,\mathrm{Re} \int_L \varphi(x)\, e^{-ix\sin\vartheta_0}\, dx = -\cos\vartheta_0 \,\mathrm{Re}\,\overline{\varphi}\,(\sin\vartheta_0) \tag{102.6p}$$

bzw.

$$T_s = -\,\mathrm{Im} \int_L \psi(x)\, e^{-ix\sin\vartheta_0}\, dx = -\,\mathrm{Im}\,\overline{\psi}\,(\sin\vartheta_0) \tag{102.6s}$$

und

$$v_B(\mathfrak{r}) \to B(\vartheta)\,\frac{e^{ir}}{\sqrt{r}}; \qquad z > 0, \qquad r \to \infty \tag{102.7}$$

$$T = \int_{-\frac{\pi}{2}}^{\frac{\pi}{2}} B(\vartheta)\, B^*(\vartheta)\, d\vartheta = -\sqrt{2\pi}\,\mathrm{Re}\left\{e^{\frac{i\pi}{4}}\, B(\vartheta_0)\right\}. \tag{102.8}$$

ϑ ist der gegen die Schirmnormale gemessene *Beugungswinkel*, ϑ_0 der ebenso gemessene *Einfallswinkel* der ebenen Welle $v_0 = \exp(x\sin\vartheta_0 + z\cos\vartheta_0)$.

g 2) Vektorielles Problem.

Auf dieses läßt sich alles Vorhergehende sinngemäß übertragen. Die Formeln werden sogar formal einfacher, da die Unterscheidung zwischen p- und s-Fall fortfällt und die elektromagnetische Bedeutung der auftretenden Größen sofort in die Augen springt.

103. Streuung. Im *Streufall* ist der *Streuquerschnitt* durch [vgl. (16.3), $\mathfrak{e}$ ist die Normale der Hüllfläche]

$$Q = \frac{1}{|\overline{\mathfrak{S}}_0|} \oint (\mathfrak{e}\,\overline{\mathfrak{S}}_S)\, d\sigma = \mathrm{Re} \oint ([\mathfrak{E}_S\, \mathfrak{H}_S^*]\, \mathfrak{e})\, d\sigma \tag{103.1}$$

gegeben. Dabei soll vorausgesetzt werden, daß eine in Richtung $\mathfrak{n}_0$ *linear polarisierte* ebene Welle der Ausbreitungsrichtung $\mathfrak{e}_0$ mit der Darstellung $\mathfrak{E}_0 = \mathfrak{n}_0\, e^{i(\mathfrak{e}_0 \mathfrak{r})}$, $\mathfrak{H}_0 = [\mathfrak{e}_0\, \mathfrak{n}_0]\, e^{i(\mathfrak{e}_0 \mathfrak{r})}$ auf einen berandeten Schirm (S) bzw. einen Körper endlichen Volumens mit der Oberfläche (S) auffällt. Die Felddarstellung ist dann durch

$$\left.\begin{aligned} \mathfrak{E}(\mathfrak{r}) &= \mathfrak{n}_0\, e^{i(\mathfrak{e}_0 \mathfrak{r})} + \mathfrak{E}_S(\mathfrak{r}) \\ \mathfrak{H}(\mathfrak{r}) &= [\mathfrak{e}_0\, \mathfrak{n}_0]\, e^{i(\mathfrak{e}_0 \mathfrak{r})} + \mathfrak{H}_S(\mathfrak{r}) \end{aligned}\right\} \tag{103.2}$$

gegeben, wobei das *Streufeld* mit Hilfe des auf der Oberfläche der streuenden Objekte fließenden *Flächenstromes* $\mathfrak{J}$ dargestellt werden kann [vgl. (51.1) und (77.1)]:

$$\left.\begin{aligned} \mathfrak{E}_S(\mathfrak{r}) &= i \,\mathrm{rot\,rot} \oint_S \mathfrak{J}(\hat{\mathfrak{r}}')\, G(\mathfrak{r} - \hat{\mathfrak{r}}')\, d\hat{\mathfrak{r}}', \\ \mathfrak{H}_S(\mathfrak{r}) &= \mathrm{rot} \oint_S \mathfrak{J}(\hat{\mathfrak{r}}')\, G(\mathfrak{r} - \hat{\mathfrak{r}}')\, d\hat{\mathfrak{r}}'. \end{aligned}\right\} \tag{103.3}$$

Läßt man die Hüllfläche in (103.1) mit der Oberfläche des streuenden Objekts *zusammenfallen*, so folgt mit der *Randbedingung* $\hat{\mathfrak{E}}_S(\hat{\mathfrak{r}}) = -\hat{\mathfrak{E}}_0(\hat{\mathfrak{r}})$ und der Bedeutung des Flächenstromes $\mathfrak{J}$ (vgl. Ziff. 51 und 77)

$$Q = \mathrm{Re} \oint_S (\mathfrak{n}_0\, \mathfrak{J}(\hat{\mathfrak{r}}))\, e^{-i(\mathfrak{e}_0 \hat{\mathfrak{r}})}\, d\hat{\mathfrak{r}}. \tag{103.4}$$

Da das Streufeld im Raume außerhalb des streuenden Objekts *quellenfrei* ist $[\mathrm{div}\,\overline{\mathfrak{S}}_S = 0]$ können wir die Hüllfläche in (103.1) andererseits auch wieder ins

Unendliche verlegen (s. Fig. 52). Dort gilt die *asymptotische* Darstellung [vgl. (69.3)]

$$\left.\begin{aligned}\mathfrak{E}_S(\mathfrak{r}) &\to -\frac{i}{4\pi}\left[\mathfrak{e}\left[\mathfrak{e}\,\overline{\mathfrak{J}}(\mathfrak{e})\right]\right]\frac{e^{ir}}{r}\\ \mathfrak{H}_S(\mathfrak{r}) &\to +\frac{i}{4\pi}\left[\mathfrak{e}\,\overline{\mathfrak{J}}(\mathfrak{e})\right]\frac{e^{ir}}{r}\end{aligned}\right\}\quad r\to\infty; \tag{103.5}$$

dabei ist $\mathfrak{e}$ der Einheitsvektor in der Richtung von $\mathfrak{r}$ ($\mathfrak{r}=\mathfrak{e}r$) und $\overline{\mathfrak{J}}$ die Größe

$$\overline{\mathfrak{J}}(\mathfrak{e}) = \oint_S \mathfrak{J}(\hat{\mathfrak{r}})\, e^{-i(\mathfrak{e}\hat{\mathfrak{r}})}\, d\hat{\mathfrak{r}}, \tag{103.6}$$

die im Falle des *ebenen Schirms* die Bedeutung der *Fourier-Transformierten* des *Flächenstromes* hat. Mit (103.6) läßt sich nun (103.4) in die einfache Form setzen

$$Q = \mathrm{Re}\left(\mathfrak{n}_0\,\overline{\mathfrak{J}}(\mathfrak{e}_0)\right). \tag{103.7}$$

In dieser Formel kommt das elektromagnetische Analogon des Theorems von LEVINE und SCHWINGER[1] zum Ausdruck, das den Zusammenhang des Streuquerschnittes mit dem Fraunhoferschen Fernfeld (103.5) in Richtung $\mathfrak{e}_0$ der einfallenden ebenen Welle herstellt. Gl. (103.7) leistet also auch hier wieder die Integration über alle Richtungen $\mathfrak{e}$, die nach (103.1) zunächst auszuführen ist, wenn man dort das asymptotische Feld (103.5) einsetzt [vgl. (19.2)]:

$$Q = \frac{1}{16\pi^2}\oint\left\{\left(\overline{\mathfrak{J}}(\mathfrak{e})\,\overline{\mathfrak{J}}^*(\mathfrak{e})\right) - \left(\mathfrak{e}\,\overline{\mathfrak{J}}(\mathfrak{e})\right)\left(\mathfrak{e}\,\overline{\mathfrak{J}}^*(\mathfrak{e})\right)\right\}d\omega.$$

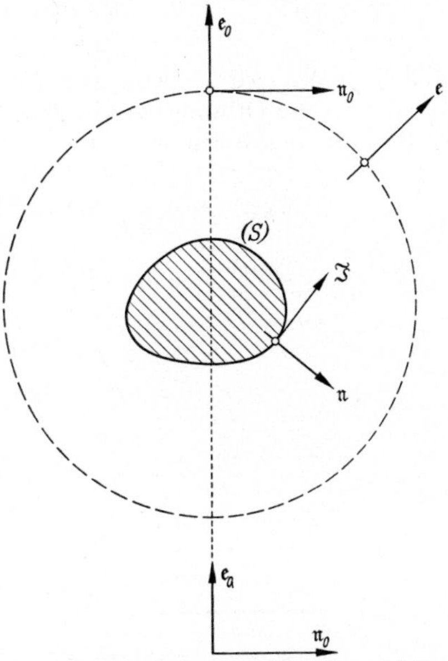

Fig. 52. Zur Ableitung des „*optischen Theorems*" über den Streuquerschnitt für elektromagnetische Strahlung.

104. Beugung. *Beim Beugungsproblem* interessieren wir uns wieder für den *Durchlaßquerschnitt*

$$T = \frac{1}{|\mathfrak{S}_0|}\int(\mathfrak{e}\,\overline{\mathfrak{S}}_B)\,d\sigma = \mathrm{Re}\int(\mathfrak{e}\,[\mathfrak{E}_B\,\mathfrak{H}_B^*]\,d\sigma, \tag{104.1}$$

wobei die Integration entweder über die *Öffnung* (L) zu erstrecken ist (dann ist für $\mathfrak{e}$ die in den Raum $z>0$ weisende Normale $\mathfrak{n}$ des ebenen Schirms einzusetzen, da die Anregung aus dem Raum $z<0$ erfolgen soll) oder über die unendlich große *Halb*kugel im Raume $z>0$. Nach der elektromagnetischen Fassung des *Babinetschen Theorems* (s. Ziff. 27) besteht wieder ein einfacher Zusammenhang zwischen dem Beugungsproblem und dem dazu *komplementären* Streuproblem in der Weise, daß man die elektrische und magnetische Feldstärke der Streuwelle vertauschen muß, um die elektrische und magnetische Komponente (letztere bis auf das Vorzeichen) des Beugungsfeldes in Raum $z>0$ zu erhalten. Dabei sind dann allerdings auch die elektrische und magnetische Feldstärke der *einfallenden* Welle zu vertauschen (erstere unter Vorzeichenumkehr). Diese Vertauschungen spielen jedoch bei der Bildung des Poyntingschen Vektors $\mathfrak{S}_B$

[1] Vgl. H.C. VAN DE HULST: Physica, Haag **15**, 740 (1949). — H. LEVINE u. J. SCHWINGER: Comm. Pure Appl. Math. **3**, 355 (1950). — G. TORALDO DI FRANCIA: R. C. Accad. naz. Lincei Roma **8**, 359 (1950). — D.S. JONES: Phil. Mag. **46**, 957 (1955).

und $\mathfrak{S}_0$ keine Rolle. Daher gilt auch hier wieder der einfache Zusammenhang

$$2T = Q \tag{104.2}$$

für Durchlaß- und Streuquerschnitt *komplementärer ebener Schirme.*

Da nach Gl. (26.11) $[\mathfrak{n}\mathfrak{H}_B] = [\mathfrak{n}\mathfrak{H}_0]$ in den Punkten der Öffnung (L) ist, so ergibt sich aus (104.1), wenn wir über die *Öffnung* integrieren und für $\mathfrak{H}_0$ den Wert $[\mathfrak{e}_0 \mathfrak{n}_0]\, e^{i(\mathfrak{e}_0 \mathfrak{r})}$ einsetzen

$$T = \mathrm{Re} \int_L \big([\mathfrak{e}_0 \mathfrak{n}_0]\, \mathfrak{L}(\hat{\mathfrak{r}})\big)\, e^{-i(\mathfrak{e}_0 \hat{\mathfrak{r}})}\, d\hat{\mathfrak{r}}, \tag{104.3}$$

dabei ist $\mathfrak{L} = [\mathfrak{n}\mathfrak{E}] = [\mathfrak{n}\mathfrak{E}_B]$ der Wert der Tangentialkomponente des elektrischen Feldes in der Öffnung wie in Ziff. 52. Andererseits läßt sich das *Fernfeld* nach Ziff. 69 in der Form

$$\left.\begin{aligned} \mathfrak{E}_B(\mathfrak{r}) &\to \pm \frac{i}{2\pi}\, [\mathfrak{e}\, \overline{\mathfrak{L}}(\mathfrak{e})]\, \frac{e^{ir}}{r} \\ \mathfrak{H}_B(\mathfrak{r}) &\to \pm \frac{i}{2\pi}\, [\mathfrak{e}\,[\mathfrak{e}\, \overline{\mathfrak{L}}(\mathfrak{e})]]\, \frac{e^{ir}}{r} \end{aligned}\right\}\ \mathfrak{r} = \mathfrak{e}\, r,\ r \to \infty,\ z \gtrless 0 \tag{104.4}$$

darstellen, dabei ist

$$\overline{\mathfrak{L}}(\mathfrak{e}) = \int_L \mathfrak{L}(\hat{\mathfrak{r}})\, e^{-i(\mathfrak{e}\hat{\mathfrak{r}})}\, d\hat{\mathfrak{r}} \tag{104.5}$$

die Fourier-Transformierte des *„magnetischen Flächenstroms“* $\mathfrak{L}(\hat{\mathfrak{r}})$ in der Öffnung. Vergleicht man (104.3) mit (104.5), so ergibt sich der folgende einfache Zusammenhang zwischen Durchlaßquerschnitt und Fernfeld:

$$T = \mathrm{Re}\big([\mathfrak{e}_0 \mathfrak{n}_0]\, \overline{\mathfrak{L}}(\mathfrak{e}_0)\big). \tag{104.6}$$

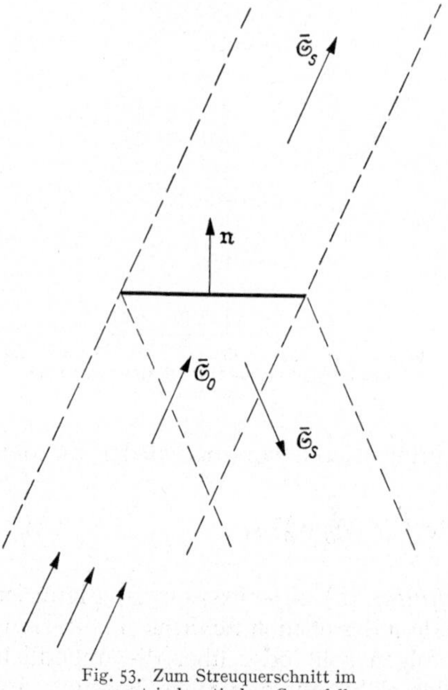

Fig. 53. Zum Streuquerschnitt im geometrisch-optischen Grenzfall.

105. Der geometrisch-optische Grenzfall. Im nächsten Abschnitt (IIIh) werden wir den Fall betrachten, daß der größte Durchmesser des streuenden Objekts bzw. der beugenden Öffnung noch klein gegen die Wellenlänge λ der einfallenden Welle ist (Rayleighscher Grenzfall). Der entgegengesetzte Grenzfall ist, was die Wellenlängenabhängigkeit betrifft, schwerer zu erfassen. Nur der strikte Grenzfall der geometrischen Optik ($\lambda \to 0$) läßt sich leicht übersehen. Wir betrachten einen ebenen Schirm (S) der Fläche S. Im geometrisch optischen Grenzfall gilt für den von der *Vorderseite* des Schirmes (von der Strahlungsquelle aus beurteilt) durch Reflexion in den unteren Halbraum gestreuten Energiefluß (s. Fig. 53) $\oint (\mathfrak{e}\,\overline{\mathfrak{S}}_S)\, d\sigma = (\mathfrak{n}\,\mathfrak{e}_0)\, |\overline{\mathfrak{S}}_0|\, S$. Da nun der Streuquerschnitt definitionsgemäß nur mit Hilfe des *Streufeldes* zu berechnen ist, dem im *ganzen Raum* noch das Feld der einfallenden Welle zu überlagern ist, um das Gesamtfeld zu erhalten, so trägt auch das *geometrisch optisch abgeschattete Gebiet hinter* dem Schirm zur Streuung bei. In diesem Gebiet ist die Streuwelle etwa im skalaren Fall durch $v_S = -v_0$ gegeben (da dann durch $v_0 + v_S = 0$ die Schattenwirkung beschrieben wird). Der in den oberen Halbraum gestreute Energiefluß ist also durch $\oint (\mathfrak{e}\,\overline{\mathfrak{S}}_S)\, d\sigma = (\mathfrak{n}\,\mathfrak{e}_0)$

$|\mathfrak{S}_0|\, S$ gegeben. Damit ergibt sich für den Streuquerschnitt nach (100.2)

$$Q = 2\,(\mathfrak{n}\,\mathfrak{e}_0)\, S \quad (\lambda \to 0) \quad (S \text{ Fläche des streuenden Schirmes}). \qquad (105.1)$$

Im betrachteten Grenzfall ist also der Streuquerschnitt *doppelt* so groß, wie der der in der Richtung $\mathfrak{e}_0$ einfallenden ebenen Welle dargebotene *geometrische* Querschnitt $S' = (\mathfrak{n}\,\mathfrak{e}_0)\, S$ des Schirmes. Mit anderen Worten hat der Streukoeffizient des Schirmes im Grenzfall $\lambda \to 0$ den Wert 2. Der Transmissionskoeffizient hat dann den Wert 1. Entsprechendes gilt auch für beliebig gekrümmte Körper[1], gleichgültig ob skalar oder vektoriell gerechnet wird. Der Wert (105.1) kann als Hauptglied einer *asymptotischen Entwicklung* des Streuquerschnittes nach Potenzen der Wellenlänge aufgefaßt werden. Erst das nächste Glied zeigt einen Einfluß der Randbedingung auf dem Schirm sowie der Polarisation und hängt in für die entsprechende Randbedingung charakteristischer Weise von der Wellenlänge ab. Für ebene berandete Schirme erhält man es unter Umständen am einfachsten mit Hilfe der geometrischen Beugungstheorie von J. B. KELLER, indem man den Beitrag *mehrfach* gebeugter Strahlen berücksichtigt[2] (vgl. Ziff. 44). Sowohl die Kirchhoffsche wie die Braunbeksche Näherung (vgl. Abschn. IIa und b) liefern *nur das geometrisch-optische Hauptglied* (105.1) (wenn man die asymptotische Auswertung dieser Näherungen nicht „*überzieht*", was zu falschen Zusatztermen führt). Eine strenge Erfassung des hochfrequenten Grenzfalls $\lambda \to 0$ (einschließlich höherer Näherungen) mit Hilfe der Integralgleichungstheorie wird in Abschn. B für den Spalt[3] (vgl. Ziff. 124) und die Kreisscheibe[4] (Ziff. 134) durchgeführt.

h) Stationäre Darstellungen (Variationsprinzip von LEVINE und SCHWINGER).

106. Einleitung. Zum Abschluß des allgemeinen Teils wollen wir eine Methode zur Berechnung von Beugungsfeldern betrachten, die eine Mittelstellung zwischen den heuristischen und den strengen Verfahren der Beugungstheorie einnimmt: Es handelt sich um die „*Methode der stationären Darstellung*" von J. SCHWINGER[5]. LEVINE und SCHWINGER haben sie zuerst zur Berechnung des Transmissionskoeffizienten der kreisrunden Öffnung herangezogen[6].

Mathematisch gesehen beruht diese Methode auf dem bekannten Zusammenhang zwischen der Theorie der linearen *Integralgleichungen* und der *Variationsrechnung*. Er besteht im wesentlichen darin, daß sich die Lösung einer *linearen* Integralgleichung auch als Extremale eines Variationsprinzips definieren läßt, das die zu variierende Funktion *bilinear* enthält. Zur angenäherten Bestimmung der Extremale kann man dann etwa das „*Ritzsche Verfahren*" benutzen, indem man für die Extremale einen „geeigneten" Funktionsverlauf mit einer Anzahl von Para-

[1] Vgl. z.B. L. BRILLOUIN: J. Appl. Phys. **20**, 1110 (1949). — H. WERGELAND: Avh. Norske Vidensk. Akad. math.-naturw. Kl. **1**, No. 9, Oslo 1945. — H.C. VAN DE HULST: Optics of Spherical Particles. Amsterdam 1946. — D. SINCLAIR: J. Opt. Soc. Amer. **37**, 475 (1947). — K.S. SIFRIN: Bull. Acad. Sci. URSS. **14**, 64 (1950).

[2] J.B. KELLER: N.Y. Univ. Res. Rep. No. EM-92 (1956). — S.N. KARP u. J.B. KELLER: N.Y. Univ. Res. Rep. No. EM-143 (1959).

[3] K. WESTPFAHL: Ann. Phys. **4**, 283 (1959).

[4] H. LEVINE: N. Y. Univ. Res. Rep. No. EM-84 (1955) Techn. Rep. 51, Appl. Math. a. Stat. Lab., Stanford Univ. 1956. Für Körper endlichen Volumens vgl. D. S. JONES: Proc. Roy. Soc. Lond. A **239**, 338 (1957); **240**, 206 (1957). — D.S. JONES u. G.B. WHITHAM: Proc. Cambridge Phil. Soc. **53**, 691 (1957). — Siehe Ziff. 146 u. 151.

[5] Vgl. dazu die einleitenden Bemerkungen bei B.A. LIPPMAN u. J. SCHWINGER: Phys. Rev. **79**, 469 (1950). — Siehe auch F.E. BORGNIS u. C.H. PAPAS: Randwertprobleme der Mikrowellenphysik (Berlin: Springer 1955), wo zahlreiche Beispiele nach dieser Methode behandelt werden.

[6] H. LEVINE u. J. SCHWINGER: Phys. Rev. **74**, 958, 1212 (1948); **75**, 1423 (1949).

metern ansetzt, die dann mit Hilfe des stationären Charakters der Funktionals bestimmt werden können. Die praktische Bedeutung der Methode der stationären Darstellung beruht aber weniger auf dieser Möglichkeit als vielmehr darauf, daß man auch stationäre Funktionale konstruieren kann, die selbst eine unmittelbare physikalische Bedeutung besitzen.

Ein entsprechender Sachverhalt ist in der Elektrostatik als *Thomsonscher Satz* bekannt. Er besagt, daß sich die Ladung auf der Oberfläche eines Leiters so verteilt, daß die gesamte *elektrostatische Feldenergie* W ein *Extremum* (hier ein Minimum) annimmt. Wir wollen hier zur Veranschaulichung der Methode ein eng mit dem Thomsonschen Satz verwandtes, aber im Hinblick auf die Beugungstheorie leicht modifiziertes und verallgemeinertes Problem betrachten. Wie beim Thomsonschen Satz fragen wir nach der Ladungsverteilung η auf einer geschlossenen Fläche (S), geben aber nicht die Gesamtladung, sondern das elektrische Potential (gegen das Unendliche) φ auf (S) vor. [Gilt insbesondere $\varphi = \text{const}$, so ist der Innenraum von (S) feldfrei und kann als leitend angesehen werden.] Die Feldenergie W läßt sich folgendermaßen als bilineares Funktional bezüglich η darstellen

$$W = \frac{1}{8\pi} \oint_S d\hat{\mathfrak{r}} \oint_S d\hat{\mathfrak{r}}' \, \frac{\eta(\mathfrak{r})\,\eta(\hat{\mathfrak{r}}')}{|\hat{\mathfrak{r}} - \hat{\mathfrak{r}}'|}, \tag{106.1}$$

indem man in die Darstellung der Feldenergie

$$W = \tfrac{1}{2} \oint_S \eta(\hat{\mathfrak{r}})\, \varphi(\hat{\mathfrak{r}})\, d\hat{\mathfrak{r}} \tag{106.2}$$

den Ausdruck für das Potential φ der Ladungsverteilung η auf (S) einsetzt

$$\varphi(\mathfrak{r}) = \frac{1}{4\pi} \oint_S \frac{\eta(\hat{\mathfrak{r}}')}{|\hat{\mathfrak{r}} - \hat{\mathfrak{r}}'|}\, d\hat{\mathfrak{r}}'. \tag{106.3}$$

Subtrahiert man nun von Gl. (106.1) die Größe $2W$ nach Gl. (106.2), so folgt

$$-W[\eta] = \frac{1}{8\pi} \oint_S d\hat{\mathfrak{r}} \left\{ \oint_S \frac{\eta(\hat{\mathfrak{r}})\,\eta(\hat{\mathfrak{r}}')}{|\hat{\mathfrak{r}} - \hat{\mathfrak{r}}'|}\, d\hat{\mathfrak{r}}' - 8\pi\,\eta(\hat{\mathfrak{r}})\,\varphi(\hat{\mathfrak{r}}) \right\}. \tag{106.4}$$

Es soll nun gezeigt werden, daß *dieser* Ausdruck für W bezüglich der Ladungsverteilung η *„stationär"* ist, d.h. daß sich W in erster Näherung nicht ändert, wenn man die Ladungsverteilung η, die sich auf (S) eingestellt hat, infinitesimal um den willkürlichen Betrag $\delta\eta(\mathfrak{r})$ abändert. In der Tat gilt für die Variation von (106.4)

$$-4\pi\,\delta W[\eta] = \oint_S d\hat{\mathfrak{r}} \left\{ \oint_S \frac{\eta(\hat{\mathfrak{r}}')}{|\hat{\mathfrak{r}} - \hat{\mathfrak{r}}'|}\, d\hat{\mathfrak{r}}' - 4\pi\,\varphi(\hat{\mathfrak{r}}) \right\} \delta\eta(\hat{\mathfrak{r}}), \tag{106.5}$$

und dies verschwindet, da η zufolge (106.3) der Integralgleichung

$$\oint_S \frac{\eta(\hat{\mathfrak{r}}')}{|\hat{\mathfrak{r}} - \hat{\mathfrak{r}}'|}\, d\hat{\mathfrak{r}}' = 4\pi\,\varphi(\hat{\mathfrak{r}}) \tag{106.6}$$

genügt. Anstelle von (106.4) können wir jedoch auch ein in η *homogenes* Funktional angeben, das ebenfalls die durch die Integralgleichung (106.6) definierte Ladungsdichte zur Extremale hat. Es hat ebenfalls die Bedeutung der gesamten

Feldenergie W und ergibt sich einfach aus (106.1) und (106.2):

$$W[\eta] = 2\pi \frac{\left\{\oint\limits_S \eta(\mathfrak{r})\,\varphi(\mathfrak{r})\,d\mathfrak{r}\right\}^2}{\oint\limits_S d\mathfrak{r} \oint\limits_S d\mathfrak{r}'\,\frac{\eta(\mathfrak{r})\,\eta(\mathfrak{r}')}{|\mathfrak{r}-\mathfrak{r}'|}}. \tag{106.7}$$

Man kann nun wieder leicht zeigen, daß das Funktional (106.7) bezüglich einer Variation von η stationär ist, wenn η der Integralgleichung (106.6) genügt (s. unten).

Homogene Funktionale der Form (106.7) sind für die Theorie der stationären Darstellung typisch und haben ebenso wie in dem eben erläuterten Falle der Elektrostatik auch in der Beugungstheorie ein unmittelbares physikalisches Interesse. An die Stelle der Flächenladung tritt jetzt der *Flächenstrom*; an diejenige der Feldenergie der *Streu-* bzw. *Transmissionskoeffizient*. Diese Größe läßt sich, wie wir gezeigt haben — vgl. Ziff. 100 und 102 — im wesentlichen als Imaginärteil des Fernfeldes in der Einfallsrichtung der anregenden ebenen Welle darstellen. Daher ist zu erwarten, daß auch das *Fernfeld* in einer *beliebigen* Richtung eine stationäre Darstellung zuläßt. Dies ist in der Tat der Fall. Darüber hinaus läßt sich auch das Feld in *jedem beliebigen Punkt* als homogenes Funktional des Flächenstroms darstellen, das gegenüber Abweichungen des Flächenstroms von der korrekten Verteilung — die durch die Integrodifferentialgleichungen von Abschnitt IIIa definiert ist — in erster Ordnung „*unempfindlich*" ist. Solche Funktionale lassen sich als *Wechselwirkungsterme* des *gesuchten* Feldes mit geeigneten *Hilfsfeldern* konstruieren.

Die Darstellung physikalisch relevanter Größen als stationäre Funktionale des Flächenstromes hat nun insofern eine große praktische Bedeutung, als schon durch das Einsetzen von groben Näherungen für den Flächenstrom erstaunlich gute Näherungen für die durch die Funktionale stationär dargestellten Feldgrößen resultieren. Allerdings ist es im allgemeinen nicht möglich, die Güte einer solchen Näherung von vornherein zu übersehen, vielmehr kann sie meistens erst nachträglich durch Vergleich mit strengen Lösungen oder mit dem Experiment konstatiert werden. Außerdem ist die Möglichkeit einer wünschenswerten schrittweisen Verbesserung der so gewonnenen Näherung nicht ohne weiteres gegeben. Eine solche Verbesserung führt nämlich nur über eine genauere Kenntnis des Flächenstromes, die wiederum nur durch eine entsprechend genau durchgeführte Auflösung der diesen definierenden Integrodifferentialgleichungen gewonnen werden kann.

Um diese Auflösung kommt man also bei gesteigerten Genauigkeitsansprüchen letzten Endes doch nicht herum. Demgegenüber liefert die Methode von SCHWINGER — bei plausiblen Annahmen über den Flächenstrom — für die stationär dargestellten Größen ein qualitativ richtiges Verhalten im *gesamten Frequenzbereich.* Der Grund dafür liegt eben gerade in der Darstellung als *stationäres* Funktional des Flächenstromes, wobei es auf die Einzelheiten des Funktionsverlaufes dann nicht so sehr ankommt. Den Vorzug verdienen in dieser Hinsicht die *homogenen* Funktionale, bei denen überdies die absolute Größe des Flächenstromes nicht eingeht. Es sei noch erwähnt, daß man im allgemeinen nicht weiß, ob das zugrunde gelegte Funktional für den extremalen Flächenstrom ein Maximum oder ein Minimum annimmt, so daß es bisher ungewiß ist, ob das mit Hilfe einer Näherungsfunktion berechnete Funktional unterhalb oder oberhalb des extremalen Wertes liegt[1].

[1] Vgl. jedoch die Arbeit von D. S. JONES: N. Y. Univ. Res. Rep. No. EM-78 (1955).

Das allgemeine Schema zur Konstruktion stationärer Funktionale $X[\eta]$ einer Funktion $\eta(\mathfrak{r})$, die einer linearen inhomogenen Integralgleichung erster Art mit dem *symmetrischen* Kern $K(\hat{\mathfrak{r}}, \hat{\mathfrak{r}}')$ und der Inhomogenität $f(\hat{\mathfrak{r}})$ genügt:

$$\oint_S \eta(\hat{\mathfrak{r}}')\, K(\hat{\mathfrak{r}}, \hat{\mathfrak{r}}')\, d\hat{\mathfrak{r}}' = f(\hat{\mathfrak{r}}), \tag{106.8}$$

ist folgender: Eine Größe X sei darstellbar in der Form

$$X = \oint_S f(\hat{\mathfrak{r}})\, \eta(\hat{\mathfrak{r}})\, d\hat{\mathfrak{r}}, \tag{106.9}$$

dann läßt sich X zufolge der Integralgleichung (106.8) auch in der Gestalt

$$-X[\eta] = \oint_S d\hat{\mathfrak{r}}\, \eta(\hat{\mathfrak{r}}) \left\{\oint_S K(\hat{\mathfrak{r}}, \hat{\mathfrak{r}}')\, \eta(\hat{\mathfrak{r}}')\, d\hat{\mathfrak{r}}' - 2f(\hat{\mathfrak{r}})\right\} \tag{106.10}$$

oder in der homogenen Form

$$X[\eta] = \frac{\left\{\oint_S \eta(\hat{\mathfrak{r}})\, f(\hat{\mathfrak{r}})\, d\hat{\mathfrak{r}}\right\}^2}{\oint_S d\hat{\mathfrak{r}} \oint_S \eta(\hat{\mathfrak{r}})\, K(\hat{\mathfrak{r}}, \hat{\mathfrak{r}}')\, \eta(\hat{\mathfrak{r}}')\, d\hat{\mathfrak{r}}'} \tag{106.11}$$

darstellen. Es läßt sich nun leicht zeigen, daß *beide* Funktionale (106.10) und (106.11) bezüglich willkürlicher infinitesimaler Abänderungen der durch (106.8) definierten Funktion η in erster Ordnung stationär sind. Bildet man nämlich die Variation von (106.10) — unter Beachtung der Symmetrie von $K(\hat{\mathfrak{r}}, \hat{\mathfrak{r}}')$ —, so folgt

$$-\delta X[\eta] = 2\oint_S d\hat{\mathfrak{r}} \left\{\oint_S \eta(\hat{\mathfrak{r}}')\, K(\hat{\mathfrak{r}}, \hat{\mathfrak{r}}')\, d\hat{\mathfrak{r}}' - f(\hat{\mathfrak{r}})\right\} \delta\eta(\hat{\mathfrak{r}}), \tag{106.10'}$$

und dies verschwindet wegen (106.8). Ebenso berechnet sich die Variation von (106.11) aus der Gleichung

$$\left.\begin{aligned} &\delta X[\eta] \cdot \oint_S d\hat{\mathfrak{r}} \oint_S \eta(\hat{\mathfrak{r}})\, K(\hat{\mathfrak{r}}, \hat{\mathfrak{r}}')\, \eta(\hat{\mathfrak{r}}')\, d\hat{\mathfrak{r}}' \\ &\quad = -2\oint_S d\hat{\mathfrak{r}} \left\{X \oint_S \eta(\hat{\mathfrak{r}}')\, K(\hat{\mathfrak{r}}, \hat{\mathfrak{r}}')\, d\hat{\mathfrak{r}}' - f(\hat{\mathfrak{r}}) \oint_S \eta(\hat{\mathfrak{r}}')\, f(\hat{\mathfrak{r}}')\, d\hat{\mathfrak{r}}'\right\} \delta\eta(\hat{\mathfrak{r}}). \end{aligned}\right\} \tag{106.12}$$

Hier verschwindet die rechte Seite ebenfalls, da der Faktor von $f(\hat{\mathfrak{r}})$ in der geschweiften Klammer nach (106.9) gleich X ist und η der Integralgleichung (106.8) genügen soll.

Im folgenden werden wir es außer mit der Integralgleichung (106.8) auch mit einer ähnlich gebauten Integrodifferentialgleichung zu tun haben (vgl. Abschn. IIIa). Es lassen sich dann zu (106.10) und (106.11) analoge Funktionale konstruieren, deren stationären Charakter man entsprechend Gl. (106.10') und (106.12) beweist, wobei aber noch eine *partielle Integration* auszuführen ist. Bei berandeten Flächenstücken *(Schirmen)* ist dann dafür Sorge zu tragen, daß der ausintegrierte Term *verschwindet*. Dies leistet aber gerade die *Kantenbedingung*.

h 1) Stationäre Darstellung skalarer Beugungsfelder.

Bei der Behandlung des skalaren Problems für ebene unendlich dünne Schirme (S) mit Löchern (L) können wir uns auf den p-Fall (d.h. die Randbedingung $v = 0$, vgl. Ziff. 4) beschränken, da dann der s-Fall (Randbedingung $\partial v/\partial n = 0$) vermöge des *Babinetschen Prinzips* mit erledigt ist (vgl. Ziff. 27). Jedoch wollen wir uns wieder den beiden möglichen geometrischen Situationen anpassen und zwischen *Streufall* [der Schirm (S) liegt ganz im Endlichen] und *Beugungsfall* [die Öffnung (L) liegt ganz im Endlichen] unterscheiden. (S) und (L) sollen sich dabei stets zur *vollen* Ebene $z=0$ ergänzen (vgl. Ziff. 26). Zunächst sei an die Felddarstellung mit Hilfe des elektrischen Flächenstroms auf (S) bzw. des „magnetischen" Flächenstroms auf (L) erinnert (vgl. Ziff. 46 und 47):

Streufall

$$\left.\begin{aligned} v(\mathfrak{r}) &= v_0(\mathfrak{r}) + v_S(\mathfrak{r}), \quad z \gtrless 0 \\ v_S(\mathfrak{r}) &= -\int_S \psi(\hat{\mathfrak{r}}')\, G(\mathfrak{r}-\hat{\mathfrak{r}}')\, d\hat{\mathfrak{r}}', \end{aligned}\right\} \tag{I}$$

Beugungsfall

$$\left.\begin{aligned} v(\mathfrak{r}) &= v_B(\mathfrak{r}) + \begin{cases} 0, & z>0 \\ v_0(\mathfrak{r}) - v^0(\mathfrak{r}), & z<0 \end{cases} \\ v_B(\mathfrak{r}) &= \pm 2 \int_L \varphi(\hat{\mathfrak{r}}') \frac{\partial}{\partial z'} G(\mathfrak{r}-\hat{\mathfrak{r}}')\, d\hat{\mathfrak{r}}', \quad z \gtrless 0. \end{aligned}\right\} \tag{II}$$

Der „elektrische Flächenstrom" $\psi(\hat{\mathfrak{r}})$ auf dem Schirm (S) ist dabei durch die Integralgleichung

$$\int_S \psi(\hat{\mathfrak{r}}')\, G(\hat{\mathfrak{r}}-\hat{\mathfrak{r}}')\, d\hat{\mathfrak{r}}' = v_0(\hat{\mathfrak{r}}), \quad \hat{\mathfrak{r}} \text{ auf } (S) \tag{III}$$

definiert — vgl. (46.2p) —, während wir für die Bestimmung des „magnetischen Flächenstroms" $\varphi(\hat{\mathfrak{r}})$ auf (L) die Integrodifferentialgleichung (48.4p) zugrunde legen wollen:

$$\int_L \{\varphi(\hat{\mathfrak{r}}') + \widehat{\operatorname{grad}}'\varphi(\hat{\mathfrak{r}}')\,\widehat{\operatorname{grad}}\}\, G(\hat{\mathfrak{r}}-\hat{\mathfrak{r}}')\, d\hat{\mathfrak{r}}' = \frac{1}{2}\frac{\partial}{\partial z} v_0(\hat{\mathfrak{r}}), \quad \hat{\mathfrak{r}} \text{ auf } (L), \tag{IV}$$

wobei hier noch die Kantenbedingung $\varphi=0$ längs des Randes (C) von (L) zu berücksichtigen ist.

107. Ritzsches Verfahren. Wir zeigen zunächst, daß die Größe ψ bzw. φ *Extremale des Variationsproblems*

$$\int_S d\hat{\mathfrak{r}}\, \psi(\hat{\mathfrak{r}}) \left\{ \int_S G(\hat{\mathfrak{r}}-\hat{\mathfrak{r}}')\, \psi(\hat{\mathfrak{r}}')\, d\hat{\mathfrak{r}}' - 2 v_0(\hat{\mathfrak{r}}) \right\} = \text{Extr.} \tag{107.1}$$

bzw.

$$\left.\begin{aligned} \int_L d\hat{\mathfrak{r}} \Big\{ \int_L d\hat{\mathfrak{r}}' [\varphi(\hat{\mathfrak{r}})\,\varphi(\hat{\mathfrak{r}}') - \widehat{\operatorname{grad}}\,\varphi(\hat{\mathfrak{r}})\,\widehat{\operatorname{grad}}'\,\varphi(\hat{\mathfrak{r}}')]\, G(\mathfrak{r}-\hat{\mathfrak{r}}') \\ - \varphi(\hat{\mathfrak{r}}) \frac{\partial}{\partial z} v_0(\hat{\mathfrak{r}}) \Big\} = \text{Extr.} \end{aligned}\right\} \tag{107.2}$$

ist. Notwendige Bedingung dafür ist das Verschwinden der Variation von (107.1) bzw. (107.2) bezüglich einer beliebigen Variation von ψ bzw. φ. Führt man diese Variation aus, so folgt in der Tat infolge der Symmetrie der Greenschen Funktion $G(\hat{\mathfrak{r}}-\hat{\mathfrak{r}}') = G(\hat{\mathfrak{r}}'-\hat{\mathfrak{r}})$

$$\int_S \left\{ \int_S \varphi(\hat{\mathfrak{r}}')\, G(\hat{\mathfrak{r}}-\hat{\mathfrak{r}}')\, d\hat{\mathfrak{r}}' - v_0(\hat{\mathfrak{r}}) \right\} \delta\varphi(\hat{\mathfrak{r}})\, d\hat{\mathfrak{r}} = 0 \tag{107.1'}$$

bzw.

$$\left.\begin{aligned} \int_L d\hat{\mathfrak{r}} \Big\{ 2\int_L [\varphi(\hat{\mathfrak{r}}')\,\delta\varphi(\hat{\mathfrak{r}}) - \widehat{\operatorname{grad}}'\,\varphi(\hat{\mathfrak{r}}')\,\widehat{\operatorname{grad}}\,\delta\varphi(\hat{\mathfrak{r}})]\, G(\hat{\mathfrak{r}}-\hat{\mathfrak{r}}')\, d\hat{\mathfrak{r}}' \\ - \frac{\partial}{\partial z} v_0(\hat{\mathfrak{r}})\, \delta\varphi(\hat{\mathfrak{r}}) \Big\} \\ = \int_L d\hat{\mathfrak{r}} \Big\{ 2\int_L [\varphi(\hat{\mathfrak{r}}') + \widehat{\operatorname{grad}}'\,\varphi(\hat{\mathfrak{r}}')\,\widehat{\operatorname{grad}}]\, G(\hat{\mathfrak{r}}-\hat{\mathfrak{r}}') - \frac{\partial v_0(\hat{\mathfrak{r}})}{\partial z} \Big\} \delta\varphi(\hat{\mathfrak{r}}) = 0. \end{aligned}\right\} \tag{107.2'}$$

Der Übergang von der ersten zur zweiten Zeile der Gl. (107.2′) entspricht dabei der üblichen Umformung mittles partieller Integration, wobei zur Unterdrückung eines ausintegrierten Terms die Kantenbedingung $\varphi = 0$ längs (C) herangezogen werden muß. Da nun die linke Seite von (107.1′) bzw. (107.2′) für im übrigen beliebige Variationen $\delta\psi$ bzw. $\delta\varphi$ verschwinden soll, so muß jeweils die geschweifte Klammer Null sein. Dies führt gerade auf die Gl. (III) bzw. (IV) zurück.

Das Variationsproblem (107.1) bzw. (107.2) ist also mit der Integralgleichung (III) bzw. der Integrodifferentialgleichung (IV) äquivalent. Zur angenäherten Bestimmung der Extremalen machen wir einen *Ritzschen Ansatz*

$$\psi(\hat{\mathfrak{r}}) = \sum_{\nu=1}^{N} a_\nu \psi_\nu(\hat{\mathfrak{r}}) \quad \text{bzw.} \quad \varphi(\hat{\mathfrak{r}}) = \sum_{\nu=1}^{N} b_\nu \varphi_\nu(\hat{\mathfrak{r}}) \tag{107.3}$$

mit einer passend zu wählenden Folge einer beliebigen Zahl N von Funktionen $\psi_\nu(\hat{\mathfrak{r}})$ bzw. $\varphi_\nu(\hat{\mathfrak{r}})$ [letztere sollen auf dem Rande (C) von (L) verschwinden]. Hierbei ist es zweckmäßig, die durch die Kantenbedingung gelieferte Information auszunutzen, die für ψ bzw. φ ein Randverhalten wie $\varrho^{-\frac{1}{2}}$ bzw. $\varrho^{\frac{1}{2}}$ fordert [$\varrho =$ Abstand vom Rande von (S) bzw. (L); vgl. Ziff. 23]; besonders dann, wenn Schirm bzw. Öffnung hauptsächlich aus Randzonen bestehen (d.h. wenn die Abmessungen von Schirm bzw. Öffnung in die Größenordnung der Wellenlänge rücken oder gar noch kleiner sind). Setzt man (107.3) in (107.1) bzw. (107.2) ein, so nimmt das entsprechende Variationsproblem folgende Form an

$$\delta \sum_{\nu=1}^{N} a_\nu \left\{ \sum_{\mu=1}^{N} a_\mu C_{\nu\mu} - 2c_\nu \right\} = 0 \tag{107.4}$$

bzw.

$$\delta \sum_{\nu=1}^{N} b_\nu \left\{ \sum_{\mu=1}^{N} b_\mu D_{\nu\mu} - 2d_\nu \right\} = 0, \tag{107.5}$$

wobei die $C_{\nu\mu}$ und c_ν bzw. $D_{\nu\mu}$ und d_ν folgende Bedeutung haben

$$\left.\begin{aligned} C_{\nu\mu} &= \int_S d\hat{\mathfrak{r}} \int_S d\hat{\mathfrak{r}}'\, \psi_\nu(\hat{\mathfrak{r}})\, G(\hat{\mathfrak{r}} - \hat{\mathfrak{r}}')\, \psi_\mu(\hat{\mathfrak{r}}') \\ c_\nu &= \int_S v_0(\hat{\mathfrak{r}})\, \psi_\nu(\hat{\mathfrak{r}})\, d\hat{\mathfrak{r}} \end{aligned}\right\} \tag{107.6}$$

bzw.

$$\left.\begin{aligned} D_{\nu\mu} &= \int_L d\hat{\mathfrak{r}} \int_L d\hat{\mathfrak{r}}' \{\varphi_\nu(\hat{\mathfrak{r}})\, \varphi_\mu(\hat{\mathfrak{r}}') - \widehat{\operatorname{grad}}\, \varphi_\nu(\hat{\mathfrak{r}})\, \widehat{\operatorname{grad}}'\, \varphi_\mu(\hat{\mathfrak{r}}')\}\, G(\hat{\mathfrak{r}} - \hat{\mathfrak{r}}') \\ d_\nu &= \frac{1}{2} \int_L \frac{\partial v_0(\hat{\mathfrak{r}})}{\partial z}\, \varphi_\nu(\hat{\mathfrak{r}})\, d\hat{\mathfrak{r}}. \end{aligned}\right\} \tag{107.7}$$

Die Variation in (107.4) bzw. (107.5) bezieht sich jetzt auf die a_ν bzw. b_ν und muß für beliebige δa_ν bzw. δb_ν verschwinden. Dies liefert für die a_ν bzw. b_ν das Gleichungssystem

$$\left.\begin{aligned} \sum_{\nu=1}^{N} a_\nu C_{\nu\mu} &= c_\mu \\ \text{bzw.} \qquad \sum_{\nu=1}^{N} b_\nu D_{\nu\mu} &= d_\mu \end{aligned}\right\} \quad \mu = 1, 2, \ldots N, \tag{107.8}$$

aus dem die a_ν bzw. b_ν zu bestimmen sind. Ein Gleichungssystem dieser Art ist uns bereits in Ziff. 63 bei der näherungsweisen Auflösung der mit (III) äquivalenten *dualen Integralgleichung* (60.8*p*) begegnet (dort hatten wir uns auf den zweidimensionalen Fall beschränkt). Es läßt sich nun leicht zeigen, daß auch die dort eingeführten Koeffizienten (63.3) und (63.6) mit unseren hier durch Gl. (107.6) eingeführten übereinstimmen (bis auf den irrelevanten Faktor $-8\pi^2 i$). In der Tat ergibt sich Übereinstimmung zwischen (63.6) und (107.6) für die $C_{\nu\mu}$, wenn wir in Gl. (107.6) die *Fourier-Darstellung* der *Greenschen Funktion*

$$G(\mathfrak{x}-\mathfrak{x}') = \frac{i}{4} H_0^1(|x-x'|) = \frac{i}{4\pi} \int_{-\infty}^{+\infty} \frac{e^{-i(x-x')\alpha}}{\sqrt{1-\alpha^2}} \, d\alpha \tag{107.9}$$

einsetzen — vgl. (8.3a) und (60.1) —, die Integrationsreihenfolge vertauschen und beachten, daß $\overline{\psi}_\nu(\alpha) = \int_{-\infty}^{\infty} \psi_\nu(x)\, e^{-i\alpha x}\, dx$ [die $\psi_\nu(x)$ wollen wir wie in Ziff. 63 *reell* wählen]. Entsprechendes gilt für die c_ν. Es sei jedoch hervorgehoben, daß bei der Herleitung der Gl. (107.8) über das Variationsprinzip *nirgends* von einer *Orthogonalität* oder *Vollständigkeit* der Funktionenfolge ψ_ν bzw. φ_ν Gebrauch gemacht werden mußte.

Ein bekannter Nachteil des Ritzschen Verfahrens besteht darin, daß die Bestimmung der Koeffizienten a_ν bzw. b_ν *nicht endgültig* ist, d.h. die Koeffizienten für $\nu \leqq N$ ändern sich, wenn im Ritzschen Ansatz (107.3) weitere ψ_ν bzw. φ_ν hinzugenommen werden ($\nu > N$). Sind jedoch die Abmessungen des streuenden oder beugenden Objekts *klein* gegen die Wellenlänge, so zeigt sich, daß diese Abänderung darin besteht, daß höhere Potenzen des Verhältnisses eines Objektdurchmessers zur Wellenlänge auftreten[1]. Insbesondere hat MAGNUS[2] für den Fall der kreisförmigen Öffnung die algebraischen Eigenschaften des Gleichungssystems (107.8) für $N\to\infty$ untersucht, und zwar für eine spezielle Wahl der Funktionenfolge φ_ν[3], die der Kantenbedingung genügt. Er zeigt, daß das Gleichungssystem (107.8) eindeutig auflösbar ist, wenn $\varepsilon = ka < 1$ ist (k Wellenzahl, a Radius der Öffnung) und wird dann zu *konvergenten Entwicklungen* der Koeffizienten b_ν nach steigenden Potenzen in ε geführt. JONES[4] hat allgemein gezeigt, daß nur die Verwendung der „*statischen*" ψ_ν bzw. φ_ν aus Ziff. 93 zu einer strengen Erfassung des Rayleighschen (langwelligen) Grenzfalles führt [vgl. dazu auch Ziff. 123 und 135].

108. Stationäre Darstellung des Streu- und Durchlaßquerschnitts. Wir wollen im folgenden die *einfallende* Welle zu einer *ebenen* Welle spezialisieren, die in der Richtung $\mathfrak{e}_0$ einfallen möge ($\mathfrak{e}_0^2 = 1$), die Amplitude können wir dabei auf 1 normieren:

$$v_0(\mathfrak{r}) = e^{i(\mathfrak{e}_0 \mathfrak{r})} \tag{108.1}$$

Wir schreiben nun die Gln. (III) und (IV) nochmals hin, spezialisieren jedoch die rechts stehende Inhomogenität mit Hilfe von (108.1)

$$\int_S \psi(\mathfrak{e}_0, \mathfrak{x}')\, G(\mathfrak{x}-\mathfrak{x}')\, d\mathfrak{x}' = e^{i(\mathfrak{e}_0 \mathfrak{x})}, \quad \mathfrak{x} \textit{ auf } (S) \tag{108.2}$$

---

[1] Vgl. H. LEVINE u. J. SCHWINGER, l. c. — A.T. DE HOOP: Appl. Sci. Res. B **4**, 151 (1954) für die Kreisscheibe bzw. kreisförmige Öffnung; sowie A. T. DE HOOP: Proc. Acad. Wet. Amsterd. B **58**, 401 (1955) für den Spalt.

[2] W. MAGNUS: N. Y. Univ. Res. Rep. No. EM-32 (1951). — Quart. Appl. Math. **11**, 77 (1953). — N. Y. Univ. Res. Rep. No. EM-80 (1955).

[3] Für eine orthogonalisierte Linearkombination der Magnusschen Funktionenfolge findet man entsprechendes bei A. T. DE HOOP, l. c. Diese Funktionenfolge stimmt mit der „statischen" aus Ziff. 93 überein.

[4] D. S. JONES: N. Y. Univ. Res. Rep. No. EM-78 (1955).

bzw.

$$\left.\begin{aligned}&\int\limits_L \{\varphi(\mathfrak{e}_0,\hat{\mathfrak{r}}') + \widehat{\operatorname{grad}}'\varphi(\mathfrak{e}_0,\hat{\mathfrak{r}}')\,\widehat{\operatorname{grad}}\}\,G(\hat{\mathfrak{r}}-\hat{\mathfrak{r}}')\,d\hat{\mathfrak{r}}' = \frac{i}{2}(\mathfrak{n}\,\mathfrak{e}_0)\,\mathrm{e}^{i(\mathfrak{e}_0\hat{\mathfrak{r}})},\\ &\qquad\qquad\hat{\mathfrak{r}}\ \mathit{auf}\ (L), \qquad (\mathfrak{n} = \text{Schirmnormale}).\end{aligned}\right\}\tag{108.3}$$

Dabei haben wir die Einfallsrichtung $\mathfrak{e}_0$ mit in das Argument der Flächenströme aufgenommen um anzudeuten, daß es sich um denjenigen Flächenstrom handelt, der auf (S) bzw. (L) durch eine in der Richtung $\mathfrak{e}_0$ einfallenden ebenen Welle erzeugt wird. Für den *Streu-* bzw. *Durchlaßquerschnitt* gilt nun im *p-Fall* die Darstellung [vgl. (100.3 p) und (102.3 p)]

$$\left.\begin{aligned}Q_p(\mathfrak{e}_0) &= -\operatorname{Im}\int\limits_S \psi(\mathfrak{e}_0,\hat{\mathfrak{r}})\,\mathrm{e}^{-i(\mathfrak{e}_0\hat{\mathfrak{r}})}\,d\hat{\mathfrak{r}},\\ T_p(\mathfrak{e}_0) &= -(\mathfrak{n}\,\mathfrak{e}_0)\operatorname{Re}\int\limits_L \varphi(\mathfrak{e}_0,\hat{\mathfrak{r}})\,\mathrm{e}^{-i(\mathfrak{e}_0\hat{\mathfrak{r}})}\,d\hat{\mathfrak{r}}.\end{aligned}\right\}\tag{108.4}$$

Durch eine einfache Verallgemeinerung des in den Gln. (106.8) bis (106.12) entwickelten Formalismus erhält man nun für Q und T mit Hilfe der Gln. (108.2) und (108.3) homogene *stationäre Darstellungen.* Für Q ergibt sich unmittelbar

$$Q_p(\mathfrak{e}_0) = -\operatorname{Im}\frac{\int\limits_S \psi(\mathfrak{e}_0,\hat{\mathfrak{r}})\,\mathrm{e}^{-i(\mathfrak{e}_0\hat{\mathfrak{r}})}\,d\hat{\mathfrak{r}}\int\limits_S \psi(-\mathfrak{e}_0,\hat{\mathfrak{r}})\,\mathrm{e}^{i(\mathfrak{e}_0\hat{\mathfrak{r}})}\,d\hat{\mathfrak{r}}}{\int\limits_S d\hat{\mathfrak{r}}\int\limits_S d\hat{\mathfrak{r}}'\,\psi(-\mathfrak{e}_0,\hat{\mathfrak{r}})\,G(\hat{\mathfrak{r}}-\hat{\mathfrak{r}}')\,\psi(\mathfrak{e}_0,\hat{\mathfrak{r}}')},\tag{108.5}$$

das zweite Integral im Zähler ist nämlich zufolge (108.2) gleich dem Nenner. Um die entsprechende Darstellung für T zu finden, multiplizieren wir zunächst (108.3) mit $\varphi(-\mathfrak{e}_0,\hat{\mathfrak{r}})$ und integrieren über (L)

$$\left.\begin{aligned}&(\mathfrak{n}\,\mathfrak{e}_0)\int\limits_L \varphi(-\mathfrak{e}_0,\hat{\mathfrak{r}})\,\mathrm{e}^{i(\mathfrak{e}_0\hat{\mathfrak{r}})}\,d\hat{\mathfrak{r}}\\ &\quad= -2i\int\limits_L d\hat{\mathfrak{r}}\int\limits_L d\hat{\mathfrak{r}}'\,\varphi(-\mathfrak{e}_0,\hat{\mathfrak{r}})\,\{\varphi(\mathfrak{e}_0,\hat{\mathfrak{r}}') + \widehat{\operatorname{grad}}'\varphi(\mathfrak{e}_0,\hat{\mathfrak{r}}')\,\widehat{\operatorname{grad}}\}\,G(\hat{\mathfrak{r}}-\hat{\mathfrak{r}}')\\ &\quad= -2i\int\limits_L d\hat{\mathfrak{r}}\int\limits_L d\hat{\mathfrak{r}}'\,\{\varphi(-\mathfrak{e}_0,\hat{\mathfrak{r}})\,\varphi(\mathfrak{e}_0,\hat{\mathfrak{r}}') - \widehat{\operatorname{grad}}\,\varphi(-\mathfrak{e}_0,\hat{\mathfrak{r}})\,\widehat{\operatorname{grad}}'\varphi(\mathfrak{e}_0,\hat{\mathfrak{r}}')\}\cdot\\ &\qquad\qquad\cdot G(\hat{\mathfrak{r}}-\hat{\mathfrak{r}}').\end{aligned}\right\}\tag{108.6}$$

Hier haben wir in der letzten Zeile eine partielle Integration durchgeführt und berücksichtigt, daß φ zufolge der Kantenbedingung auf dem Rande von (L) verschwindet. Mit Hilfe von (108.6) können wir nun die Größe T aus (108.4) auch in die Form setzen

$$\left.\begin{aligned}&T_p(\mathfrak{e}_0) = -\frac{(\mathfrak{n}\,\mathfrak{e}_0)^2}{2}\cdot\\ &\cdot\operatorname{Im}\frac{\int\limits_L \varphi(\mathfrak{e}_0,\hat{\mathfrak{r}})\,\mathrm{e}^{-i(\mathfrak{e}_0\hat{\mathfrak{r}})}\,d\hat{\mathfrak{r}}\int\limits_L \varphi(-\mathfrak{e}_0,\hat{\mathfrak{r}})\,\mathrm{e}^{i(\mathfrak{e}_0\hat{\mathfrak{r}})}\,d\hat{\mathfrak{r}}}{\int\limits_L d\hat{\mathfrak{r}}\int\limits_L d\hat{\mathfrak{r}}'\,\{\varphi(-\mathfrak{e}_0,\hat{\mathfrak{r}})\,\varphi(\mathfrak{e}_0,\hat{\mathfrak{r}}') - \widehat{\operatorname{grad}}\,\varphi(-\mathfrak{e}_0,\hat{\mathfrak{r}})\,\widehat{\operatorname{grad}}'\varphi(\mathfrak{e}_0,\hat{\mathfrak{r}}')\}\,G(\hat{\mathfrak{r}}-\hat{\mathfrak{r}}')}.\end{aligned}\right\}\tag{108.7}$$

Das zweite Integral des Zählers von (108.7) ist nämlich zufolge (108.6) bis auf den Faktor $\frac{i}{2}(\mathfrak{n}\,\mathfrak{e}_0)$ gleich dem Nenner. Es läßt sich nun wieder leicht zeigen, daß das Funktional (108.5) bzw. (108.7) *stationär* ist bezüglich willkürlicher unabhängiger infinitesimaler Abweichungen der Flächenströme $\psi(\mathfrak{e}_0,\hat{\mathfrak{r}})$ und $\psi(-\mathfrak{e}_0,\hat{\mathfrak{r}})$ bzw. $\varphi(\mathfrak{e}_0,\hat{\mathfrak{r}})$ und $\varphi(-\mathfrak{e}_0,\hat{\mathfrak{r}})$ von ihrem durch die entsprechenden Gln. (108.2) bzw. (108.3) festgelegten Verlauf. Die etwas umständlichen Darstellungen (108.5) und (108.7) sind also dann von Vorteil, wenn man — unter Umgehung der Auflösung der Gln. (108.2) bzw. (108.3) — Näherungswerte für Q bzw. T zu gewinnen sucht, indem man mit plausiblen Ansätzen für ψ bzw. φ in die stationären Darstellungen eingeht.

In Abschn. Ib, Ziff. 123 und Ic, Ziff. 135 von Teil B werden wir die Methode der stationären Darstellung auf die Beugung am Spalt und an der Kreisscheibe anwenden. Bezüglich zahlreicher anderer Anwendungen vergleiche man die Literatur[1].

Denkt man sich sämtliche in (108.5) bzw. (108.7) auftretenden Größen in Potenzreihen nach dem Verhältnis ε eines charakteristischen Schirm- bzw. Öffnungsdurchmessers zur Wellenlänge im Sinne von Ziff. 91 *entwickelt*, so ergeben sich für Q bzw. T *Potenzreihen in* ε, deren *erstes Glied* jeweils lautet[2]

$$Q_p^0 = 2\,T_s^0 = \frac{4\pi\,\varepsilon^2 \left\{\int\limits_S \psi^0(\hat{\mathfrak{r}})\,d\hat{\mathfrak{r}}\right\}^4}{\left\{\int\limits_S d\hat{\mathfrak{r}} \int\limits_S d\hat{\mathfrak{r}}'\,\frac{\psi^0(\hat{\mathfrak{r}})\,\psi^0(\hat{\mathfrak{r}}')}{|\hat{\mathfrak{r}}-\hat{\mathfrak{r}}'|}\right\}^2} \tag{108.8}$$

bzw.

$$T_p^0 = \frac{1}{2}\,Q_s^0 = \frac{2\pi}{3}\,(\mathfrak{n}\,\mathfrak{e}_0)^2\,\varepsilon^6\,\frac{\left\{\int\limits_L \varphi^0(\hat{\mathfrak{r}})\,d\hat{\mathfrak{r}}\right\}^4}{\left\{\int\limits_L d\hat{\mathfrak{r}} \int\limits_L d\hat{\mathfrak{r}}'\,\frac{\widehat{\operatorname{grad}}\,\varphi^0(\hat{\mathfrak{r}})\,\widehat{\operatorname{grad}}'\,\varphi^0(\hat{\mathfrak{r}}')}{|\hat{\mathfrak{r}}-\hat{\mathfrak{r}}'|}\right\}^2}. \tag{108.9}$$

Dies sind also die Werte von Q und T im *Rayleighschen Grenzfall* sehr großer Wellenlänge. Dabei haben wir auch jeweils die Größen angegeben, die sich auf das (im Sinne des *Babinetschen Prinzips*) *komplementäre* Problem beziehen [vgl. Gl. (102.1)]. Wie wir in Ziff. 92 gesehen haben, ist ψ^0 nichts anderes als die *statische Ladungsdichte*, die sich auf den Schirm (S) einstellt, wenn er auf konstantes Potential gebracht wird. Daher ergibt sich mit Hilfe von (106.7) und mit $\varphi=1$, $W=\frac{C}{2}\,\varphi^2=\frac{C}{2}$

$$Q_p^0 = 2\,T_s^0 = \frac{C^2}{4\pi}, \tag{108.10}$$

wobei C die elektrostatische *Kapazität* des Schirmes (S) ist[3]. Andererseits zeigt (108.9) die typische Wellenlängenabhängigkeit (λ^{-4}) der Streuintensität *kleiner* Streuer (Rayleigh)[4].

109. Fernfeldamplitude in stationärer Darstellung. Ganz entsprechend wie für den Streu- bzw. Durchlaßquerschnitt ergeben sich für die *Fernfeldamplituden*

[1] J.W. Miles: J. Acoust. Soc. Amer. **17**, 259, 272 (1946). — Quart. Appl. Math. **7**, 45 (1949). — Phys. Rev. **75**, 695 (1949). — J. Appl. Phys. **20**, 760 (1949). — J. M. Blatt u. J.D. Jackson: Phys. Rev. **76**, 18 (1949). — T. Kato: Phys. Rev. **80**, 475 (1950). — Progr. Theoret. Phys. **6**, 295 (1951). — H. Levine: J. Acoust. Soc. Amer. **22**, 48 (1950); **23**, 307 (1951). — N.Y. Univ. Res. Rep. No. EM-84 (1955). — C.H. Papas: J. Appl. Phys. **21**, 318 (1950). — H. Levine u. C.H. Papas: J. Appl. Phys. **22**, 29 (1951). — A.A. Oliner: Polytechnic Inst. Brooklyn 1951. — J. Sevick u. J.E. Storer: Cruft Laboratory, Harvard Univ. Techn. Rep. No. 149 (1952); J. Appl. **25**, 369 (1954). — L.S. Sheingold: J. Appl. Phys. **24**, 415 (1953). — C.T. Tai: J. Appl. Phys. **20**, 1076 (1949); **23**, 909 (1952). — J. Shmoys: J. Opt. Soc. Amer. **41**, 324 (1951). — A. Levitas u. M. Lax: J. Acoust. Soc. Amer. **23**, 316 (1951). — S. J. Rubinow: Phys. Rev. **96**, 218 (1954). — Eine Übersicht über verschiedene Anwendungen findet man bei W. Sollfrey: N. Y. Univ. Res. Rep. No. EM-11 (1949). — N. Marcuvitz: Wave Guiste Handbook. New York-Toronto-London: McGraw-Hill 1951. — F.E. Borgnis u. C.H. Papas: l. c.

[2] Vgl. H. Levine u. J. Schwinger: l. c.

[3] Beim Vergleich von (108.8) mit (106.7) beachte man, daß die Integrationsvariable $\hat{\mathfrak{r}}$ in beiden Gleichungen um den Faktor ε verschieden definiert ist.

[4] Die Abhängigkeit von der Linearabmessung a des Streuers und der Wellenlänge λ ist $a^6\,\lambda^{-4}$.

(Fraunhofersches Feld) des Streu- bzw. Beugungsproblems [vgl. (96.2) und (96.2a)]

$$\left.\begin{aligned} A_p(\mathfrak{e}_0,\mathfrak{e}) &= -\frac{1}{4\pi}\int\limits_S \psi(\mathfrak{e}_0,\hat{\mathfrak{r}})\,e^{-i(\mathfrak{e}\hat{\mathfrak{r}})}\,d\hat{\mathfrak{r}} \\ \text{bzw.}\qquad B_p(\mathfrak{e}_0,\mathfrak{e}) &= \frac{i}{2\pi}(\mathfrak{n}\mathfrak{e})\int\limits_S \varphi(\mathfrak{e}_0,\hat{\mathfrak{r}})\,e^{-i(\mathfrak{e}\hat{\mathfrak{r}})}\,d\hat{\mathfrak{r}} \end{aligned}\right\} \tag{109.1}$$

die *stationären Darstellungen*

$$A_p(\mathfrak{e}_0,-\mathfrak{e}) = -\frac{1}{4\pi}\,\frac{\int\limits_S \psi(\mathfrak{e}_0,\hat{\mathfrak{r}})\,e^{i(\mathfrak{e}\hat{\mathfrak{r}})}\,d\hat{\mathfrak{r}}\cdot\int\limits_S \psi(\mathfrak{e},\hat{\mathfrak{r}})\,e^{i(\mathfrak{e}_0\hat{\mathfrak{r}})}\,d\hat{\mathfrak{r}}}{\int\limits_S d\hat{\mathfrak{r}}'\int\limits_S d\hat{\mathfrak{r}}''\,\psi(\mathfrak{e}_0,\hat{\mathfrak{r}}')\,G(\hat{\mathfrak{r}}'-\hat{\mathfrak{r}}'')\,\psi(\mathfrak{e},\hat{\mathfrak{r}}'')} \tag{109.2}$$

($\mathfrak{n}$ Schirmnormale, $\mathfrak{e}$ Einheitsvektor in Richtung des Aufpunktes $\mathfrak{r}=\mathfrak{e}r$) bzw.

$$\left.\begin{aligned} B_p(\mathfrak{e}_0,-\mathfrak{e}) &= -\frac{(\mathfrak{n}\mathfrak{e})(\mathfrak{n}\mathfrak{e}_0)}{4\pi}\cdot \\ &\cdot\frac{\int\limits_L \varphi(\mathfrak{e}_0,\hat{\mathfrak{r}})\,e^{i(\mathfrak{e}\hat{\mathfrak{r}})}\,d\hat{\mathfrak{r}}\cdot\int\limits_L \varphi(\mathfrak{e},\hat{\mathfrak{r}})\,e^{i(\mathfrak{e}_0,\hat{\mathfrak{r}})}\,d\hat{\mathfrak{r}}}{\int\limits_L d\hat{\mathfrak{r}}'\int\limits_L d\hat{\mathfrak{r}}''\,\{\varphi(\mathfrak{e}_0,\hat{\mathfrak{r}}')\,\varphi(\mathfrak{e},\hat{\mathfrak{r}}'') - \widehat{\operatorname{grad}}'\,\varphi(\mathfrak{e}_0\hat{\mathfrak{r}}')\,\widehat{\operatorname{grad}}''\,\varphi(\mathfrak{e},\hat{\mathfrak{r}}'')\}\,G(\hat{\mathfrak{r}}'-\hat{\mathfrak{r}}'')}. \end{aligned}\right\} \tag{109.3}$$

Diese Ausdrücke sind nämlich wieder stationär bezüglich der ersten Variation von $\psi(\mathfrak{e}_0,\hat{\mathfrak{r}})$ und $\psi(\mathfrak{e},\hat{\mathfrak{r}})$ bzw. $\varphi(\mathfrak{e}_0,\hat{\mathfrak{r}})$ und $\varphi(\mathfrak{e},\hat{\mathfrak{r}})$, wenn die exakten Werte dieser Flächenströme die entsprechenden Integralgleichungen (108.2) bzw. (108.3) befriedigen. Dabei ist ersichtlich $\psi(\mathfrak{e}_0,\hat{\mathfrak{r}})$ derjenige Strom, der von einer in der Richtung $\mathfrak{e}_0$ einfallenden ebenen Welle auf (S) erzeugt wird, $\psi(\mathfrak{e},\hat{\mathfrak{r}})$ hingegen entspricht einer in Richtung $\mathfrak{e}$ (Beobachtungsrichtung) einfallenden Welle. Einfalls- und Beobachtungsrichtung gehen hier ganz symmetrisch ein. Physikalisch bedeutet das die *Vertauschbarkeit von Einfalls- und Beobachtungsrichtung*. In der Tat folgt aus (109.2) bzw. (109.3) zufolge der Symmetrie der Greenschen Funktion das „*Reziprozitätsgesetzt*“

$$\left.\begin{aligned} A_p(\mathfrak{e},-\mathfrak{e}_0) &= A_p(\mathfrak{e}_0,-\mathfrak{e}) \\ \text{bzw.}\qquad B_p(\mathfrak{e},-\mathfrak{e}_0) &= B_p(\mathfrak{e}_0,-\mathfrak{e}). \end{aligned}\right\} \tag{109.4}$$

Entwickelt man wieder nach Potenzen von ε, so erhält man beispielsweise im Streufall aus (109.2) in nullter Näherung, vgl. (106.7)

$$A_p^0 = -\frac{\varepsilon\left\{\int\limits_S \psi^0(\hat{\mathfrak{r}})\,d\hat{\mathfrak{r}}\right\}^2}{\int\limits_L d\hat{\mathfrak{r}}\int\limits_L d\hat{\mathfrak{r}}'\,\frac{\psi^0(\hat{\mathfrak{r}})\,\psi^0(\hat{\mathfrak{r}}')}{|\hat{\mathfrak{r}}-\hat{\mathfrak{r}}'|}} = -\frac{C}{4\pi}. \tag{109.5}$$

Dies ist das bekannte Rayleighsche Ergebnis[1], für den *Zusammenhang zwischen Fernfeldamplitude und statischer Kapazität C des Schirmes, wenn dessen Abmessungen klein gegen die Wellenlänge sind* (vgl. Ziff. 96).

110. Stationäre Darstellung beliebiger linearer Feldgrößen. Auch jede andere *lineare Feldgröße* läßt sich als homogenes stationäres Funktional darstellen, worauf zuerst ERDÉLYI[2] aufmerksam gemacht hat. In diese Funktionale geht neben dem von der einfallenden Welle erzeugten Flächenstrom noch ein geeignet zu

[1] Lord RAYLEIGH: l. c. Fußote 3, S. 372.
[2] A. ERDÉLYI: Atti Accad. Sci. Torino **87**, 281 (1952/53).

wählender *Hilfsstrom* ein. Wir erläutern dies am Beispiel der *stationären Darstellung des Feldes in einen beliebigen Feldpunkt.* Dabei beschränken wir uns auf den *Streufall,* lassen jedoch wie in Gl. (I) auf S. 395 eine beliebige einfallende Welle v_0 zu. Das in Gl. (I) definierte Streufeld v_S läßt sich nun folgendermaßen darstellen

$$v_S(\mathfrak{r}) = -\frac{\int\limits_S \psi(\hat{\mathfrak{r}}')\, G(\mathfrak{r}-\hat{\mathfrak{r}}')\, d\hat{\mathfrak{r}}' \cdot \int\limits_S \psi_0(\mathfrak{r},\hat{\mathfrak{r}}')\, v_0(\hat{\mathfrak{r}}')\, d\hat{\mathfrak{r}}'}{\int\limits_S d\hat{\mathfrak{r}}' \int\limits_S d\hat{\mathfrak{r}}''\, \psi(\hat{\mathfrak{r}}')\, G(\hat{\mathfrak{r}}'-\hat{\mathfrak{r}}'')\, \psi_0(\mathfrak{r},\hat{\mathfrak{r}}'')}. \tag{110.1}$$

Dabei ist $\psi(\hat{\mathfrak{r}})$ der durch die einfallende Welle v_0 auf (S) hervorgerufene — durch Gl. (III) auf S. 395 definierte — Flächenstrom, während $\psi_0(\mathfrak{r},\hat{\mathfrak{r}})$ derjenige Flächenstrom ist, der auf (S) infolge einer im Aufpunkt $\mathfrak{r}$ angebrachten *Punktsingularität* (von $\mathfrak{r}$ ausgehende *Kugelwelle*) entsteht. $\psi_0(\mathfrak{r},\hat{\mathfrak{r}})$ ist also durch die zu Gl. (III) analoge Integralgleichung

$$\int\limits_S \psi_0(\mathfrak{r},\hat{\mathfrak{r}}'')\, G(\hat{\mathfrak{r}}'-\hat{\mathfrak{r}}'')\, d\hat{\mathfrak{r}}'' = G(\mathfrak{r}-\hat{\mathfrak{r}}') \tag{110.2}$$

zu definieren. Die Identität von (110.1) mit der zweiten Zeile von Gl. (I) folgt aus der Tatsache, daß das zweite Integral des Zählers in (110.1) zufolge Gl. (III) auf S. 395 mit dem Nenner übereinstimmt. Im Gegensatz zu Gl. (I) ist aber (110.1) stationär bezüglich beliebiger unabhängiger Variationen von ψ und ψ_0, wobei die exakten Werte dieser Größen durch die Integralgleichungen (III) und (110.2) definiert sind. Für eine angenäherte Berechnung des Streufeldes $v_S(\mathfrak{r})$ hat man also für die *beiden* Flächenströme $\psi(\hat{\mathfrak{r}})$ und $\psi_0(\mathfrak{r},\hat{\mathfrak{r}})$ geeignete Näherungen einzusetzen.

Wählt man insbesondere für $v_0(\mathfrak{r})$ eine vom Punkt $\mathfrak{r}_0$ ausgehende Kugelwelle $v_0(\mathfrak{r}) = G(\mathfrak{r}-\mathfrak{r}_0)$, so folgt aus (110.1) die Darstellung

$$v_S(\mathfrak{r}_0,\mathfrak{r}) = -\frac{\int\limits_S \psi(\mathfrak{r}_0,\hat{\mathfrak{r}}')\, G(\mathfrak{r}-\hat{\mathfrak{r}}')\, d\hat{\mathfrak{r}}' \cdot \int\limits_S \psi(\mathfrak{r},\hat{\mathfrak{r}}')\, G(\mathfrak{r}_0-\hat{\mathfrak{r}}')\, d\hat{\mathfrak{r}}'}{\int\limits_S d\hat{\mathfrak{r}}' \int\limits_S d\hat{\mathfrak{r}}''\, \psi(\mathfrak{r}_0,\hat{\mathfrak{r}}')\, G(\hat{\mathfrak{r}}'-\hat{\mathfrak{r}}'')\, \psi(\mathfrak{r},\hat{\mathfrak{r}}'')}, \tag{110.1'}$$

aus der man die allgemeine Reziprozität

$$v_S(\mathfrak{r},\mathfrak{r}_0) = v_S(\mathfrak{r}_0,\mathfrak{r}) \tag{110.3}$$

abliest.

Die Beschränkung auf ebene Schirme im vorangehenden ist unwesentlich. Für Körper endlichen Volumens lassen sich ganz entsprechende Überlegungen durchführen. Für den p-Fall können die vorangehenden Formeln für das Streuproblem direkt übernommen werden, wenn man den Schirm (S) durch die Oberfläche des streuenden Körpers ersetzt.

h 2) Vektorielle Felder in stationärer Darstellung.

Auf den räumlichen elektromagnetischen Fall lassen sich die vorangehenden Überlegungen ohne weiteres übertragen. Wir können uns dabei auf das *Streuproblem* beschränken, da das nach dem *Babinetschen Theorem* damit zusammenhängende *komplementäre* Problem ein *Beugungsproblem* ist, vgl. Ziff. 27 und 59.

111. Flächenstrom als Extremale eines Variationsprinzips. Zunächst zeigen wir, daß der durch die Integrodifferentialgleichung (55.3)

$$\int\limits_S \{\mathfrak{J}(\hat{\mathfrak{r}}') + \widehat{\operatorname{div}}'\,\mathfrak{J}(\hat{\mathfrak{r}}')\,\widehat{\operatorname{grad}}\}\, G(\hat{\mathfrak{r}}-\hat{\mathfrak{r}}')\, d\hat{\mathfrak{r}}' = i\,\hat{\mathfrak{E}}_0(\hat{\mathfrak{r}}) \tag{111.1}$$

definierte Flächenstrom *Extremale* des *Variationsproblems*

$$\int\limits_S d\hat{\mathfrak{r}}\left\{\int\limits_S d\hat{\mathfrak{r}}'[\mathfrak{J}(\hat{\mathfrak{r}})\,\mathfrak{J}(\hat{\mathfrak{r}}')-\widehat{\operatorname{div}}\,\mathfrak{J}(\hat{\mathfrak{r}})\,\widehat{\operatorname{div}}'\,\mathfrak{J}(\hat{\mathfrak{r}}')]\,G(\hat{\mathfrak{r}}-\hat{\mathfrak{r}}')+2i\,\hat{\mathfrak{E}}_0(\hat{\mathfrak{r}})\,\mathfrak{J}(\hat{\mathfrak{r}})\right\}=\text{Extr.} \tag{111.2}$$

ist. Durch Bildung der Variation bezüglich $\mathfrak{J}$ folgt nämlich

$$\int\limits_S d\hat{\mathfrak{r}}\left\{\int\limits_S[\mathfrak{J}(\hat{\mathfrak{r}}')+\widehat{\operatorname{div}}'\,\mathfrak{J}(\hat{\mathfrak{r}}')\,\widehat{\operatorname{grad}}]\,G(\hat{\mathfrak{r}}-\hat{\mathfrak{r}}')-i\,\hat{\mathfrak{E}}_0(\hat{\mathfrak{r}})\right\}\delta\mathfrak{J}(\hat{\mathfrak{r}})=0. \tag{111.3}$$

Dabei haben wir bereits die übliche Umformung mittels partieller Integration vorgenommen und berücksichtigt, daß der ausintegrierte Term verschwindet, wenn nur solche Vergleichsfunktionen $\mathfrak{J}$ zugelassen werden, die die *Kantenbedingung* $\mathfrak{J}_\perp=0$ längs des Randes (C) von (S) erfüllen. Soll der obige Ausdruck für im übrigen beliebige $\delta\mathfrak{J}$ verschwinden, so muß die geschweifte Klammer Null sein; wir kommen also zur Gl. (111.1) zurück. Damit ist gezeigt, daß (111.1) und (111.2) äquivalente Probleme sind.

Wir machen nun zur Bestimmung der Extremale $\mathfrak{J}$ wieder einen *Ritzschen Ansatz*

$$\mathfrak{J}(\hat{\mathfrak{r}})=\sum_{\nu=1}^{N}a_\nu\,\mathfrak{B}_\nu(\hat{\mathfrak{r}}) \tag{111.4}$$

mit einer geeignet gewählten Funktionenfolge $\mathfrak{B}_\nu(\hat{\mathfrak{r}})$, die der *Kantenbedingung* $\mathfrak{B}_{\nu\perp}=0$ längs (C) genüge. Das Variationsproblem (111.2) nimmt dann wieder die Form

$$\delta\sum_{\nu=1}^{N}a_\nu\left\{\sum_{\mu=1}^{N}a_\mu\,C_{\nu\mu}-2c_\nu\right\}=0 \tag{111.5}$$

an, wobei

$$\left.\begin{aligned}C_{\nu\mu}&=\int\limits_S d\hat{\mathfrak{r}}\int\limits_S d\hat{\mathfrak{r}}'\,\{\mathfrak{B}_\nu(\hat{\mathfrak{r}})\,\mathfrak{B}_\mu(\hat{\mathfrak{r}}')-\widehat{\operatorname{div}}\,\mathfrak{B}_\nu(\hat{\mathfrak{r}})\,\widehat{\operatorname{div}}'\,\mathfrak{B}_\mu(\hat{\mathfrak{r}}')\}\,G(\hat{\mathfrak{r}}-\hat{\mathfrak{r}}')\\ c_\nu&=i\int\limits_S\mathfrak{B}_\nu(\hat{\mathfrak{r}})\,\hat{\mathfrak{E}}_0(\hat{\mathfrak{r}})\,d\hat{\mathfrak{r}}\end{aligned}\right\} \tag{111.6}$$

gesetzt wurde. Die Variation bezüglich der a_ν liefert dann für diese a_ν das Gleichungssystem

$$\sum_{\nu=1}^{N}a_\nu\,C_{\nu\mu}=c_\mu,\qquad \mu=1,2,\ldots,N. \tag{111.7}$$

Dieses System ist wieder das bei $\nu=N$ abgebrochene System (70.5) da sich mit Hilfe der Fourier-Darstellung (67.1) für die Greensche Funktion $G(\mathfrak{r}-\mathfrak{r}')$ leicht nachweisen läßt, daß die in (70.6) definierten Koeffizienten mit (111.6) übereinstimmen (bis auf unwesentliche Faktoren; die $\mathfrak{B}_\nu$ seien reell). Bei der Ableitung über das Variationsproblem braucht jedoch wieder nirgends von einer Orthogonalität oder Vollständigkeit der $\mathfrak{B}_\nu$ Gebrauch gemacht zu werden.

112. Stationäre Darstellung des Fernfeldes des Hertzschen Vektors. Wir geben hier nur noch eine stationäre Darstellung der *Fernfeldamplitude* des *Hertzschen Vektors* [vgl. (53.1) und (69.2), (69.2a)]

$$\left.\begin{aligned}\mathfrak{Z}_S(\mathfrak{r})&=i\int\limits_S\mathfrak{J}(\hat{\mathfrak{r}}')\,G(\hat{\mathfrak{r}}'-\hat{\mathfrak{r}})\,d\hat{\mathfrak{r}}',\\ \mathfrak{Z}_S(\mathfrak{r})&\to\frac{i}{4\pi}\,\frac{e^{ir}}{r}\int\limits_S\mathfrak{J}(\hat{\mathfrak{r}})\,e^{-i(\mathfrak{e}\hat{\mathfrak{r}})}\,d\hat{\mathfrak{r}}\quad(\mathfrak{r}=\mathfrak{e}\,r,\quad r\to\infty)\end{aligned}\right\} \tag{112.1}$$

also der Größe

$$\overline{\mathfrak{J}}(\mathfrak{e})=\int\limits_S\mathfrak{J}(\hat{\mathfrak{r}})\,e^{-i(\mathfrak{e}\hat{\mathfrak{r}})}\,d\hat{\mathfrak{r}}. \tag{112.2}$$

Dabei kann (S) ein beliebiger (ebener oder gekrümmter) berandeter Schirm oder die Oberfläche eines beliebig gestalteten Körpers sein. Wir wollen uns im folgenden jedoch auf *ebene* Schirme beschränken, dann ist $\overline{\mathfrak{J}}$ die *Fourier-Transformierte* des Flächenstromes $\mathfrak{J}$; vgl. Ziff. 67. Bei gekrümmten Flächen hat man lediglich zu beachten, daß die Normale $\mathfrak{n}$ variabel ist, also jeweils mit unter das entsprechende Integral genommen werden muß. Aus $\overline{\mathfrak{J}}$ ergibt sich das *Fernfeld* des Streufeldes in der Gestalt [vgl. (103.5)]

$$\left.\begin{aligned} \mathfrak{E}_S(\mathfrak{r}) &\to -\frac{i}{4\pi}[\mathfrak{e}[\mathfrak{e}\overline{\mathfrak{J}}(\mathfrak{e})]]\frac{e^{ir}}{r} \\ \mathfrak{H}_S(\mathfrak{r}) &\to \frac{i}{4\pi}[\mathfrak{e}\overline{\mathfrak{J}}(\mathfrak{e})]\frac{e^{ir}}{r} \end{aligned}\right\}\quad \mathfrak{r} = \mathfrak{e}r, \quad r\to\infty. \tag{112.3}$$

Wir wollen jetzt die anregende Welle $\mathfrak{E}_0$ zu einer in der Richtung $\mathfrak{e}_0$ einfallenden, in Richtung $\mathfrak{n}_0$ *linear polarisierten ebenen Welle* spezialisieren ($\mathfrak{n}_0\mathfrak{e}_0 = 0$): $\mathfrak{E}_0(\mathfrak{r}) = \mathfrak{n}_0\, e^{i(\mathfrak{e}_0\mathfrak{r})}$. Gl. (111.1) nimmt dann die Form

$$\int_S \{\mathfrak{J}(\mathfrak{e}_0, \hat{\mathfrak{r}}') + \widehat{\operatorname{div}}'\,\mathfrak{J}(\mathfrak{e}_0, \hat{\mathfrak{r}}')\,\widehat{\operatorname{grad}}\}\, G(\hat{\mathfrak{r}} - \hat{\mathfrak{r}}')\, d\hat{\mathfrak{r}}' = i[[\mathfrak{n}\,\mathfrak{n}_0]\,\mathfrak{n}]\, e^{i(\mathfrak{e}_0\hat{\mathfrak{r}})}, \quad \hat{\mathfrak{r}}\ \mathit{auf}\ (S) \tag{112.4}$$

an. Für $\overline{\mathfrak{J}}$ in (112.2) erhält man jetzt die folgende Darstellung [dabei soll wieder die Einfallsrichtung $\mathfrak{e}_0$ mit in das Argument aufgenommen, also $\overline{\mathfrak{J}}(\mathfrak{e}_0, \mathfrak{e})$ statt $\overline{\mathfrak{J}}(\mathfrak{e})$ geschrieben werden; ferner ist $\mathfrak{n}_1$ die gemäß (112.3) zu $\mathfrak{e}$ gehörige Polarisationsrichtung]:

$$\left.\begin{aligned} &\left(\mathfrak{n}_1\overline{\mathfrak{J}}(\mathfrak{e}_0, -\mathfrak{e})\right) = \left(\mathfrak{n}_0\overline{\mathfrak{J}}(\mathfrak{e}, -\mathfrak{e}_0)\right) \\ &= \frac{i\int_S (\mathfrak{n}_0\mathfrak{J}(\mathfrak{e}, \hat{\mathfrak{r}}))\, e^{i(\mathfrak{e}_0\hat{\mathfrak{r}})}\, d\hat{\mathfrak{r}} \int_S (\mathfrak{n}_1\mathfrak{J}(\mathfrak{e}_0, \hat{\mathfrak{r}}))\, e^{i(\mathfrak{e}\hat{\mathfrak{r}})}\, d\hat{\mathfrak{r}}}{\int_S d\hat{\mathfrak{r}}' \int_S d\hat{\mathfrak{r}}'' \{\mathfrak{J}(\mathfrak{e}, \hat{\mathfrak{r}}')\,\mathfrak{J}(\mathfrak{e}_0, \hat{\mathfrak{r}}'') - \widehat{\operatorname{div}}'\,\mathfrak{J}(\mathfrak{e}, \hat{\mathfrak{r}}')\,\widehat{\operatorname{div}}''\,\mathfrak{J}(\mathfrak{e}_0, \hat{\mathfrak{r}}'')\}\, G(\hat{\mathfrak{r}}' - \hat{\mathfrak{r}}'')}. \end{aligned}\right\} \tag{112.5}$$

Die Übereinstimmung mit (112.2) ergibt sich wieder aus der Bemerkung, daß das erste Integral des Zählers von (112.5) mit dem Faktor i gerade gleich dem Nenner ist. Man bestätigt dies mit Hilfe der Integrodifferentialgleichung (112.4) und entsprechender partieller Integration unter Heranziehung der Kantenbedingung $\mathfrak{J}_\perp = 0$. Entsprechend läßt sich auch wieder zeigen, daß das Funktional (112.5) *stationär* ist bezüglich unabhängiger Variationen der Ströme $\mathfrak{J}(\mathfrak{e}_0, \hat{\mathfrak{r}})$ und $\mathfrak{J}(\mathfrak{e}, \hat{\mathfrak{r}})$, deren exakte Werte je durch die entsprechende Gl. (112.4) festgelegt sind.

Eine stationäre Darstellung für den *Streuquerschnitt* $Q(\mathfrak{e}_0)$ ergibt sich daraus mit Hilfe von (103.7), indem man den Ausdruck (112.5) in die Beziehung

$$Q(\mathfrak{e}_0) = \operatorname{Re}\left(\mathfrak{n}_0\overline{\mathfrak{J}}(\mathfrak{e}_0, \mathfrak{e}_0)\right) \tag{112.6}$$

einsetzt[1].

B. Spezielle Beugungsprobleme.

Im folgenden sollen die im Teil A besprochenen allgemeinen Methoden auf spezielle Fälle angewandt und dadurch näher erläutert werden. Hinsichtlich des zu behandelnden Stoffes wird dabei keine Vollständigkeit erstrebt, sondern wir beschränken uns auf die einfachsten und bekanntesten Beispiele[2]. Insbesondere sollen die zahlreichen Arbeiten über die Beugung an Objekten komplizierterer

[1] Vgl. dazu H. LEVINE u. J. SCHWINGER: Comm. Pure Appl. Math. **3**, 355 (1950).

[2] Eine Zusammenstellung der neueren Literatur zur Beugungstheorie findet sich in den Darstellungen von C. J. BOUWKAMP: Diffraction Theory, Progr. Phys. (Lond.) **17**, 35—100 (1954); W. FRANZ: Theorie der Beugung elektromagnetischer Wellen, Berlin-Göttingen-Heidelberg: Springer 1957; B. NOBLE: Methods based on the Wiener-Hopf Technique, London-New York-Paris-Los Angeles: Pergamon Press 1958, auf die wir schon mehrfach hingewiesen haben.

geometrischer Struktur, wie sie im Zusammenhang mit der Entwicklung der Mikrowellentechnik erschienen sind (Hohlleiterprobleme usw.), nicht berücksichtigt werden. Dafür werden wir die wenigen herausgegriffenen Beispiele zum Teil mehrmals mit Hilfe verschiedener Methoden in Angriff nehmen, um die inneren Zusammenhänge der verschiedenen Lösungswege zu beleuchten. Weiter wollen wir uns auf den Fall einer Strahlungsquelle im Unendlichen beschränken, d. h. die einfallende Strahlung als eine ebene Welle voraussetzen. Die Verallgemeinerung der Problemstellung auf den Fall einer punktförmigen oder linearen Strahlungsquelle im Endlichen (einfallende Kugel- oder Zylinderwelle) ist in manchen der betrachteten Beispiele ohne weiteres möglich, bietet jedoch methodisch nichts wesentlich Neues.

In einem ersten Abschnitt wenden wir uns zunächst der Beugung am *ebenen Schirm* zu und behandeln dann in einem zweiten Abschnitt die Beugung an räumlich ausgedehnten Objekten. In methodischer Hinsicht sind beide Abschnitte nicht streng voneinander geschieden; doch ist, wie ein Blick auf den allgemeinen Teil zeigt, für den ersten Abschnitt eine reichhaltigere Auswahl an Lösungsmethoden verfügbar.

I. Beugung an ebenen Schirmen.

a) Beugung an der Halbebene.

Die am längsten bekannte strenge Lösung eines Beugungsproblems, die sich zudem in geschlossener Form mit Hilfe eines Fresnelschen Integrals angeben läßt, ist die Beugung an der Halbebene. Dieses Problem läßt sich als Spezialfall der Beugung am *parabolischen Zylinder* behandeln, in dessen Koordinaten die Wellengleichung separierbar ist[1]. Jedoch gibt es mehrere Methoden, mit deren Hilfe das Problem der Beugung an der unendlich dünnen Halbebene direkt gelöst werden kann. Als erster hat A. Sommerfeld (1896) nach einem heuristischen Verfahren *verzweigte Lösungen* der Wellengleichung konstruiert, die auf Riemannschen Flächen mit einem Verzweigungspunkt eindeutig sind (Ziff. 113). Nach dem Spiegelungsverfahren (vgl. Abschn. AI f) läßt sich damit neben der Halbebene auch das Randwertproblem für einen *Keil* lösen (Ziff. 114). In neuerer Zeit sind das Wiener-Hopf-Verfahren und die Methode der singulären Integralgleichungen (Abschn. AIII c) zur systematischen Begründung des Sommerfeldschen Ergebnisses herangezogen worden (Ziff. 115). Der physikalische Grund für die relativ einfache Gestalt der Lösung liegt in der Tatsache, daß die Geometrie des Problems keine Länge enthält, die sich mit der Wellenlänge vergleichen läßt (die Ausdehnung der Halbebene ist unendlich groß, der Krümmungsradius der Kante unendlich klein). Für die wesentlich kompliziertere Gestalt der Lösung bei Existenz einer Vergleichslänge geben die folgenden Abschnitte Beispiele.

113. Sommerfelds Methode der verzweigten Lösungen. *α) Konstruktion der verzweigten Lösung.* Der einseitig durch eine gerade Kante ($x=0$, $z=0$) längs der y-

[1] Den auf der konvexen Seite angestrahlten parabolischen Zylinder behandeln P. S. Epstein: Diss. München 1914. — G. Condelli: Nuov. Cim. **11**, 277 (1916). — J. Brillouin: C. R. Acad. Sci., Paris **229**, 513 (1949). — W. Chester: Quart. J. Mech. **5**, 196 (1952). — J. Acoust. Soc. Amer. **24**, 324 (1952). — I. Kay: N.Y. Univ. Res. Rep. No. EM-53 (1953). — S.O. Rice: Bell. Syst. Techn. J. **33**, 417 (1954). — J.B. Keller u. B.R. Levy: N.Y. Univ. Res. Rep. No. EM-147 (1957). — Für den Fall, daß der parabolische Zylinder auf der konkaven Seite angestrahlt wird (parabolischer Zylinderspiegel) vgl. H. Lamb: Lond. Math. Soc. (2) **4**, 190 (1906). — W. Magnus: Jber. dtsch. Math.-Ver. **50**, 140 (1940). — Z. Physik **118**, 343 (1941). — H. Hochstadt: N.Y. Univ. Res. Rep. No. EM-89 (1956). — G.A. Grinberg, N. N. Lebedev, I.P. Skalskaia u. I. S. Uflyand: J. Exp. Theor. Phys. USSR. **30**, 528 (1956).

Achse begrenzte ebene Schirm ($x>0, z=0$) liege in der xy-Ebene (vgl. Fig. 54). Der Einfall der Strahlung aus dem Unendlichen erfolge *senkrecht* zur Kante, so daß sich das räumliche auf ein zweidimensionales Beugungsproblem in der xz-Ebene und damit das elektromagnetische auf ein skalares Beugungsproblem reduziert (vgl. Ziff. 4). Unter Verwendung ebener Polarkoordinaten r, φ in der xz-Ebene wird die aus der Richtung φ_0 (vgl. Fig. 54) einfallende ebene Welle:

$$v_0(r, \varphi) = \mathrm{e}^{-ikr\cos(\varphi-\varphi_0)}. \tag{113.1}$$

Zur Lösung des Problems verwenden wir nach dem Vorbilde von SOMMERFELD[1] das in Ziff. 28 entwickelte Verfahren der *verzweigten Lösungen*. Wir ergänzen die schlichte xz-Ebene zu einer *zweiblättrigen Riemannschen Fläche*, indem wir zum „*physikalischen*" Blatt $0<\varphi<2\pi$ ein „*mathematisches*" $-2\pi<\varphi<0$ hinzufügen. Wir haben dann die in φ mit 4π periodischen Lösungen der Wellengleichung $\Delta v+k^2 v=0$ zu betrachten.

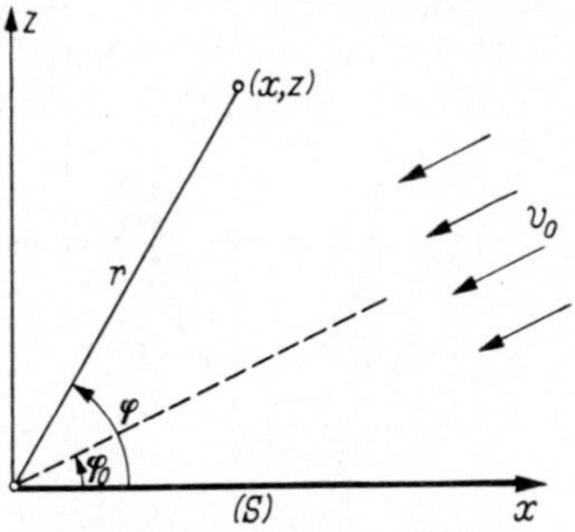

Fig. 54. Zur Beugung an der Halbebene.

Die von einer Lichtquelle im Unendlichen des physikalischen Blattes herrührende zweiwertige Lösung (vgl. Ziff. 28) erhalten wir durch geeignete Abänderung der entsprechenden einwertigen Lösung v_0 von Gl. (113.1). Hierzu formen wir v_0 zunächst um. Es sei $A_0(z)$ eine komplexe Funktion, die in $z=0$ einen einfachen Pol mit dem Residuum $1/2\pi i$ besitzt. Statt (113.1) können wir dann auf Grund des Cauchyschen Satzes schreiben

$$v_0 = \oint A_0(\beta-\varphi_0)\,\mathrm{e}^{-ikr\cos(\varphi-\beta)}\,d\beta \tag{113.2}$$

mit geschlossenem Integrationsumlauf um $\beta=\varphi_0$. Wir setzen insbesondere

$$A_0(z) = \frac{1}{2\pi}\cdot\frac{1}{\mathrm{e}^{iz}-1}. \tag{113.3}$$

[1] A. SOMMERFELD: Göttinger Nachr. **1894**, 338; **1895**, 268. — Math. Ann. **45**, 263 (1894); **47**, 317 (1896). — Zusammenfassende Darstellungen bei P. EPSTEIN: Enzyklopädie der mathematischen Wissenschaften, Bd. V, 3, Art. 24. Leipzig 1919. — G. WOLFSOHN: Handbuch der Physik, Bd. 20, Kap. 7. Berlin 1928. — A. SOMMERFELD in PH. FRANK u. R. v. MISES: Differential- und Integralgleichungen der Mechanik und Physik, Bd. II, Kap. 13 bzw. 20. Braunschweig 1927 bzw. 1934. — A. SOMMERFELD: Vorlesungen über theoretische Physik, Bd. IV, § 38. Wiesbaden 1950. — B.B. BAKER u. E.T. COPSON: The Mathematical Theory of Huygens, Principle, 2. Aufl., Kap. 4. Oxford 1950. — A. RUBINOWICZ: Die Beugungswelle in der Kirchhoffschen Theorie der Beugung, Kap. IV. Warschau 1957. — M. BORN u. E. WOLF: Prinziples of Optics, Kap. 11. London-New York-Paris-Los Angeles: Pergamon Press 1959. — Verallgemeinerte Lösungen (für allgemeinere einfallende Wellen) bzw. andere Lösungsmethoden bei H. POINCARÉ: Acta math. **20**, 313 (1897). — A. SOMMERFELD: Proc. Lond. Math. Soc. **28**, 395 (1897). — Z. Math. Phys. **46**, 11 (1901). — H. CARSLAW: Proc. Lond. Math. Soc. **30**, 121 (1899). — Proc. Edinb. Math. Soc. **19**, 71 (1901). — H. LAMB: Proc. Lond. Math. Soc. **4**, 190 (1906); **8**, 422 (1910). — C.W. OSEEN: Ark. Math. Astr. Fys. **7**, Nr. 25, 34, 40 (1911). — A. WIEGREFE: Ann. Phys. **39**, 449 (1912); **42**, 1241 (1913) (zum Teil fehlerhaft). — A. LANDÉ: Ann. Physik **48**, 521 (1915). — H.M. MACDONALD: Proc. Lond. Math. Soc. **14**, 410 (1915). — C. RAMAN u. K. KRISHNAN: Proc. Roy. Soc. Lond. A **116**, 254 (1927). — E.T. HANSON: Phil. Trans. Roy. Soc. Lond. A **237**, 48 (1938). — F. FRIEDLANDER: Proc. Roy. Soc. Lond. A **186**, 322 (1946). — Quart. J. Mech. Appl. Math. **4**, 344 (1951). — E.T. COPSON: Proc. Roy. Soc. Lond. A **202**, 277 (1950). — P.C. CLEMMOW: Quart. J. Mech. Appl. Math. **3**, 377 (1950). — Proc. Roy. Soc. Lond. A **205**, 286 (1951). — T.B.A. SENIOR: Proc. Roy. Soc. Lond. A **213**, 436 (1952). — Quart. J. Mech. Appl. Math. **6**, 101 (1953). — A.S. PETERS u. J.J. STOKER: Comm. Pure Appl. Math. **7**, 565 (1954). — J.W. WANDAKUROW: J. Exp. Theor. Phys. USSR. **26**, 3 (1954). — B.D. WOODS: Quart. J. Mech. Appl. Math. **10**, 90 (1957). — S.N. KARP: N.Y. Univ. Res. Rep. No. EM-108 (1957). — J.R. WAIT: Canad. J. Phys. **35**, 693 (1957). — W.E. WILLIAMS: Quart. J. Mech. Appl. Math. **10**, 210 (1957); Canad. J. Phys. **38**, 507 (1960). — A.P. BURGER: Proc. Roy. Soc. Lond. A **252**, 411 (1959).

Durch die Substitution $\beta=\gamma+\varphi$ geht (113.2) mit der Abkürzung $\varphi-\varphi_0=\psi$ in die Form

$$v_0=\int_C A_0(\gamma+\psi)\,\mathrm{e}^{-ikr\cos\gamma}\,d\gamma \tag{113.4}$$

mit $\gamma=-\psi$ umschließendem Integrationsweg über. Durch Ausweitung des Umlaufes erhält man den in Fig. 55 gezeichneten aus vier Teilen zusammengesetzten Weg. In den schraffierten Gebieten der γ-Ebene hat der Exponent $-ikr\cdot\cos\gamma$ einen negativen Realteil; der Integrand verschwindet daher im Unendlichen dieser Gebiete, und der Weg darf in der angezeigten Weise ins Unendliche geführt werden. Wegen der Periodizität des Integranden heben sich die Integrale längs D_1 und D_2 gegenseitig weg, und es bleibt als Ergebnis der Umformung nur das Integral längs des aus zwei Ästen zusammengesetzten Weges C übrig, was in Gl. (113.4) schon vermerkt ist.

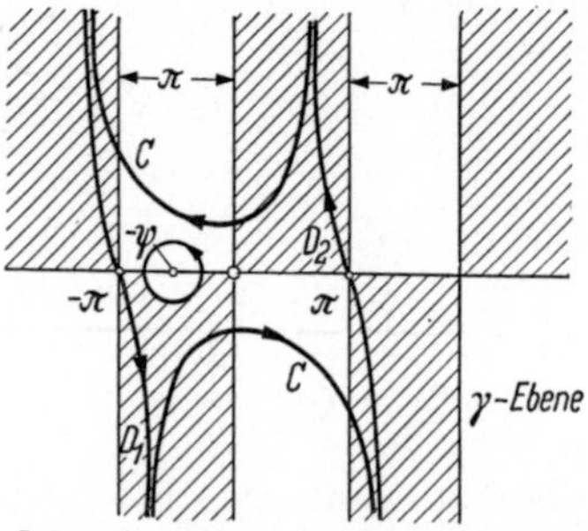

Fig. 55. Integrationswege in der komplexen γ-Ebene für die Darstellung der einfallenden Welle nach Sommerfeld, Gl. (113.4).

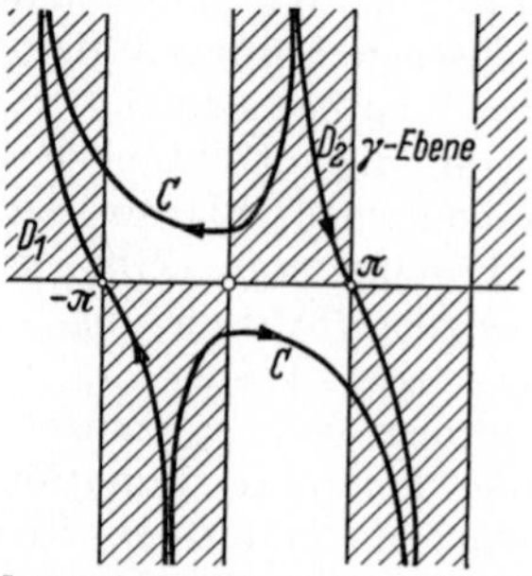

Fig. 56. Integrationsweg für Gl. (113.4a); Umkehrung der Integrationsrichtung auf D_1 und D_2 gegenüber Fig. 55.

Für die gesuchte *zweiwertige Lösung* setzen wir analog den Gln. (113.2) und (113.3) an:

$$u(r,\varphi)=\int A(\beta-\varphi_0)\,\mathrm{e}^{-ikr\cos(\varphi-\beta)}\,d\beta \tag{113.2a}$$

mit

$$A(z)=\frac{1}{4\pi}\cdot\frac{1}{\mathrm{e}^{\frac{iz}{2}}-1}. \tag{113.3a}$$

(113.2a) genügt bei beliebiger Wahl des Integrationsweges der Wellengleichung. Nach Durchführung der Substitution $\beta=\gamma+\varphi$ legen wir den Weg fest, indem wir den Weg C von Gl. (113.4) übernehmen:

$$u=\int_C A(\gamma+\psi)\,\mathrm{e}^{-ikr\cos\gamma}\,d\gamma. \tag{113.4a}$$

Ersichtlich ist u in φ mit 4π periodisch. Weiter haben wir zu zeigen, daß die Welle u von einer Quelle im Unendlichen des „*physikalischen*“ *Blattes* herrührt und im übrigen der Ausstrahlungs- sowie der Kantenbedingung genügt.

Wir untersuchen das Verhalten für $r\to\infty$. Zu diesem Zwecke deformieren wir den Weg C in die beiden umgekehrt wie in Fig. 55 durchlaufenen Wege D_1 und D_2 (vgl. Fig. 56), die ganz auf schraffiertem Gebiet liegen und daher für $r\to\infty$ einzeln verschwinden. Hinzu tritt, wenn der Pol $\gamma=-\psi$ von A sich zwischen $-\pi$ und π befindet, noch ein Umlauf um diesen Pol, der durch Residuenbildung die einfallende Welle v_0 liefert. Wir haben demnach zwei Fälle zu unterscheiden und erhalten als Grenzwert von u für $r\to\infty$:

$$u_\infty=\begin{cases} v_0 & \text{für } |\psi|<\pi \quad \text{„beleuchtetes Gebiet“} \\ 0 & \text{für } |\psi|>\pi \quad \text{„Schattengebiet“}. \end{cases} \tag{113.5}$$

Der Einfall der Welle v_0 erfolgt hiernach, wie gefordert, nur aus der Richtung $\varphi=\varphi_0\,(\psi=0)$ des „physikalischen" Blattes, während die entsprechende Richtung $\varphi=\varphi_0\pm 2\pi\,(\psi=\pm 2\pi)$ des „*mathematischen" Blattes* dem Schattengebiet angehört.

Durch die Parallelverschiebung $\gamma=\eta\mp\pi$ gehen D_1 und D_2 in den gemeinsamen Weg D von Fig. 57 über, der von oben nach unten durchlaufen werde, und man erhält mit der Abkürzung

$$\Phi(\eta)=-A(\eta-\pi+\psi)+A(\eta+\pi+\psi)=\frac{1}{4\pi i}\cdot\frac{1}{\cos\frac{\eta+\psi}{2}} \tag{113.6}$$

als neuen mit Gl. (113.4a) gleichbedeutenden Ausdruck

$$u=u_\infty+\int_D \Phi(\eta)\,\mathrm{e}^{ikr\cos\eta}\,d\eta. \tag{113.7}$$

Das Verhalten des Integrals für $r\to\infty$ ergibt sich durch Anwendung der Sattelpunktsmethode auf die Umgebung des Sattelpunktes $\eta=0$ zu

$$\Phi(0)\,\mathrm{e}^{ikr}\int\mathrm{e}^{-ikr\frac{\eta^2}{2}}\,d\eta=\Phi(0)\,\mathrm{e}^{i\left(kr-\frac{\pi}{4}\right)}\sqrt{\frac{2\pi}{kr}}. \tag{113.8}$$

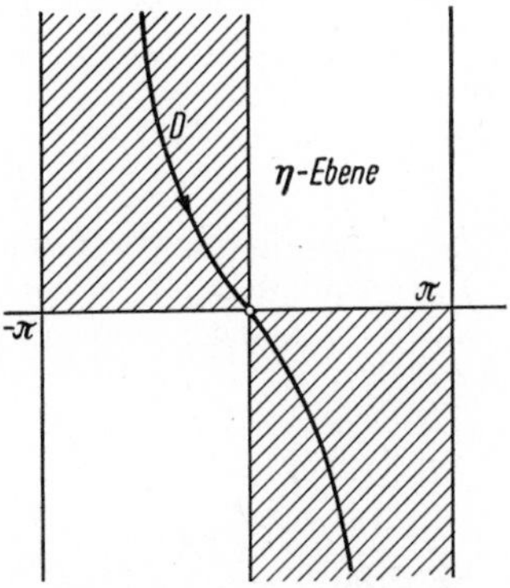

Fig. 57. Integrationsweg entsprechend der Substitution $\eta=\gamma\mp\pi$.

Das ist eine auslaufende Zylinderwelle, in Einklang mit der Ausstrahlungsbedingung. Das asymptotische Verhalten von u ist, gegenüber dem Grenzwert u_∞ verschärft, nach (113.6) bis (113.8) gegeben durch

$$u\to u_\infty-\frac{1}{2\sqrt{2\pi kr}\cos\frac{\psi}{2}}\cdot\mathrm{e}^{i\left(kr+\frac{\pi}{4}\right)}\quad \textit{für } r\to\infty. \tag{113.9}$$

Die Formeln (113.7) und (113.9) werden an den Schattengrenzen $|\psi|=\pi$ wegen $\cos\frac{\psi}{2}=0$ ungültig. Daß u sich auch in diesen Richtungen trotzdem regulär verhält, erkennt man aus der Darstellung (113.4a).

Schließlich bestätigen wir, daß die Kantenbedingung erfüllt ist, die die Endlichkeit von u für $r\to 0$ fordert. Offenbar konvergiert das Integral in (113.7) wegen (113.6) auch für $r=0$; u bleibt also für $r\to 0$ tatsächlich endlich.

β) Darstellung durch ein Fresnelsches Integral. Die Welle u läßt sich in ein *Fresnelsches Integral* umformen. Wir betrachten zunächst das Schattengebiet $|\psi|>\pi$ und verwenden (113.7) mit $u_\infty=0$. Durch Spiegelung am Punkte $\eta=0$ geht die obere in die untere Hälfte des Weges D über, und es ergibt sich mit

$$\Phi(\eta)+\Phi(-\eta)=\frac{1}{\pi i}\cdot\frac{\cos\frac{\eta}{2}\cdot\cos\frac{\psi}{2}}{\cos\eta+\cos\psi} \tag{113.10}$$

unter Abspaltung der ebenen Welle v_0 als Faktor:

$$u=v_0\cdot f(r,\psi),\qquad f=\frac{1}{\pi i}\cos\frac{\psi}{2}\int_0^{\frac{\pi}{2}-i\infty}\mathrm{e}^{ikr(\cos\eta+\cos\psi)}\cdot\frac{\cos\frac{\eta}{2}\,d\eta}{\cos\eta+\cos\psi}. \tag{113.11}$$

Durch Differentiation entsteht

$$\frac{\partial f}{\partial r}=\frac{k}{\pi}\cos\frac{\psi}{2}\int_0^{\frac{\pi}{2}-i\infty}\mathrm{e}^{ikr(\cos\eta+\cos\psi)}\cos\frac{\eta}{2}\,d\eta, \tag{113.12}$$

was sich wegen $\cos\eta + \cos\psi = 2\left(\cos^2\frac{\psi}{2} - \sin^2\frac{\eta}{2}\right)$ mit Hilfe der Substitution $(1+i)\sqrt{kr}\sin\frac{\eta}{2} = z$ zu

$$\frac{\partial f}{\partial r} = \sqrt{\frac{k}{2\pi r}}\cos\frac{\psi}{2}\, e^{2ikr\cos^2\frac{\psi}{2} - \frac{i\pi}{4}} \tag{113.13}$$

ausrechnen läßt. Integration nach r unter Verwendung der Integrationsvariablen $\tau = 2\sqrt{\frac{kr}{\pi}}\cos\frac{\psi}{2}$ liefert

$$f = \frac{e^{-\frac{i\pi}{4}}}{\sqrt{2}}\int\limits_{-\infty}^{\varrho} e^{\frac{i\pi\tau^2}{2}}\,d\tau, \qquad \varrho = 2\sqrt{\frac{kr}{\pi}}\cos\frac{\psi}{2}. \tag{113.14}$$

Die Integrationskonstante ist dabei dadurch festgelegt, daß f im Schattengebiet für $r\to\infty$, d.i. $\varrho\to-\infty$ wegen $|\psi| > \pi$, verschwinden muß. Der Ausdruck für die Welle u wird schließlich nach (113.11)

$$u(r,\varphi) = \frac{1}{\sqrt{2}}\, e^{-i\left\{kr\cos(\varphi-\varphi_0) + \frac{\pi}{4}\right\}} \int\limits_{-\infty}^{2\sqrt{\frac{kr}{\pi}}\cos\frac{\varphi-\varphi_0}{2}} e^{\frac{i\pi}{2}\tau^2}\,d\tau. \tag{113.15}$$

Er ist als analytische Funktion von ψ in der ganzen Riemannschen Fläche gültig. Insbesondere liefert er für $r\to\infty$ nicht nur im Schattengebiet $(\varrho\to-\infty)$, sondern auch im beleuchteten Gebiet $(\varrho\to\infty)$ das richtige Verhalten von Gl. (113.5).

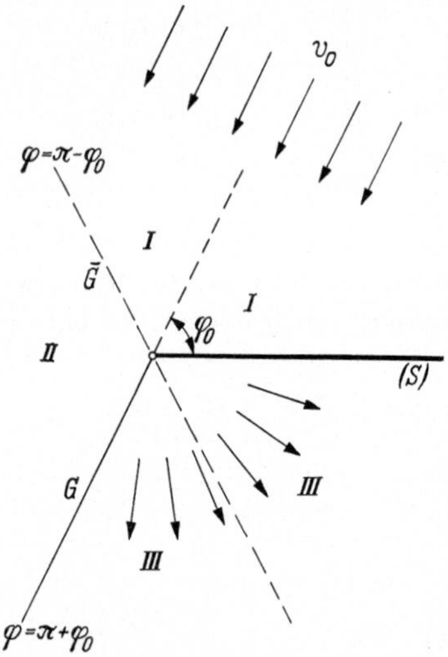

Fig. 58. Gebietseinteilung bei der Halbebene durch Schattengrenze G und Reflexionsgrenze $\bar{G}$.

114. Diskussion der Lösung und Verallgemeinerungen. In Fig. 58 sind die Verhältnisse beim Problem der Halbebene vom Standpunkte der geometrischen Optik veranschaulicht Der physikalische Raum wird durch die Schattengrenzen G und $\bar{G}$ der einfallenden und der am Schirm reflektierten Strahlung in die drei Gebiete I, II und III zerlegt. I und II sind beleuchtet. III liegt im geometrischen Schatten.

Um die Lösung des Beugungsproblems zu gewinnen, bilden wir nach der Vorschrift von Ziff. 28 die an (S) gespiegelte Welle $\bar{u}$, indem wir in u den Winkel φ durch $-\varphi$ ersetzen. Die Lösung ist dann $v = u \mp \bar{u}$, wobei sich das obere bzw. untere Vorzeichen auf die Randbedingung $v = 0$ bzw. $\partial v/\partial z = 0$ am Schirm bezieht, entsprechend einem parallel bzw. senkrecht zur Kante polarisierten elektrischen Vektor (vgl. Ziff. 4).

Wir gehen von der Darstellung (113.7) für u aus, in der die der geometrischen Optik entsprechende nur im „beleuchteten" Gebiet vorhandene ebene Welle u_∞ als besonderes Glied abgespalten ist. Letzteres fassen wir mit dem entsprechenden Anteil der gespiegelten Welle $\bar{u}$ zu v_g zusammen, so daß gilt

$$v_g(r,\varphi) = \left\{\begin{array}{ll} e^{-ikr\cos(\varphi-\varphi_0)} \mp e^{-ikr\cos(\varphi+\varphi_0)} & \textit{in } \mathrm{I} \\ e^{-ikr\cos(\varphi-\varphi_0)} & \textit{in } \mathrm{II} \\ \qquad 0 & \textit{in } \mathrm{III}. \end{array}\right\} \tag{114.1}$$

Zusammenfassung von (113.6) mit dem durch Vorzeichenumkehr von φ entstehenden Glied liefert

$$\Phi(\eta)\mp\bar{\Phi}(\eta)=\frac{1}{4\pi i}\left(\frac{1}{\cos\frac{\eta+\varphi-\varphi_0}{2}}\mp\frac{1}{\cos\frac{\eta-\varphi-\varphi_0}{2}}\right). \tag{114.2}$$

Da der Integrationsweg D (vgl. Fig. 57) symmetrisch zum Nullpunkt liegt und der Exponentialfaktor im Integranden von (113.7) in η gerade ist, können wir im zweiten Summanden von (114.2) η durch $-\eta$ ersetzen und erhalten nach einiger Rechnung für die beiden Polarisationsfälle

$$v(r,\varphi)=u\mp\bar{u}=v_g(r,\varphi)\mp\frac{1}{\pi i}\frac{\sin}{\cos}\left(\frac{\varphi_0}{2}\right)\int\limits_D e^{ikr\cos\eta}\frac{\sin}{\cos}\left(\frac{\eta+\varphi}{2}\right)\frac{d\eta}{\cos(\eta+\varphi)+\cos\varphi_0}. \tag{114.3}$$

Entsprechend gewinnen wir die für die Beobachtung maßgeblichen asymptotischen Verhältnisse aus (113.9):

$$v(r,\varphi)\to v_g(r,\varphi)-\frac{e^{i\left(kr+\frac{\pi}{4}\right)}}{2\sqrt{2\pi kr}}\left\{\frac{1}{\cos\frac{\varphi-\varphi_0}{2}}\mp\frac{1}{\cos\frac{\varphi+\varphi_0}{2}}\right\}\quad \textit{für}\quad r\to\infty. \tag{114.4}$$

Das zweite Glied in (114.3), (114.4) stellt die *Beugungswelle* dar. Diese interferiert in den beleuchteten Gebieten I und II mit v_g (*Youngsches Prinzip*, vgl. Ziff. 32). Im geometrischen Schatten III tritt die Beugungswelle isoliert auf und ist daher am besten der experimentellen Untersuchung zugänglich. Hier läßt sie sich in der Tat beobachten[1], einschließlich der zu erwartenden Polarisationseffekte. Geringfügige Abweichungen zwischen Experiment und Theorie sind daraus verständlich, daß die Voraussetzungen unendlich geringer Dicke (scharfe Schneide) und idealer Leitfähigkeit des Schirms im Experiment nicht hinreichend erfüllt sind.

Wir diskutieren die Beugungswelle für $r\to\infty$ oder genauer $kr\gg 1$. Ihre Intensität wächst nach (114.4) in *der Nähe der Schattengrenzen* $\varphi=\pi\pm\varphi_0$ stark an. Hier ist jeweils nur einer der beiden Summanden der Beugungswelle ausschlaggebend. Insbesondere ist in der Nähe von G, wo $\bar{u}$ auch zu v_g nichts beiträgt, $\bar{u}$ gegenüber u ganz zu vernachlässigen. Es *verschwindet daher dort der Einfluß der Polarisation.* Führen wir durch $\varphi=\pi+\varphi_0+\delta$ den gegen die Schattengrenze G gemessenen Winkel δ ein, so ist der fragliche Winkelbereich durch $|\delta|\ll 1$ gekennzeichnet. Ist darüber hinaus $|\delta|\lesssim\frac{1}{\sqrt{kr}}$, so wird (114.4) unbrauchbar. Wir verwenden daher zur Beschreibung des Übergangs zwischen beleuchtetem Gebiet II und Schattengebiet III die strenge Formel (113.15) für u unter Vernachlässigung von $\bar{u}$, die mit δ anstelle φ lautet

$$v\to u=v_0\frac{e^{-\frac{i\pi}{4}}}{\sqrt{2}}\int\limits_{-\infty}^{-2\sqrt{\frac{kr}{\pi}}\sin\frac{\delta}{2}}e^{\frac{i\pi}{2}\tau^2}\,d\tau,\qquad kr\gg 1,\qquad |\delta|\ll 1. \tag{114.5}$$

Das Ergebnis stimmt im betrachteten Bereich mit der Kirchhoffschen Näherung (vgl. Ziff. 116) überein.

[1] L. G. Gouy: C. R. Acad. Sci., Paris **96**, 697 (1883); **98**, 1573 (1884); **100**, 977 (1885). — Ann. Chim. Phys. **8**, 145 (1886). — W. Wien: Wied. Ann. **28**, 117 (1886). — E. Maey: Wied. Ann. **49**, 69 (1893). — F. Jentzsch: Ann. Phys. **84**, 292 (1927). — J. Savornin: Ann. de Phys. **11**, 129 (1939). — A. Rubinowicz: l. c. Kap. V, § 9. — Versuche mit Mikrowellen bei C.W. Horton u. R.B. Watson: J. Appl. Phys. **21**, 16 (1950). — B.N. Harden: Proc. Inst. Electr. Engrs. **99** III, 229 (1952). — R.D. Kodis: J. Appl. Phys. **23**, 249 (1952). — R.V. Row: J. Appl. Phys. **24**, 1448 (1953).

Da das Beugungsbild (114.5) *für die Umgebung der Schattengrenze von der gewählten Randbedingung unabhängig* ist, dürfen wir vermuten, daß hier auch das Material des Schirms ohne Einfluß ist. Das wird durch die Beobachtung bestätigt[1].

Eine interessante Illustration des Gesamtfeldes v für die Beugung an der Halbebene gibt eine Arbeit von Braunbek und Laukien[2], aus der die Fig. 59 bis 61 entnommen sind. Die Bilder beziehen sich auf den senkrecht von unten erfolgenden Einfall einer ebenen elektromagnetischen Welle, deren magnetische Feldstärke parallel zur beugenden Kante schwingt (Randbedingung $\partial v/\partial z = 0$, $v =$ magnetische Feldstärke) und erfassen den Umkreis etwa einer Wellenlänge um die Kante. In den Fig. 59 und 60 sind die Kurven konstanter Phase und konstanter Amplitude des Magnetfeldes wiedergegeben, in Fig. 61 der Verlauf des zeitlich gemittelten Energiestromes. Energiestrom und Phasenkurven sind zueinander *orthogonal*. Die Abbildungen lassen erkennen, daß auf der linken, offenen Seite die einfallende Welle durch den rechts befindlichen Schirm nur wenig gestört ist. Auf der Rückseite des Schirmes erfolgt die Strahlung qualitativ in Form einer von der Kante ausgehenden Zylinderwelle mit radial und nach rechts abnehmender Intensität. Es ist bemerkenswert, daß sich dieses Bild schon in so geringem

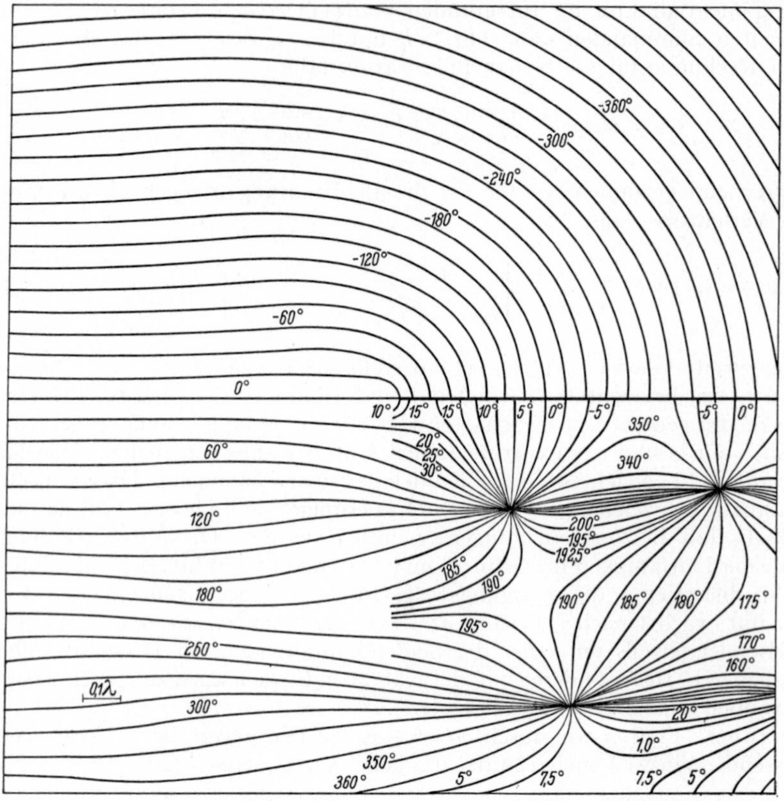

Fig. 59. Kurven konstanter Phase bei senkrechtem Einfall (von unten) auf die Halbebene (nach Braunbek und Laukien).

[1] Neuere Versuche hierzu: K.L. McDonald u. F.S. Harris: J. Opt. Soc. Amer. **42**, 321 (1952).

[2] W. Braunbek u. G. Laukien: Optik **9**, 174 (1952).

Abstand von der Kante ausprägt, obgleich die Kante ja tatsächlich nicht strahlt. Vor dem Schirm ist das Bild im wesentlichen durch die Überlagerung von einfallender und reflektierter Welle bestimmt; besonders eigenartig ist dabei der Verlauf des mittleren Energiestromes.

Eine Verallgemeinerung der bisherigen Betrachtungen ist die Theorie der *Beugung am Keil*[1]. Auch hierbei wird der „physikalische" Raum (=Außenraum

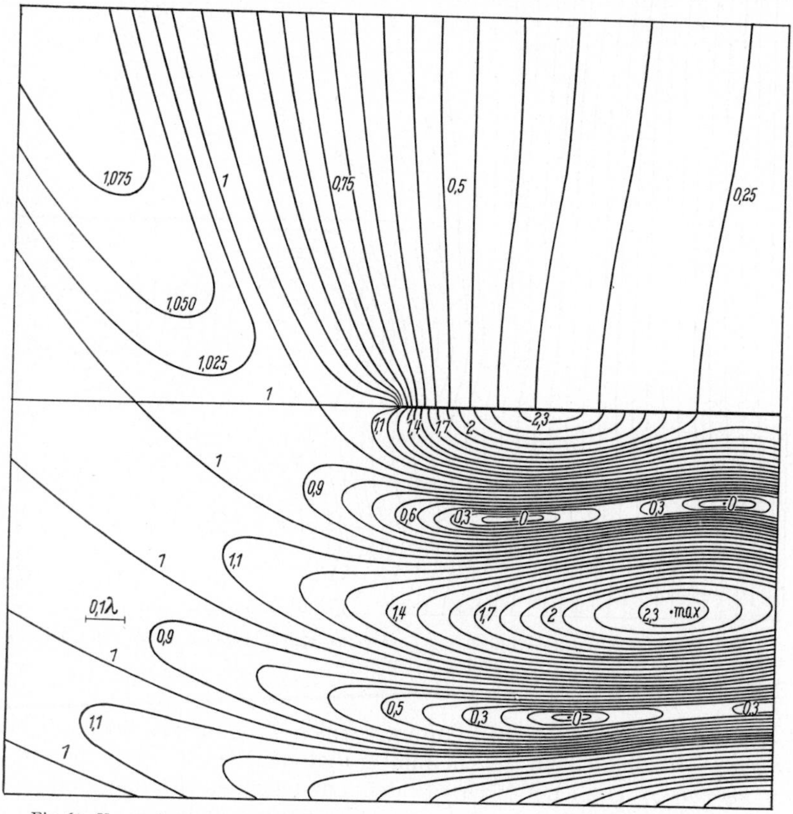

Fig. 60. Kurven konstanter Amplitude bei senkrechtem Einfall (nach BRAUNBEK und LAUKIEN).

[1] A. SOMMERFELD: Math. Ann. **47**, 317 (1896). — H. S. CARSLAW: Phil. Mag. **5**, 374 (1903). — Proc. Lond. Math. Soc. **18**, 291 (1920). — F. REICHE: Ann. Physik **37**, 131 (1912). — H.M. MACDONALD: Electric Waves, S. 186. Cambridge 1902. — Proc. Lond. Math. Soc. **14**, 410 (1915). — A. WIEGREFE: Ann. Physik **39**, 449 (1912). — T. J. I'A. BROMWICH: Proc. Lond. Math. Soc. **14**, 450 (1916). — A. RUBINOWICZ: Math. Ann. **96**, 648 (1927). — W. SOLLFREY: N.Y. Univ. Res. Rep. No. EM-45 (1952). — H. G. GARNIER: Bull. Soc. Roy. Sci. Liège **21**, 119, 207 (1952). — G. HERGLOTZ: Math. Ann. **124**, 219 (1952). — F. OBERHETTINGER: Comm. Pure Appl. Math. **7**, 551 (1954). — R. TEISSEYRE: Bull. Acad. Pol. Sci., Cl. III **3**, 157, 523 (1955). — Nuovo Cim. X **2**, 869 (1955). — Bull. Acad. Pol. Sci., Cl. III **4**, 433 (1956). — Dielektrische Keile bzw. Keile mit endlicher Leitfähigkeit (Impedanz-Grenzbedingung) behandeln D. S. JONES u. F. B. PIDDUCK: Quart. J. Math. **1**, 229 (1950). — L. B. FELSEN: McGill Symposium, Montreal 1953. — T. B. A. SEMIOR: Univ. of Michigan, Studies in Radar Cross Section **25** (1957). — F.C. KARAL u. S.N. KARP: Comm. Pure Appl. Math. **11**, 495 (1958). — N.Y. Univ. Res. Rep. No. EM-123 (1959). — G.D. MALYUGHINETZ: Sov. Phys. Doklady **3**, 752 (1958). — Ann. Phys. **6**, 107 (1960). — W.E. WILLIAMS: Proc. Cambridge Phil. Soc. **55**, 195 (1959). — S.N. KARP: N.Y. Univ. Res. Rep. No. EM-129 (1959). — S.N. KARP u. F.C. KARAL: Comm. Pure Appl. Math. **12**, 435 (1959). — N.Y. Univ. Res. Rep. No. EM-124 (1959); No. EM-145 (1959); No. EM-146 (1960). — Den rechtwinkligen Doppelkeil behandelt H.M. NUSSENZVEIG: Phil. Trans. Roy. Soc. Lond. A **252**, 1, 31 (1959).

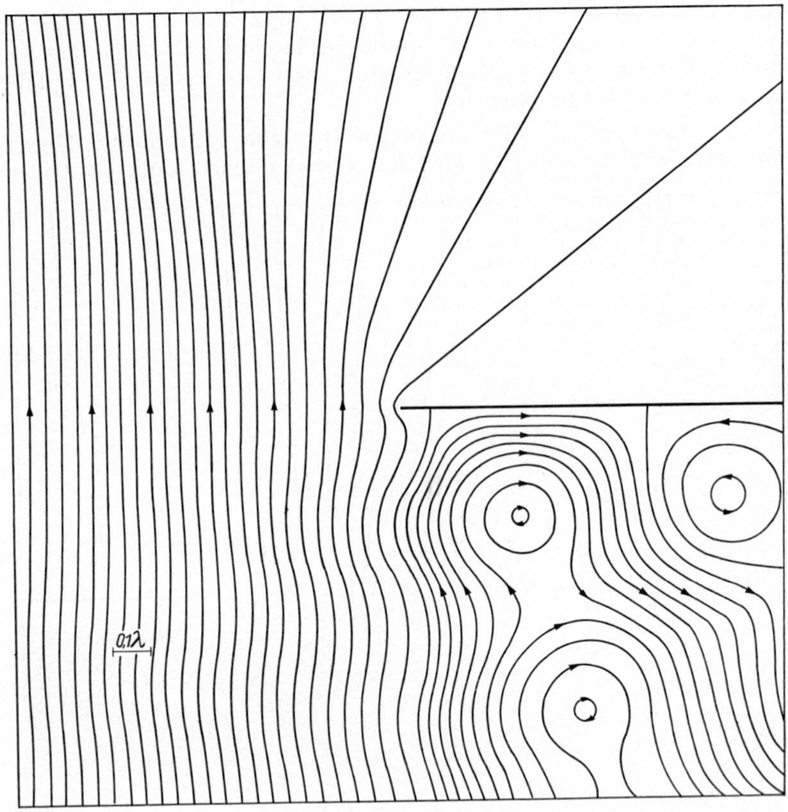

Fig. 61. Energieströmung bei senkrechtem Einfall (senkrecht zu den Kurven konstanter Phase, nach Braunbek und Laukien).

des Keils, vgl. Fig. 62) mit dem Öffnungswinkel ξ — entsprechend 2π bei der Halbebene — einschließlich der in ihm enthaltenen Quelle an seinen Begrenzungen ($\varphi = 0, \xi$) gespiegelt. Die beiden entstehenden Räume und Quellen fallen aber jetzt — im Gegensatz zu den Verhältnissen bei der Halbebene — nicht miteinander zusammen. Das Spiegelungsverfahren muß daher fortgesetzt werden, bis sich die neu entstehenden „mathematischen“ Räume mit dem „physikalischen“ Raum zu einem mehrblättrigen Riemannschen Raume zusammenschließen. Damit das in endlich vielen Schritten möglich ist, muß ξ ein rationales Vielfaches von π sein.

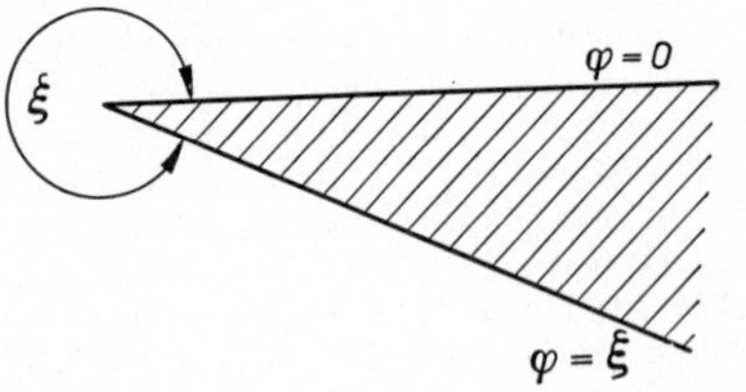

Fig. 62. Zur Beugung am Keil.

Mit $\xi = \frac{p}{m}\pi$ erhält man einen p-fachen Riemannschen Raum, der aus $2m$ Teilräumen der Öffnung ξ mit je einer Quelle zusammengesetzt ist. Interessant ist der Fall $p=1$ (Winkelspiegel von der Öffnung π/m, $m = 1, 2, 3 \ldots$), der sich im *schlichten Raum* behandeln läßt und in dem daher nur Interferenzen zwischen ebenen Wellen, jedoch keine Beugungswellen auftreten.

Mathematisch bietet der Übergang von der zweiwertigen zur p-wertigen Lösung keine Schwierigkeit. Der Umformung der zweideutigen Welle (113.2a) in ein Fresnelsches Integral entspricht eine Darstellung der p-deutigen Welle als konfluente hypergeometrische Funktion[1].

115. Direkte Lösung der Integralgleichungen für die Fourier-Amplitude. SOMMERFELDs Ansatz (113.2a) stellt eine Fourier-Transformation der verzweigten Lösung u dar, durch die die Wellenamplitude A anstelle von u als neue unbekannte Funktion eingeführt wird. Das Auffinden von A geschieht bei SOMMERFELD heuristisch. Wir wollen jetzt noch einen Weg aufzeigen, der zu einer systematischen Bestimmung der Fourier-Amplitude führt und auch bei komplizierteren Einkantenproblemen gangbar ist (Wiener-Hopf-Verfahren). In Abschn. AIIIc haben wir diesen Weg schon unter allgemeinerem Gesichtspunkt kennengelernt. Das Folgende kann als elementares Anwendungsbeispiel der dort gegebenen Theorie betrachtet werden. Wir beschränken uns auf die Behandlung des p-Falles (Randbedingung $v=0$).

Nach (49.1p) können wir die Lösung des Randwertproblems in der Gestalt

$$\left.\begin{aligned} v(x,z) &= \mathrm{e}^{ik(\alpha_0 x+\sqrt{1-\alpha_0^2}\,z)} - \frac{i}{4}\int\limits_0^\infty \psi(x')\,H_0^1\big(k\sqrt{(x-x')^2+z^2}\big)\,dx' \\ &(\alpha_0 = -\cos\varphi_0,\ \sqrt{1-\alpha_0^2} = -\sin\varphi_0) \end{aligned}\right\} \qquad (115.1)$$

darstellen (Huygenssches Prinzip). Die Belegungsdichte $\psi(x)$ ist dann zufolge der Randbedingung mit Hilfe der Integralgleichung

$$\int\limits_0^\infty \psi(x')\,H_0^1(k\,|x-x'|)\,dx' = -\,4i\,\mathrm{e}^{ik\alpha_0 x} \qquad (x>0) \qquad (115.2)$$

zu bestimmen. Sie ist vom Wiener-Hopfschen Typus (vgl. Ziff. 73); ihre Lösung mit Hilfe des Wiener-Hopf-Verfahrens wurde von COPSON durchgeführt[2]. Der erste Schritt dieses Verfahrens besteht in der Ausführung einer Fourier-Transformation. Das bedeutet physikalisch den Übergang zu einer Darstellung der Lösung durch ein Bündel ebener Wellen. Wir haben diesen Übergang bereits in Ziff. 60 betrachtet. Mit Hilfe von (60.1) geht so die Darstellung (115.1) in die folgende über

$$v(x,z) = \mathrm{e}^{ik(\alpha_0 x+\sqrt{1-\alpha_0^2}\,z)} - \frac{i}{4\pi}\int\limits_{-\infty}^{\infty} \frac{\overline{\psi}(\alpha)}{\sqrt{1-\alpha^2}}\,\mathrm{e}^{ik(\alpha x+\sqrt{1-\alpha^2}\,|z|)}\,d\alpha. \qquad (115.1')$$

Zur Bestimmung der Fourier-Transformierten $\overline{\psi}(\alpha) = \int\limits_0^\infty \psi(x)\,\mathrm{e}^{-ik\alpha x}\,dx$ dienen jetzt die aus (115.2) folgenden *dualen* Integralgleichungen [vgl. (60.8p)]

$$\left.\begin{aligned} \int\limits_{-\infty}^{\infty} \frac{\overline{\psi}(\alpha)}{\sqrt{1-\alpha^2}}\,\mathrm{e}^{ik\alpha x}\,d\alpha &= -\,4\pi i\,\mathrm{e}^{ik\alpha_0 x} \quad (x>0) \\ \int\limits_{-\infty}^{\infty} \overline{\psi}(\alpha)\,\mathrm{e}^{ik\alpha x}\,d\alpha &= 0 \qquad\qquad (x<0). \end{aligned}\right\} \qquad (115.2')$$

Sie sorgen dafür, daß die Felddarstellung (115.1′) die Randbedingung auf dem Schirm ($x>0$) erfüllt und mit ihrer z-Ableitung beim Hindurchtreten durch die

[1] W. PAULI: Phys. Rev. **54**, 924 (1938).

[2] E.T. COPSON: Quart. J. Math. **17**, 19 (1946). Vgl. auch B.B. BAKER u. E.T. COPSON: The Mathematical Theory of Huygens' Principle, 2. Aufl., S. 168ff. Oxford 1950. Eine andere Lösungsmethode verwendet W. MAGNUS: Z. Physik **117**, 168 (1941). Vgl. auch W. SCHMEIDLER: Integralgleichungen, 2. Aufl., S. 199ff. Leipzig 1955.

Öffnung ($x<0$) *stetig* ist. Die physikalische Bedeutung der Größe $\overline{\psi}(\alpha)$ ist im wesentlichen die des Fraunhoferschen Fernfeldes (vgl. Ziff. 62). Ein einfaches Lösungsverfahren, das direkt von den dualen Integralgleichungen (115.2′) ausgeht, hat Clemmow entwickelt[1]. Noch direkter ist der von uns einzuschlagende Weg über die *singulären* Integralgleichungen[2]. Diese ergeben sich, indem man Gl. (115.2′) mit $e^{-ik\alpha' x}$ multipliziert und über den jeweiligen x-Bereich integriert (vgl. Ziff. 73). Wir erhalten so die Integralgleichungen

$$\left.\begin{aligned} \oint_{-\infty}^{\infty} \frac{\overline{\psi}(\alpha')}{\sqrt{1-\alpha'^2}} \frac{d\alpha'}{\alpha'-\alpha} &= \frac{4\pi i}{\alpha-\alpha_0}, \\ \oint_{-\infty}^{\infty} \overline{\psi}(\alpha') \frac{d\alpha'}{\alpha'-\alpha} &= 0, \end{aligned}\right\} \qquad (115.2'')$$

in denen die Größen α, α' und α_0 entsprechende physikalische Bedeutungen haben [α ist der Richtungskosinus der ebenen Wellen, in die das Beugungsphänomen durch (115.1′) aufgelöst wird, wobei auch inhomogene Wellen ($\alpha>1$) beitragen]. Dem Pol $\alpha'=\alpha$ der Integranden in (115.2″) ist in der durch die Haken am Integralzeichen angedeuteten Weise in der komplexen α'-Ebene auszuweichen (ferner sind die Verzweigungspunkte $\alpha'=\pm 1$ in der aus Fig. 63 ersichtlichen Weise zu umlaufen).

Zur Lösung der singulären Integralgleichungen (115.2″) bemerken wir zunächst, daß sie nach dem Cauchyschen Satz auch in der Gestalt

$$\left.\begin{aligned} \oint_{-\infty}^{\infty} \left\{\frac{\overline{\psi}(\alpha')}{\sqrt{1-\alpha'^2}} + \frac{2}{\alpha'-\alpha_0}\right\} \frac{d\alpha'}{\alpha'-\alpha} &= 0, \\ \oint_{-\infty}^{\infty} \overline{\psi}(\alpha') \frac{d\alpha'}{\alpha'-\alpha} &= 0 \end{aligned}\right\} \qquad (115.3)$$

geschrieben werden können. Die Integranden dieser Integrale sind dann (abermals nach dem Cauchyschen Satz) notwendig von der Form

$$\left.\begin{aligned} \frac{\overline{\psi}(\alpha)}{\sqrt{1-\alpha^2}} + \frac{2}{\alpha-\alpha_0} &= \Phi^+(\alpha) \qquad (\alpha \in S^+). \\ \overline{\psi}(\alpha) &= \Phi^-(\alpha) \qquad (\alpha \in S^-). \end{aligned}\right\} \qquad (115.4)$$

Dabei ist $\Phi^+(\alpha)$ eine (vorerst beliebige) in der *oberen* α-Halbebene S^+ *holomorphe* Funktion und $\Phi^-(\alpha)$ entsprechend eine in der *unteren* Halbebene S^- holomorphe Funktion. Auf der reellen Achse müssen die beiden Gln. (115.4) *simultan* gelten, daher ergibt sich dort durch Elimination von $\overline{\psi}(\alpha)$

$$\frac{\Phi^-(\alpha)}{\sqrt{1-\alpha^2}} + \frac{2}{\alpha-\alpha_0} = \Phi^+(\alpha)$$

oder

$$\frac{\alpha-\alpha_0}{\sqrt{1-\alpha}}\, \Phi^-(\alpha) = \sqrt{1+\alpha}\,\{(\alpha-\alpha_0)\,\Phi^+(\alpha) - 2\}. \qquad (115.4')$$

---

[1] P. C. Clemmow: Proc. Roy. Soc. Lond. A **205**, 286 (1951). Siehe auch die Darstellung von P. C. Clemmow in M. Born u. E. Wolf: Principles of Optics, S. 562ff. London-New York-Paris-Los Angeles: Pergamon Press 1959. Man vgl. auch D. S. Jones: Quart. J. Math. **2**, 189 (1952), sowie B. Noble: Methods Based on the Wiener-Hopf Technique, Kap. II. London-New York-Paris-Los Angeles: Pergamon Press 1958. Dort werden die Methoden von Copson, Clemmow und Jones ausführlich nebeneinander dargestellt.

[2] H. Hönl u. K. Westpfahl: Planckfestschrift, S. 46ff. Berlin 1958.

Dabei haben wir die Wurzel $\sqrt{1-\alpha^2}$ in die beiden Faktoren $\sqrt{1+\alpha}$ und $\sqrt{1-\alpha}$ aufgespalten, die in S^+ bzw. S^- holomorph sind. Die von den Verzweigungspunkten ± 1 ausgehenden Verzweigungsschnitte sind nämlich in der in Fig. 63 angedeuteten Weise zu legen, damit die Darstellung (115.1′) der Ausstrahlungsbedingung genügt (vgl. Ziff. 60).

Somit ist die linke Seite von (115.4′) in S^-, die rechte hingegen in S^+ holomorph und daher die eine Seite die *analytische Fortsetzung* der anderen. Beide Funktionselemente zusammen definieren daher eine in der *ganzen* komplexen α-Ebene holomorphe Funktion, die somit nach dem Liouvilleschen Satz eine *Konstante* sein muß. Der Wert dieser Konstanten ergibt sich, indem man in (115.4′) $\alpha=\alpha_0$ setzt, zu $-2\sqrt{1+\alpha_0}$. Damit folgt

$$\Phi^+(\alpha)=\frac{-2}{\alpha-\alpha_0}\left(\sqrt{\frac{1+\alpha_0}{1+\alpha}}-1\right),$$

$$\Phi^-(\alpha)=-2\,\frac{\sqrt{1+\alpha_0}\,\sqrt{1-\alpha}}{\alpha-\alpha_0}$$

und daher gemäß (115.4)

$$\overline{\psi}(\alpha)=-2\,\frac{\sqrt{1+\alpha_0}\,\sqrt{1-\alpha}}{\alpha-\alpha_0}. \qquad (115.5)$$

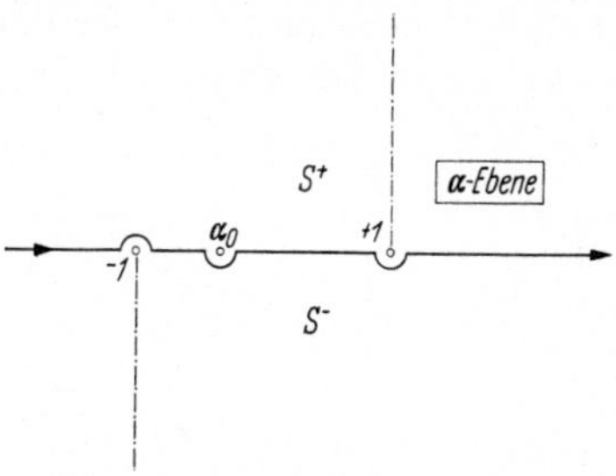

Fig. 63. Integrationsweg in der α-Ebene, Gl. (115.1′).

Die so gefundene Lösung der Integralgleichungen (115.2″) ist *eindeutig*: Wiederholt man den eben durchgeführten Gedankengang noch einmal für die *homogenen* Integralgleichungen (115.2″), so ergibt, daß die oben auftretende Konstante verschwinden muß, da andernfalls das untere Integral in (115.2″) divergiert. Eine zusätzliche Kantenbedingung erübrigt sich also (vgl. auch Ziff. 61 und 74). Mit (115.5) ist auch die (115.2) genügende Belegungsdichte gefunden:

$$\psi(x)=-\frac{k}{\pi}\sqrt{1+\alpha_0}\oint\limits_{-\infty}^{\infty}\frac{\sqrt{1-\alpha}}{\alpha-\alpha_0}\,e^{ik\alpha x}\,d\alpha. \qquad (115.6)$$

Trägt man die Lösung (115.5) in die Felddarstellung (115.1′) ein, so ergibt sich die Lösung unseres Randwertproblems in der Gestalt

$$v(x,z)=e^{ik(\alpha_0 x+\sqrt{1-\alpha_0^2}\,z)}+\frac{\sqrt{1+\alpha_0}}{2\pi i}\oint\limits_{-\infty}^{\infty}\frac{e^{ik(\alpha x+\sqrt{1-\alpha^2}\,|z|)}}{\sqrt{1+\alpha}\,(\alpha-\alpha_0)}\,d\alpha. \qquad (115.7)$$

Es bleibt noch zu zeigen, daß unsere Lösung (115.7) mit dem Ergebnis von Sommerfeld übereinstimmt. Der Vergleich läßt sich am einfachsten durch Gegenüberstellung von Gl. (114.3) (p-Fall, oberes Vorzeichen) und (115.7) durchführen. Betrachten wir insbesondere den Winkelbereich II von Fig. 58, so stellen die ersten Terme beider Ausdrücke übereinstimmend die einfallende Welle v_0 dar, so daß wir nurmehr die beiden Integrale zu vergleichen haben. Wir beschränken uns weiterhin auf $z>0$, dann gilt $\pi-\varphi_0<\varphi<\pi$. Mit der Substitution

$$\alpha=\cos\beta,\qquad \sqrt{1-\alpha^2}=\sin\beta,\qquad d\alpha=-\sin\beta\,d\beta$$

geht die reelle Achse zwischen -1 und 1 der komplexen α-Ebene in die Strecke von π bis 0 der β-Ebene über, wenn man berücksichtigt, daß hier $\sqrt{1-\alpha^2}>0$ vorausgesetzt wurde. Weiter gilt für die im betrachteten Bereich positiven Größen

$$\sqrt{1+\alpha_0}=\sqrt{2}\sin\frac{\varphi_0}{2},\qquad \sqrt{1+\alpha}=\sqrt{2}\cos\frac{\beta}{2}. \qquad (115.8)$$

Der gesamte Integrationsweg von Fig. 63 bildet sich in der β-Ebene auf den Weg von Fig. 64 ab, und man erhält mit $x = r\cos\varphi$, $z = r\sin\varphi$ aus (115.7)

$$v = v_0 + \frac{\sin\frac{\varphi_0}{2}}{\pi i}\int e^{ikr\cos(\beta-\varphi)}\,\frac{\sin\frac{\beta}{2}\,d\beta}{\cos\beta + \cos\varphi_0}\,. \tag{115.9}$$

Substituiert man weiter $\beta - \varphi = \eta$, so geht das Integral abgesehen vom Vorzeichen in das der Gl. (114.3) (oberes Vorzeichen) über mit dem in Fig. 65 gezeichneten Weg. Wegen $\pi - \varphi_0 < \varphi < \pi$ verläuft der Weg innerhalb des schraffierten Gebietes ins Unendliche und liegt der Pol $\eta = \pi - \varphi_0 - \varphi$ des Integranden links von $\eta = 0$.

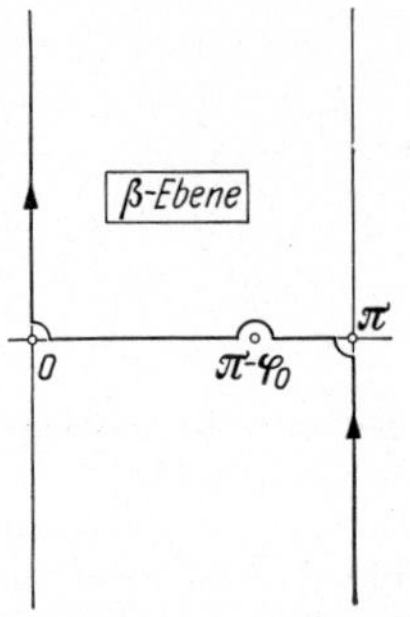

Fig. 64. Integrationsweg in der β-Ebene, Gl. (115.9).

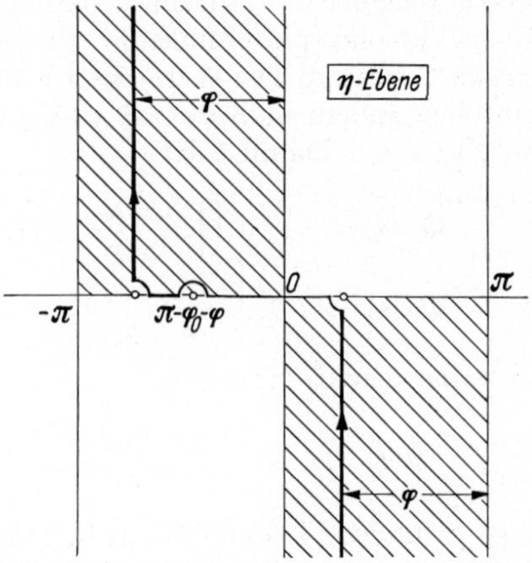

Fig. 65. Integrationsweg in der η-Ebene entsprechend Fig. 57.

Der Weg kann daher in den Weg D von Fig. 57 verschoben werden. Da er in den Fig. 65 und 57 umgekehrt durchlaufen wird, stimmt auch das Vorzeichen mit (114.3) überein.

In entsprechender Weise läßt sich das Verfahren auch auf die Beugung *elastischer* Wellen an einer Halbebene anwenden[1].

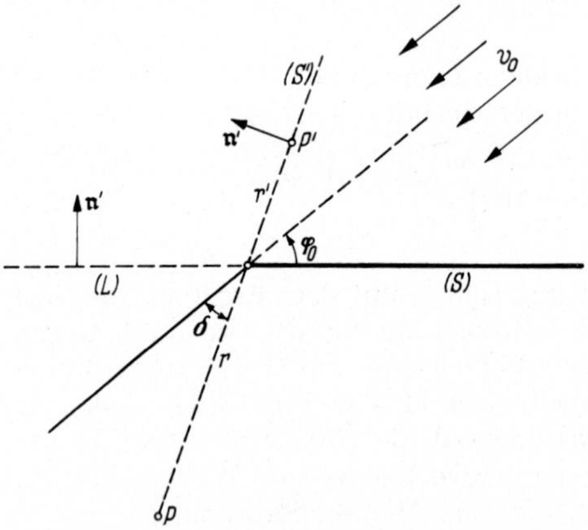

Fig. 66. Zur Kirchhoffschen Theorie der Beugung an der Halbebene.

116. Die Kirchhoffsche Lösung. Die strenge Lösbarkeit des vorliegenden Problems bietet die willkommene Möglichkeit, das praktisch wichtige Kirchhoffsche Näherungsverfahren (vgl. AII a) zu prüfen. Aus diesem Grunde soll das Problem noch nach dieser Näherungsmethode behandelt werden. Wir beschränken uns dabei auf die Betrachtung des *Fernfeldes* ($kr \gg 1$), weil die Näherung nur hier gute Resultate liefert, und schließen uns im übrigen dem Vorgehen von FRANZ[2] an.

Wir betrachten die in Fig. 66 dargestellten Verhältnisse. Die Beob-

[1] A.-W. MAUE: Z. angew. Math. Mech. **33**, 1 (1953). Vgl. auch K. WIEGHARDT: Z. Math. Phys. **55**, 60 (1907).

[2] W. FRANZ: Z. Physik **125**, 563 (1949). — Proc. Phys. Soc. Lond. A **63**, 925 (1950). Vgl. auch E. MAEY: Ann. Physik **49**, 69 (1893). — A. RUBINOWICZ: Ann. Phys. **53**, 257 (1917). — Die Beugungswelle in der Kirchhoffschen Theorie der Beugung, Kap. 4. Warschau 1957. — F. KOTTLER: Ann. Physik **70**, 405 (1923). — W. v. IGNATOWSKY: Ann. Physik **77**, 589 (1925). — B. B. BAKER u. E. T. COPSON: The Mathematical Theory of HUYGENS' Principle, 2. Aufl., S. 84ff. — PH. VAN LOC: C. R. Acad. Sci., Paris **244**, 1470 (1957).

achtung im Aufpunkte P erfolgt im Abstand r von der Kante unter dem Winkel δ gegen die Schattengrenze. Das Feld in P ist nach KIRCHHOFF durch Gl. (30.2'''):

$$v_K = \int\limits_L \left(v_0 \frac{\partial G}{\partial n'} - \frac{\partial v_0}{\partial n'} G\right) d\sigma' \tag{116.1}$$

als Integral über die Öffnung (L) gegeben. Wird dasselbe Integral über eine geschlossene oder allseitig ins Unendlich verlaufende Fläche erstreckt, so liefert es nach Gl. (8.5) v_0 oder 0 je nachdem, ob Aufpunkt und Quelle auf verschiedenen Seiten oder auf der gleichen Seite der Fläche liegen. Ersteres trifft zu bei Integration über die gesamte Schirmebene $(L)+(S)$, letzteres bei Verwendung der Fläche $(L)+(S')$, wobei (S') die dem Aufpunkt gegenüberliegende Halbebene bedeutet [vgl. Fig. 66, die dort eingezeichnete Normale $\mathfrak{n}'$ von (L) bezieht sich auf den letzteren Fall; in (116.1) ist jedoch die entgegengesetzte Normale zu verwenden]. Demnach kann Gl. (116.1) ersetzt werden durch

$$v_K = -\int\limits_{S'} \frac{\partial v_0}{\partial n'} G\, d\sigma'. \tag{116.2}$$

Dabei ist benutzt, daß $\frac{\partial G}{\partial n'} = 0$ auf (S').

Ist r' der Abstand des Integrationspunktes P' von der Kante, so gilt für die einfallende Welle (113.1) auf (S')

$$v_0 = e^{-ikr'\cos\delta}, \qquad \frac{\partial v_0}{\partial n'} = -\,i\,k \sin\delta \cdot v_0. \tag{116.3}$$

Die zweidimensionale Greensche Funktion (8.3a) ersetzen wir durch ihre asymptotische Darstellung

$$G = \frac{i}{4} H_0^{(1)}(kR) \to \frac{1+i}{4\sqrt{\pi k R}} e^{ikR} \quad \textit{für}\ kR \gg 1. \tag{116.4}$$

Mit $R = r + r'$ erhalten wir dann unter Verwendung des Wertes $v_0 = e^{ikr\cos\delta}$ der einfallenden Welle im Aufpunkt P

$$v_K \to v_0 \cdot \frac{1-i}{4} \sin\delta \int\limits_r^\infty \sqrt{\frac{k}{\pi R}}\, e^{ikR(1-\cos\delta)}\, dR. \tag{116.5}$$

Einführung der neuen Integrationsvariablen

$$\tau = -\sqrt{\frac{2kR}{\pi}(1-\cos\delta)} = -2\sqrt{\frac{kR}{\pi}} \sin\frac{\delta}{2} \tag{116.6}$$

liefert schließlich

$$v_K \to v_0 \cdot \frac{e^{-\frac{i\pi}{4}}}{\sqrt{2}} \cos\frac{\delta}{2} \int\limits_{-\infty}^{\varrho} e^{\frac{i\pi\tau^2}{2}}\, d\tau \quad \textit{für}\ kr \gg 1, \quad \varrho = -2\sqrt{\frac{kr}{\pi}} \sin\frac{\delta}{2}. \tag{116.7}$$

Gl. (116.7) stimmt mit der strengen Formel (114.5) im Gültigkeitsbereich $|\delta| \ll 1$ der letzteren überein, liefert also wie (114.5) die richtigen Abweichungen des *Fernfeldes* von der geometrischen Optik in einem schmalen Winkelbereich *in der Umgebung der Schattengrenze.* Außerhalb dieses Winkelbereichs kann die Kirchhoffsche Näherung schon deshalb nicht zutreffen, weil sich hier die Polarisation der Strahlung, d.h. die spezielle Form der Randbedingung am Schirm, bemerkbar macht, die in die Kirchhoffsche Theorie nicht eingeht.

117. Das Feld in der Ebene des Schirmes. Wir prüfen nunmehr die Brauchbarkeit der *Kirchhoffschen Ersatzwerte* für v und $\partial v/\partial z$ in der Schirmebene und beschränken uns dabei auf den Fall senkrechten Einfalls. Dann lauten die Kirchhoffschen Ersatzwerte (vgl. Ziff. 30 u. 39)

$$v \to \begin{cases} v_0 = 1 \\ 0 \end{cases} \quad \frac{\partial v}{\partial z} \to \begin{cases} \dfrac{\partial v_0}{\partial z} = -ik & \textit{in der Öffnung} \\ 0 & \textit{hinter dem Schirm.} \end{cases} \tag{116.8}$$

Die strenge Lösung setzt sich nach Ziff. 114 aus zwei Beiträgen u und $\bar{u}$ zusammen. u und $\partial u/\partial z$ entnehmen wir aus den Gln. (113.15) und setzen in der Öffnung $\varphi = \pi$ und hinter dem Schirm $\varphi = 2\pi$. Mit $\varphi_0 = \pi/2$ (senkrechter Einfall) wird dann $\varphi - \varphi_0 = \pi/2$ bzw. $3\pi/2$. Die gespiegelte Welle $\bar{u}$ geht aus u durch Vorzeichenumkehr von φ hervor, so daß bei $\bar{u}$ in (113.15) $-\varphi - \varphi_0 = -\frac{3\pi}{2}$ bzw. $-\frac{5\pi}{2}$ zu setzen ist. Zusammenfassung beider Beiträge liefert nach kurzer Umrechnung unter Benutzung der Abkürzungen

$$\Phi(x) = \int_x^\infty \frac{e^{i\left(z - \frac{\pi}{4}\right)}}{\sqrt{\pi z}}\, dz, \qquad \Psi(x) = \frac{e^{i\left(x + \frac{\pi}{4}\right)}}{\sqrt{\pi x}} \tag{116.9}$$

für die Randbedingung $v = 0$

$$v = u - \bar{u} = \begin{cases} 1 - \Phi(kr) & \textit{in der Öffnung} \\ 0 & \textit{hinter dem Schirm} \end{cases} \tag{116.10p}$$

$$\frac{\partial v}{\partial z} = \begin{cases} -ik & \textit{in der Öffnung} \\ -ik\{\Phi(kr) - \Psi(kr)\} & \textit{hinter dem Schirm} \end{cases} \tag{116.11p}$$

und für die Randbedingung $\frac{\partial v}{\partial n} = 0$

$$v = u + \bar{u} = \begin{cases} 1 & \textit{in der Öffnung} \\ \Phi(kr) & \textit{hinter dem Schirm} \end{cases} \tag{116.10s}$$

$$\frac{\partial v}{\partial z} = \begin{cases} -ik\{1 - \Phi(kr) + \Psi(kr)\} & \textit{in der Öffnung} \\ 0 & \textit{hinter dem Schirm.} \end{cases} \tag{116.11s}$$

In (116.10p) und (116.11s) ist das Verschwinden hinter dem Schirm durch die Randbedingung gefordert. Hier und ebenso in der Öffnung bei den Gln. (116.11p) und (116.10s) besteht Übereinstimmung mit Gl. (116.8) (diese Übereinstimmung folgt bereits nach den allgemeinen Überlegungen von Ziff. 26 und zwar für ebene Schirme beliebiger Gestalt). In allen anderen Fällen werden aber die Werte (116.8) erst im Abstand einiger Wellenlängen von der Kante angenommen, wo $\Phi(kr)$ und $\Psi(kr)$ praktisch auf null abgeklungen sind. In der Nähe der Kante sind demnach die Kirchhoffschen Ersatzwerte (116.8) unbrauchbar, und zwar ist der Fehler, da

$$\Phi(x) \to x^{-\frac{1}{2}}, \qquad \Phi(x) - \Psi(x) \to x^{-\frac{3}{2}} \quad \textit{für } x \to \infty \tag{116.12}$$

bei $\frac{\partial v}{\partial z}$ geringer als bei v.

Zufolge dieser Unzulänglichkeit der Kirchhoffschen Ersatzwerte in der Nähe der Kante wird die Kirchhoffsche Lösung (116.1) am Schirmrand in unzulässiger

Weise singulär und entspricht einer Ausstrahlung der Kante (vgl. Ziff. 32). Trotzdem stimmt, wie wir gesehen haben, das Fernfeld der Kirchhoffschen Lösung in der Umgebung der Einfallsrichtung mit der strengen Lösung überein.

Die modifizierten Kirchhoffschen Näherungen $v_K^{(1)}$ und $v_K^{(2)}$ erhält man nach Ziff. 35 als *antisymmetrischen* bzw. *symmetrischen* Bestandteil von v_K. FRANZ[1] korrigiert diese Näherungen mit Hilfe seines in Ziff. 37 besprochenen Verfahrens und erhält so auch außerhalb des Bereichs um die Schattengrenze eine bessere Annäherung an die strenge Lösung. Allerdings treten in höheren Näherungen die in Ziff. 38 besprochenen *Kantensingularitäten* auf.

b) Beugung am Spalt und Streifen.

Die Beugung am (unendlich langen geraden) Spalt in einem (unendlich dünnen) ebenen ideal leitenden Schirm und der komplementäre Fall der Beugung am Streifen gehört zu den separierbaren Problemen (Abschn. AI b). In der Tat läßt sich bei Einführung der Koordinaten des *elliptischen Zylinders* die Wellengleichung *separieren* und dies führt auf die Differentialgleichung der *Mathieuschen Funktionen*. (Auf diese Weise läßt sich auch ein Spalt behandeln, dessen Backen *hyperbolischen* Querschnitt haben sowie ein Zylinder *elliptischen* Querschnitts, beides für beliebigen Brechungsindex.) Da die Mathieuschen Funktionen ein vollständiges System bilden, läßt sich die Lösung unserer Randwertaufgabe (bei beliebiger Primärwelle) nach diesen Funktionen entwickeln. Diese Reihen konvergieren zwar für *alle* Werte des charakteristischen Parameters $\varepsilon = ka$ (k Wellenzahl, $2a$ Spalt- bzw. Streifenbreite), jedoch wird die Konvergenz mit wachsendem ε immer schlechter, da die Zahl der zu berücksichtigenden Reihenglieder von *derselben* Größenordnung wie ε ist. Wir wollen die Reihenentwicklung nach Mathieuschen Funktionen (die wir im folgenden der Kürze halber als strenge Lösung bezeichnen werden) hier nicht im einzelnen durchführen, sondern verweisen auf die Literatur[2] (die parallel mit der Entwicklung der Theorie der Mathieuschen Funktionen[3] entstanden ist). Die strenge Lösung läßt sich natürlich auch mit Hilfe der Methode der Integralgleichungen (Abschn. AIII a) gewinnen[4] (hier treten die Mathieuschen Funktionen als Eigenfunktionen des Kerns der Integralgleichung auf).

Wir wollen die Integralgleichungsmethode jedoch im folgenden dazu verwenden, um die beiden Grenzfälle $\varepsilon \ll 1$ und $\varepsilon \gg 1$ zu behandeln. Durch Vergleich mit der numerischen Auswertung der strengen Lösung ergibt sich, daß die so gewonnenen Formeln (wenigstens für senkrechte Inzidenz) den gesamten ε-Bereich nahezu vollständig zu erfassen vermögen.

118. Aufstellung der Integralgleichungen. Der Schirm liege in der xy-Ebene; die Schirmränder seien durch $x = \pm a$ gegeben (Spaltbreite 2a, vgl. Fig. 67). Die

[1] W. FRANZ: l. c.

[2] W. WIEN: Jber. dtsch. Math. Ver. **15**, 42 (1906). — B. SIEGER: Ann. Physik **27**, 622 (1908). — K. AICHI: Proc. Tokyo Math. Phys. Soc. **4**, 966 (1908). — M.J.O. STRUTT: Z. Physik **69**, 597 (1931). — P.M. MORSE u. P.J. RUBENSTEIN: Phys. Rev. **54**, 895 (1938). — R.J. PELLAM: J. Acoust. Soc. Amer. **11**, 396 (1940). — S. SKAVLEM: Arch. Math. Naturw. **51**, 61 (1951). — E.B. MOULLIN u. F.M. PHILLIPS: Proc. Inst. Electr. Engrs. IV **99**, 139 (1952). — B. LEVY: N.Y. Univ. Res. Rep. No. EM-121 (1958). — N.D. KAZARINOFF u. R.K. RITT: Univ. of Michigan, Res. Inst. Rep. No. 5 (1959). — J.B. KELLER u. B. R. LEVY: N.Y. Univ. Res. Rep. No. EM-147 (1959). — Siehe auch N.W. MCLACHLAN: Theory and Applications of Mathieu Functions, S. 358ff. Oxford 1947.

[3] J. MEIXNER u. F.W. SCHÄFKE: Mathieusche Funktionen und Sphäroidfunktionen. Berlin: Springer 1954.

[4] J.W. MILES: J. Math. Phys. **28**, 223 (1950). — J. DÖRR: Z. angew. Math. Phys. **3**, 427 (1952).

Ausbreitungsrichtung der einfallenden ebenen Welle sei senkrecht zu den Kanten und schließe mit der x-Achse den Winkel ϑ_0 ein:

$$v_0 = e^{ik(\alpha_0 x + \sqrt{1-\alpha_0^2}\, z)} = e^{ikr\cos(\vartheta-\vartheta_0)} \tag{118.1}$$

$$\left(\alpha_0 = \cos\vartheta_0, \quad 0 \leqq \vartheta_0 \leqq \frac{\pi}{2}\right).$$

Unterscheiden wir die Lösungen der beiden Randwertaufgaben

$$\left.\begin{aligned} &(\Delta + k^2)\, v(x,z) = 0 \\ v(x, \pm 0) = 0 \quad \text{bzw.} \quad &\frac{\partial}{\partial z} v(x, \pm 0) = 0 \qquad (|x| > a) \end{aligned}\right\} \tag{118.2}$$

durch $v_{\|}$ bzw. $v_{\perp}$, so kann die Lösung des Beugungsproblems für ein (bezüglich der elektrischen Feldstärke) *parallel* bzw. *senkrecht* zu den Schirmrändern polarisiertes elektromagnetisches Feld in der folgenden Form dargestellt werden (kartesische Komponenten)

$$\mathfrak{E} = (0, v_{\|}, 0), \quad \varkappa\,\mathfrak{H} = \frac{i}{k}\left(\frac{\partial v_{\|}}{\partial z}, 0, -\frac{\partial v_{\|}}{\partial x}\right) \tag{118.3p}$$

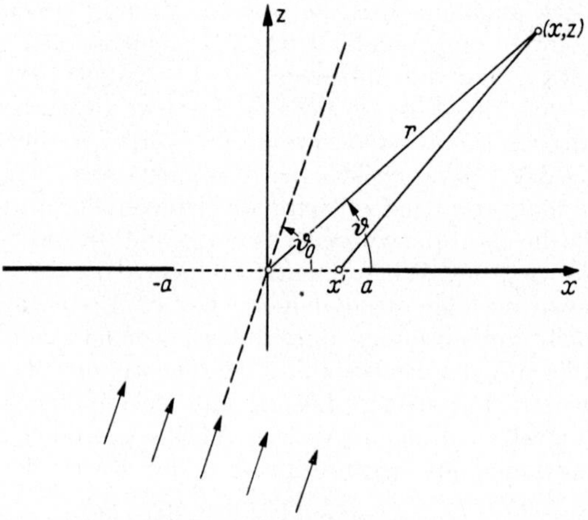

Fig. 67. Zur Beugung am Spalt.

bzw.

$$\left.\begin{aligned} &\varkappa\,\mathfrak{H} = (0, v_{\perp}, 0), \\ &\mathfrak{E} = -\frac{i}{k}\cdot \\ &\cdot\left(\frac{\partial v_{\perp}}{\partial z}, 0, -\frac{\partial v_{\perp}}{\partial x}\right). \end{aligned}\right\} \tag{118.3s}$$

Dabei bedeutet

$$k = \omega\sqrt{\varepsilon_0\mu_0}, \quad \varkappa = \sqrt{\frac{\mu_0}{\varepsilon_0}}. \tag{118.4}$$

(ω ist die Kreisfrequenz, ε_0 die Dielektrizitätskonstante und μ_0 die Permeabilität des homogenen Mediums, in das der Schirm eingebettet ist; vgl. Ziff. 4, dort wurden die beiden Polarisationen als p- und s-Fall unterschieden.)

α) Rayleighsche Integralgleichungen. Die Lösungen von (118.2) lassen sich in der Form

$$v_{\|}(x,z) = v_{\|}^{(g)}(x,z) \mp \frac{i}{2}\frac{\partial}{\partial z}\int_{-a}^{a} \varphi_{\|}(x')\, H_0^1\left(k\sqrt{(x-x')^2+z^2}\right) dx' \qquad (z \gtrless 0) \tag{118.5p}$$

bzw.

$$v_{\perp}(x,z) = v_{\perp}^{(g)}(x,z) \mp \frac{i}{2}\int_{-a}^{a} \varphi_{\perp}(x')\, H_0^1\left(k\sqrt{(x-x')^2+z^2}\right) dx' \qquad (z \gtrless 0) \tag{118.5s}$$

ansetzen [vgl. (49.3p) bzw. (50.8s): „Beugungsfall", wir haben $\varphi = \varphi_{\|}$ bzw. $\psi = \varphi_{\perp}$ gesetzt]. Dabei bedeutet

$$v_{\|}^{(g)}(x,z) = \left\{\begin{matrix} 0 & (z>0) \\ v_0(x,z) - v_0(x,-z) & (z<0) \end{matrix}\right\} \tag{118.6p}$$

bzw.

$$v_{\perp}^{(g)}(x,z) = \left\{\begin{matrix} 0 & (z>0) \\ v_0(x,z) + v_0(x,-z) & (z<0) \end{matrix}\right\} \tag{118.6s}$$

die Feldverteilung beim *Fehlen* des Spaltes. Die „Belegungsdichten“ $\varphi(x)$ haben die Bedeutung

$$\varphi_{\|}(x) = v_{\|}(x, \pm 0) \qquad (|x| < a) \tag{118.7p}$$

bzw.

$$\varphi_{\perp}(x) = \frac{\partial}{\partial z} v_{\perp}(x, \pm 0) \qquad (|x| < a), \tag{118.7s}$$

wie man mit Hilfe der für beliebige $\varphi(x)$ gültigen Beziehung

$$\lim_{z\to\pm 0} \frac{\partial}{\partial z} \int_{-a}^{a} \varphi(x')\, H_0^1\left(k\sqrt{(x-x')^2+z^2}\right) dx' = \begin{Bmatrix} \pm 2i\,\varphi(x) & (|x|<a) \\ 0 & (|x|>a) \end{Bmatrix} \tag{118.7'}$$

verifiziert. Für die $\varphi(x)$ ergeben sich aus der Forderung der Stetigkeit des Feldes und seiner z-Ableitung beim Hindurchtreten durch die Öffnung die Integralgleichungen

$$\left(\frac{d^2}{dx^2}+k^2\right)\int_{-a}^{a} \varphi_{\|}(x')\, H_0^1(k|x-x'|)\, dx' = 2k\sqrt{1-\alpha_0^2}\, e^{ik\alpha_0 x} \qquad (|x|<a) \tag{118.8p}$$

bzw.

$$\int_{-a}^{a} \varphi_{\perp}(x')\, H_0^1(k|x-x'|)\, dx' = 2i\, e^{ik\alpha_0 x} \qquad (|x|<a) \tag{118.8s}$$

[vgl. (49.4p) bzw. (50.10s)].

β) Duale Integralgleichungen. Mit Hilfe der Fourier-Darstellung

$$H_0^1\left(k\sqrt{(x-x')^2+z^2}\right) = \frac{1}{\pi}\int_{-\infty}^{\infty} e^{ik[\alpha(x-x')+\sqrt{1-\alpha^2}|z|]} \frac{d\alpha}{\sqrt{1-\alpha^2}} \tag{118.9}$$

können wir das Feld (118.5) auch in der Form

$$v_{\|}(x,z) = v_{\|}^{(g)}(x,z) + \frac{k}{2\pi}\int_{-\infty}^{\infty} \overline{\varphi}_{\|}(\alpha)\, e^{ik(\alpha x+\sqrt{1-\alpha^2}|z|)}\, d\alpha \qquad (z \lesseqgtr 0) \tag{118.10p}$$

bzw.

$$v_{\perp}(x,z) = v_{\perp}^{(g)}(x,z) \pm \frac{1}{2\pi i}\int_{-\infty}^{\infty} \frac{\overline{\varphi}_{\perp}(\alpha)}{\sqrt{1-\alpha^2}}\, e^{ik(\alpha x+\sqrt{1-\alpha^2}|z|)}\, d\alpha \qquad (z \lesseqgtr 0) \tag{118.10s}$$

darstellen [vgl. (60.3p) bzw. (66.1s)]. Hier haben wir die Größen

$$\overline{\varphi}(\alpha) = \int_{-a}^{a} \varphi(x)\, e^{-ik\alpha x}\, dx \tag{118.11}$$

für beide Polarisationsfälle eingeführt, für die sich aus (118.8p) bzw. (118.8s) die *dualen* Integralgleichungen

$$\left.\begin{aligned} &\int_{-\infty}^{\infty} \sqrt{1-\alpha^2}\,\overline{\varphi}_{\|}(\alpha)\, e^{ik\alpha x}\, d\alpha = \frac{2\pi}{k}\sqrt{1-\alpha_0^2}\, e^{ik\alpha_0 x} && (|x|<a) \\ &\int_{-\infty}^{\infty} \overline{\varphi}_{\|}(\alpha)\, e^{ik\alpha x}\, d\alpha = 0 && (|x|>a) \end{aligned}\right\} \tag{118.12p}$$

bzw.

$$\left.\begin{aligned} &\int_{-\infty}^{\infty} \frac{\overline{\varphi}_{\perp}(\alpha)}{\sqrt{1-\alpha^2}}\, e^{ik\alpha x}\, d\alpha = 2\pi i\, e^{ik\alpha_0 x} && (|x|<a) \\ &\int_{-\infty}^{\infty} \varphi_{\perp}(\alpha)\, e^{ik\alpha x}\, d\alpha = 0 && (|x|>a) \end{aligned}\right\} \tag{118.12s}$$

ergeben [vgl. (60.9p) bzw. (66.6s)]. Diese Gleichungen sorgen dafür, daß die Felddarstellung (118.10p) bzw. (118.10s) die entsprechende Randbedingung erfüllt und die Felder mit ihren z-Ableitungen beim Hindurchtreten durch die Öffnung stetig sind.

Multipliziert man die Gl. (118.12) mit $e^{-ik\alpha' x}$ und integriert über den entsprechenden x-Bereich (vgl. Ziff. 64), so ergeben sich die Integralgleichungen vom *Faltungstypus* ($\varepsilon = k a$)

$$\left.\begin{aligned} &\frac{1}{\pi}\int\limits_{-\infty}^{\infty}\sqrt{1-\alpha'^2}\,\overline{\varphi}_{\parallel}(\alpha')\,\frac{\sin\varepsilon(\alpha'-\alpha)}{\alpha'-\alpha}\,d\alpha' = \frac{2}{k}\sqrt{1-\alpha_0^2}\,\frac{\sin\varepsilon(\alpha-\alpha_0)}{\alpha-\alpha_0}\\ &\overline{\varphi}_{\parallel}(\alpha) - \frac{1}{\pi}\int\limits_{-\infty}^{\infty}\overline{\varphi}_{\parallel}(\alpha)\,\frac{\sin\varepsilon(\alpha'-\alpha)}{\alpha'-\alpha}\,d\alpha' = 0 \end{aligned}\right\}\quad(118.12'p)$$

bzw.

$$\left.\begin{aligned} &\frac{1}{\pi}\int\limits_{-\infty}^{\infty}\frac{\overline{\varphi}_{\perp}(\alpha')}{\sqrt{1-\alpha'^2}}\,\frac{\sin\varepsilon(\alpha'-\alpha)}{\alpha'-\alpha}\,d\alpha' = 2i\,\frac{\sin\varepsilon(\alpha-\alpha_0)}{\alpha-\alpha_0}\\ &\overline{\varphi}_{\perp}(\alpha) - \frac{1}{\pi}\int\limits_{-\infty}^{\infty}\overline{\varphi}_{\perp}(\alpha')\,\frac{\sin\varepsilon(\alpha'-\alpha)}{\alpha'-\alpha}\,d\alpha' = 0. \end{aligned}\right\}\quad(118.12's)$$

Für das Folgende ist es zweckmäßig auch zu einer Darstellung überzugehen, bei der die *Wechselwirkung* der beiden Spaltbacken explizit in Erscheinung tritt (d.h. den Spalt als „Streuproblem" zu behandeln). Wir wollen dabei mit der Fourier-Darstellung des Feldes beginnen. Der Übergang erfolgt dann nach Gl. (61.4p) durch Einführung der Fourier-Amplitude des *Flächenstroms* auf den Spaltbacken mittels der Beziehung

$$\overline{\psi}_{\parallel}(\alpha) = -\,2i\sqrt{1-\alpha^2}\,\{2\pi\,\delta(\alpha-\alpha_0) - k\,\overline{\varphi}_{\parallel}(\alpha)\}\qquad(118.13p)$$

bzw.

$$\overline{\psi}_{\perp}(\alpha) = -\,\frac{4\pi}{k}\,\delta(\alpha-\alpha_0) - \frac{2i}{k}\,\frac{\overline{\varphi}_{\perp}(\alpha)}{\sqrt{1-\alpha^2}}.\qquad(118.13s)$$

Mit Hilfe dieser Größen gehen die *dualen* Integralgleichungen (118.12) über in [vgl. (60.8p) mit $\overline{\psi} = \overline{\psi}_{\parallel}$ bzw. (66.5s) mit $\overline{\varphi} = \overline{\psi}_{\perp}$]

$$\left.\begin{aligned} &\int\limits_{-\infty}^{\infty}\overline{\psi}_{\parallel}(\alpha)\,e^{ik\alpha x}\,d\alpha = 0 && (|x|<a)\\ &\int\limits_{-\infty}^{\infty}\frac{\overline{\psi}_{\parallel}(\alpha)}{\sqrt{1-\alpha^2}}\,e^{ik\alpha x}\,d\alpha = -\,4\pi i\,e^{ik\alpha_0 x} && (|x|>a) \end{aligned}\right\}\quad(118.12''p)$$

bzw.

$$\left.\begin{aligned} &\int\limits_{-\infty}^{\infty}\overline{\psi}_{\perp}(\alpha)\,e^{ik\alpha x}\,d\alpha = 0 && (|x|<a)\\ &\int\limits_{-\infty}^{\infty}\sqrt{1-\alpha^2}\,\overline{\psi}_{\perp}(\alpha)\,e^{ik\alpha x}\,d\alpha = -\,\frac{4\pi}{k}\sqrt{1-\alpha_0^2}\,e^{ik\alpha_0 x} && (|x|>a). \end{aligned}\right\}\quad(118.12''s)$$

In diesen Gleichungen kommt die Wechselwirkung der beiden Spaltbacken zum Ausdruck, wenn wir die von den Flächenströmen auf den beiden getrennten Halbebenen herrührenden Fernfelder durch die Aufspaltung

$$\overline{\psi}(\alpha) = \overline{\psi}^{(1)}(\alpha) + \overline{\psi}^{(2)}(\alpha)\qquad(118.14)$$

einführen (für beide Polarisationsfälle). Die Gln. (118.12″) lassen sich dann in folgender Form schreiben

$$\left.\begin{aligned}\int_{-\infty}^{\infty}\frac{\overline{\psi}_{\|}^{(1)}(\alpha)+\overline{\psi}_{\|}^{(2)}(\alpha)}{\sqrt{1-\alpha^2}}\,e^{ik\alpha x}\,d\alpha &= -\,4\pi i\,e^{ik\alpha_0 x} & (x>a)\\ \int_{-\infty}^{\infty}\overline{\psi}_{\|}^{(1)}(\alpha)\,e^{ik\alpha x}\,d\alpha &= 0 & (x<a)\end{aligned}\right\}\tag{118.15p}$$

und

$$\left.\begin{aligned}\int_{-\infty}^{\infty}\overline{\psi}_{\|}^{(2)}(\alpha)\,e^{ik\alpha x}\,d\alpha &= 0 & (x>-a)\\ \int_{-\infty}^{\infty}\frac{\overline{\psi}_{\|}^{(2)}(\alpha)+\overline{\psi}_{\|}^{(1)}(\alpha)}{\sqrt{1-\alpha^2}}\,e^{ik\alpha x}\,d\alpha &= -\,4\pi i\,e^{ik\alpha_0 x} & (x<-a)\end{aligned}\right\}\tag{118.16p}$$

bzw.

$$\left.\begin{aligned}\int_{-\infty}^{\infty}\sqrt{1-\alpha^2}\,\{\overline{\psi}_{\perp}^{(1)}(\alpha)+\overline{\psi}_{\perp}^{(2)}(\alpha)\}\,e^{ik\alpha x}\,d\alpha &= -\,\frac{4\pi}{k}\sqrt{1-\alpha_0^2}\,e^{ik\alpha_0 x} & (x>a)\\ \int_{-\infty}^{\infty}\overline{\psi}_{\perp}^{(1)}(\alpha)\,e^{ik\alpha x}\,d\alpha &= 0 & (x<a)\end{aligned}\right\}\tag{118.15s}$$

und

$$\left.\begin{aligned}\int_{-\infty}^{\infty}\overline{\psi}_{\perp}^{(2)}(\alpha)\,e^{ik\alpha x}\,d\alpha &= 0 & (x>-a)\\ \int_{-\infty}^{\infty}\sqrt{1-\alpha^2}\,\{\overline{\psi}_{\perp}^{(2)}(\alpha)+\overline{\psi}_{\perp}^{(1)}(\alpha)\}\,e^{ik\alpha x}\,d\alpha &= -\,\frac{4\pi}{k}\sqrt{1-\alpha_0^2}\,e^{ik\alpha_0 x} & (x<-a).\end{aligned}\right\}\tag{118.16s}$$

Die Gln. (118.15) betreffen hier offenbar die Fernfeldamplitude $\overline{\psi}^{(1)}(\alpha)$, die zur Beugung einer ebenen Welle an der *rechten* Halbebene $a<x<\infty$ gehört; wobei jedoch noch eine *Wechselwirkung* mit der linken Halbebene $-\infty<x<-a$ vorhanden ist, wie durch das Glied mit $\overline{\psi}^{(2)}(\alpha)$ zum Ausdruck kommt [man vgl. die entsprechenden Formeln für die Beugung an der Halbebene (115.2′)]. Entsprechend beziehen sich die Gln. (118.16) auf die Beugung an der *linken* Halbebene. Dies zeigt sich noch deutlicher, wenn wir die auf der rechten bzw. linken Halbebene fließenden Flächenströme $\psi^{(1)}(x)$ bzw. $\psi^{(2)}(x)$ mit Hilfe der Gleichungen

$$\left.\begin{aligned}\overline{\psi}^{(1)}(\alpha) &= \int_{a}^{\infty}\psi^{(1)}(x)\,e^{-ik\alpha x}\,dx,\\ \overline{\psi}^{(2)}(\alpha) &= \int_{-\infty}^{-a}\psi^{(2)}(x)\,e^{ik\alpha x}\,dx\end{aligned}\right\}\tag{118.14′}$$

für beide Polarisationsfälle einführen. Diese genügen der Integralgleichung

$$\left\{\int_{-\infty}^{-a}\psi_{\|}^{(2)}(x')+\int_{a}^{\infty}\psi_{\|}^{(1)}(x')\right\}H_0^1(k|x-x'|)\,dx' = -4i\,e^{ik\alpha_0 x}\quad(|x|>a)\tag{118.13′p}$$

bzw.

$$\left.\begin{aligned}&\left(\frac{d^2}{dx^2}+k^2\right)\left\{\int_{-\infty}^{-a}\psi_{\perp}^{(2)}(x')+\int_{a}^{\infty}\psi_{\perp}^{(1)}(x')\right\}H_0^1(k|x-x'|)\,dx'\\ &\quad=-\,4k\sqrt{1-\alpha_0^2}\,e^{ik\alpha_0 x}\quad(|x|>a)\end{aligned}\right\}\tag{118.13′s}$$

[vgl. (49.2p) bzw. (50.9s)] oder nach einfacher Umformung

$$\left.\begin{aligned}&\int_a^\infty \{\psi_\parallel^{(1)}(x')\,H_0^1(k\,|x-x'|)+\psi_\parallel^{(2)}(-x')\,H_0^1(k\,|x+x'|)\}\,dx'\\&\qquad=-4i\,e^{ik\alpha_0 x}\\&\int_a^\infty \{\psi_\parallel^{(2)}(-x')\,H_0^1(k\,|x-x'|)+\psi_\parallel^{(1)}(x')\,H_0^1(k\,|x+x'|)\}\,dx'\\&\qquad=-4i\,e^{-ik\alpha_0 x}\end{aligned}\right\}\ (x>a)\qquad(118.13''p)$$

bzw.

$$\left.\begin{aligned}&\left(\frac{d^2}{dx^2}+k^2\right)\int_a^\infty \{\psi_\perp^{(1)}(x')\,H_0^1(k\,|x-x'|)\\&\quad+\psi_\perp^{(2)}(-x')\,H_0^1(k\,|x+x'|)\}\,dx'=-4k\sqrt{1-\alpha_0^2}\,e^{ik\alpha_0 x},\\&\left(\frac{d^2}{dx^2}+k^2\right)\int_a^\infty \{\psi_\perp^{(2)}(-x')\,H_0^1(k\,|x-x'|)\\&\quad+\psi_\perp^{(1)}(x')\,H_0^1(k\,|x+x'|)\}\,dx'=-4k\sqrt{1-\alpha_0^2}\,e^{-ik\alpha_0 x}\end{aligned}\right\}\ (x>a).\qquad(118.13''s)$$

In diesen Gleichungen wird die Wechselwirkung der rechten mit der linken Halbebene durch den jeweils zweiten Term beschrieben.

γ) Singuläre Integralgleichungen. Multiplizieren wir die Gln. (118.15), (118.16) mit $e^{-ik\alpha' x}$ und integrieren über den jeweiligen x-Bereich, so ergibt sich nach dem Verfahren von Ziff. 73 [vgl. (73.12′a,b)]

$$\left.\begin{aligned}&\oint_{-\infty}^{\infty}\left\{\frac{\overline{\psi}_\parallel^{(1)}(\alpha')+\overline{\psi}_\parallel^{(2)}(\alpha')}{\sqrt{1-\alpha'^2}}\,e^{i\varepsilon\alpha'}+2\,\frac{e^{i\varepsilon\alpha_0}}{\alpha'-\alpha_0}\right\}\frac{d\alpha'}{\alpha'-\alpha}=0\\&\oint_{-\infty}^{\infty}\overline{\psi}_\parallel^{(1)}(\alpha')\,\frac{e^{i\varepsilon\alpha'}}{\alpha'-\alpha}\,d\alpha'=0\end{aligned}\right\}\qquad(118.15'p)$$

$$\left.\begin{aligned}&\oint_{-\infty}^{\infty}\overline{\psi}_\parallel^{(2)}(\alpha')\,\frac{e^{-i\varepsilon\alpha'}}{\alpha'-\alpha}\,d\alpha'=0\\&\oint_{-\infty}^{\infty}\left\{\frac{\overline{\psi}_\parallel^{(2)}(\alpha')+\overline{\psi}_\parallel^{(1)}(\alpha')}{\sqrt{1-\alpha'^2}}\,e^{-i\varepsilon\alpha'}-2\,\frac{e^{-i\varepsilon\alpha_0}}{\alpha'-\alpha_0}\right\}\frac{d\alpha'}{\alpha'-\alpha}=0\end{aligned}\right\}\qquad(118.16'p)$$

bzw.

$$\left.\begin{aligned}&\oint_{-\infty}^{\infty}\left\{\sqrt{1-\alpha'^2}\,[\overline{\psi}_\perp^{(1)}(\alpha')+\overline{\psi}_\perp^{(2)}(\alpha')]\,e^{i\varepsilon\alpha'}-\frac{2i}{k}\sqrt{1-\alpha_0^2}\,\frac{e^{i\varepsilon\alpha_0}}{\alpha'-\alpha_0}\right\}\frac{d\alpha'}{\alpha'-\alpha}=0\\&\oint_{-\infty}^{\infty}\overline{\psi}_\perp^{(1)}(\alpha')\,\frac{e^{i\varepsilon\alpha'}}{\alpha'-\alpha}\,d\alpha'=0\end{aligned}\right\}\qquad(118.15's)$$

$$\left.\begin{aligned}&\oint_{-\infty}^{\infty}\overline{\psi}_\perp^{(2)}(\alpha')\,\frac{e^{-i\varepsilon\alpha'}}{\alpha'-\alpha}\,d\alpha'=0\\&\oint_{-\infty}^{\infty}\left\{\sqrt{1-\alpha'^2}\,[\overline{\psi}_\perp^{(1)}(\alpha')+\overline{\psi}_\perp^{(2)}(\alpha')]\,e^{-i\varepsilon\alpha'}+\frac{2i}{k}\sqrt{1-\alpha_0^2}\,\frac{e^{-i\varepsilon\alpha_0}}{\alpha'-\alpha_0}\right\}\frac{d\alpha'}{\alpha'-\alpha}=0.\end{aligned}\right\}\qquad(118.16's)$$

Durch diese Gleichungen wird der Spalt besonders übersichtlich als ein System von zwei gekoppelten Halbebenen beschrieben [vgl. Gl. (115.2″)]. Da sich die

Lösung für die Beugung an jeweils einer isolierten Halbebene bei beliebiger einfallender Welle angeben läßt, so lassen sich die Gln. (118.15) bzw. (118.16) nach $\overline{\psi}^{(1)}$ bzw. $\overline{\psi}^{(2)}$ auflösen (man denke sich den Kopplungsterm in diesen Gleichungen als „zusätzliche einfallende Welle“ aufgefaßt). Wir haben dies Verfahren in Ziff. 74 bereits erörtert; im vorliegenden Fall ergibt sich diese Auflösung am einfachsten wie folgt. Zunächst spalten wir die Wurzel

$$\sqrt{1-\alpha^2} = \sqrt{1+\alpha}\,\sqrt{1-\alpha} \tag{118.17}$$

in einen in der *oberen* α-Halbebene S^+ holomorphen Faktor $\sqrt{1+\alpha}$ und einen in der *unteren* Halbebene S^- holomorphen Faktor $\sqrt{1-\alpha}$ auf (*Faktorisierung*; man vgl. die Lage der Verzweigungsschnitte in Fig. 40). Beispielsweise besagt nun Gl. (118.15′*p*), daß der Integrand der oberen bzw. unteren Zeile dieser Gleichungen in S^+ bzw. S^- holomorph sein muß (Cauchyscher Satz). Wir können aber diese Integranden mit dem Faktor $\sqrt{1+\alpha'}$ bzw. $\frac{1}{\sqrt{1-\alpha'}}$ multiplizieren, ohne daß jene Eigenschaft verloren geht. Anstelle von (118.15′*p*) können wir also auch schreiben

$$\left.\begin{aligned}
&\oint\limits_{-\infty}^{\infty}\left\{\frac{\overline{\psi}_{\|}^{(1)}(\alpha')+\overline{\psi}_{\|}^{(2)}(\alpha')}{\sqrt{1-\alpha'}}\,e^{i\varepsilon\alpha'}+2\sqrt{1+\alpha'}\,\frac{e^{i\varepsilon\alpha_0}}{\alpha'-\alpha_0}\right\}\frac{d\alpha'}{\alpha'-\alpha}=0,\\
&\oint\limits_{-\infty}^{\infty}\frac{\overline{\psi}_{\|}^{(1)}(\alpha')}{\sqrt{1-\alpha'}}\,\frac{e^{i\varepsilon\alpha'}}{\alpha'-\alpha}\,d\alpha'=0.
\end{aligned}\right\} \tag{118.15″p}$$

Durch Subtraktion dieser beiden Gleichungen ergibt sich, zusammen mit den entsprechend behandelten übrigen Gln. (118.15′) und (118.16′), ein Gleichungssystem, das sich bei Einführung der neuen Größen

$$\hat{\psi}_{\|}^{(1)}(\alpha)=\frac{e^{i\varepsilon\alpha}}{\sqrt{1-\alpha}}\,\overline{\psi}_{\|}^{(1)}(\alpha),\qquad \hat{\psi}_{\|}^{(2)}(\alpha)=\frac{e^{-i\varepsilon\alpha}}{\sqrt{1+\alpha}}\,\overline{\psi}_{\|}^{(2)}(\alpha) \tag{118.18p}$$

$$\hat{\psi}_{\perp}^{(1)}(\alpha)=\sqrt{1-\alpha}\,e^{i\varepsilon\alpha}\,\overline{\psi}_{\perp}^{(1)}(\alpha),\qquad \hat{\psi}_{\perp}^{(2)}(\alpha)=\sqrt{1+\alpha}\,e^{-i\varepsilon\alpha}\,\overline{\psi}_{\perp}^{(2)}(\alpha) \tag{118.18s}$$

in der Gestalt

$$\left.\begin{aligned}
&\hat{\psi}_{\|}^{(1)}(\alpha)-\frac{1}{2\pi i}\oint\limits_{-\infty}^{\infty}\sqrt{\frac{1+\alpha'}{1-\alpha'}}\,e^{2i\varepsilon\alpha'}\,\hat{\psi}_{\|}^{(2)}(\alpha')\,\frac{d\alpha'}{\alpha'-\alpha}=-2\sqrt{1+\alpha_0}\,\frac{e^{i\varepsilon\alpha_0}}{\alpha-\alpha_0}\\
&\hat{\psi}_{\|}^{(2)}(\alpha)+\frac{1}{2\pi i}\oint\limits_{-\infty}^{\infty}\sqrt{\frac{1-\alpha'}{1+\alpha'}}\,e^{-2i\varepsilon\alpha'}\,\hat{\psi}_{\|}^{(1)}(\alpha')\,\frac{d\alpha'}{\alpha'-\alpha}=2\sqrt{1-\alpha_0}\,\frac{e^{-i\varepsilon\alpha_0}}{\alpha-\alpha_0}
\end{aligned}\right\} \tag{118.19p}$$

bzw.

$$\left.\begin{aligned}
&\hat{\psi}_{\perp}^{(1)}(\alpha)-\frac{1}{2\pi i}\oint\limits_{-\infty}^{\infty}\sqrt{\frac{1-\alpha'}{1+\alpha'}}\,e^{2i\varepsilon\alpha'}\,\hat{\psi}_{\perp}^{(2)}(\alpha')\,\frac{d\alpha'}{\alpha'-\alpha}=-\frac{2}{ik}\sqrt{1-\alpha_0}\,\frac{e^{i\varepsilon\alpha_0}}{\alpha-\alpha_0}\\
&\hat{\psi}_{\perp}^{(2)}(\alpha)+\frac{1}{2\pi i}\oint\limits_{-\infty}^{\infty}\sqrt{\frac{1+\alpha'}{1-\alpha'}}\,e^{-2i\varepsilon\alpha'}\,\hat{\psi}_{\perp}^{(1)}(\alpha')\,\frac{d\alpha'}{\alpha'-\alpha}=\frac{2}{ik}\sqrt{1+\alpha_0}\,\frac{e^{-i\varepsilon\alpha_0}}{\alpha-\alpha_0}
\end{aligned}\right\} \tag{118.19s}$$

schreiben läßt. Wir erhalten also jeweils ein System *gekopplter singulärer Integralgleichungen vom Cauchyschen Typ* (vgl. Ziff. 74). Aus der Symmetrie der Gleichungen folgt übrigens

$$\overline{\psi}^{(2)}(\alpha,\alpha_0)=\overline{\psi}^{(1)}(-\alpha,-\alpha_0) \tag{118.20}$$

für beide Polarisationsfälle.

Nach dem in Ziff. 74 im Anschluß an Gl. (74.20′) dargelegten Verfahren zur Vermeidung der auf dem Integrationsweg gelegenen wesentlich singulären Stelle des Faktors $e^{\pm 2i\varepsilon\alpha}$ können wir die Gln. (118.19) in die Form

$$\hat{\psi}_{\parallel}^{(1)}(\alpha,\alpha_0)+\frac{1}{2\pi i}\oint_{-\infty}^{\infty} A_{\parallel}(\alpha')\,\hat{\psi}_{\parallel}^{(1)}(-\alpha',-\alpha_0)\,\frac{d\alpha'}{\alpha'-\alpha}=-2\sqrt{1+\alpha_0}\,\frac{e^{i\varepsilon\alpha_0}}{\alpha-\alpha_0} \qquad (118.19'p)$$

bzw.

$$\hat{\psi}_{\perp}^{(1)}(\alpha,\alpha_0)+\frac{1}{2\pi i}\oint_{-\infty}^{\infty} A_{\perp}(\alpha')\,\hat{\psi}_{\perp}^{(1)}(-\alpha',-\alpha_0)\,\frac{d\alpha'}{\alpha'-\alpha}=-\frac{2}{ik}\sqrt{1-\alpha_0}\,\frac{e^{i\varepsilon\alpha_0}}{\alpha-\alpha_0} \qquad (118.19's)$$

bringen. Hier haben wir von (118.20) Gebrauch gemacht und die Größen

$$A_{\parallel}(\alpha)=\frac{\sqrt{1+\alpha}}{2\pi i}\oint_{-\infty}^{\infty}\frac{e^{2i\varepsilon\alpha'}}{\sqrt{1-\alpha'}}\,\frac{d\alpha'}{\alpha'-\alpha} \qquad (118.21p)$$

bzw.

$$A_{\perp}(\alpha)=\frac{1}{2\pi i\sqrt{1+\alpha}}\oint_{-\infty}^{\infty}\sqrt{1-\alpha'}\,e^{2i\varepsilon\alpha'}\,\frac{d\alpha'}{\alpha'-\alpha} \qquad (118.21s)$$

eingeführt. Der Übergang von (118.19) zu (118.19′) erfolgt durch Zerlegung des Faktors $e^{2i\varepsilon\alpha}/\sqrt{1-\alpha}$ bzw. $e^{2i\varepsilon\alpha}\sqrt{1-\alpha}$ in je einen in S^+ und S^- holomorphen Term mit Hilfe von (74.4). Ferner ist zu beachten, daß $\hat{\psi}^{(1)}(\alpha)$ in S^- und $\hat{\psi}^{(2)}(\alpha)$ in S^+ holomorph ist.

Eine strenge Lösung unserer Integralgleichungen in *geschlossener* Form ist bisher nicht gelungen. Im folgenden ist es unsere Aufgabe Näherungslösungen für *kleine* und *große* ε zu gewinnen.

b1) Lösung für den engen Spalt

Den für Mikrowellen leicht realisierbaren Fall, daß die Wellenlänge klein gegen den Spalt ist ($\varepsilon \ll 1$), wollen wir mit Hilfe des Rayleighschen Verfahrens (vgl. AIII f1) behandeln[1]. Anschließend werfen wir auch einen Blick auf die Methode zur Lösung der dualen Integralgleichungen (Ziff. 63) und die Variationsmethode (Ziff. 107).

119. Lösung der Rayleighschen Integralgleichungen. Für $\varepsilon \ll 1$ sind die Integralgleichungen (118.8) der geeignete Ausgangspunkt. Zunächst kann man Gl. (118.8p) als Differentialgleichung für das dort auftretende Integral auffassen; sie hat die allgemeine Lösung

$$\int_{-a}^{a}\varphi_{\parallel}(x')\,H_0^1(k|x-x'|)\,dx'=A\cos k\;x+B\sin k\,x+\frac{2e^{ik\alpha_0 x}}{k\sqrt{1-\alpha_0^2}} \qquad (|x|<a). \qquad (119.1)$$

Die Konstanten A und B bleiben zunächst unbestimmt und müssen nach Auflösung der Integralgleichung (119.1) aus der *Kantenbedingung*

$$\varphi_{\parallel}(a)=\varphi_{\parallel}(-a)=0 \qquad (119.2)$$

bestimmt werden. Im folgenden wollen wir uns auf *senkrechte* Inzidenz beschränken ($\alpha_0=0$). Dann gilt aus Symmetriegründen $\varphi_{\parallel}(-x)=\varphi(x)$; es wird also

[1] Lord Rayleigh: Phil. Mag. **43**, 259 (1897). — Proc. Roy. Soc. Lond. A **89**, 194 (1913). — A. Sommerfeld: Vorlesungen über theoretische Physik, Bd. IV, S. 297ff. Wiesbaden 1950. — R. Müller u. K. Westpfahl: Z. Physik **134**, 245 (1953). — C. J. Bouwkamp: N.Y. Univ. Res. Rep. No. EM-50 (1953). — Rep. Progr. Phys. **17**, 35 (1954). — Y. Nomura u. S. Kantsura: J. Phys. Soc. Japan **12**, 190 (1957). Siehe auch W. Franz: Theorie der Beugung elektromagnetischer Wellen, S. 98ff. Berlin-Göttingen-Heidelberg: Springer 1957.

auch die linke Seite von (119.1) in x symmetrisch. Damit folgt $B=0$ und wir haben die beiden Integralgleichungen

$$\int_{-a}^{a} \varphi_{\parallel}(x')\, H_0^1\big(k\,|x-x'|\big)\, dx' = \frac{2}{k}\,(1+A\cos k\,x) \qquad (|x|<a) \qquad (119.3p)$$

bzw.

$$\int_{-a}^{a} \varphi_{\perp}(x')\, H_0^1(k\,|x-x'|)\, dx' = 2i \qquad (|x|<a) \qquad (119.3s)$$

für *kleine* ε zu lösen. Die zunächst willkürliche Konstante A in (119.3p) läßt sich übrigens auch eliminieren, indem man in dieser Gleichung $x=0$ setzt. Trägt man den so folgenden Wert für A in die Gl. (118.3p) ein, so ergibt sich

$$\int_{-a}^{a} \varphi_{\parallel}(x')\,\{H_0^1(k\,|x-x'|) - \cos k\,x\, H_0^1(k\,|x|)\}\, dx' = \frac{2}{k}\,(1-\cos k\,x)\,; \qquad (119.3'p)$$

dadurch geht allerdings die Symmetrie des Kerns verloren.

Mit Hilfe der Substitution

$$x = a\cos\xi\,, \qquad x' = a\cos\xi' \qquad (119.4)$$

sowie

$$i\sin\xi\,\varphi_{\parallel}(a\cos\xi) = u_{\parallel}(\xi) \qquad (119.5p)$$

bzw.

$$a\sin\xi\,\varphi_{\perp}(a\cos\xi) = u_{\perp}(\xi) \qquad (119.5s)$$

nehmen die zu lösenden Gln. (119.3) die folgende Form an

$$\frac{\varepsilon}{2i}\int_{0}^{\pi} u_{\parallel}(\xi')\, H_0^1(\varepsilon\,|\cos\xi-\cos\xi'|)\, d\xi' = 1 + A\cos(\varepsilon\cos\xi) \qquad (119.6p)$$

bzw.

$$\frac{1}{2i}\int_{0}^{\pi} u_{\perp}(\xi')\, H_0^1(\varepsilon\,|\cos\xi-\cos\xi'|)\, d\xi' = 1\,. \qquad (119.6s)$$

α) *Entwicklungsverfahren.* Um die Lösung dieser Integralgleichungen nach dem Verfahren von Abschn. AIII f1 nach *steigenden* Potenzen von ε zu entwickeln, gehen wir von der Reihe[1]

$$\frac{\pi}{2i}\, H_0^1(x) = \ln\frac{\gamma x}{2i} - \frac{x^2}{4}\left(\ln\frac{\gamma x}{2i} - 1\right) + \frac{x^4}{64}\left(\ln\frac{\gamma x}{2i} - \frac{3}{2}\right) + \cdots \qquad (119.7)$$

($\ln\gamma = 0{,}5772\ldots$, Eulersche Konstante) aus. Damit ergibt sich für unseren Kern die Entwicklung

$$\left.\begin{aligned}
&\frac{1}{2i} H_0^1(\varepsilon\,|\cos\xi-\cos\xi'|) = K_0(\xi,\xi') + \varepsilon^2 K_2(\xi,\xi') + \varepsilon^4 K_4(\xi,\xi') + \cdots\\
&\text{mit}\\
&K_0(\xi,\xi') = \frac{1}{\pi}\ln\left(\frac{\gamma\varepsilon}{2i}\,|\cos\xi-\cos\xi'|\right)\\
&K_2(\xi,\xi') = \frac{1}{4\pi}\,(\cos\xi-\cos\xi')^2\,\{1-\pi K_0(\xi,\xi')\}\\
&K_4(\xi,\xi') = \frac{1}{64\pi}\,(\cos\xi-\cos\xi')^4\left\{\pi K_0(\xi,\xi') - \frac{3}{2}\right\}.
\end{aligned}\right\} \qquad (119.7')$$

[1] Vgl. W. MAGNUS u. F. OBERHETTINGER: Formeln und Sätze für die speziellen Funktionen der mathematischen Physik, 2. Aufl., S. 25. Berlin: Springer 1948.

Bei zylindrischen Beugungsproblemen ergibt sich also zufolge (119.7) keine reine Entwicklung nach steigenden Potenzen in ε, sondern die Entwicklungskoeffizienten enthalten noch den langsam veränderlichen $\ln \frac{\gamma\varepsilon}{2i}$ (im Gegensatz zum räumlichen Problem, vgl. Ziff. 91). Da die Inhomogenitäten rechts in Gl. (119.6) in ε gerade sind, so können in der Reihenentwicklung von $u_{\parallel}(\xi)$ nur *ungerade*, in der von $u_{\perp}(\xi)$ nur *gerade* Potenzen von ε vorkommen:

$$u_{\parallel}(\xi) = \varepsilon\, u_{\parallel}^{(1)}(\xi) + \varepsilon^3 u_{\parallel}^{(3)}(\xi) + \varepsilon^5 u_{\parallel}^{(5)}(\xi) + \cdots, \tag{119.8p}$$

$$u_{\perp}(\xi) = u_{\perp}^{(0)}(\xi) + \varepsilon^2 u_{\perp}^{(2)}(\xi) + \varepsilon^4 u_{\perp}^{(4)}(\xi) + \cdots. \tag{119.8s}$$

Setzen wir die Reihen (119.7′), (119.8) in (119.6) ein und entwickeln wir auch die Inhomogenitäten nach ε, so ergibt sich durch Vergleich der Koeffizienten gleicher Potenzen von ε ein sukzessives Gleichungssystem für die einzelnen Ordnungen in (119.8). Dabei ist zu beachten, daß auch die Konstante A in (119.6p) von ε abhängt:

$$A = -1 + \varepsilon^2 A_2 + \varepsilon^4 A_4 + \varepsilon^6 A_6 + \cdots \tag{119.8′}$$

[das erste Glied dieser Reihe ergibt sich aus der Forderung, daß die Inhomogenität rechts in (119.6p) kein Glied mit ε^0 enthalten darf]. Damit ergibt sich

$$\left.\begin{aligned}
&\int_0^\pi u_{\parallel}^{(1)}(\xi')\,K_0(\xi,\xi')\,d\xi' = A_2 + \frac{1}{2}\cos^2\xi,\\
&\int_0^\pi u_{\parallel}^{(3)}(\xi')\,K_0(\xi,\xi')\,d\xi' = A_4 - \frac{A_2}{2}\cos^2\xi - \frac{1}{24}\cos^4\xi - \int_0^\pi u_{\parallel}^{(1)}(\xi')\,K_2(\xi,\xi')\,d\xi',\\
&\int_0^\pi u_{\parallel}^{(5)}(\xi')\,K_0(\xi,\xi')\,d\xi' = A_6 - \frac{A_4}{2}\cos^2\xi + \frac{A_2}{24}\cos^4\xi + \frac{1}{720}\cos^6\xi -\\
&\qquad - \int_0^\pi u_{\parallel}^{(3)}(\xi')\,K_2(\xi,\xi')\,d\xi' - \int_0^\pi u_{\parallel}^{(1)}(\xi')\,K_4(\xi,\xi')\,d\xi'
\end{aligned}\right\} \tag{119.9p}$$

bzw.

$$\left.\begin{aligned}
&\int_0^\pi u_{\perp}^{(0)}(\xi')\,K_0(\xi,\xi')\,d\xi' = 1,\\
&\int_0^\pi u_{\perp}^{(2)}(\xi')\,K_0(\xi,\xi')\,d\xi' = -\int_0^\pi u_{\perp}^{(0)}(\xi')\,K_2(\xi,\xi')\,d\xi',\\
&\int_0^\pi u_{\perp}^{(4)}(\xi')\,K_0(\xi,\xi')\,d\xi' = -\int_0^\pi u_{\perp}^{(2)}(\xi')\,K_2(\xi,\xi')\,d\xi' - \int_0^\pi u_{\perp}^{(0)}(\xi')\,K_4(\xi,\xi')\,d\xi'.
\end{aligned}\right\} \tag{119.9s}$$

β) Statisches Problem. Die hier auftretenden Integralgleichungen zur sukzessiven Berechnung der $u^{(\nu)}(\xi)$ enthalten sämtlich den „*statischen Kern*“ $K_0(\xi,\xi')$, für den sich die Eigenfunktionen leicht angeben lassen[1]. Mit Hilfe der Reihenentwicklung

$$\ln|\cos\xi - \cos\xi'| = -\ln 2 - 2\sum_{\nu=1}^{\infty}\frac{\cos\nu\xi\cos\nu\xi'}{\nu} \tag{119.10}$$

ergibt sich nämlich

$$\left.\begin{aligned}
&K_0(\xi,\xi') = \frac{p}{\pi} - \frac{2}{\pi}\sum_{\nu=1}^{\infty}\frac{\cos\nu\xi\cos\nu\xi'}{\nu}\\
\text{mit}\quad &\\
&p = \ln\frac{\gamma\varepsilon}{4i} = \ln\frac{\gamma\varepsilon}{4} - \frac{\pi i}{2}.
\end{aligned}\right\} \tag{119.10′}$$

[1] Vgl. W. SCHMEIDLER: Integralgleichungen mit Anwendungen in Physik und Technik, 2. Aufl., S. 67. Leipzig 1955.

D.h. die $\cos \nu \xi$ sind die gesuchten *Eigenfunktionen* von $K_0(\xi, \xi')$ (vgl. Ziff. 93). In der Tat gilt zufolge der Orthogonalitätsrelation

$$\frac{1}{\pi}\int_0^\pi \cos \nu \xi \cos \mu \xi \, d\xi = \begin{cases} 1 & (\nu = \mu = 0) \\ \frac{\delta_{\nu\mu}}{2} & (\mu + \nu \neq 0), \end{cases}$$

$$\int_0^\pi \cos \nu \xi' \, K_0(\xi, \xi') \, d\xi' = \begin{cases} p & (\nu = 0) \\ -\frac{1}{\nu} \cos \nu \xi & (\nu > 0). \end{cases} \tag{119.10''}$$

Damit lassen sich die Integralgleichungen (119.9) — die wir in der Form

$$\frac{1}{\pi}\int_0^\pi u(\xi') \ln\left(\frac{\gamma \varepsilon}{2i} |\cos \xi - \cos \xi'|\right) d\xi' = f(\xi) \tag{119.11}$$

schreiben können — nach diesen Eigenfunktionen entwickeln, d.h. als Fourier-Cosinus-Reihen darstellen. Die Lösung von (119.11) läßt sich übrigens auch in die geschlossene Form

$$u(\xi) = -\frac{1}{\pi}\int_0^\pi \frac{df(\xi')}{d\xi'} \frac{\sin \xi'}{\cos \xi' - \cos \xi} d\xi' + \frac{1}{\pi p}\int_0^\pi f(\xi') \, d\xi' \tag{119.11'}$$

bringen[1]. Im *s-Fall* ist jedoch die Entwicklung

$$u_\perp(\xi) = \sum_{\nu=0}^{\infty} a_\perp^{(2\nu)} \cos 2\nu \xi \tag{119.12s}$$

mit

$$a_\perp^{(0)} = \frac{f_\perp^{(0)}}{p}, \quad a_\perp^{(2\nu)} = -2\nu f_\perp^{(2\nu)} \quad (\nu > 0) \tag{119.12's}$$

für das Folgende bequemer, da sich *abbrechende* Fourier-Reihen ergeben. Dabei bedeuten die $f_\perp^{(2\nu)}$ die Fourier-Cosinus-Koeffizienten der Inhomogenität $f_\perp(\xi)$ rechts in (119.9s), deren Fourier-Zerlegung nur Glieder der Form $\cos 2\nu \xi$ enthält. Im *p-Fall* erweist es sich zufolge der Kantenbedingung (119.2) und Gl. (119.5p) als zweckmäßig, die Lösung in der Form

$$\left.\begin{aligned} u_\parallel(\xi) &= \frac{1}{2}\sum_{\nu=0}^{\infty} a_\parallel^{(2\nu+1)} \{\cos 2\nu \xi - \cos(2\nu+2)\xi\} \\ &= \sin \xi \sum_{\nu=0}^{\infty} a_\parallel^{(2\nu+1)} \sin(2\nu+1)\xi \end{aligned}\right\} \tag{119.12p}$$

anzusetzen. Mit (119.10'') ergibt sich dann für die $a_\parallel^{(2\nu+1)}$

$$\left.\begin{aligned} a_\parallel^{(1)} &= \frac{2 f_\parallel^{(0)}}{p} \\ a_\parallel^{(2\nu+1)} &= a_\parallel^{(2\nu-1)} - 4\nu f_\parallel^{(2\nu)} \quad (\nu > 0). \end{aligned}\right\} \tag{119.12'p}$$

Dabei sind die $f_\parallel^{(2)\nu}$ wieder die Fourier-Cosinus-Koeffizienten der Inhomogenität $f_\parallel(\xi)$ rechts in (119.9p), deren Fourier-Zerlegung auch hier nur Glieder der Form $\cos 2\nu \xi$ enthält. Für die erste Näherung $u_\parallel^{(1)}(\xi)$ ergibt sich aus der ersten Gl. (119.9p) mit (119.12p) und (119.12'p)

$$a_\parallel^{(1)} = \frac{4A_2 + 1}{2p}, \quad a_\parallel^{(3)} = a_\parallel^{(1)} - 1 \tag{119.13p}$$

[1] Vgl. W. Schmeidler: l. c.

und damit, da hier alle $a_{\parallel}^{(2\nu+1)}$ bis auf $a_{\parallel}^{(1)}$ verschwinden,

$$u_{\parallel}^{(1)}(\xi) = \tfrac{1}{2}(1 - \cos 2\xi) = \sin^2 \xi \tag{119.14p}$$

$$A_2 = \frac{2p-1}{4}. \tag{119.13'p}$$

Aus der ersten Gl. (119.9s) ergibt sich mit (119.12s) und (119.12's)

$$u_{\perp}^{(0)} = \frac{1}{p}. \tag{119.14s}$$

γ) Höhere Näherungen. Die für die höheren Näherungen benötigten Integrale in den Inhomogenitäten rechts in (119.9) lassen sich leicht berechnen, wenn man die „*höheren Kerne*“ $K_2, K_4, \ldots$ ebenfalls in Fourier-Cosinus-Reihen entwickelt. Zu diesem Zweck braucht man nur die Reihe (119.10′) für K_0 in (119.7′) einführen und die cos-Potenzen und Produkte mit Hilfe der Formel

$$2\cos\nu\xi\cos\mu\xi = \cos(\mu+\nu)\xi + \cos(\mu-\nu)\xi$$

geeignet zusammenfassen. Man erhält

$$\left.\begin{aligned} K_2(\xi,\xi') &= -\frac{p}{4\pi} - \frac{2p+1}{16\pi}(\cos 2\xi + \cos 2\xi') \\ &\quad - \frac{1}{12\pi}\left(\cos 2\xi - \frac{1}{8}\cos 4\xi\right)\left(\cos 2\xi' - \frac{1}{8}\cos 4\xi'\right) + \cdots \\ K_4(\xi,\xi') &= \frac{3}{256\pi}(3p-1) + \frac{6p-1}{192\pi}\cos 2\xi + \frac{1}{512\pi}\left(p + \frac{7}{12}\right)\cos 4\xi + \cdots, \end{aligned}\right\} \tag{119.15}$$

dabei haben wir nur diejenigen Glieder angeschrieben, die bei der Berechnung von $u_{\parallel}^{(3)}$, $u_{\perp}^{(2)}$ und $u_{\perp}^{(4)}$ benötigt werden. Die Auflösung der weiteren Integralgleichungen (119.9) ergibt folgende Werte für die Fourier-Cosinus-Koeffizienten der Reihen (119.12), wenn wir sogleich die ersten drei Näherungen in (119.8) zusammenfassen

$$\left.\begin{aligned} a_{\parallel}^{(1)} &= \varepsilon - \frac{\varepsilon^3}{4}\left(p - \frac{3}{4}\right) + \frac{\varepsilon^5}{16}\left(p^2 - \frac{5}{4}p + \frac{7}{16}\right) + \cdots, \\ a_{\parallel}^{(3)} &= - \frac{\varepsilon^3}{48} + \frac{\varepsilon^5}{384}\left(3p - \frac{15}{8}\right) + \cdots, \\ a_{\parallel}^{(5)} &= \frac{\varepsilon^5}{5120} + \cdots \end{aligned}\right\} \tag{119.15p}$$

bzw.

$$\left.\begin{aligned} a_{\perp}^{(0)} &= \frac{1}{p} + \frac{\varepsilon^2}{4p} + \frac{\varepsilon^4}{64}\left(\frac{1}{2p^2} + \frac{3}{4p} - 1\right) + \cdots, \\ a_{\perp}^{(2)} &= - \frac{\varepsilon^2}{4}\left(\frac{1}{2p} + 1\right) - \frac{\varepsilon^4}{48}\left(\frac{3}{2p} - 1\right) + \cdots, \\ a_{\perp}^{(4)} &= \frac{\varepsilon^4}{512}\left(\frac{1}{p} + \frac{4}{3}\right) + \cdots. \end{aligned}\right\} \tag{119.15s}$$

Die damit gefundene Lösung (119.12) ist im p- bzw. s-Fall bis auf Fehler der Größenordnung ε^7 bzw. ε^6 *exakt*; allerdings ist über die Konvergenz der Reihen (119.8) bzw. (119.15) nichts bekannt. Man ist bisher noch darauf angewiesen, ihre Brauchbarkeit durch numerischen Vergleich mit der strengen Lösung zu beurteilen (s. Ziff. 124).

δ) Feldgrößen in der Öffnung. Geht man mittels (119.4) und (119.5) zu den ursprünglich eingeführten Größen (118.7) in der Öffnung zurück, so ergibt sich anstelle der Fourier-Cosinus-Reihen (119.12) eine Darstellung mittels *Tschebyscheffscher Polynome.* In der Tat ergibt sich zunächst aus (119.4)

$$\left.\begin{aligned} \sin(2\nu+1)\,\xi &= \sin\left[(2\nu+1)\arccos\frac{x}{a}\right] \\ &= (-1)^{\nu}\cos\left[(2\nu+1)\arcsin\frac{x}{a}\right] = U_{2\nu+1}\left(\frac{x}{a}\right) = \sqrt{1-\left(\frac{x}{a}\right)^2}\,U^*_{2\nu}\left(\frac{x}{a}\right) \\ \text{bzw.}\quad & \\ \cos 2\nu\,\xi &= \cos\left(2\nu\arccos\frac{x}{a}\right) = (-1)^{\nu}\cos\left(2\nu\arcsin\frac{x}{a}\right) = T_{2\nu}\left(\frac{x}{a}\right), \end{aligned}\right\} \quad (119.16)$$

wobei die $T_{2\nu}$ bzw. $U^*_{2\nu}$ die Tschebyscheffschen Polynome 2ν-ten Grades erster bzw. zweiter Art sind, während die U_ν als Tschebyscheffsche Funktionen zweiter Art bezeichnet werden[1]. Setzt man (119.16) in die Reihen (119.12) ein, so ergibt sich mit (119.5) die Darstellung $(|x| \leqq a)$

$$\varphi_{\parallel}(x) = -i\sqrt{1-\left(\frac{x}{a}\right)^2}\sum_{\nu=0}^{\infty} a_{\parallel}^{(2\nu+1)}\,U^*_{2\nu}\left(\frac{x}{a}\right) \quad (119.17p)$$

bzw.

$$\varphi_{\perp}(x) = \frac{1}{\sqrt{a^2-x^2}}\sum_{\nu=0}^{\infty} a_{\perp}^{(2\nu)}\,T_{2\nu}\left(\frac{x}{a}\right). \quad (119.17s)$$

Mit Hilfe der Koeffizienten (119.15) und der expliziten Ausdrücke für die Tschebyscheffschen Polynome ergibt sich hieraus bis zu den Gliedern in ε^3 bzw. ε^2 *)

$$\varphi_{\parallel}(x) = -i\sqrt{1-\left(\frac{x}{a}\right)^2}\cdot\varepsilon\left\{1-\varepsilon^2\left[\frac{1}{4}\ln\frac{\gamma\varepsilon}{4i}-\frac{5}{24}+\frac{1}{12}\left(\frac{x}{a}\right)^2\right]+\cdots\right\} \quad (119.17'p)$$

$$\varphi_{\perp}(x) = \frac{1}{\ln\frac{\gamma\varepsilon}{4i}\sqrt{a^2-x^2}}\left\{1+\frac{\varepsilon^2}{2}\left[\frac{1}{2}\ln\frac{\gamma\varepsilon}{4i}+\frac{3}{4}-\left(\ln\frac{\gamma\varepsilon}{4i}+\frac{1}{2}\right)\left(\frac{x}{a}\right)^2\right]+\cdots\right\}. \quad (119.17's)$$

Man findet hier also das in Ziff. 23 diskutierte Verhalten der Belegungsdichten bei Annäherung an die Schirmränder wieder.

120. Fernfeld. Fourier-Methode. α) *Fernfeld.* Von größerem physikalischem Interesse als die Feldgrößen in der Öffnung ist das *Fernfeld* hinter dem Spalt. Für dieses ergibt sich durch asymptotische Auswertung der Gln. (118.5) mit

$$\sqrt{(x-x')^2+z^2} \to r - x'\cos\vartheta \qquad (r\to\infty,\ \vartheta<\pi)$$

$$\left.\begin{aligned} v_{\parallel}(r,\vartheta) &\to \frac{k\,e^{i\left(kr+\frac{\pi}{4}\right)}}{i\sqrt{2\pi k r}}\sin\vartheta\int_{-a}^{a}\varphi_{\parallel}(x')\,e^{-ikx'\cos\vartheta}\,dx' \\ &= \frac{k\,e^{i\left(kr+\frac{\pi}{4}\right)}}{i\sqrt{2\pi k r}}\sin\vartheta\,\overline{\varphi}_{\parallel}(\cos\vartheta) \end{aligned}\right\} \quad (120.1p)$$

bzw.

$$\left.\begin{aligned} v_{\perp}(r,\vartheta) &\to -\frac{e^{i\left(kr+\frac{\pi}{4}\right)}}{\sqrt{2\pi k r}}\int_{-a}^{a}\varphi_{\perp}(x')\,e^{-ikx'\cos\vartheta}\,dx' \\ &= -\frac{e^{i\left(kr+\frac{\pi}{4}\right)}}{\sqrt{2\pi k r}}\,\overline{\varphi}_{\perp}(\cos\vartheta) \end{aligned}\right\} \quad (120.1s)$$

---

[1] Vgl. MAGNUS-OBERHETTINGER: l. c. S. 103/104.

* Vgl. dazu die Ergebnisse nach der strengen Theorie bei F. B. MOULLIN u. F. M. PHILLIPS: Proc. Inst. Electr. Engrs. IV **99**, 137 (1952).

(vgl. Ziff. 62). Führen wir hier die Größen $u(\xi)$ aus (119.5) ein sowie die für diese Größen gefundenen Fourier-Reihen (119.12), so ergibt sich

$$\left.\begin{aligned} v_{\parallel}(r,\vartheta) \to &-\frac{e^{i\left(kr+\frac{\pi}{4}\right)}}{\sqrt{2\pi k r}} \sin\vartheta\cdot\varepsilon\sum_{\nu=0}^{\infty} a_{\parallel}^{(2\nu)}\cdot \\ &\cdot\frac{1}{2}\int_0^{\pi}\{\cos 2\nu\xi-\cos(2\nu+2)\xi\}\,e^{-i\varepsilon\cos\vartheta\cos\xi}\,d\xi \end{aligned}\right\} \qquad (120.1'p)$$

bzw.

$$v_{\perp}(r,\vartheta) \to -\frac{e^{i\left(kr+\frac{\pi}{4}\right)}}{\sqrt{2\pi k r}}\sum_{\nu=0}^{\infty} a_{\perp}^{(2\nu+1)}\int_0^{\pi}\cos 2\nu\xi\, e^{-i\varepsilon\cos\vartheta\cos\xi}\,d\xi\,. \qquad (120.1's)$$

Mit Hilfe der Integraldarstellung der Bessel-Funktionen

$$\int_0^{\pi}\cos 2\nu\xi\, e^{ix\cos\xi}\,d\xi=(-1)^{\nu}\pi J_{2\nu}(x) \qquad (120.2)$$

und der Rekursionsformel

$$J_{2\nu}(x)+J_{2\nu+2}(x)=2\,\frac{2\nu+1}{x}J_{2\nu+1}(x) \qquad (120.3)$$

ergibt sich daraus die Darstellung

$$\left.\begin{aligned} v_{\parallel}(r,\vartheta) \to &-\sqrt{\frac{\pi}{2kr}}\,e^{i\left(kr+\frac{\pi}{4}\right)}\sin\vartheta\cdot \\ &\cdot\sum_{\nu=0}^{\infty}(-1)^{\nu}(2\nu+1)\,a_{\parallel}^{(2\nu+1)}\,\frac{J_{2\nu+1}(\varepsilon\cos\vartheta)}{\cos\vartheta} \end{aligned}\right\} \qquad (120.1''p)$$

bzw.

$$v_{\perp}(r,\vartheta) \to -\sqrt{\frac{\pi}{2kr}}\,e^{i\left(kr+\frac{\pi}{4}\right)}\sum_{\nu=0}^{\infty}(-1)^{\nu}a_{\perp}^{(2\nu)}J_{2\nu}(\varepsilon\cos\vartheta)\,. \qquad (120.1''s)$$

Wenn wir hier für die Koeffizienten $a_{\parallel}^{(2\nu+1)}$ und $a_{\perp}^{(2\nu)}$ unsere Potenzreihendarstellung (119.15) einführen, so müssen wir konsequenterweise auch die Besselschen Funktionen nach steigenden Potenzen von ε entwickeln. Auf diese Weise ergibt sich

$$\left.\begin{aligned} v_{\parallel}(r,\vartheta) \to &-\sqrt{\frac{\pi}{2kr}}\,e^{i\left(kr+\frac{\pi}{4}\right)}\sin\vartheta\cdot\frac{\varepsilon^2}{2}\left\{1-\frac{\varepsilon^2}{8}\left[2p-\frac{3}{2}+\cos^2\vartheta\right]\right. \\ &\left.+\frac{\varepsilon^4}{16}\left[p^2-\frac{5p}{4}+\frac{7}{16}+\frac{1}{2}\left(p-\frac{2}{3}\right)\cos^2\vartheta+\frac{1}{12}\cos^4\vartheta\right]+\cdots\right\} \end{aligned}\right\} \qquad (120.4p)$$

bzw.

$$\left.\begin{aligned} v_{\perp}(r,\vartheta) \to &-\sqrt{\frac{\pi}{2kr}}\,e^{i\left(kr+\frac{\pi}{4}\right)}\cdot\frac{1}{p}\left\{1+\frac{\varepsilon^2}{4}\sin^2\vartheta\right. \\ &\left.-\frac{\varepsilon^4}{32}\left[\frac{p}{2}-\frac{1}{4p}-\frac{3}{8}-\left(p-\frac{3}{2}\right)\cos^2\vartheta-\frac{1}{2}\cos^4\vartheta\right]+\cdots\right\}. \end{aligned}\right\} \qquad (120.4s)$$

Wir kommen auf diese Gleichungen weiter unten noch zurück; hier wollen wir zunächst darauf hinweisen, daß sich durch Vergleich von (120.1) mit (120.4) folgende Entwicklung für die $\overline{\varphi}_{\parallel}(\alpha)$ und $\overline{\varphi}_{\perp}(\alpha)$ ergibt

$$\left.\begin{aligned} \overline{\varphi}_{\parallel}(\alpha) = \frac{\pi a}{2i}\,\varepsilon&\left\{1-\frac{\varepsilon^2}{8}\left[2p-\frac{3}{2}+\alpha^2\right]\right. \\ &\left.+\frac{\varepsilon^4}{16}\left[p^2-\frac{5p}{4}+\frac{7}{16}+\left(p-\frac{2}{3}\right)\frac{\alpha^2}{2}+\frac{\alpha^4}{12}\right]+\cdots\right\} \end{aligned}\right\} \qquad (120.5p)$$

bzw.

$$\overline{\varphi}_{\perp}(\alpha)=\frac{\pi}{p}\left\{1+\frac{\varepsilon^2}{4}[1-\alpha^2]-\frac{\varepsilon^4}{32}\left[\frac{p}{2}-\frac{1}{4p}-\frac{3}{8}-\left(p-\frac{3}{2}\right)\alpha^2-\frac{\alpha^4}{2}\right]+\cdots\right\}. \tag{120.5s}$$

β) Lösung der dualen Integralgleichungen. Wir wollen noch kurz zeigen, wie sich die Größen $\overline{\varphi}_{\parallel}(\alpha)$ und $\overline{\varphi}_{\perp}(\alpha)$ direkt durch Lösung der dualen Integralgleichungen (118.12) bestimmen lassen[1]. Dies mag zur Erläuterung des in Ziff. 63 besprochenen Verfahrens dienen. Die Gln. (118.12) lassen sich für senkrechte Inzidien ($\alpha_0=0$) zufolge der dann gültigen Symmetrierelation $\overline{\varphi}(-\alpha)=\overline{\varphi}(\alpha)$ in der Form schreiben ($x=a\eta$)

$$\left.\begin{aligned}\int_0^\infty \sqrt{1-\alpha^2}\,\overline{\varphi}_{\parallel}(\alpha)\cos(\varepsilon\alpha\eta)\,d\alpha&=\frac{\pi}{k}\quad(0<\eta<1)\\ \int_0^\infty \overline{\varphi}_{\parallel}(\alpha)\cos(\varepsilon\alpha\eta)\,d\alpha&=0\quad(\eta>1)\end{aligned}\right\} \tag{120.6p}$$

bzw.

$$\left.\begin{aligned}\int_0^\infty \frac{\overline{\varphi}_{\perp}(\alpha)}{\sqrt{1-\alpha^2}}\cos(\varepsilon\alpha\eta)\,d\alpha&=\pi i\quad(0<\eta<1)\\ \int_0^\infty \overline{\varphi}_{\perp}(\alpha)\cos(\varepsilon\alpha\eta)\,d\alpha&=0\quad(\eta>1).\end{aligned}\right\} \tag{120.6s}$$

Nach dem Verfahren von Ziff. 63 haben wir zunächst nach einem orthogonalen Funktionensystem Ausschau zu halten, das die *homogenen* Integralgleichungen (120.6) gliedweise erfüllt (sich also als Fourier-Integral über den Bereich $|\eta|\leqq 1$ darstellen läßt). Ein solches ist

$$\left.\begin{aligned}\frac{J_\nu(\varepsilon\alpha)}{(\varepsilon\alpha)^\mu}&=\frac{i^{\nu-\mu}}{2^\nu\sqrt{\pi}\,\Gamma(\nu+\frac{1}{2})}\int_{-1}^{1}e^{i\varepsilon\alpha\eta}\frac{d^{\nu-\mu}}{d\eta^{\nu-\mu}}(1-\eta^2)^{\nu-\frac{1}{2}}\,d\eta\\ &(0\leqq\mu\leqq\nu,\quad \nu=0,1,2,\ldots),\end{aligned}\right\} \tag{120.7}$$

wobei der Faktor von $e^{i\varepsilon\alpha\eta}$ im Integranden für die unten vorzunehmende Spezialisierung im wesentlichen eines der Tschebyscheffschen Polynome ist, die bezüglich des Intervalls $|\eta|\leqq 1$ orthogonal und vollständig sind[2], was für das Folgende maßgebend ist. Wir machen daher den Ansatz

$$\overline{\varphi}_{\parallel}(\alpha)=\frac{\pi}{ik}\sum_{\nu=0}^{\infty}(-1)^\nu(2\nu+1)\,a_{\parallel}^{(2\nu+1)}\frac{J_{2\nu+1}(\varepsilon\alpha)}{\alpha} \tag{120.8p}$$

$$\overline{\varphi}_{\perp}(\alpha)=\pi\sum_{\nu=0}^{\infty}(-1)^\nu a_{\perp}^{(2\nu)}J_{2\nu}(\varepsilon\alpha) \tag{120.8s}$$

(wobei die hinzugefügten Faktoren für das Folgende bequem sind), womit der *Symmetrie-* und *Kantenbedingung* genüge getan wird. Nach Ziff. 61 muß nämlich $\overline{\varphi}_{\parallel}(\alpha)$ wie $\alpha^{-\frac{3}{2}}$ und $\overline{\varphi}_{\perp}(\alpha)$ wie $\alpha^{-\frac{1}{2}}$ für $|\alpha|\to\infty$ abnehmen, da die Belegungsdichten $\varphi_{\parallel}(x)$ bzw. $\varphi_{\perp}(x)$ nur dann die richtige Kantensingularität aufweisen (bei der Fourier-Analyse ist für die Art der Singularität des Wellenfeldes das Verhalten der Fourier-Transformierten für $|\alpha|\to\infty$ maßgebend). Es läßt sich hier auch explizit zeigen, daß die Ansätze (120.8) die homogenen Integralgleichungen (120.6) gliedweise erfüllen. In der Tat folgt dies mit Hilfe des (geeignet spezialisierten)

[1] E. GROSCHWITZ u. H. HÖNL: Z. Physik **131**, 305 (1952). — H. HÖNL u. E. ZIMMER: Z. Physik **135**, 196 (1953). — C. J. TRANTER: Quart. J. Mech. Appl. Math. **7**, 317 (1954).

[2] Vgl. MAGNUS-OBERHETTINGER: l. c. S. 104.

Sonine-Schafheitlinschen Integrals[1]

$$\int_0^\infty \frac{J_{2\nu+1}(\varepsilon\alpha)}{\alpha}\cos(\varepsilon\alpha\eta)\,d\alpha = \begin{cases} \dfrac{\cos[(2\nu+1)\arcsin\eta]}{2\nu+1} = \dfrac{(-1)^\nu}{2\nu+1}U_{2\nu+1}(\eta) & (0<\eta<1) \\ 0 & (\eta>1) \end{cases} \tag{120.9p}$$

bzw.

$$\int_0^\infty J_{2\nu}(\varepsilon\alpha)\cos(\varepsilon\alpha\eta)\,d\alpha = \begin{cases} \dfrac{\cos(2\nu\arcsin\eta)}{\varepsilon\sqrt{1-\eta^2}} = (-1)^\nu\dfrac{T_{2\nu}(\eta)}{\varepsilon\sqrt{1-\eta^2}} & (0<\eta<1) \\ 0 & (\eta>1). \end{cases} \tag{120.9s}$$

Mit (120.9) und den Orthogonalitätsrelationen

$$\left.\begin{aligned} &\int_0^\infty J_{2\nu+1}(\varepsilon\alpha)\,J_{2\mu+1}(\varepsilon\alpha)\frac{d\alpha}{\alpha} = \frac{\delta_{\nu\mu}}{4\nu+2} \\ &\int_{-1}^{1}\frac{U_{2\nu+1}(\eta)\,U_{2\mu+1}(\eta)}{\sqrt{1-\eta^2}}\,d\eta = \frac{\pi}{2}\,\delta_{\nu\mu} \end{aligned}\right\} \tag{120.9'p}$$

bzw.

$$\left.\begin{aligned} &\int_0^\infty J_{2\nu}(\varepsilon\alpha)\,J_{2\nu}(\varepsilon\alpha)\,\frac{d\alpha}{\alpha} = \frac{\delta_{\nu\mu}}{4\nu} \qquad (\nu+\mu\neq 0) \\ &\int_{-1}^{1}\frac{T_{2\nu}(\eta)\,T_{2\mu}(\eta)}{\sqrt{1-\eta^2}}\,d\eta = \begin{cases} \pi & (\mu=\nu=0) \\ \dfrac{\pi}{2}\,\delta_{\nu\mu} & (\mu+\nu\neq 0) \end{cases} \end{aligned}\right\} \tag{120.9's}$$

sind zugleich auch die Entwicklungen von $\cos(\varepsilon\alpha\eta)$ nach den $J_{2\nu+1}(\varepsilon\alpha)/\alpha$ bzw. $J_{2\nu}(\varepsilon\alpha)$ oder nach den $U_{2\nu+1}(\eta)$ bzw. $T_{2\nu}(\eta)$ gegeben $(0<\eta<1,\ -\infty<\alpha<\infty)$:

$$\cos(\varepsilon\alpha\eta) = 2\sum_{\nu=0}^{\infty}(-1)^\nu(2\nu+1)\,\frac{U_{2\nu+1}(\eta)}{\varepsilon\sqrt{1-\eta^2}}\,\frac{J_{2\nu+1}(\varepsilon\alpha)}{\alpha} \tag{120.10p}$$

bzw.

$$\cos(\varepsilon\alpha\eta) = J_0(\varepsilon\alpha) + 2\sum_{\nu=1}^{\infty}(-1)^\nu\,T_{2\nu}(\eta)\,J_{2\nu}(\varepsilon\alpha). \tag{120.10s}$$

Setzt man nun die Entwicklungen (120.8) und (120.10) in die *inhomogene* Integralgleichung (120.6) ein und entwickelt man auch die Inhomogenität nach den $U_{2\nu+1}(\eta)$ bzw. $T_{2\nu}(\eta)$, so ergibt sich durch Koeffizientenvergleich

$$\sum_{\nu=0}^{\infty} a_{\parallel}^{(2\nu+1)}\,C_{\parallel}^{(\nu\mu)} = \delta_{\mu 0} \tag{120.11p}$$

bzw.

$$\sum_{\nu=0}^{\infty} a_{\perp}^{(2\nu)}\,C_{\perp}^{(\nu\mu)} = \delta_{\mu 0} \tag{120.11s}$$

mit

$$C_{\parallel}^{(\nu\mu)} = -\frac{2i}{\varepsilon}(2\nu+1)(-1)^\nu\int_0^\infty J_{2\nu+1}(\varepsilon\alpha)\,J_{2\mu+1}(\varepsilon\alpha)\,\frac{\sqrt{1-\alpha^2}}{\alpha^2}\,d\alpha \tag{120.12p}$$

bzw.

$$C_{\perp}^{(\nu\mu)} = -i(-1)^\nu\int_0^\infty J_{2\nu}(\varepsilon\alpha)\,J_{2\mu}(\varepsilon\alpha)\,\frac{d\alpha}{\sqrt{1-\alpha^2}}. \tag{120.12s}$$

Damit ist die Lösung der dualen Integralgleichungen (120.6) im Prinzip für beliebige ε auf das lineare Gleichungssystem (120.11) für die $a^{(\nu)}$ zurückgeführt.

[1] Vgl. MAGNUS-OBERHETTINGER: l. c. S. 51.

Eine Lösung dieses Systems ist bisher allerdings nur für $\varepsilon \ll 1$ gelungen. In diesem Fall lassen sich die Integrale (120.12) durch Potenzreihen in ε darstellen[1]; entwickelt man auch die $a^{(\nu)}$ in solche Potenzreihen, so ergibt sich — falls man sich auf eine endliche Potenz von ε beschränkt — durch Koeffizientenvergleich ein abbrechendes Gleichungssystem für die Entwicklungskoeffizienten. Auf diesem Wege gelangt man zu den Koeffizienten (119.15) zurück[2]. Auch der Weg über das *Variationsprinzip* (Ziff. 107) führt mit einem Ritzschen Ansatz der Form (119.17) auf das Gleichungssystem (120.11), (120.12)[2]. Vergleicht man die Methoden hinsichtlich des Rechenaufwandes, so verdient die eingangs dargestellte Rayleighsche Störungsrechnung sicher den Vorzug, zumal sie nur mit elementaren Funktionen operiert. Demgegenüber ist die systematische Auswertung der Integrale (120.12) ungleich mühsamer[1].

γ) Lösungen der Integralgleichungen (118.12′). Etwas einfacher gestaltet sich die Behandlung der Integralgleichungen (118.12′), die für $\alpha_0 = 0$ lauten

$$\left.\begin{aligned} &\frac{1}{\pi}\int_{-\infty}^{\infty}\sqrt{1-\alpha'^2}\,\overline{\varphi}_{\|}(\alpha')\,\frac{\sin\varepsilon(\alpha'-\alpha)}{\alpha'-\alpha}\,d\alpha' = \frac{2}{k}\,\frac{\sin\varepsilon\alpha}{\alpha} \\ &\overline{\varphi}_{\|}(\alpha) - \frac{1}{\pi}\int_{-\infty}^{\infty}\overline{\varphi}_{\|}(\alpha')\,\frac{\sin\varepsilon(\alpha'-\alpha)}{\alpha'-\alpha}\,d\alpha' = 0 \end{aligned}\right\} \qquad (120.13\,p)$$

bzw.

$$\left.\begin{aligned} &\frac{1}{\pi}\int_{-\infty}^{\infty}\frac{\overline{\varphi}_{\perp}(\alpha')}{\sqrt{1-\alpha'^2}}\,\frac{\sin\varepsilon(\alpha'-\alpha)}{\alpha'-\alpha}\,d\alpha' = 2i\,\frac{\sin\varepsilon\alpha}{\alpha} \\ &\overline{\varphi}_{\perp}(\alpha) - \frac{1}{\pi}\int_{-\infty}^{\infty}\overline{\varphi}_{\perp}(\alpha')\,\frac{\sin\varepsilon(\alpha'-\alpha)}{\alpha'-\alpha}\,d\alpha' = 0. \end{aligned}\right\} \qquad (120.13\,s)$$

Die jeweils homogene Gl. (120.13) ist in der Literatur als *Batemansche Integralgleichung* bekannt[3]. Ihre allgemeine Lösung läßt sich zufolge der Beziehung

$$\frac{1}{\pi}\int_{-\infty}^{\infty}\frac{J_\nu(\varepsilon\alpha')}{\alpha'^{\mu}}\,\frac{\sin\varepsilon(\alpha'-\alpha)}{\alpha'-\alpha}\,d\alpha' = \frac{J_\nu(\varepsilon\alpha)}{\alpha^{\mu}} \qquad (0 \leqq \mu \leqq \nu,\ \nu = 0, 1, 2, \ldots) \qquad (120.14)$$

als Linearkombination von Lösungen der Gestalt (120.7) darstellen. Bei Berücksichtigung der Kantenbedingung wird man so wieder auf die Ansätze (120.8) in Gestalt *Neumannscher Reihen* geführt, die die *homogene* Gl. (120.13) gliedweise erfüllen. Setzt man die Reihen (120.8) in die *inhomogenen* Gln. (120.13) ein, so folgt

$$\left.\begin{aligned} &\sum_{\nu=0}^{\infty}(-1)^{\nu}(2\nu+1)\,a_{\|}^{(2\nu+1)}\cdot \\ &\quad\cdot\int_{-\infty}^{\infty}\sqrt{1-\alpha'^2}\,\frac{J_{2\nu+1}(\varepsilon\alpha')}{\alpha'}\,\frac{\sin\varepsilon(\alpha'-\alpha)}{\alpha'-\alpha}\,d\alpha' = 2i\,\frac{\sin\varepsilon\alpha}{\alpha} \end{aligned}\right\} \qquad (120.13'\,p)$$

---

[1] C. J. Bouwkamp: Proc. Kon. Ned. Akad. Wet. **53**, 654 (1950). — A.T. de Hoop: Proc. Kon. Ned. Akad. Wet. **58**, 325 (1955).

[2] A.T. de Hoop: Proc. Kon. Ned. Akad. Wet. **58**, 401 (1955).

[3] Siehe für das Folgende E.C. Titchmarch: Theory of Fourier-Integrals, S. 349ff. Oxford 1937.

bzw.

$$\sum_{\nu=0}^{\infty}(-1)^{\nu} a_{\perp}^{(2\nu)} \int_{-\infty}^{\infty} \frac{J_{2\nu}(\varepsilon\alpha')}{\sqrt{1-\alpha'^2}} \frac{\sin\varepsilon(\alpha'-\alpha)}{\alpha'-\alpha} d\alpha' = 2i \frac{\sin\varepsilon\alpha}{\alpha}. \tag{120.13's}$$

Multiplizieren wir hier die obere Gleichung mit $J_{2\mu+1}(\varepsilon\alpha)/\alpha$ die untere mit $J_{2\mu}(\varepsilon\alpha)$ und integrieren über alle $\alpha\,(-\infty<\alpha<\infty)$, so folgt mit (120.14)

$$\sum_{\nu=0}^{\infty}(-1)^{\nu}(2\nu+1)\, a_{\parallel}^{(2\nu+1)} \int_{0}^{\infty} \frac{\sqrt{1-\alpha^2}}{\alpha^2} J_{2\nu+1}(\varepsilon\alpha) J_{2\mu+1}(\varepsilon\alpha)\, d\alpha = \frac{i\varepsilon}{2}\delta_{\mu 0}$$

$$\sum_{\nu=0}^{\infty}(-1)^{\nu} a_{\perp}^{(2\nu)} \int_{0}^{\infty} J_{2\nu}(\varepsilon\alpha) J_{2\mu}(\varepsilon\alpha) \frac{d\alpha}{\sqrt{1-\alpha^2}} = i\,\delta_{\mu 0}$$

und dies stimmt mit dem Gleichungssystem (120.11), (120.12) überein.

121. Transmissionskoeffizient. Der zeitliche Mittelwert des Energiestromes durch den Spalt (pro Längeneinheit) bezogen auf den nach der geometrischen Optik durch den Spalt (im Zeitmittel) tretenden Energiestrom *(Transmissionskoeffizient)* ist für beide Polarisationsfälle durch

$$\tau = \frac{1}{2\varepsilon\sqrt{1-\alpha_0^2}} \operatorname{Im} \int_{-a}^{a} \left\{ v^* \frac{\partial v}{\partial z} \right\}_{z=0} dx \tag{121.1}$$

gegeben (vgl. Ziff. 102). Aus der Felddarstellung (118.5) mit (118.7) und (118.8) folgt nun

$$v_{\parallel}(x,\pm 0) = \varphi_{\parallel}(x), \qquad \frac{\partial}{\partial z} v_{\parallel}(x,\pm 0) = i k\sqrt{1-\alpha_0^2}\, e^{i k \alpha_0 x} \qquad (|x|<a) \tag{121.2p}$$

bzw.

$$v_{\perp}(x,\pm 0) = e^{i k \alpha_0 x}, \qquad \frac{\partial}{\partial z} v_{\perp}(x,\pm 0) = \varphi_{\perp}(x) \qquad (|x|<a). \tag{121.2s}$$

Setzt man dies in (121.1) ein, so ergibt sich bei Beachtung von (118.11)

$$\tau_{\parallel} = \frac{1}{2a} \operatorname{Re} \int_{-a}^{a} \varphi_{\parallel}(x)\, e^{-ik\alpha_0 x} dx = \frac{1}{2a} \operatorname{Re} \overline{\varphi}_{\parallel}(\alpha_0) \tag{121.3p}$$

bzw.

$$\tau_{\perp} = \frac{1}{2\varepsilon\sqrt{1-\alpha_0^2}} \operatorname{Im} \int_{-a}^{a} \varphi_{\perp}(x)\, e^{-ik\alpha_0 x} dx = \frac{1}{2\varepsilon\sqrt{1-\alpha_0^2}} \operatorname{Im} \overline{\varphi}_{\perp}(\alpha_0). \tag{121.3s}$$

Die Integrale in (121.3) lassen sich leicht ausführen, wenn wir die Substitution (119.4), (119.5) benützen und für die $u(\xi)$ ihre Darstellung durch Fourier-Reihen (119.12) einsetzen. So ergibt sich für senkrechte Inzidenz ($\alpha_0 = 0$)

$$\tau_{\parallel} = \frac{1}{2} \operatorname{Im} \int_{0}^{\pi} u_{\parallel}(\xi)\, d\xi = \frac{\pi}{4} \operatorname{Im} a_{\parallel}^{(1)} = \frac{1}{2a} \operatorname{Re} \overline{\varphi}_{\parallel}(0) \tag{121.3'p}$$

bzw.

$$\tau_{\perp} = \frac{1}{2\varepsilon} \operatorname{Im} \int_{0}^{\pi} u_{\perp}(\xi)\, d\xi = \frac{\pi}{2\varepsilon} \operatorname{Im} a_{\perp}^{(0)} = \frac{1}{2\varepsilon} \operatorname{Im} \overline{\varphi}_{\perp}(0). \tag{121.3's}$$

Setzt man hier die Entwicklung (119.15) oder (120.5) ein, so ergibt sich übereinstimmend

$$\tau_{\|} = \frac{\pi^2 \varepsilon^3}{32}\left\{1 + \frac{5\varepsilon^2}{16}\left(1 - \frac{8}{5}\ln\frac{\gamma\varepsilon}{4}\right) + \cdots\right\} \tag{121.4p}$$

bzw.

$$\tau_{\perp} = \frac{\pi^2}{\left(4\ln^2\frac{\gamma\varepsilon}{4} + \pi^2\right)\varepsilon}\left\{1 + \frac{\varepsilon^2}{4} + \frac{\varepsilon^4}{64}\left(\frac{3}{4} + \frac{4\ln\frac{\gamma\varepsilon}{4}}{4\ln^2\frac{\gamma\varepsilon}{4} + \pi^2}\right) + \cdots\right\}. \tag{121.4s}$$

Interessanterweise ist also für $\varepsilon \ll 1$ die Durchlässigkeit des Spaltes für senkrecht zu den Spalträndern polarisierte elektromagnetische Wellen wesentlich größer (um einen Faktor $\sim \varepsilon^4$) als für parallel polarisierte Felder: bei beliebig polarisierter Primärstrahlung ist *die gebeugte Welle nahezu senkrecht zum Spalt polarisiert.*

b2) Lösung für den weiten Spalt.

Der in der Lichtoptik gegebene Fall, daß die Wellenlänge sehr viel kleiner als die Spaltbreite $2a$ ist ($\varepsilon \gg 1$), läßt sich ebenfalls mit Hilfe der Integralgleichungen von Ziff. 118 systematisch behandeln. Hier ergibt sich eine *asymptotische* Reihe, die nach *halbzahligen negativen* Potenzen von ε fortschreitet. Außerdem soll ein Vergleich mit der herkömmlichen Kirchhoffschen Theorie durchgeführt werden.

122. Asymptotische Lösung. *α) Schwarzschildsches Verfahren.* Beim breiten Spalt ist es naturgemäß, von der Überlagerung der Beugungsfelder der beiden die Spaltbacken bildenden Halbebenen auszugehen und die Wechselwirkung der beiden Halbebenen durch eine Störungsrechnung zu berücksichtigen. Diesen Gedanken hat SCHWARZSCHILD[1] durchgeführt, indem er ein Iterationsverfahren im Anschluß an die Sommerfeldsche Lösung für die Halbebene (Abschn. BI a) entwickelte; er konnte zeigen, daß sein Verfahren für *alle ε konvergiert.* Eine wesentliche Vereinfachung erreicht man durch Übertragung des Schwarzschildschen Verfahrens auf die Fernfeldamplitude[2]. Dies läuft darauf hinaus, die Integralgleichungen (118.19) durch *Iteration* im Sinne der Neumannschen Reihe zu lösen. Es ergibt sich so aus (118.19) mit (118.20)

$$\overline{\psi}^{(1)}(\alpha, \alpha_0) = \sum_{\nu=0}^{\infty} \omega^{(\nu)}(\alpha, \alpha_0) \tag{122.1}$$

mit

$$\omega_{\|}^{(0)}(\alpha, \alpha_0) = -2\sqrt{1+\alpha_0}\,\frac{e^{i\varepsilon\alpha_0}}{\alpha - \alpha_0} \tag{122.2p}$$

$$\omega_{\|}^{(\nu)}(\alpha, \alpha_0) = \frac{1}{2\pi i}\oint_{-\infty}^{\infty}\sqrt{\frac{1+\alpha'}{1-\alpha'}}\,e^{2i\varepsilon\alpha'}\,\omega_{\|}^{(\nu-1)}(-\alpha', -\alpha_0)\,\frac{d\alpha'}{\alpha' - \alpha} \qquad (\nu > 0) \tag{122.3p}$$

bzw.

$$\omega_{\perp}^{(0)}(\alpha, \alpha_0) = -\frac{2}{ik}\sqrt{1-\alpha_0}\,\frac{e^{i\varepsilon\alpha_0}}{\alpha - \alpha_0} \tag{122.2s}$$

$$\omega_{\perp}^{(\nu)}(\alpha, \alpha_0) = \frac{1}{2\pi i}\oint_{-\infty}^{\infty}\sqrt{\frac{1-\alpha'}{1+\alpha'}}\,e^{2i\varepsilon\alpha'}\,\omega_{\perp}^{(\nu-1)}(-\alpha', -\alpha_0)\,\frac{d\alpha'}{\alpha' - \alpha} \qquad (\nu > 0). \tag{122.3s}$$

---

[1] K. SCHWARZSCHILD: Math. Ann. **55**, 177 (1902). Eine Weiterentwicklung des Schwarzschildschen Verfahrens bei E.N. FOX: Phil. Trans. Roy. Soc. Lond. A **241**, 71 (1948); **242**, 1 (1949). — Proc. Roy. Soc. Lond. A **221**, 398 (1952).

[2] H. HÖNL u. K. WESTPFAHL: Planckfestschrift. Berlin 1958. — K. WESTPFAHL: Ann. Physik **4**, 283 (1959).

Die nullte Näherung ist im wesentlichen die Fernfeldamplitude der an der rechten Halbebene gebeugten einfallenden ebenen Welle [*ohne* Berücksichtigung der Wechselwirkung, vgl. (115.5)]. Die in dieser Näherung auf den Spaltbacken fließenden Flächenströme führen zu Strahlungsfeldern, die ihrerseits an der jeweils anderen Halbebene gebeugt werden. Dies wird durch die erste Näherung (122.3) berücksichtigt und so fort. Wir können nun den Schwarzschildschen Konvergenzbeweis auch für (122.1) in Anspruch nehmen. Das Schwarzschildsche Verfahren liefert jedoch in seinen einzelnen Schritten *keine* Entwicklung nach fallenden Potenzen des Parameters ε. Eine solche Reihe ist aber (obwohl vermutlich asymptotisch, d.h. divergent) zur Darstellung der Feldgrößen für $\varepsilon \gg 1$ besonders geeignet.

β) Asymptotische Lösung. Um die *asymptotische* Entwicklung der Lösung zu erhalten[1], geht man am einfachsten von den Integralgleichungen (118.19′) aus und entwickelt die $A(\alpha)$ asymptotisch für $\varepsilon \gg 1$ (s. unten)

$$A_{\parallel}(\alpha) \to \varepsilon^{-\frac{1}{2}} A_{\parallel}^{(1)}(\alpha) + \varepsilon^{-\frac{3}{2}} A_{\parallel}^{(3)}(\alpha) + \cdots \tag{122.4p}$$

bzw.

$$A_{\perp}(\alpha) \to \varepsilon^{-\frac{3}{2}} A_{\perp}^{(3)}(\alpha) + \varepsilon^{-\frac{5}{2}} A_{\perp}^{(5)}(\alpha) + \cdots . \tag{122.4s}$$

Entsprechend entwickeln wir die Lösung in der Form

$$\hat{\psi}_{\parallel}^{(1)}(\alpha) \to \chi_{\parallel}^{(0)}(\alpha) + \varepsilon^{-\frac{1}{2}} \chi_{\parallel}^{(1)}(\alpha) + \varepsilon^{-1} \chi_{\parallel}^{(2)}(\alpha) + \cdots \tag{122.5p}$$

bzw.

$$\hat{\psi}_{\perp}^{(1)}(\alpha) \to \chi_{\perp}^{(0)}(\alpha) + \varepsilon^{-\frac{3}{2}} \chi_{\perp}^{(3)}(\alpha) + \varepsilon^{-\frac{5}{2}} \chi_{\perp}^{(5)}(\alpha) + \cdots, \tag{122.5s}$$

wobei wir uns im folgenden auf das erste, die Wechselwirkung der Spaltbacken berücksichtigende Glied beschränken wollen. Trägt man (122.4) und (122.5) in die Integralgleichungen (118.19′) ein, so ergibt sich durch Vergleich der Koeffizienten der negativen Potenzen von ε das Gleichungssystem

$$\left.\begin{aligned} \chi_{\parallel}^{(0)}(\alpha,\alpha_0) &= -2\sqrt{1+\alpha_0}\,\frac{e^{i\varepsilon\alpha_0}}{\alpha-\alpha_0} \\ \chi_{\parallel}^{(1)}(\alpha,\alpha_0) &= \frac{-1}{2\pi i}\oint_{-\infty}^{\infty} A_{\parallel}^{(1)}(\alpha')\,\chi_{\parallel}^{(0)}(-\alpha',-\alpha_0)\,\frac{d\alpha'}{\alpha'-\alpha} \end{aligned}\right\} \tag{122.6p}$$

bzw.

$$\left.\begin{aligned} \chi_{\perp}^{(0)}(\alpha,\alpha_0) &= -\frac{2}{ik}\sqrt{1-\alpha_0}\,\frac{e^{i\varepsilon\alpha_0}}{\alpha-\alpha_0} \\ \chi_{\perp}^{(3)}(\alpha,\alpha_0) &= \frac{-1}{2\pi i}\oint_{-\infty}^{\infty} A_{\perp}^{(3)}(\alpha')\,\chi_{\perp}^{(0)}(-\alpha',-\alpha_0)\,\frac{d\alpha'}{\alpha'-\alpha}. \end{aligned}\right\} \tag{122.6s}$$

Wir brauchen also gar keine Integralgleichung mehr zu lösen, sondern können die Wechselwirkung durch Quadraturen berechnen (entsprechendes gilt für die höheren Näherungen). Wie wir gleich sehen werden, lassen sich überdies die Integrationen

[1] K. WESTPFAHL: Ann. Physik **4**, 283 (1959). Vgl. auch die Behandlung des breiten Spaltes bei A.P. BURGER: Thesis Delft 1955. — R. TIMMAN: Trans. Inst. Rad. Engrs. AP-**4**, 209 (1956). — J. IMAI: Trans. Inst. Rad. Engrs. AP-**4**, 323 (1956). — P.C. CLEMMOW: Trans. Inst. Radio Engrs. AP-**4**, 282 (1956). — S.N. KARP u. A. RUSSEK: J. Appl. Phys. **27**, 886 (1956). — J.B. KELLER: N.Y. Univ. Res. Rep. No. EM-92 (1956). — J. Appl. Phys. **28**, 426 (1957). —H. LEVINE: Stanford Univ. Appl. Math. a. Stat. Lab. Techn. Rep. No. 61 (1957). — J. Appl. Phys. **30**, 1673 (1959). — B. NOBLE: Methods based on the Wiener-Hopf Technique, S. 203ff. London-New York-Paris-Los Angeles: Pergamon Press 1958. — R.F. MILLAR: Proc. Cambridge Phil. Soc. **54**, 479, 497 (1958). — H. HÖNL u. K. WESTPFAHL: Planckfestschrift, S. 35. Berlin 1958. — S.N. KARP u. J.B. KELLER: N.Y. Univ. Res. Rep. No. EM-143 (1959). — Für Zylinderwellen siehe C.L. TANG: Harvard Univ. Cruft Lab. Techn. Rep. No. 297 (1959).

mittels Residuenkalkül mühelos auswerten. Um die Größen (118.21) für $\varepsilon \gg 1$ asymptotisch zu entwickeln, betrachten wir zunächst das Integral

$$\hat{A}(\alpha) = \frac{1}{2\pi i} \oint_{-\infty}^{\infty} \frac{e^{2i\varepsilon(\alpha'-\alpha)}}{\sqrt{1-\alpha'}} \frac{d\alpha'}{\alpha'-\alpha}; \tag{122.7}$$

insbesondere für $\varepsilon = 0$ ergibt sich mittels Residuenkalkül

$$\hat{A}_{\varepsilon=0}(\alpha) = \frac{-1}{\sqrt{1-\alpha}}. \tag{122.7'}$$

Differenzieren wir (122.7) nach ε, so ergibt sich

$$\frac{\partial \hat{A}}{\partial \varepsilon} = \frac{1}{\pi} \int_{-\infty}^{\infty} \frac{e^{2i\varepsilon(\alpha'-\alpha)}}{\sqrt{1-\alpha'}} d\alpha' = \frac{2}{\pi} \int_{0}^{-i\infty} \frac{e^{-2i\varepsilon(\gamma'-\gamma)}}{\sqrt{\gamma'}} d\gamma', \tag{122.8}$$

dabei haben wir rechts die Substitution $1-\alpha = \gamma$, $1-\alpha' = \gamma'$ vorgenommen und den Integrationsweg so deformiert, daß er mit den beiden Ufern des Verzweigungsschnittes von $\sqrt{\gamma'}$ in der unteren γ'-Halbebene zusammenfällt. Mit der weiteren Substitution $2\gamma'\varepsilon = \sigma^2$, $d\gamma' = \sqrt{2\gamma'/\varepsilon}\, d\sigma$ geht (12.28) wegen

$$\int_{0}^{\infty} e^{\pm i\sigma^2} d\sigma = \frac{\sqrt{\pi}}{2} e^{\pm \frac{i\pi}{4}} \tag{122.9}$$

über in

$$\frac{\partial \hat{A}}{\partial \varepsilon} = \sqrt{\frac{2}{\pi\varepsilon}}\, e^{i\left[2\varepsilon(1-\alpha) - \frac{\pi}{4}\right]}. \tag{122.8'}$$

Damit erhält man für die Größen (122.7) die Darstellung

$$\hat{A}(\alpha) = \sqrt{\frac{2}{\pi}}\, e^{-\frac{i\pi}{4}} \int_{\infty}^{\varepsilon} \frac{e^{2i\xi(1-\alpha)}}{\sqrt{\xi}} d\xi, \tag{122.7''}$$

dabei haben wir die untere Grenze des Integrals so gewählt, daß für $\varepsilon = 0$ der Wert (122.7′) resultiert. Substituiert man nämlich noch $2\gamma\xi = \sigma^2$, $d\xi = \sqrt{2\xi/\gamma}\, d\sigma$, so folgt für $\hat{A}(\alpha)$ das *Fresnelsche Integral*

$$\hat{A}(\alpha) = \frac{2\, e^{-\frac{i\pi}{4}}}{\sqrt{\pi}\sqrt{1-\alpha}} \int_{\infty}^{\sqrt{2\varepsilon(1-\alpha)}} e^{i\sigma^2} d\sigma \tag{122.7'''}$$

und dies geht für $\varepsilon = 0$ mit (122.9) in (122.7′) über. Für $\varepsilon \gg 1$, $\alpha \neq 1$ (oder für $|\alpha| \gg 1$, $\alpha \in S^-$) folgt nun aus (122.7″) durch partielle Integration die asymptotische Entwicklung[1]

$$\hat{A}(\alpha) \to \frac{e^{i\left[2\varepsilon(1-\alpha) + \frac{\pi}{4}\right]}}{\sqrt{2\pi\varepsilon}\,(\alpha-1)} \left\{1 + \frac{i}{4\varepsilon} \frac{1}{\alpha-1} - \frac{3}{16\varepsilon^2} \frac{1}{(\alpha-1)^2} + \cdots\right\}. \tag{122.10}$$

Die hier auftretende Singularität $\alpha = 1$ ist für den strengen Ausdruck (122.7) jedoch keine wesentlich singuläre Stelle, wie das nach (122.10) der Fall zu sein scheint [die asymptotische Darstellung (122.10) ist jedoch für die Umgebung der

[1] Vgl. MAGNUS-OBERHETTINGER: l. c. S. 126.

Stelle $\alpha=1$ unbrauchbar], sondern ein Verzweigungspunkt. Dies kommt durch die Umformung [unter Verwendung von (122.9)]

$$\left.\begin{aligned}\hat{A}(\alpha) &= \frac{-1}{\sqrt{1-\alpha}}\left\{1-\frac{2\,e^{-\frac{i\pi}{4}}}{\sqrt{\pi}}\int\limits_0^{\sqrt{2\varepsilon(1-\alpha)}} e^{i\sigma^2}d\sigma\right\}\\ &= \frac{-1}{\sqrt{1-\alpha}}\left\{1-\frac{2\,e^{-\frac{i\pi}{4}}}{\sqrt{\pi}}\sqrt{2\varepsilon(1-\alpha)}\left[1+\frac{2i\varepsilon}{3}(1-\alpha)+\cdots\right]\right\}\end{aligned}\right\} \quad (122.10')$$

zum Ausdruck. Bei Verwendung von (122.10) für $\varepsilon\gg 1$ müssen wir daher der Stelle $\alpha=1$ in der unteren α-Halbebene S^- ausweichen, wo $\hat{A}(\alpha)$ holomorph ist. Mit Hilfe von $\hat{A}(\alpha)$ lassen sich die Größen (118.21) wie folgt darstellen

$$A_{\parallel}(\alpha)=\sqrt{1+\alpha}\,e^{2i\varepsilon\alpha}\hat{A}(\alpha) \quad (122.11\,p)$$

bzw.

$$A_{\perp}(\alpha)=\frac{1-\alpha}{\sqrt{1+\alpha}}e^{2i\varepsilon\alpha}\hat{A}(\alpha)+\frac{e^{i\left(2\varepsilon+\frac{\pi}{4}\right)}}{\sqrt{2\pi\varepsilon}\sqrt{1+\alpha}}. \quad (122.11\,s)$$

Dabei ergibt sich (122.11 *s*) mit Hilfe der Umformung

$$\oint\limits_{-\infty}^{\infty}\sqrt{1-\alpha'}\,e^{2i\varepsilon\alpha'}\frac{d\alpha'}{\alpha'-\alpha}=(1-\alpha)\oint\limits_{-\infty}^{\infty}\frac{e^{2i\varepsilon\alpha'}}{\sqrt{1-\alpha'}}\frac{d\alpha'}{\alpha'-\alpha}-\int\limits_{-\infty}^{\infty}\frac{e^{2i\varepsilon\alpha'}}{\sqrt{1-\alpha'}}d\alpha'$$

bei Beachtung von (122.8), (122.8'). Der letzte Term in (122.11 *s*) kann auch fortgelassen werden, da er in S^+ holomorph ist und somit beim Einsetzen von (122.11 *s*) in (118.19'*s*) keinen Beitrag liefert [$\hat{\psi}_{\perp}^{(1)}(-\alpha,-\alpha_0)$ ist ebenfalls in S^+ holomorph]. Setzt man nun (122.10) in (122.11) ein, so ergibt sich die asymptotische Entwicklung [$\varepsilon\gg 1$, $\alpha\neq 1$ (oder $|\alpha|\gg 1$, $\alpha\in S^-$)]

$$A_{\parallel}(\alpha)\to\frac{e^{i\left(2\varepsilon+\frac{\pi}{4}\right)}}{\sqrt{2\pi\varepsilon}}\frac{\sqrt{1+\alpha}}{\alpha-\underset{\smile}{1}}\left\{1+\frac{i}{4\varepsilon}\frac{1}{\alpha-\underset{\smile}{1}}+\cdots\right\} \quad (122.11'\,p)$$

bzw.

$$A_{\perp}(\alpha)\to\frac{e^{i\left(2\varepsilon-\frac{\pi}{4}\right)}}{4\varepsilon\sqrt{2\pi\varepsilon}}\frac{1}{\sqrt{1+\alpha}\,(\alpha-\underset{\smile}{1})}\left\{1+\frac{3i}{4\varepsilon}\frac{1}{\alpha-\underset{\smile}{1}}+\cdots\right\}. \quad (122.11'\,s)$$

In diesen Formeln ist der die analytische Situation erschwerende Faktor $e^{\pm 2i\varepsilon\alpha}$ verschwunden: die Größen $A_{\parallel}(\alpha)$ und $A_{\perp}(\alpha)$ zeigen für $|\alpha|\to\infty$ ein *algebraisches* Verhalten. In (122.4) ist also

$$A_{\parallel}^{(1)}(\alpha)=\frac{e^{i\left(2\varepsilon+\frac{\pi}{4}\right)}}{\sqrt{2\pi}}\frac{\sqrt{1+\alpha}}{\alpha-\underset{\smile}{1}} \quad (122.12\,p)$$

bzw.

$$A_{\perp}^{(3)}(\alpha)=\frac{e^{i\left(2\varepsilon-\frac{\pi}{4}\right)}}{4\sqrt{2\pi}}\frac{1}{\sqrt{1+\alpha}\,(\alpha-\underset{\smile}{1})} \quad (122.12\,s)$$

zu setzen. Trägt man (122.12) in (122.6) ein, so ergibt sich

$$\left.\begin{aligned}\chi_{\parallel}^{(1)}(\alpha,\alpha_0) &= -\frac{e^{i\left(2\varepsilon+\frac{\pi}{4}\right)}}{i\pi\sqrt{2\pi}}\sqrt{1-\alpha_0}\,e^{-i\varepsilon\alpha_0}\int\limits_{-\infty}^{\infty}\frac{\sqrt{1+\alpha'}\,d\alpha'}{(\alpha'-\underset{\smile}{1})(\alpha'-\underset{\smile}{\alpha_0})(\alpha'-\underset{\smile}{\alpha})}\\ &= -2\,\frac{e^{i\left(2\varepsilon+\frac{\pi}{4}\right)}}{\sqrt{\pi}}\frac{\sqrt{1-\alpha_0}\,e^{-i\varepsilon\alpha_0}}{(\alpha-1)(\alpha_0-1)}\end{aligned}\right\} \quad (122.13\,p)$$

bzw.

$$\left.\begin{aligned}\chi_{\perp}^{(3)}(\alpha,\alpha_0) &= \frac{e^{i\left(2\varepsilon+\frac{\pi}{4}\right)}}{4\pi i\sqrt{2\pi k}}\sqrt{1+\alpha_0}\,e^{-i\varepsilon\alpha_0}\int\limits_{-\infty}^{\infty}\frac{d\alpha'}{\sqrt{1+\alpha'}\,(\alpha'-\underset{\smile}{1})\,(\alpha'-\underset{\frown}{\alpha}_0)\,(\alpha'-\underset{\frown}{\alpha})}\\ &= \frac{e^{i\left(2\varepsilon+\frac{\pi}{4}\right)}}{4\sqrt{\pi k}}\,\frac{\sqrt{1+\alpha_0}\,e^{-i\varepsilon\alpha_0}}{(\alpha-1)(\alpha_0-1)}\,.\end{aligned}\right\} \tag{122.13s}$$

Nach diesem Muster lassen sich auch weitere Glieder der Entwicklung (122.5) mit relativ geringem Rechenaufwand bestimmen.

Geht man von den beiden oben berechneten Gliedern der $\hat{\psi}^{(1)}$ in (122.5) mit Hilfe von (118.18), (118.14) und (118.20) zu den Größen

$$\overline{\psi}_{\parallel}(\alpha) = \sqrt{1-\alpha}\,e^{-i\varepsilon\alpha}\,\hat{\psi}_{\parallel}^{(1)}(\alpha,\alpha_0) + \sqrt{1+\alpha}\,e^{i\varepsilon\alpha}\,\hat{\psi}_{\parallel}^{(1)}(-\alpha,-\alpha_0) \tag{122.14p}$$

bzw.

$$\overline{\psi}_{\perp}(\alpha) = \frac{e^{-i\varepsilon\alpha}}{\sqrt{1-\alpha}}\,\hat{\psi}_{\perp}^{(1)}(\alpha,\alpha_0) + \frac{e^{i\varepsilon\alpha}}{\sqrt{1+\alpha}}\,\hat{\psi}_{\perp}^{(1)}(-\alpha,-\alpha_0) \tag{122.14s}$$

über, so ergibt sich mit (122.6) und (122.13) für die asymptotische Lösung

$$\overline{\psi}_{\parallel}(\alpha) \to \overline{\psi}_{\parallel}^{(0)}(\alpha) + \varepsilon^{-\frac{1}{2}}\,\overline{\psi}_{\parallel}^{(1)}(\alpha) + \cdots \tag{122.14'p}$$

bzw.

$$\overline{\psi}_{\perp}(\alpha) \to \overline{\psi}_{\perp}^{(0)}(\alpha) + \varepsilon^{-\frac{3}{2}}\,\overline{\psi}_{\perp}^{(3)}(\alpha) + \cdots \tag{122.14's}$$

mit den wechselwirkungsfreien Termen

$$\left.\begin{aligned}\overline{\psi}_{\parallel}^{(0)}(\alpha) &= -2\left\{\sqrt{(1-\alpha)(1+\alpha_0)}\,\frac{e^{-i\varepsilon(\alpha-\alpha_0)}}{\alpha-\underset{\smile}{\alpha}_0} - \sqrt{(1+\alpha)(1-\alpha_0)}\,\frac{e^{i\varepsilon(\alpha-\alpha_0)}}{\alpha-\underset{\frown}{\alpha}_0}\right\}\\ &= -4\pi i\sqrt{1-\alpha^2}\,\delta(\alpha-\alpha_0)\\ &\quad -2\left\{\sqrt{(1-\alpha)(1+\alpha_0)} - \sqrt{(1+\alpha)(1-\alpha_0)}\right\}\frac{\cos\varepsilon(\alpha-\alpha_0)}{\alpha-\alpha_0}\\ &\quad +2i\left\{\sqrt{(1-\alpha)(1+\alpha_0)} + \sqrt{(1+\alpha)(1-\alpha_0)}\right\}\frac{\sin\varepsilon(\alpha-\alpha_0)}{\alpha-\alpha_0}\end{aligned}\right\} \tag{122.15p}$$

bzw.

$$\left.\begin{aligned}\overline{\psi}_{\perp}^{(0)}(\alpha) &= -\frac{2}{ik}\left\{\sqrt{\frac{1-\alpha_0}{1-\alpha}}\,\frac{e^{-i\varepsilon(\alpha-\alpha_0)}}{\alpha-\underset{\smile}{\alpha}_0} - \sqrt{\frac{1+\alpha_0}{1+\alpha}}\,\frac{e^{i\varepsilon(\alpha-\alpha_0)}}{\alpha-\underset{\frown}{\alpha}_0}\right\} = -\frac{4\pi}{k}\,\delta(\alpha-\alpha_0)\\ &\quad -\frac{2}{ik}\left\{\left[\sqrt{\frac{1-\alpha_0}{1-\alpha}} - \sqrt{\frac{1+\alpha_0}{1+\alpha}}\right]\frac{\cos\varepsilon(\alpha-\alpha_0)}{\alpha-\alpha_0}\right.\\ &\quad \left. +i\left[\sqrt{\frac{1-\alpha_0}{1-\alpha}} + \sqrt{\frac{1+\alpha_0}{1+\alpha}}\right]\frac{\sin\varepsilon(\alpha-\alpha_0)}{\alpha-\alpha_0}\right\}.\end{aligned}\right\} \tag{122.15s}$$

Dabei haben wir von der Beziehung

$$\frac{1}{\alpha-\underset{\smile}{\alpha}_0} - \frac{1}{\alpha-\underset{\frown}{\alpha}_0} = 2\pi i\,\delta(\alpha-\alpha_0) \tag{122.16}$$

Gebrauch gemacht. Ferner ergibt sich die Wechselwirkungs-Korrektur

$$\overline{\psi}_{\parallel}^{(1)}(\alpha) = -\frac{2}{\sqrt{\pi}}\,e^{i\left(2\varepsilon+\frac{\pi}{4}\right)}\left\{\frac{e^{-i\varepsilon(\alpha+\alpha_0)}}{\sqrt{(1-\alpha)(1-\alpha_0)}} + \frac{e^{i\varepsilon(\alpha+\alpha_0)}}{\sqrt{(1+\alpha)(1+\alpha_0)}}\right\} \tag{122.17p}$$

bzw.

$$\overline{\psi}_{\perp}^{(3)}(\alpha) = \frac{e^{i\left(2\varepsilon+\frac{\pi}{4}\right)}}{4\sqrt{\pi k}}\left\{\sqrt{\frac{1+\alpha_0}{1-\alpha}}\,\frac{e^{-i\varepsilon(\alpha+\alpha_0)}}{(1-\alpha)(1-\alpha_0)} + \sqrt{\frac{1-\alpha_0}{1+\alpha}}\,\frac{e^{i\varepsilon(\alpha+\alpha_0)}}{(1+\alpha)(1+\alpha_0)}\right\}. \tag{122.17s}$$

Die Diskussion dieses Ergebnisses erfolgt in Ziff. 124. Das Auftreten des δ-Terms in (122.15) entspricht unserer Behandlung des Spaltes als „Streuproblem" [vgl. Ziff. 61 und (118.13)].

123. Kirchhoffsche Lösung. Stationäre Darstellung. Wir wollen die oben entwickelten asymptotischen Lösungen des Randwertproblems mit zwei Näherungsausdrücken vergleichen, die sich mit Hilfe der Kirchhoffschen Theorie (Ziff. 30) bzw. der stationären Darstellung (Ziff. 109) ergeben.

α) Kirchhoffsche Lösung. Die Kirchhoffsche Theorie ersetzt das Randwertproblem durch folgendes *Sprungwertproblem*: gesucht ist diejenige Lösung v_K der Wellengleichung, die dieselbe Singularität wie die einfallende Welle v_0 besitzt und beim Hindurchtreten durch den *Schirm* die *Sprünge*

$$\{v_K\}_+ - \{v_K\}_- = v_0\,, \quad \left\{\frac{\partial v_K}{\partial z}\right\}_+ - \left\{\frac{\partial v_K}{\partial z}\right\}_- = \frac{\partial v_0}{\partial z}$$

aufweist; beim Hindurchtreten durch die *Öffnung* soll v_K und $\partial v_K/\partial z$ hingegen stetig sein (v_K ist dadurch bei Hinzunahme der Ausstrahlungsbedingung eindeutig bestimmt). Dieses (hier zweidimensionale) Problem, das durch das *Kirchhoffsche Integral*

$$v_K(x, z) = \begin{Bmatrix} 0 \\ v_0 \end{Bmatrix} - \frac{i}{4} \int\limits_{-a}^{a} \left\{ v_0 \frac{\partial}{\partial z} + \frac{\partial v_0}{\partial z} \right\} H_1^0\left(k\sqrt{(x-x')^2 + z^2}\right) dx' \quad (z \gtrless 0) \tag{123.1}$$

gelöst wird, können wir auch durch ein zu (118.10) analoges Fourier-Integral

$$v_K(x, z) = \begin{Bmatrix} 0 \\ v_0 \end{Bmatrix} + \frac{1}{2\pi i} \int\limits_{-\infty}^{\infty} \{\varphi_K^{(1)}(\alpha) \pm \varphi_K^{(2)}(\alpha)\}\, e^{ik(\alpha x + \sqrt{1-\alpha^2}|z|)} \frac{d\alpha}{\sqrt{1-\alpha^2}} \quad (z \gtrless 0) \tag{123.1'}$$

lösen. Für die Fourier-Amplituden $\varphi_K^{(1)}$ und $\varphi_K^{(2)}$ ergeben sich mit Hilfe der oben angeführten Sprung- bzw. Stetigkeitsrelationen die Beziehungen

$$\int\limits_{-\infty}^{\infty} \varphi_K^{(1)}(\alpha)\, e^{ik\alpha x} d\alpha = \begin{cases} 0 & (|x| > a) \\ \pi i \sqrt{1-\alpha_0^2}\, e^{ik\alpha_0 x} & (|x| < a) \end{cases} \tag{123.2}$$

und

$$\int\limits_{-\infty}^{\infty} \frac{\varphi_K^{(2)}(\alpha)}{\sqrt{1-\alpha^2}}\, e^{ik\alpha x} d\alpha = \begin{cases} 0 & (|x| > a) \\ \pi i\, e^{ik\alpha_0 x} & (|x| < a). \end{cases} \tag{123.2'}$$

Durch Fourier-Umkehrung folgt daraus

$$\left.\begin{aligned} \varphi_K^{(1)}(\alpha) &= i\sqrt{1-\alpha_0^2}\, \frac{\sin\varepsilon(\alpha-\alpha_0)}{\alpha-\alpha_0}\,, \\ \varphi_K^{(2)}(\alpha) &= i\sqrt{1-\alpha^2}\, \frac{\sin\varepsilon(\alpha-\alpha_0)}{\alpha-\alpha_0}\,. \end{aligned}\right\} \tag{123.2''}$$

Das sich damit ergebende Fernfeld des Sprungwertproblems werden wir in Ziff. 124 mit demjenigen vergleichen, das sich aus der asymptotischen Lösung des Randwertproblems ergeben hat.

β) Stationäre Darstellung. In (109.3) haben wir eine Darstellung des Fernfeldes mit Hilfe der Feldgrößen in der Öffnung angegeben, die *stationär* ist bezüglich kleiner Abweichungen dieser Größen gegenüber ihren exakten Werten. Wir wollen diese Darstellung hier auf die Größe $\overline{\varphi}_{\|}(\alpha)$ bzw. $\overline{\varphi}_{\perp}(\alpha)$ übertragen, die mit dem Fernfeld durch die Beziehung (120.1) zusammenhängen. Es ergibt sich dann auf dem in Ziff. 109 angegebenen Wege

$$\left.\begin{aligned}\overline{\varphi}_{\|}(-\alpha,\alpha_0) &= \frac{2}{k}\sqrt{1-\alpha_0^2}\cdot\\ &\cdot\frac{\int\limits_{-a}^{a}\varphi_{\|}(x,\alpha_0)\,e^{ik\alpha x}\,dx\int\limits_{-a}^{a}\varphi_{\|}(x,\alpha)\,e^{ik\alpha_0 x}\,dx}{\int\limits_{-a}^{a}dx'\int\limits_{-a}^{a}dx\left\{\varphi_{\|}(x',\alpha_0)\,\varphi_{\|}(x,\alpha)-\frac{d\varphi_{\|}(x,\alpha_0)}{dx}\,\frac{d\varphi_{\|}(x',\alpha)}{dx'}\right\}H_0^1(k\,|x-x'|)}\end{aligned}\right\}\qquad(123.3\,p)$$

bzw.

$$\overline{\varphi}_{\perp}(-\alpha,\alpha_0) = 2i\,\frac{\int\limits_{-a}^{a}\varphi_{\perp}(x,\alpha_0)\,e^{ik\alpha x}\,dx\int\limits_{-a}^{a}\varphi_{\perp}(x,\alpha)\,e^{ik\alpha_0 x}\,dx}{\int\limits_{-a}^{a}dx\int\limits_{-a}^{a}dx'\,\varphi_{\perp}(x,\alpha_0)\,H_0^1(k\,|x-x'|)\,\varphi_{\perp}(x',\alpha)}.\qquad(123.3\,s)$$

Diese Darstellungen sind also im Gegensatz zu (118.11) stationär, d.h. unempfindlich gegen kleine Abweichungen der $\varphi_{\|}$ bzw. $\varphi_{\perp}$ gegenüber ihren durch die Integralgleichungen (118.8) definierten exakten Werten. [Das zweite Argument dieser Größen in (123.3) gibt jeweils den Cosinus des Einfallswinkels der ebenen Welle an, für den die Integralgleichungen (118.8) zu lösen sind.]

Wir wollen uns hier auf senkrechte Incidenz ($\alpha_0 = 0$) beschränken und den Transmissionskoeffizienten mit Hilfe von (121.3) berechnen. Für diesen ergibt sich beispielsweise im *s-Fall*

$$\tau_{\perp} = \frac{1}{\varepsilon}\,\mathrm{Re}\,\frac{\left\{\int\limits_{-a}^{a}\varphi_{\perp}(x)\,dx\right\}^2}{\int\limits_{-a}^{a}dx\int\limits_{-a}^{a}dx'\,\varphi_{\perp}(x)\,H_0^1(k\,|x-x'|)\,\varphi_{\perp}(x')}.\qquad(123.4\,s)$$

Die hier eingehende Größe $\varphi_{\perp}(x)$ haben wir in Gl. (119.17*s*) bzw. (119.17′*s*) berechnet; sie ist an den Kanten singulär und oszilliert um einen Mittelwert. Der Vorteil der stationären Darstellung (123.4*s*) ist nun der, daß es zur angenäherten Darstellung von $\tau_{\perp}$ auf die genaue Verteilung der Größe $\varphi_{\perp}(x)$ gar nicht ankommt. Wir wollen deshalb diese Gleichung mit Hilfe der sehr groben Annäherung eines über die gesamte Öffnung konstanten Wertes von $\varphi_{\perp}$ auswerten. Da der Wert dieser Konstanten zufolge der Homogenität der Darstellung (123.4*s*) irrelevant ist, setzen wir $\varphi_{\perp}(x) \equiv 1$. Damit ergibt sich[1]

$$\tau_{\perp} = \frac{\int\limits_0^{2\varepsilon}J_0(\xi)\,d\xi - J_1(2\varepsilon)}{\left\{\int\limits_0^{2\varepsilon}J_0(\xi)\,d\xi - J_1(2\varepsilon)\right\}^2 + \left\{\int\limits_0^{2\varepsilon}N_0(\xi)\,d\xi - N_1(2\varepsilon) - \frac{1}{\pi\,\varepsilon}\right\}^2}\qquad(123.5\,s)$$

(die hier eingehenden Größen sind die Besselschen bzw. Neumannschen Funktionen). Der numerische Vergleich von (123.5 *s*) mit den Werten nach der strengen Lösung zeigt eine qualitative Übereinstimmung im gesamten ε-Bereich (s. Ziff. 124).

124. Ergebnisse. Diskussion. Zum Abschluß dieses Abschnittes wollen wir die wichtigsten Ergebnisse zusammenstellen, ergänzen und diskutieren.

α) Ergebnisse. In Polarkoordinaten lautet die Felddarstellung (118.10)

$$\left.\begin{aligned}v_{\|}(r,\vartheta) &= \left\{\begin{matrix}0\\ e^{ikr\cos(\vartheta-\vartheta_0)} - e^{ikr\cos(\vartheta+\vartheta_0)}\end{matrix}\right\}\\ &\quad-\frac{k}{2\pi}\int\limits_D\overline{\varphi}_{\|}(\cos\vartheta')\,e^{ikr\cos(\vartheta'\mp\vartheta)}\sin\vartheta'\,d\vartheta'\quad(\vartheta\lessgtr\pi)\end{aligned}\right\}\qquad(124.1\,p)$$

[1] Nach A. Erdélyi u. C.H. Papas: Proc. Nat. Acad. Sci. **40**, 128 (1954).

bzw.

$$\left.\begin{aligned} v_\perp(r,\vartheta) &= \begin{Bmatrix} 0 \\ e^{ikr\cos(\vartheta-\vartheta_0)} + e^{ikr\cos(\vartheta+\vartheta_0)} \end{Bmatrix} \\ &\mp \frac{1}{2\pi i}\int\limits_D \overline{\varphi}_\perp(\cos\vartheta')\, e^{ikr\cos(\vartheta'\mp\vartheta)}\, d\vartheta' \qquad (\vartheta \lessgtr \pi). \end{aligned}\right\} \tag{124.1 s}$$

Der Integrationsweg D in der ϑ'-Ebene stimmt hier mit demjenigen in Fig. 64 auf S. 416 überein. Für $r\to\infty$, $\vartheta<\pi$ erhält man hieraus mit Hilfe der *Sattelpunktmethode* das Fernfeld [vgl. (120.1), wir nehmen den Cosinus des Einfallswinkels ϑ_0 als zweites Argument auf]

$$v_\parallel(r,\vartheta) \to \frac{k\, e^{i\left(kr+\frac{\pi}{4}\right)}}{i\sqrt{2\pi k r}} \sin\vartheta\, \overline{\varphi}_\parallel(\cos\vartheta, \cos\vartheta_0) \tag{124.2p}$$

bzw.

$$v_\perp(r,\vartheta) \to -\frac{e^{i\left(kr+\frac{\pi}{4}\right)}}{\sqrt{2\pi k r}} \overline{\varphi}_\perp(\cos\vartheta, \cos\vartheta_0)\,. \tag{124.2s}$$

Die in (124.1), (124.2) auftretenden Fourier-Amplituden $\overline{\varphi}_\parallel$ bzw. $\overline{\varphi}_\parallel$ sind dabei mit Hilfe der Integralgleichungen (118.12) oder (118.12′) zu bestimmen. Die Lösung dieser Integralgleichungen lautet

für $\varepsilon \ll 1$ [vgl. (120.5)][1]

$$\left(p = \ln\frac{\gamma\varepsilon}{4} - \frac{i\pi}{2}, \qquad \varepsilon = k a, \qquad \cos\vartheta = \alpha, \qquad \cos\vartheta_0 = \alpha_0\right)$$

$$\left.\begin{aligned} \overline{\varphi}_\parallel(\alpha,\alpha_0) &= \frac{\pi a}{2i}\sqrt{1-\alpha_0^2}\cdot\varepsilon\left\{1 + \frac{\varepsilon^2}{8}\left[\frac{3}{2} - 2p - \alpha_0^2 + \alpha_0\alpha - \alpha^2\right]\right. \\ &+ \frac{\varepsilon^4}{16}\left[\frac{7}{16} + p^2 - p\left(\frac{5}{4} - \frac{\alpha_0^2}{2}\right) - \frac{\alpha_0^2}{3} + \frac{\alpha_0^4}{12} + \frac{1-\alpha_0^2}{6}\alpha_0\alpha\right. \\ &\left.\left. - \frac{1}{2}\left(\frac{2}{3} - p - \frac{2\alpha_0^2}{3}\right)\alpha^2 - \frac{\alpha_0\alpha^3}{6} + \frac{\alpha^4}{12}\right] + \cdots\right\} \end{aligned}\right\} \tag{124.3p}$$

bzw.

$$\left.\begin{aligned} \overline{\varphi}_\perp(\alpha,\alpha_0) &= \frac{\pi}{p}\left\{1 + \frac{\varepsilon^2}{2}\left[\frac{1-\alpha_0^2}{2} - p\,\alpha_0\alpha - \frac{\alpha^2}{2}\right] - \frac{\varepsilon^4}{16}\left[\frac{p}{4} - \frac{1}{8p}\right.\right. \\ &- \frac{1}{4}\left(\frac{3}{4} - 3\alpha_0^2 + \alpha_0^4\right) - \frac{p\,\alpha_0^2}{2} + 2p\left(\frac{1}{4} + p + \frac{\alpha_0^2}{2}\right)\alpha_0\alpha \\ &\left.\left. + \left(\frac{3}{4} - \frac{p}{2} + (p-1)\,\alpha_0^2\right)\alpha^2 + p\,\alpha_0\alpha^3 - \frac{\alpha^4}{4}\right] + \cdots\right\}; \end{aligned}\right\} \tag{124.3s}$$

für $\varepsilon \gg 1$ [vgl. (122.15), (122.17) und (118.13)]

$$\left.\begin{aligned} \overline{\varphi}_\parallel(\alpha,\alpha_0) &\to \frac{1}{ik}\left\{\sqrt{\frac{1-\alpha_0}{1-\alpha}}\, e^{i\varepsilon(\alpha-\alpha_0)} - \sqrt{\frac{1+\alpha_0}{1+\alpha}}\, e^{-i\varepsilon(\alpha-\alpha_0)}\right\}\frac{1}{\alpha-\alpha_0} \\ &- \frac{e^{i\left(2\varepsilon-\frac{\pi}{4}\right)}}{k\sqrt{\pi}}\cdot\frac{\varepsilon^{-\frac{1}{2}}}{\sqrt{1-\alpha^2}}\left\{\frac{e^{i\varepsilon(\alpha+\alpha_0)}}{\sqrt{(1+\alpha)(1+\alpha_0)}} + \frac{e^{-i\varepsilon(\alpha+\alpha_0)}}{\sqrt{(1-\alpha)(1-\alpha_0)}}\right\} + \cdots \end{aligned}\right\} \tag{124.4p}$$

bzw.

$$\left.\begin{aligned} \overline{\varphi}_\perp(\alpha,\alpha_0) &\to \left\{\sqrt{(1-\alpha)(1+\alpha_0)}\, e^{i\varepsilon(\alpha-\alpha_0)} - \sqrt{(1+\alpha)(1-\alpha_0)}\, e^{-i\varepsilon(\alpha-\alpha_0)}\right\}\frac{1}{\alpha-\alpha_0} \\ &+ \frac{e^{i\left(2\varepsilon-\frac{\pi}{4}\right)}}{8\sqrt{\pi}}\cdot\varepsilon^{-\frac{3}{2}}\left\{\frac{\sqrt{(1-\alpha)(1-\alpha_0)}}{(1+\alpha)(1+\alpha_0)}\, e^{i\varepsilon(\alpha+\alpha_0)} + \frac{\sqrt{(1+\alpha)(1+\alpha_0)}}{(1-\alpha)(1-\alpha_0)}\, e^{-i\varepsilon(\alpha+\alpha_0)}\right\} + \cdots. \end{aligned}\right\} \quad (1$$

[1] Wir geben hier in Ergänzung der Rechnungen von Ziff. 119 und 120 die Größen für einen beliebigen Einfallswinkel ϑ_0 an, vgl. A.T. DE HOOP: Proc. Kon. Ned. Akad. Wet. B **58**, 401 (1955).

Für das *Fernfeld* hinter dem Spalt ergibt sich damit aus (124.2)

für $\varepsilon \ll 1$

$$\left.\begin{aligned} v_{\parallel}(r,\vartheta) \to & -\frac{1}{2}\sqrt{\frac{\pi}{2kr}}\, e^{i\left(kr+\frac{\pi}{4}\right)} \sin\vartheta \sin\vartheta_0 \cdot \\ & \cdot \varepsilon^2 \Big\{ 1 + \frac{\varepsilon^2}{8}\left[\frac{3}{2} - 2p - \cos^2\vartheta_0 + \cos\vartheta_0\cos\vartheta - \cos^2\vartheta\right] \\ & + \frac{\varepsilon^4}{16}\Big[\frac{7}{16} + p^2 - \frac{5p}{4} + \left(\frac{p}{2} - \frac{1}{3}\right)\cos^2\vartheta_0 + \frac{\cos^4\vartheta_0}{12} \\ & + \frac{\sin^2\vartheta_0}{6}\cos\vartheta_0\cos\vartheta - \frac{1}{2}\left(\frac{2}{3} - p - \frac{2}{3}\cos^2\vartheta_0\right)\cos^2\vartheta \\ & - \frac{1}{6}\cos\vartheta_0\cos^3\vartheta + \frac{\cos^4\vartheta}{12}\Big] + \cdots \Big\} \end{aligned}\right\} \quad (124.5\,p)$$

bzw.

$$\left.\begin{aligned} v_{\perp}(r,\vartheta) \to & -\frac{1}{p}\sqrt{\frac{\pi}{2kr}}\, e^{i\left(kr+\frac{\pi}{4}\right)} \Big\{ 1 + \frac{\varepsilon^2}{2}\left[\frac{\sin^2\vartheta_0}{2} - p\cos\vartheta_0\cos\vartheta - \frac{\cos^2\vartheta}{2}\right] \\ & - \frac{\varepsilon^4}{16}\Big[\frac{p}{4} - \frac{1}{8p} - \frac{1}{4}\left(\frac{3}{4} - 3\cos^2\vartheta_0 + \cos^4\vartheta_0\right) - \frac{p}{2}\cos^2\vartheta_0 \\ & + 2p\left(\frac{1}{4} + p + \frac{\cos^2\vartheta_0}{2}\right)\cos\vartheta_0\cos\vartheta + \left(\frac{3}{4} - \frac{p}{2} + (p-1)\cos^2\vartheta_0\right) \cdot \\ & \cdot \cos^2\vartheta + p\cos\vartheta_0\cos^3\vartheta - \frac{\cos^4\vartheta}{4}\Big] + \cdots \Big\}; \end{aligned}\right\} \quad (124.5\,s)$$

für $\varepsilon \gg 1$

$$\left.\begin{aligned} v_{\parallel}(r,\vartheta) \to & \sqrt{\frac{2}{\pi kr}}\, e^{i\left(kr+\frac{\pi}{4}\right)} \Big\{ \sin\left(\frac{\vartheta-\vartheta_0}{2}\right) \cdot \\ & \cdot \frac{\cos\varepsilon(\cos\vartheta - \cos\vartheta_0)}{\cos\vartheta - \cos\vartheta_0} - i\sin\left(\frac{\vartheta+\vartheta_0}{2}\right)\frac{\sin\varepsilon(\cos\vartheta - \cos\vartheta_0)}{\cos\vartheta - \cos\vartheta_0} \\ & + \frac{e^{i\left(2\varepsilon+\frac{\pi}{4}\right)}}{\sqrt{\pi}\sin\vartheta\sin\vartheta_0} \cdot \varepsilon^{-\frac{1}{2}}\Big[\cos\left(\frac{\vartheta-\vartheta_0}{2}\right)\cos\varepsilon(\cos\vartheta + \cos\vartheta_0) \\ & - i\cos\left(\frac{\vartheta+\vartheta_0}{2}\right)\sin\varepsilon(\cos\vartheta + \cos\vartheta_0)\Big] + \cdots \Big\} \end{aligned}\right\} \quad (124.5'\,p)$$

bzw.

$$\left.\begin{aligned} v_{\perp}(r,\vartheta) \to & \sqrt{\frac{2}{\pi kr}}\, e^{i\left(kr+\frac{\pi}{4}\right)} \Big\{ -\sin\left(\frac{\vartheta-\vartheta_0}{2}\right)\frac{\cos\varepsilon(\cos\vartheta - \cos\vartheta_0)}{\cos\vartheta - \cos\vartheta_0} \\ & - i\sin\left(\frac{\vartheta+\vartheta_0}{2}\right)\frac{\sin\varepsilon(\cos\vartheta - \cos\vartheta_0)}{\cos\vartheta - \cos\vartheta_0} - \frac{e^{i\left(2\varepsilon-\frac{\pi}{4}\right)}}{32\sqrt{\pi}} \cdot \\ & \cdot \varepsilon^{-\frac{3}{2}}\left[\frac{\tan\frac{\vartheta}{2}\tan\frac{\vartheta_0}{2}}{\cos\frac{\vartheta}{2}\cos\frac{\vartheta_0}{2}}\, e^{i\varepsilon(\cos\vartheta+\cos\vartheta_0)} + \frac{\cot\frac{\vartheta}{2}\cot\frac{\vartheta_0}{2}}{\sin\frac{\vartheta}{2}\sin\frac{\vartheta_0}{2}}\, e^{-i\varepsilon(\cos\vartheta+\cos\vartheta_0)}\right] + \cdots \Big\}. \end{aligned}\right\} \quad (124.5'\,s)$$

Schließlich ergibt sich für die Kirchhoffsche Lösung mittels (123.2″)

$$v_K(r,\vartheta) \to -i\,\frac{e^{i\left(kr+\frac{\pi}{4}\right)}}{\sqrt{2\pi kr}}\,(\sin\vartheta + \sin\vartheta_0)\,\frac{\sin\varepsilon(\cos\vartheta - \cos\vartheta_0)}{\cos\vartheta - \cos\vartheta_0}. \quad (124.5'')$$

Berechnet man das Absolutquadrat des Fernfeldes, so erhält man die *Fernfeld-intensität* $I_\parallel$ bzw. $I_\perp$. Es ergibt sich bei Beschränkung auf die wesentlichsten Glieder

für $\varepsilon \ll 1$

$$\left.\begin{aligned} I_\parallel &= \frac{\pi\,\varepsilon^4}{8kr}\sin^2\vartheta\sin^2\vartheta_0\,\cdot\\ &\cdot\left\{1+\frac{\varepsilon^2}{4}\left[\frac{3}{2}-2\ln\frac{\gamma\,\varepsilon}{4}-\cos^2\vartheta_0+\cos\vartheta_0\cos\vartheta-\cos^2\vartheta\right]+\cdots\right\}\end{aligned}\right\}\qquad(124.6p)$$

bzw.

$$\left.\begin{aligned} I_\perp &= \frac{2\pi}{\left(4\ln^2\frac{\gamma\,\varepsilon}{4}+\pi^2\right)k\,r}\,\cdot\\ &\cdot\left\{1+\frac{\varepsilon^2}{2}\left[\sin^2\vartheta_0-2\ln\frac{\gamma\,\varepsilon}{4}\cos\vartheta_0\cos\vartheta-\cos^2\vartheta\right]+\cdots\right\};\end{aligned}\right\}\qquad(124.6s)$$

für $\varepsilon \gg 1$ (*ohne* Wechselwirkungsterme für beide Polarisationsfälle übereinstimmend)

$$\left.\begin{matrix} I_\parallel\\ I_\perp\end{matrix}\right\} = \frac{2}{\pi\,k\,r}\left\{\sin\vartheta\sin\vartheta_0\left[\frac{\sin\varepsilon(\cos\vartheta-\cos\vartheta_0)}{\cos\vartheta-\cos\vartheta_0}\right]^2+\frac{1}{4\sin^2\left(\frac{\vartheta+\vartheta_0}{2}\right)}+\cdots\right\};\qquad(124.6'ps)$$

für die Kirchhoffsche Lösung

$$I_K = \frac{1}{2\pi\,k\,r}(\sin\vartheta+\sin\vartheta_0)^2\left\{\frac{\sin\varepsilon(\cos\vartheta-\cos\vartheta_0)}{\cos\vartheta-\cos\vartheta_0}\right\}^2.\qquad(124.6'')$$

Um die *Polarisationsverhältnisse* besser übersehen zu können, setzen wir den Quotienten der Fernfelder für die beiden Polarisationen in die Form

$$\frac{v_\parallel}{v_\perp}\to A\,e^{i\delta},$$

dann ergibt sich aus (124.5), (124.5′) in niedrigster Näherung

für $\varepsilon \ll 1$

$$A = \frac{\varepsilon^4}{4}\sqrt{4\ln^2\frac{\gamma\,\varepsilon}{4}+\pi^2}\sin\vartheta\sin\vartheta_0,\quad \tan\delta = -\frac{\pi}{2\ln\frac{\gamma\,\varepsilon}{4}};\qquad(124.7)$$

für $\varepsilon \gg 1$

$$A = 1,\quad \tan\frac{\delta}{2} = -\frac{\sin\left(\frac{\vartheta+\vartheta_0}{2}\right)}{\sin\left(\frac{\vartheta-\vartheta_0}{2}\right)}\tan\varepsilon(\cos\vartheta-\cos\vartheta_0).\qquad(124.7')$$

Über die Durchlässigkeit des Spaltes gibt der *Transmissionskoeffizient* Auskunft, der am einfachsten mit Hilfe der Beziehung (121.3) nämlich

$$\tau_\parallel = \frac{1}{2a}\,\mathrm{Re}\,\overline{\varphi}_\parallel(\alpha_0,\alpha_0)\qquad(124.8p)$$

bzw.

$$\tau_\perp = \frac{1}{2\varepsilon\sqrt{1-\alpha_0^2}}\,\mathrm{Im}\,\overline{\varphi}_\perp(\alpha_0,\alpha_0)\qquad(124.8s)$$

berechnet werden kann. Mit (124.3), (124.4) ergibt sich

für $\varepsilon \ll 1$

$$\left.\begin{aligned}\tau_\parallel = \frac{\pi^2\varepsilon^3}{32}\sqrt{1-\alpha_0^2}&\left\{1+\frac{\varepsilon^2}{2}\left[\frac{5}{8}-\ln\frac{\gamma\,\varepsilon}{4}-\frac{\alpha_0^2}{2}\right]\right.\\ &\left.+\frac{\varepsilon^4}{16}\left[\frac{109}{96}-\frac{\pi^2}{4}+3\ln^2\frac{\gamma\,\varepsilon}{4}-\ln\frac{\gamma\,\varepsilon}{4}\left(\frac{7}{2}-2\alpha_0^2\right)-\frac{17}{16}\alpha_0^2+\frac{5}{12}\alpha_0^4\right]+\cdots\right\}\end{aligned}\right\}\qquad(124.9p)$$

bzw.

$$\left.\begin{aligned}\tau_\perp = {} & \frac{\pi^2}{\left(4\ln^2\frac{\gamma\varepsilon}{4}+\pi^2\right)\sqrt{1-\alpha_0^2}\,\varepsilon}\left\{1+\frac{\varepsilon^2}{4}\left[1-2\alpha_0^2\right]\right.\\ & \left.+\frac{\varepsilon^4}{32}\left[\frac{3}{8}+\frac{2\ln\frac{\gamma\varepsilon}{4}}{4\ln^2\frac{\gamma\varepsilon}{4}+\pi^2}+\left(4\ln^2\frac{\gamma\varepsilon}{4}+\pi^2-3\right)\alpha_0^2+3\alpha_0^4\right]+\cdots\right\};\end{aligned}\right\}\quad(124.9s)$$

für $\varepsilon \gg 1$ [1]

$$\left.\begin{aligned}\tau_\parallel = 1 & -\frac{\varepsilon^{-\frac{3}{2}}}{2\sqrt{\pi}\sqrt{1-\alpha_0^2}}\left\{\frac{\cos\left[2\varepsilon(1-\alpha_0)-\frac{\pi}{4}\right]}{1-\alpha_0}+\frac{\cos\left[2\varepsilon(1+\alpha_0)-\frac{\pi}{4}\right]}{1+\alpha_0}\right\}\\ & +\varepsilon^{-2}\frac{\cos 4\varepsilon}{2\pi\sqrt{1-\alpha_0^2}}+\frac{\varepsilon^{-\frac{5}{2}}}{4\sqrt{\pi}\sqrt{1-\alpha_0^2}}\left\{\frac{\cos\left[2\varepsilon(3-\alpha_0)-\frac{3\pi}{4}\right]}{2\pi(1-\alpha_0)}\right.\\ & +\frac{\cos\left[2\varepsilon(3+\alpha_0)-\frac{3\pi}{4}\right]}{2\pi(1+\alpha_0)}+\left(\frac{1}{8}-\frac{1}{1-\alpha_0}\right)\frac{\sin\left[2\varepsilon(1-\alpha_0)-\frac{\pi}{4}\right]}{1-\alpha_0}\\ & \left.+\left(\frac{1}{8}-\frac{1}{1+\alpha_0}\right)\frac{\sin\left[2\varepsilon(1+\alpha_0)-\frac{\pi}{4}\right]}{1+\alpha_0}\right\}+\cdots\end{aligned}\right\}\quad(124.9'p)$$

bzw.

$$\left.\begin{aligned}\tau_\perp = 1 & -\frac{\varepsilon^{-\frac{5}{2}}}{16\sqrt{\pi}}\left\{\sqrt{\frac{1+\alpha_0}{1-\alpha_0}}\,\frac{\sin\left[2\varepsilon(1-\alpha_0)-\frac{\pi}{4}\right]}{(1-\alpha_0)^2}\right.\\ & \left.+\sqrt{\frac{1-\alpha_0}{1+\alpha_0}}\,\frac{\sin\left[2\varepsilon(1+\alpha_0)-\frac{\pi}{4}\right]}{(1+\alpha_0)^2}\right\}\\ & +\frac{3\varepsilon^{-\frac{7}{2}}}{32\sqrt{\pi}}\left\{\sqrt{\frac{1+\alpha_0}{1-\alpha_0}}\left(\frac{1}{8}+\frac{1}{1-\alpha_0}\right)\frac{\cos\left[2\varepsilon(1-\alpha_0)-\frac{\pi}{4}\right]}{(1-\alpha_0)^2}\right.\\ & \left.+\sqrt{\frac{1-\alpha_0}{1+\alpha_0}}\left(\frac{1}{8}+\frac{1}{1+\alpha_0}\right)\frac{\cos\left[2\varepsilon(1+\alpha_0)-\frac{\pi}{4}\right]}{(1+\alpha_0)^2}\right\}\\ & +\varepsilon^{-4}\frac{\cos 4\varepsilon}{128\pi\sqrt{1-\alpha_0^2}}+\cdots.\end{aligned}\right\}\quad(124.9's)$$

Für das *komplementäre* Problem der Streuung am *Streifen* der Breite $2a$ ergibt sich nach dem *Babinetschen Theorem* (27.4′) mit Hilfe der Lösung (124.1) die Darstellung

$$u_\parallel(r,\vartheta) = \mathrm{e}^{ikr\cos(\vartheta-\vartheta_0)} + \frac{1}{2\pi i}\int\limits_D \overline{\varphi}_\perp(\cos\vartheta')\,\mathrm{e}^{ikr\cos(\vartheta'\mp\vartheta)}\,d\vartheta' \qquad (\vartheta \lessgtr \pi) \qquad (124.10p)$$

[1] In Ergänzung zu Ziff. 122 werden zwei weitere Glieder der asymptotischen Entwicklung angegeben, vgl. S.R. SESHADRI: Harvard Univ. Cruft Lab. Sci. Rep. No. 17 u. 20 (1958). — R.W.P. KING u. T.T. WU: The Scattering and Diffraction of Waves. Cambridge, Mass. (1959).

bzw.

$$u_{\perp}(r,\vartheta) = e^{ikr\cos(\vartheta-\vartheta_0)} \pm \frac{k}{2\pi}\int\limits_D \overline{\varphi}_{\parallel}(\cos\vartheta')\, e^{ikr\cos(\vartheta'\mp\vartheta)}\sin\vartheta'\,d\vartheta' \quad (\vartheta \lesseqgtr \pi). \quad (124.10s)$$

Die Lösungen $u_{\parallel}$ bzw. $u_{\perp}$ beziehen sich hier wieder auf die beiden Polarisationsfälle (p- und s-Fall), während die Größen $\overline{\varphi}_{\parallel}$ und $\overline{\varphi}_{\perp}$ *dieselben* sind, wie bei der Lösung für den Spalt. Der *Streukoeffizient* des Streifens ergibt sich damit wie folgt aus dem Transmissionskoeffizienten des Spaltes

$$\sigma_{\parallel} = 2\tau_{\perp}, \quad \sigma_{\perp} = 2\tau_{\parallel}. \quad (124.11)$$

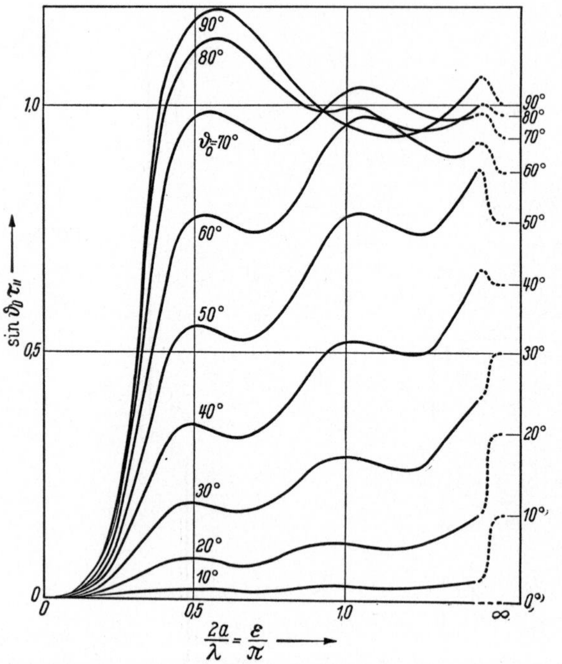

Fig. 68. Transmissionskoeffizient $\tau_{\parallel}$ für den Spalt (p-Fall) für verschiedene Einfallswinkel als Funktion von $\varepsilon = ka$ nach MORSE und RUBENSTEIN.

β) Diskussion. Das Beugungsfeld des Spaltes zeigt für kleine und große ε ein grundsätzlich verschiedenes Verhalten.

Für *kleine* ε wirkt der Spalt *stark polarisierend*, indem die $\parallel$-Welle um einen Faktor ε^4 schlechter durchgelassen wird wie die $\perp$-Welle: die elektrische Feldstärke schwingt im Beugungsfeld hinter dem engen Spalt nahezu senkrecht zu den Spalträndern (wie schon oben im Anschluß an den Transmissionskoeffizienten erwähnt). Dies Verhalten — das schon HERTZ beim Durchgang von Mikrowellen durch Drahtgitter beobachtet hat[1] — wird durch die Kantenbedingung erzwungen, indem im $\parallel$-Fall das $\mathfrak{E}$-Feld ($\mathfrak{E}_y$) in Kantennähe *verschwindet*, während im $\perp$-Fall das $\mathfrak{E}$-Feld ($\mathfrak{E}_x$) dort *singulär* wird [für $\varepsilon \ll 1$ besteht die gesamte Öffnung aus Kantenzone, vgl. (119.17')].

Für *große* ε unterscheiden sich die beiden Polarisationsfälle in nullter Näherung (ohne Wechselwirkung der Spaltbacken) nur hinsichtlich der *Phase* des Fernfeldes, während die Amplituden gleich sind. Dies hat zur Folge, daß linear polarisierte Strahlung durch den Spalt im allgemeinen elliptisch polarisiert, natürliches Licht nicht polarisiert wird. In der *Einfallsrichtung* $\vartheta = \vartheta_0$ stimmen die *Fernfelder nullter Näherung für beide Polarisationsfälle untereinander und mit der Kirchhoffschen Lösung nahezu überein.* [Genauer gesagt, stimmen die Imaginärteile der Winkelverteilung des Fernfeldes für $\vartheta = \vartheta_0$ genau überein und sind $\sim\varepsilon$; die Realteile sind — soweit vorhanden — dagegen von der Größenordnung ε^0, vgl. (124.5') und (124.5'')]. Dies zeigt sich noch deutlicher bei der Fernfeldintensität: der erste Term in (124.6' p, s) stimmt für $\vartheta = \vartheta_0$ mit (124.6'') genau überein; da dieser Term aber dann ersichtlich $\sim\varepsilon^2$ wird, fällt der zweite additive Term in (124.6' p, s) demgegenüber nicht ins Gewicht (er liefert einen sehr schwachen Schleier, der sich

[1] Neuere experimentelle Untersuchungen bei G.F. HULL: J. Phys. **17**, 559 (1949).

dem Kirchhoffschen Interferenzbild überlagert). Aus der Übereinstimmung des Fernfeldes des Sprungwertproblems mit dem Hauptglied der asymptotischen Lösung beider Randwertprobleme in der Nähe der Einfallsrichtung erklärt sich die gute Übereinstimmung der Kirchhoffschen Theorie mit dem Experiment für kleine Beugungswinkel[1].

Bei den auf der Wechselwirkung der Spaltbacken herrührenden Gliedern in (124.5′) macht sich der Einfluß der Randbedingung (bzw. Polarisation) — abgesehen von der verschiedenen Winkelabhängigkeit — in der unterschiedlichen Größenordnung bezüglich ε bemerkbar. Der Faktor

$$\exp\left[i\left(2\varepsilon \pm \frac{\pi}{4}\right)\right] \Big/ \sqrt{2\varepsilon}$$

bei diesen Korrekturtermen kann dahingehend gedeutet werden, daß die Wechselwirkung durch Zylinderwellen vermittelt wird, die zwischen den beiden Spaltkanten ausgetauscht werden.

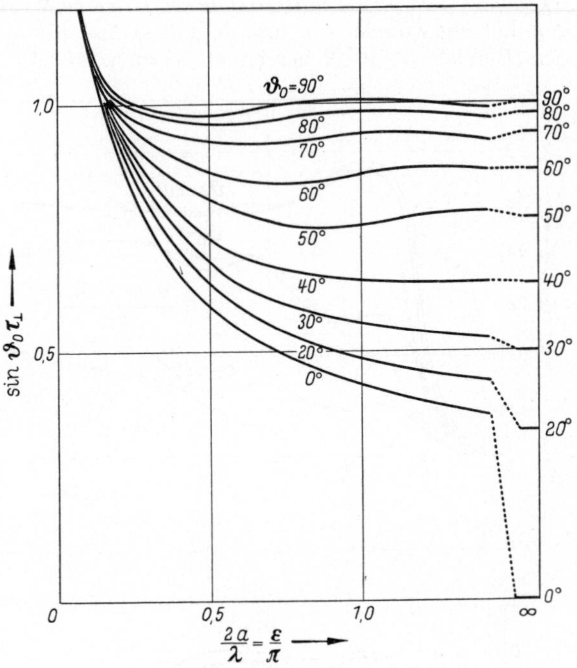

Fig. 69. Transmissionskoeffizient $\tau_\perp$ für den Spalt (s-Fall) nach MORSE und RUBENSTEIN.

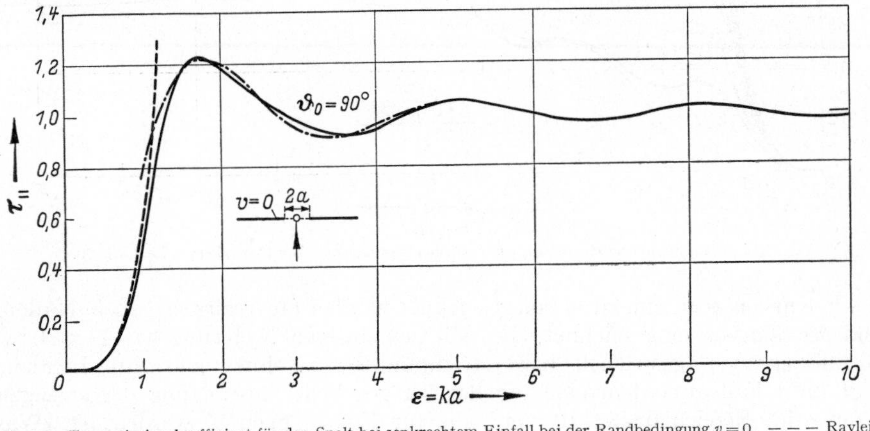

Fig. 70. Transmissionskoeffizient für den Spalt bei senkrechtem Einfall bei der Randbedingung $v=0$. — — — Rayleighsche Näherung, Gl. (124.9p); —·—·— asymptotisch, Gl. (124.9′p); —— streng nach SKAVLEM.

[1] Diese Übereinstimmung besteht auch noch für im endlichen gelegene Aufpunkte (Fresnelsche Beugung). Für diese findet sich eine numerische Auswertung des Kirchhoffschen Integrals bei E. v. LOMMEL: Abh. bayer. Akad. **15**, 531 (1886). — Neuere experimentelle Untersuchungen bei W. HARTNAGEL u. E. KAPPLER: Z. Naturforsch. **4**a, 498 (1949). — H. BURKHARDT: Abh. bayer. Akad. **64**, 1 (1954) (für Licht). — L.R. ALLDREDGE: Harvard Univ. Cruft Lab. Techn. Rep. No. 176 (1953). — J.L. HIRSCHFELD u. C.M. ZIEMAN: J. Appl. Phys. **26**, 135 (1955) (für Mikrowellen).

Das *Zwischengebiet* zwischen dem schmalen und breiten Spalt läßt mit Hilfe der eingangs erwähnten strengen Lösung in Gestalt einer Reihenentwicklung nach Mathieu-Funktionen numerisch überbrücken. Zunächst gibt Fig. 68 und 69 den Verlauf des *Transmissionskoeffizienten* wieder, wie er mit Hilfe der strengen Lösung von Morse und Rubenstein[1] für verschiedene Einfallswinkel für den Bereich $0 \leqq \varepsilon < 5$ berechnet worden ist. In Fig. 70 bis 74 sind einzelne

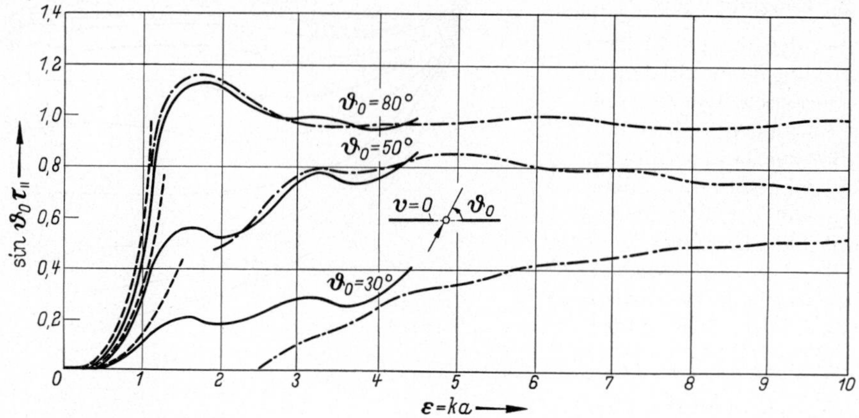

Fig. 71.

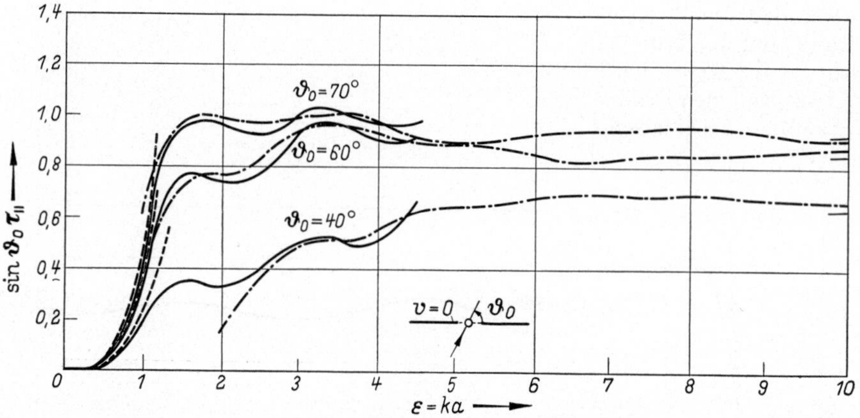

Fig. 72.

Fig. 71/72. Transmissionskoeffizient für den Spalt bei verschiedenen Einfallswinkeln, analog Fig. 70.

dieser Kurven noch einmal herausgezeichnet worden (ausgezogen) und außerdem sind die Kurven eingezeichnet, die sich aus unseren Näherungen (124.9) bzw. (124.9′) ergeben (gestrichelt bzw. strichpunktiert[2]). Für senkrechte Incidenz liegt im p-Fall außerdem eine tabellarisch gegebene Auswertung der strengen Lösung im Bereich $0 \leqq \varepsilon \leqq 10$ vor[3], die für Fig. 70 benutzt worden ist. Was zunächst die dreigliedrige Reihenentwicklung (124.9) nach *steigenden* Potenzen

[1] P.M. Morse u. P. J. Rubenstein: Phys. Rev. **54**, 895 (1938).

[2] Nach K. Westpfahl: Ann. Phys. **4**, 283 (1959). — Bei den asymptotischen Formeln ist nur das *erste* Korrekturglied berücksichtigt. Kurven für den Transmissionskoeffizienten, bei denen alle *drei* Korrekturterme berücksichtigt sind, finden sich bei R.W.P. King u. T.T. Wu: The Scattering and Diffraction of Waves, S. 119 u. 121.

[3] S. Skavlem: Arch. Math. Naturvid. **51**, 61 (1951). — S.N. Karp u. A. Russek: N.Y. Univ. Res. Rep. No. EM-75 (1955).

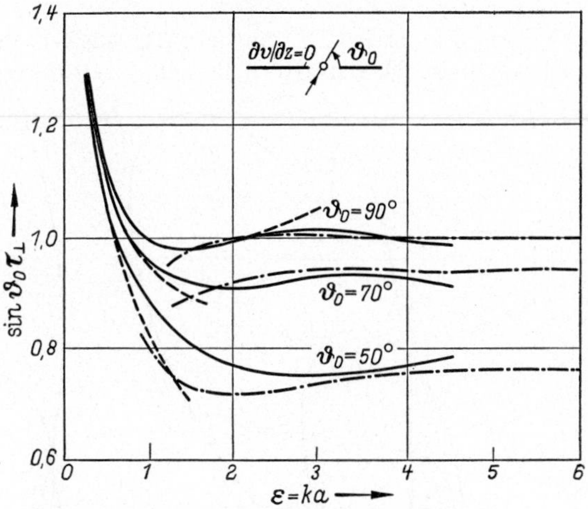

Fig. 73.

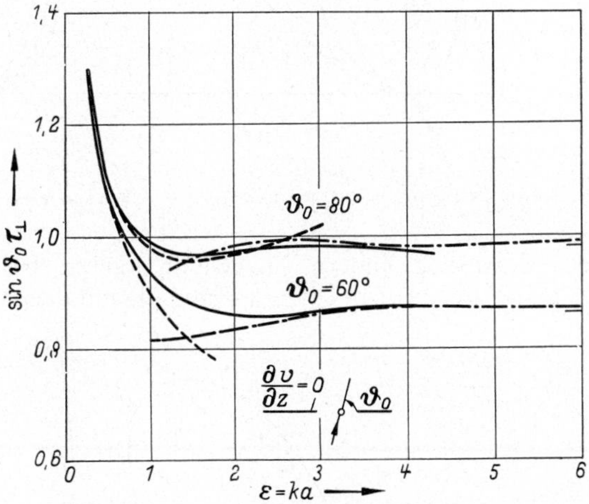

Fig. 74.

Fig. 73/74. Transmissionskoeffizient für den Spalt bei der Randbedingung $\partial v/\partial z = 0$ für verschiedene Einfallswinkel, vgl. Text zu Fig. 70.

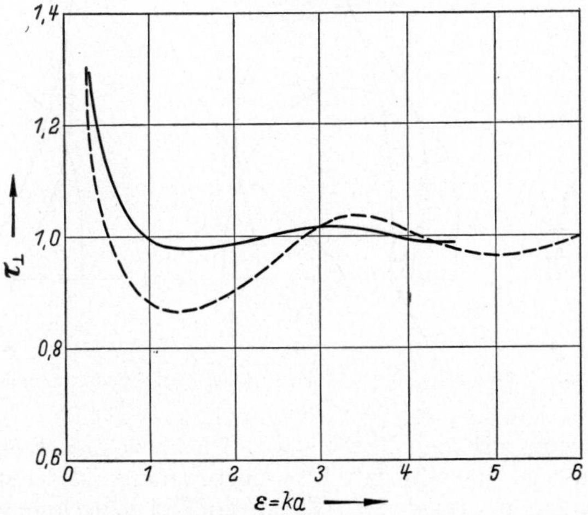

Fig. 75. Transmissionskoeffizient für den Spalt bei der Randbedingung $\partial v/\partial z = 0$ mittels stationärer Darstellung unter Zugrundelegung einer konstanten Testfunktion nach ERDÉLYI und PAPAS (gestrichelt) und streng nach MORSE-RUBENSTEIN (ausgezogen).

in ε *(Rayleighsche Näherung)* betrifft, so ist sie nach Ausweis der Figuren nur im Bereich $0 \leqq \varepsilon < 1$ brauchbar. Dies dürfte sich auch durch Berechnung weiterer

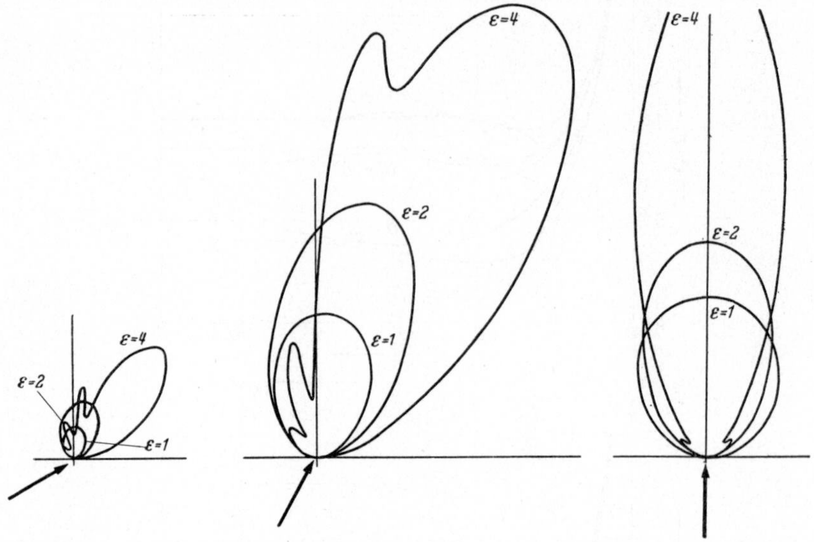

Fig. 76. Strahlungscharakteristik für den Spalt bei der Randbedingung $v = 0$ für verschiedene Einfallsrichtungen.

Reihenglieder nicht wesentlich ändern [im s-Fall ergeben bereits die ersten *beiden* Glieder in (124.9s) eine bessere Übereinstimmung mit den strengen Werten,

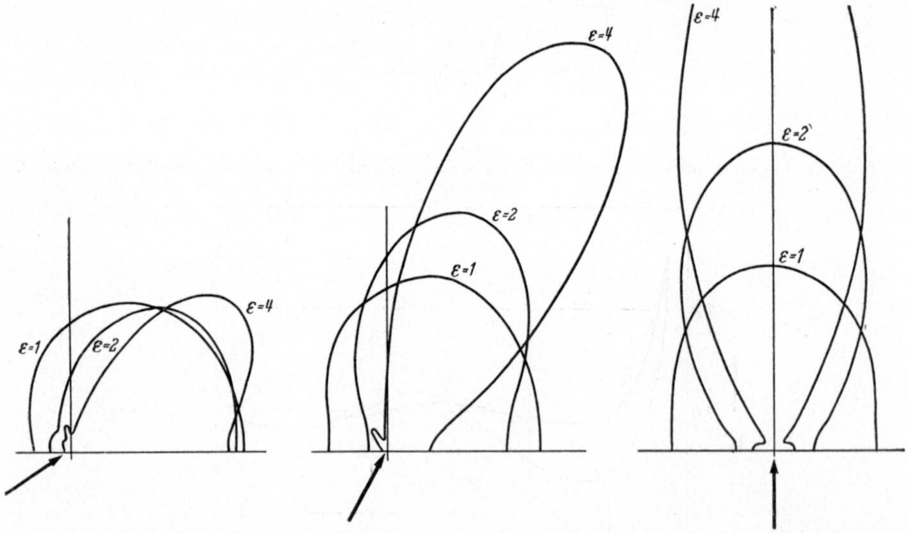

Fig. 77. Strahlungscharakteristik für den Spalt bei der Randbedingung $\partial v/\partial z = 0$ für verschiedene Einfallsrichtungen.

als das Mitnehmen des dritten Gliedes $\sim \varepsilon^4$]. Die *asymptotischen* Entwicklungen (124.9′) liefern zum Teil eine sehr gute Übereinstimmung mit der strengen Lösung (besonders für senkrechte Inzidenz). Die fortlaufend schlechter werdende Übereinstimmung bei abnehmendem Einfallswinkel rührt daher, daß für streifende Inzidenz die Formeln (124.9′) unbrauchbar werden (vgl. Ziff. 122). Durch eine

Abwandlung der Methode von Ziff. 122 hat LEVINE[1] für den Durchlaßquerschnitt $T_\perp = 2a\sqrt{1-\alpha_0^2}\,\tau_\perp$ des Spalts (pro Längeneinheit, vgl. Ziff. 99) bei *streifender Inzidenz* $\alpha_0 = 1$ die folgende asymptotische Darstellung gefunden[2]

$$\left.\begin{aligned} T_\perp = \frac{2a}{\sqrt{2}\pi}\Big\{ & 2\varepsilon^{-\frac{1}{2}} - \frac{\varepsilon^{-\frac{3}{2}}}{8} + \frac{3\varepsilon^{-\frac{5}{2}}}{256} + \frac{\varepsilon^{-\frac{7}{2}}}{64}\left[\frac{15}{64} - \frac{\sin(4\varepsilon+\pi/4)}{\sqrt{2}\pi}\right] \\ & - \frac{\varepsilon^{-\frac{9}{2}}}{1024}\left[\frac{525}{256} - 21\,\frac{\cos(4\varepsilon+\pi/4)}{\sqrt{2}\pi}\right] + \cdots\Big\} \end{aligned}\right\} \tag{124.12}$$

Andererseits ist der Spalt im $\|$-Fall bei streifender Inzidenz vollkommen undurchlässig ($T_\| = 0$).

Fig. 75 gibt einen Vergleich des nach (123.5 s) berechneten Transmissionskoeffizienten (stationäre Darstellung) mit der strengen Lösung[3]. Trotz der groben Näherung für die Feldgröße in der Öffnung ergibt die stationäre Darstellung also einen im gesamten ε-Bereich qualitativ richtigen Verlauf. Fig. 76 und 77 zeigen die Winkelverteilung des Fernfeldes für beide Polarisationsfälle bei verschiedenen Einfallswinkeln und Spaltbreiten (nach MORSE-RUBENSTEIN).

c) Beugung an der Kreisscheibe und Kreisblende.

Das Problem der Beugung an der Kreisscheibe läßt sich sowohl im skalaren (akustischen) als auch im vektoriellen (elektromagnetischen) Fall in den Koordinaten des abgeplatteten Rotationsellipsoids *separieren*. Die Lösung des Randwertproblems ergibt sich auf diesem Wege in Gestalt einer Reihe nach *Sphäroidfunktionen* (Abschn. c1). Bei der Bestimmung der Koeffizienten dieser Reihe erweist sich die *Kantenbedingung* (Abschn. A I d2) als wesentlich; so ist die exakte Form der Reihenlösung erst relativ spät gefunden und bis zur numerischen Auswertung vorangetrieben worden [BOUWKAMP 1941 (akustisch), MEIXNER und ANDREJEWSKI 1950 (elektromagnetisch)]. Die Reihen konvergieren für alle $\varepsilon = ka$ (k Wellenzahl, a Radius der Kreisscheibe), und zwar ist die Zahl der zu berücksichtigenden Reihenglieder wieder von derselben Größenordnung wie der Parameter ε (man vgl. die entsprechenden Verhältnisse bei der Reihendarstellung für die Beugung an Zylinder und Kugel in Abschn. II). Die numerische Auswertung der Reihen nach Sphäroidfunktionen ist bisher für den Parameter-Bereich $0 \leqq \varepsilon \leqq 10$ durchgeführt worden.

Für den *statischen Grenzfall* $\varepsilon \ll 1$ und den daran anschließenden ε-Bereich bis etwa $\varepsilon \approx 1$ ist eine Reihenentwicklung der Lösung nach steigenden Potenzen von ε nützlich. Diese kann zwar aus der Darstellung nach Sphäroidfunktionen gewonnen werden, jedoch ist es einfacher, die ersten Glieder direkt durch eine Störungsrechnung im Anschluß an den Rayleighschen Grenzfall (A III f) mit Hilfe der Integralgleichung für die Flächenbelegung (A III a) zu berechnen (Abschn. c2).

Der *hochfrequente Grenzfall* ($\varepsilon \gg 1$) läßt sich bisher mit Hilfe der Reihe nach Sphäroidfunktionen analytisch noch nicht erfassen. Mit anderen Worten: der geometrisch-optische Grenzfall und die daran anschließende asymptotische Entwicklung nach fallenden (gebrochenen) Potenzen von ε lassen sich aus der Reihenentwicklung noch nicht deduzieren. Das analytische Hilfsmittel dazu wäre die Watson-Transformation (vgl. Abschn. B II a, b), jedoch sind die hier erforder-

[1] H. LEVINE: Stanford Univ. Appl. Math. and Stat. Lab. Techn. Rep. No. 61 (1957). — J. Appl. Phys. **30**, 1673 (1959).

[2] Die drei letzten Korrekturglieder finden sich bei S.R. SESHADRI u. T.T. WU: Harvard Univ. Cruft Lab. Sci. Rep. No. 23 (1958). — Trans. Inst. Rad. Engrs. AP-**8**, 37 (1960).

[3] Nach A. ERDÉLYI u. C.H. PAPAS: Proc. Nat. Acad. Sci. **40**, 128 (1954). Vgl. auch J.W. MILES: Phys. Rev. **75**, 695 (1949).

lichen asymptotischen Darstellungen der Sphäroidfunktionen für beliebige Indices bisher noch nicht vollständig bekannt. In Abschn. c3 wird der Grenzfall $\varepsilon \gg 1$ zunächst mit Hilfe des heuristischen Braunbekschen Verfahrens (A II b, Ziff. 39) behandelt. Die Ergebnisse lassen sich durch *asymptotische* Lösung der Integralgleichungen für den Flächenstrom bzw. die Fernfeldamplitude (A III b) reproduzieren und durch höhere Näherungen ergänzen. Dadurch wird der Anschluß an die numerisch noch zu bewältigende Auswertung der Reihe nach Sphäroidfunktionen für $\varepsilon = 10$ hergestellt.

Setzt man die „statischen“ Werte der Belegungsdichten (aus Abschn. c2) in die *stationäre Darstellung* des Fernfeldes (A III g) ein, so ergibt eine (eigentlich inkonsequente) Auswertung dieser Darstellung für *beliebige* ε für den *Streukoeffizienten* einen Verlauf, der im gesamten ε-Bereich mit der strengen Lösung (wenigstens qualitativ) übereinstimmt (Abschn. c4).

c1) Direkte Lösung.

125. Die Wellengleichung in abgeplattet-rotationselliptischen Koordinaten. Sphäroidfunktionen. Die geeigneten Koordinaten zur Behandlung des Problems der Kreisscheibe sind die des abgeplatteten Rotationsellipsoids[1] ξ, η, φ (vgl. Fig. 78). Ihr Zusammenhang mit den kartesischen Koordinaten ist:

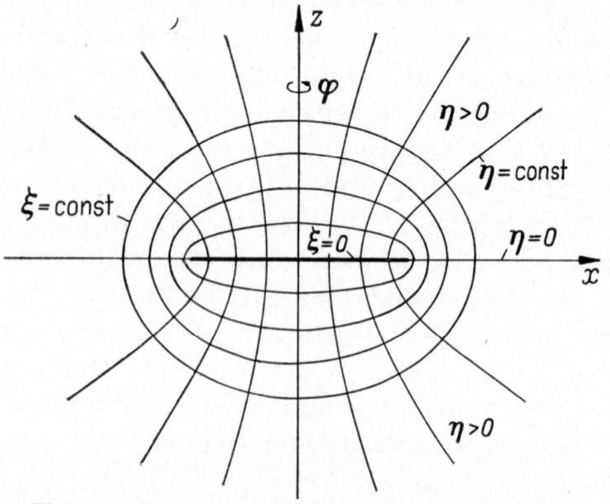

Fig. 78. Separationskoordinaten bei der Beugung an der Kreisscheibe.

$$\left.\begin{aligned} x &= a\sqrt{(1+\xi^2)(1-\eta^2)}\cos\varphi \\ y &= a\sqrt{(1+\xi^2)(1-\eta^2)}\sin\varphi \\ z &= a\,\xi\,\eta \end{aligned}\right\} \qquad (125.1)$$

und ihr Wertebereich:

$$\left.\begin{aligned} 0 &< \xi < \infty, \\ -1 &< \eta < 1, \\ 0 &< \varphi < 2\pi. \end{aligned}\right\} \qquad (125.2)$$

Die Flächen $\xi = \text{const}$ bzw. $|\eta| = \text{const}$ sind Rotationsellipsoide bzw. -hyperboloide. Sie entarten im Grenzfall $\xi = 0$ bzw. $\eta = 0$ zur Kreisscheibe bzw. Kreisblende vom Radius a. Kreisscheibe und -blende ergänzen sich zur vollen xy-Ebene. $|\eta| = 1$ ist die Rotationsachse (z-Achse). Die Koordinate η wechselt an der Kreisscheibe sprunghaft ihr Vorzeichen. In weitem Abstand von der Kreisscheibe gehen die elliptischen in Kugelkoordinaten r, ϑ, φ über, entsprechend dem Zusammenhang

$$r = a\,\xi, \qquad \cos\vartheta = \eta, \qquad \varphi = \varphi \qquad \textit{für } \xi \to \infty. \qquad (125.3)$$

Die Wellengleichung $\Delta v + k^2 v = 0$ lautet in unseren Koordinaten

$$\frac{\partial}{\partial\xi}\left[(1+\xi^2)\frac{\partial v}{\partial\xi}\right] + \frac{\partial}{\partial\eta}\left[(1-\eta^2)\frac{\partial v}{\partial\eta}\right] + \left(\frac{1}{1-\eta^2} - \frac{1}{1+\xi^2}\right)\frac{\partial^2 v}{\partial\varphi^2} + \varepsilon^2(\xi^2+\eta^2)\,v = 0 \qquad (125.4)$$

mit der Abkürzung $\varepsilon = k a$. Der Separationsansatz

$$v = f_1(\xi)\,f_2(\eta)\,e^{i m \varphi}, \qquad m = 0, \pm 1, \pm 2, \ldots \qquad (125.5)$$

[1] Vgl. W. Magnus u. F. Oberhettinger: Formeln und Sätze für die speziellen Funktionen der mathematischen Physik, 2. Aufl., S. 198. Berlin 1948.

führt zu den gewöhnlichen Differentialgleichungen

$$-[(1+\xi^2)\,f_1']'+\left\{-\frac{m^2}{1+\xi^2}+\lambda-\varepsilon^2(1+\xi^2)\right\}f_1=0, \tag{125.6a}$$

$$[(1-\eta^2)\,f_2']'+\left\{-\frac{m^2}{1-\eta^2}+\lambda-\varepsilon^2(1-\eta^2)\right\}f_2=0 \tag{125.6b}$$

mit dem Separationsparameter λ. Ihre Lösungen sind die Sphäroidfunktionen[1], auf die wir jetzt kurz eingehen wollen.

Die Differentialgleichung (125.6b) besitzt in $\eta=\pm 1$ singuläre Stellen der Bestimmtheit und verhält sich dort wie die Differentialgleichung der zugeordneten Kugelfunktionen, in die sie für $\varepsilon=0$ übergeht. Wie bei den Kugelfunktionen $P_n^m(\eta)$ sind die Eigenwerte λ_n^m $(n=|m|, |m|+1, |m|+2, \ldots)$ des Separationsparameters λ durch die Forderung der Endlichkeit der Lösung in $\eta=\pm 1$ festgelegt. Die Lösungen selbst werden mit $ps_n^m(\eta, -\varepsilon^2)$ bezeichnet und so normiert, daß gilt

$$ps_n^m(\eta, 0) = P_n^m(\eta). \tag{125.7}$$

Da Gl. (125.6b) bei Vorzeichenumkehr von η unverändert bleibt, sind ihre Lösungen ps abwechselnd gerade oder ungerade Funktionen von η. Wie die entsprechenden Kugelfunktionen sind sie gerade bzw. ungerade bei geradem bzw. ungeradem $n+m$.

Bei der Lösung der Differentialgleichung (125.6a) ist der Separationsparameter $\lambda=\lambda_n^m$ als vorgegeben zu betrachten. Die einzige singuläre Stelle der Differentialgleichung im Variabilitätsbereich von ξ ist der Grenzpunkt $\xi=\infty$. Für $\xi\to\infty$ vereinfacht sich (125.6a) zu

$$(\xi^2 f_1')' + \varepsilon^2\,\xi^2\, f_1 = 0 \tag{125.8}$$

mit den beiden Lösungen

$$f_1 = \frac{e^{\pm i\varepsilon\xi}}{\xi}, \tag{125.9}$$

die wegen (125.3) eine aus- und eine einlaufende Kugelwelle darstellen. Die entsprechenden Lösungen von (125.6a) zum Eigenwert $\lambda=\lambda_n^m$ bezeichnet man mit $S_n^{m\,(3)}(-i\xi, i\varepsilon)$ und $S_n^{m\,(4)}(-i\xi, i\varepsilon)$, wobei der noch willkürliche konstante Faktor durch

$$S_n^{m\,(3,4)}(-i\,\xi, i\,\varepsilon) \to (\mp\, i)^{n+1}\,\frac{e^{\pm i\varepsilon\xi}}{\varepsilon\,\xi} \quad \textit{für } \xi\to\infty \tag{125.10}$$

festgelegt ist. Aufspaltung in Real- und Imaginärteil:

$$S_n^{m\,(3,4)} = S_n^{m\,(1)} \pm i\, S_n^{m\,(2)} \tag{125.11}$$

liefert die beiden reellen Lösungen $S_n^{m\,(1,2)}(-i\xi, i\varepsilon)$, die sich asymptotisch wie stehende Kugelwellen verhalten. Ersetzt man in Gl. (125.6b) η durch $\pm i\xi$, so geht die Gleichung in (125.6a) über. $ps_n^m(-i\xi, -\varepsilon^2)$ ist daher ebenfalls eine Lösung von (125.6a). Es ist bis auf einen konstanten Faktor mit $S_n^{m\,(1)}(-i\xi, i\varepsilon)$ identisch. Hieraus folgt, daß die Reihenentwicklung von $S_n^{m\,(1)}$ wie die von ps_n^m nur gerade oder ungerade Potenzen von ξ enthält, je nachdem $n+m$ gerade oder ungerade ist. Insbesondere gilt somit

$$\left.\begin{aligned} S_n^{m\,(1)}(-i\,0, i\,\varepsilon) &= 0 \text{ für } n+m \text{ ungerade}\\ S_n^{m\,(1)\prime}(-i\,0, i\,\varepsilon) &= 0 \text{ für } n+m \text{ gerade}\end{aligned}\right\}. \tag{125.11a}$$

[1] J. Meixner u. F. W. Schäfke: Mathieusche Funktionen und Sphäroidfunktionen. Berlin—Göttingen—Heidelberg: Springer 1954. Das letzte Kapitel enthält einen Abschnitt über Beugungsprobleme, auf den sich die folgenden Ausführungen größtenteils stützen. Siehe auch J. A. Stratton: Spheroidal Wave Functions. New York 1956.

Hierin bedeutet ′ die Ableitung nach der ersten Variablen $-i\xi$ von S_n^m. Um die Eindeutigkeit der durch die Gln. (125.10) und (125.11) definierten Funktionen S_n^m zu gewährleisten, denken wir uns die komplexe $-i\xi$-Ebene zwischen den singulären Punkten $-i\xi = \pm 1$ aufgeschnitten. Aus diesem Grunde wurde im Argument von $S_n^{m(1)}$ der Gl. (125.11a) $-i\,0$ statt einfach 0 geschrieben.

Die aus den betrachteten speziellen Sphäroidfunktionen aufgebaute räumliche Welle (125.5) ist beim Durchgang durch die Kreisscheibe $\xi = 0$ im allgemeinen unstetig, da η sich hierbei sprunghaft ändert. Im übrigen ist sie stetig und eindeutig. Durch Überlagerung gewinnt man die allgemeinste Welle mit denselben Eigenschaften, wie wir sie zur Behandlung des Problems der Kreisscheibe benötigen.

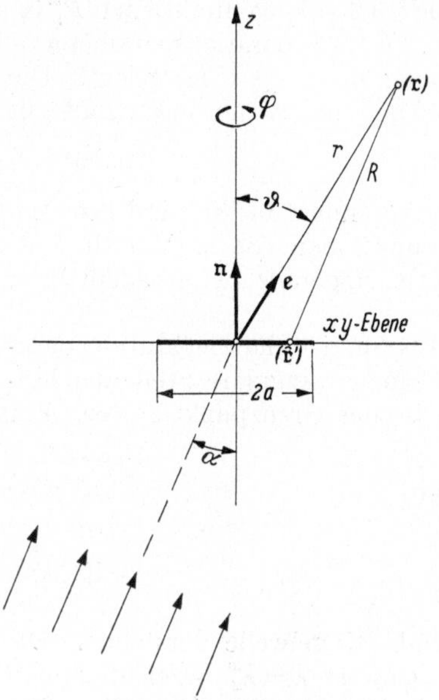

Fig. 79. Geometrische Verhältnisse bei der Beugung an der Kreisscheibe.

Für das Folgende brauchen wir insbesondere die Darstellung der einfallenden ebenen Welle v_0. Die Einfallsebene sei die xz-Ebene, der Einfallswinkel sei α (vgl. Fig. 79), so daß gilt

$$v_0 = e^{ik(x\sin\alpha + z\cos\alpha)}. \tag{125.12}$$

Die Entwicklung nach Sphäroidfunktionen lautet

$$\left.\begin{aligned} v_0 = \sum_{n=0}^{\infty} \sum_{m=-n}^{n} (2n+1)\, i^{n+2m} \cdot \\ \cdot S_n^{m(1)}(-i\xi, i\varepsilon)\, ps_n^m(\eta, -\varepsilon^2) \cdot \\ \cdot ps_n^{-m} \cdot (\cos\alpha, -\varepsilon^2)\, e^{im\varphi}. \end{aligned}\right\} \tag{125.13}$$

126. Akustisches Streuproblem. Wir zerlegen den gesamten Wellenvorgang v in einfallende und gestreute Welle

$$v = v_0 + v_S. \tag{126.1}$$

Setzen wir die Kreisscheibe als schallhart voraus, so hat die Streuwelle neben der Wellengleichung (125.4) die Randbedingung

$$\frac{\partial}{\partial\xi}(v_0 + v_S) = 0 \qquad \textit{für } \xi = 0 \tag{126.2}$$

zu erfüllen. Ferner gilt die Ausstrahlungsbedingung, die mit Rücksicht auf (125.3) lautet

$$\xi\left(\frac{\partial}{\partial\xi} - i\varepsilon\right) v_S \to 0 \qquad \textit{für } \xi \to \infty. \tag{126.3}$$

Der allgemeinste Ansatz einer auslaufenden Welle ist wegen (125.10)

$$v_S = \sum_{n=0}^{\infty} \sum_{m=-n}^{n} A_n^m\, S_n^{m(3)}(-i\xi, i\varepsilon)\, ps_n^m(\eta, -\varepsilon^2)\, e^{im\varphi}. \tag{126.4}$$

Die Konstanten A_n^m ergeben sich aus (126.2) unter Benutzung von (125.13) durch Koeffizientenvergleich:

$$A_n^m = -(2n+1)\, i^{n+2m} \cdot \frac{S_n^{m(1)\prime}(-i\,0, i\varepsilon)}{S_n^{m(3)\prime}(-i\,0, i\varepsilon)}\, ps_n^{-m}(\cos\alpha, -\varepsilon^2). \tag{126.5}$$

In weitem Abstand von der Kreisscheibe nimmt die Beugungswelle nach (126.4), (125.10) und (125.3) die Gestalt an:

$$v_S \to \frac{e^{ikr}}{kr} \sum_{n=0}^{\infty} \sum_{m=-n}^{n} A_n^m (-i)^{n+1} ps_n^m(\cos\vartheta, -\varepsilon^2)\, e^{im\varphi} \qquad \textit{für } r \to \infty. \tag{126.6}$$

Von der Kantenbedingung wurde im Vorangegangenen nicht explizite Gebrauch gemacht (vgl. hierzu Ziff. 24, die elliptischen Koordinaten gehen in der Nähe der Kante bis auf den Faktor $1/\sqrt{a}$ direkt in die dort benutzten parabolischen Koordinaten über).

Im Falle der schallweichen Kreisscheibe mit der Randbedingung $v_0 + v_S = 0$ für $\xi = 0$ anstelle von Gl. (126.2) verläuft die Rechnung entsprechend. Das Babinetsche Prinzip (vgl. Ziff. 27) erlaubt es ferner, die Ergebnisse für die Kreisscheibe auf den Fall der Beugung an der kreisförmigen Öffnung im ebenen Schirm *(Kreisblende)* zu übertragen. In engem Zusammenhang mit dem Streuproblem steht die Aufgabe, die akustische Abstrahlung einer in vorgegebener Weise schwingenden *kreisförmigen Membran* zu berechnen. Der *Streuwelle* v_S entspricht hier die *abgestrahlte Welle* v_S. Die Randbedingung ist, wie in Gl. (126.2), eine Bedingung für $\partial v_S/\partial \xi$ auf der Kreisfläche $\xi = 0$. Der einfachste Fall ist die starr schwingende Kreisplatte, die sog. *Kolbenmembran*. Er ist analytisch identisch mit dem Streuproblem bei senkrecht einfallender Strahlung. Dieser Spezialfall ist ausgiebig numerisch diskutiert worden[1].

Wir erwähnen noch, daß sich die Rechnungen ohne Schwierigkeit auf die Streuung am abgeplatteten *Rotationsellipsoid* mit der Oberfläche $\xi = \xi_0$ verallgemeinern lassen. Die Formeln bleiben die gleichen, nur ist in Gl. (126.5) 0 durch ξ_0 zu ersetzen. Ferner erzielt man den Übergang vom abgeplatteten zum gestreckten Rotationsellipsoid durch die Substitutionen $-i\xi \to \xi$, $-i\xi_0 \to \xi_0$, $i\varepsilon \to \varepsilon$. Dieser letztere Fall ist auch numerisch behandelt worden[2].

127. Elektromagnetisches Streuproblem[3]. Wir legen dieselben geometrischen Verhältnisse (vgl. Fig. 79) und Koordinaten zugrunde wie im akustischen Fall. Das elektrische Feld der einfallenden Welle sei durch Gl. (125.12) gegeben:

$$E_0 = e^{ik(x \sin\alpha + z \cos\alpha)} \tag{127.1}$$

mit der Entwicklung (125.13). Für die kartesischen Komponenten des elektromagnetischen Feldes gilt dann, je nach der Polarisation des elektrischen Vektors, a) senkrecht oder b) parallel zur Einfallsebene:

$$\left.\begin{aligned} &\text{a)}\quad \mathfrak{E}_0 = (0, E_0, 0), \quad \varkappa\mathfrak{H}_0 = (-E_0\cos\alpha, 0, E_0\sin\alpha) \\ &\text{b)}\quad \mathfrak{E}_0 = (E_0\cos\alpha, 0, -E_0\sin\alpha), \quad \varkappa\mathfrak{H}_0 = (0, E_0, 0). \end{aligned}\right\} \tag{127.1'}$$

Zur Lösung des Beugungsproblems benutzen wir die Methode des *Hertzschen Vektors* $\mathfrak{Z}$, den wir parallel zur Ebene des Beugungsschirms annehmen können (vgl. Ziff. 7). Das vollständige elektromagnetische Feld läßt dann gemäß (6.3)

---

[1] Man vgl. zu diesem Problemkreis: R.C. MACLAURIN: Trans. Cambridge Phil. Soc. **17**, 41 (1898). — E.T. HANSON: Phil. Trans. Roy. Soc. Lond. A **232**, 223 (1933). — L. GUTIN: Techn. Physics USSR. **4**, 404 (1937). — C.J. BOUWKAMP: Diss. Groningen 1941. — R.D. SPENCE: J. Acoust. Soc. Amer. **20**, 380 (1948); **21**, 98 (1949). — Phys. Rev. **73**, 1267 (1948). — R.D. SPENCE u. A. LEITNER: Phys. Rev. **74**, 349 (1948). — A. STORRUSTE: Nor. Vid. Selsk. Forh. **21**, 84, 88 (1948). — A. STORRUSTE u. H. WERGELAND: Nor. Vid. Selsk. Forh. **21**, 38, 43 (1948). — Phys. Rev. **73**, 1397 (1948). — J. MEIXNER u. U. FRITZE: Z. angew. Phys. **1**, 535 (1949). — A. LEITNER: J. Acoust. Soc. Amer. **21**, 331 (1949). — T. NIMURA: Sci. Rep. Tôhoku Univ. B **1/2**, 381 (1951). — T. NIMURA u. Y. WATANABE: Techn. Rep. Tôhoku Imp. Univ. Sendai **14**, 79 (1950). — J. Acoust. Soc. Amer. **25**, 76 (1953). — F.M. WIENER: J. Acoust. Soc. Amer. **21**, 334 (1949); **22**, 47 (1950); **23**, 697 (1951). — J. AWATANI: Mem. Inst. Sci. Industr. Res. Osaka Univ. **9**, 24 (1952).

[2] R.D. SPENCE u. S. GRANGER: J. Acoust. Soc. Amer. **23**, 701 (1951).

[3] Vgl. F. MÖGLICH: Ann. Phys. **83**, 609 (1927). — J. MEIXNER: Nachr. Akad. Wiss. Göttingen: **2**, 74 (1946) (beide fehlerhaft). — J. MEIXNER: Z. Naturforsch. **3**a, 506 (1948). — J. MEIXNER u. W. ANDREJEWSKI: Ann. Phys. **7**, 157 (1950). — C. FLAMMER: J. Appl. Phys. **24**, 1224 (1953).

in der Form

$$\left.\begin{array}{ll} \mathfrak{E} = \operatorname{rot}\operatorname{rot}\mathfrak{Z}, & \varkappa\,\mathfrak{H} = -\,i\,k\operatorname{rot}\mathfrak{Z} \\ (k = \omega\sqrt{\varepsilon_0\,\mu_0}, & \varkappa = \sqrt{\mu_0/\varepsilon_0}) \end{array}\right\} \qquad (127.2)$$

darstellen. (Dabei ist ω die Kreisfrequenz und ε_0, μ_0 sind die Materialkonstanten des homogenen Mediums, in das der Schirm eingebettet ist.) Die einfallende Welle (127.1′) ist durch den Hertzschen Vektor

$$\text{a)}\quad \mathfrak{Z}_x^0 = 0, \quad \mathfrak{Z}_y^0 = \frac{E_0}{k^2}; \qquad \text{b)}\quad \mathfrak{Z}_x^0 = \frac{E_0}{k^2\cos\alpha}, \quad \mathfrak{Z}_y^0 = 0 \qquad (127.3)$$

darstellbar. (Bei der Anwendung der Formeln des allgemeinen Teils ist hier und im folgenden zu beachten, daß dort $k = 1$ gesetzt wurde. Die dortigen Formeln sind daher durch Faktoren k dimensionell zu vervollständigen.)

Gesucht ist die Streuwelle mit dem Hertzschen Vektor $\mathfrak{Z}_S$, die die einfallende Welle $\mathfrak{Z}_0$ zur Gesamtwelle $\mathfrak{Z} = (\mathfrak{Z}_x, \mathfrak{Z}_y, 0)$ des Beugungsvorganges ergänzt:

$$\mathfrak{Z} = \mathfrak{Z}_0 + \mathfrak{Z}_S. \qquad (127.4)$$

Sie hat den folgenden Bedingungen zu genügen:

1. Der Wellengleichung (7.2)

$$(\Delta + k^2)\,\mathfrak{Z}_{x,y}^{(S)} = 0, \qquad (127.5)$$

2. der Randbedingung (7.3), (7.4)

$$\left.\begin{array}{l} \mathfrak{Z}_x = \dfrac{\partial\Phi}{\partial x}, \quad \mathfrak{Z}_y = \dfrac{\partial\Phi}{\partial y}, \\ \left(\dfrac{\partial^2}{\partial x^2} + \dfrac{\partial^2}{\partial y^2} + k^2\right)\Phi = 0 \end{array}\right\} \quad \text{für } \xi = 0, \qquad (127.6)$$

3. der Ausstrahlungsbedingung (126.3)

$$\xi\left(\frac{\partial}{\partial\xi} - i\,\varepsilon\right)\mathfrak{Z}_{x,y}^{(S)} \to 0 \quad \text{für} \quad \xi \to \infty \quad \text{und} \qquad (127.7)$$

4. der Kantenbedingung (25.3)

$$\left.\begin{array}{c} \dfrac{\partial}{\partial\xi} \\ \dfrac{\partial}{\partial\eta} \end{array}\right\} (\mathfrak{Z}_x^{(S)}\cos\varphi + \mathfrak{Z}_y^{(S)}\sin\varphi) = 0 \quad \text{für } \xi = \eta = 0. \qquad (127.8)$$

Bei der Anwendung von Gl. (25.3) wurde, wie schon früher, davon Gebrauch gemacht, daß in Kantennähe elliptische und parabolische Koordinaten im wesentlichen identisch sind. Die Gln. (127.5) und (127.8) gelten zunächst für die Gesamtwelle $\mathfrak{Z}$ und, da die einfallende Welle $\mathfrak{Z}_0$ ihnen genügt, folglich auch für $\mathfrak{Z}_S$.

Die $\mathfrak{Z}_S$ auferlegten Bedingungen (127.5) bis (127.8) sind bezüglich eines Vorzeichenwechsels von z bzw. η symmetrisch. Die Streuwelle hat daher auf Vorder- und Rückseite des Schirmes dieselbe Gestalt, was die Diskussion der Ergebnisse der Theorie (vgl. Ziff. 128) vereinfacht.

Zur Lösung spalten wir die Streuwelle in zwei Bestandteile:

$$\mathfrak{Z}_S = \mathfrak{Z}_1 + \mathfrak{Z}_2, \qquad (127.9)$$

die für sich den Forderungen (127.5) und (127.7) genügen sollen und die wir daher analog Gl. (126.4) als auslaufende Wellen ansetzen:

$$\mathfrak{Z}_x^{(1,2)} \pm i\,\mathfrak{Z}_y^{(1,2)} = \sum_{n=0}^{\infty}\sum_{m=-n}^{n} A_{n(\pm)}^{m(1,2)}\, S_n^{m(3)}(-\,i\,\xi, i\,\varepsilon)\, ps_n^m(\eta, -\,\varepsilon^2)\, e^{i m\varphi}. \qquad (127.10)$$

$\mathfrak{Z}_1$ legen wir durch die Randbedingung

$$\mathfrak{Z}_0 + \mathfrak{Z}_1 = 0 \quad \text{für } \xi = 0 \tag{127.11}$$

fest und können dann die Koeffizienten $A_{n(\pm)}^{m(1)}$ durch Vergleich von (127.10) mit (127.3), (127.1) und (125.13) berechnen:

$$\left.\begin{array}{ll} \text{a)} & A_{n(\pm)}^{m(1)} = \mp \dfrac{i}{k^2} \\ \text{b)} & A_{n(\pm)}^{m(1)} = - \dfrac{1}{k^2 \cos\alpha} \end{array}\right\} \cdot (2n+1)\, i^{n+2m} \frac{S_n^{m(1)}(-i\,0, i\,\varepsilon)}{S_n^{m(3)}(-i\,0, i\,\varepsilon)}\, p s_n^{-m}(\cos\alpha, -\varepsilon^2). \tag{127.12}$$

$\mathfrak{Z}_2$ muß nunmehr die Randbedingung (127.6) für sich allein befriedigen. Schreiben wir die allgemeine Lösung der zweidimensionalen Wellengleichung für Φ in ebenen Polarkoordinaten ϱ, φ auf der Kreisscheibe mit Besselschen Funktionen J_m und unbestimmten Konstanten U_m in der Form an

$$\Phi(\varrho, \varphi) = \sum_{m=-\infty}^{\infty} U_m\, i^m J_m(k\varrho)\, e^{i m \varphi}, \tag{127.13}$$

so folgt aus (127.6) mit $\mathfrak{Z}_2$ statt $\mathfrak{Z}$

$$\mathfrak{Z}_x^{(2)} \pm i\,\mathfrak{Z}_y^{(2)} = (\mathfrak{Z}_\varrho^{(2)} \pm i\,\mathfrak{Z}_\varphi^{(2)})\, e^{\pm i\varphi} = i\,k \sum_{m=-\infty}^{\infty} U_{m\mp1}\, i^m J_m(k\varrho)\, e^{i m\varphi} \quad \textit{für } \xi = 0. \tag{127.14}$$

Dabei wurde die Rekursionsformel der Besselschen Funktion

$$J_m'(z) \mp \frac{m}{z} J_m(z) = \mp J_{m\pm1}(z) \tag{127.15}$$

benutzt. Nunmehr gehen wir auf der Kreisscheibe von den Polarkoordinaten ϱ, φ zu den elliptischen Koordinaten η, φ und gleichzeitig von den Bessel- zu Sphäroid-Funktionen über. Hierzu setzen wir in den Gln. (125.12) und (125.13) $z=0$ bzw. $\xi=0$ und erhalten mit $\alpha=\pi/2$ eine auf der Kreisscheibe gültige Reihenentwicklung für die ebene Welle e^{ikx}, die wir mit der bekannten Darstellung

$$e^{ikx} = \sum_{m=-\infty}^{\infty} i^m J_m(k\varrho)\, e^{i m\varphi} \tag{127.16}$$

vergleichen. Dabei ergibt sich

$$J_m(k\varrho) = \sum_{n=|m|}^{\infty} (2n+1)\, i^{n+m} S_n^{m(1)}(-i\,0, i\,\varepsilon)\, p s_n^m(\eta, -\varepsilon^2)\, p s_n^{-m}(0, -\varepsilon^2). \tag{127.17}$$

Einsetzen in Gl. (127.14) liefert die Randbedingung für den zweiten Teil der Streuwelle, aus der sich die Koeffizienten $A_{n(\pm)}^{m(2)}$ des Ansatzes (127.10) berechnen:

$$\left.\begin{array}{l} A_{n(\pm)}^{m(2)} = \bar{A}_n^{m(2)} \cdot U_{m\mp1}, \\ \bar{A}_n^{m(2)} = i\,k\,(2n+1)\, i^{n+2m} \dfrac{S_n^{m(1)}(-i\,0, i\,\varepsilon)}{S_n^{m(3)}(-i\,0, i\,\varepsilon)}\, p s_n^{-m}(0, -\varepsilon^2). \end{array}\right\} \tag{127.18}$$

Es verbleibt die Bestimmung der U_m. Führen wir die Abkürzungen

$$\left.\begin{array}{l} L_m^{\pm}(\xi, \eta) = \displaystyle\sum_{n=|m|}^{\infty} A_{n(\pm)}^{m(1)}\, S_n^{m(3)}(-i\,\xi, i\,\varepsilon)\, p s_n^m(\eta, -\varepsilon^2) \\ N_m(\xi, \eta) = \displaystyle\sum_{n=|m|}^{\infty} \bar{A}_n^{m(2)}\, S_n^{m(3)}(-i\,\xi, i\,\varepsilon)\, p s_n^m(\eta, -\varepsilon^2) \end{array}\right\} \tag{127.19}$$

ein, so läßt sich (127.10) vereinfacht schreiben:

$$\mathfrak{Z}_x^{(1)} \pm i\,\mathfrak{Z}_y^{(1)} = \sum_{m=-\infty}^{\infty} L_m^{\pm}\, e^{i m\varphi}, \quad \mathfrak{Z}_x^{(2)} \pm i\,\mathfrak{Z}_y^{(2)} = \sum_{m=-\infty}^{\infty} U_{m\mp1} N_m\, e^{i m\varphi}. \tag{127.20}$$

Hiermit und mit (127.9) ergibt sich für den in der Kantenbedingung (127.8) auftretenden Ausdruck $\mathfrak{Z}_x^{(S)}\cos\varphi+\mathfrak{Z}_y^{(S)}\sin\varphi$ bis auf den Faktor $\frac{1}{2}$:

$$\left.\begin{aligned}&(\mathfrak{Z}_x^{(S)}+i\,\mathfrak{Z}_y^{(S)})\,\mathrm{e}^{-i\varphi}+(\mathfrak{Z}_x^{(S)}-i\,\mathfrak{Z}_y^{(S)})\,\mathrm{e}^{i\varphi}\\&\quad=\sum_{m=-\infty}^{\infty}[L_{m+1}^{+}+L_{m-1}^{-}+(N_{m+1}+N_{m-1})\,U_m]\,\mathrm{e}^{im\varphi}.\end{aligned}\right\}\qquad(127.21)$$

Wegen (127.12), (127.18) und (125.11a) enthalten die Reihen (127.19) nur Summanden mit geradem $n+m$ und sind daher gerade Funktionen von η. Damit ist die zweite Bedingung (127.8) von selbst erfüllt. Die erste Bedingung (127.8) muß für beliebige φ befriedigt werden und liefert die gesuchte Bestimmungsgleichung für die U_m:

$$\frac{\partial}{\partial\xi}(L_{m+1}^{+}+L_{m-1}^{-})+U_m\frac{\partial}{\partial\xi}(N_{m+1}+N_{m-1})=0\quad\textit{für}\ \xi=\eta=0.\qquad(127.22)$$

Damit ist das Streuproblem im Prinzip gelöst.

128. Diskussion des elektromagnetischen Streuproblems. Andrejewski[1]) hat die elektromagnetische Streuung an der ideal leitenden Kreisscheibe und das nach dem Babinetschen Prinzip (vgl. Ziff. 27) mit diesem Problem zugleich gelöste komplementäre Problem der Kreisblende für den Fall senkrecht auffallender Strahlung zahlenmäßig ausgewertet. Die Reihen nach Sphäroidfunktionen in den allgemeinen Formeln wurden dabei auf Grund von zum Teil eigens berechneten Tabellen der Sphäroidfunktionen numerisch aufsummiert. Die Zahl der zu berücksichtigenden Reihenglieder hängt ab von der Größe $\varepsilon=ka=$ Umfang der Kreisscheibe/Wellenlänge und ist für große ε etwa gleich dieser Größe selbst. Es handelt sich demnach um ein Berechnungsverfahren, das zwar für große Wellenlängen λ besonders schnell konvergiert, bei dem man aber auch noch bei relativ kleinen Wellenlängen mit einer nicht allzu großen Anzahl von Reihengliedern auskommt. Hierin unterscheidet sich die Methode vorteilhaft vom Rayleighschen Näherungsverfahren (vgl. Abschn. c2), das ebenfalls eine Näherung von großen Wellenlängen her darstellt, aber statt der Reihen nach Sphäroidfunktionen sehr schlecht konvergierende Potenzreihen in ε benutzt.

Die Methode der Sphäroidfunktionen erfaßt bei erträglichem Rechenaufwand etwa den Bereich $\varepsilon\leqq 10$. Der gerade noch zugängliche und daher interessanteste Fall $\varepsilon=10$ ist besonders eingehend untersucht worden. Wie die folgende Diskussion zeigt, ist mit $\varepsilon=10$ bereits der Anschluß an die für kleine Wellenlängen gültige asymptotische Lösung (bzw. die für das Fernfeld in der engeren Umgebung der Einfallsrichtung anwendbare Kirchhoffsche Lösung) gewonnen, das Gebiet mittlerer Wellenlängen also überbrückt (vgl. auch Ziff. 133 und 134).

Zunächst betrachten wir den *Streukoeffizienten* σ der Kreisscheibe und verstehen darunter das Verhältnis des gesamten Energiestroms der Streuwelle zum auf die Scheibe auftreffenden Energiestrom der ungestörten einfallenden Welle (vgl. Ziff. 103). Im Grenzfalle der geometrischen Optik ist $\sigma=2$, entsprechend der Zusammensetzung der Streuwelle aus einem reflektierten und einem die Abschattung hinter dem Schirm bewirkenden Anteil (Ziff. 105). Der Streukoeffizient liefert nach dem Babinetschen Prinzip (vgl. Ziff. 27) gleichzeitig den *Transmissionskoeffizienten* $\tau=\sigma/2$ der *Kreisblende* mit dem geometrischen Grenzwert $\tau=1$. In Fig. 80 ist $\tau=\sigma/2$ in Abhängigkeit von ε aufgetragen. Man erkennt, daß für Wellenlängen λ kleiner als der Kreisdurchmesser $2a$, entspre-

[1] W. Andrejewski: Naturwissenschaften **38**, 404 (1951). — Diss. Aachen 1952. — Z. angew. Phys. **5**, 178 (1953). Vgl. auch H. J. Schmitt: Harvard Univ. Cruft Lab. Sci. Rep. No. 14 (1957). — Y. Nomura u. S. Katsura: Sci. Rep. Res. Inst. Tôhoku Univ. B **10**, 1 (1958). — C. C.-H. Tang: Harvard Univ. Cruft Lab. Sci. Rep. No. 15 (1958).

chend $\varepsilon > \pi$, praktisch $\sigma/2 = 1$ gilt. Für größere λ sind die Abweichungen von diesem Wert stark. Für sehr große Wellenlängen nähert sich $\sigma/2$ dem Werte 0. In diesem Grenzfall wird also die Kreisblende für elektromagnetische Strahlung undurchlässig. Die ideale Leitfähigkeit des Schirmes verhindert nicht nur auf diesem selbst, sondern auch in der Öffnung die Ausbildung eines elektrischen Feldes. Für kleine ε gilt die Entwicklung[1]

$$\sigma = \frac{128}{27\pi^2}\,\varepsilon^4\left(1 + \frac{22}{25}\,\varepsilon^2 + \frac{7312}{18375}\,\varepsilon^4 + \cdots\right). \tag{128.1}$$

Zum Vergleich sind in Fig. 81 die Streukoeffizienten σ_p und σ_s für das *skalare* (akustische) Streuproblem aufgetragen[2] (der Index p bezieht sich auf die Randbedingung $v = 0$ auf dem kreisförmigen Schirm, der Index s auf die Randbedingung $\partial v/\partial z = 0$). Der Transmissions-

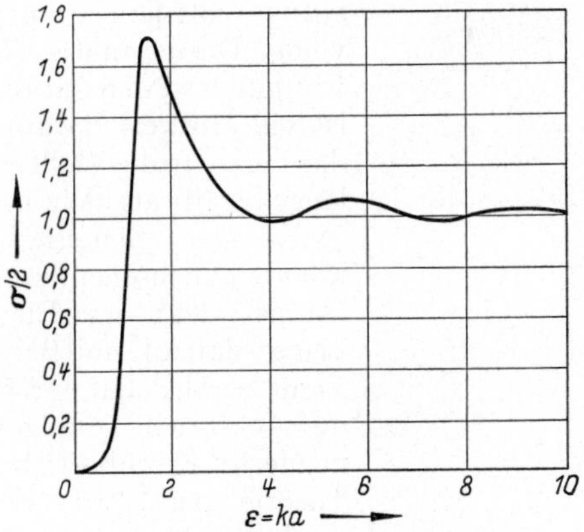

Fig. 80. Streukoeffizient σ für die Kreisscheibe bzw. Transmissionskoeffizient τ für die Kreisblende ($\tau = \sigma/2$); elektromagnetisch nach ANDREJEWSKI.

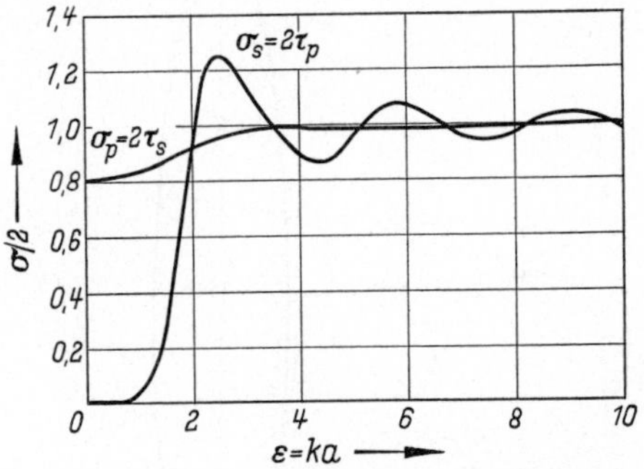

Fig. 81. Streukoeffizient σ für die Kreisscheibe bzw. Transmissionskoeffizient τ für die Kreisblende; akustisch (Index p entspricht der Randbedingung $v = 0$, s der Randbedingung $\partial v/\partial z = 0$) nach BOUWKAMP bzw. STORRUSTE und WERGELAND.

koeffizient der Kreisblende hängt mit diesen Größen gemäß dem Babinetschen Prinzip durch die Beziehungen

$$\tau_p = \tfrac{1}{2}\sigma_s, \qquad \tau_s = \tfrac{1}{2}\sigma_p \tag{128.2}$$

zusammen. Für kleine ε gilt hiei die Darstellung[3]

$$\left.\begin{aligned}\sigma_p = \frac{16}{\pi^2}\Big\{1 &+ \left(\frac{4}{9} - \frac{4}{\pi^2}\right)\varepsilon^2 + \left(\frac{71}{675} - \frac{8}{3\pi^2} + \frac{16}{\pi^4}\right)\varepsilon^4 \\ &+ \left(\frac{568}{33075} - \frac{1936}{2025\pi^2} + \frac{128}{9\pi^4} - \frac{64}{\pi^6}\right)\varepsilon^6 + \cdots\Big\},\end{aligned}\right\} \tag{128.3p}$$

$$\sigma_s = \frac{16\varepsilon^4}{27\pi^2}\left\{1 + \frac{8}{25}\,\varepsilon^2 + \frac{311}{6125}\,\varepsilon^4 + \left(\frac{2612}{496125} - \frac{4}{81\pi^2}\right)\varepsilon^6 + \cdots\right\}. \tag{128.3s}$$

Fig. 82 gibt die Richtungsverteilung der *Streuintensität* in weitem Abstand von der Kreisscheibe für den Fall $\varepsilon = 10$ im Polardiagramm wieder und zwar

[1] C. J. BOUWKAMP: Philips Res. Rep. **5**, 321, 401 (1950). — J. MEIXNER u. W. ANDREJEWSKI: Ann. Phys. **7**, 157 (1950). — C. FLAMMER: Stanford Res. Inst. Techn. Rep. No. 27 (1952). — J. Appl. Phys. **24**, 1224 (1953). Die ersten beiden Glieder werden in Ziff. 132 reproduziert.

[2] Nach C. J. BOUWKAMP: Diss. Groningen 1941. — A. STORRUSTE u. H. WERGELAND: Phys. Rev. **73**, 1397 (1948).

[3] C. J. BOUWKAMP: Diss. Groningen 1941. -- Phys. Rev. **75**, 1608 (1949). — Physica, Haag **16**, 1 (1950). Vgl. dazu Ziff. 130 und 131.

ist die Größe

$$\frac{r^2}{2a^2}\,\frac{I_S(\vartheta,\varphi)}{I_0} \tag{128.4}$$

aufgetragen. [Dabei ist $I_S(\vartheta,\varphi) = |\bar{\mathfrak{S}}_S|$ der zeitliche Mittelwert des (radial gerichteten) Pointingschen Vektors für das Fernfeld der Streuwelle und $I_0 = |\bar{\mathfrak{S}}_0|$ der zeitliche Mittelwert der Energiestromdichte der Primärwelle.] Die Darstellung bezieht sich auf einen ebenen Schnitt durch die Achse der Scheibe, der in der linken bzw. rechten Figur parallel zur Schwingungsrichtung des magnetischen bzw. elektrischen Vektors der einfallenden Strahlung geführt ist. ϑ ist der Winkel gegen die Achse. Beide Figuren zeigen Unterschiede, die als Polarisationseffekte zu verstehen sind. DieUnterschiede sind jedoch klein und verschwinden bei verkleinertem Maßstab (vgl. die für beliebiges Azimut des Achsenschnittes gültige mittlere Figur) völlig. Der geringfügige Einfluß der Polarisation ist ein Hinweis darauf, daß bei $\varepsilon = 10$ die Wellenlänge bereits als klein im Sinne der Beugungstheorie anzusehen ist. Damit steht im Einklang, daß die mittlere Figur ziemlich gut durch die vektoriell verallgemeinerte Kirchhoffsche Theorie (vgl. Ziff. 31) wiedergegeben wird, die insbesondere den richtigen Zahlenwert 12,5 des Intensitätsmaximums liefert. (Man vgl. auch die entsprechende Strahlungscharakteristik der Kugel, Ziff. 153.)

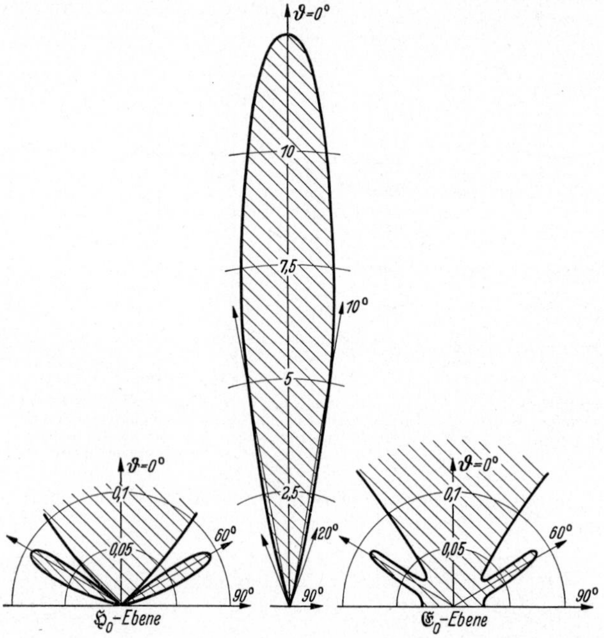

Fig. 82. Strahlungscharakteristik des Poyntingschen Vektors (links Schnitt in der $\mathfrak{H}_0$-Ebene, rechts in der $\mathfrak{E}_0$-Ebene) bei der elektromagnetischen Streuung an der Kreisscheibe für $\varepsilon = 10$ (nach Andrejewski).

Die folgenden Abbildungen beziehen sich im Gegensatz zu den vorhergehenden auf die *gesamte Feldverteilung* (einfallende Welle + Streuwelle). Zunächst zeigt Fig. 83 ebenfalls für $\varepsilon = 10$ die (zeitlich gemittelte) magnetische Energiedichte auf der Kreisscheibe bezogen auf die (zeitlich gemittelte) magnetische Energiedichte der einfallenden Welle [also die Größe $(\mathfrak{H}\,\mathfrak{H}^*)/(\mathfrak{H}_0\,\mathfrak{H}_0^*)$], im folgenden kurz relative $\mathfrak{H}$-Intensität genannt. In der Mitte der Figur sind die Niveaulinien gleicher Intensität eingezeichnet, links für die Licht-, rechts für die Schattenseite des Schirmes. Die Halbkreise sind symmetrisch zur vollen Kreisscheibe ergänzt zu denken. Der elektrische Vektor der einfallenden Strahlung schwingt horizontal. Darüber und daneben ist der Verlauf der relativen $\mathfrak{H}$-Intensität längs des horizontalen und des vertikalen Scheibendurchmessers aufgetragen. Die Ordinatenmaßstäbe für Vorder- und Rückseite unterscheiden sich um den Faktor 10. In Fig. 84 ist entsprechend die relative $\mathfrak{E}$-Intensität innerhalb der *Öffnung* einer *Kreisblende* dargestellt. Der elektrische Vektor der einfallenden Welle schwingt hier vertikal. Oben und links ist neben der theoretischen $(\varepsilon = 10)$

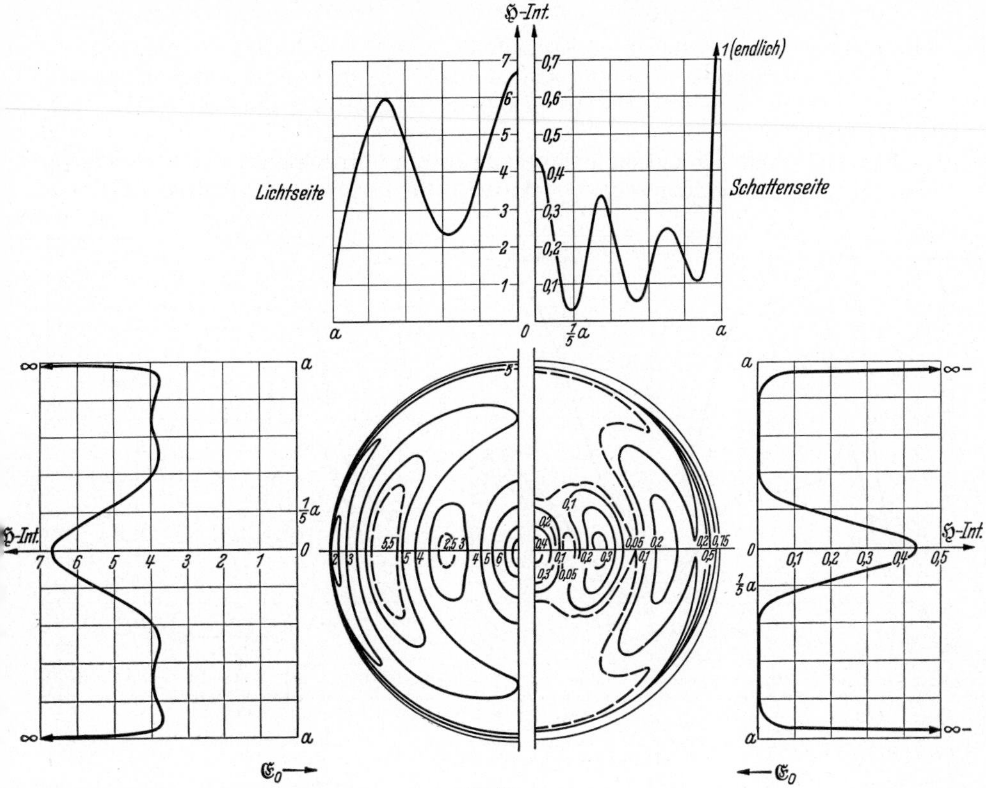

Fig. 83.

Fig. 83. Zeitlich gemittelte magnetische Energiedichte für die Beugung an der Kreisscheibe (ℌ-Intensität) für $\varepsilon = 10$; links auf der Lichtseite, rechts auf der Schattenseite (nach ANDREJEWSKI).

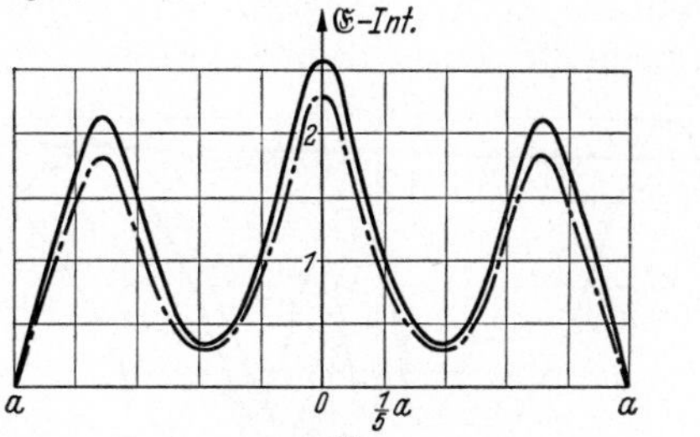

Fig. 84. Zeitlich gemittelte elektrische Energiedichte in der Öffnung einer Kreisblende (𝔈-Intensität) für $\varepsilon = 10$; die —·—·—-Kurven beziehen sich auf gemessene Werte von ANDREWS (nach ANDREJEWSKI).

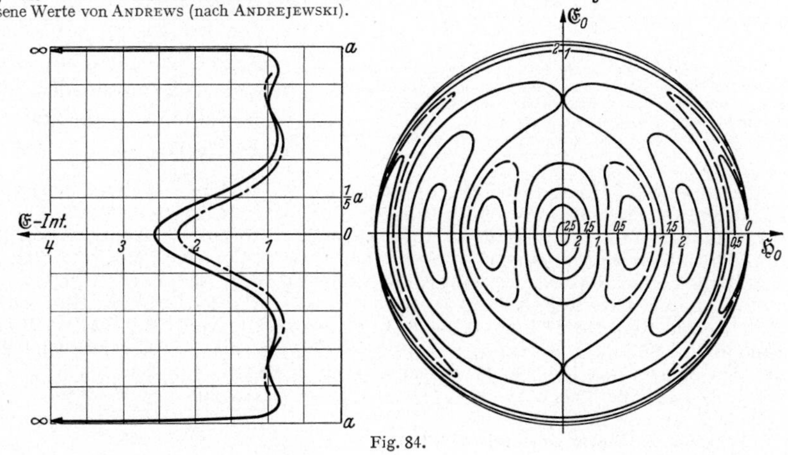

Fig. 84.

eine für $\varepsilon = 9{,}42$ gewonnene experimentelle Kurve von Andrews[1] eingetragen. Die Übereinstimmung ist ausgezeichnet. Die Fig. 83 und 84 zeigen unter anderem, daß die Intensität an der Kante im allgemeinen unendlich wird [vgl. Gl. (23.3b)].

Fig. 85 bezieht sich auf die Feldverhältnisse im Mittelpunkt der Kreisscheibe bzw. -öffnung. Aufgetragen ist die relative $\mathfrak{H}$- (für Licht- und Schattenseite) bzw.

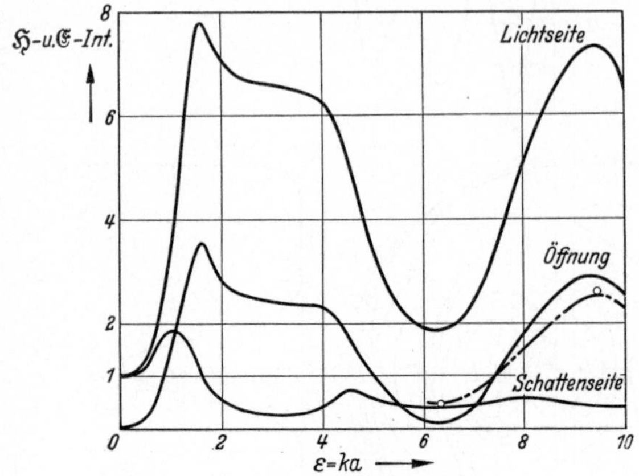

Fig. 85.

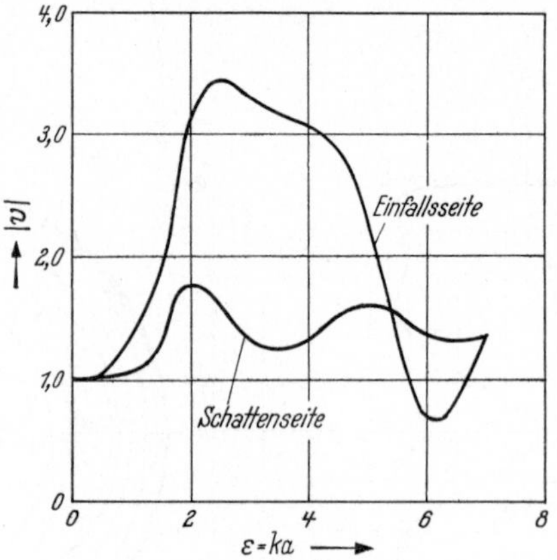

Fig. 86.

Fig. 85. Zeitlich gemittelte elektrische Energiedichte im Mittelpunkt der Öffnung einer Kreisblende und magnetische Energiedichte im Mittelpunkt einer Kreisscheibe auf deren Licht- und Schattenseite als Funktion von ε; —·—·— nach Messungen von Severin, o o Meßpunkte von Andrews (nach Andrejewski).

Fig. 86. Feldintensität im Mittelpunkt einer Kreisscheibe auf der Einfalls- und Schattenseite als Funktion von ε (Randbedingung $\partial v/\partial z = 0$, nach Meixner und Fritze).

$\mathfrak{E}$-Intensität in Abhängigkeit von ε, ferner zum Vergleich mit letzterer eine experimentelle Kurve von Severin[2]. Die geringen Abweichungen der experimentellen von der theoretischen Kurve lassen sich verstehen, wenn man annimmt, daß die im Experiment benutzte Strahlung nicht vollständig polarisiert war. Der allgemeine Verlauf der Kurven ist ziemlich unübersichtlich. Charakteristisch ist das Minimum zweier Kurven bei $\varepsilon = 2\pi$ entsprechend $\lambda = a$, das sich auch im entsprechenden Diagramm des akustischen Problems wiederfindet [vgl. Fig. 86, in der die Intensität $|v|$

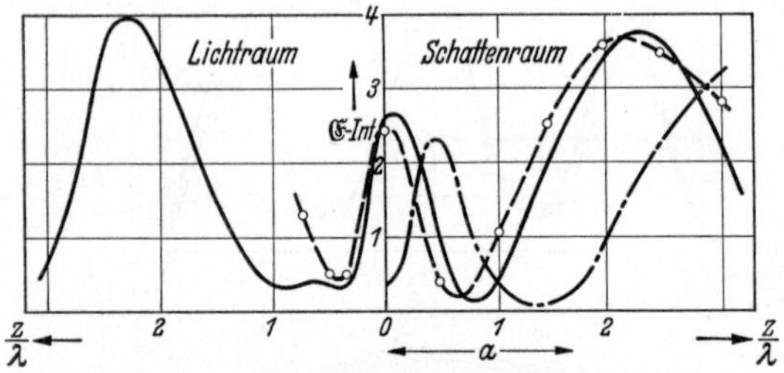

Fig. 87. Zeitlich gemittelte elektrische Energiedichte auf der Achse der kreisförmigen Öffnung als Funktion des Abstands z vom Kreismittelpunkt; links vor dem Schirm, rechts hinter dem Schirm: — theoretisch (nach Andrejewski) für $\varepsilon = 10$; —o—o experimentell (nach Andrews) für $\varepsilon = 3\pi$; —·—·— experimentell (nach Severin) für $\varepsilon = 4\pi$.

[1] C. L. Andrews: J. Appl. Phys. **21**, 761 (1950); **22**, 520 (1950). — Weitere Meßergebnisse bei C. L. Andrews: Phys. Rev. **69**, 684 (1946); **71**, 777 (1947); **74**, 1231 (1948); **78**, 344 (1950). Amer. J. Phys. **19**, 280 (1951). — R. E. Houston u. R. N. Noble: J. Appl. Phys. **22**, 1295 (1951). — Phys. Rev. **85**, 732 (1952). — G. Bekefi u. G. A. Woonton: McGrill Univ. Eaton Elec. Res. Lab. Techn. Rep. No. 241 (1952). — S. Silver, M. J. Ehrlich u. G. Held: Univ. of California, Anten. Lab. Rep. No. 185 (1952). — C. Huang u. R. D. Kodis: Harvard Univ. Cruft Lab. Techn. Rep. No. 165 (1953). — H. L. Robinson: J. Appl. Phys. **24**, 35 (1953). — M. J. Ehrlich, S. Silver u. G. Held: J. Appl. Phys. **26**, 336 (1955). — Entsprechende Ergebnisse für den akustischen Fall bei H. Primakoff, M. J. Klein, J. B. Keller u. E. L. Carstensen: J. Acoust. Soc. Amer. **19**, 132, 515 (1947). — H. Severin u. C. Starke: Acustica, Akust. Beih. **2**, 59 (1952).

[2] H. Severin: Z. Naturforsch. **1**, 487 (1946).

im Mittelpunkt der Kreisscheibe aufgetragen ist; und zwar für ein skalares Wellenfeld, das auf der Scheibe der Randbedingung $\partial v/\partial z = 0$ genügt[1] (Primärfeld $\exp ikz$)]. Fig. 87 gibt die relative $\mathfrak{E}$-Intensität auf der Achse beiderseits der Kreisöffnung wieder. Neben der für $\varepsilon = 10$ berechneten sind zwei experimentelle Kurven für $\varepsilon = 3\pi$, 4π eingezeichnet.

Die letzte Abbildung soll den Einfluß der *Kantenbedingung* auf die Lösung des Beugungsproblems veranschaulichen. In Fig. 88 ist die relative $\mathfrak{E}$-Intensität auf einem Durchmesser der Kreis*öffnung* eingezeichnet und zwar, um Polarisationseffekte auszuschließen, für zirkular polarisierte auftreffende Strahlung. Weiter ist die Intensität $|v|$ des analogen akustischen Problems eingetragen (Randbedingung $v = 0$ auf dem Schirm $\varrho \geqq a$), die sich der ersten Kurve gut anschmiegt. Schließlich ist die von Möglich[2] vor Aufstellung der Kantenbedingung durchgeführte dieser Bedingung *widersprechende* Behandlung des elektromagnetischen Beugungsproblems zum Vergleich herangezogen. Der stark abweichende Verlauf dieser letzteren Kurve zeigt, daß die Kantenbedingung das Beugungsfeld nicht nur in unmittelbarer Nähe der Kante, wie man vielleicht vermuten könnte, sondern ganz allgemein beeinflußt.

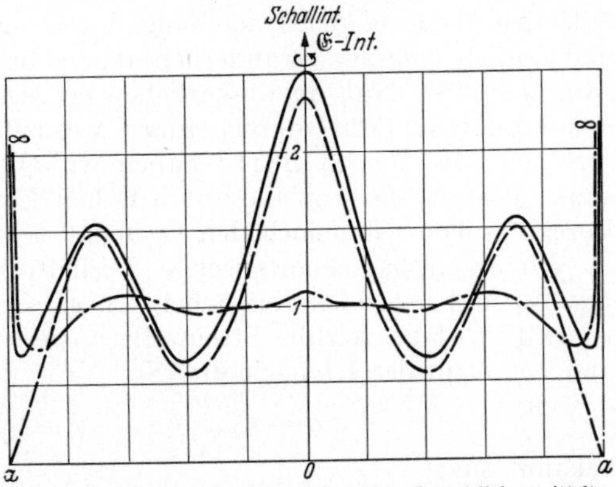

Fig. 88. Schnitt durch das Intensitätsgebirge der zeitlich gemittelten elektrischen Energiedichte in der kreisförmigen Öffnung bei zirkular polarisierter einfallender Welle: —— nach der strengen Theorie; —·—·— nach Möglich; — — akustisch (für $\varepsilon = 10$).

129. Verallgemeinerungen. Das in Ziff. 127 dargestellte Lösungsverfahren läßt sich ungeändert auf alle Fälle übertragen, in denen die einfallende elektromagnetische Strahlung durch einen parallel zur Kreisscheibe schwingenden Hertzschen Vektor darstellbar ist. Durch Verallgemeinerung des Verfahrens unter Hinzunahme einer dritten Komponente $\mathfrak{Z}_z$ des Hertzschen Vektors ist auch der allgemeine Fall einer willkürlich vorgegebenen einfallenden Welle der Behandlung zugänglich. Auf Grund des Babinetschen Prinzips (vgl. Ziff. 27) beherrscht man mit der Streuung an der Kreisscheibe gleichzeitig das komplementäre Problem, die Beugung an der Kreisblende. Besondere Fälle sind die einer punktförmigen Lichtquelle im Endlichen, repräsentiert durch einen elektrischen oder magnetischen Dipol.

Durch Differentiation nach den kartesischen Koordinaten der Strahlungsquelle gelangt man von hier aus weiter zu den Lösungen für strahlende Multipole. Meixner[3] behandelt den beliebig orientierten elektrischen Dipol für die Kreisscheibe, womit gleichzeitig der Fall des magnetischen Dipols für die Kreisblende erledigt ist. Die elektromagnetische Beugung am *Ellipsoid* ist im Gegensatz zum entsprechenden akustischen Problem (vgl. Ziff. 126) bisher noch nicht allgemein gelöst. Die Schwierigkeit liegt in der Separation der Feldvariablen

---

[1] Nach J. Meixner u. U. Fritze: Z. ang. Phys. **1**, 535 (1949).

[2] F. Möglich: Ann. Phys. **83**, 609 (1927).

[3] J. Meixner: Ann. Phys. **12**, 227 (1953). Vgl. auch J. Bardeen: Phys. Rev. **36**, 1482 (1930). — A. Leitner: N.Y. Univ. Res. Rep. No. EM-19 (1950). — A. Leitner u. R.D. Spence: J. Appl. Phys. **21**, 1001 (1950). — J.E. Storrer: J. Appl. Phys. **22**, 1058 (1951); **23**, 588 (1952).

(vgl. Ziff. 5). Für den speziellen Fall eines solenoidalen einfallenden Feldes, bei dem die eine der beiden Feldgrößen $\mathfrak{E}$ und $\mathfrak{H}$ keine azimutale Komponente, die andere nur eine solche besitzt, hat Meixner die Lösung angegeben (vgl. auch Ziff. 153). Für *elliptische* Öffnungen oder Schirme liegen bisher nur Ansätze für die Lösung des Randwertproblems vor[1].

c2) Näherung für große Wellenlängen.

130. Der Rayleighsche Grenzfall. Besonders einfache Verhältnisse liegen vor, wenn die Wellenlänge λ der einfallenden Strahlung groß ist gegenüber dem Radius a der beugenden Kreisscheibe ($ka=\varepsilon\ll 1$). Dann kann das Feld der einfallenden Welle in der Umgebung des Beugungsobjekts als räumlich konstant und zeitlich langsam veränderlich angesehen werden. Die Berechnung des Beugungsfeldes ist dann im wesentlichen ein statisches Problem. Sie wurde bereits von Lord Rayleigh[2] durchgeführt, weshalb wir vom Rayleighschen Grenzfall sprechen. In Abschn. AIII f haben wir ein konsequentes Näherungsverfahren kennengelernt, das von dieser statischen Lösung als nullter Näherung ausgeht. Vorerst wollen wir jedoch den Grenzfall selbst ins Auge fassen.

Wir legen die geometrischen Verhältnisse des Abschn. c1 zugrunde (vgl. Fig. 79) und betrachten zunächst den *akustischen Fall*. Nach den Ausführungen von Ziff. 10 läßt sich die Streuwelle v_S berechnen, wenn die *Sprungwerte* von v und $\partial v/\partial z$ auf der Kreisscheibe (S)

$$\varphi = v_+ - v_-, \qquad \psi = \left(\frac{\partial v}{\partial z}\right)_+ - \left(\frac{\partial v}{\partial z}\right)_- \tag{130.1}$$

bekannt sind:

$$v_S = \int\limits_S \left(\varphi \frac{\partial G}{\partial z'} - \psi G\right) d\sigma', \qquad G = \frac{1}{4\pi}\,\frac{e^{ikR}}{R}, \qquad R = |\mathfrak{r}-\hat{\mathfrak{r}}'|. \tag{130.2}$$

Betrachten wir, wie früher, die beiden Randbedingungen

$$(p)\quad v=0, \qquad (s)\quad \frac{\partial v}{\partial z}=0 \quad \text{auf } (S), \tag{130.3}$$

so vereinfacht sich (130.2) zu

$$(p)\quad v_S = -\int\limits_S \psi\, G\, d\sigma', \qquad (s)\quad v_S = \int\limits_S \varphi \frac{\partial G}{\partial z'}\, d\sigma'. \tag{130.4}$$

Für Aufpunkte $\mathfrak{r}=(r,\vartheta,\varphi)$ in weitem Abstand von (S) kann G bzw. $\partial G/\partial z'$ wegen $\varepsilon\ll 1$ auf (S) als konstant angesehen und unter Vernachlässigung von $\mathfrak{r}'$ gegenüber $\mathfrak{r}$ vor das Integral gezogen werden:

$$\left.\begin{aligned} &(p)\quad v_S \to -\frac{1}{4\pi}\cdot\frac{e^{ikr}}{r}\int\limits_S \psi\, d\sigma \\ &(s)\quad v_S \to -\frac{ik\cos\vartheta}{4\pi}\cdot\frac{e^{ikr}}{r}\int\limits_S \varphi\, d\sigma \end{aligned}\right\}\ \textit{für } r\to\infty. \tag{130.5}$$

---

[1] M. Kotani: Proc. Phys.-math. Soc. Japan **15**, 30 (1933). — A. Storruste: Kgl. Norske Vid. Selsk. Forh. **21**, 84, 88 (1948). — A. Storruste u. H. Wergeland: Kgl. Norske Vid. Selsk. Forh. **21**, 38 (1948). — R.D. Spence: J. Acoust. Soc. Amer. **21**, 98 (1949). — C. Huang: Harvard Univ. Cruft Lab. Techn. Rep. No. 163, 164 (1953). — J.B. Keller: J. Appl. Phys. **28**, 426 (1957). — J.B. Keller, R.M. Lewis u. B.D. Seckler: J. Appl. Phys. **28**, 570 (1957). — H. Levine u. T.T. Wu: Stanford Univ. Appl. Math. and Stat. Lab. Techn. Rep. No. 71 (1957). — Meßergebnisse bei C. Huang u. R.D. Kodis: Harvard Univ. Cruft Lab. Techn. Rep. No. 165 (1953).

[2] Lord Rayleigh: Phil. Mag. **43**, 259; **44**, 28 (1897). — Sci. Papers **4**, 283, 305 (1903). Die Arbeiten umfassen den akustischen und den elektromagnetischen Fall.

Es verbleibt die Berechnung der Sprungwerte ψ bzw. φ. Wir beschränken uns auf den Fall senkrecht einfallender Strahlung und haben dann für die einfallende Welle entsprechend Gl. (125.12)

$$v_0 = e^{ikz}. \tag{130.6}$$

Die gesuchte Lösung v des Streuproblems weicht nur in der Umgebung der Kreisscheibe (S) wesentlich von v_0 ab. Hier dürfen wir wegen $a \ll \lambda$ (λ = Wellenlänge) statt (130.6) einfach

$$v_0 = 1 \tag{130.7}$$

setzen und die Wellengleichung durch die Potentialgleichung

$$\Delta v = 0 \tag{130.8}$$

ersetzen. Im Falle der Randbedingung (p) haben wir nunmehr eine Lösung von (130.8) aufzusuchen, die auf der Kreisscheibe den Wert 0 und asymptotisch den Wert $v_0 = 1$ annimmt. Das ist eine einfache Aufgabe der Potentialtheorie. Wir lösen sie auf direktem Wege in elliptischen Koordinaten. Dann lautet Gl. (130.8) [d. i. Gl. (125.4) mit $\varepsilon = 0$]

$$\frac{\partial}{\partial\xi}\left[(1+\xi^2)\frac{\partial v}{\partial\xi}\right] + \frac{\partial}{\partial\eta}\left[(1-\eta^2)\frac{\partial v}{\partial\eta}\right] + \left(\frac{1}{1-\eta^2} - \frac{1}{1+\xi^2}\right)\frac{\partial^2 v}{\partial\varphi^2} = 0. \tag{130.9}$$

Sie ist zu lösen mit den Randbedingungen

$$v = 0 \quad \text{für } \xi = 0, \qquad v \to 1 \quad \text{für } \xi \to \infty. \tag{130.10}$$

v hänge nur von ξ ab. Dann geht (130.9) in eine gewöhnliche Differentialgleichung über. Die gesuchte Lösung ist

$$v = \frac{2}{\pi} \operatorname{arc\,tan} \xi. \tag{130.11}$$

Hieraus ergibt sich nach (130.1) mit Rücksicht auf die Symmetrieverhältnisse

$$\psi = 2\left(\frac{\partial v}{\partial z}\right)_+ = \frac{2}{a|\eta|}\left.\frac{\partial v}{\partial\xi}\right|_{\xi=0} = \frac{4}{a\pi|\eta|}. \tag{130.12}$$

Im Falle der Randbedingung (s) ergänzen wir (130.7) durch ein weiteres Glied:

$$v_0 = 1 + ikz. \tag{130.13}$$

Das Geschwindigkeitspotential (130.13) beschreibt eine homogene Strömung längs der z-Achse. Die zu behandelnde Potentialaufgabe ist jetzt die Umströmung der senkrecht zur z-Achse gestellten Kreisplatte. In elliptischen Koordinaten formuliert: (130.9) ist mit den Randbedingungen

$$\frac{\partial v}{\partial\xi} = 0 \quad \text{für } \xi = 0, \quad v \to 1 + ika \cdot \xi\eta \quad \text{für } \xi \to \infty \tag{130.14}$$

zu lösen. Mit dem Ansatz

$$v = 1 + f(\xi)\,\eta \tag{130.15}$$

erhält man

$$v = 1 + \frac{2i\varepsilon}{\pi}(1 + \xi \operatorname{arc\,tan} \xi)\,\eta \tag{130.16}$$

und hieraus nach (130.1)

$$\varphi = v_+ - v_- = \frac{4i\varepsilon}{\pi}|\eta|. \tag{130.17}$$

Wir berechnen das asymptotische Verhalten der Streuwellen nach Gl. (130.5). Mit $a\,|\eta| = \sqrt{a^2 - \varrho^2}$ (ϱ = radialer Abstand vom Scheibenmittelpunkt) erhält man zunächst

$$\int \psi\, d\sigma = 8a, \quad \int \varphi\, d\sigma = \frac{8ika^3}{3}. \tag{130.18}$$

Hieraus folgt für die Streuwelle

$$(p)\quad v_S \to -\frac{2\varepsilon}{\pi}\,\frac{e^{ikr}}{kr} \quad \text{bzw.} \quad (s)\quad v_S \to \frac{2\varepsilon^3 \cos\vartheta}{3\pi}\,\frac{e^{ikr}}{kr} \tag{130.19}$$

und nach Bildung des Absolutquadrats und Integration über die Kugelfläche für die *gesamte Streuintensität*

$$(p)\quad J_S = \frac{16a^2}{\pi} \quad \text{bzw.} \quad (s)\quad J_S = \frac{16\varepsilon^4 a^2}{27\pi}. \tag{130.20}$$

Die auf die Scheibe auffallende Intensität ist

$$J_0 = a^2 \pi. \tag{130.21}$$

Somit ergibt sich für den *Streukoeffizienten* $\sigma = \frac{J_S}{J_0}$

$$(p)\quad \sigma_p = \frac{16}{\pi^2} \quad \text{bzw.} \quad (s)\quad \sigma_s = \frac{16}{27\pi^2}\,\varepsilon^4. \tag{130.22}$$

Im Falle (p) ist σ unabhängig von λ und nur wenig kleiner als der Grenzwert der „geometrischen Akustik" (kleine λ) $\sigma = 2$ (vgl. Abschn. c1, Ziff. 128). Im Falle (s) ist σ proportional zu $(a/\lambda)^4$ und wird mit wachsender Wellenlänge beliebig klein. Auf Grund des Babinetschen Prinzips liefert (130.22) gleichzeitig den Transmissionskoeffizienten $\tau = \sigma/2$ für die Kreisblende. Dabei ist die Zuordnung der beiden Ausdrücke (130.22) zu den auf dem Schirm gültigen Randbedingungen (130.3) gegenüber dem Falle der Scheibe zu vertauschen.

Wir gehen zum *elektromagnetischen Problem* über. Der elektrische Vektor der senkrecht einfallenden Lichtwelle schwinge in x-Richtung, so daß gilt

$$\mathfrak{E}_x^0 = \varkappa\, \mathfrak{H}_y^0 = e^{ikz}. \tag{130.23}$$

In unserem Grenzfall großer Wellenlänge können die beiden Felder $\mathfrak{E}_0$, $\mathfrak{H}_0$ in der Umgebung der Kreisscheibe als homogen und statisch angesehen werden mit dem Wert:

$$\mathfrak{E}_x^0 = \varkappa\, \mathfrak{H}_y^0 = 1. \tag{130.24}$$

Von beiden wird nur das elektrische Feld durch die Anwesenheit des Leiters gestört. Die Untersuchung dieses Einflusses stellt wieder eine einfache Potentialaufgabe dar. Das elektrische Feld (130.24) wird durch das elektrische Potential

$$v_0 = -x = -a\sqrt{(1+\xi^2)(1-\eta^2)}\cos\varphi \tag{130.25}$$

beschrieben. Wir suchen ein neues Potential v, das für $\xi \to \infty$ in v_0 übergeht und [wegen v = const auf (S)] für $\xi = 0$ verschwindet. Mit dem Ansatz

$$v = f(\xi)\sqrt{1-\eta^2}\cos\varphi \tag{130.26}$$

folgt aus (130.9) die gewöhnliche Differentialgleichung

$$(1+\xi^2)\,[(1+\xi^2)\,f']' - (1+2\xi^2)\,f = 0 \tag{130.27}$$

mit der gesuchten Lösung

$$f(\xi) = -\frac{2a}{\pi}\left(\frac{\xi}{\sqrt{1+\xi^2}} + \sqrt{1+\xi^2}\,\operatorname{arc\,tan}\xi\right), \tag{130.28}$$

die sich für kleine ξ wie $-\frac{4a\xi}{\pi}$ verhält. Entsprechend Gl. (130.12) erhält man weiter für die Flächenladung $\hat{\omega}$ auf dem Schirm

$$\frac{\hat{\omega}}{\varepsilon_0} = \mathfrak{E}_z^+ - \mathfrak{E}_z^- = -2\left(\frac{\partial v}{\partial z}\right)_+ = -\frac{2}{a|\eta|}\frac{\partial v}{\partial \xi}\bigg|_{\xi=0} = \frac{8}{\pi|\eta|}\sqrt{1-\eta^2}\cos\varphi \tag{130.29}$$

oder in ebenen Polarkoordinaten ϱ, φ

$$\frac{\hat{\omega}}{\varepsilon_0} = \frac{8}{\pi}\frac{\varrho\cos\varphi}{\sqrt{a^2-\varrho^2}}. \tag{130.30}$$

Aus Gl. (130.30) läßt sich das Streufeld in weitem Abstand berechnen. Der Ladungsverteilung $\hat{\omega}$ entspricht das elektrische Moment

$$|\mathfrak{p}| = \int \hat{\omega}\, x\, d\sigma = \varepsilon_0 \frac{16}{3} a^3, \qquad \mathfrak{p} = \varepsilon_0 \frac{16}{3} a^3 \mathfrak{E}_0. \tag{130.31}$$

Das asymptotische Feld am Ort r, ϑ, φ ergibt sich als Feld eines schwingenden *elektrischen Dipols* zu

$$|\mathfrak{E}_S| = \varkappa|\mathfrak{H}_S| \to \frac{k^3}{4\pi\varepsilon_0}|\mathfrak{p}|\sqrt{1-\sin^2\vartheta\cos^2\varphi}\cdot\frac{e^{ikr}}{kr}. \tag{130.32}$$

Hieraus folgt weiter analog dem Übergang von Gl. (130.19) zu Gl. (130.22) die *gesamte Streuintensität* (zeitlicher Mittelwert des Energiestromes, vgl. Ziff. 16):

$$2\varkappa J_S = \frac{k^4}{6\pi\varepsilon_0^2}\mathfrak{p}^2 = \frac{128}{27\pi}k^4 a^6 \tag{130.33}$$

und der *Streukoeffizient* (die auf die Scheibe auffallende Primär-Intensität ist hier $2\varkappa J_0 = \pi a^2$):

$$\sigma = \frac{128}{27\pi^2}\varepsilon^4, \tag{130.34}$$

letzterer in Übereinstimmung mit dem ersten Glied von Gl. (128.1).

131. Näherungsverfahren im akustischen Fall. Wir beschränken uns auch weiterhin auf den Fall senkrecht auftreffender Strahlung und legen die Randbedingung (s) (schallharte Kreisplatte) von Gl. (130.3) zugrunde. Die Grundlage unserer Betrachtungen ist die in Abschn. AIII a1 diskutierte Integralgleichung des Streuproblems, die von verschiedenen Seiten auf das Problem der Kreisscheibe angewandt worden ist. Wir knüpfen an eine Arbeit von BOUWKAMP[1] an und erwähnen frühere Arbeiten von KING, SOMMERFELD u. a.[2]. Wir gewinnen die Integralgleichung aus Gl. (130.4), Fall s, indem wir statt nach z' (Integrationspunkt) unter Vorzeichenwechsel nach z (Aufpunkt) differenzieren und die Randbedingung $\frac{\partial v_S}{\partial z} = -\frac{\partial v_0}{\partial z}$ auf (S) fordern (vgl. Ziff. 50):

$$\lim_{z\to 0}\frac{\partial^2}{\partial z^2}\int_S \varphi G\, d\sigma' = ik \quad \textit{auf } (S). \tag{131.1}$$

[1] C. J. BOUWKAMP: Phys. Rev. **75**, 1608 (1949). — Physica, Haag **16**, 1 (1950). Andere Näherungsverfahren für kleine ka bei R.W. HART u. E.W. MONTROLL: J. Appl. Phys. **2**, 1275 (1951). — T. ANDERS: Z. Physik **135**, 219 (1953). — Y. NOMURA u. S. KATSURA: J. Phys. Soc. Japan **10**, 385 (1955). — A. LEITNER u. C.P. WELLS: Michigan State Univ. Dept. Math. and Phys. Inter. Techn. Rep. No. 1 (1955). — D.S. JONES: Comm. Pure Appl. Math. **9**, 713 (1956). — J. BAZER u. A. BROWN: N.Y. Univ. Res. Rep. No. EM-144 (1959).

[2] L.V. KING: Proc. Roy. Soc. Lond. A **153**, 1 (1936). — A. SOMMERFELD: Ann. Physik **42**, 389 (1942); **2**, 85 (1948). — H. BRAUMANN: Z. Naturforsch. **3**a, 340 (1948). — Für schräg einfallende ebene Wellen vgl. J.W. MILES: Acoustica **2**, 287 (1952). — J. Acoust. Soc. Amer. **24**, 324 (1952).

Zur sukzessiven Lösung (vgl. Ziff. 91) entwickeln wir φ und G nach Potenzen von k, indem wir setzen

$$\varphi = i k \{\varphi_0 + \varphi_1 i k + \varphi_2 (i k)^2 + \cdots\} \tag{131.2}$$

$$G = \frac{1}{4\pi}\left\{\frac{1}{R} + i k + \frac{R}{2}(i k)^2 + \cdots\right\}. \tag{131.3}$$

Hiermit zerfällt Gl. (131.1) in das Gleichungssystem

$$\lim_{z\to 0} \frac{\partial^2}{\partial z^2} \int_S \varphi_0 \cdot \frac{1}{R}\, d\sigma' = 4\pi \tag{131.4}$$

$$\lim_{z\to 0} \frac{\partial^2}{\partial z^2} \int_S \left(\varphi_1 \cdot \frac{1}{R} + \varphi_0\right) d\sigma' = 0 \tag{131.5}$$

$$\lim_{z\to 0} \frac{\partial^2}{\partial z^2} \int_S \left(\varphi_2 \cdot \frac{1}{R} + \varphi_1 + \varphi_0 \frac{R}{2}\right) d\sigma' = 0 \tag{131.6}$$

. . . .

Die zweiten Summanden der Integrale in (131.5) und (131.6) sind von den Koordinaten des Aufpunktes unabhängig, fallen daher bei der Ableitung nach z weg. Im dritten Glied von (131.6) kann die Differentiation unter dem Integral ausgeführt werden. Die ersten Glieder der drei hingeschriebenen Integrale sind Lösungen der Potentialgleichung. Diese lautet in Zylinderkoordinaten ϱ, φ, z mit Rücksicht auf die Zylindersymmetrie unter Verwendung der Abkürzung $D = \frac{1}{\varrho}\frac{\partial}{\partial \varrho}\left(\varrho \frac{\partial}{\partial \varrho}\right)$

$$\Delta v = D v + \frac{\partial^2 v}{\partial z^2} = 0. \tag{131.7}$$

Bei diesen Gliedern kann daher $\partial^2/\partial z^2$ durch $-D$ ersetzt werden. Nach diesen Umformungen kann der Grenzübergang $z \to 0$ ausgeführt werden. Das Gleichungssystem lautet nunmehr $\left(\hat{R} = \sqrt{(x - x')^2 + (z - z')^2}\right)$:

$$D \int_S \varphi_0 \cdot \frac{1}{\hat{R}}\, d\sigma' = -4\pi \tag{131.8}$$

$$D \int_S \varphi_1 \cdot \frac{1}{\hat{R}}\, d\sigma' = 0 \tag{131.9}$$

$$D \int_S \varphi_2 \cdot \frac{1}{\hat{R}}\, d\sigma' = \frac{1}{2} \int_S \varphi_0 \cdot \frac{1}{\hat{R}}\, d\sigma'. \tag{131.10}$$

Aufpunkt und Integrationspunkt liegen auf der Kreisscheibe (S).

Bei der sukzessiven Lösung der Integrodifferentialgleichungen sind die rechten Seiten jeweils bekannt. Die linken Seiten enthalten die unbekannte Funktion und sind alle von gleicher Bauart. Wir machen den Ansatz:

$$\varphi_n(\varrho) = \sum_{m=0}^{\infty} a_{nm} (a^2 - \varrho^2)^{m+\frac{1}{2}} \tag{131.11}$$

der — zusammen mit dem Umstand, daß φ_n aus Gründen des analytischen Verhaltens im Nullpunkt eine gerade Funktion von ϱ ist — dadurch nahegelegt wird, daß sich φ_n am Schirmrand $\varrho = a$ nach der Kantenbedingung (23.3), s-Fall, wie $(a - \varrho)^{\frac{1}{2}}$ verhalten muß.

Auf Grund des Ansatzes (131.11) werden die Integrale

$$J_m(\varrho) = \int_S (a^2 - \varrho'^2)^{m+\frac{1}{2}} \cdot \frac{1}{\hat{R}}\, d\sigma' \tag{131.12}$$

benötigt. Zur Ausrechnung führen wir ebene Polarkoordinaten $\hat{R}, \chi$ um den Aufpunkt $\hat{\mathfrak{r}}$ als Zentrum ein (vgl. Fig. 89, Integrationspunkt $\hat{\mathfrak{r}}'$). Mit $\varrho'^2 = \varrho^2 + \hat{R}^2 + 2\hat{R}\varrho\cos\chi$ und $d\sigma' = \hat{R}\, d\hat{R}\, d\chi$ wird dann

$$J_m(\varrho) = \int_0^{2\pi} d\chi \int_0^{R_{\max}} (a^2 - \varrho^2 - \hat{R}^2 - 2\hat{R}\varrho\cos\chi)^{m+\frac{1}{2}}\, d\hat{R}. \tag{131.13}$$

Hierin ist die obere Grenze $\hat{R} = \hat{R}_{\max}(\chi)$ durch das Verschwinden des Integranden, entsprechend $\varrho' = a$, festgelegt (vgl. Fig. 89). Spaltet man das Integral durch Auftrennung an der Stelle $\chi = \pi$ in zwei Teile und substituiert im zweiten $\chi - \pi = \chi'$, $\hat{R} = -\hat{R}'$, so erhält man nach Zusammenfassung beider Teile wieder dasselbe Integral (131.13) mit veränderten Integrationsgrenzen: χ variiert nur noch zwischen 0 und π, $\hat{R}$ durchläuft alle negativen und positiven Werte zwischen den beiden Verzweigungspunkten (Nullstellen) des Integranden. Das $\hat{R}$-Integral kann durch ein Schleifenintegral in der komplexen $\hat{R}$-Ebene ersetzt werden, das beide Verzweigungspunkte umschließt:

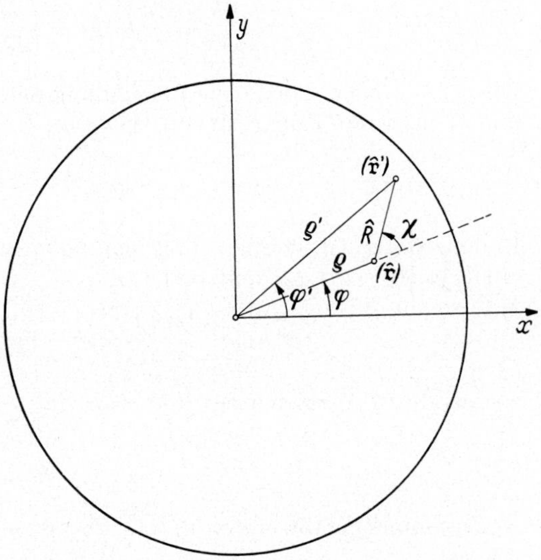

Fig. 89. Koordinaten bei der Kreisscheibe zur Auswertung des Integrals (131.13).

$$J_m(\varrho) = \tfrac{1}{2}\int_0^{\pi} d\chi \oint (a^2 - \varrho^2 - \hat{R}^2 - 2\hat{R}\varrho\cos\chi)^{m+\frac{1}{2}}\, d\hat{R}. \tag{131.14}$$

Die weitere Ausrechnung erfolgt durch Ausweitung der Integrationsschleife und Residuenbildung in $\hat{R} = \infty$.

Wir führen die Rechnung für die beiden Fälle $m = 0, 1$ durch. Für große $\hat{R}$ gilt:

$$(a^2 - \varrho^2 - \hat{R}^2 - 2\hat{R}\varrho\cos\chi)^{\frac{1}{2}} = i\left(\hat{R} + \varrho\cos\chi - \frac{a^2 - \varrho^2\sin^2\chi}{2\hat{R}} + \cdots\right), \tag{131.15}$$

$$(a^2 - \varrho^2 - \hat{R}^2 - 2\hat{R}\varrho\cos\chi)^{\frac{3}{2}} = -i\left(\hat{R}^3 + \cdots + \frac{3(a^2 - \varrho^2\sin^2\chi)^2}{8\hat{R}} + \cdots\right). \tag{131.16}$$

Residuenbildung und Ausführung der zweiten Integration liefert dann:

$$J_0(\varrho) = \frac{\pi}{2}\int_0^{\pi} (a^2 - \varrho^2\sin^2\chi)\, d\chi = \frac{\pi^2}{2}\left(a^2 - \frac{\varrho^2}{2}\right), \tag{131.17}$$

$$J_1(\varrho) = \frac{3\pi}{8}\int_0^{\pi} (a^2 - \varrho^2\sin^2\chi)^2\, d\chi = \frac{3\pi^2}{8}\left(a^4 - a^2\varrho^2 + \frac{3\varrho^4}{8}\right). \tag{131.18}$$

Zur Berechnung der linken Seiten von (131.8) bis (131.10) benötigen wir ferner die Ausdrücke

$$D J_0 = -\pi^2, \quad D J_1 = \frac{3\pi^2}{4}(-2a^2 + 3\varrho^2). \tag{131.19}$$

Nach diesen Vorbereitungen lassen sich die Integralgleichungen lösen. Aus Gl. (131.9) entnehmen wir zunächst $\varphi_1 = 0$. Die Gln. (131.8) und (131.10) schreiben sich mit (131.11) und (131.12):

$$\sum_{m=0}^{\infty} a_{0m} D J_m(\varrho) = -4\pi, \tag{131.20}$$

$$\sum_{m=0}^{\infty} a_{2m} D J_m(\varrho) = \tfrac{1}{2} \sum_{m=0}^{\infty} a_{0m} J_m(\varrho). \tag{131.21}$$

Die Gleichungen dienen zur Berechnung der a_{nm}. Aus der ersten Gleichung entnimmt man mit Rücksicht auf (131.19)

$$a_{00} = \frac{4}{\pi}, \quad a_{0m} = 0 \quad \textit{für } m \geqq 1. \tag{131.22}$$

In der zweiten Gleichung behält man links zwei Summanden bei. Sie lautet dann mit (131.19), (131.22) und (131.17):

$$-\pi^2 a_{20} + \frac{3\pi^2}{4}(-2a^2 + 3\varrho^2)\, a_{21} = \pi\left(a^2 - \frac{\varrho^2}{2}\right), \tag{131.23}$$

woraus durch Vergleich der Potenzen von ϱ folgt

$$a_{21} = -\frac{2}{9\pi}, \quad a_{20} = -\frac{2}{3\pi} a^2. \tag{131.24}$$

Zusammengefaßt lauten unsere Resultate:

$$\varphi_0 = \frac{4}{\pi}\sqrt{a^2 - \varrho^2}, \quad \varphi_1 = 0, \quad \varphi_2 = -\frac{2}{3\pi}\left\{a^2\sqrt{a^2 - \varrho^2} + \frac{1}{3}(a^2 - \varrho^2)^{\frac{3}{2}}\right\}. \tag{131.25}$$

Die nullte Näherung stimmt nach (131.2) mit unserer früheren Formel (130.17) überein. Bouwkamp hat die Rechnung bis zur siebten Näherung weitergeführt. Wir geben seine Ergebnisse in unserer Schreibweise an und benutzen dabei die Abkürzung $\sqrt{1 - \frac{\varrho^2}{a^2}} = x$:

$$\left.\begin{aligned}
\varphi_3 &= -\frac{8a^4}{9\pi^2}\, x, \qquad \varphi_4 = \frac{a^5}{30\pi}\left(x + 2x^3 + \frac{x^5}{5}\right)\\
\varphi_5 &= \frac{4a^6}{225\pi^2}\,(13x + 5x^3)\\
\varphi_6 &= -\frac{a^7}{1260\pi}\left[\left(1 - \frac{2240}{9\pi^2}\right)x + 5x^3 + 3x^5 + \frac{x^7}{7}\right]\\
\varphi_7 &= -\frac{a^8}{11025\pi^2}\,(323x + 266x^3 + 35x^5).
\end{aligned}\right\} \tag{131.26}$$

Bouwkamp verwendet bei seinen Rechnungen anstelle unseres Ansatzes (131.11) Reihen aus ungeraden Kugelfunktionen vom Argument x, was offenbar auf dasselbe herauskommt, aber bei Durchführung der Rechnung in hohen Näherungen Vorteile bietet. Da es uns hier mehr auf die prinzipielle Seite des Näherungsverfahrens ankommt, haben wir den mit den Kugelfunktionen verbundenen analytischen Apparat vermieden[1]. Bei der folgenden Diskussion beschränken wir uns auf die in Gl. (131.25) wiedergegebenen Näherungen.

In mathematischer Hinsicht bemerken wir noch, daß die homogene Integrodifferentialgleichung (131.9) die von Null verschiedene Lösung $\varphi_1 = \frac{1}{\sqrt{a^2-\varrho^2}}$ besitzt. Die Lösung der Gln. (131.8) bis (131.10) ist daher nicht eindeutig; erst die Hinzunahme der *Kantenbedingung*, die die Endlichkeit von v und φ am Rand fordert und der wir durch unseren Ansatz (131.11) Rechnung getragen haben, sorgt für Eindeutigkeit. Die Vieldeutigkeit der Gln. (131.8) bis (131.10) hängt damit zusammen, daß es sich nicht um reine Integralgleichungen, sondern um Integrodifferentialgleichungen handelt.

Als Anwendung der Theorie berechnen wir die Richtungsverteilung der abgebeugten Strahlung und den Streukoeffizienten in unserer jetzigen Näherung und verschärfen damit die Ergebnisse von Ziff. 130. Hierzu untersuchen wir die Streuwelle v_S in weitem Abstand vom Streuobjekt. Wir berechnen sie auf Grund von Gl. (130.4), s-Fall, für einen Aufpunkt mit den Kugelkoordinaten $r, \vartheta, 0$. Die ebenen Polarkoordinaten des Integrationspunktes seien ϱ', φ'. Dann gilt mit G nach Gl. (130.2) für $r \to \infty$

$$G \to \frac{1}{4\pi} \frac{e^{ik(r-\varrho' \sin\vartheta \cos\varphi')}}{r}, \qquad \frac{\partial G}{\partial z'} = -\frac{\partial G}{\partial z} \to -i k \cos\vartheta\, G \tag{131.27}$$

oder bei Entwicklung nach $k\varrho'$ und Mittelung über φ'

$$\overline{\frac{\partial G}{\partial z'}} \to -\frac{i k \cos\vartheta}{4\pi} \cdot \frac{e^{ikr}}{r} \left(1 - \frac{k^2 \varrho'^2}{4} \sin^2\vartheta + \cdots\right); \tag{131.28}$$

Die Auswertung des Integrals (130.4) liefert nunmehr mit (131.2), (131.25), (131.28) und $d\sigma' = 2\pi\varrho'\, d\varrho'$ die Streuwelle

$$v_S \to \frac{2\varepsilon^3 \cos\vartheta}{3\pi} \cdot \frac{e^{ikr}}{kr} \left\{1 + \frac{\varepsilon^2}{5}\left(1 - \frac{1}{2}\sin^2\vartheta\right)\right\}, \tag{131.29}$$

deren Amplitude in nullter Näherung mit Gl. (130.19), s-Fall, übereinstimmt. Entsprechend dem Übergang von (130.19) zu (130.22) können wir auch jetzt den Streukoeffizienten bilden und erhalten dann in unserer Näherung

$$\sigma_s = \frac{16}{27\pi^2} \varepsilon^4 \left(1 + \frac{8}{25}\varepsilon^2\right). \tag{131.30}$$

132. Näherungsverfahren im elektromagnetischen Falle. Wie beim akustischen Beugungsproblem treffe die einfallende Strahlung senkrecht auf den Schirm. Die geometrischen Verhältnisse und die Bezeichnungen der Koordinaten und Variablen seien die gleichen wie unter Ziff. 131.

Für die einfallende Welle gelte

$$\mathfrak{E}_x^0 = \varkappa\, \mathfrak{H}_y^0 = e^{ikz} \tag{132.1}$$

und dementsprechend auf der Kreisscheibe

$$\mathfrak{E}_0 = (1, 0, 0), \quad \varkappa\, \mathfrak{H}_0 = (0, 1, 0) \quad \textit{auf } (S). \tag{132.2}$$

Die gesuchte Streuwelle $\mathfrak{E}_S$, $\mathfrak{H}_S$ hat die Bedingung

$$(\mathfrak{E}_0 + \mathfrak{E}_S)_{\text{tang}} = 0 \quad \textit{auf } (S) \tag{132.3}$$

[1] Vgl. dazu auch C. J. Bouwkamp: Proc. Kon. Ned. Akad. Wet. Amsterdam **52**, 987 (1949).

zu erfüllen. Wir stellen sie durch einen Hertzschen Vektor $\mathfrak{Z}_S$ dar (vgl. Ziff. 53):

$$\mathfrak{E}_S = \operatorname{rot}\operatorname{rot}\mathfrak{Z}_S, \qquad \varkappa\,\mathfrak{H}_S = -\,i\,k\operatorname{rot}\mathfrak{Z}_S. \tag{132.4}$$

Da $\mathfrak{Z}_S$ der Wellengleichung genügt, können wir statt der ersten Gleichung auch schreiben

$$\mathfrak{E}_S = \operatorname{grad}\operatorname{div}\mathfrak{Z}_S + k^2\,\mathfrak{Z}_S. \tag{132.5}$$

Der Hertzsche Vektor ist im wesentlichen mit dem Vektorpotential identisch und läßt sich durch den Flächenstrom $\mathfrak{J} = [\mathfrak{n}, \mathfrak{H}_+ - \mathfrak{H}_-]$ auf dem Schirm in der Form ausdrücken:

$$\mathfrak{Z}_S = -\frac{\varkappa}{i\,k}\int\limits_S G\,\mathfrak{J}\,d\sigma'. \tag{132.6}$$

Nunmehr liefert die Randbedingung (132.3) mit (132.2), (132.5) und (132.6) die zweikomponentige Vektorgleichung (vgl. Ziff. 54):

$$(\widehat{\operatorname{grad}}\,\widehat{\operatorname{div}} + k^2)\int\limits_S G\,\mathfrak{J}\,d\sigma' = \frac{i\,k}{\varkappa}\,\hat{\mathfrak{E}}_0 = \frac{i\,k}{\varkappa}\,(1, 0) \qquad \textit{auf } (S). \tag{132.7}$$

Gl. (132.7) enthält keine Ableitungen nach z, sondern nur solche nach x und y. Wir dürfen daher schon vor Ausführung der Differentiationen $z = z' = 0$ setzen. Dementsprechend wollen wir auch im folgenden alle Differentialoperationen nicht als räumliche, sondern als ebene Operationen bezüglich der Variablen x, y bzw. x', y' allein ansehen und mit einem Dach (^) versehen (vgl. Abschn. A III a 2), sowie z bzw. z' bei allen Differentiationen festhalten, auch dann, wenn aus Konvergenzgründen vorübergehend $z \neq z'$ angenommen wird.

Die Integro-Differentialgleichung (132.7) für den Flächenstrom $\mathfrak{J}$ bildet den Ausgangspunkt unseres Näherungsverfahrens. Aus ihr folgt durch Rotationsbildung die weitere Gleichung

$$\widehat{\operatorname{rot}}\int\limits_S G\,\mathfrak{J}\,d\sigma' = 0 \qquad \textit{auf } (S). \tag{132.8}$$

Die Auflösung der Gleichungen ist gegenüber dem akustischen Problem dadurch erschwert, daß jetzt keine axiale Symmetrie vorliegt. Der Flächenstrom $\mathfrak{J}$ bzw. seine kartesischen Komponenten $\mathfrak{J}_x$, $\mathfrak{J}_y$ hängen daher nicht von ϱ allein, sondern auch vom Winkel φ ab (ϱ, φ ebene Polarkoordinaten). Bezüglich der φ-Abhängigkeit liegen die Verhältnisse besonders einfach, wenn wir statt des Stromes selbst seine *Quell-* und *Wirbeldichte*

$$q = \widehat{\operatorname{div}}\,\mathfrak{J}, \qquad \mathfrak{w} = \widehat{\operatorname{rot}}\,\mathfrak{J} \qquad (\mathfrak{w} = \mathfrak{n}\,w,\ \mathfrak{n}\ \text{Schirmnormale}) \tag{132.9}$$

als Unbekannte einführen. Bei diesen Größen läßt sich nämlich, wie wir im Laufe der Rechnung sehen werden, die Winkelabhängigkeit als Faktor abspalten:

$$q = f(\varrho)\cdot\cos\varphi, \qquad w = g(\varrho)\cdot\sin\varphi. \tag{132.9a}$$

Die Verwendung von q und w als Unbekannten anstelle $\mathfrak{J}_x$, $\mathfrak{J}_y$ erfordert allerdings noch eine Umformung der Gln. (132.7) und (132.8) sowie einige weitere Betrachtungen allgemeiner Art. Doch steht diesen Komplikationen eine erhebliche Vereinfachung bei der Auflösung der Integralgleichungen gegenüber.

Zur Umformung der Integralgleichungen benutzen wir die Beziehungen

$$\widehat{\operatorname{div}}\int\limits_S G\,\mathfrak{J}\,d\sigma' = \int\limits_S G\,q\,d\sigma', \qquad \widehat{\operatorname{rot}}\int\limits_S G\,\mathfrak{J}\,d\sigma' = \int\limits_S G\,\mathfrak{w}\,d\sigma'. \tag{132.10}$$

Sie folgen, wenn wir den Differentialoperator unter das Integral ziehen, dann statt nach x, y nach x', y' differenzieren und schließlich partiell integrieren. Nach der Kantenbedingung (23.4) wächst der kantenparallele Flächenstrom bei Annäherung an die Kante $\varrho \to a$ wie $(a-\varrho)^{-\frac{1}{2}}$ und infolgedessen die Wirbeldichte wie $(a-\varrho)^{-\frac{3}{2}}$ an. Das letzte Flächenintegral in Gl. (132.10) ist daher divergent; das gleiche gilt für das zugehörige, bei der partiellen Integration auftretende, in Gl. (132.10) jedoch weggelassene, Linienintegral längs des Schirmrandes. Man vermeidet die Divergenzschwierigkeiten, indem man die Flächenintegrale ähnlich wie in Gl. (131.14) als komplexe Schleifenintegrale auffaßt und bei der radialen Integration unter Hinzunahme eines Faktors $\frac{1}{2}$ den Weg in der komplexen ϱ'-Ebene von $\varrho'=0$ ausgehend um den Verzweigungspunkt $\varrho'=a$ herum wieder nach $\varrho'=0$ führt. Die partielle Integration läßt sich dann ohne Gefährdung der Konvergenz durchführen; das letzte Flächenintegral bleibt endlich, ein Linienintegral tritt nicht auf. Auch im folgenden wollen wir alle vorkommenden Flächenintegrale über den Schirm in entsprechendem Sinne verstehen und bedenkenlos partiell integrieren, ohne uns um Divergenzen und Linienintegrale am Schirmrand zu kümmern. Mit diesem Vorgehen machen wir sehr wesentliche Voraussetzungen über das Verhalten der Stromverteilung am Schirmrand, die aber tatsächlich erfüllt sind. Um auch den zweiten Summanden von Gl. (132.7) links durch q und w auszudrücken, führen wir die Funktion

$$F(\hat{R}) = \frac{1}{4\pi i k}\int_0^{\hat{R}} \frac{e^{ikr}-1}{r}\,dr, \qquad \hat{R} = \sqrt{(x-x')^2+(y-y')^2} \tag{132.11}$$

ein, die der Differentialgleichung

$$\hat{\Delta} F = \left(\frac{\partial^2}{\partial x^2}+\frac{\partial^2}{\partial y^2}\right)F = \frac{1}{\hat{R}}\frac{d}{d\hat{R}}\left(\hat{R}\frac{dF}{d\hat{R}}\right) = G(\hat{R}) \tag{132.11a}$$

genügt. Nunmehr können wir schreiben

$$\int_S G\,\mathfrak{J}\,d\sigma' = \hat{\Delta}\int_S F\,\mathfrak{J}\,d\sigma' = (\widehat{\operatorname{grad}}\,\widehat{\operatorname{div}} - \widehat{\operatorname{rot}}\,\widehat{\operatorname{rot}})\int_S F\,\mathfrak{J}\,d\sigma' \tag{132.11b}$$

und durch entsprechende Umformung wie in Gl. (132.10) entsteht

$$\int_S G\,\mathfrak{J}\,d\sigma' = \widehat{\operatorname{grad}}\int_S F\,q\,d\sigma' - \widehat{\operatorname{rot}}\int_S F\,\mathfrak{w}\,d\sigma'. \tag{132.11c}$$

Mit (132.10) und (132.11c) lauten die Integralgleichungen (132.7) und (132.8) nunmehr

$$\widehat{\operatorname{grad}}\int_S (G+k^2F)\,q\,d\sigma' - k^2\,\widehat{\operatorname{rot}}\int_S F\,\mathfrak{w}\,d\sigma' = \frac{ik}{\varkappa}(1,0) \tag{132.12a}$$

$$\int_S G\,w\,d\sigma' = 0. \tag{132.12b}$$

Die erste dieser Gleichungen dient zur Bestimmung von q, aus der zweiten gewinnt man w. Da die Integralgleichung (132.12b) homogen ist, legt sie w nur bis auf einen konstanten Faktor fest. Um diese Willkür zu beseitigen, betrachten wir die Beziehungen

$$\int_S q\,x\,d\sigma = -\int_S \mathfrak{J}_x\,d\sigma, \qquad \int_S w\,y\,d\sigma = \int_S \mathfrak{J}_x\,d\sigma, \tag{132.13}$$

die man durch partielle Integration unter Benutzung von Gl. (132.9) beweist. Addition beider Gleichungen liefert die Integrabilitätsbedingung

$$\int_S (q\,x + w\,y)\,d\sigma = 0, \tag{132.14}$$

der q und w genügen müssen, wenn eine zugehörige im Scheibenmittelpunkt endliche Stromverteilung mit dem vorausgesetzten Verhalten am Schirmrand existieren soll. Die Bedingung tritt als Zusatzforderung zu den Integralgleichungen (132.12a), (132.12b) hinzu.

Nunmehr gehen wir zur näherungsweisen Lösung der Integralgleichungen über und setzen analog (131.2), (131.3) an:

$$\left.\begin{aligned} q &= \frac{i\,k}{\varkappa}\,[q_0 + q_1\cdot i\,k + q_2 (i\,k)^2 + \cdots] \\ w &= \frac{i\,k}{\varkappa}\,[w_0 + w_1\cdot i\,k + w_2 (i\,k)^2 + \cdots] \end{aligned}\right\} \tag{132.15}$$

$$\left.\begin{aligned} G &= \frac{1}{4\pi}\left[\frac{1}{\hat R} + i\,k + \frac{\hat R}{2}(i\,k)^2 + \cdots\right] \\ F &= \frac{1}{4\pi}[\hat R + \cdots] \\ G + k^2 F &= \frac{1}{4\pi}\left[\frac{1}{\hat R} + i\,k - \frac{\hat R}{2}(i\,k)^2 + \cdots\right]. \end{aligned}\right\} \tag{132.16}$$

Hiermit zerfällt das Gleichungssystem (132.12a, b) in sukzessiv zu lösende Gleichungen für die einzelnen Näherungen. Die Korrekturen erster Näherung q_1, w_1 verschwinden aus denselben Gründen wie im akustischen Falle und seien daher sogleich weggelassen. Für die nullte und zweite Näherung erhalten wir

$$\left.\begin{matrix}\dfrac{\partial}{\partial x}\\[2mm] \dfrac{\partial}{\partial y}\end{matrix}\right\}\int\limits_S q_0\cdot\frac{1}{\hat R}\,d\sigma' = \begin{cases}4\pi\\ 0,\end{cases} \qquad \int\limits_S w_0\cdot\frac{1}{\hat R}\,d\sigma' = 0, \tag{132.17a, b}$$

$$\left.\begin{matrix}\dfrac{\partial}{\partial x}\\[2mm] \dfrac{\partial}{\partial y}\end{matrix}\right\}\int\limits_S q_2\cdot\frac{1}{\hat R}\,d\sigma' = \left\{\begin{matrix}\dfrac{\partial}{\partial x}\\[2mm] \dfrac{\partial}{\partial y}\end{matrix}\right\}\int\limits_S q_0\,\frac{\hat R}{2}\,d\sigma' \left\{\begin{matrix}-\dfrac{\partial}{\partial y}\\[2mm] +\dfrac{\partial}{\partial x}\end{matrix}\right\}\int\limits_S w_0\,\hat R\,d\sigma' \tag{132.18a}$$

$$\int\limits_S w_2\cdot\frac{1}{\hat R}\,d\sigma' = -\int\limits_S w_0\,\frac{\hat R}{2}\,d\sigma'. \tag{132.18b}$$

Hierzu treten nach (132.14) und (132.15) die Integrabilitätsbedingungen

$$\int\limits_S (q_n\,x + w_n\,y)\,d\sigma = 0, \qquad n = 0, 2. \tag{132.14a}$$

Entsprechend Gl. (131.11) setzen wir im Einklang mit Gl. (132.9a) an

$$q_n = x\sum_{m=1}^{\infty} a_{n\,m}(a^2 - \varrho^2)^{m-\frac{3}{2}} \tag{132.19a}$$

$$w_n = y\sum_{m=0}^{\infty} b_{n\,m}(a^2 - \varrho^2)^{m-\frac{3}{2}}. \tag{132.19b}$$

Der Beginn der Summation mit $m=1$ bzw. 0 trägt der Kantenbedingung Rechnung, nach der sich bei Annäherung an die Kante q wie $(a-\varrho)^{-\frac{1}{2}}$, w wie $(a-\varrho)^{-\frac{3}{2}}$ verhalten muß. Mit (132.19a, b) lassen sich die Integrale (132.14) ausrechnen und liefern

$$b_{n\,0} = \sum_{m=1}^{\infty}\frac{a^{2m}}{(2m+1)\,(2m-1)}\,(a_{n\,m} + b_{n\,m}) \tag{132.14b}$$

als neue Form der Integrabilitätsbedingungen.

Für das folgende benötigen wir die beiden Integraltypen

$$\left.\begin{aligned} K_{mp}(x,y) &= \int\limits_S (a^2-\varrho'^2)^{m-\frac{3}{2}}\, x'\, \hat{R}^{p-1}\, d\sigma' \\ L_{mp}(x,y) &= \int\limits_S (a^2-\varrho'^2)^{m-\frac{3}{2}}\, y'\, \hat{R}^{p-1}\, d\sigma', \end{aligned}\right\} \tag{132.20}$$

die auseinander durch Vertauschung von x und y hervorgehen. Ihre Berechnung geschieht nach den Methoden von Gl. (131.12) bis (131.18). Dabei benutzt man zweckmäßig die aus Fig. 89 folgenden Beziehungen

$$x'-x=\hat{R}\cos(\varphi+\chi), \qquad y'-y=\hat{R}\sin(\varphi+\chi). \tag{132.21}$$

Man erhält so

$$\left.\begin{aligned} K_{00} &= 0, & K_{02} &= \frac{\pi^2}{2}\,x \\ K_{10} &= \frac{\pi^2}{2}\,x, & K_{12} &= -\frac{\pi^2}{4}\,x\left(a^2-\frac{\varrho^2}{4}\right) \\ K_{20} &= \frac{\pi^2}{4}\,x\left(a^2-\frac{3}{4}\varrho^2\right), & L_{mp}(x,y) &= K_{mp}(y,x). \end{aligned}\right\} \tag{132.22}$$

Wir beginnen mit Gl. (132.17a), die integriert lautet

$$\int\limits_S q_0\,\frac{1}{\hat{R}}\,d\sigma' = 4\pi\,x \tag{132.23}$$

und nach (132.19a) und (132.22) die Lösung

$$q_0 = \frac{8}{\pi}\,\frac{x}{\sqrt{a^2-\varrho^2}} \tag{132.24}$$

besitzt. Für w_0 ergibt sich aus (132.17b), (132.19b) und (132.22)

$$w_0 = b_{00}\,\frac{y}{(a^2-\varrho^2)^{\frac{3}{2}}}. \tag{132.25}$$

b_{00} bestimmt sich aus der Integrabilitätsbedingung (132.14b) mit $a_{01}=8/\pi$ als einzigem von null verschiedenen Koeffizienten unter der Summe zu

$$b_{00} = \frac{8}{3\pi}\,a^2. \tag{132.26}$$

Wir gehen zur nächsten Näherung über und berechnen die rechte Seite von Gl. (132.18a). Dabei erhält man nach (132.24) bis (132.26) und (132.20) sowie (132.22)

$$\left.\begin{matrix}\dfrac{\partial}{\partial x}\\[2mm] \dfrac{\partial}{\partial y}\end{matrix}\right\}\frac{4}{\pi}\,K_{12}\left\{\begin{matrix}-\dfrac{\partial}{\partial y}\\[2mm] +\dfrac{\partial}{\partial x}\end{matrix}\right\}\frac{8a^2}{3\pi}\,L_{02} = -\pi\left\{\begin{matrix}\dfrac{\partial}{\partial x}\\[2mm] \dfrac{\partial}{\partial y}\end{matrix}\right\}x\left(a^2-\frac{\varrho^2}{4}\right)-\left\{\begin{matrix}\dfrac{4\pi}{3}\,a^2\\[2mm] 0\end{matrix}\right. . \tag{132.27}$$

Nach Integration bezüglich x bzw. y lautet nunmehr Gl. (132.18a)

$$\int\limits_S q_2\cdot\frac{1}{\hat{R}}\,d\sigma' = \pi\,x\left(-\frac{7}{3}\,a^2+\frac{\varrho^2}{4}\right). \tag{132.28}$$

Behält man im Ansatz (132.19a) für q_2 zwei Summenglieder bei, so wird die linke Seite von (132.28)

$$a_{21}K_{10}+a_{22}K_{20} = \frac{\pi^2}{2}\,x\left\{a_{21}+a_{22}\left(\frac{a^2}{2}-\frac{3}{8}\varrho^2\right)\right\}. \tag{132.29}$$

Durch Koeffizientenvergleich folgt

$$a_{22} = -\frac{4}{3\pi}, \qquad a_{21} = -\frac{4a^2}{\pi} \tag{132.30}$$

und somit

$$q_2 = -\frac{16}{3\pi} \cdot \frac{x}{\sqrt{a^2-\varrho^2}} \left(a^2 - \frac{\varrho^2}{4}\right). \tag{132.31}$$

An dieser Stelle brechen wir unsere Näherungsrechnung ab. Die gewonnenen Resultate reichen aus, um am asymptotischen Beugungsfeld (130.32) und am Streukoeffizienten (130.34) die nächste Korrektur anzubringen. Um das Feld in beliebigen Aufpunkten durch q und w ausdrücken zu können, verallgemeinern wir zunächst die Umformung von Gl. (132.11c). Anstelle von Gl. (132.11) schreiben wir jetzt

$$F(\hat{R}, z) = \frac{1}{4\pi i k} \int\limits_{\infty}^{\hat{R}} \frac{e^{ik\sqrt{r^2+z^2}}}{r}\, dr. \tag{132.32}$$

Dann gilt die Gl. (132.11a) entsprechende Differentialgleichung

$$\left(\frac{\partial^2}{\partial x^2} + \frac{\partial^2}{\partial y^2}\right) F = \frac{1}{\hat{R}} \frac{\partial}{\partial \hat{R}} \left(\hat{R} \frac{\partial F}{\partial \hat{R}}\right) = G(R), \qquad R = \sqrt{\hat{R}^2 + z^2} \tag{132.33}$$

und die Umformung der Gln. (132.11b, c) läßt sich im wesentlichen unverändert durchführen.

Wir betrachten jetzt das asymptotische Verhalten des Hertzschen Vektors $\mathfrak{Z}_S$, der sich nach (132.6), (132.11c) und (132.32) zu

$$\mathfrak{Z}_S = -\frac{\varkappa}{ik} \left\{ \int \widehat{\operatorname{grad}} F \cdot q \, d\sigma' - \int [\widehat{\operatorname{grad}} F, \mathfrak{w}] \, d\sigma' \right\} \tag{132.33a}$$

berechnet. Hierin ist die Gradientbildung nach unserer Verabredung bei festgehaltenem z auszuführen. Nach Gl. (132.32) gilt ($\hat{R}$, φ, z = Zylinderkoordinaten mit $\hat{\mathfrak{r}}$ als Nullpunkt, vgl. Fig. 89)

$$\widehat{\operatorname{grad}}_{\hat{R}} F = \frac{\partial F}{\partial \hat{R}} = \frac{1}{4\pi i k} \frac{e^{ikR}}{\hat{R}}, \qquad \widehat{\operatorname{grad}}_{\varphi} F = \frac{1}{\hat{R}} \frac{\partial F}{\partial \varphi} = 0 \tag{132.34}$$

und für einen Aufpunkt in weitem Abstand r in der Richtung $\mathfrak{e} = (\vartheta, \varphi)$:

$$\widehat{\operatorname{grad}}_{\hat{R}} F = \frac{1}{4\pi i k \sin\vartheta} \cdot \frac{e^{ik[r - (\hat{\mathfrak{r}}' \mathfrak{e})]}}{r}, \qquad \widehat{\operatorname{grad}}_{\varphi} F = 0. \tag{132.34a}$$

Mit den Abkürzungen

$$Q(\mathfrak{e}) = \int e^{-ik(\hat{\mathfrak{r}}' \mathfrak{e})} q \, d\sigma', \qquad W(\mathfrak{e}) = \int e^{-ik(\hat{\mathfrak{r}}' \mathfrak{e})} w \, d\sigma' \tag{132.35}$$

wird dann der Hertzsche Vektor nach Gl. (132.33a):

$$\left.\begin{aligned} \mathfrak{Z}_{\hat{R}}^{(S)} &= \frac{\varkappa Q}{4\pi k^2 \sin\vartheta} \frac{e^{ikr}}{r} \\ \mathfrak{Z}_{\varphi}^{(S)} &= \frac{\varkappa W}{4\pi k^2 \sin\vartheta} \frac{e^{ikr}}{r} \end{aligned}\right\} \text{für } r \to \infty. \tag{132.36}$$

Seine zur Ausstrahlungsrichtung $\mathfrak{e}$ senkrechten Komponenten liefern nach Gl. (132.5) das asymptotische Beugungsfeld

$$\left.\begin{aligned} \mathfrak{E}_{\vartheta}^{(S)} &= k^2 \mathfrak{Z}_{\vartheta}^{(S)} = k^2 \cos\vartheta \, \mathfrak{Z}_{\hat{R}}^{(S)} \\ \mathfrak{E}_{\varphi}^{(S)} &= k^2 \mathfrak{Z}_{\varphi}^{(S)}. \end{aligned}\right\}. \tag{132.36a}$$

Bei der Ausrechnung der Integrale benutzen wir

$$(\mathfrak{r}'\mathfrak{e}) = \sin\vartheta\,(x'\cos\varphi + y'\sin\varphi)\,, \tag{132.37}$$

entwickeln die Exponentialfunktion und streichen sogleich alle Glieder, die wegen des Faktors x bzw. y in Gl. (132.19a, b) aus Symmetriegründen verschwinden. Wir erhalten dann

$$\left.\begin{aligned} Q &= -\,i\,k\sin\vartheta\cos\varphi\cdot\\ &\quad\cdot\left\{\int q\,x'\,d\sigma' - \frac{k^2}{6}\sin^2\vartheta\int q\,x'\,(x'^2\cos^2\varphi + 3\,y'^2\sin^2\varphi)\,d\sigma' + \cdots\right\}\\ W &= -\,i\,k\sin\vartheta\sin\varphi\cdot\\ &\quad\cdot\left\{\int w\,y'\,d\sigma' - \frac{k^2}{6}\sin^2\vartheta\int w\,y'\,(3\,x'^2\cos^2\varphi + y'^2\sin^2\varphi)\,d\sigma' + \cdots\right\}. \end{aligned}\right\} \tag{132.35a}$$

Im Ausdruck für W verwenden wir die Integrabilitätsbedingung (132.14) und ersparen uns auf diese Weise die Berechnung der zweiten Näherung für w. Die Integrationen lassen sich nach Einsetzen von (132.15), (132.24) bis (132.26) und (132.31) elementar ausführen und liefern:

$$\left.\begin{aligned} Q &= \frac{16}{3}\,\frac{\varepsilon^2}{k\varkappa}\sin\vartheta\cos\varphi\left(1 + \frac{8}{15}\,\varepsilon^2 - \frac{1}{10}\,\varepsilon^2\sin^2\vartheta\right)\\ W &= \frac{16}{3}\,\frac{\varepsilon^2}{k\varkappa}\sin\vartheta\sin\varphi\left(-\,1 - \frac{8}{15}\,\varepsilon^2 + \frac{1}{6}\,\varepsilon^2\sin^2\vartheta\right). \end{aligned}\right\} \tag{132.35b}$$

Bildung der *gesamten Streuintensität*

$$2\varkappa\,J_S = \oint\left(|\mathfrak{E}_\vartheta^{(S)}|^2 + |\mathfrak{E}_\varphi^{(S)}|^2\right)d\sigma \tag{132.38a}$$

durch Einsetzen von (132.36a), (132.36) und (132.35b) und Integration über die Kugel führt nach Division durch die auf den Schirm auftreffende Intensität $2\varkappa\,J_0 = a^2\pi$ zum Streukoeffizienten in zweiter Näherung

$$\sigma = \frac{128\,\varepsilon^4}{27\,\pi^2}\left(1 + \frac{22}{25}\,\varepsilon^2\right), \tag{132.38b}$$

wie in Gl. (128.1) bereits angegeben.

Obgleich wir die Stromverteilung $\mathfrak{J}$ selbst nicht benötigt haben, um zu unserem Resultat (132.38b) zu gelangen, geben wir sie der Vollständigkeit halber noch an. Sie ergibt sich durch Integration der Gln. (132.9) in nullter Näherung zu

$$\mathfrak{J}_x = -\frac{i\,k}{\varkappa}\,\frac{16}{3\pi}\,\frac{a^2 - x^2 - y^2/2}{\sqrt{a^2 - \varrho^2}}\,,\qquad \mathfrak{J}_y = \frac{i\,k}{\varkappa}\,\frac{8}{3\pi}\,\frac{x\,y}{\sqrt{a^2 - \varrho^2}}\,. \tag{132.39}$$

Im Prinzip lassen sich gesamte Streuintensität und Streukoeffizient statt aus dem Fernfeld auch aus dem Nahfeld und zwar wieder aus seinem Streuanteil $\mathfrak{E}_S$, $\mathfrak{H}_S$ berechnen (vgl. Ziff. 103). Da das Streufeld für sich den Maxwellschen Gleichungen genügt, entspringt der ins Unendliche ausgestrahlte Energiestrom aus dem Beugungsschirm und kann durch Integration der Normalkomponente des Pointingschen Vektors über beide Seiten der Schirmfläche gewonnen werden. Dabei ist das tangentielle elektrische Streufeld auf dem Schirm $\mathfrak{E}_x^{(S)} = -\,\mathfrak{E}_x^0 = -\,1$, also homogen und von nullter Ordnung in k. Beim Magnetfeld kommt es, da beide Seiten des Schirms zu berücksichtigen sind, auf die Differenz der beiderseitigen Tangentialkomponente an, also auf den Flächenstrom.

Dieser ist nach den Gln. (132.9) und (132.15) von erster Ordnung in k, aber bis zur zweiten Näherung rein imaginär, d.h. gegenüber dem elektrischen Feld um 90° phasenverschoben. Er ist also reiner Blindstrom und liefert keinen Energiefluß nach außen. Erst die dritte Näherung liefert einen reellen Stromanteil von der Ordnung k^4 und führt zum ersten Glied in Gl. (132.38b).

Als erster hat Bethe[1] die Integralgleichungsmethode auf das vorliegende elektromagnetische Beugungsproblem angewandt. Systematisch ausgebaut und in höheren Näherungen durchgeführt wurde das Verfahren vor allem durch Bouwkamp[2]. Bouwkamp löst wie bei seiner Behandlung des akustischen Problems direkt die ursprünglichen Integrodifferentialgleichungen (132.7) sowie (132.8), während Marcuwitz[3] schrittweise vorgeht, indem er zuerst eine Differentialgleichung und danach eine reine Integralgleichung löst. Wir sind bei unseren Rechnungen in gewissem Sinne umgekehrt vorgegangen als letzterer, da wir zur Gewinnung von $\mathfrak{J}$ aus q und w noch nachträglich die Differentialgleichungen (132.9) zu lösen haben.

c 3) Näherung für kleine Wellenlängen.

133. Die Kirchhoffsche Lösung. Das althergebrachte, für kleine Wellenlängen anwendbare Näherungsverfahren ist dasjenige von Kirchhoff (vgl. Abschn. A II a). Es ist jedoch bekannt, daß diese Methode in ihrer ursprünglichen Gestalt nur für das Fernfeld und auch hier nur in der Nähe der geometrisch-optischen Schattengrenzen zutreffende Ergebnisse liefert, wie wir das insbesondere beim Problem der Halbebene (vgl. Ziff. 116) und bei der Beugung am Spalt (vgl. Ziff. 124) gesehen haben. Im Gegensatz dazu gibt das im folgenden Abschnitt zu besprechende modifizierte Näherungsverfahren von Braunbek (Ziff. 39) das Beugungsfeld im ganzen Raum wieder.

Wir betrachten den akustischen Fall und behalten die geometrischen Verhältnisse der vorangehenden Abschnitte bei (Schirm in xy-Ebene, Einfall von der Seite negativer z). Nach der Helmholtzschen Integralformel (8.5) läßt sich das Feld v hinter der Schirmebene $(S)+(L)$ $[(S)=$ Schirm, $(L)=$ Öffnung$]$, also für $z>0$, durch die Werte von v und $\partial v/\partial z$ in dieser Ebene darstellen:

$$v=\int\limits_{S+L}\left(v\frac{\partial G}{\partial z'}-\frac{\partial v}{\partial z'}G\right)d\sigma',\qquad G=\frac{e^{ikR}}{4\pi R},\qquad R=|\mathfrak{r}-\hat{\mathfrak{r}}'|. \tag{133.1}$$

Die zu Gl. (133.1) führenden Überlegungen von Ziff. 8 bleiben gültig, wenn wir die Greensche Funktion des unendlichen Raumes $G(\mathfrak{r}-\mathfrak{r}')$ durch eine der beiden Greenschen Funktionen des Halbraumes $G(\mathfrak{r}-\mathfrak{r}')\pm G(\mathfrak{r}_S-\mathfrak{r}')$ ersetzen, wobei $\mathfrak{r}_S=(x,y,-z)$ der Spiegelpunkt des Aufpunktes $\mathfrak{r}=(x,y,z)$ ist. Wir erhalten damit die beiden mit Gl. (133.1) gleichberechtigten Darstellungen (vgl. Ziff. 34):

$$v=-2\int\limits_{S+L}\frac{\partial v}{\partial z'}G\,d\sigma'=2\int\limits_{S+L}v\frac{\partial G}{\partial z'}\,d\sigma'. \tag{133.2}$$

---

[1] H. A. Bethe: Phys. Rev. **66**, 163 (1944). Vgl. auch E. T. Copson: Proc. Roy. Soc. A, **186**, 100 (1946).

[2] C. J. Bouwkamp: Proc. Kon. Ned. Akad. Wet. Amst. **52**, 987 (1949); **53**, 654 (1950). — Philips Res. Rep. **5**, 321, 401 (1950). Zusammenfassender Bericht: N.Y. Univ. Res. Rep. No. EM-50 (1953). Vgl. auch die Versuchsergebnisse bei H. Severin: Z. angew. Phys. **2**, 499 (1950). — H. Severin u. W. v. Baeckmann: Z. angew. Phys. **3**, 22 (1951). — M. J. Ehrlich: Diss. Univ. of California 1951.

[3] N. Marcuwitz: Appendix zu C. J. Bouwkamp: New York Univ. Res. Rep. No. EM-50 (1953).

Insbesondere ergeben sich für die einfallende Welle v_0 für $z>0$ die Darstellungen

$$v_0 = -2\int\limits_{S+L} \frac{\partial v_0}{\partial z'}\, G\, d\sigma' = 2\int\limits_{S+L} v_0 \frac{\partial G}{\partial z'}\, d\sigma'. \qquad (133.3)$$

Die bisherigen Formeln gelten exakt. Wir erhalten aus Gl. (133.2) zwei Näherungslösungen v im Sinne von KIRCHHOFF, indem wir die Integration nur über die Öffnung (L) erstrecken und hier v durch v_0 ersetzen. Subtrahieren wir hiervon die einfallende Welle v_0 in der Gestalt (133.3), so erhalten wir zwei Ausdrücke für die Streuwelle v_S [vgl. (35.2a), (35.3a)]

$$v_S^{(1)} = 2\int\limits_S \frac{\partial v_0}{\partial z'}\, G\, d\sigma', \qquad v_S^{(2)} = -2\int\limits_S v_0 \frac{\partial G}{\partial z'}\, d\sigma'. \qquad (133.4)$$

Beide Darstellungen liefern, wie wir sehen werden, im allgemeinen verschiedene Ergebnisse. Stimmen sie in gewissen räumlichen Bereichen überein, so kann uns das als Anhaltspunkt dafür dienen, daß die Näherungen dort zutreffen. Die gewöhnliche Kirchhoffsche Näherung[1] geht anstatt von Gl. (133.2) direkt von Gl. (133.1) aus und ist das Mittel der beiden Näherungen (133.4). Wir nehmen wieder senkrechten Einfall an. Dann entsteht aus Gl. (133.4) bei Verwendung der Abkürzung

$$J = \int\limits_S G\, d\sigma' \qquad (133.5)$$

mit Rücksicht auf Gl. (130.6)

$$v_S^{(1)} = 2ikJ, \qquad v_S^{(2)} = 2\frac{\partial J}{\partial z}. \qquad (133.6)$$

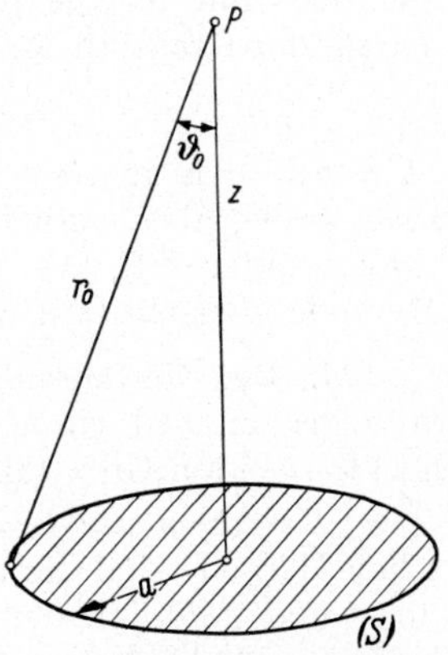

Fig. 90. Bezeichnungen bei der Beugung an der Kreisscheibe (Poissonsche Beugung).

Wir wenden die Formeln auf die Kreisscheibe an und betrachten zunächst das Feld auf der Achse hinter der Scheibe im Abstand z. Die Integration ergibt mit den aus Fig. 90 ersichtlichen Bezeichnungen

$$J = \frac{1}{2ik}\left(e^{ikr_0} - e^{ikz}\right) \qquad (133.7)$$

und hieraus

$$v_S^{(1)} = e^{ikr_0} - e^{ikz}, \qquad v_S^{(2)} = e^{ikr_0}\cos\vartheta_0 - e^{ikz}. \qquad (133.8)$$

Beide Ergebnisse stimmen nur für kleine ϑ_0, also in weitem Abstand von der Scheibe, überein.

Die Berechnung des Fernfeldes ist geläufig. Mit Gl. (131.27) und den dortigen Bezeichnungen erhält man mit Hilfe der Integrale

$$\left.\begin{aligned} &\int\limits_0^{2\pi} e^{-ik\varrho'\sin\vartheta\cos\varphi'}\, d\varphi' = 2\pi\, J_0(k\varrho'\sin\vartheta) \\ &\int\limits_0^{a} J_0(k\varrho'\sin\vartheta)\,\varrho'\, d\varrho' = a\,\frac{J_1(ka\sin\vartheta)}{k\sin\vartheta} \end{aligned}\right\} \qquad (133.9)$$

[1] Eingehende analytische und numerische Berechnungen auf Grund des Kirchhoffschen Integrals für im Endlichen gelegene Aufpunkte (Fresnelsche Beugung) bei E. v. LOMMEL: Abh. bayer. Akad. **15**, 233 (1884). — Auswertungen mit Hilfe des Rubinowiczschen Linienintegrals bei R. G. MIRAMANOW: C. R. Acad. Sci. URSS. **61**, 617 (1948); **67**, 65 (1949).

(J_0 und J_1 sind die Besselschen Funktionen nullter und erster Ordnung) für $r\to\infty$ den Wert

$$J\to\frac{a}{2k\sin\vartheta}\,J_1(k\,a\sin\vartheta)\,\frac{e^{ikr}}{r}, \tag{133.9'}$$

und damit ($\varepsilon=k\,a$)

$$\left.\begin{array}{l} v_S^{(1)}\to 1\\ v_S^{(2)}\to\cos\vartheta\end{array}\right\}\cdot\frac{i\,\varepsilon}{\sin\vartheta}\,J_1(\varepsilon\sin\vartheta)\,\frac{e^{ikr}}{kr}. \tag{133.10}$$

Übereinstimmung zwischen $v_S^{(1)}$ und $v_S^{(2)}$ besteht nur für kleine Winkel ϑ. Wir diskutieren noch die gesamte Streuintensität und den *Streukoeffizienten*. Da v_S von $\vartheta=0$ aus mit wachsendem ϑ wegen $\varepsilon\gg 1$ schnell abfällt, geben die kleinen Winkel den Ausschlag, und beide Formeln (133.10) liefern im Grenzfalle $\varepsilon\to\infty$ dasselbe. Für den Streukoeffizienten erhält man mit Hilfe des (dimensionell um einen Faktor k^{-1} ergänzten) optischen Theorems (100.8′ps) (das in Strenge allerdings nur für die Lösung eines gemischten Randwertproblems gilt) sofort den für den Grenzfall der geometrischen Optik zu fordernden Wert (vgl. Ziff. 105)

$$\sigma=2. \tag{133.11}$$

σ läßt sich aus (133.9) und (133.10) auch genauer ausrechnen, indem man zwar große, aber endliche ε voraussetzt. Doch zeigen die folgenden Betrachtungen unter Ziff. 134, daß hiermit der Gültigkeitsbereich der Kirchhoffschen Methode überschritten wird, den Ergebnissen daher keine Bedeutung zukommt.

134. Das Verfahren von BRAUNBEK. Asymptotische Lösung. Wir wollen im folgenden noch ein heuristisches und ein strenges Verfahren zur Erfassung des hochfrequenten Grenzfalles $\varepsilon\gg 1$ behandeln, die zum gleichen Ergebnis führen.

α) Verfahren von Braunbek. Die unbefriedigenden Resultate der Kirchhoffschen Methode sind darauf zurückzuführen, daß die benutzten Ersatzrandwerte für v und $\partial v/\partial n$ in der Schirmebene zu grob sind. Sie geben zwar die Verhältnisse im Abstand einiger Wellenlängen vom Schirmrand sowohl in der Öffnung als auch hinter dem Schirm richtig wieder, nicht jedoch in der Nähe des Randes. BRAUNBEK[1] trägt diesem Umstand dadurch Rechnung, daß er die Kirchhoffschen Ersatzwerte entsprechend korrigiert (Ziff. 39). Er entnimmt die Werte für v und $\partial v/\partial n$ in Randnähe der Sommerfeldschen Lösung des Halbebenen-Problems. Das ist für Wellenlängen $\lambda\ll a$ erlaubt, da für solche λ die Krümmung des Schirmrandes vernachlässigt werden kann.

Bei der *Kirchhoffschen Lösung* wurde in Gl. (133.2) gesetzt

$$\left.\begin{array}{lll} v_K=v_0=1, & \dfrac{\partial v_K}{\partial z}=\dfrac{\partial v_0}{\partial z}=i\,k & \textit{auf } (L),\\ v_K=0, & \dfrac{\partial v_K}{\partial z}=0 & \textit{auf } (S).\end{array}\right\} \tag{134.1}$$

Anstelle dieser Werte sind, wenn wir uns für die Randbedingung $\partial v/\partial n=0$ entscheiden (s-Fall), die *Sommerfeldschen Werte* der Gln. (116.10s), (116.11s) zu verwenden, wobei in Gl. (116.11s) wegen der anderen Einfallsrichtung in den dortigen Rechnungen noch das Vorzeichen umzukehren ist. Demnach sind die Werte (134.1) durch die *Braunbekschen Zusätze*

$$\left.\begin{array}{lll} \delta v_B=0, & \delta\dfrac{\partial v_B}{\partial z}=i\,k\big(-\Phi(k\,\xi)+\Psi(k\,\xi)\big) & \textit{auf } (L)\\ \delta v_B=\Phi(k\,\xi), & \delta\dfrac{\partial v_B}{\partial z}=0 & \textit{auf } (S)\end{array}\right\} \tag{134.2}$$

[1] W. BRAUNBEK: Z. Physik **127**, 381, 405 (1950). — Übertragung des Braunbek-Verfahrens auf den elektromagnetischen Fall bei W. FRAHN: Dipl.-Arbeit, Techn. Hochschule, Aachen 1951.

zu korrigieren, wobei wir den Abstand vom Schirmrand mit ξ bezeichnet haben. Mit (134.2) ergeben die beiden Ausdrücke (133.2) die folgenden *Korrekturen* der *Streuwelle:*

$$\left.\begin{aligned} \delta v_S^{(1)} &= 2ik\int_L [\Phi(k\xi') - \Psi(k\xi')]\, G\, d\sigma' \\ \delta v_S^{(2)} &= 2\int_S \Phi(k\xi')\,\frac{\partial G}{\partial z'}\, d\sigma'. \end{aligned}\right\} \tag{134.3}$$

Mit den Abkürzungen

$$J_\pm = \int_{L,S} \Phi(k\xi')\, G\, d\sigma', \qquad K = \int_L \Psi(k\xi')\, G\, d\sigma' \tag{134.4}$$

entsteht hieraus

$$\delta v_S^{(1)} = 2ik\,(J_+ - K), \qquad \delta v_S^{(2)} = -2\,\frac{\partial J_-}{\partial z}. \tag{134.5}$$

Wir berechnen zunächst die Korrektur des Beugungsfeldes auf der Achse. Dabei setzen wir, da die Beiträge zu (134.4) nur von einem schmalen Streifen längs des Schirmrandes herrühren, mit den Bezeichnungen von Fig. 90:

$$d\sigma' = 2\pi a\, d\xi', \qquad G = \frac{e^{ik(r_0 \pm \xi' \sin\vartheta_0)}}{4\pi r_0} \tag{134.6}$$

und erhalten

$$\left.\begin{aligned} J_\pm &= \frac{a}{2}\,\frac{e^{ikr_0}}{r_0}\int_0^\infty \Phi(k\xi')\, e^{\pm ik\xi'\sin\vartheta_0}\, d\xi' \\ K &= \frac{a}{2}\,\frac{e^{ikr_0}}{r_0}\int_0^\infty \Psi(k\xi')\, e^{ik\xi'\sin\vartheta_0}\, d\xi', \end{aligned}\right\} \tag{134.7}$$

was sich mit den Funktionen (116.9) streng auswerten läßt. Im ersten Integral ist zunächst partiell zu integrieren. Beide Integrale lassen sich dann unter mehrmaliger Anwendung von $\Phi(0) = 1$ auswerten. Dabei ergibt sich

$$\left.\begin{aligned} J_\pm &= \pm\frac{ia}{2k\sin\vartheta_0}\left(1 - \frac{1}{\sqrt{1 \pm \sin\vartheta_0}}\right)\frac{e^{ikr_0}}{r_0}, \\ K &= \frac{ia}{2k\cdot\sqrt{1+\sin\vartheta_0}}\;\frac{e^{ikr_0}}{r_0} \end{aligned}\right\} \tag{134.8}$$

und weiter nach Gl. (134.5) mit $a = r_0 \sin\vartheta_0$

$$\left.\begin{aligned} \delta v_S^{(1)} &= e^{ikr_0}\left(\sqrt{1+\sin\vartheta_0} - 1\right), \\ \delta v_S^{(2)} &= e^{ikr_0}\left(\sqrt{1+\sin\vartheta_0} - \cos\vartheta_0\right). \end{aligned}\right\} \tag{134.9}$$

Dabei wurde die Differentiation nach z nur an dem schnell veränderlichen Exponentialfaktor ausgeführt. (Dieses Vorgehen bedarf in unmittelbarer Nähe des Schirms ($z \lesssim \lambda$) noch einer genaueren Untersuchung[1].)

Gl. (134.9) korrigiert die Kirchhoffschen Ausdrücke (133.8) einheitlich zu

$$v_S = v_S^{(1)} + \delta v_S^{(1)} = v_S^{(2)} + \delta v_S^{(2)} = e^{ikr_0}\sqrt{1+\sin\vartheta_0} - e^{ikz}. \tag{134.10}$$

Der erste Summand in Gl. (134.10) rechts, stellt das Gesamtfeld $v = v_0 + v_S$ dar und nimmt insbesondere im Mittelpunkt der Scheibe ($r_0 = a$, $\vartheta_0 = \pi/2$) den Wert $v = e^{ika}\sqrt{2}$ an. Hiernach ist die Feldintensität $|v|^2$ im Zentrum hinter der Scheibe doppelt so groß wie bei der einfallenden Welle (Poissonscher Fleck). Das steht

[1] Vgl. dazu C. J. BOUWKAMP: Progr. Phys. **17**, 56 (1954). — W. BRAUNBEK: Z. Physik **138**, 80 (1954).

in Einklang mit der auf Grund der strengen Theorie gezeichneten Fig. 86, untere Kurve, die sich mit wachsendem $\varepsilon = k a$ unter Oszillationen dem Wert $|v| = \sqrt{2}$ nähert. Im Gegensatz hierzu liefern die Kirchhoffschen Formeln (133.8) die völlig falschen Werte $v = 1$ bzw. 0.

Wir gehen zur Betrachtung des Fernfeldes über[1]. Für ebene Polarkoordinaten $\varrho' = a \pm \xi'$, φ' in der Schirmebene ergibt sich das Flächenelement in Randnähe zu

$$d\sigma' = a\, d\varphi'\, d\xi'. \tag{134.11}$$

Mit G nach Gl. (131.27) und mittels Gl. (133.9) erhält man für die Größen (134.4) die Darstellung

$$\left.\begin{aligned} J_\pm &= \frac{a}{2}\,\frac{e^{ikr}}{r}\int_0^\infty \Phi(k\,\xi')\, J_0\big(k(a\pm\xi')\sin\vartheta\big)\, d\xi' \\ K &= \frac{a}{2}\,\frac{e^{ikr}}{r}\int_0^\infty \Psi(k\,\xi')\, J_0\big(k(a+\xi')\sin\vartheta\big)\, d\xi'. \end{aligned}\right\} \tag{134.12}$$

Für die weitere Rechnung setzen wir $\varepsilon \sin\vartheta \gg 1$ voraus. Das reicht aus, da für kleine ϑ bereits die Kirchhoffsche Näherung (133.10) richtige Resultate gab. Unter Verwendung der asymptotischen Darstellung der Bessel-Funktion

$$J_0\big(k(a\pm\xi')\sin\vartheta\big) \to \sqrt{\frac{2}{\pi\, k\, a\sin\vartheta}}\,\cos\left\{k(a\pm\xi')\sin\vartheta - \frac{\pi}{4}\right\}, \tag{134.13}$$

in der wir unter der Wurzel ξ' gegenüber a vernachlässigt haben, läßt sich (134.12) nach demselben Verfahren wie Gl. (134.7) auswerten. Dabei ergibt sich

$$\left.\begin{aligned} J_\pm &\to \pm\frac{i\,a^2}{\sqrt{8\pi\,\varepsilon^3\sin^3\vartheta}}\cdot\left\{\left(1-\frac{1}{\sqrt{1\pm\sin\vartheta}}\right)e^{i\left(\varepsilon\sin\vartheta-\frac{\pi}{4}\right)}\right. \\ &\qquad\left. -\left(1-\frac{1}{\sqrt{1\mp\sin\vartheta}}\right)e^{-i\left(\varepsilon\sin\vartheta-\frac{\pi}{4}\right)}\right\}\frac{e^{ikr}}{r} \\ K &\to \frac{i\,a^2\sin\vartheta}{\sqrt{8\pi\,\varepsilon^3\sin^3\vartheta}}\cdot\left\{\frac{1}{\sqrt{1+\sin\vartheta}}\,e^{i\left(\varepsilon\sin\vartheta-\frac{\pi}{4}\right)}+\frac{1}{\sqrt{1-\sin\vartheta}}\,e^{-i\left(\varepsilon\sin\vartheta-\frac{\pi}{4}\right)}\right\}\frac{e^{ikr}}{r} \end{aligned}\right\} \tag{134.14}$$

und hieraus nach Gl. (134.5)

$$\left.\begin{aligned} \delta v_S^{(1)} &\to \frac{\varepsilon^{\frac{1}{2}}}{\sqrt{2\pi\sin^3\vartheta}}\left\{\left(\sqrt{1+\sin\vartheta}-1\right)e^{i\left(\varepsilon\sin\vartheta-\frac{\pi}{4}\right)}\right. \\ &\qquad\left. -\left(\sqrt{1-\sin\vartheta}-1\right)e^{-i\left(\varepsilon\sin\vartheta-\frac{\pi}{4}\right)}\right\}\frac{e^{ikr}}{kr} \\ \delta v_S^{(2)} &\to \frac{\varepsilon^{\frac{1}{2}}}{\sqrt{2\pi\sin^3\vartheta}}\left\{\left(\sqrt{1+\sin\vartheta}-\cos\vartheta\right)e^{i\left(\varepsilon\sin\vartheta-\frac{\pi}{4}\right)}\right. \\ &\qquad\left. -\left(\sqrt{1-\sin\vartheta}-\cos\vartheta\right)e^{-i\left(\varepsilon\sin\vartheta-\frac{\pi}{4}\right)}\right\}\frac{e^{ikr}}{kr}. \end{aligned}\right\} \tag{134.15}$$

Andererseits gehen die Kirchhoffschen Näherungen (133.10) für große $\varepsilon\sin\vartheta$ in

$$\left.\begin{aligned} v_S^{(1)} &= 1 \\ v_S^{(2)} &= \cos\vartheta \end{aligned}\right\}\cdot\frac{2i\,\varepsilon^{\frac{1}{2}}}{\sqrt{2\pi\sin^3\vartheta}}\,\sin\left(\varepsilon\sin\vartheta-\frac{\pi}{4}\right)\cdot\frac{e^{ikr}}{kr} \tag{134.16}$$

über. Zusammenfassung von (134.15) und (134.16) liefert einheitlich

$$v_S \to \frac{\varepsilon^{\frac{1}{2}}}{\sqrt{2\pi\sin^3\vartheta}}\left\{\sqrt{1+\sin\vartheta}\cdot e^{i\left(\varepsilon\sin\vartheta-\frac{\pi}{4}\right)}-\sqrt{1-\sin\vartheta}\cdot e^{-i\left(\varepsilon\sin\vartheta-\frac{\pi}{4}\right)}\right\}\frac{e^{ikr}}{kr}. \tag{134.17}$$

[1] Man vgl. dazu auch die Auswertung der Flächenintegrale (134.4) mit Hilfe des Prinzips der stationären Phase bei J.B. Keller, R.M. Levis u. B.D. Seckler: N.Y. Univ. Res. Rep. No. EM-96 (1956). — J. Appl. Phys. **28**, 570 (1957).

Gl. (134.17) ist im Bereich $\varepsilon \sin \vartheta \gg 1$ gültig. Andererseits stellt Gl. (133.10) deren Doppeldeutigkeit für $\vartheta \ll 1$ verschwindet, eine in diesem Bereich gültige Näherung dar. Die Braunbeksche Korrektur ist hier gegenüber (133.10) zu vernachlässigen. Beide Ausdrücke (133.10) und (134.17) zusammen erfassen das *Fernfeld in allen Winkelbereichen.* Im Bereich $\frac{1}{\varepsilon} \ll \sin \vartheta \ll 1$ sind beide Formeln gültig. Daß sie hier übereinstimmen, zeigt der Vergleich von (134.16) und (134.17).

β) Asymptotische Lösung. Das heuristische Braunbeksche Verfahren läßt sich im hier betrachteten Falle der Kreisscheibe durch direkte asymptotische Lösung des maßgeblichen Randwertproblems streng begründen[1]. Wir werden zu diesem Zweck die entsprechende Integralgleichung nach einer zu Ziff. 122 analogen Methode für $\varepsilon \gg 1$ asymptotisch lösen. Auf diese Weise läßt sich das Braunbeksche Ergebnis als erstes Glied der asymptotischen Entwicklung des Randwertproblems nach fallenden (gebrochenen) Potenzen von $k a = \varepsilon$ bestätigen. Darüber hinaus können weitere Glieder der asymptotischen Entwicklung berechnet werden. Diese sind insbesondere zur Ermittlung des asymptotischen Verhaltens des *Streuquerschnittes* notwendig, da die Braunbeksche Näherung nur den geometrischen Grenzwert liefert.

Es erleichtert die analytische Situation, wenn wir mit Hilfe des Babinetschen Theorems (Ziff. 27) vom s-Fall für die Kreisscheibe zum p-Fall für die Kreisblende übergehen. Neben dem Randwert $v=0$ für $z=0$, $\varrho > a$ ist dann nach (26.3′p) noch der Normalgradient in der Öffnung bekannt: $v_z = i k$ für $z=0$, $\varrho < a$. Setzt man dies in die erste Darstellung (133.2) ein, so folgt (wir verwenden Zylinderkoordinaten ϱ, φ, z; das Problem ist rotationssymmetrisch) für $z>0$

$$v(\varrho, z) = -\frac{i k}{2\pi} \int_0^a d\varrho' \, \varrho' \int_0^{2\pi} \frac{e^{ikR}}{R} d\varphi' - \frac{1}{2\pi} \int_a^\infty d\varrho' \, \varrho' \, \psi(\varrho') \int_0^{2\pi} \frac{e^{ikR}}{R} d\varphi' \tag{134.18}$$

mit

$$\psi(\varrho) = v_z(\varrho, +0) \qquad (\varrho > a). \tag{134.19}$$

Die Randbedingung liefert für $\psi(\varrho)$ die Integralgleichung

$$\int_a^\infty d\varrho' \, \varrho' \psi(\varrho') \int_0^{2\pi} \frac{e^{ik\hat{R}}}{\hat{R}} d\varphi' = -i k \int_0^a d\varrho' \, \varrho' \int_0^{2\pi} \frac{e^{ik\hat{R}}}{\hat{R}} d\varphi' \qquad (\varrho > a) \tag{134.20}$$

mit

$$\hat{R} = \sqrt{\varrho^2 + \varrho'^2 - 2\varrho\varrho' \cos(\varphi - \varphi')}.$$

Bevor wir diese Gleichung asymptotisch lösen, berechnen wir noch das zu (134.18) gehörige Fernfeld. Führen wir zu diesem Zweck neben den Zylinderkoordinaten noch räumliche Polarkoordinaten r, ϑ, φ ein, so ergibt sich mit Hilfe der Darstellung

$$\frac{e^{ikR}}{R} \to \frac{e^{ikr}}{r} e^{-ik\varrho' \sin\vartheta \cos(\varphi - \varphi')}$$

und den Integralen (133.9) aus (134.18) für $r \to \infty$

$$v(r, \vartheta) \to -\frac{e^{ikr}}{kr} \left\{ i\varepsilon \frac{J_1(\varepsilon \sin\vartheta)}{\sin\vartheta} + k \int_a^\infty \psi(\varrho') \, J_0(k\varrho' \sin\vartheta) \, \varrho' \, d\varrho' \right\}. \tag{134.21}$$

[1] H. LEVINE: N.Y. Univ. Res. Rep. No. EM-84 (1955). — Stanford Univ. Appl. Math. and Stat. Lab., Techn. Rep. No. 51 (1956). — H. LEVINE u. T. T. WU: Stanford Univ. Math. and Stat. Lab., Techn. Rep. No. 71 (1957). — K. WESTPFAHL: Ann. Physik (im Erscheinen).

Unter der Voraussetzung $\varepsilon \sin\vartheta \gg 1$ können wir dies mit Hilfe der asymptotischen Darstellung der Zylinderfunktionen

$$\left.\begin{aligned} J_0(x) &\to \sqrt{\frac{2}{\pi x}}\cos\left(x-\frac{\pi}{4}\right), \qquad J_1(x) \to \sqrt{\frac{2}{\pi x}}\sin\left(x-\frac{\pi}{4}\right) \\ H_0^1(x) &\to \sqrt{\frac{2}{\pi x}}\exp\left(x-\frac{\pi}{4}\right) \qquad (|x|\gg 1) \end{aligned}\right\} \tag{134.22}$$

näherungsweise auch in der folgenden Form schreiben

$$\left.\begin{aligned} v(r,\vartheta) \to &-\frac{e^{ikr}}{kr}\left\{\frac{2i\varepsilon^{\frac{1}{2}}}{\sqrt{2\pi\sin^3\vartheta}}\sin\left(\varepsilon\sin\vartheta-\frac{\pi}{4}\right)\right. \\ &\left.+\frac{k^{\frac{1}{2}}e^{\frac{i\pi}{4}}}{\sqrt{2\pi\sin^3\vartheta}}\left[\overline{\psi}(\sin\vartheta)-i\,\overline{\psi}(-\sin\vartheta)\right]\right\} \qquad (\varepsilon\sin\vartheta\gg 1) \end{aligned}\right\} \tag{134.23}$$

mit

$$\overline{\psi}(\alpha) = \int_a^\infty \psi(\varrho)\, e^{-ik\alpha\varrho}\sqrt{\varrho}\, d\varrho. \tag{134.24}$$

Zur asymptotischen Lösung der Integralgleichung (134.20) übergehend verwenden wir die Sommerfeldsche Darstellung[1]

$$\frac{e^{ikR}}{R} = \frac{ik}{2}\int_{-\infty}^{\infty} H_0^1(k\alpha\hat{R})\, e^{ik\sqrt{1-\alpha^2}|z|}\frac{\alpha\, d\alpha}{\sqrt{1-\alpha^2}} \tag{134.25}$$

[der Zweig der Wurzel $\sqrt{1-\alpha^2}$ ist wie bei der Fourier-Darstellung in (60.1) zu wählen] und das Additionstheorem

$$H_0^1(k\alpha\hat{R}) = \sum_{n=-\infty}^{\infty} e^{in(\varphi-\varphi')}\cdot\left\{\begin{matrix} J_n(k\alpha\varrho)\, H_n^1(k\alpha\varrho') & (\varrho<\varrho') \\ H_n^1(k\alpha\varrho)\, J_n(k\alpha\varrho') & (\varrho>\varrho'), \end{matrix}\right\} \tag{134.26}$$

dann ergibt sich mit (133.9)

$$\left.\begin{aligned} &\int_a^\infty d\varrho'\,\varrho'\,\psi(\varrho')\int_{-\infty}^{\infty}\frac{d\alpha\cdot\alpha}{\sqrt{1-\alpha^2}}\left\{\begin{matrix} J_0(k\alpha\varrho')\, H_0^1(k\alpha\varrho) & (\varrho'<\varrho) \\ H_0^1(k\alpha\varrho')\, J_0(k\alpha\varrho) & (\varrho'>\varrho) \end{matrix}\right\} \\ &\qquad = \pi i a\int_{-\infty}^{\infty} J_1(\varepsilon\alpha)\, H_0^1(k\alpha\varrho)\frac{d\alpha}{\sqrt{1-\alpha^2}} \qquad (\varrho>a). \end{aligned}\right\} \tag{134.27}$$

Mit Hilfe der Darstellungen (134.22) erkennt man leicht, daß die beiden α-Integranden in der oberen α-Halbebene exponentiell verschwinden; wir können daher als α-Integrationsweg auch die beiden Ufer des von 1 nach $1+i\infty$ laufenden Verzweigungsschnittes verwenden (vgl. Fig. 40). Für $\varepsilon\gg 1$ dürfen wir dann überall die Näherung (134.22) verwenden. Damit ergibt sich (wir kehren anschließend zum ursprünglichen α-Integrationsweg zurück)

$$\left.\begin{aligned} &\int_a^\infty d\varrho'\sqrt{\varrho'}\,\psi(\varrho')\int_{-\infty}^{\infty}\left\{e^{ik\alpha(\varrho-\varrho')} - i\, e^{ik\alpha(\varrho+\varrho')}\right\}\frac{d\alpha}{\sqrt{1-\alpha^2}} \\ &\qquad = \sqrt{a}\oint_{-\infty}^{\infty}\left\{e^{ik\alpha(\varrho-a)} + i\, e^{ik\alpha(\varrho+a)}\right\}\frac{d\alpha}{\alpha\sqrt{1-\alpha^2}} \equiv f(\varrho) \qquad (\varrho>a). \end{aligned}\right\} \tag{134.28}$$

---

[1] Magnus-Oberhettinger: l. c. S. 48, die Formel des Textes ergibt sich mit Hilfe der Halbumlaufrelation $H_0^2(e^{-i\pi}x) = -H_0^1(x)$.

(Die zunächst im Exponenten $\varrho-\varrho'$ zu setzenden Absolutstriche können fortbleiben, da nur der gerade Teil der Exponentialfunktion zum α-Integral beiträgt; Haken am Integralzeichen bedeuten, daß den Polen auf dem reellen Integrationsweg durch entsprechende unendlich kleine Halbkreise in die komplexe α-Ebene auszuweichen ist.) Zunächst können wir Gl. (134.28) mit Hilfe der Fourier-Darstellung der Hankel-Funktion (60.1) in der nachstehenden Form schreiben

$$\pi\int_a^\infty \sqrt{\varrho'}\,\psi(\varrho')\,\{H_0^1(k\,|\varrho-\varrho'|)-i\,H_0^1(k\,|\varrho+\varrho'|)\}\,d\varrho'=f(\varrho)\qquad(\varrho>a)\,. \tag{134.29}$$

Diese Gleichung läßt sich folgendermaßen interpretieren. Die Belegungsdichte $\psi(\varrho)$ auf dem Schirm ist in erster asymptotischer Näherung im wesentlichen dieselbe, wie diejenige auf einer *Halbebene*, deren Kante mit einer Tangente der kreisförmigen Öffnung zusammenfällt [vgl. (115.2)]. Das ist aber genau der Ausgangspunkt der Braunbekschen Konzeption. In zweiter asymptotischer Näherung ist eine Wechselwirkung mit einer im Abstand $2a$ gegenüberliegenden (kantenparallelen) Halbebene zu berücksichtigen. Dies kommt durch das zweite Glied in der geschweiften Klammer zum Ausdruck. Durch Berücksichtigung weiterer Glieder der asymptotischen Entwicklungen (134.22) läßt sich in höheren Näherungen auch der Einfluß der Krümmung der Schirmkante (sowie höhere Wechselwirkungen der Kantenelemente) erfassen.

Das Problem ist also in unserer Näherung demjenigen der Beugung am Spalt weitgehend analog [vgl. (118.13″p)] und dementsprechend können wir das in Ziff. 122 entwickelte Lösungsverfahren fast wörtlich übernehmen. Zunächst kehren wir zu Gl. (134.28) zurück und schreiben sie mit Hilfe von (134.24) in der Gestalt

$$\int_{-\infty}^{\infty}\left\{\overline{\psi}(\alpha)-i\,\overline{\psi}(-\alpha)\right\}\frac{e^{ik\alpha\varrho}}{\sqrt{1-\alpha^2}}\,d\alpha=f(\varrho)\qquad(\varrho>a)\,. \tag{134.30}$$

Multiplizieren wir diese Gleichung mit $e^{-ik\alpha'\varrho}$ und integrieren über $\varrho>a$ so folgt [vgl. (115.2″)]

$$\left.\begin{aligned}\oint_{-\infty}^{\infty}\left\{[\overline{\psi}(\alpha')-i\,\overline{\psi}(-\alpha')]\,e^{i\varepsilon\alpha'}-\sqrt{a}\,\frac{1+i\,e^{2i\varepsilon\alpha'}}{\alpha'}\right\}\frac{d\alpha'}{\sqrt{1-\alpha'^2}\,(\alpha'-\alpha)}&=0\\ \oint_{-\infty}^{\infty}\overline{\psi}(\alpha')\,\frac{e^{i\varepsilon\alpha'}}{\alpha'-\alpha}\,d\alpha'&=0.\end{aligned}\right\} \tag{134.30'}$$

Die untere dieser Gleichungen enthält die aus (134.24) folgende Aussage, daß $\overline{\psi}(\alpha)\,e^{i\varepsilon\alpha}$ in der *unteren* α-Halbebene holomorph ist. Die obere Gleichung besagt entsprechend, daß der dortige Integrand in der *oberen* Halbebene holomorph ist. Die genannten Eigenschaften der beiden Integranden bleibt erhalten, wenn wir den oberen mit $\sqrt{1+\alpha'}$, den unteren mit $1/\sqrt{1-\alpha'}$ multiplizieren. Subtrahiert man die so entstehenden Gleichungen, so ergibt sich [vgl. (118.19p)]

$$\left.\begin{aligned}&\overline{\psi}(\alpha)\,\frac{e^{i\varepsilon\alpha}}{\sqrt{1-\alpha}}+\frac{1}{2\pi}\oint_{-\infty}^{\infty}\overline{\psi}(-\alpha')\,\frac{e^{i\varepsilon\alpha'}}{\sqrt{1-\alpha'}}\,\frac{d\alpha'}{\alpha'-\alpha}\\ &\quad=-\frac{\sqrt{a}}{2\pi i}\oint_{-\infty}^{\infty}\frac{1+i\,e^{2i\varepsilon\alpha'}}{\alpha'\sqrt{1-\alpha'}}\,\frac{d\alpha'}{\alpha'-\alpha}\equiv\hat{f}(\alpha)\,.\end{aligned}\right\} \tag{134.31}$$

Führen wir hier wieder die Abkürzung

$$\hat{\psi}(\alpha) = \frac{e^{i\varepsilon\alpha}}{\sqrt{1-\alpha}}\,\overline{\psi}(\alpha) \tag{134.32}$$

sowie die durch (118.21 p) definierte Größe $A_{\|}(\alpha)$ ein, so nimmt (134.31) die Gestalt

$$\hat{\psi}(\alpha) - \frac{1}{2\pi}\oint\limits_{-\infty}^{\infty} \hat{\psi}(-\alpha')\,A_{\|}(\alpha')\,\frac{d\alpha'}{\alpha'-\alpha} = \hat{f}(\alpha) \tag{134.1'}$$

an.

Wir interessieren uns hier nur für die ersten beiden Glieder der asymptotischen Entwicklung

$$\hat{\psi}(\alpha) \to \hat{\psi}_0(\alpha) + \varepsilon^{-\frac{1}{2}}\,\hat{\psi}_1(\alpha) + \cdots \tag{134.33}$$

der Lösung von (134.31′). (Die Berechnung weiterer Glieder ist nur sinnvoll, wenn die Integralgleichung zuvor im Sinne des oben erwähnten Einflusses der Krümmung der Randkurve ergänzt wird.) Zunächst haben wir die Inhomogenität $\hat{f}(\alpha)$ asymptotisch zu entwickeln. Auf Grund der Umformung

$$\frac{1}{2\pi i}\oint\limits_{-\infty}^{\infty} \frac{1+i\,e^{2i\varepsilon\alpha'}}{\alpha'\sqrt{1-\alpha'}}\,\frac{d\alpha'}{\alpha'-\alpha} = \frac{1}{\alpha}\left(1-\frac{1}{\sqrt{1-\alpha}}\right) + i\,\frac{e^{2i\varepsilon\alpha}}{\alpha}\left\{\hat{A}(\alpha)-\hat{A}(0)\right\} \tag{134.34}$$

[mit der durch (122.7) definierten Größe $\hat{A}(\alpha)$] ergibt sich leicht mit Hilfe von (122.10) die gesuchte Entwicklung

$$\hat{f}(\alpha) \to -\sqrt{a}\left\{\frac{1}{\alpha}\left(1-\frac{1}{\sqrt{1-\alpha}}\right) - \frac{e^{i\left(2\varepsilon-\frac{\pi}{4}\right)}}{\sqrt{2\pi\varepsilon}\,(\alpha-\mathfrak{z})} + \cdots\right\}. \tag{134.35}$$

Trägt man dies sowie die Entwicklung (122.4 p) mit dem durch (122.12 p) gegebenen Koeffizienten $A_{\|}^{(1)}(\alpha)$ in (134.31′) ein, so ergibt sich durch Vergleich der Koeffizienten von ε^0 und $\varepsilon^{-\frac{1}{2}}$

$$\hat{\psi}_0(\alpha) = \frac{\sqrt{a}}{\alpha}\left(\frac{1}{\sqrt{1-\alpha}} - 1\right), \tag{134.36a}$$

$$\hat{\psi}_1(\alpha) = \sqrt{\frac{a}{2\pi}}\,\frac{e^{i\left(2\varepsilon-\frac{\pi}{4}\right)}}{\alpha-\mathfrak{z}} + \frac{1}{2\pi}\oint\limits_{-\infty}^{\infty}\hat{\psi}_0(-\alpha')\,A_{\|}^{(1)}(\alpha')\frac{d\alpha'}{\alpha'-\alpha} = \sqrt{\frac{a}{\pi}}\,\frac{e^{i\left(2\varepsilon-\frac{\pi}{4}\right)}}{\alpha-\mathfrak{z}}. \tag{134.36b}$$

Geht man hier mittels (134.32) zu $\overline{\psi}(\alpha)$ über, so ergibt sich die gesuchte Lösung in der einfachen Form

$$\overline{\psi}(\alpha) \to \sqrt{a}\left\{\frac{1-\sqrt{1-\alpha}}{\alpha}\,e^{-i\varepsilon\alpha} - \frac{\varepsilon^{-\frac{1}{2}}}{\sqrt{\pi}}\,\frac{e^{i\left\{\varepsilon(2-\alpha)-\frac{\pi}{4}\right\}}}{\sqrt{1-\alpha}} + \cdots\right\}. \tag{134.37}$$

Tragen wir dies Ergebnis schließlich in Gl. (134.23) ein und gehen mit Hilfe des Babinetschen Theorems (27.7) wieder zur Kreisscheibe zurück, so folgt für $z>0$, $\varepsilon\sin\vartheta \gg 1$

$$\left.\begin{aligned} v_S(r,\vartheta) \to \frac{e^{ikr}}{kr}\Bigg\{&\frac{\varepsilon^{\frac{1}{2}}}{\sqrt{2\pi\sin^3\vartheta}}\Big(\sqrt{1+\sin\vartheta}\,e^{i\left(\varepsilon\sin\vartheta-\frac{\pi}{4}\right)} \\ &- \sqrt{1-\sin\vartheta}\,e^{-i\left(\varepsilon\sin\vartheta-\frac{\pi}{4}\right)}\Big) + \frac{e^{i\left(2\varepsilon+\frac{\pi}{4}\right)}}{\pi\sqrt{2\sin\vartheta}}\cdot \\ &\cdot\left(\frac{e^{i\left(\varepsilon\sin\vartheta+\frac{\pi}{4}\right)}}{\sqrt{1+\sin\vartheta}} - \frac{e^{-i\left(\varepsilon\sin\vartheta+\frac{\pi}{4}\right)}}{\sqrt{1-\sin\vartheta}}\right) + \cdots\Bigg\}.\end{aligned}\right\} \tag{134.38}$$

Dabei haben wir das aus $\overline{\psi}_0$ sich ergebende Glied mit dem ersten Term in (134.23) zusammengefaßt; das Ergebnis stimmt mit (134.17) genau überein. Das Braunbek-Verfahren liefert also in der Tat das Hauptglied der asymptotischen Entwicklung der Lösung des Randwertproblems. Dabei ist die Braunbek-Korrektur (134.15) von *derselben* Größenordnung, wie die Kirchhoffsche Lösung (134.16). Das nächste [in (134.38) angegebene] Glied ist um den Faktor $\varepsilon^{-\frac{1}{2}}$ kleiner als das Hauptglied (entsprechendes gilt von den weiteren Gliedern).

Für die Umgebung der Einfallsrichtung $\vartheta \ll 1$ ($\varepsilon \sin\vartheta$ nicht $\gg 1$) müssen wir auf (134.21) zurückgreifen. Wir wollen uns hier auf die Berechnung des Streukoeffizienten σ beschränken. Schreiben wir die Streuwelle in der Form $v_S \to (1/r) \exp kr \cdot A(\vartheta)$, so folgt mit Hilfe von (100.8′*ps*) und (134.21) zunächst streng

$$\sigma = \frac{4}{k\,a^2} \operatorname{Im} A(0) = 2 + \frac{4}{k\,a^2} \operatorname{Im} \int_a^\infty \psi(\varrho)\,\varrho\,d\varrho. \tag{134.39}$$

[Vorzeichenumkehr gegenüber (134.21) infolge des Übergangs zum komplementären Problem.] In unserer Näherung, die nur Korrekturterme berücksichtigt, die gegenüber dem Hauptglied um eine Größenordnung $\varepsilon^{-\frac{1}{2}}$ kleiner sind, ergibt sich mit Hilfe von (134.24)

$$\int_a^\infty \psi(\varrho)\,\varrho\,d\varrho \to \sqrt{a}\,\overline{\psi}(0). \tag{134.40}$$

Setzt man hier (134.37) ein, so ergibt sich zunächst für die Streuamplitude in der *Einfallsrichtung*

$$A(0) \to \frac{1}{k}\left\{\frac{i\,\varepsilon^2}{2} + \frac{\varepsilon}{2} - \frac{\varepsilon^{\frac{1}{2}}}{\sqrt{\pi}}\,e^{i\left(2\varepsilon - \frac{\pi}{4}\right)} + \cdots\right\}. \tag{134.41}$$

Bedienen wir uns der Sprechweise der „geometrischen Beugungstheorie" (Abschn. AIIc), so können wir sagen, daß die gegenüber (134.38) veränderte Größenordnung dieser Amplitude durch die Fokussierung der gebeugten Strahlen auf der Symmetrieachse zustande kommt. Dabei entspricht der erste Term in (134.41) dem geometrisch-optischen Strahl, der zweite den einfach gebeugten und der dritte den zweifach gebeugten Strahlen. Bemerkenswerterweise ist in der unmittelbaren Umgebung der Einfallsrichtung die Kirchhoffsche Amplitude des Fernfeldes [erster Term in (134.41)] um einen Faktor ε größer als die Braunbeksche Korrektur (zweiter Term), im Gegensatz zu allen anderen Richtungen, wo diese beiden Beiträge, wie wir gesehen haben, von der gleichen Größenordnung sind. Wir finden also auch hier das schon bei der Halbebene (Ziff. 116) und beim Spalt (Ziff. 124) gewonnene Ergebnis bestätigt, daß die Kirchhoffsche Lösung in der Umgebung der Einfallsrichtung (aber auch nur hier) das Hauptglied des Fernfeldes der Lösung des Randwertproblems liefert.

Trägt man (134.41) in (134.39) ein, so gibt die Braunbeksche Korrektur keinen Beitrag und es folgt

$$\sigma_s \to 2 - \frac{4\,\varepsilon^{-\frac{3}{2}}}{\sqrt{\pi}} \sin\left(2\varepsilon - \frac{\pi}{4}\right) + \cdots. \tag{134.42s}$$

LEVINE und WU (l. c. S. 485) haben zwei weitere Glieder dieser asymptotischen Entwicklung sowie die entsprechende für den p-Fall berechnet; ihr Ergebnis lautet

$$\left.\begin{aligned} \sigma_s \to 2 &- \frac{4\,\varepsilon^{-\frac{3}{2}}}{\sqrt{\pi}} \sin\left(2\varepsilon - \frac{\pi}{4}\right) - \varepsilon^{-2}\left\{\frac{1}{2} - \frac{2}{\pi}\sin\left(4\varepsilon - \frac{\pi}{2}\right)\right\} \\ &+ \frac{\varepsilon^{-\frac{5}{2}}}{\sqrt{\pi}}\left\{\frac{1}{2}\cos\left(2\varepsilon - \frac{\pi}{4}\right) - \frac{1}{\pi}\sin\left(6\varepsilon - \frac{3\pi}{4}\right)\right\} + \cdots \end{aligned}\right\} \tag{134.42′s}$$

bzw.

$$\sigma_p \to 2 - \frac{\varepsilon^{-2}}{2} + \frac{\varepsilon^{-\frac{5}{2}}}{2\sqrt{\pi}} \cos\left(2\varepsilon - \frac{\pi}{4}\right) + \cdots. \tag{134.42p}$$

Schließlich finden sie für eine unter dem Winkel α einfallende ebene Welle den Streukoeffizienten (s-Fall)

$$\left.\begin{aligned} \sigma_s \to 2 &- \frac{4\varepsilon^{-\frac{3}{2}}}{\sqrt{\pi}} \sin\left(2\varepsilon - \frac{\pi}{4}\right) J_0(2\varepsilon \sin\alpha) \\ &- \varepsilon^{-2}\left\{\frac{1}{2} - \frac{2}{\pi}\sin\left(4\varepsilon - \frac{\pi}{2} + 2\varepsilon\sin\alpha\right) J_0(\varepsilon\sin^2\alpha)\right\} + \cdots. \end{aligned}\right\} \tag{134.43}$$

Das Ergebnis (134.42s, p) erhält man auch mit Hilfe der geometrischen Beugungstheorie bei Berücksichtigung der *zweifach* gebeugten Strahlen[1] (vgl. Ziff. 44). Das Verhalten des Streuquerschnittes der Kreisscheibe für $\varepsilon \gg 1$ ist also demjenigen für den Streifen der Breite $2a$ verwandt (vgl. Ziff. 124); die Abhängigkeit von der Wellenlänge ist im s-Fall für beide Probleme im wesentlichen die gleiche, während sich im p-Fall beim Streukoeffizienten der Kreisscheibe noch ein monotones Glied der Größenordnung ε^{-2} überlagert. In Fig. 91 a ist der exakte Verlauf der Streukoeffizienten σ_p und σ_s noch einmal aufgetragen (vgl. Ziff. 128), zusammen mit der asymptotischen Darstellung für σ_s

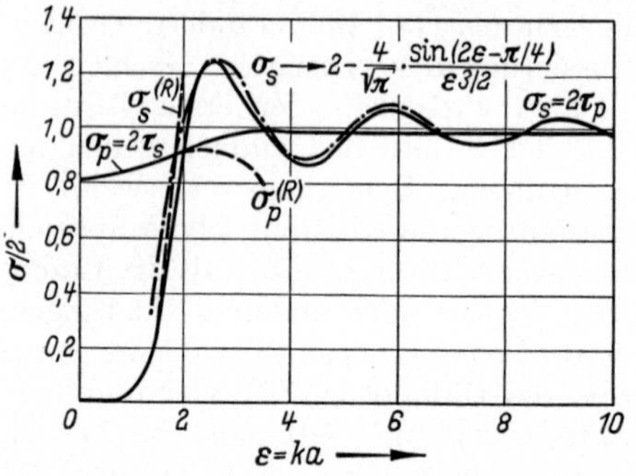

a

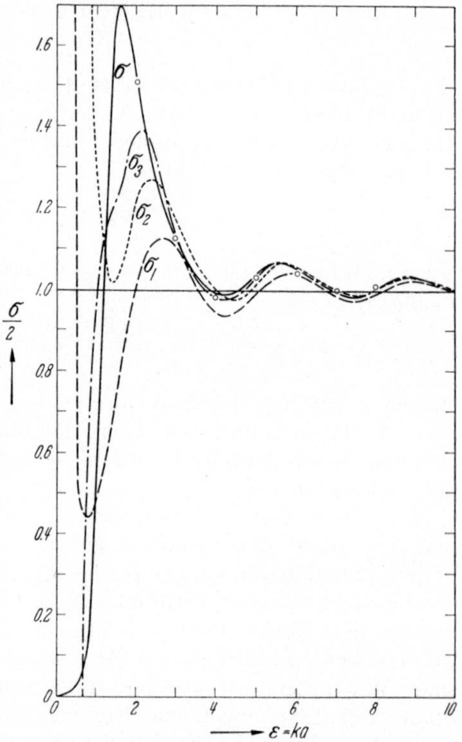

b

Fig. 91 a und b. Streukoeffizient σ für die Kreisscheibe bzw. Transmissionskoeffizient τ für die Kreisblende, a akustisch: —— streng (vgl. Fig. 81); — — Rayleighsche Näherung ($\varepsilon \ll 1$, nach Bouwkamp); —·—·— asymptotisch ($\varepsilon \gg 1$, nach Lévine); b elektromagnetisch: —— streng (nach Andrejewski, vgl. Fig. 80); — — — erste, ····· zweite, —·—·— dritte asymptotische Näherung (nach Seshadri und Wu); o o Meßwerte (nach Huang).

nach Gl. (134.42s). Außerdem sind noch die Kurven eingetragen, die sich mit Hilfe der viergliedrigen Potenzreihendarstellung (128.3p, s) ergeben (deren erstes Glied die Rayleighsche Näherung ist). Die Verhältnisse liegen hier wieder ähnlich, wie bei der Streuung am Streifen (Ziff. 124); die Potenzreihen konvergieren schlecht (im p-Fall etwas besser als im s-Fall), während die asymptotischen Darstellungen bis herunter zu mäßig großen ε sehr brauchbare Näherungen liefern. Für das elektromagnetische Streuproblem ist die asymptotische Lösung des

[1] Vgl. J. B. Keller: N.Y. Univ. Res. Rep. No. EM-92 (1956). — S. N. Karp u. J. B. Keller: N.Y. Univ. Res. Rep. No. EM-143 (1959).

Randwertproblems von SESHADRI und WU[1] durchgeführt worden. Für den Streukoeffizienten der Kreisscheibe ergibt sich (senkrechte Inzidenz einer linear polarisierten ebenen Welle):

$$\left.\begin{aligned} \sigma \to 2 &- \frac{2\varepsilon^{-\frac{3}{2}}}{\sqrt{\pi}} \sin\left(2\varepsilon - \frac{\pi}{4}\right) + \varepsilon^{-2}\left\{\frac{3}{2} + \frac{1}{\pi}\sin\left(4\varepsilon - \frac{\pi}{2}\right)\right\} \\ &- \frac{\varepsilon^{-\frac{5}{2}}}{\sqrt{\pi}}\left\{\frac{7}{2}\cos\left(2\varepsilon - \frac{\pi}{4}\right) + \frac{1}{2\pi}\sin\left(6\varepsilon - \frac{3\pi}{4}\right)\right\} + \cdots. \end{aligned}\right\} \tag{134.44}$$

Fig. 91b gibt einen Vergleich der den drei Korrekturtermen in (134.44) entsprechenden Näherungen untereinander und mit dem strengen Verlauf nach ANDREJEWSKI (vgl. Fig. 80). Außerdem sind noch einige Meßwerte von HUANG[2] eingetragen.

c 4) Das Variationsprinzip

135. Der akustische Fall. LEVINE und SCHWINGER[3] haben das akustische und das elektromagnetische Beugungsproblem auf ein Variationsprinzip zurückgeführt (vgl. Abschn. A III h) und auf das von uns diskutierte spezielle Problem angewandt. Wir beschränken uns hier auf die Behandlung des akustischen Problems und stützen uns dabei auf die Integralgleichung (131.1), die sich auf den Fall der Randbedingung $\partial v/\partial z = 0$ auf der Kreisscheibe bezieht. Indem wir von vornherein $z = 0$ annehmen und als Ausgleich dafür unter Einführung eines Parameters $\varkappa$ die Greensche Funktion $G(R)$ durch $G\left(\sqrt{R^2+\varkappa^2}\right)$ ersetzen, schreiben wir Gl. (131.1) in der Form

$$\lim_{\varkappa\to 0} \int\limits_S \varphi' \frac{\partial^2 G}{\partial \varkappa^2}\, d\sigma' = i\, k \quad \textit{auf } (S). \tag{135.1}$$

Diese Gleichung läßt sich aus dem Variationsprinzip

$$\delta \left\{\lim_{\varkappa\to 0} \iint\limits_{SS} \frac{\partial^2 G}{\partial \varkappa^2}\, \varphi\, \varphi'\, d\sigma\, d\sigma' - 2 i\, k \int\limits_S \varphi\, d\sigma\right\} = 0 \tag{135.2}$$

für die unbekannte Funktion φ herleiten, wie man unmittelbar sieht. Gl. (135.2) ist im wesentlichen gleichbedeutend mit der Forderung, das Doppelintegral in (135.2) bei festgehaltener Normierung $\int\limits_S \varphi\, d\sigma$ von φ zum Extremum zu machen. In dieser geringfügig abgeänderten Formulierung des Variationsproblems kommt dem Faktor $-2i\,k$ in Gl. (135.2) die Rolle eines Lagrangeschen Multiplikators zu.

Wir behandeln das Variationsproblem nach dem *Ritzschen Verfahren* (vgl. Ziff. 107) und machen unter Einführung zweier Parameter a_1, a_2 den Ansatz

$$\varphi = a_1 \sqrt{a^2 - \varrho^2} + a_2 (a^2 - \varrho^2)^{\frac{3}{2}}, \tag{135.3}$$

der durch (131.11) nahegelegt wird. Während es sich aber dort um eine Approximation für große Wellenlängen handelte, sind jetzt die Parameter so zu bestimmen, daß die Lösung für eine *beliebige* vorgegebene Wellenlänge möglichst gut angenähert wird.

---

[1] S. R. SESHADRI u. T. T. WU: Harvard Univ. Cruft Lab. Sci. Rep. No. 16 (1958). — Trans. Inst. Rad. Engrs. AP-**8**, 27 (1960). Bezüglich der Behandlung des hochfrequenten Grenzfalles mit Hilfe einer stationären Darstellung vgl. C. HUANG: Harvard Univ. Cruft Lab. Techn. Rep. No. 164 (1953). — C. HUANG, R. D. KODIS u. H. LEVINE: J. Appl. Phys. **26**, 151 (1955). — H. H. CHANG: Harvard Univ. Cruft Lab. Sci. Rep. No. 2 (1955).

[2] C. HUANG: l. c. 1. — Fig. 91b ist der Monographie von R. W. P. KING u. T. T. WU: The Scattering and Diffraction of Waves, Cambridge Mass. 1959 entnommen.

[3] H. LEVINE u. J. SCHWINGER: Phys. Rev. **74**, 958, 1212 (1948); **75**, 1423, 1608 (1949) (akustisch). — Comm. Pure Appl. Math. **3**, 355 (1950) (elektromagnetisch).

Verwendung des Ansatzes (135.3) in Gl. (135.2) führt auf die beiden Integraltypen

$$\left.\begin{aligned} C_{nm} &= \lim_{\varkappa\to 0} \iint\limits_{S\,S} \frac{\partial^2 G}{\partial \varkappa^2} (a^2-\varrho^2)^{n-\frac{1}{2}} (a^2-\varrho^2)^{m-\frac{1}{2}}\, d\sigma\, d\sigma' \\ B_n &= \int\limits_S (a^2-\varrho^2)^{n-\frac{1}{2}}\, d\sigma \end{aligned}\right\} \tag{135.4}$$

und für die zu variierende Funktion in (135.2) zu dem Ausdruck

$$C_{11} a_1^2 + 2 C_{12} a_1 a_2 + C_{22} a_2^2 - 2 i k (B_1 a_1 + B_2 a_2). \tag{135.5}$$

Aufsuchung des Extremums liefert

$$\left.\begin{aligned} C_{11} a_1 + C_{12} a_2 &= i k B_1 \\ C_{12} a_1 + C_{22} a_2 &= i k B_2 \end{aligned}\right\} \tag{135.6}$$

und weiter

$$a_1 = \frac{i k}{D} \begin{vmatrix} B_1 & C_{12} \\ B_2 & C_{22} \end{vmatrix}, \qquad a_2 = \frac{i k}{D} \begin{vmatrix} C_{11} & B_1 \\ C_{12} & B_2 \end{vmatrix}, \qquad D = \begin{vmatrix} C_{11} & C_{12} \\ C_{12} & C_{22} \end{vmatrix}, \tag{135.7}$$

womit unsere Aufgabe im Prinzip gelöst ist[1].

Zur Gewinnung des Streukoeffizienten σ_s (s-Fall) berechnen wir die Streuwelle in weitem Abstand r für den Streuwinkel $\vartheta = 0$ nach Gl. (130.4s) und erhalten mit Rücksicht auf (135.3), (135.4)

$$v_S \to -\frac{\partial}{\partial z} \frac{e^{ikr}}{4\pi r} \int\limits_S \varphi\, d\sigma = -\frac{i k}{4\pi} \cdot \frac{e^{ikr}}{r} (B_1 a_1 + B_2 a_2). \tag{135.8}$$

Hieraus ergibt sich nach (100.8$'p, s$), durch einen Faktor $1/k$ dimensionell vervollständigt, mit (100.6) die gesamte Streuintensität J_S und nach Division durch $a^2\pi$ der Streukoeffizient

$$\sigma_s = -\frac{1}{a^2\pi} \operatorname{Im}\left[i (B_1 a_1 + B_2 a_2)\right] \tag{135.9}$$

oder unter Berücksichtigung von Gl. (135.7)

$$\sigma_s^{(2)} = \frac{k}{a^2\pi} \operatorname{Im}\left(\frac{C_{22} B_1^2 - 2 C_{12} B_1 B_2 + C_{11} B_2^2}{D}\right). \tag{135.10}$$

Die Schreibweise $\sigma_s^{(2)}$ für den Streukoeffizienten soll darauf hindeuten, daß die Näherungsrechnung mit einem zweigliedrigen Ansatz (135.3) durchgeführt wurde. Verwenden wir statt dessen einen eingliedrigen Ansatz, so sind nur die Integrale B_1, C_{11} beizubehalten und alle anderen zu streichen. Man erhält dann anstelle (135.10) als Streukoeffizienten erster Näherung

$$\sigma_s^{(1)} = \frac{k}{a^2\pi} \operatorname{Im}\left(\frac{B_1^2}{C_{11}}\right). \tag{135.10a}$$

---

[1] Entwickelt man die Koeffizienten a_1, a_2 in (135.7) nach $\varepsilon = k a$, so ergeben sich genau die (131.25) entsprechenden Werte. Infolge des stationären Charakters von (135.5) ist jedoch zu erwarten, daß eine Auswertung von (135.7) für beliebige ε brauchbare Ergebnisse für einen größeren ε-Bereich liefert, als die Reihenentwicklung nach ε (vgl. $\sigma_s^{(R)}$ in Fig. 91a mit $\sigma^{(1,2)}$ in Fig. 92). Ergänzt man den Ansatz (135.3) zu einer unendlichen Reihe im Sinne von (131.11), so ergibt sich anstelle von (135.6) ein unendliches Gleichungssystem, über das eingehende Untersuchungen vorliegen. W. Magnus: N. Y. Univ. Res. Rep. No. EM-32 (1951). — Quart. Appl. Math. **11**, 77 (1953). — N. Y. Univ. Res. Rep. No. EM-80 (1956). — A. T. de Hoop: Appl. Sci. Res. B **4**, 151 (1954).

Es bleiben noch einige Worte über die Auswertung der Integrale B_n und C_{nm} zu sagen. Die B_n berechnen sich elementar zu

$$B_1 = \frac{2\pi}{3} a^3, \quad B_2 = \frac{2\pi}{5} a^5. \tag{135.11}$$

Zur Bestimmung der C_{nm} mit $d\sigma = \varrho\, d\varrho\, d\varphi$, $d\sigma' = \varrho'\, d\varrho'\, d\varphi'$ benötigen wir verschiedene Beziehungen aus der Theorie der Bessel-Funktionen und zwar die Sommerfeldsche Formel[1]

$$G = \frac{e^{ik\sqrt{R^2+\varkappa^2}}}{4\pi\sqrt{R^2+\varkappa^2}} = \frac{1}{4\pi}\int\limits_0^\infty J_0(\tau R)\, e^{-\varkappa\sqrt{\tau^2-k^2}} \cdot \frac{\tau\, d\tau}{\sqrt{\tau^2-k^2}} \tag{135.12}$$

mit $\sqrt{\tau^2-k^2} = -i\sqrt{k^2-\tau^2}$ für $\tau < k$, das Additionstheorem der Bessel-Funktionen

$$J_0(\tau \hat{R}) = \sum_{\nu=-\infty}^{\infty} J_\nu(\tau\varrho)\, J_\nu(\tau\varrho')\, e^{i\nu(\varphi-\varphi')}, \qquad \hat{R} = \sqrt{\varrho^2 - \varrho'^2 - 2\varrho\varrho'\cos(\varphi-\varphi')} \tag{135.13}$$

und die Formel von Sonine[2]

$$J_{\nu+\mu+1}(z) = \frac{z^{\nu+1}}{2^\nu \Gamma(\nu+1)} \int\limits_0^{\pi/2} J_\mu(z\sin\vartheta)\, \sin^{\mu+1}\vartheta\, \cos^{2\nu+1}\vartheta \cdot d\vartheta. \tag{135.14}$$

Geht man mit (135.13) in (135.12) und hiermit in (135.4) ein, so verschwinden bei der Winkelintegration alle höheren Bessel-Funktionen mit $\nu \neq 0$. Die beiden verbleibenden radialen Integrale haben bis auf die Vertauschung von n und m die gleiche Gestalt

$$2\pi \int\limits_0^a J_0(\tau\varrho)\, (a^2-\varrho^2)^{n-\frac{1}{2}}\, \varrho\, d\varrho \tag{135.15}$$

und lassen sich mit der Substitution $\varrho = a\sin\vartheta$ nach Gl. (135.14) ausrechnen:

$$\left.\begin{aligned} &2\pi a^{2n+1} \int\limits_0^{\pi/2} J_0(\tau a \sin\vartheta)\cos^{2n}\vartheta \cdot \sin\vartheta\, d\vartheta \\ &\qquad = \pi\, \Gamma(n+\tfrac{1}{2})\, (2a)^{n+\frac{1}{2}}\, \tau^{-n-\frac{1}{2}}\, J_{n+\frac{1}{2}}(\tau a). \end{aligned}\right\} \tag{135.16}$$

Zusammenfassung der verschiedenen Ausdrücke liefert schließlich nach Ausführung der Differentiation nach $\varkappa$ und des Grenzüberganges $\varkappa \to 0$ mit der Substitution $\tau a = z$

$$\left.\begin{aligned} C_{nm} = {} & \pi\, \Gamma(n+\tfrac{1}{2})\, \Gamma(m+\tfrac{1}{2})\, 2^{n+m-1} a^{2n+2m-1} \cdot \\ & \cdot \int\limits_0^\infty J_{n+\frac{1}{2}}(z)\, J_{m+\frac{1}{2}}(z)\, z^{-(n+m)} \sqrt{z^2-\varepsilon^2}\, dz. \end{aligned}\right\} \tag{135.17}$$

Das stehengebliebene Integral läßt sich noch durch ziemlich umständliche Rechnungen auf Besselsche und Struvesche Funktionen und einfache Integrale über solche Funktionen zurückführen und wird dadurch der numerischen Auswertung zugänglich.

136. Diskussion der Ergebnisse. Das von uns behandelte Problem ist das der Kreisscheibe mit der Randbedingung $\partial v/\partial n = 0$. Levine und Schwinger gehen vom damit äquivalenten Problem der Kreisöffnung im ebenen Schirm mit der Randbedingung $v = 0$ aus. Die Rechnung ist in beiden Fällen genau die gleiche, nur betrachten Levine und Schwinger entsprechend ihrem anderen Ausgangs-

[1] W. Magnus u. F. Oberhettinger: Formeln und Sätze für die speziellen Funktionen der mathematischen Physik, 2. Aufl., S. 48. Berlin: Springer 1948. — G.N. Watson: Theory of Besselfunctions, S. 416. Cambridge: Cambridge University Press 1944.

[2] W. Magnus u. F. Oberhettinger: l. c. S. 44. — G.N. Watson: l. c. S. 373.

punkt statt des Streukoeffizienten den Transmissionskoeffizienten $\tau_p = \sigma_s/2$ und erhalten den in Fig. 92 wiedergegebenen Verlauf in Abhängigkeit von $\varepsilon = ka$. σ_s ist nach unseren Gln. (135.10a) und (135.10) in erster und zweiter Näherung dargestellt. Zum Vergleich ist noch einmal die Kurve nach der strengen Theorie

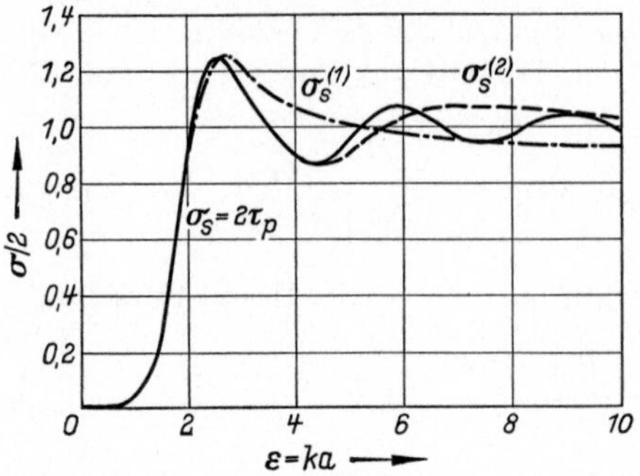

Fig. 92.

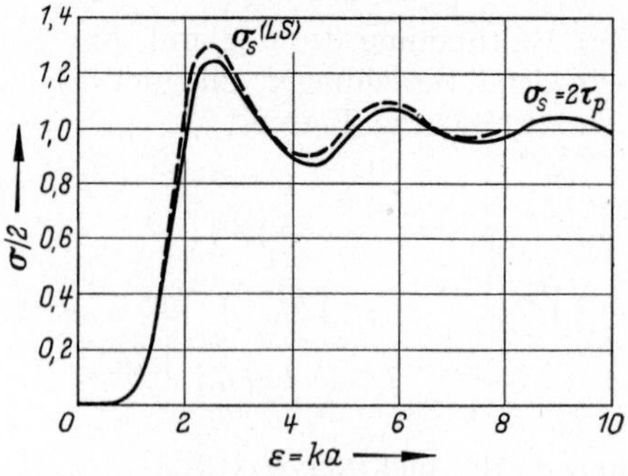

Fig. 93.

Fig. 92. Streukoeffizient σ für die Kreisscheibe bzw. Transmissionskoeffizient τ für die Kreisblende, akustisch: —— streng; —·—·— nach Levine und Schwinger mittels stationärer Darstellung mit eingliedriger Testfunktion für den Bereich $\varrho < a$; — — mit zweigliedriger Testfunktion.

Fig. 93. Dasselbe wie in Fig. 92 bei Benutzung einer Testfunktion für den Bereich $\varrho > a$ (nach Levine und Schwinger).

von Abschn. c1, Ziff. 128, eingetragen. Die Übereinstimmung der nach dem Variationsprinzip gewonnenen Resultate mit der strengen Theorie ist ausgezeichnet und in Anbetracht des Umstandes, daß das Ritzsche Verfahren mit nur zwei verfügbaren Parametern durchgeführt wurde, erstaunlich gut. Levine und Schwinger haben dasselbe Problem noch einmal auf Grund eines zweiten Variationsprinzips (vgl. Ziff. 107) behandelt, bei dem anstelle der auf der Kreisfläche definierten Funktion φ die in der Schirmebene außerhalb des Kreises definierte Funktion ψ als Unbekannte auftritt [vgl. Gl. (130.4)]. Die mit einem einzigen Ritzschen Parameter durchgeführte Rechnung liefert für den Streukoeffizienten σ_s die in Fig. 93 wiedergegebene Kurve, die für große ε noch besser als Fig. 92, für kleinere ε weniger gut mit den Ergebnissen der strengen Theorie übereinstimmt.

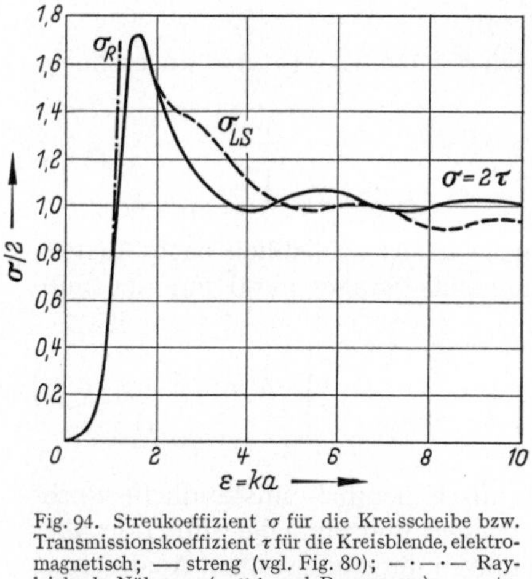

Fig. 94. Streukoeffizient σ für die Kreisscheibe bzw. Transmissionskoeffizient τ für die Kreisblende, elektromagnetisch; —— streng (vgl. Fig. 80); —·—·— Rayleighsche Näherung ($\varepsilon \ll 1$, nach Bouwkamp); — — stationäre Darstellung nach Levine und Schwinger mittels statischer Testfunktion.

Auf die entsprechende Behandlung des elektromagnetischen Problems gehen wir nicht ein. Sie liefert für den Streukoeffizienten die in Fig. 94 wiedergegebene gestrichelte Kurve[1], die für $\varepsilon \lesssim 2$ praktisch mit dem Verlauf von σ nach der strengen Theorie (ausgezogene Kurve, vgl. Ziff. 128) übereinstimmt. Außerdem ist noch eine strichpunktierte Kurve eingezeichnet, die mit Hilfe der Potenzreihe (128.1) berechnet worden ist. Diese Reihe (deren erstes Glied die *Rayleighsche Näherung* ist) ist demnach — obwohl dreigliedrig — nur für $\varepsilon \lesssim 1$ brauchbar.

[1] Nach H. Levine u. J. Schwinger: Comm. Pure Appl. Math. **3**, 355 (1950).

II. Beugung an konvexen Körpern ohne Kanten.

a) Beugung am Kreiszylinder.

Wie die in dem vorangehenden Abschn. I behandelten drei Beispiele ebener Schirme, gehört auch die Beugung am Kreiszylinder zu den *separierbaren* Problemen. Durch Separation der Wellengleichung in Zylinderkoordinaten r, ϑ ist die Randwertaufgabe wohl zuerst von Lord RAYLEIGH (1882) gelöst worden. Die sich ergebende Reihendarstellung nach trigonometrischen Funktionen (für die ϑ-Abhängigkeit) und ganzzahligen Zylinderfunktionen (für die r-Abhängigkeit) ist seither Gegenstand zahlreicher Arbeiten geworden. Um den Anschluß an Abschn. AIII d herzustellen, wollen wir jedoch im folgenden das Problem mit Hilfe der Integralgleichung für den Flächenstrom lösen, was natürlich zum gleichen Ergebnis führt. Die Reihen konvergieren nur dann mit (für die numerische Rechnung) brauchbarer Schnelligkeit, wenn der Zylinderradius a die Wellenlänge λ der einfallenden Welle nicht wesentlich überschreitet $\left(\text{für } \varepsilon = ka = \frac{2\pi a}{\lambda} \ll 1\right.$ ergibt sich die *Rayleigh-Streuung*$\left.\right)$. Die Reihen konvergieren zwar für alle ε, jedoch ist die Zahl der zu berücksichtigenden Reihenglieder von derselben Größenordnung wie ε. Mit höherem numerischen Aufwand (Rechenmaschinen) lassen sich die Reihen noch bis etwa $\varepsilon = 10$ praktisch auswerten (LOWAN-MORSE-FESHBACH-LAX 1946). Die einzelnen Reihenglieder kann man als die Strahlung entsprechender (linearer) Multipole deuten. Mit wachsendem ε müssen laufend mehr *(ungedämpfte) Partialwellen* berücksichtigt werden, so daß die Strahlungscharakteristik fortschreitend komplizierter wird. Erst im Grenzfall $\varepsilon \to \infty$ stellen sich die einfachen Verhältnisse der geometrischen Optik ein.

Während der Rayleighsche Grenzfall ($\varepsilon \ll 1$) einer Reihenentwicklung nach *steigenden* Potenzen von ε entspricht, hat man im geometrisch-optischen Grenzfall nach einer asymptotischen Entwicklung nach *fallenden* (gebrochenen) Potenzen von ε zu suchen. Diese kann man nach DEBYE (1908) dadurch erhalten, daß man die strenge Lösung durch ein doppeltes Fourier-Integral darstellt und dieses mit Hilfe der Methode der stationären Phase (bzw. der Sattelpunktmethode) auswertet. Die Ergebnisse DEBYEs gehen jedoch über den geometrisch-optischen Grenzfall nicht hinaus. Erst neuere Untersuchungen (FOCK 1946, FRANZ und DEPPERMANN 1952) haben gezeigt, daß die an den geometrisch-optischen Grenzfall anschließende asymptotische Entwicklung gegenüber dem entsprechenden Problem bei ebenen Schirmen (Abschn. BI) etwas Neues bietet. Es treten nämlich neben der Reihe nach fallenden Potenzen in ε noch Glieder auf, die sich als eine Art *Oberflächenwelle* oder besser „*Kriechwelle*" interpretieren lassen. Dieser Sachverhalt läßt sich im Sinne der geometrischen Beugungstheorie (KELLER 1955, vgl. Abschn. AII c) folgendermaßen beschreiben: Die von der Schattengrenze aus auf der Oberfläche des glatten beugenden Körpers entlang laufenden „*gebeugten Strahlen*" werden durch fortlaufend tangential abgespaltenen Sekundärstrahlen exponentiell geschwächt, so daß den gebeugten Strahlen eine (beim Umlaufen des Zylinders) um so stärker gedämpfte Welle entspricht, einen je längeren Bogen sie mit der Oberfläche gemeinsam haben. (Bei den ebenen Schirmen brauchen die gebeugten Strahlen lediglich um die unendlich stark gekrümmte Kante herumzulaufen, so daß keine Dämpfung verursacht wird.) Anders ausgedrückt kann man sagen, die geometrisch-optische Stromverteilung auf der Oberfläche ist bei mäßig großem ε durch „*Kriechströme*" zu korrigieren, die von der Schattengrenze ausgehend um den Körper herumlaufen und zufolge der Abstrahlung längs der Kriechstrecke exponentiell gedämpft sind. Diese Kriechströme ergeben sich als Lösungen der (sinngemäß vereinfachten) *homogenen* Integralgleichungen für die Oberflächen-ströme von Abschn. AIII d, Ziff. 76. Dem entspricht es, daß sich eine unendliche Folge von Dämpfungskonstanten ergibt (die naturgemäß unabhängig von der Art der Anregung sind; man kann hier von *gedämpften Partialwellen* sprechen). Die von den Kriechströmen abgestrahlten Kriechwellen — deren Dämpfungskonstante von der Größenordnung $\varepsilon^{\frac{1}{3}}$ ist, die sich also bei mäßig großem ε deutlich bemerkbar machen — sind in der Theorie der drahtlosen Telegraphie längs der kugelförmigen Erde seit langem als „*Residuenwellen*" bekannt. Sie werden nämlich nach dem Vorgang von Watson (1918) dadurch gewonnen, daß man die entsprechende Reihendarstellung mit Hilfe eines in der komplexen Ebene des Zeigers durch Residuenbildung auswertbaren Integrals darstellt (Ziff. 140). Diese Watson-Transformation liefert auch beim Zylinder den direkten analytischen Zugang zum Phänomen der Kriechwellen, ausgehend von der strengen Reihenentwicklung (Franz, Imai 1954). Wir wollen im folgenden die erwähnten Methoden in ihren Zusammenhängen mit einiger Ausführlichkeit darstellen, da die dabei auftretenden physikalischen Gesichtspunkte für alle Beugungsphänomene bei glatten Körpern charakteristisch sind. Bei dem praktisch wichtigeren, aber komplizierten Problem der Kugel, können wir uns dann vergleichsweise kurz fassen.

a 1) Reihendarstellung nach ungedämpften Partialwellen.

137. Lösung der Integralgleichungen. Auf den (unendlich langen) ideal leitenden Zylinder vom Radius a falle eine ebene Welle, deren Ausbreitungsrichtung senkrecht zur Zylinderachse sei (z-Achse eines Polarkoordinatensystems r, ϑ, z, s. Fig. 95):

$$v_0(r,\vartheta) = \mathrm{e}^{-ikr\cos\vartheta}. \tag{137.1}$$

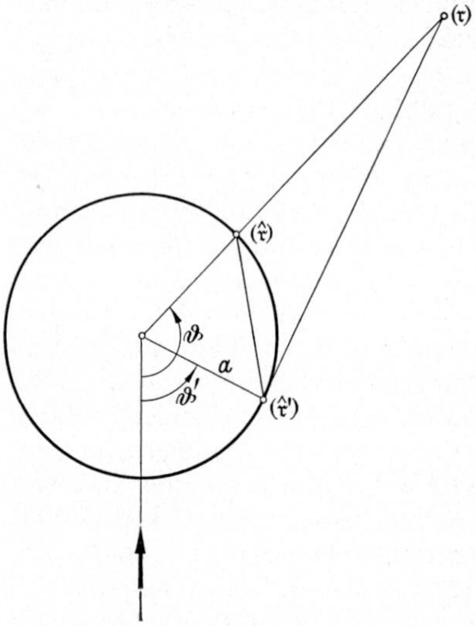

Fig. 95. Zur Beugung am Kreiszylinder.

Wir haben dann für die beiden Polarisationsfälle folgende (von z unabhängige) *Randwertprobleme* zu lösen

$$(\Delta + k^2)\, v(r,\vartheta) = 0 \tag{137.2}$$

$$\textit{Randbedingung}\left\{\begin{aligned} &v\,(a,\vartheta) = 0 \quad (p\text{-Fall}) \\ &\frac{\partial v\,(a,\vartheta)}{\partial r} = 0 \quad (s\text{-Fall}). \end{aligned}\right\} \tag{137.3}$$

Ihre Lösung können wir nach (76.1 p, s) in der Gestalt

$$\left.\begin{aligned} p\text{-}\textit{Fall}\quad v_{\|}(r,\vartheta) &= \mathrm{e}^{-ikr\cos\vartheta} \\ &\quad - \frac{ia}{4}\int\limits_0^{2\pi} \psi_{\|}(\vartheta')\, H_0^1(kR)\, d\vartheta', \end{aligned}\right\} \tag{137.4p}$$

$$s\text{-}\textit{Fall}\qquad v_{\perp}(r,\vartheta) = \mathrm{e}^{-ikr\cos\vartheta} + \frac{ia}{4}\int\limits_0^{2\pi} \psi_{\perp}(\vartheta')\,\frac{\partial}{\partial a} H_0^1(kR)\, d\vartheta' \tag{137.4s}$$

mit

$$R = |\mathfrak{r} - \hat{\mathfrak{r}}'| = \sqrt{r^2 + a^2 - 2ar\cos(\vartheta - \vartheta')} \tag{137.5}$$

darstellen. Die Indices $\|$ bzw. $\perp$ sollen andeuten, daß die elektrische Feldstärke der durch

$$p\text{-}\textit{Fall}\qquad \mathfrak{E} = \mathfrak{z}\, v_{\|}, \quad \varkappa\,\mathfrak{H} = \frac{i}{k}\,[\mathfrak{z}\,\mathrm{grad}\, v_{\|}] \tag{137.4'p}$$

bzw.

s-Fall $$\mathfrak{E} = \frac{-i}{k}[\mathfrak{z}\,\mathrm{grad}\,v_\perp], \quad \varkappa\,\mathfrak{H} = \mathfrak{z}\,v_\perp \tag{137.4′s}$$

dargestellten elektromagnetischen Felder parallel bzw. senkrecht zur Zylinderachse polarisiert ist (vgl. Ziff. 4). (Dabei bedeutet $\mathfrak{z}$ den Einheitsvektor in Richtung der Zylinderachse, $k = \omega\sqrt{\varepsilon_0\mu_0}$, $\varkappa = \sqrt{\mu_0/\varepsilon_0}$; ferner ω die Kreisfrequenz, ε_0 die Dielektrizitätskonstante, μ_0 die Permeabilität des homogenen Mediums, in das der Zylinder eingebettet ist.) Die Flächenstromdichten $\psi_\parallel = \left(\frac{\partial v_\parallel}{\partial r}\right)_{r=a}$ bzw. $\psi_\perp = (v_\perp)_{r=a}$ sind hierbei aus den Integralgleichungen (76.6*p*, 7*s*) zu bestimmen. Mit

$$|\hat{\mathfrak{r}} - \hat{\mathfrak{r}}'| = 2a\left|\sin\frac{\vartheta-\vartheta'}{2}\right| \tag{137.5′}$$

und $(ka = \varepsilon)$

$$\left.\begin{aligned}\left\{\frac{\partial}{\partial r}H_0^1(kR)\right\}_{r=a} &= \left\{\frac{\partial}{\partial a}H_0^1(kR)\right\}_{r=a} = \frac{1}{2}\frac{\partial}{\partial a}H_0^1\left(2\varepsilon\left|\sin\frac{\vartheta-\vartheta'}{2}\right|\right)\\ &= -k\,H_1^1\left(2\varepsilon\left|\sin\frac{\vartheta-\vartheta'}{2}\right|\right)\left|\sin\frac{\vartheta-\vartheta'}{2}\right|\end{aligned}\right\} \tag{137.6}$$

nehmen diese Integralgleichungen hier folgende Form an

$$\psi_\parallel(\vartheta) + \frac{\varepsilon}{2i}\int_0^{2\pi}\psi_\parallel(\vartheta')\,H_1^1\left(2\varepsilon\left|\sin\frac{\vartheta-\vartheta'}{2}\right|\right)\left|\sin\frac{\vartheta-\vartheta'}{2}\right|d\vartheta' = -2ik\cos\vartheta\,\mathrm{e}^{-i\varepsilon\cos\vartheta} \tag{137.7p}$$

bzw.

$$\psi_\perp(\vartheta) - \frac{\varepsilon}{2i}\int_0^{2\pi}\psi_\perp(\vartheta')\,H_1^1\left(2\varepsilon\left|\sin\frac{\vartheta-\vartheta'}{2}\right|\right)\left|\sin\frac{\vartheta-\vartheta'}{2}\right|d\vartheta' = 2\,\mathrm{e}^{-i\varepsilon\cos\vartheta}. \tag{137.7s}$$

Zur Lösung dieser Fredholmschen Integralgleichungen zweiter Art entwickeln wir den Kern (137.6) in eine Fourier-Reihe. Mit Hilfe des Additionstheorems[1]

$$\left.\begin{aligned}&H_0^1\left(k\sqrt{r^2+r'^2-2rr'\cos(\vartheta-\vartheta')}\right)\\ &\qquad= \sum_{n=-\infty}^{\infty}\mathrm{e}^{in(\vartheta-\vartheta')}\cdot\begin{cases}J_n(kr)\,H_n^1(kr') & (r<r')\\ J_n(kr')\,H_n^1(kr) & (r>r')\end{cases}\end{aligned}\right\} \tag{137.8}$$

also

$$H_0^1\left(2\varepsilon\left|\sin\frac{\vartheta-\vartheta'}{2}\right|\right) = \sum_{n=-\infty}^{\infty}J_n(\varepsilon)\,H_n^1(\varepsilon)\,\mathrm{e}^{in(\vartheta-\vartheta')} \tag{137.8′}$$

ergibt sich die gesuchte Darstellung in der Form

$$\left.\begin{aligned}\frac{a}{4i}\frac{\partial}{\partial a}H_0^1\left(2\varepsilon\left|\sin\frac{\vartheta-\vartheta'}{2}\right|\right) &= -\frac{\varepsilon}{2i}H_1^1\left(2\varepsilon\left|\sin\frac{\vartheta-\vartheta'}{2}\right|\right)\left|\sin\frac{\vartheta-\vartheta'}{2}\right|\\ &= \frac{\varepsilon}{4i}\sum_{n=-\infty}^{\infty}\{J_n'(\varepsilon)\,H_n^1(\varepsilon) + J_n(\varepsilon)\,H_n^{1\prime}(\varepsilon)\}\,\mathrm{e}^{in(\vartheta-\vartheta')}\end{aligned}\right\} \tag{137.9}$$

(wobei wir hier und im folgenden die Ableitungen der Zylinderfunktionen nach ihrem Argument durch Striche kennzeichnen). Entwickeln wir auch die Lösung ψ

[1] Vgl. W. Magnus u. F. Oberhettinger: Formeln und Sätze für die speziellen Funktionen der mathematischen Physik, 2. Aufl., S. 31. Berlin-Göttingen-Heidelberg: Springer 1948.

in eine Fourier-Reihe

$$\psi(\vartheta) = \sum_{n=-\infty}^{\infty} a^{(n)} \, e^{n i \left(\vartheta - \frac{\pi}{2}\right)} \tag{137.10}$$

sowie die Inhomogenitäten rechts in (137.7) mit Hilfe der Darstellung für die ebene Welle

$$e^{-ikr\cos\vartheta} = \sum_{n=-\infty}^{\infty} J_n(kr) \, e^{i n \left(\vartheta - \frac{\pi}{2}\right)}, \tag{137.10'}$$

so ergibt sich durch Eintragen von (137.9, 10) in (137.7) die Beziehung (oberes Vorzeichen für den p-Fall, unteres für den s-Fall)

$$a^{(n)} \left\{1 \pm \frac{i\pi\varepsilon}{2} \left[J_n'(\varepsilon) \, H_n^1(\varepsilon) + J_n(\varepsilon) \, H_n^{1\prime}(\varepsilon)\right]\right\} = \begin{Bmatrix} 2k \, J_n'(\varepsilon) \\ 2 J_n(\varepsilon). \end{Bmatrix} \tag{137.11}$$

Mit Hilfe der Wronskischen Determinante

$$\frac{i\pi\varepsilon}{2} \left\{J_n'(\varepsilon) \, H_n^1(\varepsilon) - J_n(\varepsilon) \, H_n^{1\prime}(\varepsilon)\right\} = 1 \tag{137.12}$$

ergibt sich daraus

$$a_{\parallel}^{(n)} = -\frac{2ik}{\pi\varepsilon} \cdot \frac{1}{H_n^1(\varepsilon)} \tag{137.13p}$$

$$a_{\perp}^{(n)} = \frac{2i}{\pi\varepsilon} \cdot \frac{1}{H_n^{1\prime}(\varepsilon)}. \tag{137.13s}$$

Für die Dichte des axial bzw. azimutal auf dem Zylindermantel fließenden Flächenstromes ergibt sich also

$$\psi_{\parallel}(\vartheta) = -\frac{2ik}{\pi\varepsilon} \sum_{n=-\infty}^{\infty} \frac{e^{i n \left(\vartheta - \frac{\pi}{2}\right)}}{H_n^1(\varepsilon)} \tag{137.14p}$$

$$\psi_{\perp}(\vartheta) = \frac{2i}{\pi\varepsilon} \sum_{n=-\infty}^{\infty} \frac{e^{i n \left(\vartheta - \frac{\pi}{2}\right)}}{H_n^{1\prime}(\varepsilon)}. \tag{137.14s}$$

Trägt man diese Darstellung in (137.4) ein, so ergibt sich unter Verwendung von (137.8) und (137.10′) das Feld in der Form

$$v_{\parallel}(r, \vartheta) = \sum_{n=-\infty}^{\infty} \left\{J_n(kr) - \frac{J_n(\varepsilon)}{H_n^1(\varepsilon)} \, H_n^1(kr)\right\} e^{i n \left(\vartheta - \frac{\pi}{2}\right)} \tag{137.15p}$$

bzw.

$$v_{\perp}(r, \vartheta) = \sum_{n=-\infty}^{\infty} \left\{J_n(kr) - \frac{J_n'(\varepsilon)}{H_n^{1\prime}(\varepsilon)} \, H_n^1(kr)\right\} e^{i n \left(\vartheta - \frac{\pi}{2}\right)}. \tag{137.15s}$$

Im folgenden wollen wir diese beiden Reihen zusammengefaßt in der Form

$$v(r, \vartheta) = \sum_{n=-\infty}^{\infty} \left\{J_n(kr) - \frac{\Omega \, J_n(\varepsilon)}{\Omega \, H_n^1(\varepsilon)} \, H_n^1(kr)\right\} e^{i n \left(\vartheta - \frac{\pi}{2}\right)} \tag{137.15'}$$

schreiben, wobei sich für $\Omega = 1$ die Lösung für den p-Fall bzw. für $\Omega = \partial/\partial\varepsilon$ diejenige für den s-Fall ergibt. Dies sind die Rayleighschen Reihen für die strenge Lösung unseres Beugungsproblems[1].

[1] Lord RAYLEIGH: Phil. Mag. (4) **12**, 86 (1881). Diese und die meisten der folgenden Arbeiten behandeln sogleich den allgemeineren Fall eines Zylinders von beliebigem Brechnungsindex und einer einfallenden Zylinderwelle. Eine schräg zur Zylinderachse einfallende ebene Welle behandeln P. WELLMANN: Z. Astrophys. **14**, 195 (1937) (fehlerhaft). — J. R. WAIT: Canad. J. Phys. **33**, 189 (1955). — R. BURBERG: Z. Naturforsch. **11** a, 300 (1956). Im Endlichen gelegene Quellpunkte behandeln F. OBERHETTINGER: Ann. Phys. **43**, 136 (1943). — R. D. KODIS: J. Appl. Phys. **23**, 249 (1952).

Der *Streukoeffizient* ist nach (101.7) [durch einen Faktor $k^{-\frac{1}{2}}$ dimensionell ergänzt] durch

$$\sigma = -\frac{1}{a}\sqrt{\frac{2\pi}{k}}\,\mathrm{Re}\left\{e^{\frac{i\pi}{4}} A(\pi)\right\} \tag{137.16}$$

gegeben, dabei bedeutet $A(\vartheta)$ die Amplitude des Fernfeldes der Streuwelle (s. unten).

Mit Hilfe des aus (137.15′) asymptotisch folgenden *Streufeldes* $(r\to\infty)$

$$v_S(r,\vartheta) \to \frac{e^{ikr}}{\sqrt{r}} A(\vartheta) = -\sqrt{\frac{2}{\pi k r}}\, e^{i\left(kr-\frac{\pi}{4}\right)} \sum_{n=-\infty}^{\infty} \frac{\Omega J_n(\varepsilon)}{\Omega H_n^1(\varepsilon)}\, e^{in(\vartheta-\pi)} \tag{137.17}$$

ergibt sich somit aus (137.16) die folgende Darstellung für den Streukoeffizienten

$$\sigma = \frac{2}{\varepsilon}\,\mathrm{Re} \sum_{n=-\infty}^{\infty} \frac{\Omega J_n(\varepsilon)}{\Omega H_n^1(\varepsilon)}\,. \tag{137.18}$$

138. Diskussion. Die an RAYLEIGH anschließende Literatur[1] beschäftigt sich hauptsächlich mit Anwendungen auf akustische Probleme sowie solche der Mikrowellentechnik, bei denen der Parameter $\varepsilon = ka$ die Größenordnung 1 besitzt, so daß man bei der numerischen Behandlung mit wenigen Gliedern der Reihen (137.15) auskommt. In neuerer Zeit ist durch Tabulierung der durch die Reihen dargestellten Funktionen (und entsprechender Hilfsfunktionen) der Bereich bis $\varepsilon = 10$ zugänglich gemacht worden[2].

Wir wollen zunächst einen Blick auf den *Rayleighschen Grenzfall* $\varepsilon \ll 1$ werfen. Hier ergibt sich durch Entwicklung der *Streuwelle* (137.17) nach Potenzen von ε in niedrigster Näherung ($\ln\gamma = 0{,}5772$ Eulersche Konstante)

$$v_{\parallel}^{(S)}(r,\vartheta) \to \sqrt{\frac{\pi}{2kr}}\, e^{i\left(kr+\frac{\pi}{4}\right)} \left(\frac{1}{\ln\frac{\varepsilon\gamma}{2} - \frac{i\pi}{2}} + \cdots\right) \tag{138.1p}$$

bzw.

$$v_{\perp}^{(S)}(r,\vartheta) \to -\sqrt{\frac{\pi}{2kr}}\, e^{i\left(kr+\frac{\pi}{4}\right)} \varepsilon^2 \left(\frac{1}{2} + \cos\vartheta + \cdots\right). \tag{138.1s}$$

---

[1] Ältere Untersuchungen und zusammenfassende Darstellungen bei W. v. IGNATOWSKY: Ann. Phys. **18**, 495 (1905); **23**, 905 (1907). — W. SEITZ: Ann. Physik **16**, 746 (1905); **19**, 554 (1906); **21**, 1013 (1900). — C. SCHÄFER u. F. GROSSMANN: Ann. Physik **31**, 455 (1910). — C. SCHÄFER u. J. MERZKIRCH: Z. Physik **13**, 166 (1923). — KOBAYASHI-IWAO: Ann. Physik **43**, 861 (1914). — G. THILO: Ann. Physik **62**, 531 (1920). — Lord RAYLEIGH: Theory of Sound, 2. Aufl., Bd. 2. London 1926. — A. SOMMERFELD in P. FRANK u. R. v. MISES: Die Differential- und Integralgleichungen der Mechanik und Physik, Bd. II, Kap. 13 bzw. 20. Braunschweig 1927 bzw. 1934. — G. WOLFSOHN: Handbuch der Physik, Bd. 20, Kap. 7. Berlin 1928. — J.A. STRATTON: Electromagnetic Theory. New York 1941. — F.E. BORGNIS u. C.H. PAPAS: Randwertprobleme der Mikrowellenphysik. Berlin-Göttingen-Heidelberg: Springer 1955. — Die neuere Literatur findet man zusammengestellt bei C.J. BOUWKAMP: Progr. Phys. (Lond.) **17**, 35 (1954) § 11. — Erwähnt seien P.S. CARTER: Proc. Inst. Radio Engrs. **31**, 671 (1943). — G. SINCLAIR: Proc. Inst. Radio Engrs. **39**, 660 (1951). — J.J. FARAN: J. Acoust. Soc. Amer. **23**, 405 (1951); **25**, 115 (1953). — R.W. HART u. E.W. MONTROLL: J. Appl. Phys. **22**, 1278 (1951). — N. SAITO u. Y. IKEDA: J. Phys. Soc. Japan **6**, 305 (1951). — W.S. LUCKE: J. Appl. Phys. **22**, 14 (1951). — D.T. LAIRD u. H. COHEN: J. Acoust. Soc. Amer. **24**, 46 (1952). — E.W. MONTROLL u. J.M. GREENBERG: Phys. Rev. **86**, 889 (1952). — C.T. TAI: J. Appl. Phys. **23**, 909 (1952). — S.T. WILES u. A.B. MCLAY: Canad. J. Phys. **32**, 372 (1954). — Eine eingehende Übersicht über die Ergebnisse der Theorie und Anwendungen bei H.C. VAN DE HULST: Light Scattering by Small Particles, Kap. 15. New York u. London 1957. — R.W.P. KING u. T.T. WU: The Scattering and Diffraction of Waves, Kap. 2. Cambridge, Mass. 1959.

[2] Umfangreiches Tabellenmaterial bei A.N. LOWAN, P.M. MORSE, H. FESHBACH u. M. LAX: Scattering and Radiation from Circular Cylinders and Spheres, Tables of Amplitudes and Phase Angles, Washington, D.C., V.S. Navy (1946); M. LAX u. H. FESHBACH: J. Acoust. Soc. Amer. **20**, 108 (1948).

Aus (137.16) erhält man damit für den Streukoeffizienten [in (138.1 s) muß man noch das Glied mit ε^4 berechnen, da die angeschriebenen Glieder noch keinen Beitrag zu (137.16) liefern]:

$$\sigma_{\parallel} = \frac{2\pi^2}{\varepsilon\left(4\ln^2\frac{\gamma\,\varepsilon}{2} + \pi^2\right)} + \cdots \tag{138.2p}$$

bzw.

$$\sigma_{\perp} = \frac{3\pi^2\varepsilon^3}{8} + \cdots . \tag{138.2s}$$

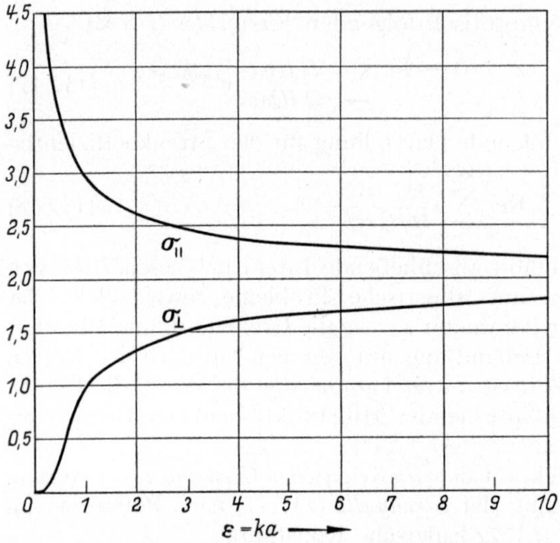

Fig. 96. Streukoeffizient für den ideal leitenden Kreiszylinder für die beiden Polarisationsfälle ($\sigma_{\parallel}$: elektrischer Vektor schwingt parallel zur Zylinderachse, $\sigma_{\perp}$: senkrecht zur Achse).

Das Verhalten des Streukoeffizienten für $\varepsilon \ll 1$ ist also demjenigen des Streifens der Breite $2a$ weitgehend analog [vgl. (121.4) mit (124.11)]. Die Streustrahlung ist (bei beliebig polarisierter Primärstrahlung) nahezu parallel zur Zylinderachse polarisiert.

Für größere ε ergibt sich durch numerische Auswertung der Reihe (137.18) der in Fig. 96 dargestellte Verlauf des Streukoeffizienten. In Fig. 97 ist die Intensität der *Rückwärtsstreuung* — genauer gesagt die Größe[1] $\frac{2}{a}\,|A(0)|^2$ — als Funktion von ε aufgetragen, die durch numerische Berechnung der Reihe (137.17) gewonnen worden ist[2]. Die hier für den s-Fall auftretenden Schwankungen lassen sich deuten als Interferenzen der *reflektierten Welle* mit den um den Zylinder herumgelaufenen *Kriechwellen* (Ziff. 146). (Im p-Fall sind die Kriechwellen so stark gedämpft, daß praktisch keine Interferenzen mehr auftreten.)

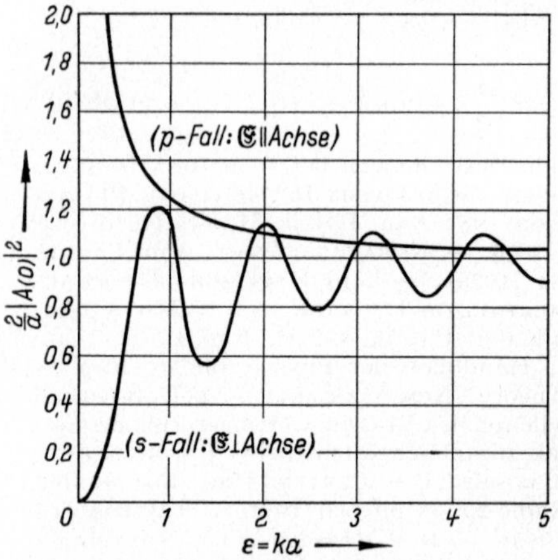

Fig. 97. Rückstreuung beim ideal leitenden Kreiszylinder für die beiden Polarisationsfälle.

Für den s-Fall ist das *Gesamtfeld auf der Oberfläche des Zylinders* im Verhältnis zur einfallenden Welle — also die Größe $\psi_{\perp}(\vartheta)\,e^{i\,\varepsilon\cos\vartheta}$ — in Fig. 120 auf S. 536 aufgetragen[3], und zwar links die Größe $20\log^{10}|\psi_{\perp}(\vartheta)|$ (in der in der Akustik üblichen Dezibel-Skala), rechts die Phasendifferenz zwischen $\psi_{\perp}(\vartheta)$ und $v_0(a,\vartheta)$, d. h. arc $\{\psi_{\perp}(\vartheta)\,e^{i\,\varepsilon\cos\vartheta}\}$. Diese Kurven stellen eine numerische Auswertung der Reihe (137.14 s) im Bereich $0 \leqq \varepsilon \leqq 10$ dar, mit ϑ als Parameter. Im folgenden Abschnitt

[1] Im geometrisch-optischen Grenzfall ($\varepsilon \to \infty$) hat diese Größe den Wert $\frac{2}{a}\,|A(0)|^2 \to 1$. Dies werden wir in Ziff. 146 bestätigt finden; es ergibt sich aber auch schon durch elementare geometrisch-optische Überlegungen.

[2] Beides nach H.C. VAN DE HULST: l. c.

[3] Nach F.M. WIENER: J. Acoust. Soc. Amer. **19**, 444 (1947).

wollen wir uns noch etwas eingehender mit der analytischen Darstellung des an die geometrische Optik anschließenden hochfrequenten Grenzfalles $\varepsilon \gg 1$ beschäftigen. Für diese Darstellung — die bis herunter zu mäßig großen ε brauchbar ist — benötigen wir zunächst einige Resultate aus der Theorie der Zylinderfunktionen.

139. Zur Darstellung der Zylinderfunktionen. Im folgenden soll eine Übersicht über das Verhalten der Zylinderfunktionen bei großem (reellen positiven) Argument aber beliebigem (auch komplexen) Index gegeben werden. Diese gewinnt man nach dem Vorgang von DEBYE[1] durch Anwendung der *Sattelpunktmethode* auf die Sommerfeldsche Integraldarstellung der Zylinderfunktionen:

$$Z_\nu(x) = \frac{1}{\pi}\int\limits_C e^{i x \cos\alpha + i\nu\left(\alpha - \frac{\pi}{2}\right)}\, d\alpha. \tag{139.1}$$

Dabei ergibt sich $H_\nu^1(x)$, $H_\nu^2(x)$ oder $2J_\nu(x)$, je nachdem, ob als Integrationsweg C in der α-Ebene der Weg C_1, C_2 oder C_0 in Fig. 98 gewählt wird. (Aus Konvergenzgründen muß C im Unendlichen auf schraffiertem Gebiet verlaufen, wo Täler des Integranden liegen.) Wir wollen den Exponenten des Integranden von (139.1) durch $i\left\{\sigma(\alpha) + \frac{\pi}{4}\right\}$ abkürzen, wobei $\sigma(x)$ folgende Bedeutung hat

$$\left.\begin{aligned}\sigma(\alpha) + \frac{\pi}{4} = x\cos\alpha \\ + \nu\left(\alpha - \frac{\pi}{2}\right).\end{aligned}\right\} \tag{139.2}$$

Es sind dann die *Sattelpunkte* α_s durch $\partial\sigma/\partial\alpha = 0$ festgelegt, d.h.

$$\left.\begin{aligned}\sin\alpha_s = \frac{\nu}{x}, \\ \alpha_s = \arcsin\frac{\nu}{x}.\end{aligned}\right\} \tag{139.3}$$

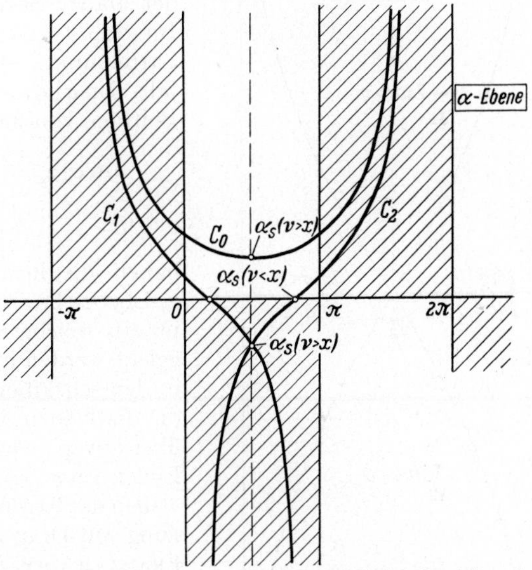

Fig. 98. Integrationswege bei der Sommerfeldschen Darstellung der Zylinderfunktionen (Sattelpunktsmethode).

Im Streifen $0 < \operatorname{Re}\alpha < \pi$ gibt es für jedes x und ν stets *zwei* Sattelpunkte; sie liegen wegen $\sin(\pi - \alpha_s) = \sin\alpha_s$ symmetrisch bezüglich des Punktes $\alpha = \pi/2$. Entwickelt man den Exponenten im Sattelpunkt

$$\sigma(\alpha) = \sigma(\alpha_s) - \frac{x}{2}\cos\alpha_s(\alpha - \alpha_s)^2 + \cdots \tag{139.2'}$$

und berechnet das nach Einsetzen von (139.2′) in (139.1) entstehende Laplace-Integral, so ergibt sich für die Beiträge der beiden Sattelpunkte

$$Z_\nu(x) \to (\pm)\, Q(\alpha_s)\, e^{\pm i\sigma(\alpha_s)}. \tag{139.4}$$

---

[1] P. DEBYE: Math. Ann. **67**, 535 (1909). — Abh. bayer. Akad. 1910. Vgl. auch G.N. WATSON: Theory of Besselfunctions, Kap. 8. Cambridge 1944. — W. FRANZ: Theorie der Beugung elektromagnetischer Wellen, Ziff. 13 und 14. Berlin 1957. — Z. angew. Math. Mech. **40**, 385 (1960).

Die hier eingeführten Größen haben bei Beachtung von (139.3) folgende Bedeutung

$$Q(\alpha_s) = \sqrt{\frac{2}{\pi\, x \cos\alpha_s}} = \begin{cases} \sqrt{\frac{2}{\pi}}\,(x^2-\nu^2)^{-\frac{1}{4}} & (139.5\,\mathrm{a}) \\ \sqrt{\frac{2}{\pi}}\,(\nu^2-x^2)^{-\frac{1}{4}}\,\mathrm{e}^{\frac{i\pi}{4}} & (139.5\,\mathrm{b}) \end{cases}$$

und

$$\sigma(\alpha_s) + \frac{\pi}{4} = \begin{cases} x\cos\alpha_s + \nu\left(\alpha_s - \frac{\pi}{2}\right) = x\left\{\cos\alpha_s + \left(\alpha_s - \frac{\pi}{2}\right)\sin\alpha_s\right\} & (139.6\,\mathrm{a}) \\ \sqrt{x^2-\nu^2} - \nu \arccos\frac{\nu}{x} & (139.6\,\mathrm{b}) \\ -i\left(\sqrt{\nu^2-x^2} - \nu\,\mathrm{Ar\,Cos}\,\frac{\nu}{x}\right) = -i\left(\sqrt{\nu^2-x^2} - \nu\ln\frac{\nu+\sqrt{\nu^2-x^2}}{x}\right) & (139.6\,\mathrm{c}) \end{cases}$$

[dabei sind das Vorzeichen vor (139.4) und die Zweige der hier auftretenden mehrdeutigen Funktionen noch festzulegen]. Das obere Vorzeichen im Exponenten von (139.4) gilt für den Sattelpunkt α_s, das untere für $\pi-\alpha_s$. Es ist also der eine oder der andere Sattelpunkt maßgebend, je nachdem $\mathrm{Im}\,\sigma(\alpha_s) \lessgtr 0$ ist (der Beitrag des jeweils anderen Sattelpunkts ist dann exponentiell klein). Nur falls $\mathrm{Im}\,\sigma(\alpha_s) = 0$ ist, liefern *beide* Sattelpunkte Beiträge von gleichem Betrage. Die Linien

$$\left.\begin{aligned} \mathrm{Im}\,\sigma(\alpha_s) = 0 \rightarrow \mathrm{Im}\Big\{&\cos\alpha_s \\ &+ \left(\alpha_s - \frac{\pi}{2}\right)\sin\alpha_s\Big\} = 0 \end{aligned}\right\} \quad (139.7)$$

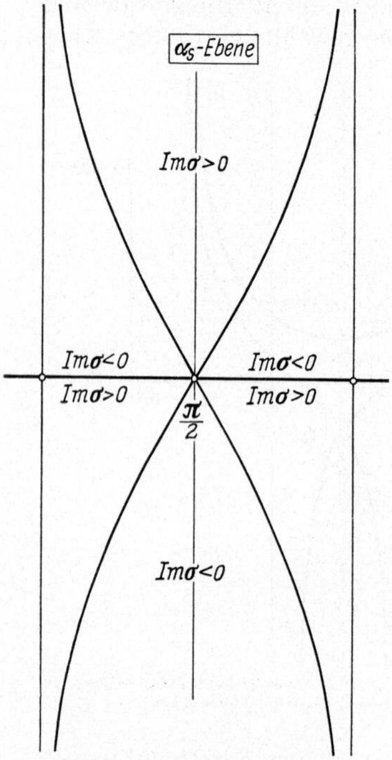

Fig. 99. Gebietsaufteilung der α_s-Ebene durch die Linien $\mathrm{Im}\,\sigma = 0$, Gl. (139.7).

haben die in Fig. 99 angedeutete Lage in der α_s-Ebene. Es ist nun noch zu untersuchen, durch jeweils welche Sattelpunkte die Wege in Fig. 98 gelegt werden müssen, damit sie die beiden Täler in den schraffierten Gebieten längs Fallinien über die Paßhöhen verbinden und wann dieser Weg über zwei gleich hohe Paßstellen (die auf den Linien $\mathrm{Im}\,\sigma = 0$ liegen) geführt werden muß. Wir wollen das Ergebnis (für dessen detaillierte Begründung auf Debye und in vereinfachter Form auf Franz zu verweisen ist) in der ν-Ebene darstellen, deren rechte Halbebene durch die konforme Abbildung $\nu = x\sin\alpha_s$ aus dem Streifen $0 < \mathrm{Re}\,\alpha_s < \frac{\pi}{2}$ der α_s-Ebene in der in Fig. 100 angedeuteten Weise hervorgeht. In die Felder, in die die ν-Ebene durch die Linien $\mathrm{Im}\,\sigma = 0$ eingeteilt wird, sind die jeweils dort gültigen asymptotischen Darstellungen der Zylinderfunktionen eingetragen, wie sie sich aus den Beiträgen der jeweils maßgeblichen Sattelpunkte gemäß (139.4) ergeben. In der (schraffierten) Umgebung der Linien $\mathrm{Im}\,\sigma = 0$ sind bei jeweils einer der Zylinderfunktionen *beide* Sattelpunkte zu berücksichtigen, wodurch sich die in Fig. 100 angegebenen *trigonometrischen* Darstellungen ergeben. Dort liegen offenbar die *Nullstellen* der entsprechenden Zylinderfunktionen. Die Darstellungen in der linken Halbebene ergeben sich aus denjenigen der rechten mit Hilfe der Beziehungen

$$\left.\begin{aligned} H_\nu^1(x) = \mathrm{e}^{-i\pi\nu} H_{-\nu}^1(x), \quad H_\nu^2(x) = \mathrm{e}^{i\pi\nu} H_{-\nu}^2(x) \\ 2 J_\nu(x) = \mathrm{e}^{-i\pi\nu} H_{-\nu}^1(x) + \mathrm{e}^{i\pi\nu} H_{-\nu}^2(x). \end{aligned}\right\} \quad (139.8)$$

Ferner ist zu beachten, daß für $0 < \mathrm{Re}\,\alpha_s < \frac{\pi}{2}$ dem Übergang $\nu \to -\nu$ der Übergang $\alpha_s \to -\alpha_s$ entspricht; somit folgt nach (139.6a)

$$\sigma(-\nu, -\alpha_s) = \sigma(\nu, \alpha_s) + \pi\nu. \tag{139.9}$$

Die Zweige der Funktionen in (139.5, 6) sind so zu wählen, daß für reelle positive ν in (139.5a, 6b) $(x^2 - \nu^2)^{-\frac{1}{4}} > 0$, $0 < \arccos\frac{x}{\nu} < \frac{\pi}{2}$ für $\nu < x$ und $0 < \alpha_s < \frac{\pi}{2}$ und in (139.5b, 6c) $(\nu^2 - x^2)^{-\frac{1}{4}} > 0$, $\mathrm{Ar\,Cos}\,\frac{\nu}{x} > 0$ für $\nu > x$ und $\mathrm{Im}\,\alpha_s > 0$ wird. Die

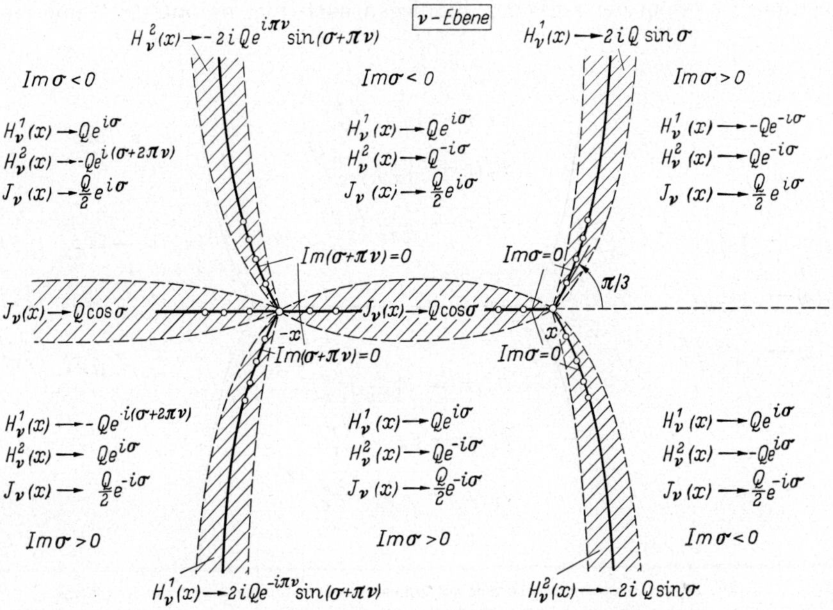

Fig. 100. Zur Debyeschen asymptotischen Darstellung der Zylinderfunktionen $Z_\nu(x)$ $(x \gg 1)$ in den einzelnen Bereichen der ν-Ebene nach Gl. (139.4–6).

Punkte $\nu = \pm x$ sind Verzweigungspunkte der Debyeschen Darstellung; die Verzweigungsschnitte sind längs der Linien $\mathrm{Im}\,\sigma = 0$ zu legen. Beim Überschreiten eines Verzweigungsschnittes ändert sich die Darstellung jeweils der Zylinderfunktion, die auf dem Verzweigungsschnitt trigonometrisch dargestellt wird.

Für *reelle* positive ν ergibt sich aus Fig. 100 mit (139.5, 6) insbesondere

für $\nu < x$

$$\left.\begin{aligned} H_\nu^{1,2}(x) &\to \sqrt{\frac{2}{\pi}}\,(x^2-\nu^2)^{-\frac{1}{4}} \exp\left\{\pm i\left(\sqrt{x^2-\nu^2} - \nu\arccos\frac{\nu}{x} - \frac{\pi}{4}\right)\right\} \\ J_\nu(x) &\to \sqrt{\frac{2}{\pi}}\,(x^2-\nu^2)^{-\frac{1}{4}} \cos\left(\sqrt{x^2-\nu^2} - \nu\arccos\frac{\nu}{x} - \frac{\pi}{4}\right), \end{aligned}\right\} \tag{139.10}$$

für $\nu > x$

$$\left.\begin{aligned} H_\nu^{1,2}(x) &\to \mp i\sqrt{\frac{2}{\pi}}\,(\nu^2-x^2)^{-\frac{1}{4}} \exp\left(\nu\ln\frac{\nu+\sqrt{\nu^2-x^2}}{x} - \sqrt{\nu^2-x^2}\right) \\ J_\nu(x) &\to \frac{1}{\sqrt{2\pi}}\,(\nu^2-x^2)^{-\frac{1}{4}} \exp\left\{-\left(\nu\ln\frac{\nu+\sqrt{\nu^2-x^2}}{x} - \sqrt{\nu^2-x^2}\right)\right\}. \end{aligned}\right\} \tag{139.11}$$

Die Zylinderfunktionen sind also für $\nu < x$ mit ν dem Betrage nach nur sehr langsam veränderlich, während für $\nu > x$ $\left(\text{wegen } \nu \ln \frac{\nu + \sqrt{\nu^2 - x^2}}{x} - \sqrt{\nu^2 - x^2} > 0\right)$ J_ν mit wachsendem ν stärker als exponentiell abnimmt. $H_\nu^{1,2}$ nimmt dann entsprechend zu. Für *komplexe* ν ergibt sich das Verhalten der Zylinderfunktionen für $|\nu| \to \infty$ in den einzelnen Feldern von Fig. 100 mit Hilfe von (139.6c) für $|\nu| \gg x$ in der in Fig. 101 dargestellten Weise. (Abgesehen von der nächsten Umgebung der Linien, auf denen die Nullstellen der Zylinderfunktionen liegen; dort nehmen diese wie $\nu^{-\frac{1}{2}}$ ab.)

Im folgenden benötigen wir noch die *Nullstellen* ν_n und ν_n' von $H_\nu^1(x)$ und der Ableitung $H_\nu^{1\prime}(x)$ in der ν-Ebene. Sie liegen nach Fig. 100 auf der Linie reeller

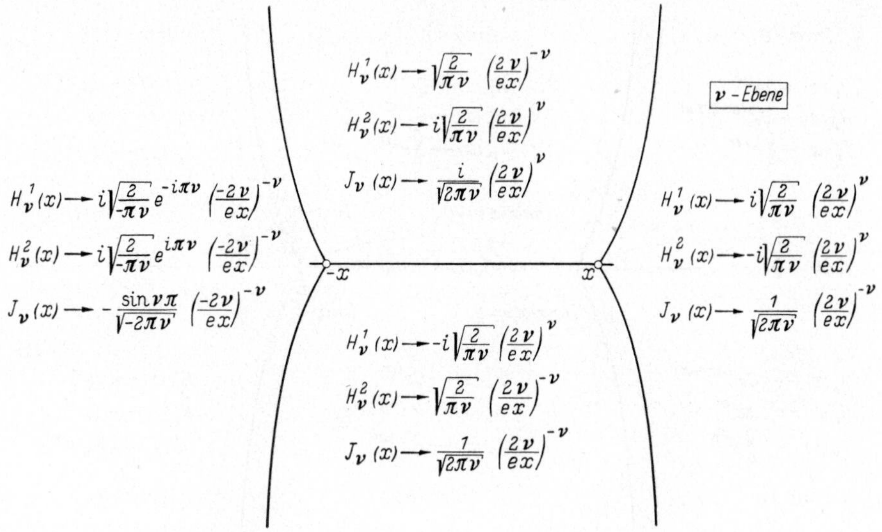

Fig. 101. Zur asymptotischen Darstellung der Zylinderfunktionen für das Unendliche der ν-Ebene.

σ im *ersten* Quadranten und [wegen (139.8)] diametral entgegengesetzt im dritten Quadranten der ν-Ebene (mit ν_n, ν_n' ist auch $-\nu_n$, $-\nu_n'$ Nullstelle). Zu ihrer Bestimmung haben wir mit (139.6a) die Gleichungen

$$\sin\sigma = 0 \to x\left\{\cos\alpha_s + \left(\alpha_s - \frac{\pi}{2}\right)\sin\alpha_s\right\} - \frac{\pi}{4} = -n\pi \qquad (139.12)$$

und

$$\cos\sigma = 0 \to x\left\{\cos\alpha_s + \left(\alpha_s - \frac{\pi}{2}\right)\sin\alpha_s\right\} - \frac{\pi}{4} = -(2n+1)\frac{\pi}{2} \qquad (139.12')$$

(n ganze Zahl > 0, das negative Zeichen rechts sorgt dafür, daß die Nullstellen in den ersten Quadranten fallen). Wegen $x \gg 1$ muß also für nicht zu große n der Betrag $\left|\alpha_s - \frac{\pi}{2}\right| \ll 1$ sein; entwickelt man die linke Seite der obigen Gleichungen nach $\alpha_s - \frac{\pi}{2}$, so ergibt sich ein erstes Glied mit $\left(\alpha_s - \frac{\pi}{2}\right)^3$. Zieht man die Wurzel und geht vermöge $\nu = x\sin\alpha_s = x\left\{1 - \frac{1}{2}\left(\alpha_s - \frac{\pi}{2}\right)^2 + \cdots\right\}$ zu ν über, so ergibt sich

$$\nu_n = x + \frac{x^{\frac{1}{3}}}{2}\left(\frac{3\pi}{4}\right)^{\frac{2}{3}} e^{\frac{i\pi}{3}} (4n-1)^{\frac{2}{3}} \qquad (n = 1, 2, \ldots) \qquad (139.13)$$

und

$$\nu_n' = x + \frac{x^{\frac{1}{3}}}{2}\left(\frac{3\pi}{4}\right)^{\frac{2}{3}} e^{\frac{i\pi}{3}} (4n+1)^{\frac{2}{3}} \qquad (n = 0, 1, 2, \ldots). \tag{139.13'}$$

(Die dritte Einheitswurzel ist hier so gewählt, daß ν_n und ν_n' in den ersten Quadranten fallen.) Die ersten Glieder dieser unendlichen Folge von Nullstellen liegen für nicht zu große x in der Nähe des Verzweigungspunktes $\nu = x$ der Debyeschen Näherung. Für $\nu \to x$ bzw. $\alpha_s \to \pi/2$ werden jedoch die Debyeschen Näherungen *unbrauchbar*, da für $\alpha_s = \pi/2$ beide Sattelpunkte (α_s und $\pi - \alpha_s$) zusammenfallen: die übliche Sattelpunktmethode liefert singuläre Beiträge [vgl. (139.5a, b)].

Um diese Singularität zu vermeiden, muß man in der Entwicklung (139.2') ein weiteres (kubisches) Glied mitnehmen. Am zweckmäßigsten entwickelt man $\sigma(\alpha)$ in (139.2) für Sattelpunkte in der Nähe von $\alpha = \pi/2$ nicht im Sattelpunkt selbst, sondern im Punkt $\alpha = \pi/2$:

$$\sigma(\alpha) = (\nu - x)\left(\alpha - \frac{\pi}{2}\right) + \frac{x}{6}\left(\alpha - \frac{\pi}{2}\right)^3 + \cdots. \tag{139.14}$$

Damit geht (139.1) in die Gestalt

$$Z_\nu(x) \to \frac{1}{\pi}\int\limits_C e^{i(\nu - x)\left(\alpha - \frac{\pi}{2}\right) + \frac{ix}{6}\left(\alpha - \frac{\pi}{2}\right)^3} d\alpha \tag{139.15}$$

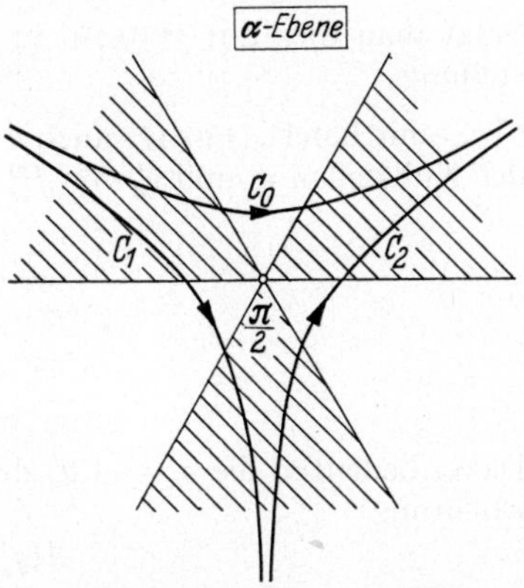

Fig. 102. Integrationswege zur Darstellung der Zylinderfunktionen für den Fall, daß Argument und Index nahezu gleich sind, Gl. (139.15).

über. Das Relief des Integranden weist zufolge der dritten Potenz im Exponenten in einiger Entfernung vom Punkt $\alpha = \pi/2$ drei Täler zwischen drei Höhenzügen in der in Fig. 102 angedeuteten Weise auf (Täler schraffiert). Die Integrationswege C in Fig. 98 können also jetzt folgendermaßen gewählt werden

$$\left.\begin{aligned} C_1&: \quad -\infty\, e^{-\frac{i\pi}{3}} \to +\infty\, e^{-\frac{i\pi}{3}} \\ C_2&: \quad -\infty\, e^{\frac{i\pi}{3}} \to +\infty\, e^{\frac{i\pi}{3}} \\ C_0&: \quad -\infty \to +\infty. \end{aligned}\right\} \tag{139.16}$$

Mit Hilfe der den drei verschiedenen Wegen angepaßten Substitution

$$\tau = \left(\frac{x}{6}\right)^{\frac{1}{3}}\left(\alpha - \frac{\pi}{2}\right)\begin{Bmatrix} e^{\pm\frac{i\pi}{3}} \\ -1 \end{Bmatrix}$$

erhält man so aus (139.15)

$$\left.\begin{aligned} H_\nu^{1,2}(x) &\to \frac{2}{\pi}\, e^{\mp\frac{i\pi}{3}}\left(\frac{6}{x}\right)^{\frac{1}{3}} A(q) \\ J_\nu(x) &\to \frac{1}{\pi}\left(\frac{6}{x}\right)^{\frac{1}{3}} A(q). \end{aligned}\right\} \tag{139.17}$$

Dabei bedeutet

$$A(q) = \tfrac{1}{2}\int\limits_{-\infty}^{\infty} e^{i(q\tau - \tau^3)}\, d\tau = \int\limits_0^{\infty} \cos(\tau^3 - q\tau)\, d\tau \tag{139.18}$$

das *Airysche Integral*, dessen Argument bei den drei Zylinderfunktionen (139.17) (in der dort eingehaltenen Reihenfolge) jeweils die Bedeutung

$$q = (\nu - x)\left(\frac{6}{x}\right)^{\frac{1}{3}}\begin{Bmatrix} e^{\mp\frac{i\pi}{3}} \\ -1 \end{Bmatrix} \tag{139.19}$$

hat.

Die Darstellung (139.17) (auch als Hankel-Approximation[1] bezeichnet) ergänzt die Debyeschen Näherungen (auch als Tangensapproximation bezeichnet) hinsichtlich der Umgebung von $\nu = x$ und geht in diese über, wenn ν nicht zu nahe an x liegt. In der Tat läßt sich dann das Airysche Integral seinerseits mittels der Sattelpunktmethode durch Entwicklung des Exponenten in den beiden Sattelpunkten $\tau_s = \pm\sqrt{q/3}$ asymptotisch auswerten:

$$A(q) \to \frac{\sqrt{\pi}}{(3q)^{\frac{1}{4}}} \cos\left\{2\left(\frac{q}{3}\right)^{\frac{3}{2}} - \frac{\pi}{4}\right\}. \tag{139.18'}$$

Setzt man dies mit (139.19) in (139.17) ein, so ergibt sich die Debyesche Darstellung.

Somit liefert (139.17) auch eine gegenüber (139.13, 13') genauere Berechnung der Nullstellen ν_n und ν_n' von $H_\nu^1(x)$ und $H_\nu^{1\prime}(x)$:

$$\left.\begin{aligned} \nu_n &= x + \left(\frac{x}{6}\right)^{\frac{1}{3}} q_n \, e^{\frac{i\pi}{3}} \\ \nu_n' &= x + \left(\frac{x}{6}\right)^{\frac{1}{3}} q_n' \, e^{\frac{i\pi}{3}}. \end{aligned}\right\} \tag{139.20}$$

Dabei bedeuten die q_n und q_n' die Nullstellen des Airyschen Integrals und seiner Ableitung:

$$A(q_n) = 0, \qquad A'(q_n') = 0. \tag{139.20'}$$

Die ersten fünf Nullstellen sind in Tabelle 1 in Ziff. 141 angegeben.

Als erste Anwendung vorstehender Ergebnisse wollen wir die Darstellungen (139.10, 11) in die Reihen (137.14) für die Flächenstromdichten einsetzen, wobei der Fall $\varepsilon \gg 1$ ins Auge gefaßt werden soll. Zunächst bringen wir diese Reihen mit Hilfe von (139.8) in die Gestalt

$$\psi_{\parallel}(\vartheta) = -\frac{2ik}{\pi\varepsilon} \sum_{n=0}^{\infty} (2 - \delta_{n0}) \frac{e^{-\frac{i\pi}{2}n}}{H_n^1(\varepsilon)} \cos n\vartheta \tag{139.21 p}$$

bzw.

$$\psi_{\perp}(\vartheta) = \frac{2i}{\pi\varepsilon} \sum_{n=0}^{\infty} (2 - \delta_{n0}) \frac{e^{-\frac{i\pi}{2}n}}{H_n^{1\prime}(\varepsilon)} \cos n\vartheta. \tag{139.21 s}$$

Mit Hilfe von (139.10, 11) erkennt man nun, daß die Glieder dieser Reihen bis $n \approx \varepsilon$ einen mit n nur sehr langsam veränderlichen Betrag haben, während die Phase in unübersichtlicher Weise von Glied zu Glied wechselt. Erst für $n > \varepsilon$ beginnen die Glieder mit fortschreitendem n stark (stärker als exponentiell) abzunehmen. Darauf beruht es, daß die Reihen zwar für alle ε konvergent sind, jedoch für große ε die Zahl der zu berücksichtigenden Reihenglieder $\approx \varepsilon$ ist. Entsprechendes gilt auch für die anderen Reihen in Ziff. 137. Für $\varepsilon \gg 1$ müssen wir also nach anderen Darstellungen Ausschau halten.

---

[1] $A(q)$ läßt sich nämlich durch eine Hankel-Funktion vom Index $\frac{1}{3}$ bzw. durch

$$A(q) = \frac{\pi}{3}\left(\frac{q}{3}\right)^{\frac{1}{2}} \left\{ J_{\frac{1}{3}}\left[2\left(\frac{q}{3}\right)^{\frac{3}{2}}\right] + J_{-\frac{1}{3}}\left[2\left(\frac{q}{3}\right)^{\frac{3}{2}}\right] \right\}$$

darstellen.

a2) Reihendarstellung nach gedämpften Partialwellen.

140. Watson-Transformation. Für $\varepsilon \gg 1$ hilft eine erstmals von WATSON[1] angegebene Reihentransformation weiter, die neuerdings von FRANZ und IMAI[2] auf die Beugung am Zylinder angewandt worden ist.

Die Watson-Transformation besteht zunächst darin, eine unendliche Reihe der Form

$$v = \sum_{n=-\infty}^{\infty} A_n \mathrm{e}^{in\vartheta} \tag{140.1}$$

in das Integral

$$v = \frac{i}{2} \oint \frac{\mathrm{e}^{i\nu(\vartheta-\pi)}}{\sin \pi\nu} A_\nu \, d\nu \tag{140.2}$$

umzuformen, wobei der Integrationsweg in der ν-Ebene die reelle Achse in der in Fig. 103 dargestellten Weise umläuft. In der Tat führt — falls A_ν auf der reellen Achse keine Pole hat — das Integral (140.2) nach dem Cauchyschen Satz auf die Summe (140.1) zurück, da der Faktor von A_ν für alle ganzzahligen $\nu = n$ Pole erster Ordnung mit den Residuen

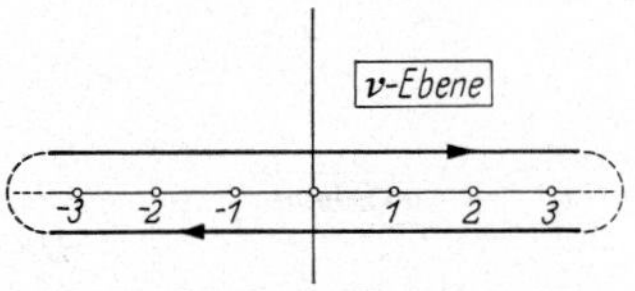

Fig. 103. Zur Watson-Transformation: Integrationsweg zu Gl. (140.2).

$$\operatorname{Res}\left\{\frac{\mathrm{e}^{i\nu(\vartheta-\pi)}}{\sin \pi\nu}\right\}_{\nu=n} = \frac{\mathrm{e}^{in(\vartheta-\pi)}}{\pi \cos \pi n} = \frac{\mathrm{e}^{in\vartheta}}{\pi}$$

besitzt. Ist der Koeffizient A_ν überdies symmetrisch $(A_{-\nu} = A_\nu)$, so ergibt sich aus (140.2), [wenn wir für den in der unteren Halbebene verlaufenden Teil des Integrationsweges die Variable ν durch $-\nu$ ersetzen]:

$$v = i \int_{-\infty}^{\infty} \frac{\cos \nu(\vartheta - \pi)}{\sin \pi\nu} A_\nu \, d\nu. \tag{140.2'}$$

Dabei ist als Integrationsweg eine Parallele zur reellen Achse in der oberen Halbebene zu wählen (oder auch die reelle Achse selbst, unter Umgehung aller ganzzahligen Werte von ν in der durch den Haken am Integral angedeuteten Weise). Der Vorteil der Watson-Transformation besteht nun in der Möglichkeit einer geeigneten Verlegung des Integrationsweges. Im vorliegenden Fall handelt es sich um die Reihen (137.15′), bei denen A_ν die Form

$$\left.\begin{aligned} A_\nu &= \frac{\mathrm{e}^{-\frac{i\pi}{2}\nu}}{\Omega H_\nu^1(\varepsilon)} \{\Omega H_\nu^1(\varepsilon) J_\nu(kr) - \Omega J_\nu(\varepsilon) H_\nu^1(kr)\} \\ &= \frac{\mathrm{e}^{-\frac{i\pi}{2}\nu}}{2\Omega H_\nu^1(\varepsilon)} \{\Omega H_\nu^1(\varepsilon) \cdot H_\nu^2(kr) - \Omega H_\nu^2(\varepsilon) \cdot H_\nu^1(kr)\} \end{aligned}\right\} \tag{140.3}$$

hat. Dies ist wegen (139.8) in ν symmetrisch, so daß wir (140.2′) anwenden können. Wir deformieren nun den Integrationsweg in der in Fig. 104 angedeuteten Weise in einen Umlauf um die Reihe der Wurzeln ν_s von

$$\Omega H_{\nu_s}^1(\varepsilon) = 0, \tag{140.4}$$

die nach Ziff. 139 im ersten Quadranten der ν-Ebene liegen, sowie einen unendlich großen Halbkreis in der oberen Halbebene. Mit Hilfe des in Fig. 101 ange-

[1] G.N. WATSON: Proc. Roy. Soc. Lond. A **95**, 83 (1918).

[2] W. FRANZ: Z. Naturforsch. **9**a, 705 (1954). — Theorie der Beugung elektromagnetischer Wellen. Berlin: Springer 1957. — I. IMAI: Z. Physik **137**, 31 (1954). — Für die Beugung eines ebenen Wellenstoßes vgl. F.G. FRIEDLANDER: Comm. Pure Appl. Math. **7**, 705 (1954). — Wir folgen im wesentlichen der zusammenfassenden Darstellung von FRANZ.

gebenen Verhaltens der Zylinderfunktionen im Unendlichen der ν-Ebene läßt sich zeigen, daß der Integrand von (140.2′) mit (140.3) mit Ausnahme der Umgebung der Nullstellenreihen von $\Omega H_\nu^1(\varepsilon)$ stärker als exponentiell verschwindet (bezüglich der ins einzelne gehenden Begründung sei auf FRANZ verwiesen). Da die ν_s Pole erster Ordnung von A_ν sind, so können wir also das in Rede stehende Integral in die Summe der Residuen dieser Pole verwandeln:

$$v(r,\vartheta)=\pi\sum_s\left\{\frac{\Omega H_\nu^2(\varepsilon)}{\frac{\partial}{\partial\nu}\Omega H_\nu^1(\varepsilon)}\right\}_{\nu_s}\frac{\cos\nu_s(\pi-\vartheta)}{\sin\pi\nu_s}\,e^{-\frac{i\pi}{2}\nu_s}\cdot H^1_{\nu_s}(kr). \qquad (140.5)$$

Diese Gleichung stellt die Lösung unseres Beugungsproblems als Summe von „*Residuenwellen*“ dar, von denen wir im folgenden zeigen wollen, daß sie *gedämpften Partialwellen* entsprechen. Die Konvergenz der Reihe folgt aus der Tatsache, daß die durch sie dargestellte Funktion in Strenge mit derjenigen übereinstimmt, die durch die Rayleighschen Reihen dargestellt wird.

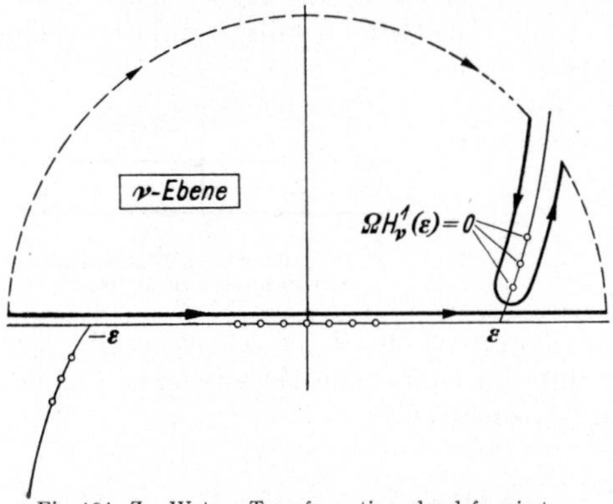

Fig. 104. Zur Watson-Transformation: der deformierte Integrationsweg bleibt an den Polen ν_s hängen.

Wir wollen hier noch eine Bemerkung über den methodischen Unterschied der Rayleighschen Reihen (137.15′) und der Watsonschen (140.5) machen. Erstere können als Entwicklung des Randwertproblems nach *azimutalen Eigenfunktionen* $H_n^1(kr)\,e^{in\vartheta}$ aufgefaßt werden. [Die Ganzzahligkeit von n wird durch die Forderung der *Eindeutigkeit* erzwungen; man kann hier auch von *erzwungenen* Schwingungen sprechen, die im *Nullpunkt* angeregt werden (der jedoch nicht zum Feldgebiet gehört)]. Andererseits kann die Residuenreihe als eine Entwicklung des Problems nach *radialen Eigenfunktionen* $H^1_{\nu_s}(kr)\,e^{i\nu_s\vartheta}$ interpretiert werden. Diese erfüllen nämlich die Randbedingung zufolge (140.4) *einzeln* (sowie im Unendlichen die Ausstrahlungsbedingung). SOMMERFELD[1] hat für den analogen Fall der Kugel gezeigt, daß man die Lösung des Randwertproblems auch *direkt* nach radialen Eigenfunktionen entwickeln kann (ohne den Umweg über die Watson-Transformation). Allerdings ist jetzt die Winkelabhängigkeit nicht mehr eindeutig. Man muß sich in (140.5) die $r\vartheta$-Ebene längs des Halbstrahls $\vartheta=0$ aufgeschnitten denken. [Wegen der dadurch hereinkommenden Singularität kann man jetzt von *erzwungenen* Schwingungen sprechen, die längs des *Halbstrahls* $\vartheta=0$ angeregt werden; in der Umgebung dieses Halbstrahls ist jedoch die Darstellung (140.5) unbrauchbar und muß durch eine andere ersetzt werden (s. Ziff. 142)].

141. Asymptotische Lösung für das Schattengebiet. Der Vorteil der Reihe (140.5) besteht darin, daß sie für $\varepsilon\gg1$ *rasch konvergiert.* Um dies zu zeigen, haben wir geeignete Darstellungen der einzelnen Faktoren zu suchen. Zunächst ergeben sich die Wurzeln von (140.4) in den beiden Polarisationsfällen nach (139.13, 13′) größenordnungsmäßig (Tangensapproximation) zu

$$\nu_\parallel^{(s)}=\varepsilon+\frac{\varepsilon^{\frac13}}{2}\left(\frac{3\pi}{4}\right)^{\frac23}(4s-1)^{\frac23}\,e^{\frac{i\pi}{3}}\qquad(s=1,2,\ldots)\qquad(141.1p)$$

[1] A. SOMMERFELD: Vorlesungen über theoretische Physik, Bd. VI, S. 215ff. Wiesbaden 1947.

bzw.

$$\nu_{\perp}^{(s)} = \varepsilon + \frac{\varepsilon^{\frac{1}{3}}}{2}\left(\frac{3\pi}{4}\right)^{\frac{2}{3}}(4s+1)^{\frac{2}{3}}\,e^{\frac{i\pi}{3}} \qquad (s=0,1,2,\ldots) \tag{141.1s}$$

oder nach (139.20) genauer (Hankel-Approximation)

$$\nu^{(s)} = \varepsilon + \left(\frac{\varepsilon}{6}\right)^{\frac{1}{3}} q^{(s)}\,e^{\frac{i\pi}{3}} = \varepsilon + \frac{1+i\sqrt{3}}{2}\left(\frac{\varepsilon}{6}\right)^{\frac{1}{3}} q^{(s)}. \tag{141.1'}$$

Die $q^{(s)}$ sind dabei im p- bzw. s-Fall die Wurzeln der Gleichungen

$$A(q_{\parallel}^{(s)}) = 0 \quad \text{bzw.} \quad A'(q_{\perp}^{(s)}) = 0. \tag{141.2}$$

Franz hat die asymptotische Entwicklung noch einen Schritt weiter getrieben mit dem Ergebnis

$$\left.\begin{aligned} \nu_{\parallel}^{(s)} &= \varepsilon + \left(\frac{\varepsilon}{6}\right)^{\frac{1}{3}} q_{\parallel}^{(s)}\,e^{\frac{i\pi}{3}} - \left(\frac{6}{\varepsilon}\right)^{\frac{1}{3}} \frac{q_{\parallel}^{(s)2}}{180}\,e^{-\frac{i\pi}{3}} \\ \nu_{\perp}^{(s)} &= \varepsilon + \left(\frac{\varepsilon}{6}\right)^{\frac{1}{3}} q_{\perp}^{(s)}\,e^{\frac{i\pi}{3}} - \left(\frac{6}{\varepsilon}\right)^{\frac{1}{3}} \left\{\frac{1}{10\,q_{\perp}^{(s)}} + \frac{q_{\perp}^{(s)2}}{180}\right\} e^{-\frac{i\pi}{3}}. \end{aligned}\right\} \tag{141.1''}$$

In (141.1′) haben wir die Imaginärteile abgespalten, die sich sogleich als *Dämpfungskonstanten* herausstellen werden. Die ersten fünf Nullstellen von A und A' sind in Tabelle 1 angegeben; zusammen mit dem Wert der jeweils anderen Funktion an der Nullstelle.

Tabelle 1. *Nullstellen des Airy-Integrals und seiner Ableitung.*

s	$q_{\parallel}^{(s)}$	$A'(q_{\parallel}^{(s)})$	$q_{\perp}^{(s)}$	$A(q_{\perp}^{(s)})$
1	3,372134	− 1,05905	1,469354	1,16680
2	5,895843	1,21295	4,684712	− 0,91272
3	7,962025	− 1,30673	6,951786	0,82862
4	9,788127	1,37568	8,889027	− 0,77962
5	11,457423	− 1,43078	10,632519	0,74562

Tabelle 2. *Nullstellen von* $H_\nu^1(\varepsilon)$ *und* $H_\nu^{1\prime}(\varepsilon)$.

$\nu_{\parallel}^{(s)} = \varepsilon + \varepsilon^{\frac{1}{3}} e^{\frac{i\pi}{3}} \cdot 1{,}855757$	$\nu_{\perp}^{(s)} = \varepsilon + \varepsilon^{\frac{1}{3}} e^{\frac{i\pi}{3}} \cdot 0{,}808617$
3,244608	2,578096
4,381671	3,825715
5,386614	4,891820
6,305263	5,851301

Damit ergeben sich die in Tabelle 2 angegebenen ersten fünf Nullstellen $\nu^{(s)}$. Für $r \gg a$ (genauer für $kr - \varepsilon \gg \varepsilon^{\frac{1}{3}}$) können wir ferner für $H_{\nu_s}^1(kr)$ die Darstellung links von der Nullstellenreihe in Fig. 100 verwenden:

$$H_{\nu_s}^1(kr) \to \sqrt{\frac{2}{\pi k}}\,(r^2 - a^2)^{-\frac{1}{4}}\,e^{i\left(k\sqrt{r^2-a^2} - \nu_s \arccos\frac{a}{r} - \frac{\pi}{4}\right)}. \tag{141.3}$$

Dabei haben wir die ν_s aus (141.1′) eingesetzt und entsprechend vereinfacht. Zur Berechnung des Faktors

$$\left\{\frac{\Omega H_\nu^2(\varepsilon)}{\dfrac{\partial}{\partial \nu}\,\Omega H_\nu^1(\varepsilon)}\right\}_{\nu_s} = \frac{e^{\frac{5\pi i}{6}}}{2\sqrt{\pi}}\,\varepsilon^{\frac{1}{3}}\,C_s \tag{141.4}$$

(wobei die rechts vorgenommene Aufspaltung für das folgende bequem ist, da dann C_s ein reeller Zahlfaktor wird) bemerken wir zunächst, daß sich der Zähler mit Hilfe der Wronski-Determinante (137.12) für $\nu_s = \nu_{\parallel}^{(s)}$ bzw. $\nu_s = \nu_{\perp}^{(s)}$ in der Gestalt

$$\left.\begin{aligned} H_{\nu_s}^2(\varepsilon) &= \frac{-4}{\pi i \varepsilon H_{\nu_s}^{1\prime}(\varepsilon)} \\ \text{bzw.}\qquad H_{\nu_s}^{2\prime}(\varepsilon) &= \frac{4}{\pi i \varepsilon H_{\nu_s}^1(\varepsilon)} \end{aligned}\right\} \tag{141.5}$$

schreiben läßt. Mittels der aus der Rekursionsformel der Zylinderfunktionen asymptotisch folgenden Beziehung

$$\frac{\partial Z_\nu(x)}{\partial x} \to -\frac{\partial Z_\nu(x)}{\partial \nu} \tag{141.6}$$

und der Hankel-Approximation (139.17) ergibt sich damit für (141.4)

$$C_{\parallel}^{(s)} = 2\sqrt{\pi}\,\varepsilon^{-\frac{1}{3}}\,e^{-\frac{5\pi i}{6}} \left\{\frac{H_\nu^2(\varepsilon)}{\frac{\partial H_\nu^1(\varepsilon)}{\partial \nu}}\right\}_{\nu_{\parallel}^{(s)}} \to \frac{\pi^{\frac{3}{2}}}{3\cdot 6^{\frac{1}{3}}\{A'(q_{\parallel}^{(s)})\}^2}, \tag{141.4'p}$$

$$C_{\perp}^{(s)} = 2\sqrt{\pi}\,\varepsilon^{-\frac{1}{3}}\,e^{-\frac{5\pi i}{6}} \left\{\frac{H_\nu^{2\prime}}{\frac{\partial^2 H_\nu^1(\varepsilon)}{\partial \nu\,\partial\varepsilon}}\right\}_{\nu_{\perp}^{(s)}} \to \frac{\pi^{\frac{3}{2}}}{6^{\frac{1}{3}}\,q_{\perp}^{(s)}\{A(q_{\perp}^{(s)})\}^2}. \tag{141.4's}$$

Dabei haben wir bei (141.4′*s*) die zweite Ableitung A'' mit Hilfe der Differentialgleichung des Airy-Integrals

$$A''(q) + \frac{q}{3}A(q) = 0 \tag{141.7}$$

durch A selbst ausgedrückt. Mit Hilfe von Tabelle 1 ergeben sich für die C_s folgende Werte:

Tabelle 3. *Amplituden der Kriechwellen.*

s	$C_{\parallel}^{(s)}$	$C_{\perp}^{(s)}$
1	0,91072	1,53187
2	0,69427	0,78520
3	0,59820	0,64199
4	0,53974	0,56719
5	0,49897	0,51840

Setzen wir noch den winkelabhängigen Faktor der Reihenglieder (140.5) in die Form

$$\frac{\cos\nu(\pi-\vartheta)}{\sin\pi\nu}\,e^{-\frac{i\pi}{2}\nu} = -i\,\frac{e^{i\nu\left(\vartheta-\frac{\pi}{2}\right)} + e^{i\nu\left(\frac{3\pi}{2}-\vartheta\right)}}{1-e^{2\pi i\nu}} \tag{141.8}$$

und tragen schließlich (141.3, 4, 8) dort ein, so ergibt sich

$$\left.\begin{aligned} v(r,\vartheta) \to \varepsilon^{\frac{1}{3}}\,\frac{e^{i\left(k\sqrt{r^2-a^2}+\frac{\pi}{12}\right)}}{\sqrt{2k}\,(r^2-a^2)^{\frac{1}{4}}} \sum_s \frac{C_s}{1-e^{2\pi i\nu_s}}\,\cdot \\ \cdot\left\{e^{i\nu_s\left(\vartheta-\arccos\frac{a}{r}-\frac{\pi}{2}\right)} + e^{i\nu_s\left(\frac{3\pi}{2}-\vartheta-\arccos\frac{a}{r}\right)}\right\}. \end{aligned}\right\} \tag{141.9}$$

Die hier eingehenden Größen haben nun eine einfache geometrische Bedeutung. Wie aus Fig. 105 zu ersehen ist, sind

$$\left.\begin{aligned} &a\left(\vartheta-\arccos\frac{a}{r}-\frac{\pi}{2}\right) \\ \text{bzw.}\qquad &a\left(\frac{3\pi}{2}-\vartheta-\arccos\frac{a}{r}\right) \end{aligned}\right\} \tag{141.10}$$

die Längen derjenigen Kreisbögen, die zwei „*Strahlen*" auf dem Zylinder zurücklegen, die ihn (aus dem Unendlichen kommend) tangierend treffen um ihn zum Aufpunkt $\mathfrak{r}$ hin tangierend wieder zu verlassen. Die Argumente der winkelabhängigen Exponentialfunktionen in (141.9) nehmen nun mit (141.1') die Form

$$\left.\begin{aligned} &\left\{i\,k\left[a+\frac{q_s}{2k^{\frac{2}{3}}}\left(\frac{a}{6}\right)^{\frac{1}{3}}\right]-\frac{\sqrt{3}}{2}\left(\frac{\varepsilon}{6}\right)^{\frac{1}{3}}q_s\right\}\left(\vartheta-\operatorname{arc\,cos}\frac{a}{r}-\frac{\pi}{2}\right)\\ \text{bzw.}\quad &\left\{i\,k\left[a+\frac{q_s}{2k^{\frac{2}{3}}}\left(\frac{a}{6}\right)^{\frac{1}{3}}\right]-\frac{\sqrt{3}}{2}\left(\frac{\varepsilon}{6}\right)^{\frac{1}{3}}q_s\right\}\left(\frac{3\pi}{2}-\vartheta-\operatorname{arc\,cos}\frac{a}{r}\right)\end{aligned}\right\}\qquad(141.10')$$

an. Der hier in der eckigen Klammer zu a hinzutretende Term kann durch die Vorstellung gedeutet werden, daß die beiden Strahlen nicht unmittelbar auf der Zylinderoberfläche laufen, sondern von ihr den Abstand $\frac{q_s}{2k^{\frac{2}{3}}}\left(\frac{a}{6}\right)^{\frac{1}{3}}$ einhalten. (Eine andere Interpretationsmöglichkeit ist die einer veränderten Phasengeschwindigkeit der Strahlen auf ihrem Wege entlang der Oberfläche.) Vom Zylinder bis zum Aufpunkt legen dann beide Strahlen noch die geradlinige Strecke $\sqrt{r^2-a^2}$ zurück. Der kreisbogenförmige und der geradlinige Laufweg zusammen liefern — mit k multipliziert — die *Phasenänderung* längs des Strahls. Außerdem sorgt aber der mit wachsendem s größer werdende (positive) Imaginärteil von ν_s dafür, daß die einzelnen Residuenwellen (denen jeweils die gleichen Strahlen entsprechen) auf ihrem Weg längs der Zylinderoberfläche mit s zunehmend stärker *gedämpft* werden[1]. Wir können daher mit FRANZ auch von *Kriechwellen* sprechen. Die mit s zunehmende Dämpfung der Kriechwellen führt zu einer sehr *schnellen Konvergenz* der Reihe (141.9), solange die *Kriechstrecke* (141.10) *positiv* ist. Dies ist aber nach Fig. 105 nur dann der Fall, wenn der Aufpunkt $\mathfrak{r}$ im *geometrischen Schatten* des Zylinders liegt.

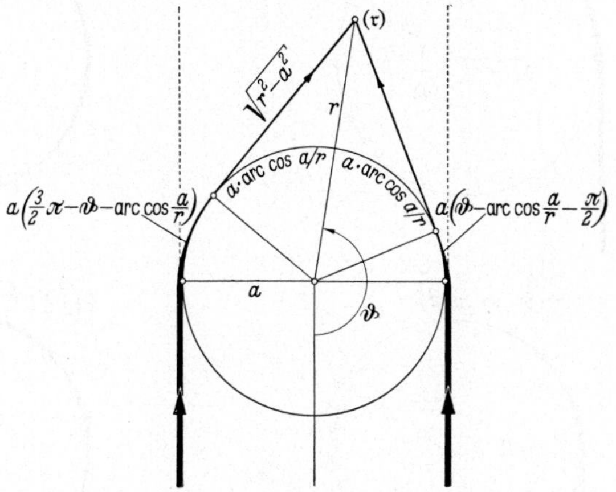

Fig. 105. Zur Theorie der Kriechwellen: Kriechstrecken, wenn der Aufpunkt im geometrischen Schatten des Zylinders liegt.

142. Asymptotische Lösung für das Lichtgebiet. Für den Fall, daß der Aufpunkt im geometrisch beleuchteten Gebiet liegt, sind die Kriechstrecken aus den Fig. 106a—d (für zwei verschiedene Lagen des Aufpunktes) zu entnehmen:

$$\left.\begin{aligned} &a\left(\frac{3\pi}{2}+\vartheta-\operatorname{arc\,cos}\frac{a}{r}\right)\\ \text{und}\quad &a\left(\frac{3\pi}{2}-\vartheta-\operatorname{arc\,cos}\frac{a}{r}\right).\end{aligned}\right\}\qquad(142.1)$$

[1] Gemeint ist natürlich keine zeitliche Dämpfung sondern eine *in* der Fortschreitungsrichtung erfolgende exponentielle Schwächung der Amplitude. Wir weisen übrigens darauf hin, daß dieses Verhalten in der Nähe der Oberfläche durch *Extrapolation* des Feldes in großer Entfernung vom Zylinder erschlossen wird. Im selben Sinne können wir sagen, daß die Residuenwellen in der Nähe der Oberfläche auch *senkrecht* zur Fortschreitungsrichtung exponentiell abnehmen (da nur die Strahlen ins Spiel kommen, die in nächster Nähe des Zylinders vorbeigehen). Vgl. dazu F. G. FRIEDLANDER: Comm. Pure Appl. Math. **7**, 705 (1954). Eine Methode zur Untersuchung des Feldes in unmittelbarer Nähe der Oberfläche bei V. A. FOCK: J. Phys. (USSR) **10**, 399 (1946) (vgl. Ziff. 144).

Damit diese Kriechstrecken in den Phasenfaktoren von (141.9) erscheinen, nimmt Franz (darin über die ursprüngliche Anwendung der Watson-Transformation hinausgehend) für den winkelabhängigen Faktor in (140.2′) folgende Aufspaltung vor

$$\cos\nu(\pi-\vartheta)=\mathrm{e}^{i\nu\pi}\cos\nu\vartheta-i\,\mathrm{e}^{i\nu\vartheta}\sin\pi\nu. \tag{142.2}$$

Setzen wir dies in (140.2′) ein [mit A_ν aus (140.3)], so ergibt sich, falls wir das Integral, das den *ersten* Term von (142.2) enthält, wieder durch Residuenbildung

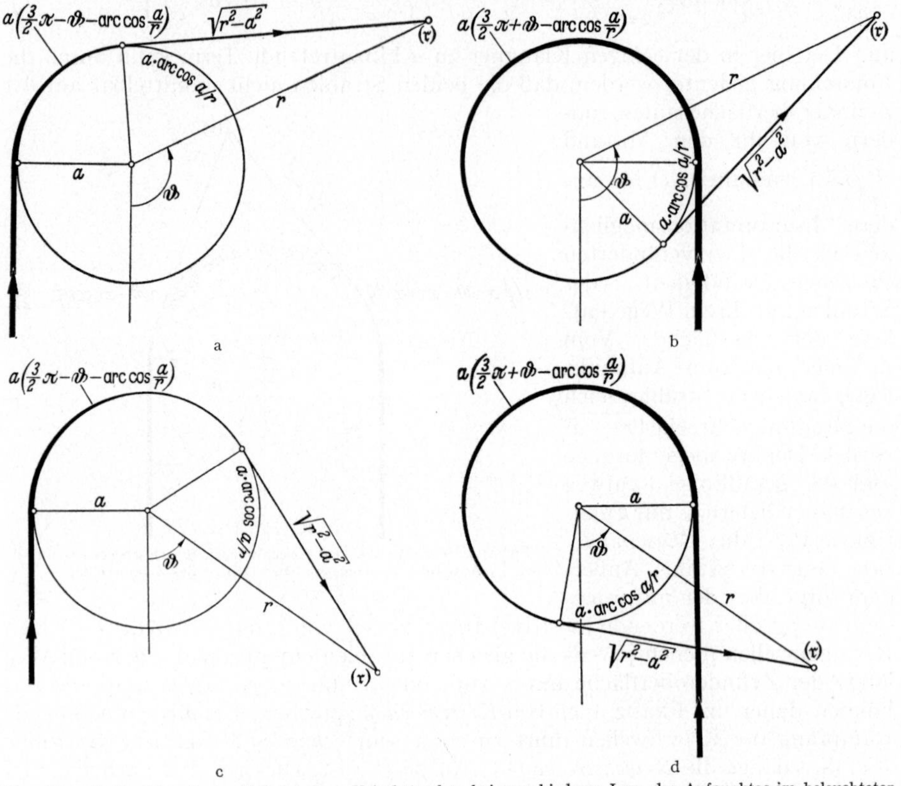

Fig. 106a—d. Zur Theorie der Kriechwellen: Kriechstrecken bei verschiedener Lage des Aufpunktes im beleuchteten Gebiet.

an den Polen ν_s auswerten [entsprechend (140.5)]

$$v(r,\vartheta)=v_g(r,\vartheta)+\pi\sum_s\left\{\frac{\Omega H_\nu^2(\varepsilon)}{\frac{\partial}{\partial\nu}\Omega H_\nu^1(\varepsilon)}\right\}_{\nu_s}\frac{\cos\nu_s\vartheta}{\sin\pi\nu_s}\,\mathrm{e}^{\frac{i\pi}{2}\nu_s}\cdot H_{\nu_s}^1(k\,r). \tag{142.3}$$

Dabei lassen wir den aus dem *zweiten* Term von (142.2) sich ergebenden Beitrag als Integral stehen:

$$v_g(r,\vartheta)=-\frac{1}{2}\oint\mathrm{e}^{i\nu\left(\vartheta-\frac{\pi}{2}\right)}\frac{\Omega H_\nu^2(\varepsilon)}{\Omega H_\nu^1(\varepsilon)}H_\nu^1(k\,r)\,d\nu. \tag{142.4}$$

Der Integrationsweg kann hier etwa als Schleife um die Polstellen ν_s herumgeführt werden (vgl. Fig. 104). Den Beitrag, der dem ersten Term von (140.3) entspricht, haben wir gleich fortgelassen, da der entsprechende Integrand innerhalb der Schleife holomorph ist. Bei dem Integranden von (142.4) ist wesentlich, daß sich der charakteristische Nenner sin $\pi\nu$ der Watson-Transformation (140.2') herausgekürzt hat. Die Pole auf der reellen Achse sind daher fortgefallen, wodurch eine Auswertung des Integrals nach der *Sattelpunktmethode* möglich wird. Die Sattelpunkte liegen nämlich auf der reellen Achse (wie wir gleich sehen werden); es besteht aber nun — im Gegensatz zu Integralen des Typs (140.2') — keine Gefahr, daß sie in die Nachbarschaft der Pole des Watsonschen Faktors $1/\sin\pi\nu$ geraten. (Da in einem solchen Fall die Sattelpunktmethode versagen würde, haben wir oben die Residuenmethode benutzt.)

Zunächst werten wir die Residuensumme in (142.3) asymptotisch aus ($\varepsilon \gg 1$, $kr - \varepsilon \gg \varepsilon^{\frac{1}{3}}$), indem wir (141.3, 4) eintragen und die Umformung

$$\frac{\cos\nu\vartheta}{\sin\pi\nu}\, e^{\frac{i\pi}{2}\nu} = -i\,\frac{e^{i\nu\left(\frac{3\pi}{2}+\vartheta\right)} + e^{i\nu\left(\frac{3\pi}{2}-\vartheta\right)}}{1-e^{2\pi i\nu}} \tag{142.5}$$

beachten:

$$\left.\begin{aligned} v(r,\vartheta) \to v_g(r,\vartheta) &+ \varepsilon^{\frac{1}{3}}\,\frac{e^{i\left(k\sqrt{r^2-a^2}+\frac{\pi}{12}\right)}}{\sqrt{2k}\,(r^2-a^2)^{\frac{1}{4}}}\cdot \\ &\cdot\sum_s \frac{C_s}{1-e^{2\pi i\nu_s}}\left\{e^{i\nu_s\left(\frac{3\pi}{2}+\vartheta-\arccos\frac{a}{r}\right)} + e^{i\nu_s\left(\frac{3\pi}{2}-\vartheta-\arccos\frac{a}{r}\right)}\right\}.\end{aligned}\right\} \tag{142.6}$$

Für $r\to\infty$ erhält man daraus mit (141.1')

$$\left.\begin{aligned} v(r,\vartheta) \to v_g(r,\vartheta) &+ \varepsilon^{\frac{1}{3}}\,\frac{e^{i\left(kr+\frac{\pi}{12}\right)}}{\sqrt{2kr}}\sum_s\frac{C_s}{1-e^{2\pi i\nu_s}}\cdot \\ &\cdot\left\{e^{\left\{i\varepsilon-\frac{\sqrt{3}-i}{2}\left(\frac{\varepsilon}{6}\right)^{\frac{1}{3}}q_s\right\}(\pi-\vartheta)} + e^{\left\{i\varepsilon-\frac{\sqrt{3}-i}{2}\left(\frac{\varepsilon}{6}\right)^{\frac{1}{3}}q_s\right\}(\pi+\vartheta)}\right\}.\end{aligned}\right\} \tag{142.6'}$$

In der Residuensumme treten also gerade die Kriechstrecken (142.1) auf, die im geometrisch beleuchteten Gebiet stets positiv sind. Die zunehmend stärkere Dämpfung der einzelnen in dieses Gebiet gelangenden Kriechwellen garantiert wiederum die schnelle Konvergenz der Summe (142.6). [Andererseits wachsen die Glieder der Reihe (141.9) im beleuchteten Gebiet zunächst stark an; die Konvergenz beginnt erst bei sehr hohen ν_s, bei denen in (141.3) ν_s/kr nicht mehr durch a/r ersetzt werden darf.] Der Nenner $1-\exp 2\pi i\nu_s$ der Reihenglieder (141.9) und (142.6) weist darauf hin, daß neben den direkten Residuenwellen auch alle jene auftreten, die erst zum Aufpunkt gelangen, nachdem sie den Zylinder mehrmals umlaufen haben (der Nenner entsteht also durch Summation über die Zahl der Umläufe in Form einer geometrischen Reihe).

143. Das geometrisch-optische Feld. Es soll jetzt noch gezeigt werden, daß die asymptotische Auswertung des Integrals (142.4) die *einfallende* und die (nach den Gesetzen der geometrischen Optik) *reflektierte* Welle liefert. Wir hatten schon gesehen, daß diese Auswertung hier zweckmäßigerweise mit Hilfe der Sattelpunktmethode zu erfolgen hat. Mit Hilfe des in Fig. 101 angegebenen Verhaltens der Zylinderfunktionen im Unendlichen der ν-Ebene läßt sich zunächst leicht zeigen, daß der Integrand von (142.4) im Unendlichen beiderseits der dem Nenner $\Omega H_\nu^1(\varepsilon)$ entsprechenden zackenförmigen Polreihe exponentiell verschwindet. Andererseits wird er in der unteren ν-Halbebene überall exponentiell groß, mit Ausnahme der trichterförmigen Nullstellen von $\Omega H_\nu^2(\varepsilon)$. Führen wir den Integrationsweg demgemäß in der in Fig. 107 angedeuteten Weise durch die erste Nullstelle von $\Omega H_\nu^2(\varepsilon)$, so muß er zwei Pässe $\hat{\nu}$ und $\check{\nu}$ links und rechts von $\nu=\varepsilon$ überwinden. Zur Ermittlung der genauen Lage dieser Sattelpunkte tragen wir in den

Integranden von (142.4) die asymptotischen Darstellungen der Zylinderfunktionen aus Fig. 100 ein (wobei wir also links und rechts von den Nullstellenreihen verschiedene Darstellungen zu benutzen haben):

$$v_g(r,\vartheta)\to \left.\begin{aligned} &\mp \frac{e^{\frac{i\pi}{4}}}{\sqrt{2\pi}}\int \frac{d\nu}{\{(k r)^2-\nu^2\}^{\frac14}}\, e^{i\left\{\nu\left(\vartheta+\arccos\frac{\nu}{\varepsilon}-\arccos\frac{\nu}{kr}-\frac{\pi}{2}\right)-2\sqrt{\varepsilon^2-\nu^2}+\sqrt{(kr)^2-\nu^2}\right\}}\\ &+\frac{e^{-\frac{i\pi}{4}}}{\sqrt{2\pi}}\int \frac{d\nu}{\{(k r)^2-\nu^2\}^{\frac14}}\, e^{i\left\{\nu\left(\vartheta-2\arccos\frac{\nu}{kr}-\frac{\pi}{2}\right)+\sqrt{(kr)^2-\nu^2}\right\}}.\end{aligned}\right\} \qquad (143.1)$$

Dabei gilt das obere bzw. untere Vorzeichen vor dem ersten Integral für den p- bzw. s-Fall. [Die im s-Fall durch Ω geforderte Differentiation nach ε braucht nur an dem schnell veränderlichen Faktor $\exp(\pm i\sigma)$ ausgeführt zu werden.] Ferner ist das erste Integral über den linken, das zweite über den rechten Teil der Schleife in Fig. 107 zu führen. In den Sattelpunkten muß die Ableitung der Exponenten nach ν verschwinden. Bezeichnen wir den Sattelpunkt links bzw. rechts von ε mit

$$\hat{\nu}=k p \quad \text{bzw.} \quad \check{\nu}=k q, \qquad (143.2)$$

so ergibt sich also für p bzw. q die Bedingung

$$\vartheta+2\arccos\frac{p}{a}=\arccos\frac{p}{r}+\frac{\pi}{2} \qquad (143.3\,\text{a})$$

bzw.

$$\vartheta=\arccos\frac{q}{r}+\frac{\pi}{2}. \qquad (143.3\,\text{b})$$

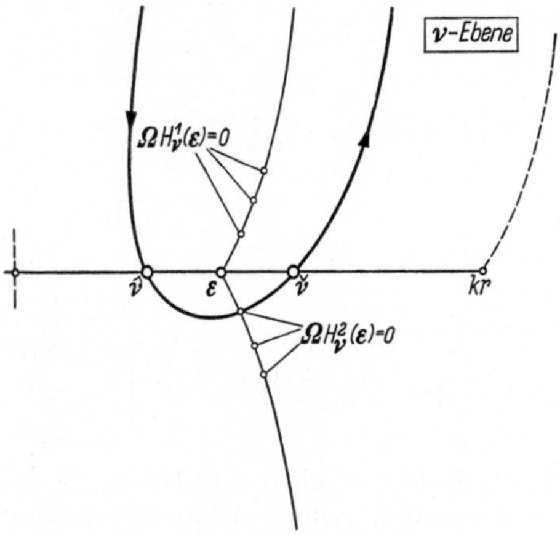

Fig. 107. Integrationsweg zur Darstellung des geometrisch-optischen Feldes: der Beitrag des linken Sattelpunktes $\hat{\nu}$ liefert die reflektierte Welle, der Beitrag des rechten Sattelpunktes die einfallende Welle.

Die Lösungen dieser Gleichungen lassen sich graphisch sehr einfach bestimmen: In Fig. 108 ist der (nach der geometrischen Optik) nach dem Aufpunkt $\mathfrak{r}$ reflektierte Strahl eingezeichnet (Einfallswinkel γ gleich Reflexionswinkel). Für seinen vor wie nach der Reflexion gleichen Abstand

$$p=a\sin\gamma \qquad (143.4\,\text{a})$$

vom Kreismittelpunkt, gilt aber gerade die Beziehung (143.3a). Ferner zeigt Fig. 109, daß die Größe

$$q=r\sin\vartheta \qquad (143.4\,\text{b})$$

in (143.3b) den Abstand bedeutet, den ein (geometrisch-optisch) einfallender Strahl (durch den Aufpunkt) vom Kreismittelpunkt hat[1]. Für die weitere Auswertung von (143.1) entwickeln wir die Exponenten in den Sattelpunkten (bis

[1] Dies gilt zwar zunächst nur für $|\pi-\vartheta|<\pi/2$, da der arc cos (q/r) in (143.3b) definitionsgemäß auf das Intervall von 0 bis $\pi/2$ festgelegt ist: Franz (l. c.) zeigt jedoch, daß die einfallende Welle $\exp(-ikr\cos\vartheta)$ stets asymptotisch durch ein Integral dargestellt werden kann, dessen Integrand mit demjenigen des zweiten Integrals in (143.1) übereinstimmt und dessen Weg über dieselben Sattelpunkte führt.

zu den quadratischen Gliedern) unter Beachtung von (143.2, 3a, b):

$$\left.\begin{aligned} v_g(r,\vartheta) \to & \\ & \mp \frac{e^{\frac{i\pi}{4}}}{\sqrt{2\pi k}\,(r^2-p^2)^{\frac{1}{4}}}\, e^{ik\left(\sqrt{r^2-p^2}-2\sqrt{a^2-p^2}\right)} \int e^{-\frac{i}{2k}\left(\frac{2}{\sqrt{a^2-p^2}}-\frac{1}{\sqrt{r^2-p^2}}\right)(\nu-\hat{\nu})^2}\,d\nu \\ & + \frac{e^{-\frac{i\pi}{4}}}{\sqrt{2\pi k}\,(r^2-q^2)^{\frac{1}{4}}}\, e^{ik\sqrt{r^2-q^2}} \int e^{\frac{i}{2k}\frac{(\nu-\check{\nu})^2}{\sqrt{r^2-q^2}}}\,d\nu. \end{aligned}\right\} \tag{143.4}$$

Mit Hilfe des Laplace-Integrals

$$\int_{-\infty}^{\infty} e^{-\alpha x^2}\,dx = \sqrt{\frac{\pi}{\alpha}}$$

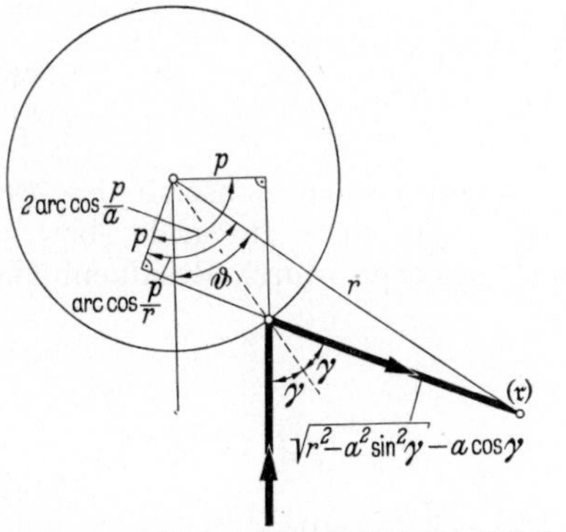

Fig. 108. Zur geometrisch-optischen Reflexion am Zylinder.

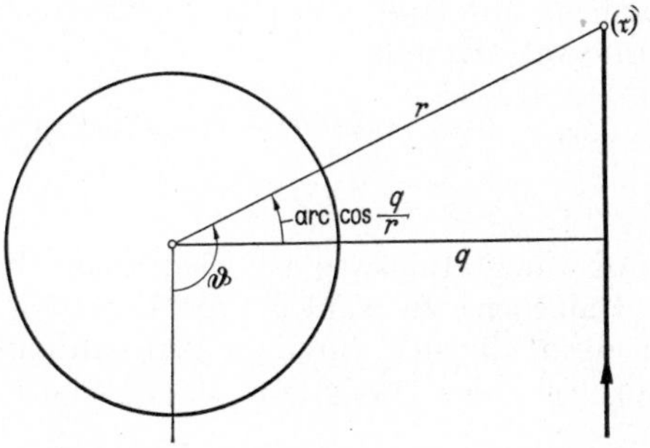

Fig. 109. Bezeichnungen zur Darstellung der einfallenden Welle.

und den Beziehungen

$$\sqrt{a^2-p^2} = a\cos\gamma, \qquad \sqrt{r^2-q^2} = -r\cos\vartheta$$

ergibt sich daraus

$$v_g \to e^{-ikr\cos\vartheta} \mp \sqrt{\frac{a\cos\gamma}{2\sqrt{r^2-a^2\sin^2\gamma}-a\cos\gamma}}\,\exp ik\left(\sqrt{r^2-a^2\sin^2\gamma}-2a\cos\gamma\right). \tag{143.5}$$

Für das *Fernfeld* $\left(r\to\infty,\ \gamma\to\frac{\vartheta}{2}\right)$ vereinfacht sich dies zu

$$v_g(r,\vartheta) \to e^{-ikr\cos\vartheta} \mp \sqrt{\frac{a}{2r}\cos\frac{\vartheta}{2}}\; e^{ik\left(r-2a\cos\frac{\vartheta}{2}\right)}. \tag{143.5'}$$

Diese Feldverteilung ist aber in genauer Übereinstimmung mit der geometrischen Optik (vgl. Ziff. 147). Schon DEBYE hatte gezeigt, daß seine eingangs erwähnte Integraldarstellung der strengen Lösung durch asymptotische Auswertung auf (143.5') führt[1]. Ergänzt man die Sattelpunktmethode durch die an sie anschlie-

[1] P. DEBYE: Phys. Z. **9**, 775 (1908). Vgl. auch H. SPOHN: Diss. Breslau 1916; Phys. Z. **21**, 444, 469, 501, 518 (1920); H. PFENNINGER: Ann. Phys. **83**, 753 (1927). Nach H. BUCERIUS: Optik **1**, 188 (1946) erhält man die Debyeschen Ergebnisse schneller, indem man die Rayleighschen Reihen im Sinne der Eulerschen Summenformel durch ein Integral ersetzt und dieses nach der Methode der stationären Phase auswertet. Auf diese Weise ergibt sich auch ein anderer Zugang zu den Residuenwellen. Für den geometrisch-optischen Grenzfall vgl. man auch W. v. IGNATOWSKY: Ann. Phys. **18**, 495 (1905); **23**, 875 (1907).

ßende asymptotische Reihe, so ergibt sie anstelle von (143.5′)

$$\left.\begin{aligned} v_g(r,\vartheta) &\to e^{-ikr\cos\vartheta} \mp \sqrt{\frac{a}{2r}\cos\frac{\vartheta}{2}}\, e^{ik\left(r-2a\cos\frac{\vartheta}{2}\right)} \cdot \\ &\cdot \left\{1 - \frac{3i}{16\varepsilon\cos\frac{\vartheta}{2}} \pm \frac{i}{2\varepsilon\cos^3\frac{\vartheta}{2}} + \cdots\right\}. \end{aligned}\right\} \tag{143.5''}$$

144. Asymptotische Darstellung der Flächenströme. Wir wollen hier noch die asymptotischen Darstellungen der Belegungsdichten $\psi_{\parallel}(\vartheta) = \left(\frac{\partial v_{\parallel}}{\partial r}\right)_{r=a}$ und $\psi_{\perp}(\vartheta) = (v_{\perp})_{r=a}$ angeben, für die wir in Ziff. 137 die Reihen (137.14) erhalten haben. Mit Hilfe von (140.2′) lassen sich diese Reihen zunächst durch folgende Integrale darstellen:

$$\left.\begin{aligned} \psi_{\parallel}(\vartheta) &= k \\ \psi_{\perp}(\eta) &= -1 \end{aligned}\right\} \cdot \frac{2}{\pi\varepsilon} \oint_{-\infty}^{\infty} \frac{e^{-\frac{i\pi}{2}\nu}}{\sin\pi\nu} \frac{\cos\nu(\vartheta-\pi)}{\Omega H_\nu^1(\varepsilon)}\, d\nu. \tag{144.1}$$

(Als Integrationsweg ist wieder eine Parallele zur reellen Achse in der *oberen* ν-Halbebene zu wählen; vgl. Fig. 104.) Wertet man diese Integrale [bzw. diejenigen, die sich durch die Aufspaltung (142.2) ergeben] durch Residuenbildung an den Polen (140.4) aus, so ergibt sich:

für die *Schattenseite* des Zylinders $\left(|\pi-\vartheta| < \frac{\pi}{2}\right)$

$$\left.\begin{aligned} \psi_{\parallel}(\vartheta) &= k \\ \psi_{\perp}(\vartheta) &= -1 \end{aligned}\right\} \cdot \frac{4i}{\varepsilon} \sum_s \frac{\cos\nu_s(\pi-\vartheta)}{\sin\pi\nu_s} \frac{e^{-\frac{i\pi}{2}\nu_s}}{\left\{\frac{\partial}{\partial\nu}\Omega H_\nu^1(\varepsilon)\right\}_{\nu_s}}, \tag{144.2}$$

für die *beleuchtete Seite* des Zylinders $\left(|\vartheta| < \frac{\pi}{2}\right)$

$$\left.\begin{aligned} \psi_{\parallel}(\vartheta) &= k \\ \psi_{\perp}(\vartheta) &= -1 \end{aligned}\right\} \cdot \left\{\frac{4i}{\varepsilon} \sum_s \frac{\cos\nu_s\vartheta}{\sin\pi\nu_s} \frac{e^{\frac{i\pi}{2}\nu_s}}{\left\{\frac{\partial}{\partial\nu}\Omega H_\nu^1(\varepsilon)\right\}_{\nu_s}} + \frac{2}{\pi i\varepsilon} \int_{-\infty}^{\infty} \frac{e^{i\nu\left(\vartheta-\frac{\pi}{2}\right)}}{\Omega H_\nu^1(\varepsilon)}\, d\nu\right\}. \tag{144.2'}$$

Die Integralterme entsprechen hier wieder den geometrisch-optischen Belegungsdichten. Die asymptotische Auswertung dieser streng gültigen Darstellungen liefert hier folgendes Ergebnis:

für $|\vartheta-\pi| < \frac{\pi}{2}$

$$\left.\begin{aligned} \psi_{\parallel}(\vartheta) &\to k\,\varepsilon^{-\frac{1}{3}} e^{-\frac{i\pi}{3}} \\ \psi_{\perp}(\vartheta) &\to 1 \end{aligned}\right\} \cdot \sum_s \frac{D_s}{1-e^{2\pi i\nu_s}} \left\{e^{i\nu_s\left(\vartheta-\frac{\pi}{2}\right)} + e^{i\nu_s\left(\frac{3\pi}{2}-\vartheta\right)}\right\} \tag{144.3}$$

mit

$$D_{\parallel}^{(s)} = -\frac{\pi}{3} \frac{6^{\frac{1}{3}}}{A'(q_{\parallel}^{(s)})} \tag{144.4p}$$

bzw.

$$D_{\perp}^{(s)} = \frac{\pi}{q_{\perp}^{(s)} A(q_{\perp}^{(s)})}; \tag{144.4s}$$

$$\left.\begin{aligned}
&\text{für } |\vartheta|<\frac{\pi}{2}\\
&\left.\begin{aligned}\psi_{\|}(\vartheta)&\to -2ik\cos\vartheta\\ \psi_{\perp}(\vartheta)&\to 2\end{aligned}\right\}\cdot e^{-i\varepsilon\cos\vartheta}\left(1\pm\frac{i}{2\varepsilon\cos^3\vartheta}\pm\cdots\right)\\
&+\left\{\begin{matrix}k\,\varepsilon^{-\frac{1}{3}}e^{-\frac{i\pi}{3}}\\ 1\end{matrix}\right\}\cdot\sum_s\frac{D_s}{1-e^{2\pi i\nu_s}}\left\{e^{i\nu_s\left(\frac{3\pi}{2}+\vartheta\right)}+e^{i\nu_s\left(\frac{3\pi}{2}-\vartheta\right)}\right\}.
\end{aligned}\right\}\qquad(144.3')$$

Mit Hilfe der Tabelle 1 in Ziff. 141 erhält man die in der folgenden Tabelle 4 angegebenen ersten fünf Koeffizienten D_s

Tabelle 4. *Anfangswerte der Kriechströme.*

s	$D_{\|}^{(s)}$	$D_{\perp}^{(s)}$
1	−1,79678	1,83243
2	1,56880	−0,73473
3	−1,45621	0,54538
4	1,38324	−0,45333
5	−1,32996	0,39627

Mit diesen Anfangswerten beginnen die Ströme von den geometrischen Schattengrenzen aus auf die geometrisch-optisch im Schatten liegende Seite des Zylinders zu kriechen. Dabei werden sie infolge Abstrahlung längs ihres Weges exponentiell geschwächt. Es sei noch erwähnt, daß FRANZ und GALLE[1] die vorstehend angegebenen Größen ν_s, C_s, D_s durch asymptotische Reihen bis einschließlich des Gliedes mit ε^{-2} vervollständigt haben.

In der Umgebung der geometrischen *Schattenränder* $\vartheta=\pi/2$ und $\vartheta=3\pi/2$ wird sowohl die Darstellung (144.3) als auch (144.3′) unbrauchbar, da dort einer der Exponenten der „konvergenzerzeugenden" Exponentialfunktionen in der jeweiligen geschweiften Klammer verschwindet. In diesem physikalisch besonders interessanten Bereich („*Halbschattenzone*") müssen also die Integrale (144.1) nach einem anderen Verfahren ausgewertet werden[2]. Zu diesem Zweck können wir zufolge des dort angegebenen Integrationsweges $\operatorname{Im}\nu>0$ voraussetzen (was weiterhin durch den Haken am Integralzeichen angedeutet sei) und somit den Watsonschen Nenner $\sin\pi\nu$ in eine konvergente geometrische Reihe entwickeln:

$$\left.\begin{aligned}\psi_{\|}(\vartheta)&=k\\ \psi_{\perp}(\vartheta)&=-1\end{aligned}\right\}\cdot\frac{2}{\pi i\varepsilon}\sum_{l=0}^{\infty}\int_{-\infty}^{\infty}\left\{e^{i\nu\left(\vartheta-\frac{\pi}{2}+2\pi l\right)}+e^{i\nu\left(\frac{3\pi}{2}-\vartheta+2\pi l\right)}\right\}\frac{d\nu}{\Omega H_\nu^1(\varepsilon)}.\qquad(144.5)$$

Der analytische Vorteil dieser Schreibweise besteht darin, daß hier die ganzzahligen Pole des Watsonschen Nenners nicht mehr auftreten. In physikalischer Hinsicht entsprechen die einzelnen Summenglieder den von den beiden Schattengrenzen $\vartheta=\pi/2$ und $\vartheta=3\pi/2$ ausgehenden Kriechströmen, die in den geometrischen Schatten hineinkriechend den Zylinder l-mal umlaufen haben (vgl. Fig. 95; $\vartheta-\pi/2$ und $3\pi/2-\vartheta$ sind die von den beiden Schattengrenzen gemessenen Winkelabstände eines Punktes der Oberfläche mit dem Azimut ϑ). Die Beiträge der

[1] W. FRANZ u. R. GALLE: Z. Naturforsch. **10**a, 374 (1955).

[2] Vgl. dazu L. WETZEL: Harvard Univ. Cruft Lab. Sci. Rep. No. 10 (1957). — R.F. GOODRICH: Studies in Radar Cross-Section XXVI. Ann Arbor: Univ. of Michigan Press (1958). Man vergleiche auch R.S. ELLIOT: J. Appl. Phys. **26**, 368 (1955). — D.S. JONES: Proc. Roy. Soc. Lond. A **239**, 338 (1957). Bei JONES findet sich eine direkte Methode zur Lösung des Randwertproblems für die Halbschattenzone (deren Winkelausdehnung von der Größenordnung $\varepsilon^{-\frac{1}{3}}$ ist).

den einzelnen Dämpfungskonstanten entsprechenden Kriechströme sind in der Darstellung (144.5) schon „aufsummiert“. Zur Auswertung der Integrale überzeugt man sich zunächst mit Hilfe der Debyeschen asymptotischen Darstellung von $H_\nu^1(\varepsilon)$ (vgl. Fig. 100, Ziff. 139), daß der Hauptbeitrag von der Umgebung der Stelle (stationärer Phase) $\nu=\varepsilon$ herrührt. Zur genaueren Auswertung tragen wir daraufhin die Hankel-Approximation (139.17) in (144.5) ein. Das Ergebnis läßt sich durch Einführung der in Gl. (139.19) definierten Variablen q in die folgende Form setzen

$$\left.\begin{aligned} \psi_{\|}(\vartheta) &\to k\,\frac{\varepsilon^{-\frac{1}{3}}}{6^{\frac{2}{3}}}\,e^{\frac{i\pi}{6}} \\ \psi_{\perp}(\vartheta) &\to \frac{i}{6} \end{aligned}\right\}\cdot\sum_{l=0}^{\infty}\left\{g(\xi_l)\,e^{i\varepsilon\left(\vartheta-\frac{\pi}{2}+2\pi l\right)}+g(\xi_l')\,e^{i\varepsilon\left(\frac{3\pi}{2}-\vartheta+2\pi l\right)}\right\} \tag{144.6}$$

mit

$$g(\xi)=\int\limits_{-\infty e^{-\frac{i\pi}{3}}}^{\infty e^{-\frac{i\pi}{3}}}\frac{e^{i\xi q}}{\Omega A(q)}\,dq \tag{144.7}$$

und

$$\left.\begin{aligned} \xi_l &= \left(\frac{\varepsilon}{6}\right)^{\frac{1}{3}} e^{\frac{i\pi}{3}}\left(\vartheta-\frac{\pi}{2}+2\pi l\right) \\ \xi_l' &= \left(\frac{\varepsilon}{6}\right)^{\frac{1}{3}} e^{\frac{i\pi}{3}}\left(\frac{3\pi}{2}-\vartheta+2\pi l\right). \end{aligned}\right\} \tag{144.8}$$

(Dabei hat Ω jetzt die Bedeutung $\Omega=1$ im $\|$-Fall bzw. $\Omega=d/dq$ im $\perp$-Fall.) Für $\xi>0$ läßt sich (144.7) durch Residuenbildung an den durch $\Omega A(q)=0$ definierten Polen q_s auswerten:

$$g(\xi)=2\pi i\sum_s\frac{e^{i\xi q_s}}{\left\{\frac{d}{dq}\,\Omega A(q)\right\}_{q_s}}. \tag{144.7'}$$

Setzt man dies in (144.6) ein, so kommt man zu Gl. (144.3) zurück. Die Darstellung (144.6) ist jedoch im Gegensatz zu (144.3) auch noch für die Umgebung der Schattenränder ($\xi=0$) brauchbar. Die Glieder mit $l>0$ können hier nach wie vor mittels der Residuenmethode ausgewertet werden, während für das den Hauptbeitrag liefernde (im wesentlichen allein in Betracht kommende) Glied mit $l=0$ die Integrale $g(\xi)$ numerisch ausgewertet werden müssen[1]. [$|g(\xi)|$ geht für im ersten Quadrat gelegene ξ-Werte mit wachsendem $|\xi|$ exponentiell zu null; vgl. (144.7′) und (144.8).] Damit läßt sich auch für die Halbschattenzone eine für $\varepsilon\gg1$ sehr genaue Berechnung der Flächenströme durchführen. Für mäßig große ε kann man die Genauigkeit noch dadurch steigern, daß man bei der Hankel-Funktion in (144.5) ein weiteres Glied in ihrer asymptotischen Darstellung berücksichtigt[2]. Die sich ergebende Darstellung ist für alle $\varepsilon\gtrsim2$ brauchbar (vgl. Ziff. 146).

Die oben gefundene asymptotische Darstellung der Flächenströme auf einem ideal leitenden Kreiszylinder läßt sich sinngemäß auch auf andere konvexe Zylinder bzw. auf beliebig konvexe Körper übertragen, falls die Krümmungsradien überall sehr groß gegen die Wellenlänge sind. In der Tat hat V. A.

[1] Tabellierungen der Funktionen (144.7) *(Fock-Funktionen)* finden sich bei V. A. Fock: J. of Phys. USSR. **10**, 130 (1946). — L. Wetzel: l. c. — N. A. Logan: Air Force Cambridge Research Center (1959).

[2] Vgl. L. Wetzel: l. c.

FOCK[1] eine entsprechende allgemeine Darstellung schon frühzeitig angegeben, indem er die Umgebung eines Punktes der geometrischen Schattengrenze auf der Oberfläche eines konvexen Körpers lokal durch ein Rotationsparaboloid ersetzte. FOCK betrachtet das Auftreten der die scharfe Schattengrenze verwischenden Kriechströme als eine Art Ausgleichsphänomen, für das er eine parabolische Differentialgleichung aufstellt. Für die Lösung dieser Gleichung erhält er gerade Funktionen des Types (144.7), die deshalb in der Literatur meist als *Fock-Funktionen* bezeichnet werden.

145. Direkte asymptotische Lösung der Integralgleichungen. Die in Ziff. 144 angegebene asymptotische Darstellung der Flächenbelegungen läßt sich auch durch direkte asymptotische Lösung der Integralgleichungen (137.7) gewinnen. Diese Lösungsmethode ist besonders deshalb von Interesse, weil sie sich auch auf beliebige glatte konvexe Zylinder, sowie (in entsprechend erweiterter Form) auf beliebige glatte (doppelt gekrümmte) konvexe Oberflächen (deren Krümmungsradien überall groß gegen die Wellenlänge sind) übertragen läßt, bei denen der Weg über die Watson-Transformation nicht gangbar ist.

Zunächst bemerken wir, daß FOCK[2] die Integralgleichungen herangezogen hat, um seine in Ziff. 144 erwähnte Darstellung der Belegungsdichten zu begründen. Im folgenden wollen wir die Methode darlegen, die FRANZ und DEPPERMANN entwickelt haben, um die in Ziff. 144 gefundenen Kriechströme als asymptotische Lösungen der Integralgleichungen zu erweisen[3].

Wir versuchen zunächst die Integralgleichung (137.7*p*) bzw. (137.7*s*) durch Iteration zu lösen, d. h. durch sukzessives Einsetzen (beginnend mit der Inhomogenität). Die so entstehenden Integrale lassen sich für $\varepsilon \gg 1$ mit Hilfe der Methode der stationären Phase asymptotisch auswerten; man findet auf diese Weise die Lösung

$$\psi_{\parallel}(\vartheta) \to \left\{ \begin{array}{ll} -2ik\cos\vartheta\, \mathrm{e}^{-i\varepsilon\cos\vartheta}\left(1+\dfrac{i}{2\varepsilon\cos^3\vartheta}-\cdots\right) & \left(|\vartheta|<\dfrac{\pi}{2}\right) \\ 0 & \left(|\pi-\vartheta|<\dfrac{\pi}{2}\right) \end{array} \right\} \quad (145.1p)$$

bzw.

$$\psi_{\perp}(\vartheta) \to \left\{ \begin{array}{ll} 2\mathrm{e}^{-i\varepsilon\cos\vartheta}\left(1-\dfrac{i}{2\varepsilon\cos^3\vartheta}+\cdots\right) & \left(|\vartheta|<\dfrac{\pi}{2}\right) \\ 0 & \left(|\pi-\vartheta|<\dfrac{\pi}{2}\right). \end{array} \right\} \quad (145.1s)$$

Es ergibt sich also hier die geometrisch-optische Verteilung der Belegungsdichten, ergänzt durch eine asymptotische Reihe nach fallenden Potenzen von ε. In der Umgebung der geometrischen Schattenränder $\vartheta = \frac{\pi}{2}, \frac{3\pi}{2}$ wird diese Entwicklung

[1] V.A. FOCK: J. Phys. USSR. **9**, 255 (1945); **10**, 130, 399 (1946). — Phil. Mag. **39**, 149 (1948). — Usp. Fiz: Nauk. **43**, 587 (1951). — Abh. Sowj. Phys. **2**, 7 (1951). — V.A. FOCK u. M. LEONTOVICH: J. Phys. USSR. **10**, 1 (1946). — Vgl. auch S. J. RABINOWITZ: Johns Hopkins Univ. Techn. Rep. No. 32 (1956). — L. WETZEL: Harvard Univ. Cruft. Lab. Sci. Rep. No. 12 (1956). — R.F. GOODRICH: Studies in Radar Cross-Section XXVI. Ann Arbor: Univ. of Michigan Press 1958.

[2] V.A. FOCK: J. Phys. USSR. **10**, 130 (1946).

[3] W. FRANZ u. K. DEPPERMANN: Ann. Phys. **10**, 361 (1952) (Zylinder). — K. DEPPERMANN u. W. FRANZ: Ann. Phys. **14**, 253 (1954) (Kugel). — Höhere Näherungen (im Sinne einer asymptotischen Entwicklung), die auch die (schwach) veränderliche Krümmung eines beliebigen konvexen Zylinders berücksichtigen, bei W. FRANZ u. K. KLANTE: Trans. Inst. Radio Engrs. AP-**7**, 568 (1959). — J.B. KELLER u. B.R. LEVY: N.Y. Univ. Res. Rep. No. EM-147 (1959). Wir folgen im wesentlichen wieder der Darstellung bei W. FRANZ: Theorie der Beugung elektromagnetischer Wellen. Berlin: Springer 1957.

unbrauchbar; dort hat man die iterierten Integrale nach einer anderen Methode auszuwerten (etwa derjenigen vom Typ des Airyschen Integrals)[1]. Infolge des Nenners $\varepsilon\cos^3\vartheta$ umfaßt diese Umgebung (Halbschattenzone) einen Winkelbereich von der Größenordnung $\varepsilon^{-\frac{1}{3}}$. Wenn wir zwar ε aber nicht $\varepsilon^{\frac{1}{3}}$ als groß gegen 1 voraussetzen, so kann dieser Übergangsbereich sich über den ganzen Zylinder ausbreiten. Innerhalb der Übergangszone muß die Belegungsdichte stetig von den Werten (145.1) auf der beleuchteten Seite auf diejenigen auf der Schattenseite abnehmen. Dieser Übergang wird gerade durch die Kriechströme vermittelt, wie wir früher gesehen hatten. Hier ergeben sie sich als Lösungen der (entsprechend modifizierten) *homogenen* Integralgleichungen (137.7). Dies läßt sich für beliebige konvexe Körper (deren Krümmungsradien überall groß gegen die Wellenlänge sind) auf die im folgenden dargestellte Weise begründen.

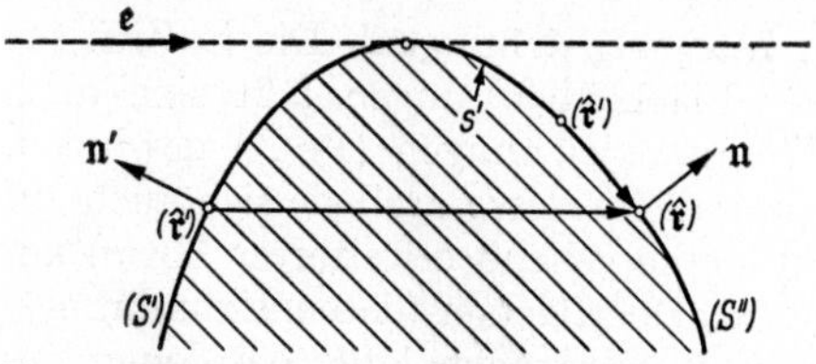

Fig. 110. Zur Beugung am konvexen Zylinder nach der Methode der Integralgleichungen.

In Fig. 110 fällt eine ebene Welle $e^{ik(\mathfrak{e}\mathfrak{r})}$ aus der Richtung $\mathfrak{e}$ auf einen konvexen Körper. Die Integralgleichungen (76.6p) bzw. (76.7s) für die Flächenbelegungen ψ_p bzw. ψ_s haben die Form

$$\psi_p(\hat{\mathfrak{r}}) + \frac{1}{2\pi}\oint_S \psi_p(\hat{\mathfrak{r}}')\,\frac{\partial}{\partial n}\,\frac{e^{ik|\hat{\mathfrak{r}}-\hat{\mathfrak{r}}'|}}{|\hat{\mathfrak{r}}-\hat{\mathfrak{r}}'|}\,d\hat{\mathfrak{r}}' = 2ik(\mathfrak{n}\,\mathfrak{e})\,e^{ik(\mathfrak{e}\hat{\mathfrak{r}})} \tag{145.2p}$$

bzw.

$$\psi_s(\hat{\mathfrak{r}}) - \frac{1}{2\pi}\oint_S \psi_s(\hat{\mathfrak{r}}')\,\frac{\partial}{\partial n'}\,\frac{e^{ik|\hat{\mathfrak{r}}-\hat{\mathfrak{r}}'|}}{|\hat{\mathfrak{r}}-\hat{\mathfrak{r}}'|}\,d\hat{\mathfrak{r}}' = 2e^{ik(\mathfrak{e}\hat{\mathfrak{r}})}. \tag{145.2s}$$

Auf der geometrisch-optisch beleuchteten Seite (S') haben wir für die Belegungsdichten $\psi(\hat{\mathfrak{r}})$ einen schnell veränderlichen Phasenfaktor der Form $e^{ik(\mathfrak{e}\hat{\mathfrak{r}})}$ zu erwarten neben einem langsam veränderlichen Amplitudenfaktor [vgl. (145.1)]. Es tritt also in den obigen über (S') erstreckten Integralen der Exponentialfaktor $\exp ik\{(\mathfrak{e}\hat{\mathfrak{r}}')+|\hat{\mathfrak{r}}-\hat{\mathfrak{r}}'|\}$ auf. Nach dem Prinzip der stationären Phase liefern daher nur diejenigen Stellen $\hat{\mathfrak{r}}'$ einen Beitrag zum Integral, in denen die Phase stationär ist, d.h. für die

$$\mathfrak{e} + \frac{\hat{\mathfrak{r}}'-\hat{\mathfrak{r}}}{|\hat{\mathfrak{r}}'-\hat{\mathfrak{r}}|} = 0.$$

Der Hauptbeitrag zu den Integralen über (S') kommt also von demjenigen Punkt $\hat{\mathfrak{r}}'$, für den $\hat{\mathfrak{r}}-\hat{\mathfrak{r}}'$ die Richtung von $\mathfrak{e}$ hat (s. Fig. 110). Dies ist nur für Punkte $\hat{\mathfrak{r}}$ auf der geometrisch-optischen Schattenseite (S'') der Oberfläche der Fall. Wir können also (145.2) in der folgenden angenäherten Form schreiben

$$\left.\begin{aligned} \psi(\hat{\mathfrak{r}}) &\pm \frac{1}{2\pi}\int_{S''}\psi(\hat{\mathfrak{r}}')\cdots = \psi_0(\hat{\mathfrak{r}}) \qquad (\hat{\mathfrak{r}}\in S') \\ \psi(\hat{\mathfrak{r}}) &\pm \frac{1}{2\pi}\left\{\int_{S'} + \int_{S''}\right\}\psi(\hat{\mathfrak{r}}')\cdots = \psi_0(\hat{\mathfrak{r}}) \qquad (\hat{\mathfrak{r}}\in S''), \end{aligned}\right\} \tag{145.3}$$

wobei ψ_0 die Inhomogenität rechts in (145.2) bedeutet und das obere Vorzeichen sich auf den p-Fall, das untere auf den s-Fall bezieht. Im geometrisch-optischen Grenzfall erwarten wir nun, daß die Belegungsdichte ψ auf der Schattenseite (S'')

[1] Zur Darstellung der Belegungen in der Halbschattenzone vgl. man auch Ziff. 144 sowie V.A. Fock, l. c. — D.S. Jones: Proc. Roy. Soc. Lond. A **239**, 338 (1957).

verschwindet [vgl. wieder (145.1)]; das ist aber nach (145.3) nur dann der Fall, wenn der Term mit dem Integral über (S') für $\mathfrak{r} \in S''$ den Wert ψ_0 rechts gerade kompensiert. Die in den Schatten hinein kriechende Belegung („Kriechstrom") muß sich also näherungsweise nach der zweiten Gl. (145.3) aus der homogenen Integralgleichung

$$\psi_p(\hat{\mathfrak{r}}) + \frac{1}{2\pi} \int_{S''} \psi_p(\hat{\mathfrak{r}}') \frac{\partial}{\partial n} \frac{e^{ik|\hat{\mathfrak{r}}-\hat{\mathfrak{r}}'|}}{|\hat{\mathfrak{r}} - \hat{\mathfrak{r}}'|} d\hat{\mathfrak{r}}' = 0 \quad (\hat{\mathfrak{r}} \in S'') \tag{145.4p}$$

bzw.

$$\psi_s(\hat{\mathfrak{r}}) - \frac{1}{2\pi} \int_{S''} \psi_s(\hat{\mathfrak{r}}') \frac{\partial}{\partial n'} \frac{e^{ik|\hat{\mathfrak{r}}-\hat{\mathfrak{r}}'|}}{|\hat{\mathfrak{r}} - \hat{\mathfrak{r}}'|} d\hat{\mathfrak{r}}' = 0 \quad (\hat{\mathfrak{r}} \in S'') \tag{145.4s}$$

bestimmen lassen. Von den Kriechströmen erwarten wir nun weiter, daß sie längs Geodäten, die von der Einfallsrichtung tangiert werden, in den Schatten fließen, wobei ihre Phase sich proportional mit der Bogenlänge s längs des Kriechweges ändert (gemessen von der Schattengrenze aus). Die Integrale in (145.4) enthalten dann neben langsam veränderlichen Faktoren den Phasenfaktor $\exp ik(s' + |\hat{\mathfrak{r}} - \hat{\mathfrak{r}}'|)$. Dieser ist dort stationär, wo die Zunahme der Bogenlänge s' gleich der Abnahme der Sehne $|\hat{\mathfrak{r}} - \hat{\mathfrak{r}}'|$ ist. Das bedeutet aber, daß im wesentlichen nur die Umgebung desjenigen Punktes $\hat{\mathfrak{r}}'$ zum Integral in (145.4) beiträgt, der auf der Geodäte kurz *vor* $\hat{\mathfrak{r}}$ liegt (s. die rechte Seite von Fig. 110).

Auf die Verhältnisse des Kreiszylinders spezialisierend, haben wir die Kriechströme aus der aus (137.7) im Sinne von (145.4) sich ergebenden homogenen Integralgleichung

$$\psi(\vartheta) = \mp \frac{\varepsilon}{2i} \int_{|\vartheta'|<\pi/2} \psi(\vartheta') H_1^1\left(2\varepsilon \left|\sin\frac{\vartheta-\vartheta'}{2}\right|\right) \left|\sin\frac{\vartheta-\vartheta'}{2}\right| d\vartheta' \quad \left(|\vartheta| < \frac{\pi}{2}\right) \tag{145.5}$$

zu bestimmen (oberes Vorzeichen für den $\|$-Fall, unteres für den $\perp$-Fall). Die oben angedeutete Aufspaltung in einen schnell veränderlichen Phasenfaktor und eine langsam veränderliche Amplitude lautet hier (mit $s = a\vartheta$)

$$\psi(\vartheta) = \hat{\psi}(\vartheta)\, e^{i\varepsilon\vartheta}. \tag{145.6}$$

Setzt man dies in die Integralgleichungen (145.5) ein und entwickelt ihren Kern asymptotisch für $\varepsilon \gg 1$, so ergibt sich

$$\hat{\psi}(\vartheta) = \mp \sqrt{\frac{\varepsilon}{4\pi}}\, e^{\frac{3\pi i}{4}} \int_{|\vartheta'|<\pi/2} \hat{\psi}(\vartheta') \sqrt{\sin\frac{|\vartheta'-\vartheta|}{2}}\, e^{i\varepsilon\left(\vartheta'-\vartheta+2\sin\frac{|\vartheta'-\vartheta|}{2}\right)} d\vartheta'. \tag{145.5'}$$

Die Phase ist hier wieder nur in der Umgebung des Punktes $\vartheta' = \vartheta$ stationär und zwar für $\vartheta' \lesssim \vartheta$. Wir können daher im Integranden nach der Größe $\vartheta - \vartheta' = \tau$ entwickeln und brauchen nur über positive τ integrieren:

$$\hat{\psi}(\vartheta) = \sqrt{\frac{\varepsilon}{8\pi}}\, e^{\frac{3\pi i}{4}} \int_0^\infty \hat{\psi}(\vartheta - \tau) \sqrt{\tau}\, e^{-\frac{i\varepsilon}{24}\tau^3} d\tau. \tag{145.5''}$$

Dabei konnten wir die obere Grenze nach ∞ verlegen, da der wesentliche Beitrag doch nur aus der Umgebung von $\tau = 0$ herrührt. Gl. (145.5'') wird durch eine Exponentialfunktion gelöst, die wir in der Form

$$\hat{\psi}(\vartheta) = e^{-\alpha\left(\frac{i\varepsilon}{24}\right)^{\frac{1}{3}}\vartheta} \tag{145.6'}$$

ansetzen wollen. Für die im Exponenten auftretende Größe α ergibt sich dann nämlich die von ε freie transzendente Gleichung

$$\int_0^\infty \sqrt{t}\, e^{\alpha t - t^3}\, dt = \pm i \sqrt{\frac{\pi}{3}}\,. \tag{145.7}$$

Die Lösungen α_s dieser Gleichung sind also im p- bzw. s-Fall zueinander konjugiert komplex. Franz[1] hat gezeigt, daß Gl. (145.7) auch in der Form

$$A\left(\frac{e^{\mp\frac{i\pi}{3}}}{4^{\frac{1}{3}}}\,\alpha\right) A'\left(\frac{e^{\mp\frac{i\pi}{3}}}{4^{\frac{1}{3}}}\,\alpha\right) = 0 \tag{145.7'}$$

geschrieben werden kann (A ist wieder das Airysche Integral). Die so gefundenen Lösungen der homogenen Integralgleichungen haben also die Form

$$\left.\begin{aligned} \psi_{\parallel}^{(s)}(\vartheta) &= k\,\varepsilon^{-\frac{1}{3}}\, e^{-\frac{i\pi}{3}} \\ \psi_{\perp}^{(s)}(\vartheta) &= 1 \end{aligned}\right\} \cdot D_s\, e^{\left\{i\varepsilon - \alpha_s \left(\frac{i\varepsilon}{24}\right)^{\frac{1}{3}}\right\}\left(\vartheta - \frac{\pi}{2}\right)} \tag{145.8}$$

(wobei von den hier hinzugefügten Faktoren gleich die Rede sein wird). Damit sie exponentiell *abnehmen*, haben wir im p-Fall α_s aus den Nullstellen des ersten Faktors von (145.7′) (oberes Vorzeichen) zu bestimmen, im s-Fall hingegen die α_s aus den Nullstellen des zweiten Faktors (unteres Vorzeichen). Damit stimmt aber die geschweifte Klammer im Exponenten von (145.8) mit den ν_s aus Gl. (141.1′) überein. Die Lösungen (145.8) stellen also genau die vom rechten Schattenrand ($\vartheta = \pi/2$) ausgehenden Kriechströme dar, wie sie früher auf Grund der Watson-Transformation gefunden wurden [vgl. (144.2)]. Entsprechend hat man noch die vom linken Schattenrand ($\vartheta = 3\pi/2$) ausgehenden Kriechströme hinzuzufügen sowie alle diejenigen, die schon mehrmals um den Zylinder herumgelaufen sind. Schreibt man den *Imaginärteil* der geschweiften Klammer im Exponenten von (145.8) in der Form $a\omega/c'$, so kann c' als die gegenüber $c = \omega/k$ verringerte Geschwindigkeit interpretiert werden, mit der die Phase der Flächenstromdichte den Zylinder umläuft. Der *Realteil* bestimmt die Dämpfung seiner Amplitude.

Die Anfangswerte D_s der Kriechwellen sind hier so zu bestimmen, daß man die Summe der Lösungen (145.8) mit samt ihren sämtlichen Ableitungen nach ϑ in der Schattengrenze stetig an diejenige Lösung anschließt, die sich durch Iteration auf der Lichtseite ergibt. Dieser Weg ist jedoch mühsam; die D_s wird man daher dem Ergebnis der Watson-Transformation (144.3) entnehmen und sie näherungsweise auch auf beliebige konvexe glatte Körper übertragen. Dabei ist dann für a der Krümmungsradius der tangentiell angestrahlten Geodäte (für den Ausgangspunkt auf der Schattenlinie) einzusetzen. Für die Kugel werden wir dies Verfahren noch rechtfertigen (Ziff. 150).

Die von den Kriechströmen abgestrahlten Fernfelder erhält man, indem man (145.8) in die Integrale (137.4) einsetzt, die für $r \to \infty$ mit $R \to r - a\cos(\vartheta - \vartheta')$ in die Form

$$v_{\parallel}^{(s)}(r, \vartheta) \to \frac{a}{\sqrt{8\pi k r}}\, e^{i\left(kr + \frac{\pi}{4}\right)} \int_0^{2\pi} \psi_{\parallel}^{(s)}(\vartheta')\, e^{-i\varepsilon\cos(\vartheta - \vartheta')}\, d\vartheta' \tag{145.9p}$$

bzw.

$$v_{\perp}^{(s)}(r, \vartheta) \to \sqrt{\frac{a\varepsilon}{8\pi r}}\, e^{i\left(kr + \frac{3\pi}{4}\right)} \int_0^{2\pi} \psi_{\perp}^{(s)}(\vartheta') \cos(\vartheta - \vartheta')\, e^{-i\varepsilon\cos(\vartheta - \vartheta')}\, d\vartheta' \tag{145.9s}$$

[1] W. Franz: Z. Naturforsch. 9a, 705 (1954) Anhang 2.

übergehen. Die asymptotische Auswertung dieser Integrale liefert Beiträge von zwei Stellen ϑ' stationärer Phase; es sind diejenigen, in denen die Tangenten durch den Aufpunkt (r, ϑ) gehen. Das Ergebnis stimmt mit (142.6′) überein.

146. Diskussion. Die Brauchbarkeit der in Ziff. 144 gegebenen asymptotischen Darstellungen der *Flächenströme* auf dem Zylindermantel wird durch die Figuren 111a—e veranschaulicht[1]. Zunächst ist in Fig. 111a der Flächenstrom

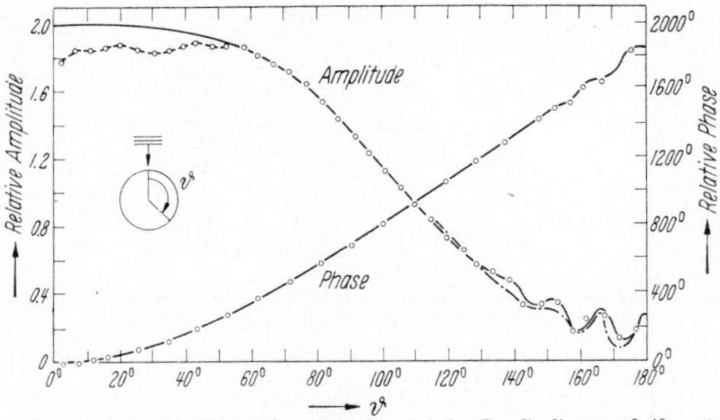

Fig. 111a. Stromverteilung auf der Oberfläche eines Zylinders bei der Randbedingung $\partial v/\partial n = 0$ ($\mathfrak{E} \perp$ Zylinderachse) nach Betrag und Phase für $\varepsilon = 12$: —— streng (nach RIBLET); —·—·— erste asymptotische Näherung, Gl. (144.6); ○○○ Meßergebnisse (nach WETZEL).

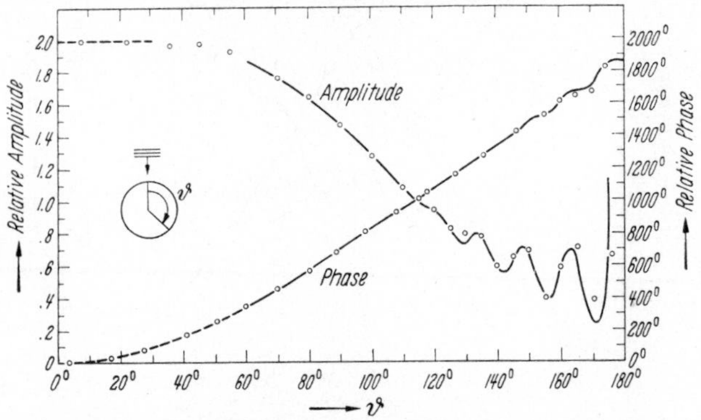

Fig. 111b. Stromverteilung auf der ideal leitenden Kugel (in der Schnittebene, in der der elektrische Vektor der einfallenden ebenen linear polarisierten Welle schwingt) nach Betrag und Phase für $\varepsilon = 12$: —— zweite asymptotische Näherung (nach WETZEL); — — — geometrisch optische Näherung; ○○○ Meßwerte (nach WETZEL).

$\psi_\perp(\vartheta)$ nach Amplitude und Phase für $\varepsilon = 12$ als Funktion von ϑ aufgetragen. Die ausgezogene Kurve ist durch numerische Auswertung der Rayleighschen Reihen gewonnen, die strichpunktierte mit Hilfe des ersten Gliedes der Darstellung (144.6) (abgesehen von der Umgebung von $\vartheta = 0$). Die eingezeichneten Punkte sind Meßwerte; die Abweichungen auf der beleuchteten Seite gehen auf Verfälschungen durch die Meßapparatur zurück. Durch Berücksichtigung des in Ziff. 144 erwähnten Korrekturterms von WETZEL läßt sich die Genauigkeit der asymptotischen Darstellung noch weiter steigern. Dies zeigt Fig. 111b zunächst für die Kugel (ausgezogene Kurve). Hier ist die Stromkomponente $\varkappa \mathfrak{J}_\vartheta(\vartheta, 0)$ nach Amplitude und Phase aufgetragen [vgl. (154.1″) und (155.11)].

Zum Vergleich sind in Fig. 111c die beiden Flächenströme auf dem Zylinder und der Kugel nochmal aufgetragen, und zwar beide mit der Wetzelschen Korrektur. Es ergibt sich also eine ausgezeichnete Übereinstimmung mit den Werten

[1] Die Figuren 111a—e sind dem Buch von R. W. P. KING u. T. T. WU: The Scattering and Diffraction of Waves. Cambridge, Mass. 1959, entnommen.

nach der strengen Theorie (schwarze Punkte). Qualitativ ist die asymptotische Darstellung (144.6) auch noch für relativ kleine ε-Werte brauchbar (vgl. Fig. 111d

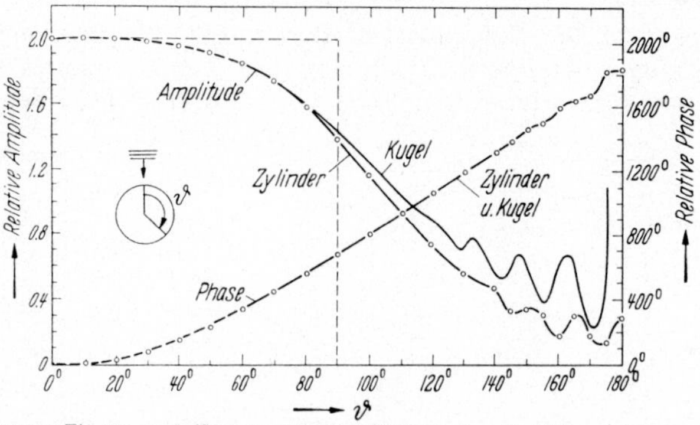

Fig. 111c. Vereinigung von Fig. 111a u. b (Stromverteilung auf Zylinder und Kugel für $\varepsilon = 12$): — zweite asymptotische Näherung (nach Wetzel); ○○○ strenge Werte (nach Riblet).

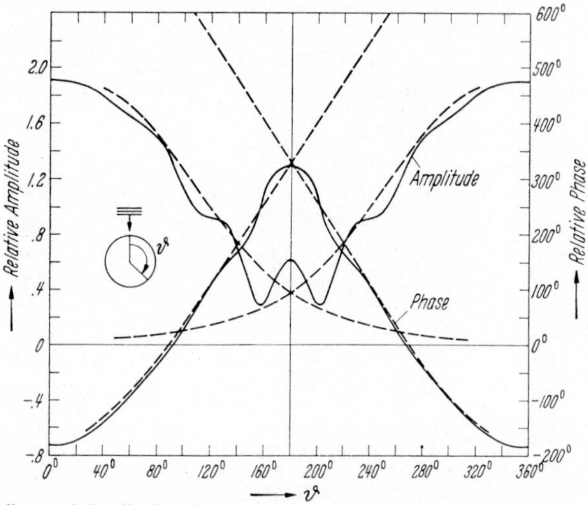

Fig. 111d. Stromverteilung nach Amplitude und Phase auf einem ideal leitenden Zylinder ($\mathfrak{E} \perp$ Zylinderachse) für $\varepsilon = 3{,}1$: — streng (nach Kodis); — — — erste asymptotische Näherung (Fock-Strom).

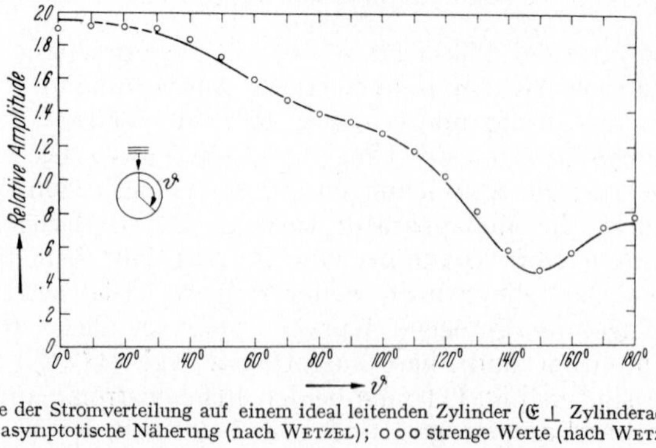

Fig. 111e. Amplitude der Stromverteilung auf einem ideal leitenden Zylinder ($\mathfrak{E} \perp$ Zylinderachse) für $\varepsilon = 2$: — zweite asymptotische Näherung (nach Wetzel); ○○○ strenge Werte (nach Wetzel).

für $\varepsilon = 3{,}1$); mit der Wetzelschen Korrektur liefert sie sogar selbst dann noch quantitativ richtige Ergebnisse (vgl. Fig. 111e für $\varepsilon = 2$).

Wenn zwar ε, nicht aber $(\varepsilon/6)^{\frac13}$ groß gegen 1 ist, so überwiegt das von den Kriechwellen herrührende Feldanteil in (142.6) die in (143.5″) angegebene Korrektur der geometrisch-optisch reflektierten Welle. Zum Beispiel ergibt sich für die *Rückstrahlung* des Zylinders ($\vartheta=0$, $r\to\infty$) aus (142.6′) und (143.5′)

$$v_S(r,0)\to A(0)\,\frac{e^{ikr}}{\sqrt{r}}=\sqrt{\frac{a}{2r}}\,e^{ik(r-2a)}\left\{1\mp 2\varepsilon^{-\frac16}\sum_s C_s\,\frac{e^{i\left(2\varepsilon-\pi\nu_s+\frac{\pi}{12}\right)}}{1-e^{2\pi i\nu_s}}\right\}. \qquad (146.1)$$

Für die in Fig. 97 aufgetragene Intensität der Rückwärtsstreuung *(Rückstreu-Koeffizient)* ergibt sich daraus

$$\frac{2}{a}\,|A(0)|^2=\left|1\mp 2\varepsilon^{-\frac13}\sum_s C_s\,\frac{\exp\left\{-\frac{\sqrt{3}\,\pi}{2}\left(\frac{\varepsilon}{6}\right)^{\frac13}q_s\right\}}{1-\exp 2\pi i\nu_s}\,e^{i\left\{\varepsilon(\pi+2)+\frac{\pi}{2}\left(\frac{\varepsilon}{6}\right)^{\frac13}q_s+\frac{\pi}{12}\right\}}\right|^2. \qquad (146.1')$$

Die hier auftretenden Interferenzen der reflektierten Welle [erstes Glied in (146.1)] mit der um den Zylinder herumgelaufenen Kriechwelle (vgl. Fig. 112a) sind für den s-Fall [$\mathfrak{E}\perp$ Zylinderachse, unteres Vorzeichen in (146.1′)] wesentlich stärker als für den p-Fall ($\mathfrak{E}\,\|$ Zylinderachse, oberes Vorzeichen), da die exponentielle Schwächung der Kriechwellen im zweiten Fall stärker ist als

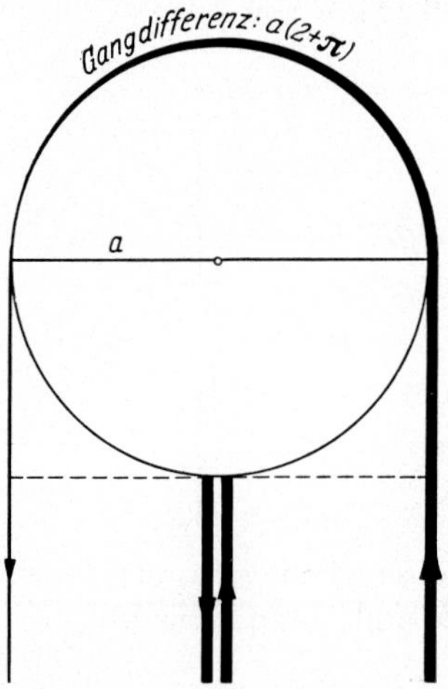

Fig. 112a. Gangdifferenz zwischen reflektierter Welle und Kriechwelle bei der Rückstrahlung.

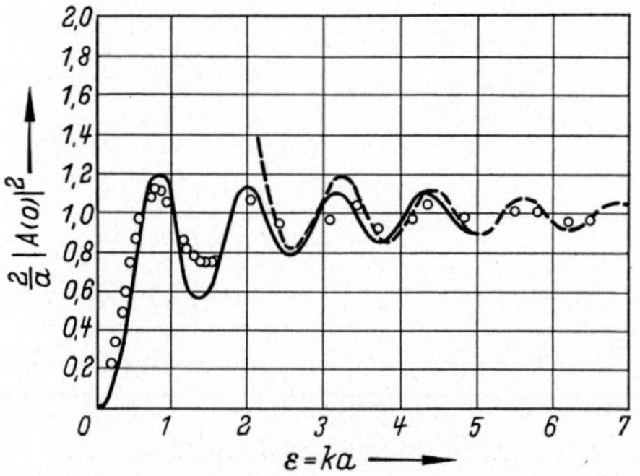

Fig. 112b. Rückstrahlung beim ideal leitenden Kreiszylinder für den s-Fall ($\mathfrak{E}\perp$ Zylinderachse): — streng (vgl. Fig. 97); — — asymptotisch nach Gl. (146.1); ○ ○ Meßwerte nach LIMBACH.

im ersteren (vgl. Ziff. 141, Tabelle 1). In Fig. 112b ist die Rückstrahlung nach (146.1′) als Funktion von ε für den s-Fall aufgetragen [zusammen mit derjenigen nach der strengen numerischen Auswertung der Rayleighschen Reihen (Fig. 97)]. Außerdem sind noch einige Meßpunkte eingetragen[1]. (Für das Verhältnis der Amplituden von Kriechwelle zu geometrisch-optischer Welle vgl. man die Diskussion der entsprechenden Verhältnisse bei der Kugel in Ziff. 151.)

Bei der Anwendung der Watson-Transformation auf die Beugung an einem Zylinder aus *transparentem* (schwach absorbierendem) Material[2] ergeben sich zusätzlich außer den geometrisch-optisch *gebrochenen* Wellen noch weitere Kriechwellen (Regenbogenterme). Neben dem Kreiszylinder ist auch der parabolische[3] und der elliptische[4] Zylinder mit Hilfe der Watson-Transformation behandelt worden.

[1] Nach A. LIMBACH: Zit. bei W. FRANZ u. K. DEPPERMANN: Ann. Phys. **10**, 361 (1952).

[2] P. BECKMANN: Diplomarbeit, Münster 1956. — W. FRANZ u. P. BECKMANN: Trans. Inst. Radio Engrs. AP-**4**, 203 (1956). — P. BECKMANN u. W. FRANZ: Z. Naturforsch. **12**a, 257 (1957).

[3] S.O. RICE: Bell. Syst. Techn. J. **33**, 417 (1954). — J.B. KELLER u. B. LEVY: N.Y. Univ. Res. Rep. No. EM-147 (1959).

[4] B. LEVY: N.Y. Univ. Res. Rep. No. EM-121 (1958). — J.B. KELLER u. B. LEVY: l. c. — N.P. KAZARINOFF u. R.K. RITT: Univ. of Michigan, Res. Inst. Rep. No. 5 (1959).

Zur asymptotischen Berechnung des *Streuquerschnittes* mit Hilfe der Amplitude der Vorwärtsstreuung nach (137.16) ist Gl. (141.9) (für $r \to \infty$) nicht geeignet, da für die Richtung $\vartheta = \pi$ die Winkelargumente der Exponentialfunktionen verschwinden. Dadurch wird aber die exponentielle Konvergenz der Reihe zerstört; ein Umstand der damit zusammenhängt, daß die Richtung der Vorwärtsstreuung mit derjenigen der geometrischen Schattengrenze zusammenfällt [zu deren beiden Seiten die verschiedenen Darstellungen (141.9) und (142.6) gelten]. Entsprechendes hatte sich auch für den Strombelag (144.3') in der Umgebung der Schattengrenze ergeben, der den wesentlichen Beitrag zur Vorwärtsstreuung abstrahlt.

Zur Berechnung der Vorwärtsstreuung hat man daher die Abstrahlung der durch (144.6) dargestellten Flächenströme in der Halbschattenzone zu ermitteln[1]. Das Ergebnis für den *Streukoeffizienten* stimmt mit dem nach anderen Methoden gewonnenen[2] überein. Besonders erwähnenswert ist die modifizierte Watson-Transformation von Beckmann und Franz[3] sowie die eigenartige funktionentheoretische Methode von Wu[4], die zu einem neuen Typus von Kriechwellen führt. Das Ergebnis von Wu lautet

für den p-Fall

$$\frac{\sigma_{\parallel}}{2} = 1 + 0{,}498\,076\,59 \cdot \varepsilon^{-\frac{2}{3}} - 0{,}011\,176\,56 \cdot \varepsilon^{-\frac{4}{3}}$$
$$\left. - 0{,}014\,686\,52 \cdot \varepsilon^{-2} + 0{,}004\,889\,45 \cdot \varepsilon^{-\frac{8}{3}} \right\} \qquad (146.2\,p)$$
$$+ 0{,}001\,793\,45 \cdot \varepsilon^{-\frac{10}{3}}$$

für den s-Fall

$$\frac{\sigma_{\perp}}{2} = 1 - 0{,}432\,119\,98 \cdot \varepsilon^{-\frac{2}{3}} - 0{,}213\,712\,36 \cdot \varepsilon^{-\frac{4}{3}}$$
$$\left. + 0{,}055\,732\,55 \cdot \varepsilon^{-2} - 0{,}000\,555\,34 \cdot \varepsilon^{-\frac{8}{3}} \right\} \qquad (146.2\,s)$$
$$+ 0{,}023\,249\,32 \cdot \varepsilon^{-\frac{10}{3}}.$$

Die Koeffizienten dieser asymptotischen Reihe ergeben sich als bestimmte Integrale über Aggregate von Airy-Funktionen und ihren Ableitungen (bzw. von drittelzahligen Bessel-Funktionen).

Der Streukoeffizient zeigt also hier im Gegensatz zu demjenigen des Streifens (Ziff. 124) keine Schwankungen, sondern nähert sich monoton seinem geometrisch-optischen Grenzwert 2. Dies folgt übrigens auch schon aus Fig. 96 und läßt sich durch den Hinweis deuten, daß beim Zylinder die Resonanzmöglichkeit entfällt, die beim Streifen durch das Zusammenwirken der Kantenströme gegeben ist. Der in Fig. 96 angegebene Verlauf ist in Fig. 113 noch einmal aufgetragen, um

---

[1] D.S. Jones: Proc. Roy. Soc. Lond. A **239**, 338 (1957).
[2] T.T. Wu u. S.I. Rubinow: J. Appl. Phys. **27**, 1032 (1956). — R.D. Kodis: Trans. Inst. Radio Engrs. AP-4, 580 (1956). — D.S. Jones u. G.B. Whitham: Proc. Cambridge Phil. Soc. **53**, 691 (1957). Vgl. auch H.C. van de Hulst: Light Scattering by Small Particles, S. 315. 1957. — Die stationäre Darstellung mit Hilfe des Strombelags der geometrischen Optik führt nicht zum richtigen Ergebnis, vgl. C.H. Papas: J. Appl. Phys. **21**, 318 (1950). — F.E. Borgnis u. C.H. Papas: Randwertprobleme der Mikrowellen-Physik, S. 56ff. Berlin-Göttingen-Heidelberg: Springer 1955. — Verbesserte Anwendungen der stationären Darstellung [die jedoch auch nicht zu einer quantitativen Übereinstimmung mit (146.2) führen] bei R.D. Kodis: Harvard Univ. Cruft Lab. Sci. Rep. Nos. 2, 3, 4, 5, 7, 8, 11. — Proc. Cambridge Phil. Soc. **54**, 512 (1958). — Für allgemeinere konvexe Körper vgl. D.S. Jones: Proc. Roy. Soc. Lond. A **240**, 206 (1957) (dort auch dreidimensionale elektromagnetische Probleme).
[3] P. Beckmann u. W. Franz: Z. Naturforsch. **12**a, 533 (1957).
[4] T.T. Wu: Harvard Univ. Cruft Lab. Techn. Rep. No. 232 (1956). — Phys. Rev. **104**, 1201 (1956).

ihn mit dem Verlauf nach Gl. (146.2) (bei Beschränkung auf das erste Korrekturglied) vergleichen zu können (gestrichelte Kurven). Außerdem sind noch die Rayleighschen Grenzkurven für $\varepsilon \ll 1$ nach Gl. (138.2) eingetragen (strichpunktiert).

Die ersten Korrekturglieder von Gln. (146.2) lassen sich in folgender Weise auf *beliebige konvexe Zylinder* übertragen[1]:

$$\sigma_{\parallel} \to 2 + \frac{0{,}9962}{k^{\frac{2}{3}} d} \left(\varrho_1^{\frac{1}{3}} + \varrho_2^{\frac{1}{3}}\right) \tag{146.3p}$$

bzw.

$$\sigma_{\perp} \to 2 - \frac{0{,}8640}{k^{\frac{2}{3}} d} \left(\varrho_1^{\frac{1}{3}} + \varrho_2^{\frac{1}{3}}\right). \tag{146.3s}$$

Dabei bedeuten ϱ_1 und ϱ_2 die Krümmungsradien des Zylinderprofils in den beiden Punkten, in denen je ein einfallender Strahl es tangiert und d den Abstand dieser beiden Strahlen (Fig. 114). Schließlich läßt sich dies Ergebnis auch für die Berechnung des Streukoeffizienten beliebiger konvexer Körper heranziehen[2], indem man die Umgebung der einzelnen Elemente ds der Schattengrenze auf deren Oberfläche durch entsprechende Zylinderstücke ersetzt. So ergibt sich die erste Korrektur zum geometrisch-optischen Streukoeffizienten der Kugel als doppelt so groß wie jene des Zylinders von gleichem Radius.

Zum Abschluß sei erwähnt, daß sich die oben durchgeführte asymptotische Entwicklung für $\varepsilon \to \infty$ als ein Spezialfall der erweiterten Luneberg-Kline-Entwicklung (vgl. Ziff. 45) auffassen läßt, die die geometrische Optik durch asymptotische Reihen korrigiert. Auch über die Feldverteilung in der *Umgebung der geometrischen Schattengrenze* (wo die bisherigen Entwicklungen versagen) liegen eingehende Untersuchungen vor[3].

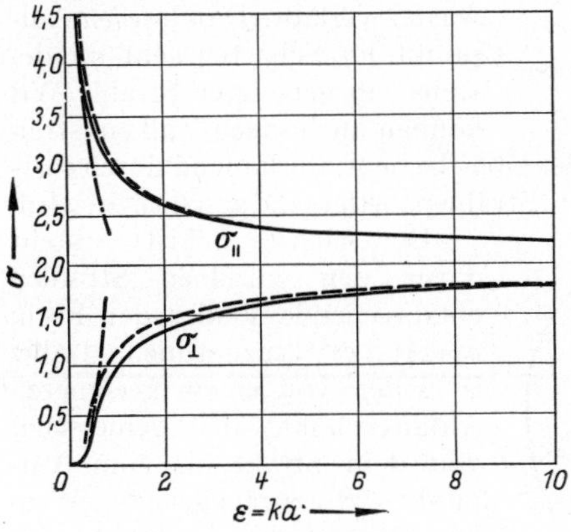

Fig. 113.

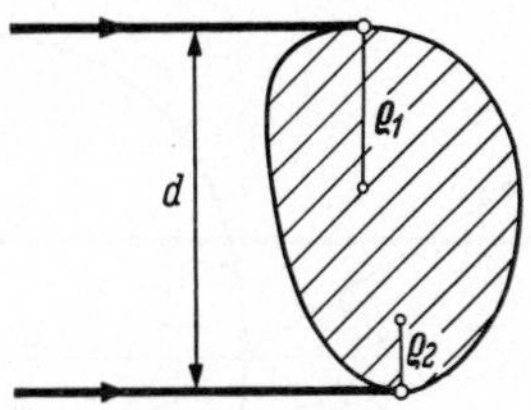

Fig. 114.

Fig. 113. Streukoeffizient des ideal leitenden Zylinders (vgl. Fig. 96): — streng; — — asymptotisch nach Gln. (146.2p) und (146.2s) bei Berücksichtigung des ersten Korrekturgliedes; - · — · — Rayleighsche Näherung nach Gl. (138.2p) und (138.2s).

Fig. 114. Zur asymptotischen Berechnung des Streuquerschnittes eines Zylinders von beliebigem Querschnitt, vgl. Gln. (146.3p) und (146.3s).

147. Geometrische Theorie der Beugung für konvexe Körper. Zum Abschluß wollen wir noch kurz den heuristischen Zugang zur asymptotischen Lösung

[1] Siehe Fußnote 1, S. 526.
[2] D. S. Jones u. G. B. Whitham: l. c. Fußnote 2, S. 526.
[3] T. T. Wu: Harvard Univ. Cruft Lab. Sci. Rep. No. 9 (1957). — T. T. Wu u. S. R. Seshadri: Harvard Univ. Cruft. Lab. Sci. Rep. No. 22 (1958).

des Randwertproblems darstellen, den J. B. KELLER[1] in seiner geometrischen Beugungstheorie für beliebige glatte konvexe Körper aufgezeigt hat (vgl. Abschn. A II c). Der Ausgangspunkt dieser Theorie ist eine erweiterte Fassung des *Fermatschen Prinzips*:

a) Die *reflektierten Strahlen* sind die extremalen Verbindungen zwischen Quellpunkt Q und Aufpunkt P, die einen *Punkt* mit der Oberfläche des Körpers gemeinsam haben.

b) Die *gebeugten Strahlen* sind die extremalen Verbindungen zwischen Q und P, die einen *Bogen* mit Oberfläche gemeinsam haben (s. Fig. 115, Q liegt hier im Unendlichen).

Jeder den Körper treffende einfallende Strahl führt gemäß dem Reflexionsgesetz zu einem reflektierten Strahl. Weder ein einfallender noch ein reflektierter Strahl können Aufpunkte im geometrischen Schatten erreichen. Außerdem führt jeder den Körper *tangierende* einfallende Strahl zu einem gebeugten Strahl, der längs einer Geodäte auf der Oberfläche weiterläuft und sie zum Aufpunkt hin tangierend wieder verläßt. Durch *jeden* Aufpunkt im Schatten geht mindestens ein gebeugter Strahl. Wir können auch sagen, daß ein streifend einfallender Strahl geodätisch längs der Oberfläche weiterlaufend durch fortwährend sich tangential abspaltende gebeugte Strahlen fortlaufend geschwächt wird.

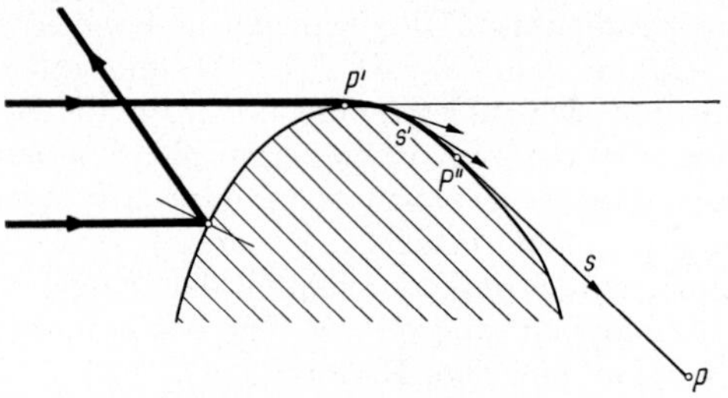

Fig. 115. Zur „geometrischen Beugungstheorie" konvexer Körper nach J. B. KELLER.

Der nächste Schritt besteht darin, den einzelnen Strahlen entsprechende Felder der Form $v = A(s)\, e^{iks}$ zuzuordnen. Dabei ist s der (von einem geeigneten Anfangspunkt aus gemessene) von dem Strahl bis zum Aufpunkt P zurückgelegte Weg. Die Amplitude A ergibt sich aus dem Energieprinzip (vgl. Ziff. 42).

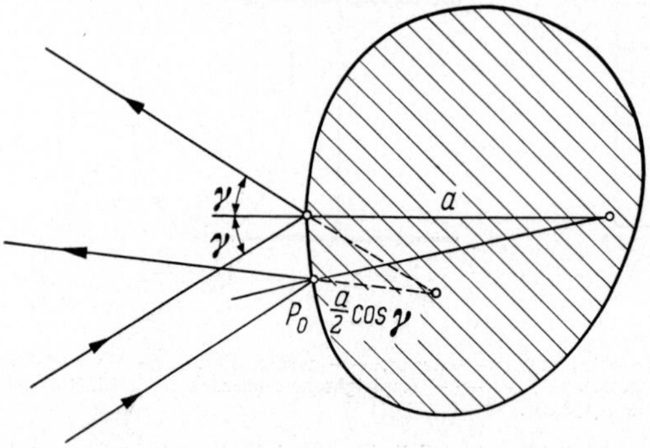

Fig. 116. Zur Berechnung des geometrisch-optisch reflektierten Feldes.

Für *konvexe Zylinder* ergibt sich z. B. die Amplitude der *reflektierten* Welle wie folgt. Zwei parallele infinitesimal benachbarte unter dem Winkel γ einfallende Strahlen (die einer einfallenden ebenen Welle entsprechen) erzeugen zwei sich schneidende infinitesimal benachbarte reflektierte Strahlen (s. Fig. 116). Da der Energiefluß durch den von ihnen begrenzten Kanal an jeder Stelle der gleiche sein muß, gilt für die Amplitude im Abstand s von der Oberfläche

$$|A(s)|^2 \left(s + \frac{a}{2}\cos\gamma\right) = |A_0|^2 \frac{a}{2}\cos\gamma. \tag{147.1}$$

[1] J. B. KELLER: Trans. Inst. Radio Engrs. AP-**4**, 312 (1956). — J. Appl. Phys. **28**, 426 (1957). — J. B. KELLER u. B. LEVY: N.Y. Univ. Res. Rep. No. EM-109 (1957). — Comm. Pure Appl. Math. **12**, 159 (1959). Vgl. auch F. G. FRIEDLANDER: Proc. Cambridge Phil. Soc. **38**, 383 (1942). Weitere Literatur bei J. B. KELLER: Calculus of Variations and its Applications, ed. L. M. GRAVES, S. 27ff. New York 1958.

Dabei ist $\frac{a}{2}\cos\gamma$ der Abstand des Schnittpunktes der reflektierten Strahlen vom Reflexionspunkt P_0 und a der Krümmungsradius der Profilkurve des Zylinders im Reflexionspunkt (vgl. Fig. 116). Die Amplitude A_0 ist diejenige der einfallenden Welle v_0 im Auftreffpunkt P_0. Für das geometrisch-optische Feld (einfallende und reflektierte Welle) haben wir somit die Darstellung

$$v_g(P) = v_0(P) \mp v_0(P_0)\sqrt{\frac{a\cos\gamma}{2s + a\cos\gamma}}\,e^{iks}. \tag{147.2}$$

Dabei haben wir gleich berücksichtigt, daß bei der Randbedingung $v=0$ das reflektierte Feld gegenüber dem einfallenden an der Oberfläche den Phasensprung π erleidet, während bei der Randbedingung $\partial v/\partial n=0$ kein Phasensprung auftritt[1].

Wir wenden uns jetzt zur Berechnung der den gebeugten Strahlen zuzuordnenden Felder, indem wir diese Strahlen schrittweise verfolgen. Zunächst nehmen wir an, daß das zum gebeugten Strahl gehörige Feld v_B im Berührungspunkt P' dem einfallenden Feld $v_0(P')$ dort proportional ist:

$$v_B(P') = B(P')\,v_0(P'). \tag{147.3}$$

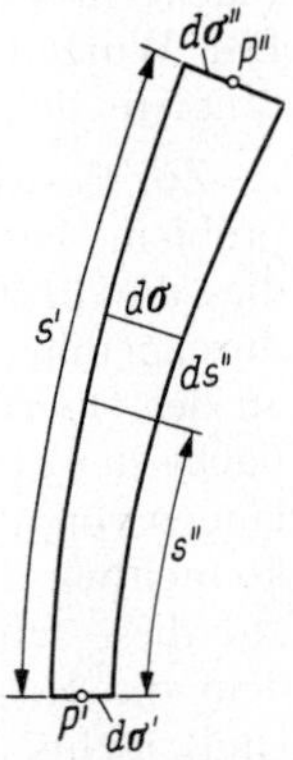

Fig. 117. Zur Geometrie zweier unendlich benachbarter Geodäten.

Dabei wird der „*Beugungskoeffizient*" B noch von den lokalen Eigenschaften der Fläche in P' abhängen (s. weiter unten). Zur Berechnung der Amplitude der gebeugten Welle beim Fortschreiten längs der Oberfläche machen wir uns die Vorstellung zu eigen, daß dabei kontinuierlich Energie abgestrahlt wird, wobei die Abstrahlrate dem jeweiligen Energiestrom proportional ist. Der Energiefluß längs eines von zwei infinitesimal benachbarten (tangential angestrahlten) Geodäten begrenzten Streifens der Breite $d\sigma$ (vgl. Fig. 117) erleidet also beim Fortschreiten um ds'' den Strahlungsverlust

$$\frac{d}{ds''}(A^2\,d\sigma) = -2\beta A^2\,d\sigma. \tag{147.4}$$

Dabei kann der „*Abstrahlungskoeffizient*" β noch von Punkt zu Punkt der Geodäte variieren. Durch Integration von (147.4) längs der Geodäte der Länge s' von P' nach P'' (Fig. 117) ergibt sich nun, wenn wir gleich zum Feld übergehen und (147.3) beachten

$$v_B(P'') = v_0(P')\,B(P')\sqrt{\frac{d\sigma'}{d\sigma''}}\,e^{iks' - \int_0^{s'}\beta(s)\,ds}. \tag{147.5}$$

Schließlich haben wir noch die Abstrahlung nach dem Aufpunkt P zu betrachten. Hierzu ist zunächst zu bemerken, daß die Oberfläche für das System der tangential von ihr ausgehenden gebeugten Strahlen eine Brennfläche ist. Daher können wir nach (42.4') das Feld in P in der Form

$$v_B(P) = A''\sqrt{\frac{\varrho_1}{s(\varrho_1 + s)}}\,e^{iks} \tag{147.6}$$

[1] Zur Berechnung höherer Näherungen des geometrisch-optischen Feldes (durch Verallgemeinerung der Luneberg-Kline-Methode) vgl. J.B. KELLER u. H.B. KELLER: J. Opt. Soc. Amer. **40**, 48 (1950). — F.G. FRIEDLANDER u. J.B. KELLER: Comm. Pure Appl. Math. **8**, 382 (1955). — J.B. KELLER, R.M. LEVIS u. B.D. SECKLER: Comm. Pure Appl. Math. **9**, 207 (1956).

schreiben, wobei s die Wegstrecke von P'' zum Aufpunkt P bedeutet und ϱ_1 wieder der längs des Strahls von P'' aus gemessene Abstand der anderen Kaustik ist, die zu dem betreffenden Strahlensystem gehört. Für die Konstante A'' machen wir die naheliegende Annahme, daß sie proportional dem in (147.5) berechneten Feld $v_B(P'')$ ist. Damit ergibt sich für (147.6) die Darstellung

$$v_B(P) = v_0(P')\,B(P')\,B(P'')\sqrt{\frac{d\sigma'}{d\sigma''}\cdot\frac{\varrho_1}{s(\varrho_1+s)}}\,\exp\left\{i\,k(s+s') - \int\limits_0^{s'}\beta(s)\,d s'\right\}. \quad (147.7)$$

Dabei muß nach dem Theorem von der *Umkehrbarkeit der Lichtwege* der Proportionalitätsfaktor $B(P'')$ in derselben Weise von den lokalen Eigenschaften der Fläche in P'' abhängen, wie der Beugungskoeffizient $B(P')$ von denen in P'. Der Wurzelfaktor ist aus der jeweiligen Geometrie der Geodäten und des sie tangierenden Strahlensystems zu bestimmen.

Zur Bestimmung der Größen B und β müssen wir die Lösung eines Randwertproblems betrachten, das *lokal* mit unserem Problem übereinstimmt. Bevor wir dies durchführen, bemerken wir, daß für die Randbedingung $v=0$ unsere oben durchgeführten Überlegungen zunächst zu versagen scheinen, da dann das Feld an der Oberfläche verschwindet. Da jedoch die Oberfläche allemal eine Brennfläche der gebeugten Strahlen ist, so wird das Feld im Abstand einiger Wellenlängen von der Oberfläche wesentlich stärker sein als in größerem Abstand. Dann können wir aber unsere obigen Betrachtungen anstatt auf die Oberfläche selbst, auf diese Oberflächenschicht beziehen, wodurch sich in unserem Grenzfall (in dem die Krümmungsradien der Fläche überall sehr groß gegen die Wellenlänge sind) nichts ändert[1].

Die von dem einfallenden Strahl und der Flächennormale in P' aufgespannte Einfallsebene schneidet die Oberfläche längs einer Kurve, deren Krümmungsradius in P' wir mit $a(P')$ bezeichnen wollen. Es soll nun angenommen werden, daß von den differentialgeometrischen Eigenschaften der Fläche in P' lediglich $a(P')$ in den Beugungskoeffizienten $B(P')$ eingeht. Entsprechend soll der Abstrahlungskoeffizient β nur vom Krümmungsradius im jeweiligen Punkt der Geodäte abhängen. Um diese Abhängigkeit zu bestimmen, wenden wir das Ergebnis unserer heuristischen Betrachtungen auf die Beugung am Kreiszylinder an und vergleichen es mit der asymptotischen Entwicklung der strengen Lösung des Randwertproblems. Fällt eine ebene Welle senkrecht auf den Zylinder auf, so sind die Geodäten Kreisbogenstücke (vgl. Fig. 105). Der Wurzelfaktor in Gl. (147.7) hat den Wert $s^{-\frac{1}{2}}$, da das von benachbarten Geodäten begrenzte Band seine Breite nicht ändert und die Schnittpunkte der tangential abgehenden Strahlen im Unendlichen liegen. Ferner ist, da der Krümmungsradius der Geodäten konstant ist, auch β konstant und $B(P') = B(P'')$. Schließlich ist $s' = a\left(\vartheta - \arccos\frac{a}{r} - \frac{\pi}{2}\right)$ und $s = \sqrt{r^2 - a^2}$ (vgl. die rechte Seite von Fig. 105). Neben dem von P'' nach P gehenden gebeugten Strahl gehen ferner auch noch alle diejenigen gebeugten Strahlen durch P, die den Zylinder l-mal umlaufen haben, bevor sie von P'' aus nach P auslaufen. Für diese Strahlen ist $s' = a\left(\vartheta - \arccos\frac{a}{r} - \frac{\pi}{2}\right) + 2l\,\pi\,a$. Außerdem gelangen auch noch gebeugte Strahlen nach P, die auf dem Zylinder die Kriechstrecke $s' = a\left(\frac{3\pi}{2} - \vartheta - \arccos\frac{a}{r}\right) + 2\pi\,l\,a$ zurückgelegt haben (vgl. die linke Seite von Fig. 105). Berücksichtigt

[1] In Ziff. 141 hatte sich gezeigt, daß die gebeugten Strahlen von der Oberfläche des beugenden Körpers einen gewissen Abstand einhalten.

man dies alles in (147.7), so ergibt sich durch Summation über l

$$v_B(P) = \frac{B^2}{(r^2-a^2)^{\frac{1}{4}}} \frac{e^{ik\sqrt{r^2-a^2}}}{1-e^{2\pi(i\varepsilon-a\beta)}} \cdot \left\{ e^{(i\varepsilon-a\beta)\left(\vartheta-\arccos\frac{a}{r}-\frac{\pi}{2}\right)} + e^{(i\varepsilon-a\beta)\left(\frac{3\pi}{2}-\vartheta-\arccos\frac{a}{r}\right)} \right\}. \tag{147.8}$$

Der Vergleich mit der asymptotischen Lösung des Randwertproblems (141.9) zeigt, daß es unendlich viele Beugungskoeffizienten B_s und Abstrahlungskoeffizienten β_s gibt, die je zu einem gebeugten Strahl gehören, wobei über die Beiträge aller Strahlen zu summieren ist. Dabei ist

$$B_s^2 = \frac{a^{\frac{1}{3}} C_s}{\sqrt{2}\, k^{\frac{1}{6}}} e^{\frac{i\pi}{12}} \tag{147.9}$$

mit den C_s aus Gl. (141.4') und

$$\beta_s = \frac{\sqrt{3}-i}{2} \left(\frac{k}{6}\right)^{\frac{1}{3}} a^{-\frac{2}{3}} q_s, \tag{147.10}$$

wobei die q_s die Nullstellen von (141.2) sind[1].

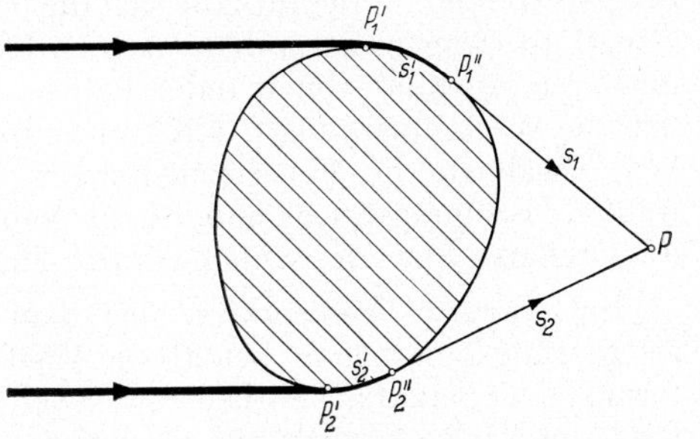

Fig. 118. Zur „geometrischen Beugung" an konvexen Zylindern nach J.B. Keller.

Für einen *beliebigen glatten konvexen Zylinder* mit *geschlossenem* Querschnitt ergibt sich damit aus (147.7) mit (147.9, 10) (vgl. Fig. 118)

$$\left.\begin{aligned} v_B(P) = \frac{e^{\frac{i\pi}{12}}}{\sqrt{2}\, k^{\frac{1}{6}}} \Bigg\{ & v_0(P_1') \frac{e^{ik(s_1+s_1')}}{\sqrt{s_1}} [a(P_1')\, a(P_1'')]^{\frac{1}{6}} \cdot \\ & \cdot \sum_s \frac{C_s \exp\left\{-\gamma_s \int_0^{s_1'} a(s)^{-\frac{2}{3}} ds\right\}}{1-\exp\left\{ikS-\gamma_s \oint a(s)^{-\frac{2}{3}} ds\right\}} \\ & + v_0(P_2') \frac{e^{ik(s_2+s_2')}}{\sqrt{s_2}} [a(P_2')\, a(P_2'')]^{\frac{1}{6}} \cdot \sum_s \frac{C_s \exp\left\{-\gamma_s \int_0^{s_2'} a(s)^{-\frac{2}{3}} ds\right\}}{1-\exp\left\{ikS-\gamma_s \oint a(s)^{-\frac{2}{3}} ds\right\}} \Bigg\} \\ & \left(\gamma_s = \frac{\sqrt{3}-i}{2} \left(\frac{k}{6}\right)^{\frac{1}{3}} q_s\right). \end{aligned}\right\} \tag{147.11}$$

Dabei ist S der Umfang des Zylinders und v_0 die einfallende ebene Welle. Für Zylinder mit offenem Querschnitt (vom Typ der Parabel) ergibt sich entsprechend nur jeweils eine der beiden Summen ohne den Nenner. Asymptotische Entwicklungen der Lösung des Randwertproblems für parabolische[2] und elliptische[3] Zylinder haben Übereinstimmung mit dem heuristisch gewonnenen Ergebnis gezeigt. Entsprechendes gilt für die Kugel[4] (sowohl für das skalare als auch das vektorielle Randwertproblem) sowie für das skalare Randwertproblem für das Spheroid[5].

[1] Höhere Näherungen dieser Größen für konvexe Zylinder von variablem Krümmungsradius bei J.B. Keller u. B. Levy: N.Y. Univ. Res. Rep. No. EM-147 (1959).

[2] S.O. Rice: Bell Syst. Techn. J. **33**, 417 (1954). — J.B. Keller u. B. Levy: N.Y. Univ. Res. Rep. No. EM-147 (1959). — Zur Beugung an Blenden endlicher Dicke vgl. man auch K. Artmann: Z. Physik **127**, 468 (1950). — Ann. Phys. **7**, 209 (1950). — V.A. Fock: Abh. Sowj. Phys. **2**, 7 (1951). — J.B. Keller: N.Y. Univ. Res. Rep. No. EM-119 (1958).

[3] B. Levy: N.Y. Univ. Res. Rep. No. EM-121 (1958). — J.B. Keller u. B. Levy: N.Y. Univ. Res. Rep. No. EM-147 (1959).

[4] B. Levy u. J.B. Keller: N.Y. Univ. Res. Rep. No. EM-109 (1957).

[5] B. Levy u. J.B. Keller: N.Y. Univ. Res. Rep. No. EM-130 (1959).

b) Beugung an der Kugel.

Das Problem der Beugung elektromagnetischer Wellen an einer Kugel (beliebigen Materials) ist bisher das einzige Beispiel eines konvexen Körpers ohne Kanten, das sich in voller Allgemeinheit vollständig durchrechnen läßt. Das physikalische Interesse an diesem Problem ist außerordentlich vielseitig.

Ein großer hierher gehöriger Problemkreis bezieht sich auf die Phänomene, die durch das Zusammenwirken sehr vieler gleichartiger kugelförmiger Teilchen bewirkt werden. (Hierauf läßt sich die Theorie der Beugung an *einer* Kugel sinngemäß übertragen, wenn die einzelnen Kugeln statistisch verteilt sind, und einen mittleren Abstand voneinander haben, der groß gegen die Wellenlänge ist, so daß die Wechselwirkung der Kugeln untereinander vernachlässigt werden kann.) Wir erwähnen die Farberscheinungen, die an Metallsuspensionen beobachtet werden, Beugungserscheinungen an Nebeltröpfchen sowie an den Teilchen der interstellaren Materie, schließlich die Theorie des Regenbogens.

Ein zweiter Problemkreis, bei dem die Lösung unserer Randwertaufgabe als Ausgangspunkt dient, betrifft die Ausbreitung von Radiowellen längs der kugelförmigen Erdoberfläche. Die Spannweite des Anwendungsbereiches der Lösung wird durch die Möglichkeit gekennzeichnet, das Verhältnis von Kugelradius a zu Wellenlänge λ in weiten Grenzen zu variieren, sowie durch die verschiedenen Lagen von Quell- und Aufpunkt.

Im folgenden soll die Lösung für einen unendlich fernen Quellpunkt (ebene linear polarisierte einfallende Welle) durchgeführt und für das Fernfeld ausgewertet werden. Wir betrachten zunächst das skalare (akustische) Beugungsproblem, das auch für die Streuung unpolarisierter elektromagnetischer Strahlung asymptotisch von Bedeutung ist (vgl. Ziff. 155). Die Übertragung der Lösungsmethode auf das vektorielle Problem geschieht mit Hilfe der Debyeschen Potentiale. Die Lösung läßt sich auch hier wieder nach zwei grundsätzlich verschiedenen Wellentypen entwickeln: a) den ungedämpften (im Kugelmittelpunkt angeregten) Partialwellen (ganzzahlige Kugelfunktionen, halbzahlige Bessel-Funktionen), b) den gedämpften (längs eines radialen Halbstrahls angeregten) Residuenwellen (komplexe Indices bei Kugel- und Bessel-Funktionen). Die Dämpfung entsteht wieder durch fortwährende tangentiale Abstrahlung der an der Kugeloberfläche entlanglaufenden Wellenfelder (Kriechwellen). Der Zusammenhang beider Darstellungsformen wird durch die Watson-Transformation vermittelt. Die Reihe der ungedämpften Partialwellen konvergiert schnell für (gegenüber der Wellenlänge) *kleine* Kugelradien, während die Residuenreihe bei *großen* Kugelradien angemessen ist. Das Zwischengebiet muß durch numerische Auswertung überbrückt werden. Wir behandeln im wesentlichen nur den Fall ideal leitender Kugeln und beschränken uns auf eine Darlegung der mathematischen Methode und ihrer physikalischen Interpretation (bezüglich der Anwendungen vgl. man die in Ziff. 153 und 155 zitierte Literatur).

b1) Akustisches Problem.

148. Lösung der Integralgleichungen. Eine ebene Welle

$$v_0(r, \vartheta) = e^{-ikr\cos\vartheta} \tag{148.1}$$

falle auf die Kugel vom Radius a (vgl. Fig. 119). Die Lösung der Randwertaufgabe für die Wellengleichung $(\Delta + k^2)\, v(r, \vartheta) = 0$ ist dann unabhängig vom Azimut φ. Sie läßt sich nach (76.1 p, s) in folgender Form darstellen *p-Fall* $[v_p(a,\vartheta)=0]$

$$v_p(r,\vartheta)=\mathrm{e}^{-ikr\cos\vartheta}-\frac{a^2}{4\pi}\int_0^{\pi}d\vartheta'\sin\vartheta'\,\psi_p(\vartheta')\int_0^{2\pi}\frac{\mathrm{e}^{ikR}}{R}\,d\varphi',\qquad(148.1\,p)$$

s-Fall $\left[\frac{\partial}{\partial r}v_s(a,\vartheta)=0\right]$

$$v_s(r,\vartheta)=\mathrm{e}^{-ikr\cos\vartheta}+\frac{a^2}{4\pi}\int_0^{\pi}d\vartheta'\sin\vartheta'\,\psi_s(\vartheta')\frac{\partial}{\partial a}\int_0^{2\pi}\frac{\mathrm{e}^{ikR}}{R}\,d\varphi'\qquad(148.1\,s)$$

mit

$$\left.\begin{aligned}R&=|\mathfrak{r}-\hat{\mathfrak{r}}'|=\sqrt{r^2+a^2-2ra\cos\Theta}\\ \cos\Theta&=\cos\vartheta\cos\vartheta'+\sin\vartheta\sin\vartheta'\cos(\varphi-\varphi').\end{aligned}\right\}\qquad(148.2)$$

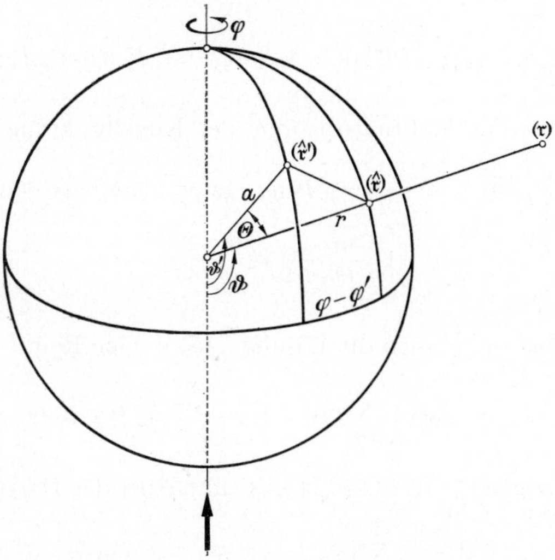

Fig. 119. Zur akustischen Beugung an der Kugel.

Die Belegungsdichten $\psi_p(\vartheta)=\frac{\partial}{\partial r}v_p(a,\vartheta)$ bzw. $\psi_s(\vartheta)=v_s(a,\vartheta)$ sind dabei aus den Integralgleichungen (76.6 *p*) bzw. (76.7 *s*) zu bestimmen. Diese nehmen hier die folgende Form an

$$\psi_p(\vartheta)+\frac{a^2}{8\pi}\int_0^{\pi}d\vartheta'\sin\vartheta'\,\psi_p(\vartheta')\frac{\partial}{\partial a}\int_0^{2\pi}\frac{\mathrm{e}^{2i\varepsilon\sin\frac{|\Theta|}{2}}}{a\sin\frac{|\Theta|}{2}}\,d\varphi'=-2ik\cos\vartheta\,\mathrm{e}^{-i\varepsilon\cos\vartheta}\qquad(148.3\,p)$$

bzw.

$$\psi_s(\vartheta)-\frac{a^2}{8\pi}\int_0^{\pi}d\vartheta'\sin\vartheta'\,\psi_s(\vartheta')\frac{\partial}{\partial a}\int_0^{2\pi}\frac{\mathrm{e}^{2i\varepsilon\sin\frac{|\Theta|}{2}}}{a\sin\frac{|\Theta|}{2}}\,d\varphi'=2\,\mathrm{e}^{-i\varepsilon\cos\vartheta}\qquad(148.3\,s)$$

$(\varepsilon=ka)$, wobei

$$|\hat{\mathfrak{r}}-\hat{\mathfrak{r}}'|=2a\sin\frac{|\Theta|}{2}=2a\sqrt{\sin^2\left(\frac{\vartheta-\vartheta'}{2}\right)+\sin\vartheta\sin\vartheta'\sin^2\left(\frac{\varphi-\varphi'}{2}\right)}\qquad(148.4)$$

den Abstand zweier Kugelpunkte bedeutet. Mit Hilfe der Entwicklung[1]

$$\frac{\mathrm{e}^{ik\sqrt{r^2+r'^2-rr'\cos\Theta}}}{\sqrt{r^2+r'^2-2rr'\cos\Theta}}=ik\sum_{n=0}^{\infty}(2n+1)\,P_n(\cos\Theta)\cdot\begin{cases}\psi_n(kr)\,\zeta_n^1(kr') & (r<r')\\ \psi_n(kr')\,\zeta_n^1(kr) & (r>r'),\end{cases}\qquad(148.5)$$

[1] Vgl. W. Magnus u. F. Oberhettinger: Formeln und Sätze für die speziellen Funktionen der mathematischen Physik, 2. Aufl., S. 31. Berlin 1948.

bei der wir uns der Heine-Sommerfeldschen Bezeichnungsweise[1]

$$\left.\begin{aligned} \psi_\nu(x) &= \sqrt{\frac{\pi}{2x}}\, J_{\nu+\frac{1}{2}}(x) \\ \zeta_\nu^{1,2}(x) &= \sqrt{\frac{\pi}{2x}}\, H^{1,2}_{\nu+\frac{1}{2}}(x) \end{aligned}\right\} \tag{148.6}$$

bedienen, ergibt sich für den Kern der Integralgleichungen (148.3) folgende „*Diagonaldarstellung*"

$$\left.\begin{aligned} \frac{a^2}{8\pi}\frac{\partial}{\partial a}\int\limits_0^{2\pi} \frac{e^{2i\varepsilon\sin\frac{|\Theta|}{2}}}{a\sin\frac{|\Theta|}{2}}\,d\varphi' &= \frac{i\varepsilon a}{2}\frac{\partial}{\partial a}\sum_{n=0}^{\infty}(2n+1)\,\psi_n(\varepsilon)\,\zeta_n^1(\varepsilon)\,P_n(\cos\vartheta)\,P_n(\cos\vartheta') \\ &= \frac{i\varepsilon^2}{2}\sum_{n=0}^{\infty}(2n+1)\,\{\psi_n'(\varepsilon)\,\zeta_n^1(\varepsilon)+\psi_n(\varepsilon)\,\zeta_n^{1\prime}(\varepsilon)\}\,P_n(\cos\vartheta)\,P_n(\cos\vartheta'). \end{aligned}\right\} \tag{148.7}$$

Dabei haben wir vom Additionstheorem der Kugelfunktionen

$$\left.\begin{aligned} P_n(\cos\Theta) &= \sum_{l=-n}^{n}(-1)^l\,P_n^l(\cos\vartheta)\,P_n^{-l}(\cos\vartheta')\,e^{il(\varphi-\varphi')} \\ P_n^{-l} &= (-1)^l\,\frac{(n-l)!}{(n+l)!}\,P_n^l \end{aligned}\right\} \tag{148.6'}$$

Gebrauch gemacht.

Entwickelt man nun auch die Lösung $\psi(\vartheta)$ in eine Reihe nach zonalen Kugelfunktionen

$$\psi(\vartheta) = \sum_{n=0}^{\infty}(2n+1)\,e^{-\frac{i\pi}{2}n}\,a_n\,P_n(\cos\vartheta) \tag{148.8}$$

sowie die Inhomogenität rechts in (148.3) mit Hilfe der Darstellung

$$e^{-ikr\cos\vartheta} = \sum_{n=0}^{\infty}(2n+1)\,e^{-\frac{i\pi}{2}n}\,\psi_n(kr)\,P_n(\cos\vartheta), \tag{148.9}$$

so lassen sich die Koeffizienten a_n leicht bestimmen. Setzt man nämlich die Darstellungen (148.7, 8, 9) in die Integralgleichungen (148.3) ein, so ergibt sich mit Hilfe der Orthogonalitätsrelation der zonalen Kugelfunktionen

$$\int\limits_0^{\pi} P_n(\cos\vartheta)\,P_{n'}(\cos\vartheta)\sin\vartheta\,d\vartheta = \frac{2\delta_{nn'}}{2n+1}$$

die folgende Beziehung (oberes Vorzeichen für den p-Fall, unteres für den s-Fall)

$$a_n\,\{1\pm i\,\varepsilon^2\,[\psi_n'(\varepsilon)\,\zeta_n^1(\varepsilon)+\psi_n(\varepsilon)\,\zeta_n^{1\prime}(\varepsilon)]\} = \begin{cases} 2k\,\psi_n'(\varepsilon) \\ 2\psi_n(\varepsilon). \end{cases} \tag{148.10}$$

Dies läßt sich noch mit Hilfe der Wronski-Determinante

$$i\,\varepsilon^2\,\{\psi_n'(\varepsilon)\,\zeta_n^1(\varepsilon)-\psi_n(\varepsilon)\,\zeta_n^{1\prime}(\varepsilon)\} = 1 \tag{148.11}$$

vereinfachen und ergibt

$$a_n^{(p)} = -\frac{ik}{\varepsilon^2\,\zeta_n^1(\varepsilon)} \tag{148.12p}$$

[1] In der angelsächsischen Literatur werden die Funktionen (148.6) meistens mit $j_\nu(x)$ bzw. $h_\nu^{1,2}(x)$ bezeichnet. Häufig werden im Anschluß an Debye auch die Funktionen $\sqrt{\pi x/2}\,J_{\nu+\frac{1}{2}}(x)$ bzw. $\sqrt{\pi x/2}\,H^{1,2}_{\nu+\frac{1}{2}}(x)$ mit $\psi_\nu(x)$ bzw. $\zeta_\nu^{1,2}(x)$ bezeichnet, die sich von (148.6) um den Faktor x unterscheiden.

bzw.

$$a_n^{(s)} = \frac{i}{\varepsilon^2 \zeta_n^{1\prime}(\varepsilon)} \tag{148.12s}$$

Für die Belegungsdichten ergeben sich damit die Darstellungen

$$\psi_p(\vartheta) = -\frac{i\,k}{\varepsilon^2} \sum_{n=0}^{\infty} (2n+1) \frac{e^{-\frac{i\pi}{2}n}}{\zeta_n^1(\varepsilon)} P_n(\cos\vartheta) \tag{148.13p}$$

bzw.

$$\psi_s(\vartheta) = \frac{i}{\varepsilon^2} \sum_{n=0}^{\infty} (2n+1) \frac{e^{-\frac{i\pi}{2}n}}{\zeta_n^{1\prime}(\varepsilon)} P_n(\cos\vartheta)\,. \tag{148.13s}$$

Setzen wir diese in unsere Felddarstellung (148.1) ein, so ergibt sich mit Hilfe der Entwicklungen (148.5, 9) die folgende Darstellung nach *ungedämpften Partialwellen:*

$$v(r,\vartheta) = \sum_{n=0}^{\infty} (2n+1)\, e^{-\frac{i\pi}{2}n} \left\{\psi_n(k\,r) - \frac{\Omega\,\psi_n(\varepsilon)}{\Omega\,\zeta_n^1(\varepsilon)} \zeta_n^1(k\,r)\right\} P_n(\cos\vartheta)\,. \tag{148.14}$$

Dabei hat der Operator Ω dieselbe Bedeutung wie in Ziff. 137 ($\Omega \equiv 1$ im p-Fall bzw. $\Omega \equiv \partial/\partial\varepsilon$ im s-Fall). Für den *Streuanteil* des *Fernfeldes* erhält man daraus mit Hilfe der asymptotischen (Hankelschen) Näherung

$$\psi_n(x) \to \frac{\sin\left(x - \frac{\pi n}{2}\right)}{x}\,, \quad \zeta_n^1(x) \to -i\,\frac{e^{i\left(x - \frac{\pi n}{2}\right)}}{x} \qquad (x \gg 1,\; n \ll x) \tag{148.15}$$

die Darstellung ($r \to \infty$)

$$v_S(r,\vartheta) \to A(\vartheta)\,\frac{e^{ikr}}{r} = i\,\frac{e^{\,kr}}{r} \sum_{n=0}^{\infty} (-1)^n (2n+1) \frac{\Omega\,\psi_n(\varepsilon)}{\Omega\,\zeta_n^1(\varepsilon)} P_n(\cos\vartheta)\,. \tag{148.16}$$

Der *Streukoeffizient* der Kugel ergibt sich aus der *Vorwärtsstreuung* mit Hilfe der allgemeinen Beziehung (100.8′ ps) (die wir noch durch den Faktor k^{-1} dimensionell zu ergänzen haben) in der Gestalt $[P_n(-1) = (-1)^n]$

$$\sigma = \frac{4}{k\,a^2}\,\mathrm{Im}\,A(\pi) = \frac{4}{\varepsilon^2}\,\mathrm{Re} \sum_{n=0}^{\infty} (2n+1) \frac{\Omega\,\psi_n(\varepsilon)}{\Omega\,\zeta_n^1(\varepsilon)}\,. \tag{148.17}$$

149. Diskussion. Für den *Rayleighschen Grenzfall* $\varepsilon \ll 1$ kann man sich der Potenzreihenentwicklung

$$\psi_n(\varepsilon) = \frac{\varepsilon^n}{1\cdot 3 \cdots (2n+1)} (1+\cdots)\,, \quad \zeta_n^1(\varepsilon) = -i\,\frac{1\cdot 3\cdots(2n-1)}{\varepsilon^{n+1}} (1+\cdots) \tag{149.1}$$

bedienen (wobei ... Potenzreihen in ε andeuten, die quadratisch beginnen). Damit erhält man aus (148.15) in niedrigster (Rayleighscher) Näherung die Streuwelle

$$v_S^{(p)}(r,\vartheta) \to -\,\varepsilon\,(1+\cdots)\,\frac{e^{ikr}}{kr} \tag{149.2p}$$

bzw.

$$v_S^{(s)}(r,\vartheta) \to -\,\varepsilon^3 \left(\frac{1}{3} + \frac{1}{2}\cos\vartheta + \cdots\right) \frac{e^{ikr}}{k\,r}\,. \tag{149.2s}$$

Bei der Randbedingung $v = 0$ ist also die Streuwelle für $\varepsilon \ll 1$ homogen, während bei $\partial v/\partial r = 0$ auch noch das Dipolglied ($\sim \cos\vartheta$) zu berücksichtigen ist.

Für den *Streukoeffizienten* ergibt sich in niedrigster Näherung

$$\sigma_p = 4 + \cdots, \qquad \sigma_s = \frac{4}{9}\,\varepsilon^4 + \cdots. \tag{149.3p}$$

Eine schallweiche Kugel (Gasblase) streut also (bei $\varepsilon \ll 1$) wesentlich stärker als eine gleich große schallharte (starre) Kugel. (Der Unterschied wird noch ausgeprägter, wenn die Frequenz der einfallenden Welle in die Nähe einer Resonanzstelle der Glasblase liegt, worauf hier nicht eingegangen werden soll[1].)

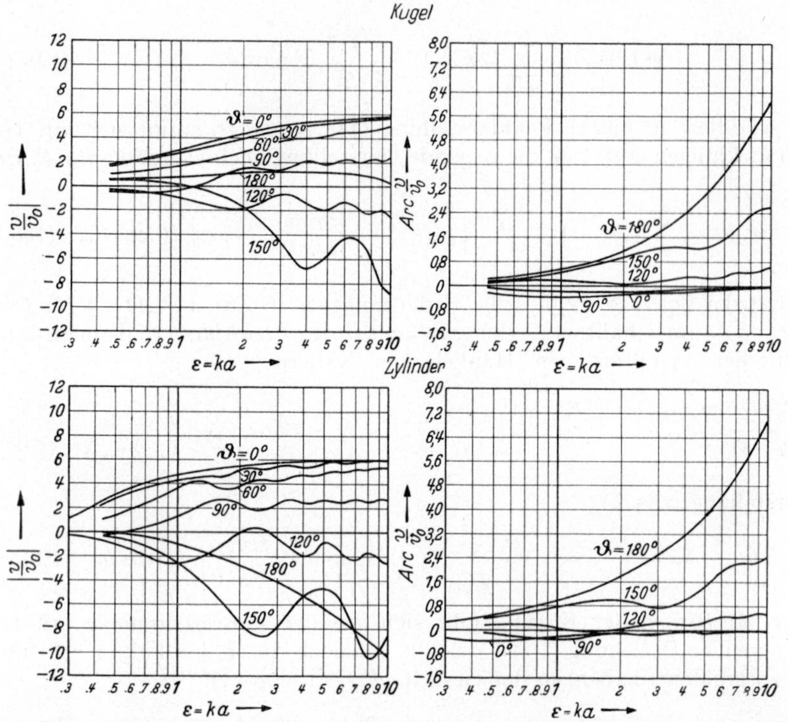

Fig. 120. Feldverteilung nach Betrag und Phase auf der Oberfläche von Kugel (obere Figuren) und Zylinder (untere Figuren) bei der Randbedingung $\partial v/\partial n = 0$ als Funktion von ε und mit ϑ als Parameter (nach Schwarz bzw. Wiener).

Bezüglich weiterer Einzelheiten sei auf die Literatur verwiesen[2]. Für größere ε kann die Struktur des Beugungsfeldes nur durch numerisches Aufsummieren der Partialwellen ermittelt werden[3]. So ist in Fig. 120 oben die Belegungsdichte $\psi_s(\vartheta) = v_s(a, \vartheta)$ im Verhältnis zur einfallenden Welle $\exp(-i\,\varepsilon\cos\vartheta)$ als Funktion von ε aufgetragen[4], und zwar links die Größe $20\log^{10}|\psi_s(\vartheta)|$, rechts die

[1] Vgl. E. Meyer u. K. Tamm: Akust. Z. **4**, 145 (1939).

[2] Zusammenfassende Darstellungen: Lord Rayleigh: The Theory of Sound, Bd. II. London 1896. — H. Lamb: Lehrbuch der Hydrodynamik (deutsch von E. Helly). Leipzig 1931. — E. Skudrzyk: Die Grundlagen der Akustik. Wien 1954.

[3] Vgl. Lord Rayleigh: Phil. Trans. Roy. Soc. Lond. A **203**, 87 (1904). — H. Stenzel: Elektr. Nachr.-Techn. **15**, 71 (1938). — H. Stenzel u. O. Brosze: Leitfaden zur Berechnung von Schallvorgängen. 2. Aufl., Berlin 1958. — K. Schwarz: Akust. Z. **8**, 91 (1943). — H. Wergeland: Avh. Norsk. Vid. Akad. Oslo **1**, No. 9 (1945). — F.M. Wiener: J. Acoust. Soc. Amer. **19**, 444 (1947). — A. Schoch: Ergebn. exakt. Naturw. **23** (1950) § 33. — R.W. Hart: J. Acoust. Soc. Amer. **23**, 323 (1951). — J. J. Faran: J. Acoust. Soc. Amer. **23**, 405 (1951). — Weitere Literatur bei C. J. Bouwkamp: Rep. Progr. Phys. Lond. **17**, 35—100 (1954) (§ 11).

[4] Nach K. Schwarz l. c.

Phasendifferenz Arc $\{\psi_s(\vartheta)\, e^{i\varepsilon\cos\vartheta}\}$ zwischen $\psi_s(\vartheta)$ (d. h. dem Feld auf der Oberfläche der schallharten Kugel) und der einfallenden Welle. In der unteren Hälfte von Fig. 120 sind die entsprechenden Größen für den Zylinder aufgetragen[1] (vgl. Ziff. 138). Fig. 121 gibt noch einmal den Betrag $|\psi_s(\vartheta)|$ wieder[2]; diesmal als Funktion des Winkels ϑ (mit ε als Parameter). Für größere ε-Werte zeigt sich bereits eine „*Schattenbildung*"; im Antipodenpunkt $\vartheta = \pi$ wird dieser Schatten jedoch wieder aufgehellt (Poissonscher Fleck), da dort die „*Kriechwellen*" gleichphasig eintreffend konvergieren (vgl. Ziff. 150). Schließlich sind in Fig. 122 die Linien $|v_s(r,\vartheta)| = \text{const}$ für $\varepsilon = 2$ eingezeichnet[3], die erkennen lassen, daß sich in einigem Abstand vor der Kugel *stehende Wellen* ausbilden.

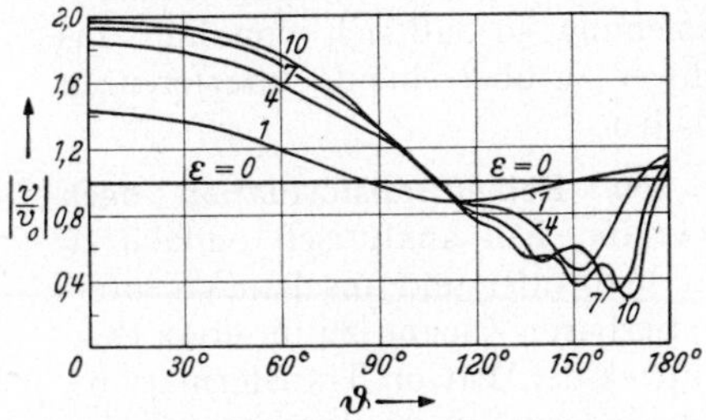

Fig. 121. Betrag des Feldes auf der Oberfläche einer Kugel (akustisch, Randbedingung $\partial v/\partial n = 0$) als Funktion von ϑ mit ε als Parameter (Poissonscher Fleck bei $\vartheta = 180°$, nach SCHWARZ).

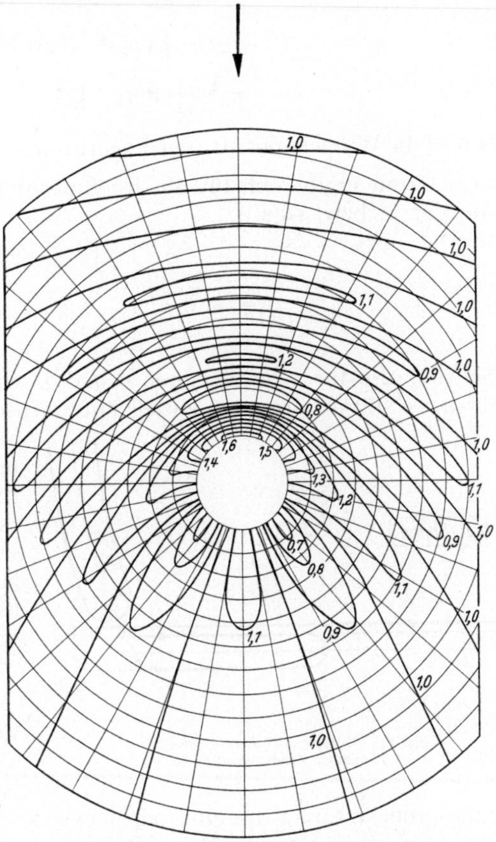

Fig. 122. Kurven konstanter Amplitude bei der Beugung einer von oben einfallenden ebenen akustischen Welle an der Kugel bei der Randbedingung $\partial v/\partial n = 0$ (nach STENZEL).

Für den anderen Grenzfall $\varepsilon \gg 1$ haben wir die Debyeschen asymptotischen Näherungen (139.10, 11) zu verwenden. Sie nehmen hier folgende Gestalt an

$$\psi_n(\varepsilon) \to \begin{cases} (1-t^2)^{-\frac{1}{4}} \dfrac{\cos\sigma}{\varepsilon} & (n < \varepsilon) \\[2ex] (t^2-1)^{-\frac{1}{4}} \dfrac{e^{-\tau}}{2\varepsilon} & (n > \varepsilon) \end{cases} \tag{149.4}$$

$$\zeta_n^1(\varepsilon) \to \begin{cases} (1-t^2)^{-\frac{1}{4}} \dfrac{e^{i\sigma}}{\varepsilon} & (n < \varepsilon) \\[2ex] (t^2-1)^{-\frac{1}{4}} \dfrac{e^{\tau}}{i\,\varepsilon} & (n > \varepsilon) \end{cases} \tag{149.5}$$

[1] Fig. 120 in dieser Form bei A. SCHOCH l. c.
[2] Nach K. SCHWARZ l. c.
[3] Nach H. STENZEL l. c.

mit

$$\left.\begin{aligned} t &= \frac{2n+1}{2\varepsilon}, \\ \sigma &= \varepsilon\left(\sqrt{1-t^2} - t\arccos t\right) - \frac{\pi}{4} \\ \tau &= \varepsilon\left\{t\ln\left(t+\sqrt{t^2-1}\right) - \sqrt{t^2-1}\right\} \end{aligned}\right\} \tag{149.6}$$

(wobei die Wurzeln positiv, der Logarithmus reell und $0 \leqq \arccos t \leqq \frac{\pi}{2}$ zu wählen ist). Damit ergibt sich für die Koeffizienten der Kugelfunktions-Reihe (148.14) (für den p- bzw. s-Fall)

$$\frac{\Omega\,\psi_n(\varepsilon)}{\Omega\,\zeta_n^1(\varepsilon)} \to \left\{\begin{aligned} &\frac{1}{2}\left(1 \pm e^{-2i\sigma}\right) \quad && (n < \varepsilon) \\ &\pm \frac{i}{2}\, e^{-2\tau} && (n > \varepsilon). \end{aligned}\right\} \tag{149.7}$$

Sie sind also für $n < \varepsilon$ zwischen 0 und 1 schnell oszillierende Größen, die dann für $n > \varepsilon$ stärker als exponentiell mit wachsendem n abnehmen. Es sind somit auch hier wieder (größenordnungsmäßig) so viele Partialwellen zu berücksichtigen, wie die Zahl ε beträgt. Sie haben eine mit n nur sehr langsam veränderliche Amplitude; jedoch besteht keine übersichtliche Phasenbeziehung, so daß sich von hier aus schwer zu übersehende Interferenzen ergeben.

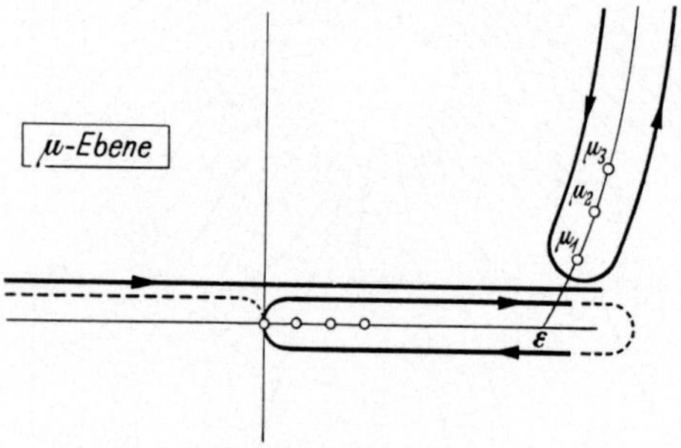

Fig. 123. Komplexe Integrationswege zur Watson-Transformation.

150. Reihentransformation nach Watson. Ein analytisch einfach zu handhabender und anschaulich interpretierbaren Zugang zu unserem Beugungsproblem für $\varepsilon \gg 1$ ergibt sich hier wieder mittels der Watson-Transformation[1]. Zunächst können wir die Reihe (148.14) als Residuensumme des Integrals

$$\left.\begin{aligned} v(r,\vartheta) = \frac{i}{2}\oint \frac{2\mu+1}{\sin\pi\mu}\,P_\mu(-\cos\vartheta)\,\frac{e^{-\frac{i\pi}{2}\mu}}{\Omega\,\zeta_\mu^1(\varepsilon)}\,\cdot \\ \cdot\left\{\Omega\,\zeta_\mu^1(\varepsilon)\cdot\psi_\mu(k\,r) - \Omega\,\psi_\mu(\varepsilon)\cdot\zeta_\mu^1(k\,r)\right\}d\mu \end{aligned}\right\} \tag{150.1}$$

auffassen, wobei der Integrationsweg die positive reelle Achse umläuft (vgl. Fig. 123). In den bei ganzzahligen $\mu = n \geqq 0$ gelegenen Polen des Integranden tritt nämlich das Residuum

$$\operatorname{Res}\left\{\frac{P_\mu(-\cos\vartheta)}{\sin\pi\mu}\right\}_{\mu=n} = \frac{P_n(-\cos\vartheta)}{\pi\cos\pi n} = \frac{1}{\pi}\,P_n(\cos\vartheta) \tag{150.2}$$

auf. Da hier der Integrand eine ungerade Funktion von $\mu + \frac{1}{2}$ ist (s. Sommerfeld l. c.), so kann als Integrationsweg auch eine in der oberen μ-Halbebene gelegene Parallele zur reellen Achse dienen (vgl. Fig. 123). Die Auswertung des Integrals erfolgt durch Deformation des Integrationsweges in eine Schleife um

[1] A. Sommerfeld: Vorlesungen über theoretische Physik, Bd. VI, S. 216ff. u. 258ff. Wiesbaden 1947. — W. Franz: Z. Naturforsch. **9**a, 705 (1954). — L. B. Felsen: Trans. Inst. Radio Engrs. AP-**5**, 1 (1957).

die Polreihe μ_s, die durch die Wurzeln der Gleichung

$$\Omega\,\zeta^1_{\mu_s}(\varepsilon) = 0 \tag{150.3}$$

gegeben ist. (Der Integrand verschwindet im Unendlichen der entsprechenden Teile der μ-Ebene, wie bei SOMMERFELD gezeigt wird.) Durch Residuenbildung in diesen Polen geht dann (150.1) in die folgende Watsonsche Reihe über

$$v(r,\vartheta) = \frac{\pi}{2}\sum_s \frac{2\mu_s+1}{\sin\pi\mu_s}\left\{\frac{\Omega\,\zeta^2_\mu(\varepsilon)}{\frac{\partial}{\partial\mu}\,\Omega\,\zeta^1_\mu(\varepsilon)}\right\}_{\mu_s} \mathrm{e}^{-\frac{i\pi}{2}\mu_s} P_{\mu_s}(-\cos\vartheta)\,\zeta^1_{\mu_s}(k\,r)\,. \tag{150.4}$$

Sie entspricht wiederum einer Entwicklung nach Partialwellen, die längs des Halbstrahls $\vartheta = 0$ angeregt werden und beim Fortschreiten in meridionaler Richtung exponentiell gedämpft sind. [Diese radialen Eigenfunktionen genügen zufolge (150.3) auch wieder *einzeln* der entsprechenden Randbedingung für $r = a$.] Zufolge (148.6) stimmen nun die Nullstellen von (150.3) asymptotisch (für $\varepsilon \gg 1$) mit denjenigen von (140.4) überein. Somit ist

$$\mu_s + \frac{1}{2} = \nu_s = \varepsilon + \left(\frac{\varepsilon}{6}\right)^{\frac{1}{3}} q_s\,\mathrm{e}^{\frac{i\pi}{3}} \tag{150.5}$$

zu setzen. Die q_s sind dabei durch (141.2) gegeben (der Index $\|$ entspricht dem p-Fall, $\perp$ dem s-Fall). Treibt man die asymptotische Entwicklung einen Schritt weiter, so ergibt sich nach FRANZ (l. c.)

im p-Fall

$$\mu_s + \frac{1}{2} = \nu_s = \varepsilon + \left(\frac{\varepsilon}{6}\right)^{\frac{1}{3}} q^{(s)}_{\|}\,\mathrm{e}^{\frac{i\pi}{3}} - \left(\frac{6}{\varepsilon}\right)^{\frac{1}{3}} \frac{q^{(s)2}_{\|}}{180}\,\mathrm{e}^{-\frac{i\pi}{3}}, \tag{150.5'}$$

im s-Fall

$$\mu_s + \frac{1}{2} = \nu_s = \varepsilon + \left(\frac{\varepsilon}{6}\right)^{\frac{1}{3}} q^{(s)}_{\perp}\,\mathrm{e}^{\frac{i\pi}{3}} - \left(\frac{6}{\varepsilon}\right)^{\frac{1}{3}}\left(\frac{7}{20 q^{(s)}_{\perp}} + \frac{q^{(s)2}_{\perp}}{180}\right)\mathrm{e}^{-\frac{i\pi}{3}}.$$

Ferner gilt asymptotisch

$$\left\{\frac{\Omega\,\zeta^2_\mu(\varepsilon)}{\frac{\partial}{\partial\mu}\,\Omega\,\zeta^1_\mu(\varepsilon)}\right\}_{\mu_s} \to \left\{\frac{\Omega\,H^2_\nu(\varepsilon)}{\frac{\partial}{\partial\nu}\,\Omega\,H^1_\nu(\varepsilon)}\right\}_{\nu_s}. \tag{150.6}$$

Mit Hilfe der für $|\mu\sin\vartheta| \gg 1$ ($\mathrm{Re}\,\mu > 0$) asymptotisch gültigen Darstellung[1]

$$P_\mu(-\cos\vartheta) = \sqrt{\frac{2}{\pi\,\mu\sin\vartheta}}\cos\left\{\left(\mu + \frac{1}{2}\right)(\pi - \vartheta) - \frac{\pi}{4}\right\} \tag{150.7}$$

und der asymptotischen Darstellungen (143.3) für die Zylinderfunktionen ergibt sich somit ein Ausdruck, der demjenigen für den Kreiszylinder (140.5) weitgehend entspricht. Zunächst folgt nämlich mit (150.5, 7)

$$\frac{1}{2}\,\frac{2\mu+1}{\sin\pi\mu_s}\,\mathrm{e}^{-\frac{i\pi}{2}\mu_s} P_{\mu_s}(-\cos\vartheta)\,\zeta^1_{\mu_s}(k\,r) \to - \frac{\varepsilon^{\frac{1}{2}}\mathrm{e}^{\frac{i\pi}{4}}}{\sqrt{k\,r\sin\vartheta}} \cdot \frac{\cos\left\{\nu_s(\pi-\vartheta) - \frac{\pi}{4}\right\}}{\cos\pi\nu_s}\,\mathrm{e}^{-\frac{i\pi}{2}\nu_s} H^1_{\nu_s}(k\,r) \tag{150.8}$$

[wobei wir $(2\mu_s+1)/\sqrt{\mu_s} \to 2\sqrt{\varepsilon}$ setzen durften]. Trägt man dies und (150.6) in (150.4) ein, so stimmt das Ergebnis bis auf den ersten Faktor rechts in (150.8) im

[1] MAGNUS-OBERHETTINGER, S. 92.

wesentlichen mit (140.5) überein. Damit können wir für $kr-\varepsilon \gg \varepsilon^{\frac{1}{3}}$ (141.9) hier in folgender Form übernehmen

$$\left.\begin{aligned} v(r,\vartheta) \to &-\frac{\varepsilon^{\frac{5}{6}}}{k}\,\frac{e^{i\left(k\sqrt{r^2-a^2}-\frac{\pi}{6}\right)}}{\sqrt{2r\sin\vartheta}\,(r^2-a^2)^{\frac{1}{4}}}\sum_s \frac{C_s}{1+e^{2\pi i\nu_s}}\Big\{e^{i\nu_s\left(\vartheta-\arccos\frac{a}{r}-\frac{\pi}{2}\right)+\frac{i\pi}{4}} \\ &+e^{i\nu_s\left(\frac{3\pi}{2}-\vartheta-\arccos\frac{a}{r}\right)-\frac{i\pi}{4}}\Big\}. \end{aligned}\right\} \tag{150.9}$$

Die Werte von ν_s bzw. C_s sind hier der Tabelle 2 bzw. Tabelle 3 in Ziff. 141 zu entnehmen (∥ bzw. ⊥ entspricht der Randbedingung $v=0$ bzw. $\partial v/\partial r=0$). Die physikalische Interpretation dieser Gleichung im Sinne der um die Kugel herumlaufenden Kriechwellen ist derjenigen der entsprechenden Gl. (141.9) für den Kreiszylinder weitgehend analog. Es treten wieder die in Fig. 105 eingezeichneten Kriechstrecken auf. Sie verlaufen hier auf den *Meridianen*, in denen die Ebene durch Einfallsrichtung, Kugelmittelpunkt und Aufpunkt die Kugel schneidet. Die Reihe konvergiert für $\varepsilon \gg 1$ nur dann sehr schnell, wenn der Aufpunkt im *geometrischen Schatten* der Kugel liegt.

Eine Komplikation gegenüber dem Fall des Zylinders tritt hier dadurch ein, daß die Kriechwellen auf dem Halbstrahl $\vartheta=\pi$ *fokussiert* werden. Dies wird in (150.9) durch die Singularität des Faktors $(\sin\vartheta)^{-\frac{1}{2}}$ angezeigt. In der Umgebung dieses Halbstrahls wird die Entwicklung (150.9) jedoch unbrauchbar, da dort die asymptotische Darstellung (150.7) nicht mehr gilt. In dieser Umgebung $[\varepsilon(\pi-\vartheta)$ nicht $\gg 1]$ kann man dagegen für $|\mu| \gg 1$ die Darstellung[1]

$$P_\mu(-\cos\vartheta) \to J_0\left((\mu+\tfrac{1}{2})(\pi-\vartheta)\right) \tag{150.10}$$

verwenden. Mit ihrer Hilfe wird die Brennlinie $\vartheta=\pi$ in die Feldverteilung

$$v(r,\vartheta) \to -\sqrt{\pi}\,\frac{\varepsilon^{\frac{4}{3}}}{2k}\,\frac{e^{i\left(k\sqrt{r^2-a^2}-\frac{\pi}{6}\right)}}{\sqrt{r}\,(r^2-a^2)^{\frac{1}{4}}}\sum_s \frac{C_s}{1+e^{2\pi i\nu_s}}\,e^{i\nu_s\left(\frac{\pi}{2}-\arccos\frac{a}{r}\right)}\,J_0\left(\nu_s(\pi-\vartheta)\right) \tag{150.9'}$$

aufgelöst. Aus dieser Formel geht außerdem hervor, daß die Kriechwellen beim Durchgang durch die Brennlinie einen *Phasenverlust* von $\pi/2$ erleiden. Die Kaustik-Eigenschaft des Halbstrahls $\vartheta=\pi$ hat ihren Grund darin, daß sich auf ihm nicht nur die Kriechwellen treffen, die von zwei Punkten der Kugelfläche ausgehen, sondern solche die von sämtlichen Punkten des *„leuchtenden" Äquators* abstrahlen (Poissonscher Fleck).

Die zur Berechnung des Streuquerschnitts nach (148.17) erforderliche Streuamplitude $A(\pi)$ des Fernfeldes $(r\to\infty)$ in der Einfallsrichtung $(\vartheta=\pi)$ läßt sich jedoch aus (150.9′) nicht berechnen. Der Aufpunkt rückt dann nämlich wieder in die Nähe der Schattengrenze (vgl. Fig. 105), was sich analytisch durch das Verschwinden des konvergenzerzeugenden Exponenten in (150.9′) bemerkbar macht (vgl. dazu Ziff. 151).

Für Aufpunkte *außerhalb des geometrischen Schattens* spalten wir nach FRANZ[2] die Kugelfunktion im Integranden von (150.1) in folgender Form auf

$$P_\mu(-\cos\vartheta) = e^{i\pi\mu}\,P_\mu(\cos\vartheta) - 2i\sin\pi\mu\;Q_\mu^{(2)}(\vartheta) \tag{150.11}$$

($Q_\mu^{(2)}$ Kugelfunktion zweiter Art). Wertet man das dem ersten Term in (150.11) entsprechende Integral (150.1) wieder durch Residuenbildung in den Polen μ_s

[1] Vgl. MAGNUS-OBERHETTINGER, S. 93.

[2] W. FRANZ: Z. Naturforsch. 9a, 705 (1954), Anhang 3. — MAGNUS-OBERHETTINGER, S. 76.

aus, so ergibt sich

$$v(r,\vartheta)=v_g(r,\vartheta)+\frac{\pi}{2}\sum_s \frac{2\mu_s+1}{\sin\pi\mu_s}\left\{\frac{\Omega\,\zeta_\mu^2(\varepsilon)}{\frac{\partial}{\partial\mu}\Omega\,\zeta_\mu^1(\varepsilon)}\right\}_{\mu_s} e^{\frac{i\pi}{2}\mu_s} P_{\mu_s}(\cos\vartheta)\,\zeta_{\mu_s}^1(kr). \quad (150.12)$$

Das dem zweiten Term entsprechende Integral

$$v_g(r,\vartheta)=-\frac{1}{2}\oint(2\mu+1)\,Q_\mu^{(2)}(\vartheta)\,e^{-\frac{i\pi}{2}\mu}\frac{\Omega\,\zeta_\mu^2(\varepsilon)}{\Omega\,\zeta_\mu^1(\varepsilon)}\zeta_\mu^1(kr)\,d\mu \quad (150.13)$$

(der Integrationsweg sei die die Pole μ_s umlaufende Schleife in Fig. 123) kann hier wieder mit Hilfe der Sattelpunktmethode ausgewertet werden, da auf der positiv reellen Achse (auf der die Sattelpunkte liegen) keine Pole mehr vorhanden sind. Bei der Auswertung kann man die asymptotische Darstellung

$$Q_\mu^{(2)}(\vartheta)\to\frac{e^{i\left\{\left(\mu+\frac{1}{2}\right)\vartheta-\frac{\pi}{4}\right\}}}{\sqrt{2\pi\mu\sin\vartheta}}\qquad(|\mu\sin\vartheta|\gg 1,\ \mathrm{Re}\,\mu>1) \quad (150.14)$$

verwenden; der Integrand von (150.13) geht dann bis auf den Faktor $\sqrt{\frac{\nu}{kr\sin\vartheta}}$ mit $\mu+\frac{1}{2}=\nu$ in denjenigen von (142.4) über. Wertet man dies Integral wie in Ziff. 143 an den beiden Sattelpunkten $\hat\nu=\varepsilon\sin\gamma$ (γ Reflexionswinkel) und $\check\nu=kr\sin\vartheta$ aus, so ergibt sich die (143.5) entsprechende Darstellung für das geometrisch-optische Feld ($\varepsilon\sin\gamma\sin\vartheta\gg 1$, oberes Vorzeichen für den p-, unteres für den s-Fall)

$$\left.\begin{aligned}v_g(r,\vartheta)&\to e^{-ikr\cos\vartheta}\mp\sqrt{\frac{a^2\sin 2\gamma}{4r\sin\vartheta\left(\sqrt{r^2-a^2\sin^2\gamma}-2a\cos\gamma\right)}}\,\cdot\\&\cdot\exp ik\left(\sqrt{r^2-a^2\sin^2\gamma}-2a\cos\gamma\right).\end{aligned}\right\} \quad (150.13')$$

Für das Fernfeld ($r\to\infty$, $\gamma\to\frac{\vartheta}{2}$, $\varepsilon\sin\frac{\vartheta}{2}\sin\vartheta\gg 1$) ergibt sich daraus (ergänzt durch das nächste Glied der asymptotischen Entwicklung)

$$\left.\begin{aligned}&v_g^{(p)}(r,\vartheta)\to e^{-ikr\cos\vartheta}-\frac{a}{2r}e^{ik\left(r-2a\cos\frac{\vartheta}{2}\right)}\left(1+\frac{i}{2\varepsilon\cos^3\frac{\vartheta}{2}}+\cdots\right)\\&\text{bzw.}\\&v_g^{(s)}(r,\vartheta)\to e^{-ikr\cos\vartheta}+\frac{a}{2r}e^{ik\left(r-2a\cos\frac{\vartheta}{2}\right)}\left(1-i\frac{1+2\cos^2\frac{\vartheta}{2}}{2\varepsilon\cos^3\frac{\vartheta}{2}}+\cdots\right).\end{aligned}\right\} \quad (150.13'')$$

Die asymptotische Auswertung von (150.12) ergibt jetzt (für $kr-\varepsilon\gg\varepsilon^{\frac{1}{3}}$, $\varepsilon\sin\vartheta\gg 1$)

$$\left.\begin{aligned}v(r,\vartheta)&\to v_g(r,\vartheta)+\frac{\varepsilon^{\frac{5}{6}}}{k}\frac{e^{i\left(k\sqrt{r^2-a^2}+\frac{\pi}{3}\right)}}{\sqrt{2r\sin\vartheta}\,(r^2-a^2)^{\frac{1}{4}}}\,\cdot\\&\cdot\sum_s\frac{C_s}{1+e^{2\pi i\nu_s}}\left\{e^{i\nu_s\left(\frac{3\pi}{2}+\vartheta-\arccos\frac{a}{r}\right)-\frac{i\pi}{4}}+e^{i\nu_s\left(\frac{3\pi}{2}-\vartheta-\arccos\frac{a}{r}\right)+\frac{i\pi}{4}}\right\}.\end{aligned}\right\} \quad (150.15)$$

Die zugehörigen Kriechwellen sind in Fig. 106a—d dargestellt. Die Reihe konvergiert für alle Aufpunkte im Gebiet außerhalb des geometrischen Schattens äußerst schnell (ausgenommen die geometrische Schattengrenze). Die Umgebung der *Rückwärtsstreuung* $\vartheta=0$ ist hier aus dem gleichen Grund auszunehmen, der bei der Vorwärtsstreuung erläutert worden ist (Fokussierung). Die asymptotische Darstellung für $|\mu \sin\vartheta| \gg 1$

$$P_\mu(\cos\vartheta) \to \sqrt{\frac{2}{\pi\,\mu\sin\vartheta}}\cos\left\{\left(\mu+\frac{1}{2}\right)\vartheta-\frac{\pi}{4}\right\} \tag{150.7'}$$

ist hier durch

$$P_\mu(\cos\vartheta) \to J_0\left(\left(\mu+\tfrac{1}{2}\right)\vartheta\right) \tag{150.10'}$$

($|\mu|\gg 1$, $|\mu\vartheta|$ nicht $\gg 1$) zu ersetzen. Damit ergibt sich anstelle von (150.15)

$$\left.\begin{aligned} v(r,\vartheta) \to v_g(r,\vartheta) + \sqrt{\pi}\,\frac{\varepsilon^{\frac{4}{3}}}{2k}\,\frac{\mathrm{e}^{i\left(k\sqrt{r^2-a^2}+\frac{\pi}{3}\right)}}{\sqrt{r}\,(r^2-a^2)^{\frac{1}{4}}}\,\cdot \\ \cdot\sum_s \frac{C_s}{1+\varepsilon^{2\pi i\nu_s}}\,\mathrm{e}^{i\nu_s\left(\frac{3\pi}{2}-\arccos\frac{a}{r}\right)}\,J_0(\nu_s\vartheta)\,. \end{aligned}\right\} \tag{150.15'}$$

Die höhere Größenordnung der Streuwelle bezüglich ε rührt wieder davon her, daß sämtliche Punkte des Äquators Kriechwellen nach den Punkten des Halbstrahls $\vartheta=0$ entsenden. [In Gl. (150.15) kommt die Beugung durch den Beitrag zweier leuchtender Punkte zustande, in (150.15′) hingegen durch eine leuchtende Linie.]

Für die *Flächenbelegungen* (148.13) ergibt sich mit Hilfe der Watson-Transformation und ihrer asymptotischen Auswertung folgende Darstellung ($\varepsilon\sin\vartheta\gg 1$)

für die *Schattenseite* $\left(\frac{\pi}{2}<\vartheta<\pi\right)$

$$\left.\begin{aligned} \psi_p(\vartheta) &\to k\,\varepsilon^{-\frac{1}{3}}\,\mathrm{e}^{-\frac{i\pi}{3}} \\ \psi_s(\vartheta) &\to 1 \end{aligned}\right\}\cdot\frac{1}{\sqrt{\sin\vartheta}}\sum_s D_s\,\frac{\mathrm{e}^{i\nu_s\left(\vartheta-\frac{\pi}{2}\right)}-i\,\mathrm{e}^{i\nu_s\left(\frac{3\pi}{2}-\vartheta\right)}}{1+\mathrm{e}^{2\pi i\nu_s}} \tag{150.16}$$

für die *Vorderseite* $\left(0<\vartheta<\frac{\pi}{2}\right)$

$$\left.\begin{aligned} &\left.\begin{aligned} \psi_p(\vartheta) &\to -2i\,k\cos\vartheta \\ \psi_s(\vartheta) &\to 2 \end{aligned}\right\}\cdot\mathrm{e}^{-i\varepsilon\cos\vartheta}\left(1\pm i\,\frac{1+\cos^2\vartheta}{2\varepsilon\cos^3\vartheta}+\cdots\right) \\ &-\left\{\begin{matrix} k\,\varepsilon^{-\frac{1}{3}}\,\mathrm{e}^{-\frac{i\pi}{3}} \\ 1 \end{matrix}\right\}\cdot\frac{1}{\sqrt{\sin\vartheta}}\sum_s D_s\,\frac{\mathrm{e}^{i\nu_s\left(\frac{3\pi}{2}+\vartheta\right)}+i\,\mathrm{e}^{i\nu_s\left(\frac{3\pi}{2}-\vartheta\right)}}{1+\mathrm{e}^{2\pi i\nu_s}}\,. \end{aligned}\right\} \tag{150.16'}$$

Der Faktor $(\sin\vartheta)^{-\frac{1}{2}}$ weist wieder auf die Fokussierung hin: Die Dichte $\psi(\vartheta)$ der längs Geodäten (Großkreisen) fortschreitenden „*Kriechströme*" muß bei Annäherung an die Kugelpole wie eben dieser Faktor wachsen, da die Geodäten dort konvergieren. In der Umgebung der Kugelpole ist die Darstellung (150.16, 16′) wieder durch eine entsprechende mit Hilfe von Bessel-Funktionen zu ersetzen und zwar ergibt sich für den Kugelpol auf der *Schattenseite* $\vartheta\approx\pi$

$$\left.\begin{aligned} \psi_p(\vartheta) &\to \sqrt{2\pi}\,k\,\varepsilon^{\frac{1}{6}}\,\mathrm{e}^{-\frac{i\pi}{3}} \\ \psi_s(\vartheta) &\to \sqrt{2\pi\,\varepsilon} \end{aligned}\right\}\cdot\sum_s D_s\,\frac{\mathrm{e}^{i\left(\frac{\pi\nu_s}{2}-\frac{\pi}{4}\right)}}{1+\mathrm{e}^{2\pi i\nu_s}}\,J_0\left(\nu_s(\pi-\vartheta)\right) \tag{150.17}$$

für den Kugelpol auf der *Vorderseite* $\vartheta\approx 0$

$$\left.\begin{aligned} &\left.\begin{aligned} \psi_p(\vartheta) &\to -2i\,k\cos\vartheta \\ \psi_s(\vartheta) &\to 2 \end{aligned}\right\}\mathrm{e}^{-i\varepsilon\cos\vartheta}\left(1\pm i\,\frac{1+\cos^2\vartheta}{2\varepsilon\cos^3\vartheta}+\cdots\right) \\ &-\left\{\begin{matrix} \sqrt{2\pi}\,k\,\varepsilon^{\frac{1}{6}}\,\mathrm{e}^{-\frac{i\pi}{3}} \\ \sqrt{2\pi\,\varepsilon} \end{matrix}\right\}\cdot\sum_s D_s\,\frac{\mathrm{e}^{i\left(\frac{3\pi\nu_s}{2}+\frac{\pi}{4}\right)}}{1+\mathrm{e}^{2\pi i\nu_s}}\,J_0(\nu_s\vartheta)\,. \end{aligned}\right\} \tag{150.17'}$$

Die Kriechströme gehen wieder von der Schattengrenze $\vartheta = \pi/2$ aus und zwar mit *denselben anfangswerten* D_s, wie beim Zylinder (Ziff. 144). In der nächsten Umgebung der Schattengrenze am Kugeläquator ($\vartheta \approx \pi/2$) werden die Reihen (150.17, 17′) unbrauchbar und sind durch die (144.6) entsprechenden *Fockschen Darstellungen* zu ersetzen:

$$\left.\begin{matrix} \psi_p(\vartheta) \to k \dfrac{\varepsilon^{-\frac{1}{6}}}{6^{\frac{2}{3}}} \mathrm{e}^{\frac{i\pi}{6}} \\ \psi_s(\vartheta) \to \dfrac{i}{6} \end{matrix}\right\} \cdot \frac{1}{\sqrt{\sin\vartheta}} \sum_{l=0}^{\infty} (-1)^l \left\{ g(\xi_l)\, \mathrm{e}^{i\varepsilon\left(\vartheta - \frac{\pi}{2} + 2\pi l\right)} - i\, g(\xi_l')\, \mathrm{e}^{i\varepsilon\left(\frac{3\pi}{2} - \vartheta + 2\pi l\right)} \right\}. \tag{150.17''}$$

Hierbei sind die Fock-Funktionen $g(\xi)$ und ihre Argumente ξ_l bzw. ξ_l' durch (174.4) und (144.8) definiert.

Die Belegungen $\psi(\vartheta)$ lassen sich auch wieder durch direkte asymptotische Lösung der Integralgleichungen (148.3) gewinnen[1]. Zu diesem Zweck hat man zunächst den Kern (148.7) für $\varepsilon \gg 1$ mittels des Prinzips der stationären Phase asymptotisch zu entwickeln. Die Phase des Integranden links in (148.7) wird für $\varphi' = \varphi$ stationär; wir können die dort vorgesehene Integration auf die nächste Umgebung dieses Punktes beschränken. Es ergibt sich so

$$\frac{a^2}{8\pi} \frac{\partial}{\partial a} \int_0^{2\pi} \frac{\mathrm{e}^{2i\varepsilon \sin\frac{|\Theta|}{2}}}{a \sin\frac{|\Theta|}{2}}\, d\varphi' \to \sqrt{\frac{\varepsilon}{4\pi}}\, \mathrm{e}^{\frac{3\pi i}{4}} \sqrt{\sin\frac{|\vartheta - \vartheta'|}{2}}\, \frac{\mathrm{e}^{2i\varepsilon \sin\frac{|\vartheta-\vartheta'|}{2}}}{\sqrt{\sin\vartheta \sin\vartheta'}}. \tag{150.18}$$

Setzen wir dies zusammen mit dem Ansatz [vgl. (146.6)]

$$\psi(\vartheta) = \frac{\hat{\psi}(\vartheta)}{\sqrt{\sin\vartheta}}\, \mathrm{e}^{i\varepsilon\vartheta} \tag{150.19}$$

[$\hat{\psi}(\vartheta)$ langsam veränderlicher Amplitudenfaktor] in die für die Kriechströme zuständigen homogenen Integralgleichungen (148.3) ein, so lauten sie (oberes Vorzeichen für den p-Fall, unteres für den s-Fall):

$$\hat{\psi}(\vartheta) = \mp \sqrt{\frac{\varepsilon}{4\pi}}\, \mathrm{e}^{\frac{3\pi i}{4}} \int \hat{\psi}(\vartheta') \sqrt{\sin\frac{|\vartheta - \vartheta'|}{2}}\, \mathrm{e}^{i\varepsilon\left(\vartheta' - \vartheta + 2\sin\frac{|\vartheta' - \vartheta'|}{2}\right)} d\vartheta'. \tag{150.20}$$

Dies stimmt aber mit (145.5′) genau überein.

151. Diskussion. Für das Amplitudenverhältnis der Kriechwellen zu der geometrisch-optisch reflektierten Welle ergibt sich nach (150.13″, 15) für $r \to \infty$, $\varepsilon \sin\vartheta \gg 1$

$$\left|\frac{v - v_g}{v_g - v_0}\right| \to \frac{\sqrt{2}\,\varepsilon^{-\frac{1}{6}}}{\sqrt{\sin\vartheta}} \left| \sum_s \frac{C_s}{1 + \mathrm{e}^{2\pi i \nu_s}} \{\mathrm{e}^{i\nu_s(\pi+\vartheta)} + i\, \mathrm{e}^{i\nu_s(\pi-\vartheta)}\} \right| \tag{151.1}$$

und nach (150.13″, 15′) für $r \to \infty$, $\varepsilon\vartheta$ nicht $\gg 1$

$$\left|\frac{v - v_g}{v_g - v_0}\right| \to \sqrt{\pi}\, \varepsilon^{\frac{1}{3}} \left| \sum_s \frac{C_s}{1 + \mathrm{e}^{2\pi i \nu_s}} \mathrm{e}^{i\pi\nu_s} J_0(\nu_s \vartheta) \right|. \tag{151.1'}$$

Diese Größe ist in Fig. 124 und 125 für $\vartheta = 0$ (Rückstrahlung) und $\vartheta = 3\pi/4$ aufgetragen[1] und zwar jeweils für die am schwächsten gedämpfte Kriechwelle, die auf der Kugel die Kriechstrecke $a\pi$ bzw. $a\pi/4$ zurückgelegt hat. Bei der Rückstrahlung ist die Kriechwelle im s-Fall bei $\varepsilon = 10$ noch mit etwa 10% beteiligt, während sie im p-Fall (zufolge der größeren Dämpfung) gänzlich vernachlässigt

[1] Vgl. dazu K. Deppermann u. W. Franz: Ann. Physik **14**, 253 (1954).

werden kann. Für $\vartheta = 3\pi/4$ ist infolge der kürzeren Kriechstrecke im s-Fall die Kriechwelle bei $\varepsilon = 100$ noch mit einer Stärke von etwa 10% vorhanden, während sie im p-Fall dann nur noch 0,2% ausmacht (immerhin erreicht sie aber bei $\varepsilon = 7$ noch einen Anteil von 10%).

Auf die Methoden zur Berechnung der *Vorwärtsstreuung* sind wir schon in Ziff. 146 kurz eingegangen[1]. Für den *Streuquerschnitt* ergibt sich nach Wu[2] die folgende asymptotische Darstellung

für den *p-Fall*

$$\left.\begin{aligned} \frac{\sigma_p}{2} \to 1 &+ 0{,}9961531 \cdot \varepsilon^{-\frac{2}{3}} - 0{,}35764983 \cdot \varepsilon^{-\frac{4}{3}} \\ &+ 0{,}2275982 \cdot \varepsilon^{-2} - 0{,}0072753 \cdot \varepsilon^{-\frac{8}{3}} - 0{,}007443 \cdot \varepsilon^{-\frac{10}{3}}, \end{aligned}\right\} \quad (151.2p)$$

für den *s-Fall*

$$\left.\begin{aligned} \frac{\sigma_s}{2} \to 1 &- 0{,}86423996 \cdot \varepsilon^{-\frac{2}{3}} - 0{,}4162852 \cdot \varepsilon^{-\frac{4}{3}} \\ &+ 0{,}7352097 \cdot \varepsilon^{-2} - 0{,}0298539 \cdot \varepsilon^{-\frac{8}{3}} + 0{,}058616 \cdot \varepsilon^{-\frac{10}{3}}. \end{aligned}\right\} \quad (151.2s)$$

(Der erste Korrekturterm ist hier doppelt so groß wie beim Zylinder.)

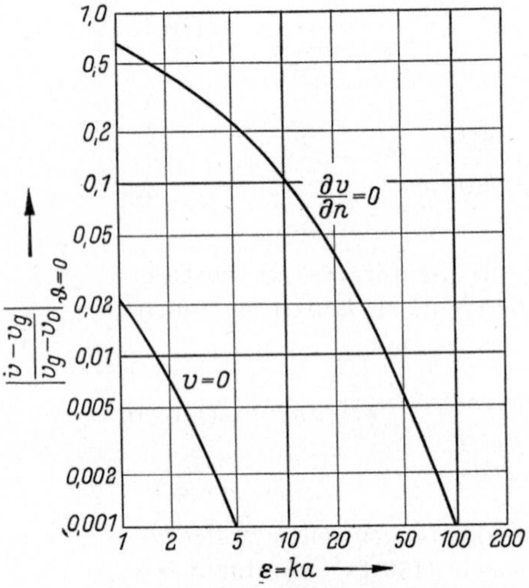

Fig. 124.

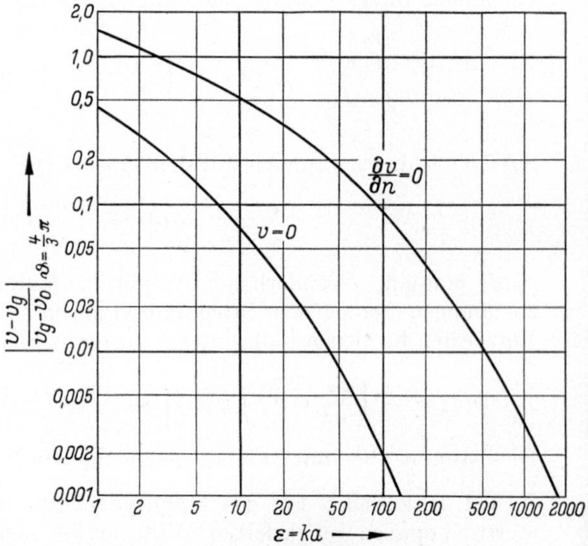

Fig. 125.

Fig. 124. Amplitudenverhältnis von Kriechwelle zu geometrisch-optisch reflektierter Welle bei der Rückstreuung ($\vartheta = 0$) an der Kugel für die beiden Randbedingungen $v = 0$ und $\partial v/\partial n = 0$ (nach Deppermann und Franz).

Fig. 125. Amplitudenverhältnis wie in Fig. 124 für Streuung in Richtung $\vartheta = \frac{3}{4}\pi$ für die beiden Randbedingungen.

b2) Elektromagnetisches Problem.

152. Lösung der Randwertaufgabe. Auf eine ideal leitende Kugel vom Radius a falle eine ebene linear polarisierte elektromagnetische Welle. Die Polarisationsverhältnisse und die zu verwendenden Polarkoordinaten sind aus Fig. 126 zu

[1] Vgl. F.P. White: Proc. Roy. Soc. Lond. A **100**, 505 (1922). — G. Kear: N.Y. Univ. Res. Rep. No. EM-86 (1955). — T.T. Wu u. S.J. Rubinow: J. Appl. Phys. **27**, 1032 (1956). — R.D. Kodis: Trans. Inst. Radio Engrs. AP-**4**, 580 (1956). — D.S. Jones u. G.B. Whitham: Proc. Cambridge Phil. Soc. **53**, 691 (1957). — D.S. Jones: Proc. Roy. Soc. Lond. A **239**, 338 (1957). — P. Beckmann u. W. Franz: Z. Naturforsch. **12**a, 533 (1957).

[2] T.T. Wu: Harvard Univ. Cruft Lab. Techn. Rep. No. 232 (1956). — Phys. Rev. **104**, 1201 (1956).

entnehmen[1]. Die einzigen nicht verschwindenden Komponenten des Primärfeldes sind durch

$$\mathfrak{E}^0_x = \varkappa\,\mathfrak{H}^0_y = e^{ikz} \qquad \left(k = \omega\sqrt{\varepsilon_0\mu_0}, \quad \varkappa = \sqrt{\mu_0/\varepsilon_0}\right) \tag{152.1}$$

gegeben[2]. Bei der Berechnung des zufolge der Anwesenheit der Kugel modifizierten Feldes handelt es sich um die Lösung folgenden Randwertproblems

$$\left.\begin{aligned} \operatorname{rot}\mathfrak{E} &= i\,\omega\,\mu_0\,\mathfrak{H} \\ \operatorname{rot}\mathfrak{H} &= -\,i\,\omega\,\varepsilon_0\,\mathfrak{E} \end{aligned}\right\} \tag{152.2}$$

$$[\mathfrak{n}\,\mathfrak{E}] = 0 \qquad (r = a) \tag{152.2'}$$

($\mathfrak{n}$ Einheitsvektor in Richtung $\mathfrak{r}$, ω Kreisfrequenz des monochromatischen Feldes, ε_0 Dielektrizitätskonstante, μ_0 Permeabilität des homogenen isotropen Mediums, in das die Kugel eingebettet ist).

Wie wir in Ziff. 6 gesehen haben, läßt sich jede Lösung von (152.2) mit Hilfe der beiden *Debyeschen Potentiale* Π_e und Π_m in der Form

$$\left.\begin{aligned} \mathfrak{E} &= \operatorname{rot}\operatorname{rot}(\mathfrak{r}\,\Pi_e) \\ &\quad + i\,k\operatorname{rot}(\mathfrak{r}\,\Pi_m), \\ \varkappa\,\mathfrak{H} &= \operatorname{rot}\operatorname{rot}(\mathfrak{r}\,\Pi_m) \\ &\quad - i\,k\operatorname{rot}(\mathfrak{r}\,\Pi_e) \end{aligned}\right\} \tag{152.3}$$

darstellen, wobei die Π Lösungen der Wellengleichung

$$(\Delta + k^2)\,\Pi(\mathfrak{r}) = 0 \tag{152.4}$$

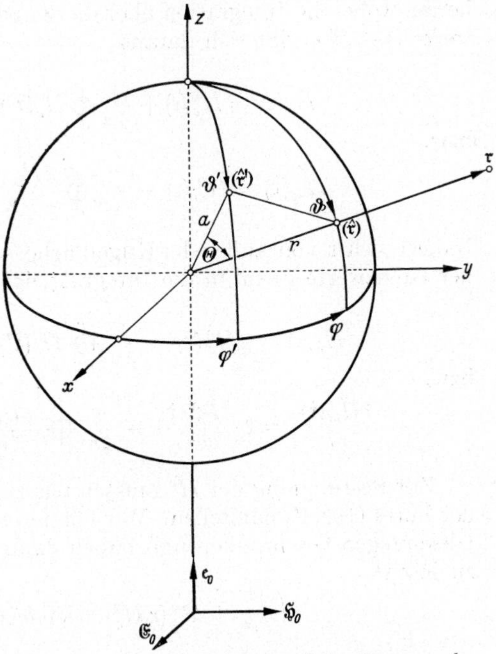

Fig. 126. Zur Theorie der elektromagnetischen Beugung an der Kugel.

sein müssen. Der Vorteil der Einführung dieser Potentiale besteht hier darin, daß sich die Randbedingung (152.2') auf sie sehr einfach übertragen läßt. Mit Hilfe der Identität

$$\operatorname{rot}\operatorname{rot}(\mathfrak{r}\,\Pi) = \nabla\frac{\partial}{\partial r}(r\,\Pi) - \mathfrak{r}\,\Delta\Pi \tag{152.5}$$

schreiben wir (152.3) zunächst in der Form

$$\left.\begin{aligned} \mathfrak{E} &= \nabla\frac{\partial}{\partial r}(r\,\Pi_e) + k^2\,\mathfrak{r}\,\Pi_e - i\,k\,[\mathfrak{r}\,\nabla]\,\Pi_m \\ \varkappa\,\mathfrak{H} &= \nabla\frac{\partial}{\partial r}(r\,\Pi_m) + k^2\,\mathfrak{r}\,\Pi_m + i\,k\,[\mathfrak{r}\,\nabla]\,\Pi_e. \end{aligned}\right\} \tag{152.3'}$$

(Das aus Π_e abgeleitete Feld hat in radialer Richtung nur eine elektrische Komponente, das aus Π_m abgeleitete nur eine magnetische.) In beiden Beiträgen von (152.3') zu $[\mathfrak{n}\,\mathfrak{E}]$ treten also die tangentialen Differentiationen $[\mathfrak{n}\,\nabla]$ auf; die ihnen unterworfenen Größen müssen zur Erfüllung der Randbedingung (152.2') verschwinden:

$$\frac{\partial}{\partial r}(r\,\Pi_e) = 0, \quad \Pi_m = 0 \qquad (r = a). \tag{152.6}$$

[1] Wir haben den Winkel ϑ hier als das *Supplement* des in den vorangegangenen Abschnitten mit ϑ bezeichneten Winkels definiert. Dadurch werden die folgenden Formeln zum Teil etwas einfacher. Beim Vergleich mit den Ergebnissen für den Zylinder und das skalare Kugelproblem ist $\vartheta \to \pi - \vartheta$ zu ersetzen und $P_n(-\cos\vartheta) = (-1)^n\,P_n(\cos\vartheta)$ zu beachten.

[2] Abgesehen von einem dimensionsbehafteten Amplitudenfaktor.

Wir haben es also nur noch mit den beiden *unabhängigen skalaren* Randwertproblemen (152.4, 6) zu tun. Zu ihrer Lösung ziehen wir das Huygenssche Prinzip (8.5) in der Form

$$\Pi(\mathfrak{r}) = \Pi^0(\mathfrak{r}) + \frac{1}{4\pi}\oint\left\{\Pi(\hat{\mathfrak{r}}')\frac{\partial}{\partial r'} - \frac{\partial\Pi(\hat{\mathfrak{r}}')}{\partial r'}\right\}\frac{e^{ik|\mathfrak{r}-\hat{\mathfrak{r}}'|}}{|\mathfrak{r}-\hat{\mathfrak{r}}'|}\,d\hat{\mathfrak{r}}' \tag{152.7}$$

heran, wobei die Integration über die Kugel zu erfolgen hat. Mit Hilfe der Randwerte (152.6) ergibt sich daraus

$$\Pi_e(\mathfrak{r}) = \Pi_e^0(\mathfrak{r}) + \frac{1}{4\pi}\oint\Pi_e(\hat{\mathfrak{r}}')\left(\frac{\partial}{\partial r'} + \frac{1}{a}\right)\frac{e^{ik|\mathfrak{r}-\hat{\mathfrak{r}}'|}}{|\mathfrak{r}-\hat{\mathfrak{r}}'|}\,d\hat{\mathfrak{r}}' \tag{152.7e}$$

bzw.

$$\Pi_m(\hat{\mathfrak{r}}) = \Pi_m^0(\mathfrak{r}) - \frac{1}{4\pi}\oint\frac{\partial\Pi_m(\hat{\mathfrak{r}}')}{\partial r'}\,\frac{e^{ik|\mathfrak{r}-\hat{\mathfrak{r}}'|}}{|\mathfrak{r}-\hat{\mathfrak{r}}'|}\,d\hat{\mathfrak{r}}'. \tag{152.7m}$$

Nähert sich $\mathfrak{r}$ von außen der Kugelfläche, so ergeben sich aus (152.7 *e, m*) mit Hilfe der Grenzwerte (9.5a, b) die Integralgleichungen

$$\Pi_e(\hat{\mathfrak{r}}) = 2\Pi_e^0(\hat{\mathfrak{r}}) + \frac{1}{2\pi}\oint\Pi_e(\hat{\mathfrak{r}}')\left(\frac{\partial}{\partial r'} + \frac{1}{a}\right)\frac{e^{ik|\mathfrak{r}-\hat{\mathfrak{r}}'|}}{|\mathfrak{r}-\hat{\mathfrak{r}}'|}\,d\hat{\mathfrak{r}}' \tag{152.8e}$$

bzw.

$$\frac{\partial\Pi_m(\hat{\mathfrak{r}})}{\partial r} = 2\frac{\partial\Pi_m^0(\hat{\mathfrak{r}})}{\partial r} - \frac{1}{2\pi}\oint\frac{\partial\Pi_m(\hat{\mathfrak{r}}')}{\partial r'}\,\frac{\partial}{\partial r}\,\frac{e^{ik|\mathfrak{r}-\hat{\mathfrak{r}}'|}}{|\mathfrak{r}-\hat{\mathfrak{r}}'|}\,d\hat{\mathfrak{r}}'. \tag{152.8m}$$

Zur Bestimmung der Π^0 müssen wir zunächst auch das Primärfeld (152.1) in der Form (152.3′) darstellen. Wir können uns dabei auf die r-Komponente dieser Gleichungen beschränken und haben dann die folgenden Differentialgleichungen zu lösen[1]

$$\left(\frac{\partial^2}{\partial r^2} + k^2\right)(r\,\Pi_e^0) = \sin\vartheta\cos\varphi\,e^{ikr\cos\vartheta}, \tag{152.9e}$$

$$\left(\frac{\partial^2}{\partial r^2} + k^2\right)(r\,\Pi_m^0) = \sin\vartheta\sin\varphi\,e^{ikr\cos\vartheta}. \tag{152.9m}$$

Mit Hilfe der aus (148.9) folgenden Entwicklung

$$\sin\vartheta\,e^{ikr\cos\vartheta} = \frac{i}{kr}\frac{\partial}{\partial\vartheta}e^{ikr\cos\vartheta} = \frac{1}{kr}\sum_{n=1}^{\infty}(2n+1)\,e^{\frac{i\pi}{2}(n-1)}\,\psi_n(kr)\,P_n^1(\cos\vartheta)$$

$$\left[\frac{d}{d\vartheta}P_n(\cos\vartheta) = -P_n^1(\cos\vartheta), \qquad P_0^1 = 0\right]$$

und der Differentialgleichung

$$\left\{\frac{d^2}{dr^2} + k^2 - \frac{n(n+1)}{r^2}\right\}\left\{\begin{matrix} r\,\psi_n(kr) \\ r\,\zeta_n(kr)\end{matrix}\right\} = 0 \tag{152.9′}$$

[1] Die (senkrechten) Projektionen eines beliebigen Vektors $\mathfrak{A}$ auf die kartesischen Achsen xyz sind mit den Projektionen auf die Richtungen der Einheitsvektoren $\mathfrak{e}_r\,\mathfrak{e}_\vartheta\,\mathfrak{e}_\varphi$ (Fig. 126 und 140) durch die Relationen

$$\begin{aligned} A_r &= A_x\sin\vartheta\cos\varphi + A_y\sin\vartheta\sin\varphi - A_z\cos\vartheta \\ A_\vartheta &= A_x\cos\vartheta\cos\varphi + A_y\cos\vartheta\sin\varphi - A_z\sin\vartheta \\ A_\varphi &= -A_x\sin\varphi + A_y\cos\varphi \end{aligned}$$

verknüpft. Ferner gilt für die Komponenten des Gradienten in Polarkoordinaten

$$\nabla\psi = \left(\frac{\partial\psi}{\partial r},\ \frac{1}{r}\frac{\partial\psi}{\partial\vartheta},\ \frac{1}{r\sin\vartheta}\frac{\partial\psi}{\partial\varphi}\right).$$

erkennt man leicht, daß (152.9) die folgende Lösung hat

$$\left.\begin{aligned} \Pi_e^0 &= \cos\varphi \\ \Pi_m^0 &= \sin\varphi \end{aligned}\right\} \cdot \frac{1}{k} \sum_{n=1}^{\infty} \frac{2n+1}{n(n+1)} e^{\frac{i\pi}{2}(n-1)} \psi_n(kr)\, P_n^1(\cos\vartheta)\,. \tag{152.10}$$

Die Lösung der Integralgleichungen (152.8) fällt nun nicht mehr schwer. Zunächst führen wir die Abkürzungen

$$\left.\begin{aligned} u_e(\vartheta,\varphi) &= \Pi_e(\hat{\mathfrak{r}}) \\ u_m(\vartheta,\varphi) &= \frac{\partial \Pi_m(\hat{\mathfrak{r}})}{\partial r} \end{aligned}\right\} \tag{152.11}$$

ein und können dann diese Integralgleichungen mit Hilfe von (148.4) in der Form

$$u_e(\vartheta,\varphi) = 2\Pi_e^0 + \frac{a^2}{8\pi} \int_0^{2\pi} d\varphi' \int_0^{\pi} d\vartheta' \sin\vartheta'\, u_e(\vartheta',\varphi') \left(\frac{\partial}{\partial a} + \frac{2}{a}\right) \frac{e^{2i\varepsilon \sin\frac{|\Theta|}{2}}}{a\sin\frac{|\Theta|}{2}} \tag{152.12e}$$

bzw.

$$u_m(\vartheta,\varphi) = 2\frac{\partial \Pi_m^0}{\partial r} - \frac{a^2}{8\pi} \int_0^{2\pi} d\varphi' \int_0^{\pi} d\vartheta' \sin\vartheta'\, u_m(\vartheta',\varphi') \frac{\partial}{\partial a} \frac{e^{2i\varepsilon \sin\frac{|\Theta|}{2}}}{a\sin\frac{|\Theta|}{2}} \tag{152.12m}$$

schreiben. Im Hinblick auf (152.10) setzen wir die Lösungen in der Form

$$\left.\begin{aligned} u_e &= \cos\varphi \\ u_m &= \sin\varphi \end{aligned}\right\} \cdot \frac{1}{k} \sum_{n=1}^{\infty} \frac{2n+1}{n(n+1)} e^{\frac{i\pi}{2}(n-1)} a_n P_n^1(\cos\vartheta) \tag{152.13}$$

an. Dann ergibt die Integration nach φ' in (152.12) mit Hilfe der Entwicklung (148.5) folgende Darstellung ($\varepsilon = ka$)

$$\left.\begin{aligned} &\frac{a^2}{8\pi}\left(\frac{\partial}{\partial a} + \frac{2}{a}\right) \int_0^{2\pi} \frac{e^{2i\varepsilon\sin\frac{|\Theta|}{2}}}{a\sin\frac{|\Theta|}{2}} \cos\varphi'\, d\varphi' \\ &= \frac{i\varepsilon a}{2} \cos\varphi \left(\frac{\partial}{\partial a} + \frac{2}{a}\right) \sum_{n=1}^{\infty} \frac{2n+1}{n(n+1)} \psi_n(\varepsilon)\, \zeta_n^1(\varepsilon)\, P_n^1(\cos\vartheta)\, P_n^1(\cos\vartheta') \\ &= \frac{\cos\varphi}{2} \sum_{n=1}^{\infty} \frac{2n+1}{n(n+1)} \{1 + 2i\varepsilon\psi_n(\varepsilon)\,[\zeta_n^1(\varepsilon) + \varepsilon\zeta_n^{1\prime}(\varepsilon)]\}\, P_n^1(\cos\vartheta)\, P_n^1(\cos\vartheta') \end{aligned}\right\} \tag{152.14e}$$

bzw.

$$\left.\begin{aligned} &\frac{a^2}{8\pi} \frac{\partial}{\partial a} \int_0^{2\pi} \frac{e^{2i\varepsilon\sin\frac{|\Theta|}{2}}}{a\sin\frac{|\Theta|}{2}} \sin\varphi'\, d\varphi' \\ &= \frac{\sin\varphi}{2} \sum_{n=1}^{\infty} \frac{2n+1}{n(n+1)} \{2i\varepsilon^2 \psi_n'(\varepsilon)\zeta_n^1(\varepsilon) - 1\}\, P_n(\cos\vartheta)\, P_n(\cos\vartheta')\,. \end{aligned}\right\} \tag{152.14m}$$

Dabei haben wir von der sich aus dem Additionstheorem (148.6′) ergebenden Formel

$$\int_0^{2\pi} d\varphi'\, P_n(\cos\Theta) \cdot \begin{cases} \cos\varphi' \\ \sin\varphi' \end{cases} = \frac{2\pi}{n(n+1)} P_n^1(\cos\vartheta)\, P_n^1(\cos\vartheta') \cdot \begin{cases} \cos\varphi \\ \sin\varphi \end{cases} \tag{152.15}$$

Gebrauch gemacht; ferner von der Wronski-Determinante (148.11). Setzt man (152.13, 14) sowie die Inhomogenität (152.10) in (152.12) ein, so ergibt sich durch zweimalige Anwendung der Orthogonalitätsrelation

$$\int\limits_0^\pi P_n^1(\cos\vartheta)\, P_{n'}^1(\cos\vartheta)\sin\vartheta\, d\vartheta = 2\,\frac{n(n+1)}{2n+1}\,\delta_{n n'}$$

folgender Wert für die Entwicklungskoeffizienten

$$a_n^{(e)} = \frac{i}{\varepsilon\,[\varepsilon\,\zeta_n^1(\varepsilon)]'} \tag{152.16e}$$

$$a_n^{(m)} = \frac{-i\,k}{\varepsilon^2\,\zeta_n^1(\varepsilon)} \tag{152.16m}$$

(dabei bedeutet der Strich ′ die Ableitung der eckigen Klammer nach ε). Damit ergeben sich die Lösungen unserer Integralgleichungen in der Form

$$\left.\begin{aligned} u_e(\vartheta,\varphi) &= -\,k^{-1}\cos\varphi \\ u_m(\vartheta,\varphi) &= \sin\varphi \end{aligned}\right\}\cdot\frac{1}{\varepsilon}\sum_{n=1}^{\infty}\frac{2n+1}{n(n+1)}\,\frac{e^{\frac{i\pi}{2}n}}{\Omega\,\varepsilon\,\zeta_n^1(\varepsilon)}\,P_n^1(\cos\vartheta)\,. \tag{152.17}$$

Hier hat der auf $\varepsilon\,\zeta_n^1(\varepsilon)$ wirkende Operator Ω im „*elektrischen*“ Fall die Bedeutung $\Omega \equiv \partial/\partial\varepsilon$, im „*magnetischen*“ hingegen $\Omega \equiv 1$.

Setzt man diese Belegungsdichten in die Darstellung (152.7) für die Debyeschen Potentiale ein, so ergibt sich unter nochmaliger Verwendung der Entwicklung (148.5) mit (152.10) die Darstellung

$$\left.\begin{aligned} \Pi_e &= \cos\varphi \\ \Pi_m &= \sin\varphi \end{aligned}\right\}\frac{i}{k}\,V(r,\vartheta) \tag{152.18}$$

mit

$$V(r,\vartheta) = \sum_{n=1}^{\infty}\frac{2n+1}{n(n+1)}\,e^{\frac{i\pi}{2}n}\left\{\psi_n(k\,r) - \frac{\Omega\,\varepsilon\,\psi_n(\varepsilon)}{\Omega\,\varepsilon\,\zeta_n^1(\varepsilon)}\,\zeta_n^1(k\,r)\right\}P_n^1(\cos\vartheta)\,. \tag{152.18′}$$

Betrachtet man an Stelle einer ideal leitenden Kugel eine solche mit den *Materiekonstanten* ε_i, μ_0, σ (Leitfähigkeit), so gilt (152.18, 18′) für das Äußere der Kugel, wenn man folgende Ersetzungen vornimmt *(Mie-Koeffizienten)*

für Π_e

$$\frac{\Omega\,\varepsilon\,\psi_n(\varepsilon)}{\Omega\,\varepsilon\,\zeta_n^1(\varepsilon)} \rightarrow \frac{\psi_n(\varepsilon)\,[x\,\psi_n(x)]'_{N\varepsilon} - N^2\,[\varepsilon\,\psi_n(\varepsilon)]'\,\psi_n(N\,\varepsilon)}{\zeta_n^1(\varepsilon)\,[x\,\psi_n(x)]'_{N\varepsilon} - N^2\,[\varepsilon\,\zeta_n^1(\varepsilon)]'\,\psi_n(N\,\varepsilon)}\,, \tag{152.19e}$$

für Π_m

$$\frac{\Omega\,\varepsilon\,\psi_n(\varepsilon)}{\Omega\,\varepsilon\,\zeta_n^1(\varepsilon)} \rightarrow \frac{\psi_n(\varepsilon)\,[x\,\psi_n(x)]'_{N\varepsilon} - [\varepsilon\,\psi_n(\varepsilon)]'\,\psi_n(N\,\varepsilon)}{\zeta_n^1(\varepsilon)\,[x\,\psi_n(x)]'_{N\varepsilon} - [\varepsilon\,\zeta_n^1(\varepsilon)]'\,\psi_n(N\,\varepsilon)}\,. \tag{152.19m}$$

Dabei bedeutet N den komplexen *Brechungsindex*

$$N = \sqrt{\frac{\varepsilon_i}{\varepsilon_0} + \frac{i\sigma}{\varepsilon_0\,\omega}}\,. \tag{152.20}$$

Wir gehen zur Darstellung des Gesamtfeldes mit Hilfe der Potentiale (152.18) nach Gl. (152.3′) über. Zunächst ergibt sich für die *radialen* Komponenten [bei Beachtung von (152.9′)]

$$\left.\begin{aligned} &\left.\begin{aligned} \mathfrak{E}_r &= \cos\varphi \\ \varkappa\,\mathfrak{H}_r &= \sin\varphi \end{aligned}\right\}\cdot\frac{1}{k\,r}\sum_{n=1}^{\infty}(2n+1)\,e^{\frac{i\pi}{2}(n-1)}\,\cdot \\ &\quad\cdot\left\{\psi_n(k\,r) - \frac{\Omega\,\varepsilon\,\psi_n(\varepsilon)}{\Omega\,\varepsilon\,\zeta_n^1(\varepsilon)}\,\zeta_n^1(k\,r)\right\}P_n^1(\cos\vartheta)\,. \end{aligned}\right\} \tag{152.21}$$

Zur übersichtlichen Darstellung der *tangentialen* Komponenten führen wir neben der Größe $V(r, \vartheta)$ noch die Größe

$$U(r, \vartheta) = \frac{1}{i k r} \frac{\partial}{\partial r} (r V) \tag{152.18''}$$

ein; dann ergibt sich

$$\left.\begin{aligned} \mathfrak{E}_\vartheta &= \cos\varphi \left(\frac{\partial U_e}{\partial \vartheta} + \frac{V_m}{\sin\vartheta} \right) \\ \mathfrak{E}_\varphi &= -\sin\varphi \left(\frac{U_e}{\sin\vartheta} + \frac{\partial V_m}{\partial \vartheta} \right) \end{aligned}\right\} \tag{152.22}$$

und

$$\left.\begin{aligned} \varkappa\, \mathfrak{H}_\vartheta &= \sin\varphi \left(\frac{V_e}{\sin\vartheta} + \frac{\partial U_m}{\partial \vartheta} \right) \\ \varkappa\, \mathfrak{H}_\varphi &= \cos\varphi \left(\frac{\partial V_e}{\partial \vartheta} + \frac{U_m}{\sin\vartheta} \right). \end{aligned}\right\} \tag{152.22'}$$

Für den *Streuanteil* des *Fernfeldes* $(r \to \infty)$ erhält man mit Hilfe von (148.15) zunächst aus (152.18′) und (152.18″)

$$\left.\begin{aligned} V_S(r, \vartheta) &\to U_S(r, \vartheta) \to -\frac{e^{ikr}}{i k r} S(\vartheta) \\ S(\vartheta) &= \sum_{n=1}^{\infty} \frac{2n+1}{n(n+1)} \frac{\Omega\, \varepsilon \psi_n(\varepsilon)}{\Omega\, \varepsilon \zeta_n^1(\varepsilon)} P_n^1(\cos\vartheta). \end{aligned}\right\} \tag{152.23}$$

Aus (152.21) erkennt man, daß für $r \to \infty$ die *radialen* Komponenten wie r^{-2} verschwinden, während nach (152.22, 22′) und (152.23) die tangentialen nur wie r^{-1} abnehmen: Das Fernfeld der Streuwelle ist *rein transversal* (in Übereinstimmung mit der Ausstrahlungsbedingung, Ziff. 18). Für die transversalen Komponenten des Streu-Fernfeldes erhält man aus (152.22, 22′) und (152.23) die Darstellung

$$\left.\begin{aligned} \mathfrak{E}_\vartheta^{(S)} &\to \varkappa\, \mathfrak{H}_\varphi^{(S)} \to i \frac{e^{ikr}}{k r} \cos\varphi\, S_\parallel(\vartheta) \\ -\mathfrak{E}_\varphi^{(S)} &\to \varkappa\, \mathfrak{H}_\vartheta^{(S)} \to i \frac{e^{ikr}}{k r} \sin\varphi\, S_\perp(\vartheta) \end{aligned}\right\} \tag{152.24}$$

mit

$$\left.\begin{aligned} S_\parallel(\vartheta) &= \frac{\partial S_e(\vartheta)}{\partial \vartheta} + \frac{S_m(\vartheta)}{\sin\vartheta} \\ S_\perp(\vartheta) &= \frac{S_e(\vartheta)}{\sin\vartheta} + \frac{\partial S_m}{\partial \vartheta} \end{aligned}\right\} \tag{152.24'}$$

oder ausführlich geschrieben

$$\left.\begin{aligned} S_\parallel(\vartheta) &= \sum_{n=1}^{\infty} \frac{2n+1}{n(n+1)} \left\{ \frac{[\varepsilon \psi_n(\varepsilon)]'}{[\varepsilon \zeta_n^1(\varepsilon)]'} \tau_n(\cos\vartheta) + \frac{\psi_n(\varepsilon)}{\zeta_n^1(\varepsilon)} \pi_n(\cos\vartheta) \right\} \\ S_\perp(\vartheta) &= \sum_{n=1}^{\infty} \frac{2n+1}{n(n+1)} \left\{ \frac{[\varepsilon \psi_n(\varepsilon)]'}{[\varepsilon \zeta_n^1(\varepsilon)]'} \pi_n(\cos\vartheta) + \frac{\psi_n(\varepsilon)}{\zeta_n^1(\varepsilon)} \tau_n(\cos\vartheta) \right\} \end{aligned}\right\} \tag{152.24''}$$

mit

$$\left.\begin{aligned} \tau_n(\cos\vartheta) &= \frac{d}{d\vartheta} P_n^1(\cos\vartheta) = -\frac{d^2}{d\vartheta^2} P_n(\cos\vartheta) \\ \pi_n(\cos\vartheta) &= \frac{1}{\sin\vartheta} P_n^1(\cos\vartheta) = \frac{-1}{\sin\vartheta} \frac{d}{d\vartheta} P_n(\cos\vartheta). \end{aligned}\right\} \tag{152.24'''}$$

Die Indices ∥ bzw. ⊥ beziehen sich hier auf die *elektrische* Feldstärke und zwar bezeichnen sie die zur *Beobachtungsebene* parallelen bzw. senkrechten Komponenten. (Die Beobachtungsebene ist die durch die Einfallsrichtung den Kugelmittelpunkt und den Aufpunkt gehende Ebene.)

Aus (152.24) erkennt man, daß die Streustrahlung im allgemeinen *elliptisch polarisiert* ist, nur wenn die Beobachtungsebene parallel oder senkrecht zur Schwingungsrichtung (des elektrischen Vektors) des Primärfeldes ist, erhält man linear polarisierte Strahlung. Ferner zeigt (152.24), daß im Fernfeld die elektrische und magnetische Feldstärke aufeinander *senkrecht* stehen (wiederum in Übereinstimmung mit der allgemeinen Forderung der Ausstrahlungsbedingung in Ziff. 18).

Zur Berechnung des *Streukoeffizienten* gehen wir am einfachsten von Gl. (103.7) aus, die einen allgemeinen Zusammenhang zwischen dem Streuquerschnitt und dem Fernfeld der *Vorwärtsstreuung* herstellt. Schreiben wir das Fernfeld der *Gesamtstrahlung* für den elektrischen Vektor allgemein in der Form ($\mathfrak{r} = \mathfrak{e} r$)

$$\mathfrak{E}(\mathfrak{r}) \to \mathfrak{n}_0 \, e^{ik(\mathfrak{e}_0 \mathfrak{e}) r} + \frac{e^{ikr}}{kr} \, \mathfrak{a}(\mathfrak{e})$$

($\mathfrak{e}_0$ Ausbreitungsrichtung der einfallenden ebenen Welle, $\mathfrak{n}_0$ ihre Polarisationsrichtung, $\mathfrak{e}$ Beobachtungsrichtung), so nimmt Gl. (103.7) für den Streuquerschnitt Q (dimensionell vervollständigt) folgende Form an

$$Q = \frac{4\pi}{k^2} \operatorname{Im} \left(\mathfrak{n}_0 \, \mathfrak{a}(\mathfrak{e}_0)\right). \tag{152.25}$$

Wir benötigen also zur Berechnung von Q lediglich das $\mathfrak{E}$-Fernfeld in der Vorwärtsrichtung $\mathfrak{e}_0$ und zwar nur die Komponente in der Polarisationsrichtung $\mathfrak{n}_0$ des Primärfeldes.

Wenden wir diese allgemeine Formel auf die Streuung an der Kugel an, so können wir an Hand der in Fig. 126 dargestellten geometrischen Verhältnisse den Streukoeffizienten $\sigma = Q/\pi a^2$ auf die Komponente $\mathfrak{E}_\vartheta$ für $r \to \infty$, $\vartheta = 0$, $\varphi = 0$ zurückführen. Mit Hilfe von (152.24) ergibt sich so aus (152.25) die Darstellung

$$\sigma = \frac{4}{\varepsilon^2} \operatorname{Re} S_\parallel(0). \tag{152.26}$$

Zur Berechnung von $S_\parallel(0)$ verwenden wir in (152.24″) die Grenzwerte[1]

$$\tau_n(1) = \pi_n(1) = \frac{n(n+1)}{2} \tag{152.27}$$

damit ergibt sich

$$\sigma = \frac{2}{\varepsilon^2} \operatorname{Re} \sum_{n=1}^{\infty} \left\{ \frac{[\varepsilon \psi_n(\varepsilon)]'}{[\varepsilon \zeta_n^1(\varepsilon)]'} + \frac{\psi_n(\varepsilon)}{\zeta_n^1(\varepsilon)} \right\}; \tag{152.26'}$$

Die *Fernfeldintensität* $I_S = |\overline{\mathfrak{S}}_S|$ (zeitlicher Mittelwert des radial gerichteten Pointingschen Vektors des Streufeldes) ergibt sich nach der allgemeinen Formel (16.3) mit Hilfe von (152.24) in der Gestalt

$$I_S(\vartheta, \varphi) = \frac{1}{2\varkappa k^2 r^2} \left\{ \cos^2\varphi \, |S_\parallel(\vartheta)|^2 + \sin^2\varphi \, |S_\perp(\vartheta)|^2 \right\}. \tag{152.28}$$

[1] Bei Verwendung des Komplement-Winkels $\vartheta \to \pi - \vartheta$ hat man von den Grenzwerten

$$\tau_n(-1) = -\pi_n(-1) = (-1)^n \frac{n(n+1)}{2}$$

Gebrauch zu machen, die aus (152.27) mit Hilfe der Beziehungen

$$\tau_n(-\cos\vartheta) = (-1)^n \tau_n(\cos\vartheta), \quad \pi_n(-\cos\vartheta) = -(-1)^n \pi_n(\cos\vartheta)$$

folgen.

Die damit zu Ende geführte Lösung unseres Beugungsproblems (für die ideal leitende Kugel) geht auf K. SCHWARZSCHILD zurück[1]. Den allgemeineren Fall der Kugel von beliebigem (infolge von Absorption komplexen) Brechungsindex haben G. MIE und P. DEBYE als erste eingehend behandelt[2]. Es läßt sich leicht zeigen, daß die Reihendarstellungen für *alle* ε konvergieren; die Zahl der zu be-rücksichtigenden Reihenglieder wird wieder durch die Größe der Zahl ε bestimmt (d.h. es ist Summation bis $n \approx \varepsilon$ erforderlich, s. Ziff. 153).

153. Diskussion. Zunächst wollen wir uns eine Übersicht über die in den Reihen (152.24'') auftretenden Koeffizienten ver-schaffen. Zu diesem Zweck schreiben wir sie in der Form

$$\frac{\Omega\,\varepsilon\,\psi_n(\varepsilon)}{\Omega\,\varepsilon\,\zeta_n^1(\varepsilon)} = \frac{1}{2}\left(1 - e^{2i\alpha_n}\right), \quad (153.1)$$

wobei die reellen Winkel α_n durch die Glei-chung

$$\tan\alpha_n = \frac{\Omega\,\varepsilon\,\psi_n(\varepsilon)}{\Omega\,\varepsilon\,\chi_n(\varepsilon)} \quad (153.2)$$

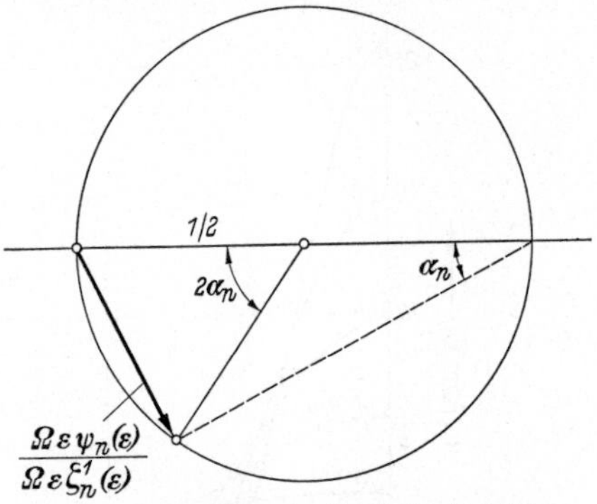

Fig. 127. Zur Darstellung des Quotienten (153.1) in der komplexen Zahlenebene.

definiert sind. $\left[\chi_n(\varepsilon) = \sqrt{\dfrac{\pi}{2\varepsilon}}\,N_{n+\frac12}(\varepsilon)\right.$ ist der Imaginärteil von $\zeta_n^1\!: \zeta_n^1 = \psi_n + i\chi_n,$ dabei ist $N_\nu(\varepsilon)$ die Neumannsche Zylinderfunktion.$\bigr]$ Die komplexen Zahlen (153.1) liegen also auf einem Kreis vom Radius $\frac12$ (vgl. Fig. 127); ihr Betrag schwankt zwischen 0 und 1:

$$\left|\frac{\Omega\,\varepsilon\,\psi_n(\varepsilon)}{\Omega\,\varepsilon\,\zeta_n^1(\varepsilon)}\right|^2 = \mathrm{Re}\left\{\frac{\Omega\,\varepsilon\,\psi_n(\varepsilon)}{\Omega\,\varepsilon\,\zeta_n^1(\varepsilon)}\right\} = \sin^2\alpha_n = \frac{1}{2}\left(1 - \cos 2\alpha_n\right). \quad (153.3)$$

Die ersten sechs Winkelfunktionen $\tau_n(\cos\vartheta)$ und $\pi_n(\cos\vartheta)$ sind in Fig. 128 dar-gestellt. Wir erhalten also im allgemeinen ein recht unübersichtliches Zusammen-wirken von *elektrischen* (aus Π_e abgeleiteten) und *magnetischen* (aus Π_m abgelei-teten) Partialwellen. Für $\varepsilon\gg 1$ können wir die Debyeschen Näherungen (149.4, 5) zur Darstellung der Koeffizienten verwenden (oberes Vorzeichen für $\Omega = \partial/\partial\varepsilon$, unteres für $\Omega = 1$)

$$\frac{\Omega\,\varepsilon\,\psi_n(\varepsilon)}{\Omega\,\varepsilon\,\zeta_n^1(\varepsilon)} \rightarrow \begin{cases}\frac12\left(1 \mp e^{-2i\sigma}\right) & (n < \varepsilon)\\[4pt] \mp\,e^{-2\tau} & (n > \varepsilon)\end{cases} \quad (153.4)$$

[mit den in (149.6) definierten Größen σ und τ]. Aus dieser Darstellung ergibt sich die Konvergenz unserer Reihen, da ihre Glieder für $n > \varepsilon$ stärker als exponentiell mit n abnehmen. Vergleicht man die Gln. (153.1) und (153.4) mit-

[1] K. SCHWARZSCHILD: Abh. bayr. Akad. **31**, 293 (1901). Vgl. auch J. J. THOMSON: Recent Researches in Electricity and Magnetism. Oxford 1893. — J. W. NICHOLSON: Roy. Astronom. Soc. **70**, 544 (1910). — J. PROUDMAN: Roy. Astronom. Soc. **73**, 535 (1913). — J. PROUDMAN, A. T. DOODSON u. G. KENNEDY: Phil. Trans. Roy. Soc. Lond. A **217**, 279 (1918).
[2] G. MIE: Ann. Physik **25**, 377 (1908). — P. DEBYE: Ann. Physik **30**, 59 (1909). Vgl. auch T. J. I'A. BROMWICH: Phil. Trans. Roy. Soc. Lond. A **220**, 175 (1920). — H. C. VAN DE HULST: Rech. Obs. Utrecht **11**, Pt. 1 (1946). — L. INFELD: Quart. Appl. Math. **5**, 113 (1947). — A. L. ADEN: J. Appl. Phys. **22**, 601 (1951). — Darstellungen der Mieschen Theorie bei H. BAT-MAN: Electrical and Optical Wave Motion. Cambridge 1915. — G. WOLFSOHN: Handbuch der Physik, Bd. 20, Kap. 7. Berlin 1928. — M. BORN: Optik. Berlin 1933. — J. A. STRATTON: Elektromagnetic Theory. New York 1941. — H. WEIL, M. L. BARASCH u. T. A. KAPLAN: Studies in Radar Cross Sections X. Ann. Arbor: Univ. of Michigan Press 1956. — M. BORN n. E. WOLF: Principles of Optics. London-New York-Paris-Los Angeles: Pergamon Press 1959.

einander, so ergibt sich für $\varepsilon \gg 1$

$$\alpha_n(\varepsilon) \to \mu \arccos\frac{\mu}{\varepsilon} - \sqrt{\varepsilon^2-\mu^2} \pm \frac{\pi}{4} \qquad \left(\mu = n + \frac{1}{2}\,, \quad n < \varepsilon\right), \tag{153.5}$$

wobei wir für σ den Wert aus (149.6) eingesetzt haben. Den Grenzfall $\varepsilon \gg 1$ werden wir in Ziff. 155 eingehender betrachten.

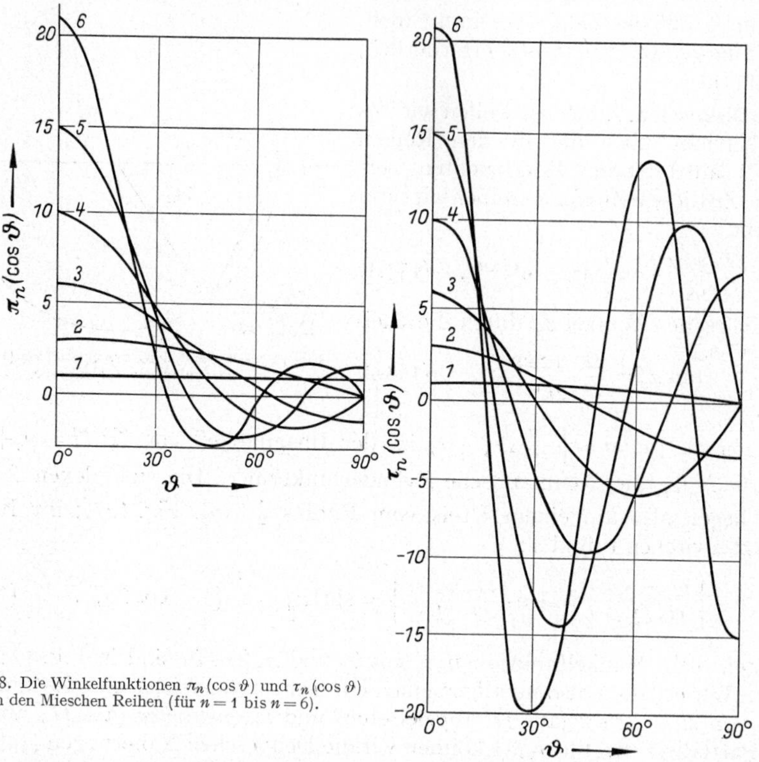

Fig. 128. Die Winkelfunktionen $\pi_n(\cos\vartheta)$ und $\tau_n(\cos\vartheta)$ in den Mieschen Reihen (für $n = 1$ bis $n = 6$).

Hier wollen wir uns zunächst mit dem *Rayleighschen Grenzfall* $\varepsilon \ll 1$ beschäftigen. Für diesen können wir die Reihenentwicklung (149.1) verwenden, mit deren Hilfe sich die folgende Darstellung ergibt

$$\left.\begin{aligned} \frac{[\varepsilon\,\psi_n(\varepsilon)]'}{[\varepsilon\,\zeta_n^1(\varepsilon)]'} &= -i\,\frac{n+1}{n} \\ \frac{\psi_n(\varepsilon)}{\zeta_n^1(\varepsilon)} &= i \end{aligned}\right\} \frac{\varepsilon^{2n+1}}{(2n+1)\{1\cdot 3\cdot 5\cdots(2n-1)\}^2}\,(1+\cdots). \tag{153.6}$$

Die elektrischen und magnetischen Partialwellen der gleichen Ordnung n sind also von *derselben* Größenordnung in ε. In niedrigster Näherung müssen wir daher sowohl die erste *elektrische* als auch die erste *magnetische* Partialwelle berücksichtigen. Mit Hilfe der Beziehungen

$$\tau_1(\cos\vartheta) = \cos\vartheta\,, \qquad \pi_1(\cos\vartheta) = 1$$

und (153.6) erhält man dann aus (152.24″) die Streuamplituden in niedrigster Näherung

$$\left.\begin{aligned} S_\parallel(\vartheta) &= -i\,\varepsilon^3\left(\cos\vartheta - \tfrac{1}{2} + \cdots\right) \\ S_\perp(\vartheta) &= -i\,\varepsilon^3\left(1 - \tfrac{1}{2}\cos\vartheta + \cdots\right). \end{aligned}\right\} \tag{153.7}$$

Trägt man diese in (152.24) ein, so ergibt sich das Streufernfeld

$$\left.\begin{aligned} \mathfrak{E}_\vartheta^{(S)} &= \varkappa\,\mathfrak{H}_\varphi^{(S)} = \varepsilon^3\cos\varphi\left(\cos\vartheta - \frac{1}{2} + \cdots\right)\frac{e^{ikr}}{k\,r} \\ -\,\mathfrak{E}_\varphi^{(S)} &= \varkappa\,\mathfrak{H}_\vartheta^{(S)} = \varepsilon^3\sin\varphi\left(1 - \frac{1}{2}\cos\vartheta + \cdots\right)\frac{e^{ik\,r}}{k\,r}\,. \end{aligned}\right\} \tag{153.8}$$

Dies ist das Fernfeld eines in Richtung von $\mathfrak{E}_0$ im Mittelpunkt der Kugel schwingenden *elektrischen Dipols* vom Moment

$$\mathfrak{p}_0 = \varepsilon_0\,a^3\,\mathfrak{E}_0\,, \tag{153.9e}$$

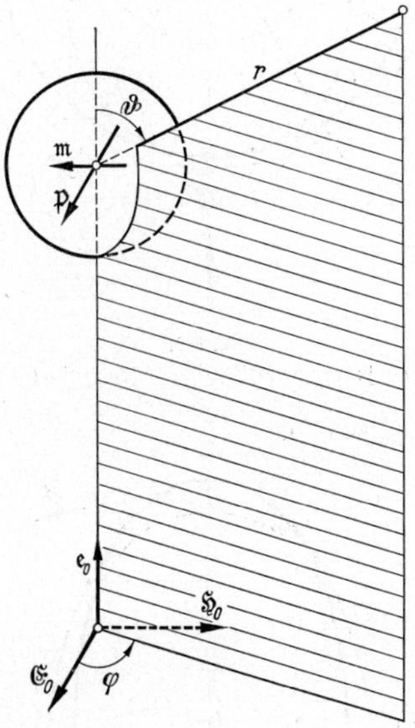

Fig. 129.

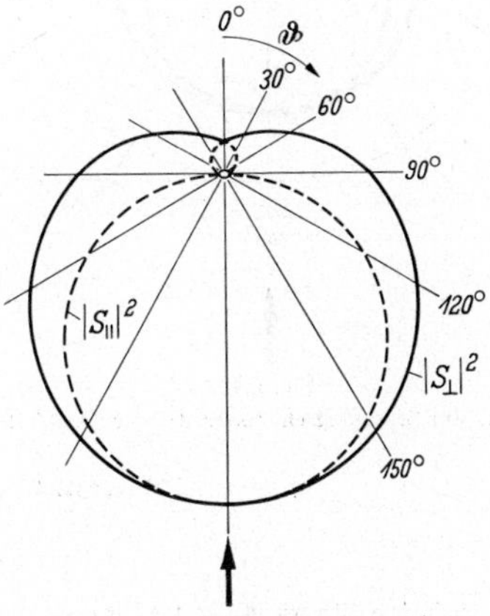

Fig. 130.

Fig. 129. Das Dipolpaar $\mathfrak{p}$ (elektrisches Dipolmoment) und $\mathfrak{m}$ (magnetisches Dipolmoment) durch deren Strahlung das Fernfeld der ideal leitenden Kugel für $\varepsilon \ll 1$ dargestellt werden kann (Rayleighsche Näherung); Beobachtungsebene schraffiert.

Fig. 130. Strahlungscharakteristik des gekreuzten Dipolpaares der Fig. 129.

dem sich das Fernfeld eines in Richtung von $-\mathfrak{H}_0$ schwingenden *magnetischen Dipols* vom Moment

$$\mathfrak{m}_0 = -\,\mu_0\,\frac{a^3}{2}\,\mathfrak{H}_0\,, \tag{153.9m}$$

überlagert. Die ϑ-Abhängigkeit des Strahlungsdiagramms dieses gekreuzten Dipolpaares (vgl. Fig. 129) ist in Fig. 130 wiedergegeben. Es zeigt eine eigentümliche Bevorzugung der *Rückwärtsstreuung*. Das durch (153.8) für $\varepsilon \ll 1$ gelöste Problem der ideal leitenden Kugel im Felde einer ebenen Welle läßt sich auch leicht direkt gewinnen, indem man das Feld in der Umgebung der Kugel als statisch behandelt (vgl. Abschn. III f)[1].

[1] Zuerst durchgeführt bei J. J. THOMSON: Recent Researches in Electricity and Magnetism, S. 437. Oxford 1893. — Für ellipsoidische Teilchen von beliebigem Brechungsindex findet sich die quasistatische Feldberechnung bei Lord RAYLEIGH: Phil. Mag. **44**, 28 (1897). — R. GANS: Ann. Physik **37**, 881 (1912). — Höhere Näherungen bei A. F. STEVENSON: J. Appl. Phys. **24**, 1143 (1953). — Anisotropes Material behandelt R. CLARK JONES: Phys. Rev. **68**, 93, 213 (1945). — Die Anwesenheit eines statischen homogenen Magnetfeldes berücksichtigt E. FICK: Z. Physik **140**, 308 (1955). — Ein ideal leitendes abgeplattetes Rotationsellipsoid behandelt C. T. TAI: Stanford Res. Inst. Techn. Rep. No. 24 (1952). — Vgl. auch G. TORALDO DI FFRANCIA: Boll. Unione Mat. Ital. **11**, 332 (1950).

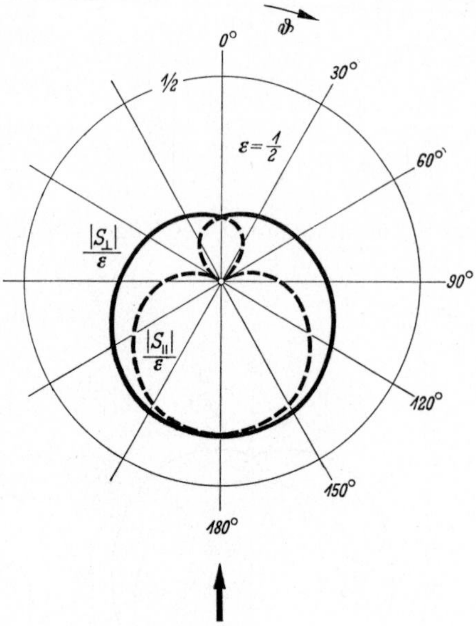

Fig. 131.

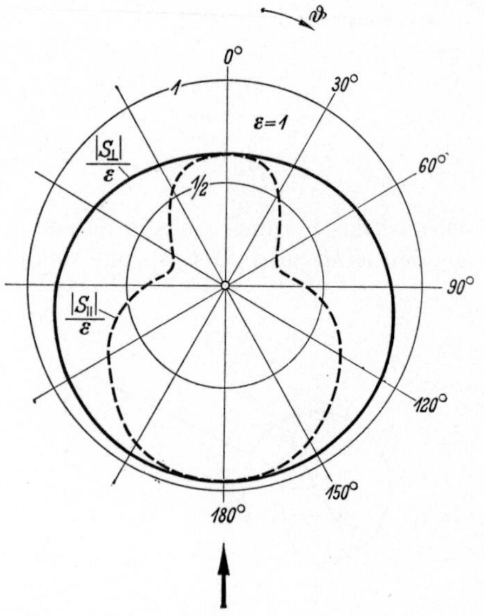

Fig. 132.

Fig. 131. Zur Strahlungscharakteristik der ideal leitenden Kugel für $\varepsilon=\frac{1}{2}$: — $|S_\perp(\vartheta)|/\varepsilon$, – – – $|S_\parallel(\vartheta)|/\varepsilon$ (nach van de Hulst).

Fig. 132. Dasselbe wie in Fig. 131 für $\varepsilon = 1$.

Fig. 133a u. b. Dasselbe wie in Fig. 131 für $\varepsilon = 3$ und 5 (zum Vergleich sind die Werte nach der Kirchhoffschen Theorie eingezeichnet, fein ausgezogene Linie).

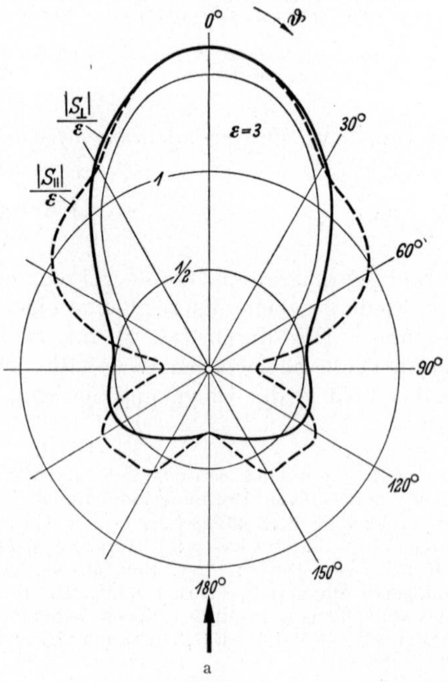

a

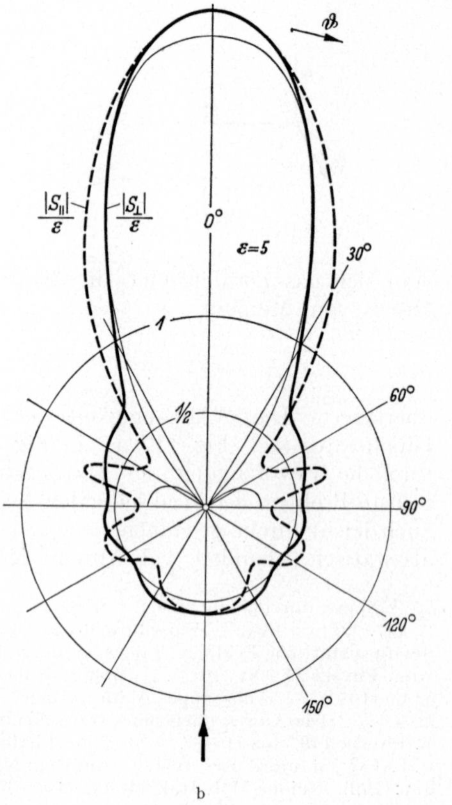

b

Die höheren Partialwellen lassen sich entsprechend als die Strahlung schwingender elektrischer und magnetischer Multipole deuten[1]. Geht man bis zu drei Partialwellen beiderlei Typs, so erhält man aus (152.26) folgenden Wert für den Streukoeffizienten

$$\sigma = \tfrac{10}{4}\,\varepsilon^4 + \tfrac{4}{5}\,\varepsilon^6 + \cdots. \qquad (153.10)$$

Für größere ε muß das Strahlungsdiagramm durch numerische Auswertung der Reihen (152.24″) ermittelt werden.

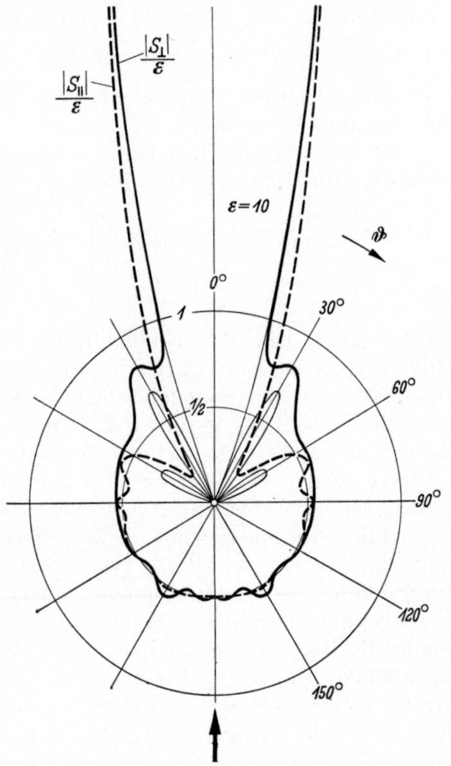

a

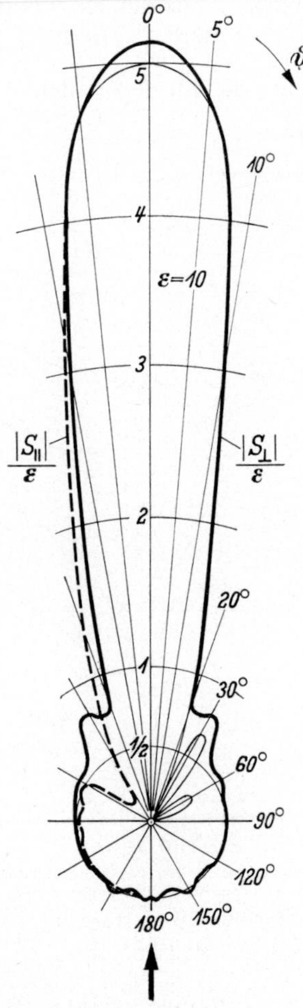

b

Fig. 134 a u. b. Dasselbe wie in Fig. 131 für $\varepsilon = 10$ (fein ausgezogene Linie: Kirchhoffsche Theorie).

Die Fig. 131 bis 134 geben einige typischen Beispiele für die mit wachsendem ε erfolgende Wandlung des Strahlungsdiagramms von der bevorzugten Rückwärtsstreuung bis zur scharf ausgeprägten Vorwärtsstreuung (Poissonscher Fleck) und zwar sind die Größen $|S_\parallel(\vartheta)|/\varepsilon$ und $|S_\perp(\vartheta)|/\varepsilon$ für $\varepsilon = \frac{1}{2}$, 1, 3, 5 und 10 als Polardiagramm aufgetragen[2]. Für $\varepsilon = \frac{1}{2}$ stimmt die Strahlungscharakteristik praktisch mit derjenigen des gekreuzten Dipolpaares (Fig. 130) überein, die sich für $\varepsilon \ll 1$ ergeben hatte. Anders für $\varepsilon = 10$, hier oszillieren die Größen zwischen 60° und 180° nur geringfügig um den Wert $|S_\parallel^{(g)}(\vartheta)|/\varepsilon = |S_\perp^{(g)}|/\varepsilon = \frac{1}{2}$, der sich nach der *geometrischen Optik* infolge der Streuung durch *Reflexion* ergibt [vgl. die folgende Ziffer, Gl. (155.21)].

[1] Vgl. dazu R. Gans u. H. Happl: Ann. Physik **29**, 277 (1909). — R. Gans: Ann. Physik **62**, 331 (1920). — T. Isnardi: Ann. Physik **62**, 573 (1920).

[2] Umgezeichnet nach v. d. Hulst: Light Scattering by Small Particles, S. 163. New York u. London 1957.

Die Schwankungen kommen durch Interferenz der geometrisch-optischen Feldverteilung mit den *Kriechwellen* zustande (vgl. Ziff. 155). Für kleinere Beugungswinkel ϑ ergibt sich eine nach $\vartheta=0$ hin steil ansteigende Beugungskeule, die ziemlich genau dem der Kirchhoffschen Theorie entsprechenden Verteilungsgesetz $\frac{|S_\parallel(\vartheta)|}{\varepsilon}=\frac{|S_\perp(\vartheta)|}{\varepsilon}=\frac{|J_1(\varepsilon\vartheta)|}{\vartheta}$ folgt [vgl. Gl. (155.15′)]. Die Kirchhoffsche Streuverteilung [die für $\vartheta=0$ den Wert $|S_\parallel(0)|/\varepsilon=|S_\perp(0)|/\varepsilon=\varepsilon/2$ liefert] ist in die Figuren mit eingetragen worden. Einen weiteren Überblick über die Strahlungscharakteristik der ideal leitenden Kugel vermitteln die Fig. 135a—c, in denen die Größen $\frac{4}{\varepsilon^2}|S_\parallel(\vartheta)|^2$ und $\frac{4}{\varepsilon^2}|S_\perp(\vartheta)|^2$ für verschiedene Werte des Parameters ε logarithmisch aufgetragen sind[1].

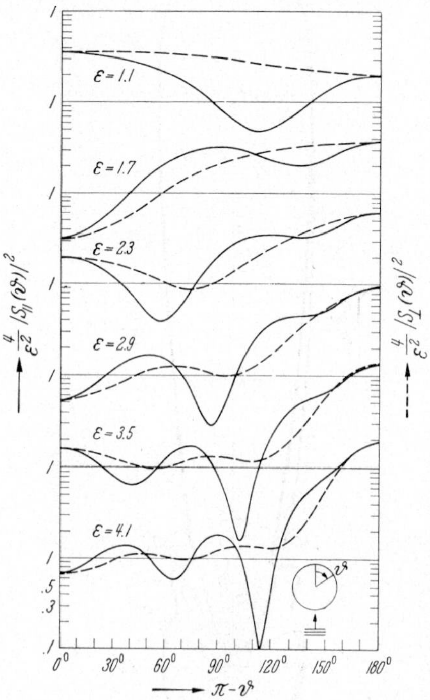

Fig. 135a. Strahlungscharakteristik der ideal leitenden Kugel für verschiedene Werte des Parameters $\varepsilon=ka$ (logarithmischer Maßstab): —— $\frac{4}{\varepsilon^2}|S_\parallel(\vartheta)|^2$; – – – $\frac{4}{\varepsilon^2}|S_\perp(\vartheta)|^2$ (nach Logan u. a.).

Fig. 136 zeigt die Intensität der *Rückstreuung*[2] für $0\leqq\varepsilon\leqq3$. Hier ist die Größe

$$\left.\begin{aligned} 4\pi r^2\frac{I_S(\pi,\varphi)}{\pi a^2 I_0} &= \frac{4}{\varepsilon^2}|S_\parallel(\pi)|^2\\ &= \frac{4}{\varepsilon^2}|S_\perp(\pi)|^2\end{aligned}\right\}\qquad(153.11)$$

aufgetragen, d.h. die Fernfeldintensität (152.28) für die Rückwärtsstreuung multipliziert mit der Kugeloberfläche $4\pi r^2$ und ins Verhältnis gesetzt zu dem auf den geometrischen Querschnitt der Kugel auftreffenden Energiestrom der Primärwelle. Diese Größe hat für die sich im Grenzfall $\varepsilon\to\infty$ einstellende isotrope Streuung den Wert 1 [vgl. Gl. (155.8′)]. Die für endlich ε auftretenden starken Schwankungen um diesen Wert lassen sich qualitativ durch die Fokussierung der von sämtlichen Punkten des Äquators abstrahlenden Kriechwellen (155.13) (die die Rückseite der Kugel umlaufen haben) verstehen. (Für eine quantitative Übereinstimmung sind die Werte von $\varepsilon\leqq3$ noch zu klein.) Die zugehörige *Phase* $\delta(\varepsilon)$ ist aus Fig. 137 zu entnehmen[3] und zwar ist sie hier gemäß der Gleichung

$$-i\,S_\parallel(\pi)=i\,S_\perp(\pi)=|S_\parallel|\,e^{-i\delta(\varepsilon)}$$

definiert. Sie beginnt bereits bei $\varepsilon\approx1{,}5$ um den asymptotischen Wert $\delta=2\varepsilon-\pi$ der geometrischen Optik [vgl. (155.21)] herumzupendeln.

Der *Streukoeffizient* $\sigma=\frac{4}{\varepsilon}\,\mathrm{Re}\,S_\parallel(0)=\frac{4}{\varepsilon}\,\mathrm{Re}\,S_\perp(0)$, der in Fig. 138 als Funktion von ε aufgetragen ist[4], steigt für $\varepsilon<1$ zunächst sehr stark an [für $\varepsilon\ll1$ wie

[1] Aus R.W.P. King u. T.T. Wu: The Scattering and Diffraction of Waves. Cambridge, Mass. 1959.

[2] Nach van de Hulst: l. c. S. 285.

[3] Nach H.C. v. d. Hulst: l. c. S. 286.

[4] Vgl. dazu F.W. Götz: Astronom. Nachr. **255**, 63 (1935). — J.L. Greenstein: Harvard Circ. No. 422 (1938). — J.C. Johnson, R.G. Eldridge u. J.R. Teorell: Sci. Reps. 4, M.I.T. Dept. of Meteorolog. 1954. — H.C. van de Hulst: l. c. S. 162.

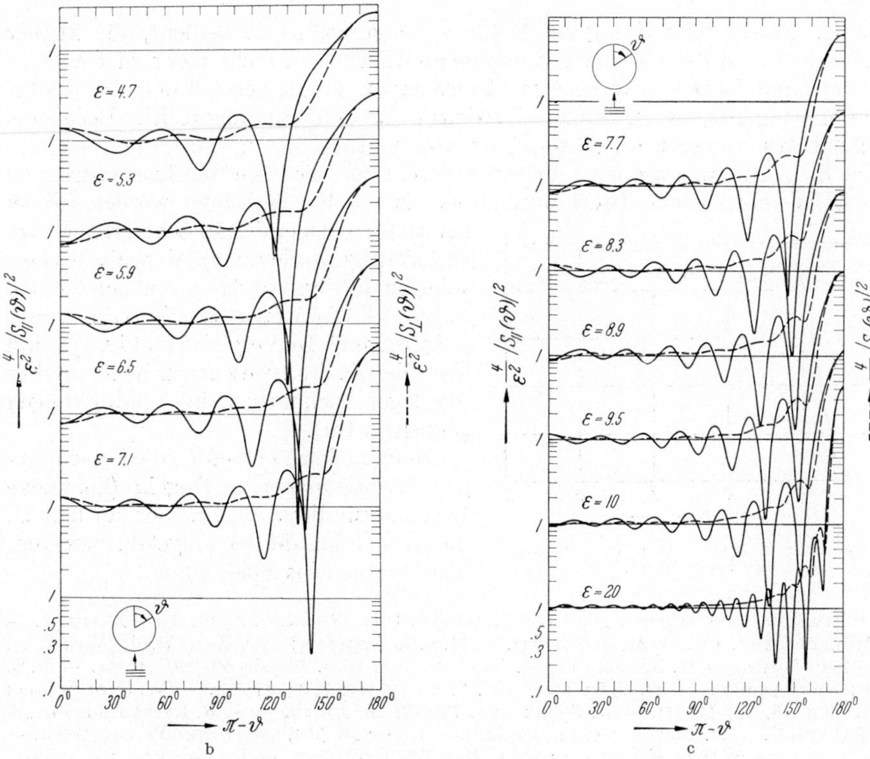

Fig. 135b u. c. Dasselbe wie Fig. 135a für verschiedene Werte von ε.

ε^4, vgl. (153.10)], erreicht bei $\varepsilon=1{,}2$ seinen Maximalwert $\sigma=2{,}28$ und fällt dann unter leichten Schwankungen sehr langsam auf seinen geometrisch-optischen Grenzwert $\sigma=2$ ab. [Für $\varepsilon\gg 1$ gilt die Darstellung (155.22), die keine Schwankungen mehr zeigt.]

Für endliche reelle Brechungsindices N komplizieren sich die Verhältnisse

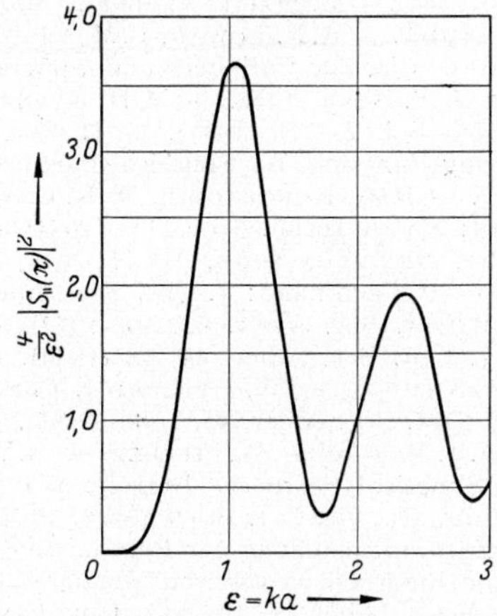

Fig. 136. Amplitude der Rückstreuung an der ideal leitenden Kugel als Funktion von ε.

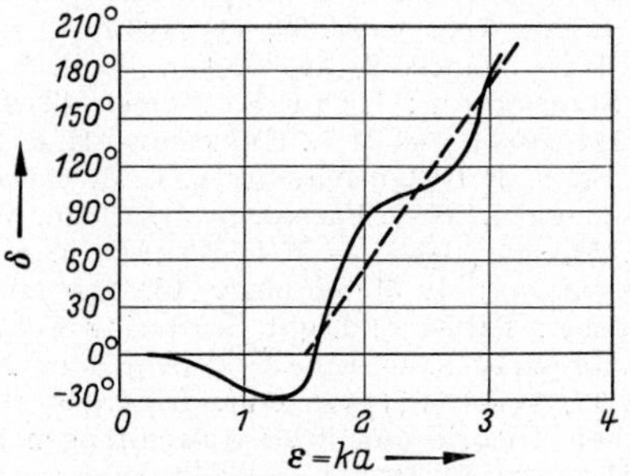

Fig. 137. Phase der Rückstreuung an der ideal leitenden Kugel als Funktion von ε (gestrichelte Linie: geometrisch-optischer Wert).

(infolge des hinzukommenden weiteren Parameters) zum Teil erheblich. Physikalisch beruht dies darauf, daß jetzt neben den Interferenzen der reflektierten mit den gebeugten Strahlen noch solche mit den (zweimal) *gebrochenen* (und innerhalb der Kugel mehrfach reflektierten) Strahlen hinzutreten. (Hier haben wir uns der Sprechweise der geometrischen Beugungstheorie bedient, für kleiner werdende ε sind die einzelnen Komponenten natürlich nicht mehr zu trennen.) Die der numerischen Auswertung und Diskussion der Reihen mit den Mie-Koeffizienten (152.19 e, m) gewidmete Literatur ist sehr umfangreich[1]. Besonders reichhaltiges numerisches Material ist von Gumprecht u. Sliepcevich[2] (maschinell) erarbeitet worden. Unter anderem ist hier die Rückwärtsstreuung für sechs verschiedene Brechungsindices bis $\varepsilon = 400$ berechnet worden (wobei bis zu 421 Glieder der Mieschen Reihen berücksichtigt worden sind). Als typisches Beispiel ist in Fig. 139 der Streukoeffizient σ für $N = 1{,}33$ (Wasser) als Funktion von ε aufgetragen[3]. Im Vergleich zu Fig. 138 sind hier die Maxima wesentlich höher und es überlagern sich noch kleine Schwankungen (Feinstruktur).

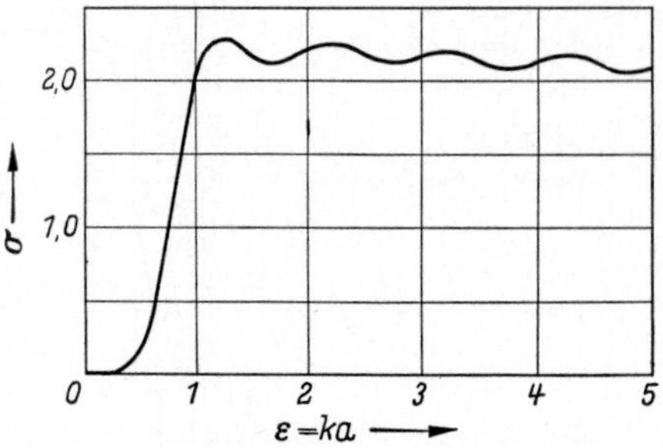

Fig. 138. Streukoeffizient der ideal leitenden Kugel nach van de Hulst.

Noch mühsamer werden die Berechnungen für *absorbierende* Kugeln (komplexe Brechungsindices N), da hier auch noch die Absorption der die Kugel durchsetzenden Strahlen ins Spiel kommt[4].

[1] Erwähnt seien Arbeiten von Lord Rayleigh: Proc. Roc. Soc. Lond. A **84**, 25 (1910). — E. Müller: Ann. Physik **35**, 500 (1911). — M.A. Schirmann: Sitzgsber. Akad. Wiss. Wien **127**, 1559 (1918). — H. Senftleben u. E. Benedict: Ann. Physik **60**, 297 (1919). — B.B. Ray: Proc. Indian. Assoc. Cultivation Sci. **7**, 10 (1921); **8**, 23 (1923). — W. Shoulejkin: Phil. Mag. **48**, 307 (1924). — R. Gans: Ann. Physik **76**, 29 (1925). — R. Feik: Ann. Physik **77**, 673 (1925). — H. Blumer: Z. Physik **32**, 119 (1925); **38**, 304, 920 (1926); **39**, 195 (1926). — J.A. Stratton u. H.G. Houghton: Phys. Rev. **38**, 159 (1939). — T. Casperson: Kolloid-Z. **60**, 151 (1932); **65**, 162 (1933). — E. Schönberg u. B. Jung: Astronom. Nachr. **253**, 261 (1934). — C. Schalén: Medd. Upsala Astron. Obs. **64** (1936). — H. Engelhard u. H. Friess: Kolloid-Z. **81**, 129 (1937). — C. Schalén: Medd. Upsala Astron. Obs. **1**, No. 2 (1939). — G.R. Paranjpe, J.G. Naik u. P.S. Vaidya: Proc. Indian Acad. Sci. A **9**, 333, 352 (1939). — R. Ruedy: Canad. J. Res. A **21**, 79, 99 (1943); A **22**, 53 (1944). — C. Schalén: Medd. Upsala Astron. Ovs. **1**, No. 9 (1945). — H. Holl: Optik **1**, 213 (1946). — A.N. Lowan, P.M. Morse, H. Feshbach u. M. Lax: Scattering and Radiation from Circular Cylinders and Spheres, Tables of Amplitudes and Phase Angles. Washington, U.S. Navy, 1946. — M.D. Barnes, A.S. Kenyon, E.M. Zaiser u. V.K. La Mer: J. Colloid Sci. **2**, 349 (1947). — H. Holl: Optik **4**, 173 (1948). — A.N. Lowan: Tables of Scattering Functions for Spherical Particles, Nat. Bur. Standards (U.S.) Appl. Math. Series 4 (1948). — H.G. Houghton u. W.R. Chalker: J. Opt. Soc. Amer. **39**, 955 (1949). — E.J. Durbin: NACA Techn. Note 2441 (1951). — E. de Bary: Optik **9**, 319 (1952). — R.O. Gumprecht, Neng-lun Sung, Jin H. Chin, u. C.M. Sliepcevich: J. Opt. Soc. Amer. **42**, 226 (1952). — B. Goldberg: J. Opt. Soc. Amer. **43**, 1221 (1953). — M.L. Herker u. H.E. Perlee: J. Opt. Soc. Amer. **43**, 49 (1953). — R.H. Boll, R.O. Gumprecht u. C.M. Sliepcevich: J. Opt. Soc. Amer. **44**, 18 (1954). — W. Heller u. W.J. Pangonis: J. Chem. Phys. **22**, 948 (1954). — W. Heller: J. Chem. Phys. **23**, 342 (1955). — M.L. Kerker u. A.L. Cox: J. Opt. Soc. Amer. **45**, 1080 (1955). — R. Penndorf: J. Meteorology **13**, 219 (1956). — W.J. Pangonis, W. Heller u. A.W. Jacobson: Tables of Light Scattering Functions for Spherical Particles. Detroit: Wayne Univ. Press 1958. — Eine Übersicht über die neuere Literatur bei C.J. Bouwkamp: Progr. Phys. **17**, 35—100 (1954), § 11. Eine sehr eingehende Zusammenstellung der Ergebnisse der Mieschen Theorie und ihrer Anwendungen in der schon mehrfach erwähnten Monographie von H.C. van de Hulst. — Näherungsmethoden für $N \approx 1$ bei R.W. Montroll u. E.W. Hart: J. Appl. Phys. **22**, 376, 1278 (1951). — E.W. Montroll u. J.M. Greenberg: Proc. Symp. Appl. Math. (Amer. Math. Soc.) **5**, 103 (1954). — Eine Übersicht über die Anwendungen in der Kolloid-Chemie bei G. Oster: Chem. Rev. **43**, 319 (1948).

[2] R.O. Gumprecht u. C.M. Sliepcevich: Light Scattering Functions for Spherical Particles: Ann Arbor: Univ. of Michigan Press 1951. — J. Phys. Chem. **57**, 90 (1953).

[3] Nach B. Goldberg: J. Opt. Soc. Amer. **43**, 1221 (1953).

[4] Erwähnt seien hier noch Arbeiten von E. Schönberg u. B. Jung: Mitt. Sternw. Breslau **4**, 61 (1937); F.T. Gucker u. S.H. Cohn: J. Colloid Sci. **8**, 555 (1953).

Die strenge Lösung des Randwertproblems für ein *Ellipsoid* (durch Entwicklung nach *Sphäroidfunktionen*) ist bisher nur für ein *Rotationsellipsoid* gelungen, das von einer ebenen linear polarisierten Welle getroffen wird, die in Richtung der Rotationsachse fortschreitet (allgemeiner für eine um die Rotationsachse symmetrische Dipolverteilung)[1].

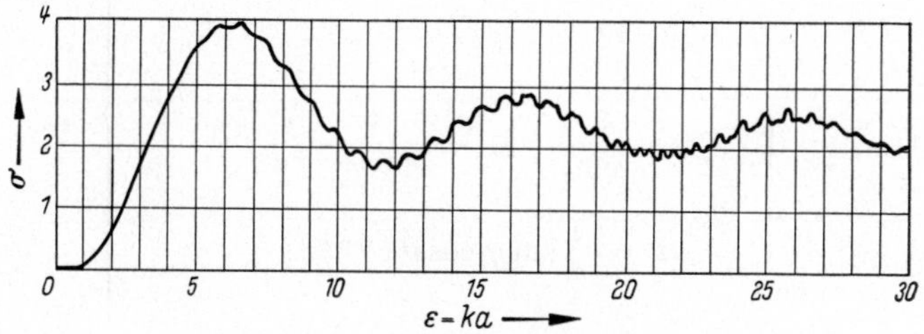

Fig. 139. Streukoeffizient für einen Wassertropfen nach GOLDBERG.

154. Die Integralgleichung für den Flächenstrom. Für die Dichte des auf der Oberfläche der Kugel fließenden Flächenstroms $\mathfrak{J} = [\mathfrak{n}\,\mathfrak{H}]$ erhält man aus (152.3')

$$\varkappa\mathfrak{J} = [\mathfrak{n}\,\nabla]\,\frac{\partial}{\partial r}\,(r\,\Pi_e) - i\,\varepsilon\,[\mathfrak{n}[\mathfrak{n}\,\nabla]]\,\Pi_m \tag{154.1}$$

mit den Komponenten

$$\left.\begin{aligned} \varkappa\mathfrak{J}_\vartheta &= -\,i\,k\,\frac{\partial u_e}{\partial\vartheta} - \frac{1}{\sin\vartheta}\,\frac{\partial u_m}{\partial\varphi} \\ \varkappa\mathfrak{J}_\varphi &= -\,\frac{i\,k}{\sin\vartheta}\,\frac{\partial u_e}{\partial\varphi} + \frac{\partial u_m}{\partial\vartheta}. \end{aligned}\right\} \tag{154.1'}$$

Dabei haben wir von (152.11) und der Randbedingung (152.6) Gebrauch gemacht. Setzt man hier die Lösung (152.17) ein, so ergibt sich

$$\left.\begin{aligned} \varkappa\mathfrak{J}_\vartheta &= \frac{\cos\varphi}{\varepsilon}\sum_{n=1}^{\infty}\frac{2n+1}{n(n+1)}\,e^{\frac{i\pi}{2}n}\left\{\frac{i\,\tau_n(\cos\vartheta)}{[\varepsilon\,\zeta_n^1(\varepsilon)]'} - \frac{\pi_n\,(\cos\vartheta)}{\varepsilon\,\zeta_n^1(\varepsilon)}\right\} \\ \varkappa\mathfrak{J}_\varphi &= -\,\frac{\sin\varphi}{\varepsilon}\sum_{n=1}^{\infty}\frac{2n+1}{n(n+1)}\,e^{\frac{i\pi}{2}n}\left\{\frac{i\,\pi_n\,(\cos\vartheta)}{[\varepsilon\,\zeta_n^1(\varepsilon)]'} - \frac{\tau_n(\cos\vartheta)}{\varepsilon\,\zeta_n^1(\varepsilon)}\right\}. \end{aligned}\right\} \tag{154.1''}$$

Um ein Beispiel für die in Ziff. 77 behandelte allgemeine Theorie zu geben, wollen wir hier noch die Integralgleichung angeben, der die Flächenstromdichte $\mathfrak{J}$ zu genügen hat. Wir schreiben zunächst die Integralgleichung (77.4) in der Form

$$\mathfrak{J}(\hat{\mathfrak{r}}) + \frac{1}{2\pi}\oint[\mathfrak{n}(\hat{\mathfrak{r}})\,[\mathfrak{J}(\hat{\mathfrak{r}}')\,\nabla]]\,\frac{e^{ik|\hat{\mathfrak{r}}-\hat{\mathfrak{r}}'|}}{|\hat{\mathfrak{r}}-\hat{\mathfrak{r}}'|}\,d\hat{\mathfrak{r}}' = 2\,[\mathfrak{n}(\hat{\mathfrak{r}})\,\mathfrak{H}_0(\hat{\mathfrak{r}})]. \tag{154.2}$$

[1] Vgl. dazu: K.F. HERTZFELD: Sitzgsber. Akad. Wiss. Wien **120**, 1587 (1911). — F. MÖGLICH: Ann. Physik **83**, 609 (1927). — A. LEITNER u. R.D. SPENCE: Phys. Rev. **79**, 199 (1950). J. Appl. Phys. **21**, 1001 (1950). — F.V. SCHULTZ: Studies in Radar Cross-Section I. Ann Arbor: Univ. of Michigan Press 1950. — J. MEIXNER: Ann. Phys. **12**, 227 (1953). — L.M. RAUCH: Studies in Radar Cross-Section IX. Ann Arbor: Univ. of Michigan Press 1953. — K.M. SIEGEL, B.H. GERE, I. MARX u. F.B. SLEATOR: Studies in Radar Cross-Section XI. Ann Arbor: Univ. of Michigan Press 1953. — K. M. SIEGEL, F.V. SCHULTZ, B.H. GERE u. F.B. SLEATOR: Trans. Inst. Radio Engrs. AP-**4**, 266 (1956). — Für das skalare Problem s. auch R.D. SPENCE u. S. GRANGER: J. Acoust. Soc. Amer. **23**, 701 (1951). — Asymptotische Darstellungen für den hochfrequenten Grenzfall (Watson-Transformation) bei R.K. RITT u. N.D. KAZARINOFF: Studies in Radar Cross-Section XXX. Ann Arbor: Univ. of Michigan Press 1958. — B. LEVY u. J.B. KELLER: N.Y. Univ. Res. Rep. No. EM-130 (1959). — N.D. KAZARINOFF u. R.K. RITT: Ann. of Phys. **6**, 277 (1959).

Zerlegen wir diese Vektorgleichung in ihre Komponenten bezüglich des Dreibeins $\mathfrak{e}_r\,\mathfrak{e}_\vartheta\,\mathfrak{e}_\varphi$ im Punkte $\hat{\mathfrak{r}}$ (vgl. Fig. 140), so ergibt sich mit (152.1) und (148.4)

$$\left.\begin{aligned}
&\mathfrak{J}_\vartheta(\hat{\mathfrak{r}}) + \frac{1}{4\pi}\oint\left\{\mathfrak{J}_r(\hat{\mathfrak{r}}')\frac{\partial}{a\,\partial\vartheta} - \mathfrak{J}_\vartheta(\hat{\mathfrak{r}}')\frac{\partial}{2\,\partial a}\right\}\frac{e^{2i\varepsilon\sin\frac{|\Theta|}{2}}}{a\sin\frac{|\Theta|}{2}}\,d\hat{\mathfrak{r}}' \\
&\qquad = -\frac{2}{\varkappa}\cos\varphi\, e^{i\varepsilon\cos\vartheta} \\
&\mathfrak{J}_\varphi(\hat{\mathfrak{r}}) - \frac{1}{4\pi}\oint\left\{\mathfrak{J}_\varphi(\hat{\mathfrak{r}}')\frac{\partial}{2\,\partial a} - \mathfrak{J}_r(\hat{\mathfrak{r}}')\frac{1}{a\sin\vartheta}\frac{\partial}{\partial\varphi}\right\}\cdot \\
&\qquad \cdot\frac{e^{2i\varepsilon\sin\frac{|\Theta|}{2}}}{a\sin\frac{|\Theta|}{2}}\,d\hat{\mathfrak{r}}' = \frac{2}{\varkappa}\sin\varphi\cos\vartheta\, e^{i\varepsilon\cos\vartheta}.
\end{aligned}\right\} \qquad (154.2')$$

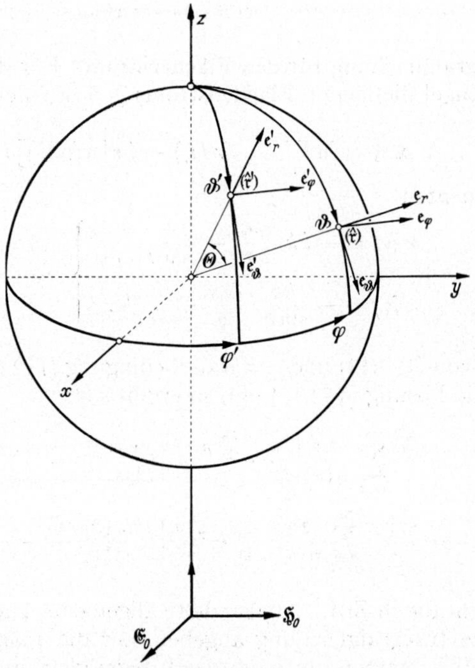

Fig. 140. Zur Umrechnung der Vektor-Komponenten bezüglich des Dreibeins $\mathfrak{e}_r$, $\mathfrak{e}_\vartheta$, $\mathfrak{e}_\varphi$ in solche bezüglich $\mathfrak{e}'_r$, $\mathfrak{e}'_\vartheta$, $\mathfrak{e}'_\varphi$.

Rechnen wir hier die Komponenten von $\mathfrak{J}(\hat{\mathfrak{r}}')$ bezüglich des Dreibeins $\mathfrak{e}_r\,\mathfrak{e}_\vartheta\,\mathfrak{e}_\varphi$ noch in diejenigen bezüglich des Dreibeins $\mathfrak{e}'_r\,\mathfrak{e}'_\varphi\,\mathfrak{e}'_\vartheta$ im Punkte $\hat{\mathfrak{r}}'$ um (vgl. Fig. 140)[1], so erhalten wir schließlich für die Komponenten

$$\mathfrak{J}_\vartheta(\hat{\mathfrak{r}}) = J_1(\vartheta,\varphi), \qquad \mathfrak{J}_\varphi(\hat{\mathfrak{r}}) = J_2(\vartheta,\varphi)$$

---

[1] Für die beiden Dreibeine gelten die Transformationsformeln

$$\begin{aligned}
\mathfrak{e}_r &= (\cos\vartheta\cos\vartheta' + \sin\vartheta\sin\vartheta'\cos(\varphi-\varphi'))\,\mathfrak{e}'_r \\
&\quad + (\sin\vartheta\cos\vartheta'\cos(\varphi-\varphi') - \cos\vartheta\sin\vartheta')\,\mathfrak{e}'_\vartheta + \sin\vartheta\sin(\varphi-\varphi')\,\mathfrak{e}'_\varphi, \\
\mathfrak{e}_\vartheta &= (\cos\vartheta\sin\vartheta'\cos(\varphi-\varphi') - \sin\vartheta\cos\vartheta')\,\mathfrak{e}'_r \\
&\quad + (\cos\vartheta\cos\vartheta'\cos(\varphi-\varphi') + \sin\vartheta\sin\vartheta')\,\mathfrak{e}'_\vartheta + \cos\vartheta\sin(\varphi-\varphi')\,\mathfrak{e}'_\varphi, \\
\mathfrak{e}_\varphi &= -\sin\vartheta'\sin(\varphi-\varphi')\,\mathfrak{e}'_r - \cos\vartheta'\sin(\varphi-\varphi')\,\mathfrak{e}'_\vartheta + \cos(\varphi-\varphi)'\,\mathfrak{e}'_\varphi.
\end{aligned}$$

folgendes System von Integralgleichungen

$$\left.\begin{aligned}
&J_1(\vartheta,\varphi)-\frac{a}{4\pi}\int_0^{2\pi}d\varphi'\int_0^{\pi}d\vartheta'\sin\vartheta'\Big\{J_1(\vartheta',\varphi')\Big(\sin(\varphi-\varphi')\frac{\partial}{\partial\varphi'}\\
&\quad+\cos(\varphi-\varphi')\frac{a}{2}\frac{\partial}{\partial a}\Big)+J_2(\vartheta',\varphi')\sin(\varphi-\varphi')\Big(\cos\vartheta'\frac{a}{2}\frac{\partial}{\partial a}-\sin\vartheta'\frac{\partial}{\partial\vartheta'}\Big)\Big\}\cdot\\
&\quad\cdot\frac{e^{2i\varepsilon\sin\frac{|\Theta|}{2}}}{a\sin\frac{|\Theta|}{2}}=-\frac{2}{\varkappa}\cos\varphi\, e^{i\varepsilon\cos\vartheta}\\
&\text{und}\\
&J_2(\vartheta',\varphi')-\frac{a}{4\pi}\int_0^{2\pi}d\varphi'\int_0^{\pi}d\vartheta'\sin\vartheta'\Big\{J_1(\vartheta',\varphi')\sin(\varphi-\varphi')\Big(\cos\vartheta'\frac{a}{2}\frac{\partial}{\partial a}\\
&\quad-\sin\vartheta'\frac{\partial}{\partial\vartheta'}\Big)-J_2(\vartheta',\varphi')\Big(\sin(\varphi-\varphi')\frac{\partial}{\partial\varphi'}+\cos(\varphi-\varphi')\frac{a}{2}\frac{\partial}{\partial a}\Big)\Big\}\cdot\\
&\quad\cdot\frac{e^{2i\varepsilon\sin\frac{|\Theta|}{2}}}{a\sin\frac{|\Theta|}{2}}=\frac{2}{\varkappa}\sin\varphi\cos\vartheta\, e^{i\varepsilon\cos\vartheta}.
\end{aligned}\right\}\quad(154.2'')$$

Die direkte Lösung dieser Gleichungen muß selbstverständlich wieder auf die Gln. (154.1″) führen, die wir oben mit Hilfe der Debyeschen Potentiale gefunden haben.

Wir wollen den Lösungsweg andeuten: Die Integralgleichungen (154.2″) sind von der Form

$$\left.\begin{aligned}
J_1-\int_0^{2\pi}d\varphi'\int_0^{\pi}d\vartheta'\sin\vartheta'(J_1K_1+J_2K_2)&=-\frac{2}{\varkappa}\cos\varphi\, e^{i\varepsilon\cos\vartheta}\\
J_2-\int_0^{2\pi}d\varphi'\int_0^{\pi}d\vartheta'\sin\vartheta'(J_1K_2-J_2K_1)&=\frac{2}{\varkappa}\sin\varphi\cos\vartheta\, e^{i\varepsilon\cos\vartheta}
\end{aligned}\right\}\quad(154.3)$$

mit den Kernen

$$\left.\begin{aligned}
K_1(\vartheta,\varphi|\vartheta',\varphi')&=\frac{a}{4\pi}\Big\{\sin(\varphi-\varphi')\frac{\partial}{\partial\varphi'}+\cos(\varphi-\varphi')\frac{a}{2}\frac{\partial}{\partial a}\Big\}\frac{e^{2i\varepsilon\sin\frac{|\Theta|}{2}}}{a\sin\frac{|\Theta|}{2}}\\
K_2(\vartheta,\varphi|\vartheta',\varphi')&=\frac{a}{4\pi}\sin(\varphi-\varphi')\Big\{\cos\vartheta'\frac{a}{2}\frac{\partial}{\partial a}-\sin\vartheta'\frac{\partial}{\partial\vartheta'}\Big\}\frac{e^{2i\varepsilon\sin\frac{|\Theta|}{2}}}{a\sin\frac{|\Theta|}{2}}.
\end{aligned}\right\}\quad(154.4)$$

Auf Grund der Identitäten

$$\left.\begin{aligned}
\frac{\partial}{\partial\vartheta'}(\sin\vartheta' K_1)+\frac{\partial K_2}{\partial\varphi'}&=-\frac{a^2}{8\pi}\sin\vartheta'\frac{\partial}{\partial\vartheta}\Big(\frac{\partial}{\partial a}+\frac{2}{a}\Big)\frac{e^{2i\varepsilon\sin\frac{|\Theta|}{2}}}{a\sin\frac{|\Theta|}{2}}\\
\frac{\partial K_1}{\partial\varphi'}-\frac{\partial}{\partial\vartheta'}(\sin\vartheta' K_2)&=\frac{a^2}{8\pi}\frac{\sin\vartheta'}{\sin\vartheta}\frac{\partial}{\partial\varphi}\Big(\frac{\partial}{\partial a}+\frac{2}{a}\Big)\frac{e^{2i\varepsilon\sin\frac{|\Theta|}{2}}}{a\sin\frac{|\Theta|}{2}}
\end{aligned}\right\}\quad(154.5)$$

liegt es nahe, die Lösung von (154.3) in der Gestalt (154.1′) anzusetzen. Trägt man nämlich (154.1′) in (154.3) ein, so lassen sich die auf u_e und u_m wirkenden

Differentiationen durch partielle Integration auf die Kerne K_1 und K_2 abwälzen, wobei gerade die Kombinationen (154.5) auftreten. Das Ergebnis läßt sich in folgender Form schreiben

$$\left.\begin{aligned} & i k \frac{\partial}{\partial\vartheta}\left\{u_e - \frac{a^2}{8\pi}\int_0^{2\pi} d\varphi' \int_0^{\pi} d\vartheta' \sin\vartheta'\, u_e \left(\frac{\partial}{\partial a} + \frac{2}{a}\right) \frac{\mathrm{e}^{2i\varepsilon\sin\frac{|\Theta|}{2}}}{a\sin\frac{|\Theta|}{2}}\right\} \\ & + \frac{1}{\sin\vartheta}\frac{\partial}{\partial\varphi}\left\{u_m + \frac{a^2}{8\pi}\int_0^{2\pi} d\varphi' \int_0^{\pi} d\vartheta' \sin\vartheta'\, u_m \left(\frac{\partial}{\partial a} + \frac{2}{a}\right) \frac{\mathrm{e}^{2i\varepsilon\sin\frac{|\Theta|}{2}}}{a\sin\frac{|\Theta|}{2}}\right\} \\ & = 2\cos\varphi\, \mathrm{e}^{i\varepsilon\cos\vartheta} \end{aligned}\right\} \tag{154.6a}$$

und

$$\left.\begin{aligned} & \frac{i k}{\sin\vartheta} \frac{\partial}{\partial\varphi}\left\{u_e - \frac{a^2}{8\pi}\int_0^{2\pi} d\varphi' \int_0^{\pi} d\vartheta' \sin\vartheta'\, u_e \left(\frac{\partial}{\partial a} + \frac{2}{a}\right) \frac{\mathrm{e}^{2i\varepsilon\sin\frac{|\Theta|}{2}}}{a\sin\frac{|\Theta|}{2}}\right\} \\ & - \frac{\partial}{\partial\vartheta}\left\{u_m + \frac{a^2}{8\pi}\int_0^{2\pi} d\varphi' \int_0^{\pi} d\vartheta' \sin\vartheta'\, u_m \left(\frac{\partial}{\partial a} + \frac{2}{a}\right) \frac{\mathrm{e}^{2i\varepsilon\sin\frac{|\Theta|}{2}}}{a\sin\frac{|\Theta|}{2}}\right\} \\ & = -2\sin\varphi\cos\vartheta\, \mathrm{e}^{i\varepsilon\cos\vartheta}. \end{aligned}\right\} \tag{154.6b}$$

Diese Gleichungen haben wir zunächst als ein System von Differentialgleichungen für die beiden in den geschweiften Klammern stehenden Größen aufzufassen. Löst man sie (durch Entwicklung nach Kugelfunktionen) nach diesen beiden Größen auf, so ergeben sich im wesentlichen die Integralgleichungen (152.12*e*, *m*). [Für u_m erhält man zunächst eine von (152.12*m*) bezüglich des Kernes und der Inhomogenität etwas abweichende Integralgleichung, die jedoch mit (152.12*m*) äquivalent ist.]

Entsprechende simultane Integralgleichungen für den Flächenstrom lassen sich auch für allgemeinere Körperformen aufstellen, bei denen *keine* Potentiale so eingeführt werden können, daß diese Gleichungen in zwei einfachere unabhängige Integralgleichungen zerfallen (wie oben für u_e und u_m). Man kann dann versuchen, die simultanen Gleichungen näherungsweise zu lösen. So haben Franz und Deppermann[1] die Integralgleichungen (154.2″) für $\varepsilon \gg 1$ asymptotisch gelöst; das Ergebnis stimmt mit demjenigen überein, das sich mit Hilfe der asymptotisch ausgewerteten Watson-Transformation der Reihen (154.1″) ergibt (vgl. Ziff. 155).

In der Tat vereinfachen sich die Integralgleichungen (154.3) für $\varepsilon \gg 1$ erheblich. Machen wir nämlich für die Komponenten des Flächenstroms den Ansatz [vgl. (150.19) und (154.1″)]

$$\left.\begin{aligned} J_1(\vartheta, \varphi) &= \frac{\cos\varphi}{\sqrt{\sin\vartheta}}\, \hat{J}_1(\vartheta)\, \mathrm{e}^{i\varepsilon\vartheta} \\ J_2(\vartheta, \varphi) &= \frac{\sin\varphi}{\sqrt{\sin\vartheta}}\, \hat{J}_2(\vartheta)\, \mathrm{e}^{i\varepsilon\vartheta}, \end{aligned}\right\} \tag{154.7}$$

so ergibt sich durch asymptotische Auswertung der φ'-Integration in (154.3) nach dem Prinzip der stationären Phase [die Phase wird für $\varphi' = \varphi$ stationär, vgl.

[1] K. Deppermann u. W. Franz: Ann. Physik **14**, 253 (1954).

(150.18)]:

$$\left.\begin{aligned} \int_0^{2\pi} d\varphi' K_1 \cdot \begin{Bmatrix}\cos\varphi'\\ \sin\varphi'\end{Bmatrix} &\to \sqrt{\frac{\varepsilon}{4\pi}}\, e^{\frac{3\pi i}{4}} \sqrt{\sin\frac{|\vartheta-\vartheta'|}{2}} \cdot \frac{e^{2i\varepsilon\sin\frac{|\vartheta-\vartheta'|}{2}}}{\sqrt{\sin\vartheta\sin\vartheta'}} \cdot \begin{Bmatrix}\cos\varphi\\ \sin\varphi\end{Bmatrix}\\ \int_0^{2\pi} d\varphi' K_2\cdot\begin{Bmatrix}\cos\varphi'\\ \sin\varphi'\end{Bmatrix} &\to 0.\end{aligned}\right\}\qquad(154.8)$$

(Dabei haben wir uns auf das Hauptglied der asymptotischen Entwicklung für $\varepsilon \gg 1$ beschränkt, zu dem nur der zweite Term von K_1 einen Beitrag liefert.)

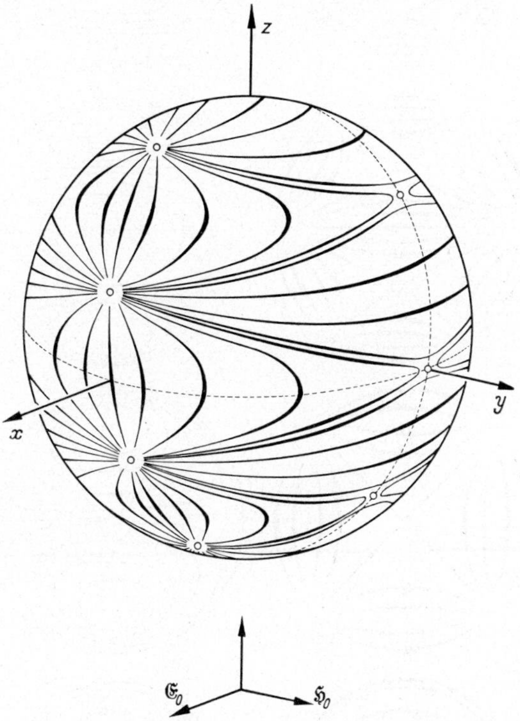

Fig. 141. Stromverteilung auf der ideal leitenden Kugel für die vierte elektrische Partialwelle.

Trägt man (154.7, 8) in die für die *Kriechströme* maßgeblichen homogenen Integralgleichungen (154.3) ein, so folgt (oberes Vorzeichen für $\hat{J}_1$, unteres für $\hat{J}_2$):

$$\hat{J}(\vartheta) \mp \sqrt{\frac{\varepsilon}{4\pi}}\, e^{\frac{3\pi i}{4}} \int \hat{J}(\vartheta') \sqrt{\sin\frac{|\vartheta-\vartheta'|}{2}} \cdot e^{i\varepsilon\left(\vartheta'-\vartheta+2\sin\frac{|\vartheta-\vartheta'|}{2}\right)} d\vartheta' = 0. \qquad (154.9)$$

Dies stimmt aber mit der entsprechenden Gl. (150.20) für das skalare Problem überein [vgl. dazu auch Gl. (155.11) der folgenden Ziff. 155].

Um ein anschauliches Bild der Stromverteilungen zu erhalten, die zur Ausstrahlung der einzelnen Partialwellen führen, zeigt zunächst Fig. 141 die Stromlinien der Flächenströme $\mathfrak{J}$ auf der Kugeloberfläche für die vierte elektrische Partialwelle. Die stromlosen Punkte, auf die die Stromlinien hin konvergieren, liegen auf dem Kreis $\varphi = 0, \pi$ und sind durch die Nullstellen von $\tau_4(\cos\vartheta)$ gegeben.

Die stromlosen Punkte, die von den Stromlinien gemieden werden, liegen dagegen auf dem Kreis $\varphi = \pm \frac{\pi}{2}$, für sie ist $\pi_4(\cos\vartheta) = 0$. Wegen $\mathfrak{J} = [\mathfrak{n}\,\mathfrak{H}]$ sind die Stromlinien die Orthogonaltrajektorien der magnetischen Kraftlinien auf der Kugel.

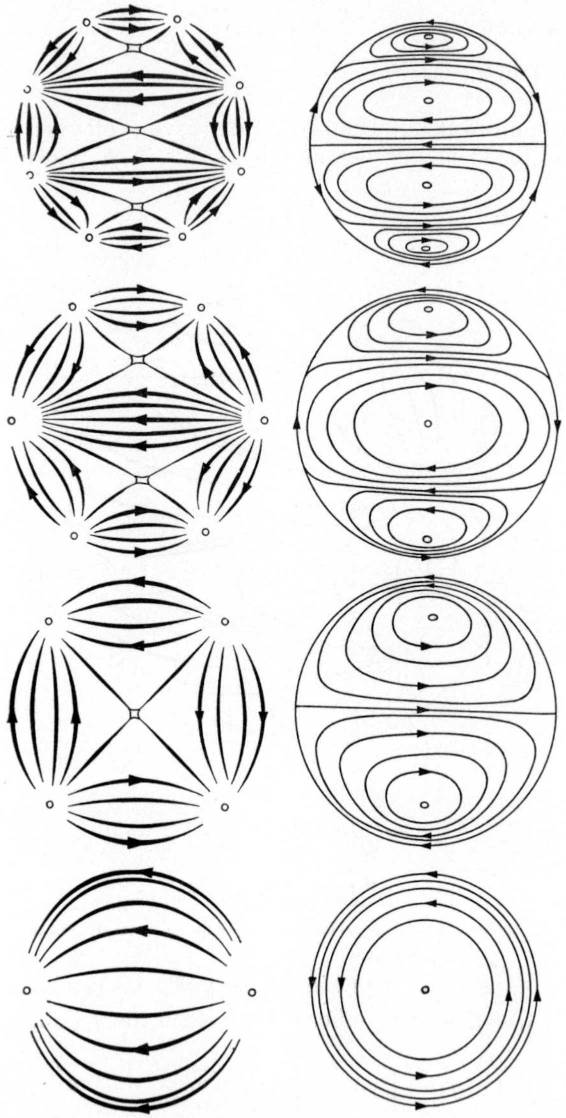

Fig. 142. Projektionen der elektrischen und magnetischen Kraftlinien des Fernfeldes bei der Beugung an der ideal leitenden Kugel für die ersten vier elektrischen Partialwellen (links $\mathfrak{E}$-Linien, rechts $\mathfrak{H}$-Linien) in zwei aufeinander senkrechten Ebenen (nach Mie).

In Fig. 142 sind rechts die Projektionen dieser magnetischen Kraftlinien in die yz-Ebene für die ersten vier elektrischen Partialwellen eingezeichnet, links die Projektionen der zugehörigen Stromlinien in die xz-Ebene[1]. Die magnetischen

[1] Nach G. Mie: Ann. Physik **25**, 377 (1908).

Kraftlinien zeigen auf allen konzentrischen Kugeln $r=\text{const}$ die gleiche Verteilung. Die elektrischen Kraftlinien zeigen im *Fernfeld*, d.h. auf der Kugel $r\to\infty$, dieselbe Verteilung wie die Stromlinien auf der Kugel $r=a$ (jedoch die

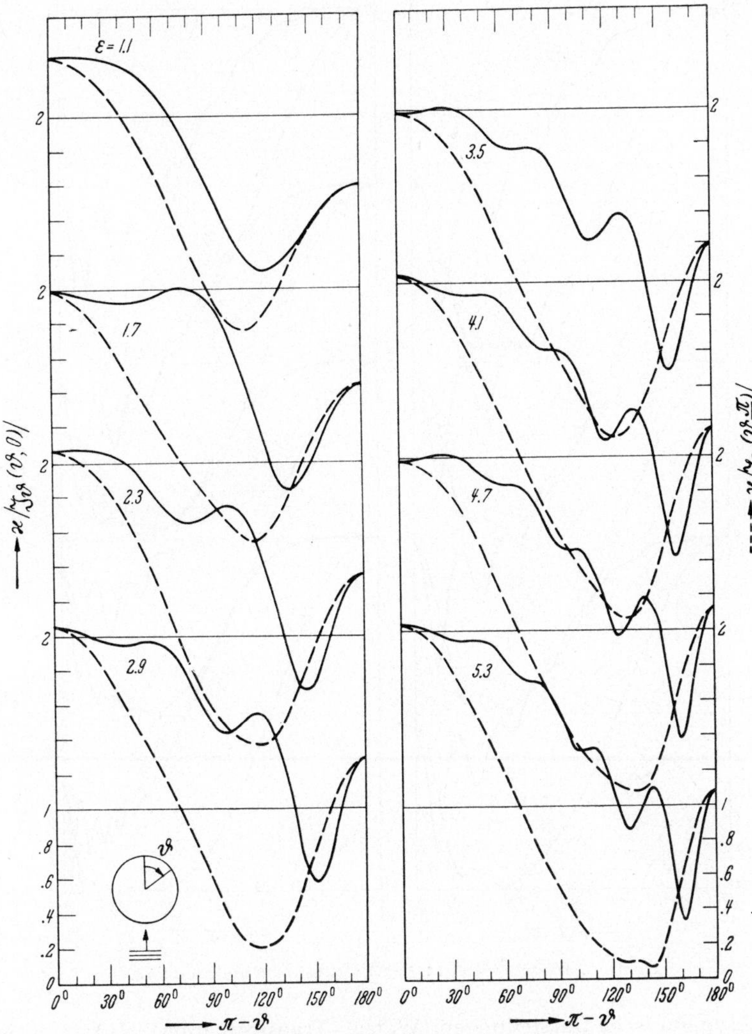

Fig. 143a. Stromverteilung auf der ideal leitenden Kugel für verschiedene Werte von $\varepsilon=ka$ als Funktion von ϑ: — $\varkappa\,|\mathfrak{J}_\vartheta(\vartheta,0)|$; – – – $\varkappa\,|\mathfrak{J}_\varphi(\vartheta,\pi/2)|$ (nach LOGAN u. a.).

umgekehrte Richtung), da sie dort auf den magnetischen Kraftlinien senkrecht stehen.

In Fig. 143a, b sind die Amplituden der in der Ebene $\varphi=0$ bzw. $\varphi=\pi/2$ rein meridionalen bzw. rein azimutalen Flächenströme als Funktion von ϑ für verschiedene Werte von ε aufgetragen[1]. Sie sind durch numerische Auswertung der Reihen (154.1″) gewonnen worden; der Poissonsche Fleck ist deutlich ausgeprägt.

[1] Die Fig. 143a, b sind dem Buch von R.W.P. KING u. T.T. WU: The Scattering and Diffraction of Waves. Cambridge, Mass. 1959, entnommen.

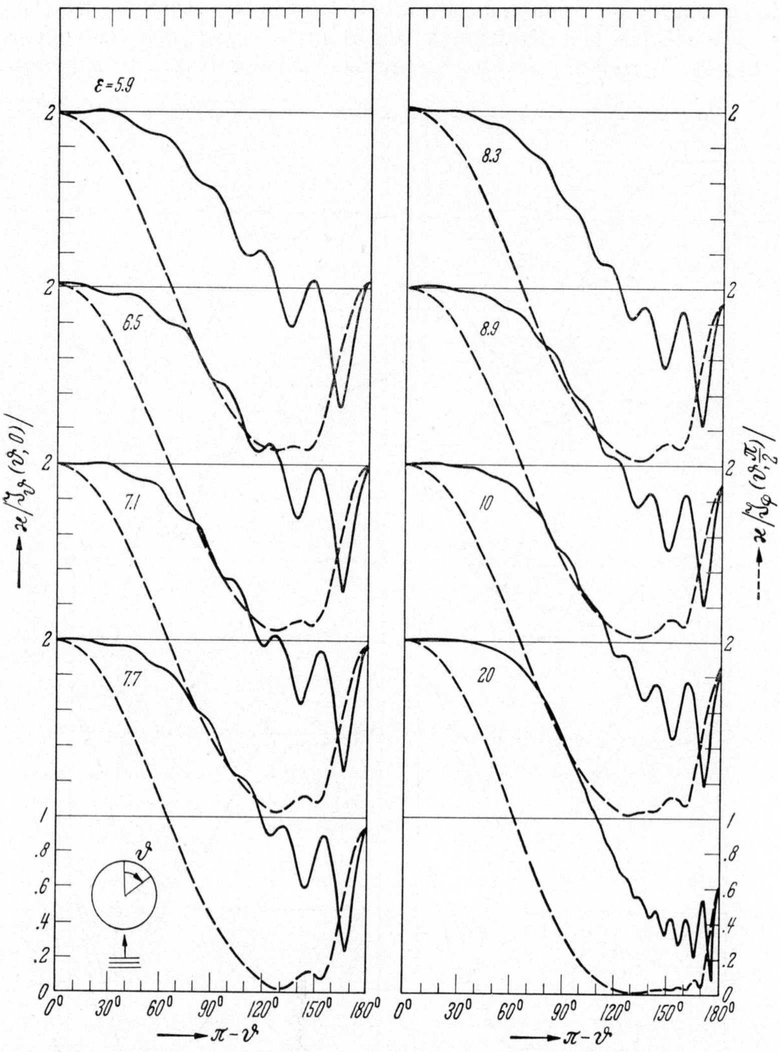

Fig. 143b. Dasselbe wie Fig. 143a für verschidene Werte von $\varepsilon = k a$.

155. Asymptotische Darstellungen (Watson-Transformation). Zur analytischen Erfassung des Grenzfalles $\varepsilon \gg 1$ sind im wesentlichen zwei Methoden entwickelt worden. Die erste verwendet für die Koeffizienten der Mieschen Reihen die asymptotischen Darstellungen (153.4) (sowie entsprechende Darstellungen für die Kugelfunktionen) und ersetzt die Summation durch eine Integration, die nach dem Prinzip der stationären Phase ausgewertet wird[1]. Auf diese Weise lassen sich die Ergebnisse der geometrischen Optik und der Fresnel-Kirchhoff-

[1] Vgl. dazu P. Debye: Ann. Physik **30**, 59 (1909). — R. Mecke: Ann. Physik **62**, 623 (1920). — G. Jobst: Ann. Physik **76**, 863 (1925); **78**, 158 (1925). — H. Blumer: Z. Physik **38**, 920 (1926). — H.C. van de Hulst: Rech. Astron. Obs. Utrecht **11**, Pt. 1 (1946). — T. Ljunggrén: Ark. Mat. Astronom. Fys. A **36**, No. 14 (1948). — Ark. Fys. **1**, No. 1 (1949). Siehe auch H.C. van de Hulst: Light Scattering by Small Particles, Kap. 12.

schen Beugungstheorie reproduzieren (Korrekturen dazu sind im allgemeinen nicht berechnet worden, da der bei der Methode hereinkommende Fehler schwer zu übersehen ist).

Die zweite (wirkungsvollere) Methode ist die schon mehrfach benutzte Watson-Transformation. Sie wurde ursprünglich für das Problem der Ausbreitung von Funksignalen längs der kugelförmigen Erde entwickelt[1]. Das dort vorliegende mathematische Problem entspricht demjenigen von Mie weitgehend. Der einzige Unterschied besteht darin, daß sich beim Radioproblem Feldquelle und Aufpunkt in unmittelbarer Nähe der Kugeloberfläche befinden. (Beschränkt man sich auf einen radial schwingenden elektrischen Dipol, so kommt man bei der Felddarstellung mit dem Debyeschen Potential Π_e alleine aus[2].)

Bei der Watson-Transformation werden die Mieschen Reihen durch Hinzufügung eines Faktors mit ganzzahligen Polen und konstanten Residuen in *Strenge* in ein Umlaufintegral in der komplexen Ebene des Index umgewandelt[3]. Dieses Integral läßt sich nach Franz für Aufpunkte im geometrisch beleuchteten Gebiet wieder in zwei Teile zerlegen, von denen der eine durch Residuenbildung und der andere asymptotisch nach der Sattelpunktmethode ausgewertet werden kann[3]. Das letztere Integral liefert genau die *geometrisch-optische* Feldverteilung, während das erstere die (bei mäßig großen ε merklich in Erscheinung tretenden) *Kriechwellen* ergibt. Wir wollen die Watson-Transformation hier für die in Gl. (152.18′) definierten Größen $V(r, \vartheta)$ kurz durchführen. Aus diesen Größen können die elektromagnetischen Feldvektoren durch Differentiation gewonnen werden; bei der Auswertung wollen wir uns auf das (transversale) Fernfeld beschränken. Schreiben wir Gl. (152.18′) in der Form

$$V(r, \vartheta) = -\frac{\partial}{\partial\vartheta}\hat{V}(r, \vartheta), \tag{155.1}$$

so können wir $\hat{V}(r, \vartheta)$ entsprechend Gl. (150.1) nach dem Cauchyschen Satz durch das Integral

$$\left.\begin{aligned}\hat{V}(r, \vartheta) = \frac{i}{2}\oint \frac{2\mu+1}{\mu(\mu+1)}\,\frac{P_\mu(-\cos\vartheta)}{\sin\pi\mu}\,\frac{e^{\frac{i\pi}{2}\mu}}{\Omega\,\varepsilon\,\zeta_\mu^1(\varepsilon)}\,\cdot&\\ \cdot\,\{\Omega\,\varepsilon\,\zeta_\mu^1(\varepsilon)\cdot\psi_\mu(k\,r) - \Omega\,\varepsilon\,\psi_\mu(\varepsilon)\cdot\zeta_\mu^1(k\,r)\}\,d\mu&\end{aligned}\right\} \tag{155.2}$$

darstellen. Als Integrationsweg kann wieder jeder der in Fig. 123 eingezeichneten Wege benutzt werden. [Der in der Summe für $\hat{V}(r, \vartheta)$ zunächst fehlende Term mit $n=0$ kann hinzugefügt werden, da er bei der Differentiation (155.1) keinen

---

[1] G.N. Watson: Proc. Roy. Soc. Lond. A **95**, 83 (1918). — O. Laporte: Ann. Physik **70**, 595 (1923). — B. van der Pol u. H. Bremmer: Phil. Mag. **24**, 141, 825 (1937); **25**, 817 (1938); **27**, 261 (1939). — Hochfrequenztechn. **51**, 181 (1938). Vgl. auch T.L. Eckersley u. G. Millington: Phil. Trans. Roy. Soc. Lond. A **237**, 273 (1938). — Phil. Mag. **27**, 517 (1939). — V.A. Fock: J. Phys. USSR. **9**, 255 (1945). — Ausführliche Darstellungen bei H. Bremmer: Terrestrial Radio Waves. New York u. Amsterdam 1949. — Ch. R. Burrows u. St. S. Attwood: Radio Wave Propagation. New York 1949. — H. Zuhrt: Elektromagnetische Strahlungsfelder. Berlin-Göttingen-Heidelberg: Springer 1953.

[2] Die entsprechende Reihendarstellung der Lösung findet sich wohl zuerst bei H. Poincaré: Palermo Rendiconti **29**, 169 (1910).

[3] F.P. White: Proc. Roy. Soc. Lond. A **100**, 505 (1922). — W. Franz: Z. Naturforsch. **9**a, 705 (1954). — H. Weil, M.L. Barasch u. T.A. Kaplan: Studies in Radar Cross Section X. Ann Arbor: Univ. of Michigan Press 1956. — L.B. Felsen: Trans. Inst. Radio Engrs. AP-**5**, 1 (1957). — W. Franz: Theorie der Beugung elektromagnetischer Wellen. Berlin-Göttingen-Heidelberg: Springer 1957. — P. Beckmann: Z. Naturforsch. **12**a, 960 (1957). Man vgl. auch H. Bucerius: Optik **1**, 188 (1946); dort wird eine Auswertung der Mieschen Reihen im Sinne der Eulerschen Summenformel vorgenommen, die zu äquivalenten Korrekturen der geometrischen Optik führt.

Beitrag liefert.] Das Integral läßt sich wieder durch Residuenbildung an denjenigen Polen μ_s auswerten, die durch die Wurzeln der Gleichung

$$\Omega\, \varepsilon\, \zeta^1_{\mu_s}(\varepsilon) = 0 \tag{155.3}$$

gegeben sind. Diese Gleichung kann für die elektrischen Partialwellen für $\varepsilon \gg 1$ durch $\Omega_e \varepsilon \zeta^1_\mu(\varepsilon) \to \varepsilon \zeta^{1\prime}_\mu(\varepsilon) = 0$ ersetzt werden. Zusammen mit $\Omega_m \varepsilon \zeta^1_\mu(\varepsilon) = \varepsilon \zeta^1_\mu(\varepsilon) = 0$ stimmt sie also mit (150.3) überein. Damit ergibt sich wie in Ziff. 150

$$\mu_s + \frac{1}{2} = \nu_s = \varepsilon + \left(\frac{\varepsilon}{6}\right)^{\frac{1}{3}} q_s\, e^{\frac{i\pi}{3}} \tag{155.4}$$

mit den durch (141.2) definierten q_s. (Der Index $\parallel$ entspricht hier dem magnetischen Fall, $\perp$ dem elektrischen.) Genauere Werte kann man nach Franz den Gleichungen

$$\left.\begin{aligned} \mu_s^{(e)} + \frac{1}{2} &= \nu_s^{(e)} = \varepsilon + \left(\frac{\varepsilon}{6}\right)^{\frac{1}{3}} q_\perp^{(s)}\, e^{\frac{i\pi}{3}} + \left(\frac{6}{\varepsilon}\right)^{\frac{1}{3}} \left(\frac{3}{20 q_\perp^{(s)}} - \frac{q_\perp^{(s)2}}{180}\right) e^{-\frac{i\pi}{3}} \\ \mu_s^{(m)} + \frac{1}{2} &= \nu_s^{(m)} = \varepsilon + \left(\frac{\varepsilon}{6}\right)^{\frac{1}{3}} q_\parallel^{(s)}\, e^{\frac{i\pi}{3}} - \left(\frac{6}{\varepsilon}\right)^{\frac{1}{3}} \frac{q_\parallel^{(s)2}}{180}\, e^{-\frac{i\pi}{3}} \end{aligned}\right\} \tag{155.4'}$$

entnehmen. Die weitere Auswertung läuft derjenigen in Ziff. 150 vollkommen parallel; die sich ergebende Residuensumme konvergiert sehr schnell, solange der Aufpunkt im geometrischen Schatten der Kugel liegt. Für Aufpunkte im Lichtgebiet ist wieder die Aufspaltung (150.11) zu verwenden. Wir bekommen also zunächst die noch streng gültigen Watsonschen Reihen

im Schattengebiet

$$\hat{V}(r,\vartheta) = \frac{\pi}{2} \sum_s \frac{2\mu_s + 1}{\mu_s(\mu_s+1)} \frac{e^{\frac{i\pi}{2}\mu_s}}{\sin \pi \mu_s} \left\{\frac{\Omega\, \varepsilon\, \zeta^2_\mu(\varepsilon)}{\frac{\partial}{\partial \mu} \Omega\, \varepsilon\, \zeta^1_\mu(\varepsilon)}\right\}_{\mu_s} P_{\mu_s}(-\cos\vartheta)\, \zeta^1_{\mu_s}(kr), \tag{155.5}$$

im Lichtgebiet

$$\hat{V}(r,\vartheta) = \hat{V}_g(r,\vartheta) + \frac{\pi}{2} \sum_s \frac{2\mu_s + 1}{\mu_s(\mu_s+1)} \frac{e^{\frac{3\pi i}{2}\mu_s}}{\sin \pi \mu_s} \left\{\frac{\Omega\, \varepsilon\, \zeta^2_\mu(\varepsilon)}{\frac{\partial}{\partial \mu} \Omega\, \varepsilon\, \zeta^2_\mu(\varepsilon)}\right\}_{\mu_s} P_{\mu_s}(\cos\vartheta)\, \zeta^1_{\mu_s}(kr) \tag{155.5'}$$

mit [vgl. (150.13)]

$$\hat{V}_g(r,\vartheta) = -\frac{1}{2} \oint \frac{2\mu+1}{\mu(\mu+1)}\, e^{\frac{i\pi}{2}\mu}\, Q^{(2)}_\mu(\vartheta)\, \frac{\Omega\, \varepsilon\, \zeta^2_\mu(\varepsilon)}{\Omega\, \varepsilon\, \zeta^1_\mu(\varepsilon)}\, \zeta^1_\mu(kr)\, d\mu. \tag{155.6}$$

Die asymptotische Auswertung ergibt dann für $r \to \infty$, $\varepsilon \sin\vartheta \gg 1$

$$\left.\begin{aligned} \hat{V}(r,\vartheta) &\to \hat{V}_g(r,\vartheta) + \frac{\varepsilon^{-\frac{7}{6}}}{kr} \frac{e^{i\left(kr + \frac{\pi}{3}\right)}}{\sqrt{2\sin\vartheta}} \cdot \\ &\cdot \sum_s \frac{C_s}{1 + e^{2\pi i \nu_s}} \left\{e^{i\nu_s\left(\frac{\pi}{2} + \vartheta\right) + \frac{i\pi}{4}} + e^{i\nu_s(2\pi - \vartheta) - \frac{i\pi}{4}}\right\}, \end{aligned}\right\} \tag{155.7}$$

wobei die C_s durch Gl. (141.4') bzw. Tabelle 3 von Ziff. 141 gegeben sind. (Der Index $\parallel$ entspricht wieder dem magnetischen Fall, $\perp$ dem elektrischen.) Für die Umgebung der *Rückwärtsstreuung* ($\vartheta \to \pi$) ist diese Darstellung entsprechend (150.15') durch die folgende zu ersetzen

$$\hat{V}(r,\vartheta) \to \hat{V}_g(r,\vartheta) + \sqrt{\pi}\, \frac{\varepsilon^{-\frac{2}{3}}}{2kr}\, e^{i\left(kr + \frac{\pi}{3}\right)} \sum_s \frac{C_s\, e^{2\pi i \nu_s}}{1 + e^{2i\pi\nu_s}}\, J_0\big(\nu_s(\pi - \vartheta)\big). \tag{155.7'}$$

Die Reihen konvergieren für große ε wieder außerordentlich schnell mit Ausnahme der Umgebung der Vorwärtsstreuung ($\vartheta \to 0$).

Gehen wir mit Hilfe von (155.1), (152.23) und (152.24') zum *Fernfeld* (152.24) der Feldvektoren über, so haben wir in (155.7) den schnell veränderlichen Phasenfaktor lediglich zweimal nach ϑ zu differenzieren [die mit $1/\sin\vartheta$ behafteten Glieder in (152.24') sind gegenüber den ϑ-Ableitungen um eine Größenordnung ε kleiner]. Es ergibt sich so für $\varepsilon \sin\vartheta \gg 1$

$$\left.\begin{aligned} S_{\parallel}(\vartheta) &\to S_{\parallel}^{(g)}(\vartheta) + \frac{\varepsilon^{\frac{5}{6}}}{\sqrt{2\sin\vartheta}}\, e^{\frac{i\pi}{12}} \sum_s C_s^{(e)} \left\{\frac{e^{i\nu\left(\frac{\pi}{2}+\vartheta\right)} - i\,e^{i\nu(2\pi-\vartheta)}}{1+e^{2\pi i\nu}}\right\}_{\nu_s^{(e)}} \\ S_{\perp}(\vartheta) &\to S_{\perp}^{(g)}(\vartheta) + \frac{\varepsilon^{\frac{5}{6}}}{\sqrt{2\sin\vartheta}}\, e^{\frac{i\pi}{12}} \sum_s C_s^{(m)} \left\{\frac{e^{i\nu\left(\frac{\pi}{2}+\vartheta\right)} - i\,e^{i\nu(2\pi-\vartheta)}}{1+e^{2\pi i\nu}}\right\}_{\nu_s^{(m)}}, \end{aligned}\right\} \tag{155.8}$$

dabei bedeuten die $S^{(g)}(\vartheta)$ die Streuamplituden des im Sinne der *geometrischen Optik reflektierten* Feldes. Für diese erhält man durch asymptotische Auswertung des Integrals (155.6) am Sattelpunkt $\hat{\mu}+\frac{1}{2} = \varepsilon\cos\vartheta$ (einschließlich Korrekturtermen, $\varepsilon \cos\frac{\vartheta}{2}\sin\vartheta \gg 1$)

$$\left.\begin{aligned} S_{\parallel}^{(g)}(\vartheta) &\to \frac{\varepsilon}{2}\, e^{-i\left(2\varepsilon\sin\frac{\vartheta}{2}+\frac{\pi}{2}\right)} \left(1 - \frac{i}{2\varepsilon\sin^3\frac{\vartheta}{2}} + \cdots\right) \\ S_{\perp}^{(g)}(\vartheta) &\to \frac{\varepsilon}{2}\, e^{-i\left(2\varepsilon\sin\frac{\vartheta}{2}-\frac{\pi}{2}\right)} \left(1 + \frac{i\cos\vartheta}{2\varepsilon\sin^3\frac{\vartheta}{2}} + \cdots\right) \end{aligned}\right\} \tag{155.8'}$$

wobei auch hier zum Hauptglied bei $S_{\parallel}^{(g)}$ nur $\hat{V}_e$, bei $S_{\perp}^{(g)}$ nur $\hat{V}_m$ beiträgt).

Bei mäßig großen ε überwiegt der durch die Kriechwellen in (155.8) dargestellte Beugungsterm wieder die Korrekturterme in (155.8'). Überhaupt herrschen weitgehend dieselben Verhältnisse wie im skalaren Fall. Die asymptotischen Darstellungen für $v(r,\vartheta)$ [Gl. (150.15)] und $\hat{V}(r,\vartheta)$ [Gl. (155.7)] unterscheiden sich nämlich nur um einen Faktor $\frac{1}{\mu_s(\mu_s+1)} \to \varepsilon^{-2}$; dieser kommt aber bei Anwendung des Operators $-\frac{\partial^2}{\partial\vartheta^2}$ auf $\hat{V}$ gerade wieder in Fortfall. Man erkennt dies auch an Hand der aus (150.7') folgenden asymptotischen Darstellung der Winkelfaktoren (152.24''')

$$\left.\begin{aligned} \tau_\mu(\cos\vartheta) &\to \sqrt{\frac{2\mu^3}{\pi\sin\vartheta}}\cos\left\{\left(\mu+\frac{1}{2}\right)\vartheta - \frac{\pi}{4}\right\} \\ \pi_\mu(\cos\vartheta) &\to \sqrt{\frac{2\mu}{\pi\sin^3\vartheta}}\sin\left\{\left(\mu+\frac{1}{2}\right)\vartheta - \frac{\pi}{4}\right\}. \end{aligned}\right\} \tag{155.9}$$

Somit gilt in niedrigster asymptotischer Näherung für $r\to\infty$, $\varepsilon\sin\vartheta \gg 1$

$$\left.\begin{aligned} \mathfrak{E}_\vartheta^{(S)} &= \varkappa\, \mathfrak{H}_\varphi^{(S)} \to \cos\varphi\, v_S^{(s)}(r,\vartheta) \\ -\mathfrak{E}_\varphi^{(S)} &= \varkappa\, \mathfrak{H}_\vartheta^{(S)} \to \sin\varphi\, v_S^{(p)}(r,\vartheta). \end{aligned}\right\} \tag{155.10}$$

(Dabei ist $v^{(s)}$ die Lösung des skalaren Randwertproblems für die Randbedingung $\partial v/\partial r = 0$, $v^{(p)}$ diejenige für $v=0$.) Damit ergibt sich für die *Fernfeldintensität* [zeitlich gemittelte Energiestromdichte, vgl. (152.28)]

$$I_S(\vartheta,\varphi) \to \frac{1}{2\varkappa}\left\{\cos^2\varphi\, |v_S^{(s)}|^2 + \sin^2\varphi\, |v_S^{(p)}|^2\right\}. \tag{155.10'}$$

Ist die einfallende Strahlung *unpolarisiert*, so ergibt sich aus (155.10′) durch Mittelung über alle Polarisationsrichtungen (d.h. über das Azimut φ) die Fernfeldintensität

$$I_S(\vartheta) = \frac{1}{4\varkappa}\{|v_S^{(s)}|^2 + |v_S^{(p)}|^2\}. \tag{155.10''}$$

Entsprechend gilt für den *Kriechanteil* der *Flächenstromdichte* in derselben Näherung

$$\left.\begin{aligned} \varkappa \mathfrak{J}_\vartheta(\vartheta, \varphi) &\to -\cos\varphi\, \psi_s(\vartheta) \\ \varkappa \mathfrak{J}_\varphi(\vartheta, \varphi) &\to \frac{1}{ik}\sin\varphi\, \psi_p(\vartheta) \end{aligned}\right\} \tag{155.11}$$

mit den Belegungsdichten $\psi(\vartheta)$ [Gl. (150.16, 16′) und (150.17″)] der beiden skalaren Probleme. Die Korrekturterme zur *geometrisch-optischen Stromverteilung* auf der *Lichtseite* der Kugel haben hier jedoch eine andere Gestalt:

$$\left.\begin{aligned} \varkappa \mathfrak{J}_\vartheta(\vartheta, \varphi) &\to -\cos\varphi \\ \varkappa \mathfrak{J}_\varphi(\vartheta, \varphi) &\to \sin\varphi\cos\vartheta \end{aligned}\right\} \cdot 2\, e^{i\varepsilon\cos\vartheta}\left(1 \pm \frac{i\sin^2\vartheta}{2\varepsilon\cos^3\vartheta} + \cdots\right). \tag{155.11'}$$

Auf den Halbstrahlen $\vartheta = 0$ und $\vartheta = \pi$ werden die Kriechwellen wieder *fokussiert*. In der Umgebung dieser Halbstrahlen haben wir die aus (150.10, 10′) folgenden asymptotischen Darstellungen

$$\left.\begin{aligned} \tau_\mu(\cos\vartheta) \\ \pi_\mu(\cos\vartheta) \end{aligned}\right\} \to \frac{\mu^2}{2}\left\{J_0\left(\left(\mu + \frac{1}{2}\right)\vartheta\right) \mp J_2\left(\left(\mu + \frac{1}{2}\right)\vartheta\right)\right\} \tag{155.12}$$

($|\mu| \gg 1$, $|\mu\vartheta|$ nicht $\gg 1$) bzw.

$$\left.\begin{aligned} \tau_\mu(-\cos\vartheta) \\ \pi_\mu(-\cos\vartheta) \end{aligned}\right\} \to \frac{\mu^2}{2}\left\{J_0\left(\left(\mu + \frac{1}{2}\right)(\pi - \vartheta)\right) \mp J_2\left(\left(\mu + \frac{1}{2}\right)(\pi - \vartheta)\right)\right\} \tag{155.12'}$$

($|\mu| \gg 1$, $|\mu(\pi - \vartheta)|$ nicht $\gg 1$) zu verwenden. Dabei haben wir von den Beziehungen $J_0' = -J_1$, $2J_1' = J_0 - J_2$, $\frac{2}{x}J_1(x) = J_0(x) + J_2(x)$ Gebrauch gemacht. Diesmal sind also beide Terme in Gl. (152.24′) von *derselben* Größenordnung. Setzt man (155.7′) unter Verwendung obiger Grenzwerte in (152.24′) ein [bei Beachtung von (152.23) und (155.1)], so ergibt sich für die *Rückstreuung* [$\varepsilon(\pi - \vartheta)$ nicht $\gg 1$]

$$\left.\begin{aligned} &\left.\begin{aligned} S_\parallel(\vartheta) &\to S_\parallel^{(g)}(\vartheta) \\ S_\perp(\vartheta) &\to S_\perp^{(g)}(\vartheta) \end{aligned}\right\} - \frac{\sqrt{\pi}}{4}\,\varepsilon^{\frac{4}{3}}\, e^{\frac{5\pi i}{3}} \cdot \\ &\quad \cdot \sum_s \left\{\left\{\frac{C_s\, e^{i\pi\nu_s}}{1 + e^{2\pi i\nu_s}}\left[J_0\left(\nu_s(\pi - \vartheta)\right) - J_2\left(\nu_s(\pi - \vartheta)\right)\right]\right\}_{\substack{e\\m}} \right. \\ &\quad \left. - \left\{\frac{C_s\, e^{i\pi\nu_s}}{1 + e^{2\pi i\nu_s}}\left[J_0\left(\nu_s(\pi - \vartheta)\right) + J_2\left(\nu_s(\pi - \vartheta)\right)\right]\right\}_{\substack{m\\e}}\right\}. \end{aligned}\right\} \tag{155.13}$$

Auf die modifizierte Watson-Transformation zur Berechnung der *Vorwärtsstreuung* (für die die obigen Residuenreihen versagen) gehen wir nicht ein[1]. Um jedoch wenigstens eine grobe Näherung zu erhalten, können wir im Sinne der ersten eingangs erwähnten Methode folgendermaßen vorgehen. Mit Hilfe der

[1] Man vgl. die in Fußnote 1 u. 2 auf S. 544 zitierte Literatur.

asymptotischen Darstellungen (153.4) nimmt (152.24′) die folgende Gestalt an

$$\left.\begin{aligned} S_{\parallel}(\vartheta) &\to \frac{1}{2}\sum_{n=1}^{\varepsilon}\frac{2n+1}{n(n+1)}\{(1-\mathrm{e}^{-2i\sigma})\,\tau_n(\cos\vartheta)+(1+\mathrm{e}^{-2i\sigma})\,\pi_n(\cos\vartheta)\}\\ S_{\perp}(\vartheta) &\to \frac{1}{2}\sum_{n=1}^{\varepsilon}\frac{2n+1}{n(n+1)}\{(1-\mathrm{e}^{-2i\sigma})\,\pi_n(\cos\vartheta)+(1+\mathrm{e}^{-2i\sigma})\,\tau_n(\cos\vartheta)\}\end{aligned}\right\} \qquad (155.14)$$

mit

$$\sigma=\sqrt{\varepsilon^2-\mu^2}-\mu\arccos\frac{\mu}{\varepsilon}-\frac{\pi}{4}\qquad\left(\mu=n+\frac{1}{2}\right). \qquad (155.14')$$

Dabei konnten wir die Summe bei $n\sim\varepsilon$ abbrechen, da die Koeffizienten der Winkelfunktionen zufolge (153.4) für $n>\varepsilon$ stärker als exponentiell verschwinden. Diesen Sachverhalt können wir so deuten, daß jedem n ein „*Strahl*" der einfallenden Welle entspricht, der im Abstand n/k am Ursprung der Kugel vorbeigeht. (Es sind dann bei der Streuung nur die Primärstrahlen wirksam, die die Kugel *treffen*, da $n\lesssim\varepsilon$.) Für $\vartheta=0$ haben die beiden Winkelfunktionen nach (152.27) den gleichen Wert $\tau_n(1)=\pi_n(1)=\frac{n(n+1)}{2}$ und der Exponentialterm in (155.14) wird somit gerade kompensiert; dies wird auch noch für kleine ϑ angenähert der Fall sein. Da ferner zufolge des Gewichtsfaktors $(2n+1)$ die großen Werte von n den Hauptbeitrag liefern, können wir die Darstellung (155.12) verwenden und erhalten aus (155.14)

$$S_{\parallel}(\vartheta)=S_{\perp}(\vartheta)\to\sum_{n=1}^{\varepsilon}\mu\,J_0(\mu\,\vartheta)\,. \qquad (155.15)$$

Ersetzen wir die Summe durch das Integral[1]

$$S_{\parallel}(\vartheta)=S_{\perp}(\vartheta)\to\int_0^{\varepsilon}\mu\,J_0(\mu\,\vartheta)\,d\mu=\varepsilon\,\frac{J_1(\varepsilon\,\vartheta)}{\vartheta}, \qquad (155.15')$$

so erhalten wir denselben Ausdruck, den die *Kirchhoffsche Theorie* für die Beugung an der Kreisscheibe liefert [vgl. (133.10)].

Um den Einfluß der mit dem Exponentialfaktor $\exp(-2i\,\sigma)$ behafteten Terme für größer werdende ϑ zu untersuchen, kann man für diese Terme die Darstellung (155.9) verwenden und erhält dann aus (155.14) die Zusätze

$$S_{\parallel}^{(g)}(\vartheta)=-S_{\perp}^{(g)}(\vartheta)\to-\sqrt{\frac{2}{\pi\sin\vartheta}}\sum_{n=1}^{\varepsilon}\sqrt{\mu}\,\mathrm{e}^{-2i\sigma}\cos\left(\mu\,\vartheta-\frac{\pi}{4}\right). \qquad (155.16)$$

Dabei haben wir die Terme mit $\pi_n(\cos\vartheta)$ gleich fortgelassen, da ihr Beitrag um eine Größenordnung in ε kleiner ist. Der Exponentialfaktor $\exp(-2i\,\sigma)$ ist nämlich eine mit n sehr schnell veränderliche Größe (gleichbleibenden absoluten Betragens); die einzelnen Summenterme in (155.16) werden sich daher gegenseitig kompensieren mit Ausnahme derjenigen n, die (angenähert) dieselbe Phase haben (Prinzip der stationären Phase). Wir werden aber gleich sehen, daß dies nur für diejenigen n in der Nachbarschaft von $\hat{n}+\frac{1}{2}=\varepsilon\cos\frac{\vartheta}{2}$ der Fall ist. In dieser Nachbarschaft können wir aber die Summe in (155.16) durch ein Integral ersetzen:

$$S_{\perp}^{(g)}(\vartheta)\to\frac{1}{\sqrt{2\pi\sin\vartheta}}\left\{\int\sqrt{\mu}\,\mathrm{e}^{i\varphi(\mu)}\,d\mu+\cdots\right\}. \qquad (155.16')$$

Dabei bedeutet ... einen entsprechend aufgebauten Integralterm, wobei die Exponenten in beiden Integranden sich in der Form

$$\varphi(\mu)=-2\sigma\pm\left(\mu\,\vartheta-\frac{\pi}{4}\right)=2\mu\arccos\frac{\mu}{\varepsilon}-2\sqrt{\varepsilon^2-\mu^2}\pm\left(\mu\,\vartheta-\frac{\pi}{4}\right)+\frac{\pi}{2} \qquad (155.17)$$

[1] S. Magnus-Oberhettinger, S. 30.

zusammenfassen lassen. Wir werten die Integrale nach dem Schema

$$\int \sqrt{\mu}\, e^{i\varphi(\mu)}\, d\mu \to \sqrt{\frac{2\pi\hat{\mu}}{|\varphi''(\hat{\mu})|}}\, e^{i\left\{\varphi(\hat{\mu})+\frac{\pi s}{4}\right\}} \qquad (s = \operatorname{sgn} \varphi''(\hat{\mu})) \qquad (155.18)$$

aus und haben dazu zunächst die Stelle $\hat{\mu}$ zu bestimmen, in deren Umgebung die Phase stationär ist. Für diese ist $\varphi'(\hat{\mu}) = 0$, also nach (155.17)[1]

$$2 \arccos \frac{\hat{\mu}}{2} \pm \vartheta = 0\,. \qquad (155.19)$$

Da hier der arc cos stets positiv ist, hat (155.19) nur für das untere Vorzeichen von ϑ eine Lösung:

$$\hat{\mu} = \varepsilon \cos \frac{\vartheta}{2}\,. \qquad (155.19')$$

Das bedeutet, daß derjenige Primärstrahl den wesentlichen Beitrag liefert, der nach dem (unendlich fernen) Aufpunkt hin reflektiert wird (vgl. Fig. 108). Damit ergibt sich aus (155.17)

$$\left.\begin{aligned} \varphi(\hat{\mu}) &= -2\varepsilon \sin \frac{\vartheta}{2} + \frac{3\pi}{4}\,, \\ \varphi''(\hat{\mu}) &= \frac{-2}{\varepsilon \sin \frac{\vartheta}{2}}\,. \end{aligned}\right\} \qquad (155.20)$$

Setzt man dies in (155.18) ein, so nimmt (155.16) die folgende Gestalt an

$$S_{\parallel}^{(g)}(\vartheta) = -S_{\perp}^{(g)}(\vartheta) \to \frac{\varepsilon}{2}\, e^{-i\left(2\varepsilon \sin\frac{\vartheta}{2} + \frac{\pi}{2}\right)}\,. \qquad (155.21)$$

Dies ist genau die nach der geometrischen Optik durch Reflexion sich ergebende Streuamplitude[2], die wir schon als Hauptglied der asymptotischen Entwicklung des Integrals (155.6) $\left(\text{für } \varepsilon \cos \frac{\vartheta}{2} \sin\vartheta \gg 1\right)$ gefunden hatten [vgl. (155.8′)]. In der Tat ist der Weg, auf dem wir das Ergebnis (155.21) hier erhalten haben, nichts anderes als eine weniger strenge Form der Aufspaltung, die wir in (155.5′, 6) in Strenge durchgeführt haben. Die Intensität der der *Reflexion* entsprechenden Streustrahlung (152.28) ist zufolge (155.21) bezüglich des Winkels ϑ *isotrop*, während die der Beugung entsprechende gemäß (155.15′) für $\vartheta = 0$ ein scharfes Maximum hat (abgesehen von Interferenzen dieser beiden Komponenten der Streustrahlung).

Für den *Streukoeffizienten* (152.26) erhält man mit Hilfe der Kirchhoffschen Näherung (155.15′) nur den geometrisch-optischen Grenzwert $\sigma = 2$. Um auf dem oben eingeschlagenen Weg eine bessere Näherung zu erhalten, muß man den Beitrag der „*Randstrahlen*" berücksichtigen, d.h. derjenigen Primärstrahlen, die die Kugel nahezu streifend treffen[3]. (Dieser Beitrag ist in der oben durchgeführten

---

[1] Da der arc cos (μ/ε) definitionsgemäß auf das Intervall 0 bis π beschränkt ist, hat er die Steigung $-1/\sqrt{\varepsilon^2 - \mu^2}$, wobei die Wurzel >0 genommen werden muß.

[2] Eine Berechnung derselben auf Grund der Prinzipien der geometrischen Optik für beliebige Brechungsindices bei Ch. Wiener: Abh. Kaiser-Leopold-Carol. Akad. Naturforsch. **73** (1907); **91** (1909). — J. Bricard: J. phys. **4**, 57 (1943). — G.E. Davis: J. Opt. Soc. Amer. **45**, 572 (1955). — Durch die in Ziff. 147 dargestellte Erweiterung der geometrischen Optik ergeben sich auch die Beugungseffekte infolge der Kriechwellen: B. Levy u. J.B. Keller: N.Y. Univ. Res. Rep. No. EM-109 (1957).

[3] Vgl. dazu T. Ljunggrén: Ark. Fysik **1**, No. 1 (1949). — Entsprechende Entwicklungen für den Fall des Zylinders bei N. Basu: Phil. Mag. **35**, 79 (1918). — T.K. Chimnayam: Phil. Mag. **37**, 9 (1919). — K. Artmann: Z. Physik **177**, 468 (1950).

Näherung deshalb nicht enthalten, weil dort die Debyeschen Näherungen verwandt worden sind, die für die Randstrahlen $n \to \varepsilon$ versagen, vgl. Ziff. 139.) Eine andere (weiterreichende) Methode besteht darin, die Abstrahlung des [durch (155.11) in Verbindung mit (150.17″) gegebenen] Strombelags auf der Kugel in der Nachbarschaft der geometrischen Schattengrenze zu berechnen[1], die im wesentlichen für die Vorwärtsstreuung verantwortlich ist (vgl. dazu Ziff. 146). Auf diesem Wege (oder mit Hilfe der eingangs erwähnten modifizierten Watson-Transformation) ergibt sich folgende asymptotische Darstellung für den Streukoeffizienten (ergänzt durch weitere Glieder der asymptotischen Entwicklung)[2]

$$\left.\begin{aligned}\frac{\sigma}{2} \to 1 &+ 0{,}6595661 \cdot \varepsilon^{-\frac{2}{3}} + 0{,}7797489 \cdot \varepsilon^{-\frac{4}{3}}\\ &- 2{,}8713350 \cdot \varepsilon^{-2} - 0{,}3385447 \cdot \varepsilon^{-\frac{8}{3}}\\ &+ 0{,}058460 \cdot \varepsilon^{-\frac{10}{3}}.\end{aligned}\right\} \qquad (155.22)$$

Der erste Korrekturterm ist hier das arithmetische Mittel der entsprechenden Korrekturterme der Streukoeffizienten (151.2*p*, *s*), die bei den beiden skalaren Streuproblemen auftreten. Man erkennt dies unmittelbar durch Vergleich der Darstellungen (148.17) und (152.26′). Der Streukoeffizient der Kugel zeigt also (im Gegensatz zu demjenigen der Kreisscheibe, vgl. Ziff. 134) asymptotisch keine Oszillationen. Dies hat seinen Grund darin, daß zur Vorwärtsstreuung (und damit auch zum Streukoeffizienten) asymptotisch nur die „Randstrahlen" (d.h. der Teil der gestreuten Strahlung, der an der Kugel streifend vorbeigeht) beitragen. Die prinzipiell vorhandene Interferenz mit den Kriechwellen kann asymptotisch vernachlässigt werden, da die zur Vorwärtsstreuung beitragenden Kriechwellen die Kugel mindestens einmal vollständig umlaufen haben müssen. (Ob jedoch die Kriechwellen für mäßig große ε nicht doch zum Streukoeffizienten beitragen, sollte im Hinblick auf Fig. 138 geprüft werden.)

Für *transparentes* Material der Kugel [reeller Brechungsindex in (152.19*e*, *m*)] ergeben sich bei der asymptotischen Auswertung zusätzlich neben den den *gebrochenen* Strahlen entsprechenden Wellen noch weitere Kriechwellen, die besonders im Zusammenhang mit dem *Regenbogenproblem* untersucht worden sind. Wir müssen uns hier auf eine Zusammenstellung der Literatur beschränken, in der sich die schrittweise Durchleuchtung dieses faszinierenden Problems widerspiegelt[3]. Die hier maßgeblichen Beugungserscheinungen in der Nähe des Grenzstrahles machen sich erst bei sehr großen Werten von ε (von der Größenordnung 10^3) deutlich bemerkbar. Für Regentropfen ist ε von der Größenordnung 10^4.

[1] Vgl. D.S. JONES: Proc. Roy.Soc. Lond. A **240**, 206 (1957).

[2] Nach T.T. WU: Phys. Rev. **104**, 1201 (1956).

[3] R. DESCARTES: Discours de la méthode pour bien conduire sa raison. Leiden 1637. — Le méteores, Discour 8. Leiden 1637. — TH. YOUNG: Phil. Trans. Roy. Soc. Lond. **22**, 8 (1804). — G.B. AIRY: Trans. Cambridge Phil. Soc. **6**, 379 (1838); **8**, 593 (1848). — Pogg. Ann., Erg.-Bd. **1**, 232 (1842). — G. STOKES: Trans. Cambridge Phil. Soc. **9**, 166 (1850). — Math. and Phys. Papers, Bd. 2, S. 332. Cambridge 1883. — E. MASCART: C. R. Acad. Sci., Paris **115**, 453 (1892). — Traité d'optique Bd. 1, S. 382, Bd. 2, S. 430. Paris 1891 u. 1893. — J.M. PERNTER: Wien. Ber. **106**, IIa, 135 (1897). — C. WIENER: Abh. Kaiser-Leopold-Carol. Akad. Naturforsch. **73** (1907); **91** (1908). — J.M. PERNTER u. F.M. EXNER: Meteorologische Optik, S. 530. Leipzig 1910. — W. MÖBIUS: Ann. Physik **33**, 1493 (1910); **40**, 736 (1913). — J. ROSENBERG: Ann. Physik **68**, 414 (1922). — B. VAN DER POL u. H. BREMMER: Phil. Mag. **24**, 857 (1937). — J. BRICARD: Ann. phys. **14**, 148 (1940). — H. BUCERIUS: Optik **1**, 188 (1946). — T. LJUNGGRÉN: Ark. Mat. Astronom. Fys. A **36**, No. 14 (1948). — W.V.R. MALKUS, R.H. BISHOP u. R.O. BRIGGS: Nat. Adv. Comm. Aeronaut. Techn. Notes No. 1622 (1948). — Eine eingehende Übersicht bei H.C. VAN DE HULST: Light Scattering by Small Particles, Kap. 13. Die Anwendung der neuerdings von P. BECKMANN: Z. Naturforsch. **12**a, 960 (1957) gegebenen Korrektur und Vervollständigung der Theorie von VAN DER POL und BREMMER auf das Regenbogenproblem steht noch aus.

Sachverzeichnis.

(Deutsch-Englisch.)

Bei gleicher Schreibweise in beiden Sprachen sind die Stichwörter nur einmal aufgeführt.

Subject Index.

(English-German.)

Where English and German spelling of a word is identical the German version is omitted.